LAMINAR
BOUNDARY LAYERS

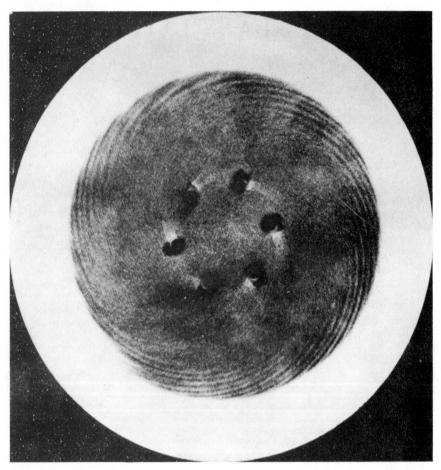

Frontispiece. Boundary-layer flow induced by a rotating disk (china-clay photograph), showing laminar flow near the centre and subsequent instability in the form of spiral vortices which cause transition to turbulent flow near the rim.

(See Gregory, Stuart, and Walker 1955)

LAMINAR
BOUNDARY LAYERS

An Account of the
Development, Structure and Stability of
Laminar Boundary Layers
in Incompressible Fluids,
together with a Description of the
Associated Experimental Techniques

Editor

L. ROSENHEAD

DOVER PUBLICATIONS, INC.

New York

Published in Canada by General Publishing Company, Ltd., 30
Lesmill Road, Don Mills, Toronto, Ontario.
Published in the United Kingdom by Constable and Company,
Ltd., 10 Orange Street, London WC2H 7EG.

This Dover edition, first published in 1988, is an unabridged and
unaltered republication of the 1966 printing of the work first
published by The Clarendon Press (Oxford University Press) in
1963 in the *Fluid Motion Memoirs* series. It is reprinted by special
arrangement with Oxford University Press, 200 Madison Ave-
nue, New York, New York 10016.

Manufactured in the United States of America
Dover Publications, Inc., 31 East 2nd Street, Mineola, N.Y.
11501

Library of Congress Cataloging-in-Publication Data

Laminar boundary layers.

Reprint. Originally published: Oxford : Clarendon Press, 1963.
Originally published in series: Fluid motion memoirs.
Bibliography: p.
Includes indexes.
1. Boundary layer. 2. Laminar flow. I. Rosenhead, Louis,
1906–
QC151.7.L35   1988   530.4′2   88-3906
ISBN 0-486-65646-2 (pbk.)

TO

THE AERONAUTICAL RESEARCH COUNCIL
OF GREAT BRITAIN

in appreciation of its work for
aeronautical science

This book has been written by

L. F. CRABTREE

G. E. GADD

N. GREGORY

C. R. ILLINGWORTH

C. W. JONES

D. KÜCHEMANN

M. J. LIGHTHILL

R. C. PANKHURST

L. ROSENHEAD (*Editor*)

L. SOWERBY

J. T. STUART

E. J. WATSON

G. B. WHITHAM

PREFACE

Laminar Boundary Layers springs from Goldstein's *Modern Developments in Fluid Dynamics* of 1938 but is almost entirely new writing. The theory of boundary layers, and the associated experimental work, have grown so considerably since the appearance of the parent publication that a comprehensive account of modern knowledge in this field needs more than the two volumes which Goldstein found adequate. The region covered by *M.D.F.D.*, together with an account of present ideas and developments in this field, has therefore been divided among the present book; another on *Incompressible Aerodynamics*, which has been written by Thwaites and a group of collaborators; and one on turbulence which still has to be completed.

The present book is principally concerned with the study of incompressible laminar boundary layers, but extensions are also made to a number of closely related topics where these throw light on the main one. In order to enable the reader to appreciate the nature and ramifications of the subject, sections have been written on the physical and aerodynamical background, the full equations of motion and their solutions, the theory of flow for small Reynolds number, and finally about the main subject—laminar boundary layers. This includes steady boundary layers in two- and three-dimensional flow, unsteady boundary layers, stability, and observational techniques. Laminar heat transfer has been touched on only lightly because a chapter on this topic is included in Howarth's *High Speed Flow*. Ideas and methods which are now principally of historical interest have been referred to only briefly or not at all.

The writers are experienced in the fields described in the chapters to which their names are attached, and also in associated regions of inquiry. What they have written frequently shows refreshing and attractive divergences of style, and the editorial prerogative has not been employed to replace by uniformity the highly personal qualities of the writing of the specialist-authors of this book. Considerable efforts were made, however, to ensure clarity, a minimum of overlap between chapters, and as much uniformity of notation as seemed reasonable. One convention about symbols may need a separate note of explanation —in two-dimensional boundary-layer theory x denotes the coordinate in the surface and z is in the direction of the normal to the surface;

this was agreed in order to facilitate transition to three-dimensional theory in the form conventionally adopted for aircraft wings, in which x, y are the coordinates in the surface and z is again in the direction of the normal. A similar convention has been adopted for the symbols used to denote components of velocity and vorticity.

Many different types of specialist now make use of the ideas, methods, and results of boundary-layer theory—applied mathematicians, engineers, and experimental physicists and chemists, working in fields as diverse as aerodynamics, hydraulics, meteorology, oceanography, heat and mass transfer, etc.; it is hoped that the present book will be useful in differing ways to all of them, and not least to young research workers coming fresh to this subject. To people in this last category I should like to emphasize the importance of understanding at least the scope and limitations of existing methods of calculating and measuring the characteristics of fluids in motion.

Collaboration between people in different towns is frequently difficult, and in the writing of this book co-operation was made more than usually difficult by the distracting demands made upon the authors by the pressure of their normal work in universities and the Scientific Civil Service. Many of the co-authors of $L.B.L.$ have been abroad for prolonged periods during the writing of the book and this has frequently produced conditions not conducive to rapid and detailed collaboration. Now that the work is done I must say to the co-authors how grateful I am to them for having worked as well as they did and often under so much difficulty.

I am grateful to members of the $L.B.L.$ Panel—G. K. Batchelor, N. Gregory, C. W. Jones, M. J. Lighthill, H. H. Pearcey (Secretary), and B. Thwaites—for their advice and help. I am particularly indebted to Pearcey, with whom I have worked so harmoniously over so many years, for having acted more as an Assistant Editor than a Secretary.

J. L. Nayler and R. W. Gandy, successive Secretaries of the Aeronautical Research Council, have helped considerably in many ways—personal, technical, and administrative. The excellence of the work of their staff in the A.R.C. office, in preparing drafts of chapters and other material, is beyond my capacity for praise; Miss E. E. Metcalfe's contribution in tracing all the figures was especially valuable.

I greatly appreciate, too, the painstaking assistance given by Mrs. J. K. Cottrell and Mrs. P. Raeder of the University of Liverpool, and Mrs. E. R. Edmondson of the National Physical Laboratory, especially in the compilation of the References and Author Index, and the Subject Index.

It is a pleasure also to be able to express to the staff of the Clarendon Press my grateful thanks for their understanding patience, for their co-operative helpfulness, and for the excellence of their work in the exercise of their craft.

Finally, the authors of this book are grateful to the Aeronautical Research Council for the invitation to write *Laminar Boundary Layers* —and, of course, to Sydney Goldstein, on whose shoulders they have attempted to stand and review what in 1961 are some of the 'modern developments in fluid dynamics'.

L. R.

December 1961

ACKNOWLEDGEMENTS

THE author of Chapter I acknowledges with gratitude the help of Sir James Gray in preparing a paragraph of Section 5.3 of his chapter. The author of Chapters VII and IX wishes to thank Dr. G. K. Batchelor of the Cavendish Laboratory; Professor C. C. Lin and Dr. W. E. Gibson of the Massachusetts Institute of Technology; Mr. P. Bradshaw, Dr. R. C. Lock, Dr. L. A. Segel, and Mr. J. Watson of the National Physical Laboratory, and Mr. L. E. Fraenkel of Imperial College for their constructive criticisms of the drafts of these two chapters.

The authors of Chapter X are indebted to Mr. D. W. Bryer, Mr. C. Salter, and Mr. A. Silverleaf of the National Physical Laboratory for many helpful comments on the draft of Chapter X.

Contributions in Chapters VI, VII, IX, and X by Dr. Gadd, Dr. Stuart, Dr. Pankhurst, and Mr. Gregory of the National Physical Laboratory are published by permission of the Director of the Laboratory.

We gratefully acknowledge the assistance given by the following in granting permission to reproduce certain figures and tables:

Acoustical Society of America for Figs. VII. 10 and 11 taken from the *Journal of the Acoustical Society of America*.

Akademie der Wissenschaften in Göttingen for Figs. II. 32, IX. 3 taken from *Nachrichten von der Gesellschaft der Wissenschaften zu Göttingen*.

Akademie-Verlag, Berlin, for Figs. VII. 9 and 18, IX. 19, and Tables IX. 1 and 2 taken from *Zeitschrift für angewandte Mathematik und Mechanik*.

Ballistics Research Laboratories, Aberdeen Proving Ground, Maryland, for Fig. II. 20.

Birkhauser Verlag, Basel, for material used in Table VIII. 1 taken from *Archiv der Mathematik*.

G. Braun, Karlsruhe, for Fig. VII. 12 taken from *Grenzschicht-Theorie* by Schlichting.

Cambridge Philosophical Society for Figs. III. 4 and 12, Table VIII. 7, and for some of the data given in Table V. 4, taken from the *Proceedings of the Cambridge Philosophical Society*.

Cambridge University Press for Figs. VII. 17, IX. 8, 23, and 25 taken from the *Journal of Fluid Mechanics*, and for Table IX. 3 taken from *The Theory of Hydrodynamic Stability* by Lin.

Clarendon Press, Oxford, for Figs. III. 9 and 10, VII. 1 and 2 taken from the *Quarterly Journal of Mechanics and Applied Mathematics*.

Sir William Farren for Fig. II. 33.

C. W. K. Gleerup, Lund, for material used in Table VIII. 1 taken from *Lunds Universitets Årsskrift*.

Indiana University Graduate Institute for Mathematics and Mechanics for Fig. IX. 4 taken from the *Journal of Rational Mechanics and Analysis*.

Institute of the Aerospace Sciences for Figs. III. 7 and 8, VIII. 4 and 12, IX. 7, 9, and 10 taken from the *Journal of the Aeronautical Sciences*.

Longmans, Green & Co. for data used in Tables I. 2, 3, and 4 taken from the twelfth edition of *Tables of Physical and Chemical Constants* by Kaye and Laby.

Max-Planck-Institut für Strömungsforschung, Göttingen, for Fig. VII. 3 taken from a *Göttingen Dissertation* by Rubach.

National Aeronautics and Space Administration for Figs. IX. 26, 27, 28, and 29 taken from a *Technical Note*, and for Figs. IX. 11, 12, 13, 22, and 30, X. 20 taken from *Technical Reports* and *Technical Notes* of the National Advisory Committee for Aeronautics.

Royal Aeronautical Society for Figs. X. 6 and 18 taken from the *Journal of the Royal Aeronautical Society*, and for parts of Table VI. 5 taken from the *Aeronautical Quarterly*.

Royal Society for Figs. VII. 14, 15, and 16, VIII. 6, IX. 5 and 24, and Table VIII. 3 taken from the *Proceedings of the Royal Society*, and for the Frontispiece and Figs. IX. 1, 2, and 21 taken from the *Philosophical Transactions*.

Springer-Verlag, Berlin, for Figs. VII. 6 and 7 taken from *Ingenieur-Archiv*.

Taylor & Francis, Ltd., for Figs. III. 3, 11, VII. 8, and Tables VIII. 5 and 6 taken from the *Philosophical Magazine*.

United States Air Force for Fig. IX. 18 taken from a *Technical Report*.

Verein Deutscher Ingenieure, Düsseldorf, for Figs. II. 26 and 27 taken from *Forschungsarbeiten auf dem Gebiet des Ingenieurwesens*.

Friedr. Vieweg & Sohn, Braunschweig, for Figs. VII. 4 and 5 taken from *Zeitschrift für Flugwissenschaften*.

We are also grateful to the Controller, H.M. Stationery Office, for the following Crown Copyright material:

Figs. II. 28, IX. 16, X. 10, 15, and 19 taken from the *Reports and Memoranda* of the Aeronautical Research Council; Figs. VII. 13, VIII. 7 and 8, X. 8, and Tables VI. 4, VIII. 4 taken from unpublished papers of the Ministry of Aviation; and Figs. IX. 20, X. 16 supplied by the National Physical Laboratory.

Finally, acknowledgement is made to the following organizations for permission to refer to unpublished papers:

Aircraft Research Association; Cornell University; David Taylor Model Basin, United States Navy Department; Kimberley Clark Corporation; Massachusetts Institute of Technology; Ministry of Aviation; National Aeronautics and Space Administration; National Physical Laboratory; Pennsylvania State University; United States Air Force Office of Scientific Research; United States Naval Ordnance Laboratory; University of Freiburg; University of Maryland.

CONTENTS

CONTENTS

II. INTRODUCTION. BOUNDARY LAYER THEORY

By M. J. LIGHTHILL

III. THE NAVIER–STOKES EQUATIONS OF MOTION

By G. B. WHITHAM

IV. FLOW AT SMALL REYNOLDS NUMBER

By c. r. illingworth

V. TWO-DIMENSIONAL BOUNDARY LAYERS

By c. w. JONES and E. J. WATSON

VI. APPROXIMATE METHODS OF SOLUTION

By G. E. GADD C. W. JONES, and E. J. WATSON

CONTENTS   xvii

VII. UNSTEADY BOUNDARY LAYERS

By J. T. STUART

VIII. THREE-DIMENSIONAL BOUNDARY LAYERS

By L. F. CRABTREE, D. KÜCHEMANN, and L. SOWERBY

IX. HYDRODYNAMIC STABILITY

By J. T. STUART

X. EXPERIMENTAL METHODS

By R. C. PANKHURST and N. GREGORY

The following figures appear as plates:

CONVENTIONS FOR REFERENCES

THE system of cross-reference within the book is as follows:

Chapters are designated by roman numerals.

Sections and equations are numbered serially within each chapter in arabic numerals. References to sections or equations within the same chapter do not carry the chapter number; others do.

Figures are numbered serially within each chapter in arabic numerals and, in addition, always carry the chapter number.

The method of referring to original papers follows, in the main, the conventions used by the Royal Society of London. All references are collected towards the end of the book in a single bibliography, arranged alphabetically by the names of the authors.

The abbreviations used in the bibliography follow the methods of the *World List of Scientific Periodicals* (1952) published by Butterworths. The abbreviations used in this book, together with the full titles and places of origin, are included in Current Paper 444 of the Aeronautical Research Council, London, which may be obtained from Her Majesty's Stationery Office, London. The Current Paper has been issued with the object of removing possible ambiguities and is strongly recommended to those who wish to consult the original works.

I

INTRODUCTION. REAL AND IDEAL FLUIDS

PART I

INTRODUCTORY ESSAY

1. External aerodynamics before boundary-layer theory

EXTERNAL aerodynamics is the study of the disturbances generated by an obstacle in a stream of air, and of the forces between the airstream and the obstacle which result from these disturbances. Its data are directly applicable to problems of locomotion through an atmosphere at rest, in which the flow at any instant is most fruitfully studied relative to a frame of reference moving along with the body, which in this frame behaves like an obstacle in a wind.

External aerodynamics was a disturbingly mysterious subject before Prandtl solved the mystery with his work on boundary-layer theory from 1904 onwards (Prandtl 1904, 1935, 1952). The trouble had been by no means the lack of a theory, but rather the existence of an almost overwhelmingly large body of theory, constructed by many of the best mathematical physicists of the nineteenth century, according to the most respectable physical principles. This theory gave, for the motion of a wide variety of shapes through the atmosphere, which it treated as a 'perfect fluid' (that is, a continuous medium of constant density whose parts act on each other only by normal pressures), the fullest information, none of which accorded with the most elementary observation of the facts.

The failure of the theory was particularly disturbing because the only known mechanical properties of the air which had been neglected, namely compressibility and viscosity, could reasonably be supposed to produce small effects in the type of problem considered. The variations of density associated with the pressure changes occurring in airflows at speeds U small compared with the speed of sound a were known to be small (of the order of $(U/a)^2$). Similarly, the coefficient of viscosity μ had such a small value that tangential stresses of the order of $\mu U/l$ (where l is a dimension characteristic of the body), occurring in the field of flow as predicted by perfect-fluid theory, would be small compared with the predicted normal pressures (of the order of ρU^2) for typical values of U and l.

In the discussions of this impasse in the latter half of the nineteenth century, there was too much concentration on only one incorrect prediction of the theory, namely that the drag should be zero in steady flow. This so-called d'Alembert paradox was really no more paradoxical than that the whole flow pattern should be incorrectly predicted. The result should indeed have been called d'Alembert's theorem, since it gave a positive indication that drag coefficients very small compared with 1 might be achieved if, by deeper understanding, shapes which would closely realize the irrotational flow predicted by perfect-fluid theory could be discovered. It is this fact that alone has made possible motion through the air at speeds greater than 100 m.p.h.

For motions through water a divergence between theory and practice also existed, but was partly camouflaged to nineteenth-century scholars by two additional physical features. First, if a body of dimension l moves through water within a distance of order l or less from the surface, a wave pattern is set up, leading to a 'wave-making resistance' (and so avoiding the abhorred prediction of zero drag!). Furthermore, the behaviour of water waves was represented fairly accurately by perfect-fluid theory, which even gave a reasonable qualitative picture of wave-making by obstacles in a stream.

Secondly, even for bodies well below the surface of the liquid, there was a clear-cut reason why the perfect-fluid theory should break down at any place where the absolute pressure predicted by theory became negative. There, cavitation of the liquid (formation of large or small bubbles of vapour) could be expected, and does actually occur. It was seen, for example, that this would set a limit to the realization of perfect-fluid flow around sharp corners, where the predicted pressure is negatively infinite. The beginnings of steady-state cavity theory were made in the theory of discontinuous flows, due to Helmholtz (1868) and Kirchhoff (1869).

On the other hand, this limitation on the theory—whose practical importance depends on the fact that for liquid flows at quite moderate speeds the dynamic pressure changes, of the order of $\pm\rho U^2$, may be comparable with the absolute pressure, whereas speeds of the order of that of sound are needed for the same to be true in gases—was allowed to obscure the existence of a quite different limitation, independent of the absolute pressure, and occurring equally for liquids and gases. Those who advocated the use of discontinuous-flow theory for flow of air past sharp corners (or for water flows when no cavity is formed) still did so on the ground that, otherwise, negative pressures would occur. It was not suspected that a quite different, and in general much less stringent, criterion for flow separation might exist, that could apply even on a smooth surface.

Now that we know that the way out of the impasse involves the recognition that viscous forces, though small, play a crucial part in determining the flow pattern, it is worth looking closely at the nineteenth-century work on viscous flow to see how this point was missed.

The irrotational flows predicted by perfect-fluid theory do actually satisfy the equations of motion of a viscous fluid (of constant density). The error in these flow patterns therefore lies entirely in the boundary condition used to determine them. Stokes (1851), in his great paper 'On the effect of the internal friction of fluids on the motion of pendulums', had shown that the condition of zero relative velocity of the fluid at a solid surface both was the most physically tenable boundary condition for the equations of motion of a viscous fluid, and led to remarkable agreement with a wide range of experiments in that problem, as it had also in the capillary-tube resistance experiments of Poiseuille (1840) and Hagen (1839). However, the fact that the perfect-fluid theory, by contrast, allowed an arbitrary relative velocity, tangential to the solid surface, between it and the fluid in contact with it, was not seriously criticized. Some writers suggested that the condition of zero relative velocity was appropriate only to slow motions, and that for fast motions a layer of fluid at rest (of constant thickness) would intervene between the solid surface and the main stream flowing over it (at arbitrary relative speed). Supporters of this view do not seem to have discussed the dynamics of such a layer, or thought about the necessarily continuous variation of velocity across it which results from viscous action, or about the effect on the fluid in this layer of the pressure gradients to which it is subjected.

All treatments of the equations of a viscous fluid during this period neglected the non-linear inertia terms. This neglect had been just permissible for Stokes's pendulums, but was not so in most problems of external aerodynamics to which the methods were tentatively applied. Stokes had realized that his own formula $3\pi\mu Ul$ for the resistance to a sphere of diameter l moving with steady velocity U was applicable only for velocities so small that the ordinary term of order $\rho U^2 l^2$ was negligible by comparison; experiments by Coulomb (1800) had shown that a transition from the quadratic to the linear dependence on velocity did occur at very low velocities. Later workers, however, for example Basset (1888), suggested optimistically that the neglect of the non-linear terms might have some value at much higher velocities. They pointed with relief to the fact that the predicted drag was at least not zero (ignoring the fact that it was far too small). They also emphasized that their linearized equation (which is in fact Laplace's equation for the vorticity) was exactly satisfied, not only in the one limiting case of very small velocities (that is, $\rho Ul/\mu \to 0$), but also in the other limiting case of a perfect fluid ($\rho Ul/\mu \to \infty$), for which the predicted vorticity was identically zero. This 'interpolation' argument would have been more convincing if the same boundary condition had been used in the two theories!

Even after the appearance of Prandtl's great paper of 1904, containing all the essentials of the solution to the mystery (although its effect on the ways of thinking of hydrodynamicists might have been quicker had it not been compressed into eight pages for acceptance by the International Congress of Mathematicians), the same type of error continued to be published. Oseen's alternative linearization of the equations of steady viscous motion (in which the squares of the departures of the velocity from its value at infinity are neglected) made a really valuable improvement in our knowledge of very slow motions (with $(\rho Ul/\mu < 1)$. However, his use of this linearization in his *Hydrodynamik* (Oseen 1927a) to discuss the behaviour of flows in the limit of small viscosity (that is, as $\rho Ul/\mu \to \infty$) was hardly valuable in 1927, since it gives results in flat disagreement with the features of the flow in this limit discovered by Prandtl (to whom no reference is made); in particular, the fact that the point of flow separation from the surface is determined by the situation in the boundary layer.

Similarly, the books appearing in the last fifty years which have given the fullest accounts of perfect-fluid theory have mostly failed to include the essential information without which knowledge of perfect-fluid theory is useless—that is, knowledge of the broad criteria that determine whether or not boundary-layer separation will prevent a particular solution from corresponding closely to any real flow (except momentarily after the flow has just been started from rest). Many such books continue the old confusion between the cavitation and separation conditions. Others construct ingeniously a vast variety of irrotational flows, and then give them realistic names which suggest that the flows can occur in practice, although the majority include enormous adverse pressure gradients along some surface, or even flow along a wall containing a pronounced corner. University instruction in fluid dynamics has often suffered from being based too closely on books of this type.

It is certainly not necessary for every worker in fluid dynamics to have studied the detailed mathematics of boundary-layer theory, as set out in the later chapters of this book. On the other hand, any useful teaching of the subject must include at least the salient qualitative facts brought to light by Prandtl, which need crowd out of a course on fluid dynamics only a very moderate amount of other material. An attempt is made, in the following chapter, to give ·a broad synopsis of this fundamental knowledge which has successfully transformed external aerodynamics from a mystery into a science.

PART II

PHYSICAL BACKGROUND OF THE FLOWS TO BE STUDIED

We shall confine ourselves, as far as any systematic exposition in this book is concerned (but without excluding occasional excursions), to those flows in which the fluid density may be regarded as constant. It is desirable to begin with a review of the conditions under which this assumption is valid in external aerodynamics, of the physical properties of the air which are called into play in determining flows of this type, and of the conditions under which liquid motions are of an essentially similar character.

2. Conditions under which density variation may be neglected in external aerodynamics

2.1. *Air in equilibrium*

In external aerodynamics, density changes arise not directly from the flow, but indirectly, through pressure changes and temperature changes. Now, from a fundamental point of view, the temperature T of air in equilibrium is the constant which governs the distribution of energy among its molecules. The Maxwell–Boltzmann law, that states of energy ϵ are occupied in proportion to $e^{-\epsilon/kT}$, where $k = 1\cdot38 \times 10^{-16}$ ergs $(^{\circ}\text{K})^{-1}$ is Boltzmann's constant, gives (Guggenheim 1955, Tolman 1948) that the average translational energy per molecule is $\frac{3}{2}kT$, corresponding (at $T = 15^{\circ}$ C $= 288^{\circ}$ K) to a root-mean-square speed of 510 m/sec for the N_2 molecules which make up four-fifths of the whole, 480 m/sec for the other main constituent, O_2, 430 m/sec for A (present to 1 per cent.), and 630 m/sec for such H_2O molecules as may be present. A further important part of the internal energy is an average rotational energy kT per molecule of N_2 or O_2.

Vibration of molecules gives by comparison only a very small addition to the internal energy, except at high temperatures. This is because the energy ϵ of the first vibrating state of O_2 has $\epsilon/k = 2{,}230°$ K and that of N_2 has $\epsilon/k = 3{,}340°$ K, both values making $e^{-\epsilon/kT}$ negligible at ordinary temperatures. A further small (negative) contribution, which becomes important only at high pressures (particularly when combined with low temperature), is the potential energy of attraction of such clusters of molecules as may be temporarily formed by the forces of cohesion (Mayer and Mayer 1940, Fowler and Guggenheim 1939).

The pressure force acting across a surface in air at rest is generated on a molecular scale by momentum transport, resulting from the fact that molecules crossing the surface, say from left to right, have always a positive left–right component of momentum, while those crossing it the other way have a negative one. It follows that the pressure p (force per unit area of surface) is twice the kinetic energy per unit volume of the translational motions of molecules normal to the surface. Since this kinetic energy is $\frac{1}{2}kT$ per molecule on the average, we have

$$p = 2(\tfrac{1}{2}kT)N\rho = RT\rho, \tag{1}$$

where N is the number of molecules per unit mass, ρ is the density, and $R = kN$. Thus, R is inversely proportional to the mean molecular weight; in fact

$$R = 2{\cdot}87 \times 10^6 \, (1-0{\cdot}378h)^{-1} \text{ cm}^2 \text{ sec}^{-2} \, (°\text{K})^{-1} \tag{2}$$

for air containing a proportion h of H_2O molecules.

More accurately still, the pressure force includes in addition the resultant of the forces acting between pairs of molecules instantaneously on opposite sides of the surface, which to a first approximation gives

$$p = RT\rho + a_1(T)\rho^2, \tag{3}$$

where $a_1(T)$ is a 'virial coefficient' including positive terms due to the repulsive forces involved in close encounters and negative ones due to the longer-range forces of cohesion, the latter terms being greater for $T < 500°$ K. The correction is, however, not more than $0{\cdot}2$ per cent. at atmospheric density.

The pressure of the H_2O molecules alone is ph; when this reaches the vapour pressure of water, $p_v(T)$ (see Table I. 1), the air is said to be

TABLE I. 1
Vapour pressure of water

T (°C)	0	5	10	15	20	25	30	35	40
p_v (mb)	6·1	8·7	12·3	17·0	23·3	31·6	42·3	56·0	73·5

'saturated', and condensation on to any liquid surface with sufficiently large radius of curvature can take place (see Section 4.3), with an energy liberation of $2 \cdot 5 \times 10^{10}$ ergs per gm of H_2O. Ordinary atmospheric air contains enough 'nuclei of condensation' for such precipitation to occur fairly rapidly with ph only a little greater than $p_v(T)$.

2.2 Air in motion

By air in motion, with *uniform* velocity **v**, we mean simply air in one of the states of equilibrium described above but with the additional velocity **v** superimposed on that of every molecule. Then each molecular species has the mean velocity **v**, as well as the appropriate standard deviation of velocity (of the order of 500 m/sec) noted above. When **v** is very much smaller than this standard deviation, almost half the molecules at any instant have a negative velocity component in the direction of **v**. It is not surprising, therefore, that obstacles in such an airflow can make their presence felt far upstream.

It is of course with non-uniform motion that we are concerned in aerodynamics. Exact equilibrium is then impossible, as each bit of air is continuously having momentum, energy or volume added or removed. However, the tendency to revert to an equilibrium state, expressed by the second law of thermodynamics, is a very rapid one for air at atmospheric pressure. Each molecule makes about 10^{10} collisions per second (Meyer 1899, Chapman and Cowling 1952), and after 10^{-9} sec, when an average of 10 collisions per molcule has occurred, the degree of approximation to which they have produced the equilibrium state appropriate to new values of the momentum, energy, and volume is high. Only the vibrational energy of the molecules still lags behind. The lag of this very small fraction of the total internal energy makes an appreciable effect only in sound waves, where by being repeatedly generated with alternate sign it gradually converts into heat the energy carried by the wave.

Now, in a time 10^{-9} sec, the molecules traverse a distance of less than 1 micron (10^{-4} cm). Therefore, air flowing under conditions which vary little over a distance of 1 micron must everywhere be very nearly in an equilibrium state, and we can correctly speak of the pressure and temperature at any point of the flow, and regard them as related to the density approximately by equation (1).

2.3. Temperature changes in external aerodynamics

We return now to the question, under what conditions the density can be regarded as constant. Equation (1)' shows that the density changes will be a very small fraction of the density, provided that both the pressure and the temperature changes are very small fractions of the absolute pressure and temperature, respectively.

Now, in external aerodynamics, temperature changes arise principally (Emmons 1958, Sears 1954a, Howarth 1953) from the conversion of the kinetic energy of the bulk motion into internal energy, and conversely from the utilization of internal energy to accelerate the bulk motion. It is clear enough, from the magnitudes of the root-mean-square speeds of the molecules relative to the bulk motion, that, if the latter is but a small fraction of 500 m/sec, then the relative change of internal energy and so also of absolute temperature, due to exchange with the energy of the bulk motion, must be small, of the order of the square of this fraction.

To get a more precise estimate of the temperature changes involved, we recall from Section 2.1 that approximately the internal energy E amounts to $\frac{5}{2}kT$ per molecule, which is $\frac{5}{2}RT$ per gm. It follows that, if the kinetic energy of an airstream of velocity U is converted into internal energy, the temperature rises by $U^2/5R$. At the substantial speed $U = 100$ m/sec this is only $7°$ K, a relatively small fraction of the absolute temperature.

In most flows the temperature rise where fluid is brought to rest (notably, at the surface of any obstacle) is somewhat less than this, particularly as a result of energy loss due to work done on adjacent fluid. In steady flow this tends to cause the kinetic energy drop to be balanced by a rise not in the internal energy E but in the enthalpy,

$$H = E+p/\rho \doteq E+RT \doteq \tfrac{7}{2}RT, \tag{4}$$

leading to a temperature rise of approximately $U^2/7R$, which is only $5°$ K in the case $U = 100$ m/sec mentioned above.

It follows that an obstacle held in a stream of temperature T_∞ will reach in due course a final temperature T_f near to $T_\infty+U^2/7R$. However, the passage to this final temperature may take a considerable time in the case of an obstacle of large heat capacity, and we often wish to know at what rate heat is transferred from the stream to such an obstacle when the temperature T_w of its surface is less than T_f—or at what rate the obstacle loses heat when $T_w > T_f$. A knowledge of these rates is also essential if we wish to be able to maintain the body surface at a temperature $T_w \neq T_f$.

In 'heat-transfer' problems of this type, the condition that $U^2/7R$ is a very small fraction of T_∞ does *not* ensure that temperature variations generally are a small fraction of the absolute temperature. The fluid in immediate contact with the surface has the temperature T_w of the surface (see Section 3.2 below), and the transition from this value to temperatures typical of the stream must take place continuously—in fact, across a thin boundary layer (which may, however, separate from the surface). Such a boundary layer can be studied by simplified methods, applicable to problems with small temperature variation, only if $(T_w-T_\infty)/T_\infty$ as well as $U^2/7RT_\infty$ is very small.

In regions of the flow where the streamlines are crowded together, and the flow has accelerated to a velocity v greater than U, the temperature is normally below the value T_∞, and in steady flow is close to $T_\infty+(U^2-v^2)/7R$. This drop in temperature, due to the conversion of enthalpy into kinetic energy of the bulk motion, does not much exceed, in general, the rise in temperature found at points where the fluid is brought to rest. It would be equal to it where $v = U\sqrt{2}$, and we shall see that a consequence of the boundary-layer theory is that v/U is limited (particularly in flows of practical utility, where the obstacles have low drag) and hardly ever exceeds $\sqrt{2}$, at least in order of magnitude (see also Thwaites 1960). The requirements that $U^2/7RT_\infty$ and $(T_w-T_\infty)/T_\infty$ are very small are therefore unaltered by consideration of the high-velocity regions, and may be taken as our principal guide.

On the other hand, it should be kept in mind that places where the temperature drops below T_∞ even by only a few degrees, due either to acceleration of the flow or to the body surface being cooler than the main stream, may possibly be regions of condensation of H_2O. Table I. 1 shows that, for a given value of h, quite a small drop in temperature may be sufficient to make $p_v(T) < ph$, the counter-effect of such drop in pressure as may also be present (in the case of acceleration of the flow) being negligible. Condensation can lead to considerable departures of flow behaviour from that found in dry air, both because of the heat released and because the droplets do not necessarily follow the air streamlines.

2.4. *Pressure changes in external aerodynamics*

We must now discuss when pressure changes will be small compared with the absolute pressure.

First, consider the hydrostatic pressure variation. Over a vertical distance l this is ρgl. Therefore, flows with length scale l very small compared with $p/\rho g = RT/g$ (which has the large value 8·4 km for $T = 288°$ K, and is the height in which be pressure would drop by a factor e in an atmosphere at constant temperature T) have hydro-static pressure variation small compared with the absolute pressure.

Next, the dynamic pressure variation can be completely separated from the hydrostatic pressure variation, at least in flows where the density variations are small—in other words, flows in which the same pressure distribution is required to balance the weight of the fluid as when the fluid is at rest. The reason for this is that the difference of the exact pressure distribution from the hydrostatic distribution balances the dynamic forces (inertial and viscous) and is independent of gravity. It is the order of magnitude of this dynamic pressure distribution alone which is studied in the rest of this section, the word 'dynamic' being for the most part suppressed.

A rough working rule, valid under most circumstances, is that, pressure being molecular momentum transport per unit area, the varia-tions of pressure over fields of flow in external aerodynamics are of the order of magnitude of the momentum transport, ρU^2 per unit area, due to bulk convection with velocity U in the main stream. In cases of steady flow, the perfect-fluid theory (Lamb 1932) gives a clear indica-tion of this with the Bernoulli equation $p + \frac{1}{2}\rho v^2 = \text{constant}$ (whose connexion with the rule $H + \frac{1}{2}v^2 = \text{constant}$ mentioned in Section 2.3 is that in a perfect fluid no energy dissipation occurs and therefore $\Delta H = (\Delta p)/\rho$ in any change). This gives a maximum pressure $p_\infty + \frac{1}{2}\rho U^2$, attained at a stagnation point, but no clear minimum.

On the other hand, perfect-fluid theory gives also a theorem that, even in unsteady flow, the minimum pressure is attained on the boundary (Lamb 1932, p. 47), and, although extremely low values of this minimum are predicted for some shapes of obstacle, they are not observed experimentally, and we shall see that the boundary-layer theory gives good reasons why very low pressures on the boundary cannot be achieved, at least in most steady flows. Modifications due to viscosity include the possibility of terms of order $\mu U/l$ in the maxi-mum pressure (see, for example, Homann 1936a), which, however, are small compared with $\frac{1}{2}\rho U^2$ in most practical flows, and in the others are still small compared with the absolute pressure. Also, especially low pressures are found in the interior of any discrete vortices that are produced in the flow. There are, in fact, many flows where density variations are negligible except within such vortices, where the low pressure produces a substantial density reduction, but the effect on the flow as a whole can nevertheless be neglected.

If these very localized filaments of low density be ignored, and if we remember that some cases of unsteady flow may need further study later (Section 6), we are left with the broad general rule that dynamic pressure variations are a small fraction of the absolute pressure if $\rho U^2/p \doteq U^2/RT$ is small. But if this is so, and provided also that $(T_w-T_\infty)/T_\infty$ is small, then temperature variations are a small fraction of the absolute temperature (Section 2.3); and, if, finally, gl/RT is small (to control the hydrostatic pressure variations) then density variations are a small fraction of the density.

These three conditions (which are discussed further in Section 2.7) are not, however, in general sufficient in *internal* aerodynamics. For example, in the flow of compressed air or steam down a long pipe, even at velocities such that U^2/RT is very small, the accumulated effect of wall friction along the length of the pipe can reduce the pressure to a modest fraction of its value at the entry. A similar effect is found in bearings where air is used as the lubricant, and many other counter-examples exist.

2.5. Solenoidality of the velocity field

The main use to be made of the conclusion that relative density changes are small is to infer that the fluid velocity field is solenoidal (like the electrostatic field in a region free of charge). Geometrically, this means that the magnitude of the velocity varies along any 'elementary streamtube' (thin tube to which the velocity vector is everywhere tangential) inversely as the cross-sectional area—a result of great value in the interpretation of flow-visualization photographs, as well as in flow prediction. Analytically, it means that the divergence of the velocity field,

$$\text{div } \mathbf{v} = \frac{\partial v_x}{\partial x} + \frac{\partial v_y}{\partial y} + \frac{\partial v_z}{\partial z} \tag{5}$$

(where v_x means the velocity component in the x-direction, etc.), is zero. This simple equation needs only to be combined with the three equations of momentum and the boundary conditions to give a complete specification of the conditions governing the flow.

However, there are limitations to the validity of the conclusion that the velocity field is solenoidal to close approximation if relative density changes are small. The divergence div $\mathbf{v}$ (Weatherburn 1944) is the rate of increase of volume of a fluid element, per unit volume. This, in turn, is minus the rate of increase of density per unit density, and can be written

$$\text{div } \mathbf{v} = -\frac{1}{\rho}\frac{D\rho}{Dt}. \tag{6}$$

The rate of change $D\rho/Dt$ is in two parts. One part, which alone is present in steady flow, is due to convection with the velocity **v** itself, and does not invalidate the inference that the velocity field is closely solenoidal. In unsteady flow, however, there is a further part, the local rate of change of ρ due to fluctuations of the flow, which at very high frequencies can become important.

2.6. *Unsteady flow and sound waves*

In external aerodynamics, such unsteadiness is due to oscillations in the position, attitude, or shape of the obstacle, which either are harmonic with radian frequency ω or, in more general cases, can usefully be Fourier-analysed into such harmonic components. If we consider one harmonic component at a time, the right-hand side of equation (6) is of order $\omega p_\omega / p_\infty$, where p_ω is the amplitude of the transient pressures of frequency ω. If U_ω is a typical velocity associated with these fluctuations, then p_ω contains terms of order $\omega \rho U_\omega l$, since differences in p_ω over distances of order l have to generate rates of change of momentum (per unit volume) of order $\omega \rho U_\omega$. Terms of order $\rho U U_\omega$ are also present in p_ω, but these cannot invalidate the solenoidality condition if those already mentioned do not. (These estimates can also be derived from the unsteady form of Bernoulli's equation for irrotational flow.) Now, individual terms in div **v** have fluctuations with frequency ω of amplitude U_ω / l. Hence, the condition that $\omega p_\omega / p_\infty$ be negligible compared with these is that

$$\rho \omega^2 l^2 / p_\infty \ll 1. \tag{7}$$

If condition (7) is not satisfied, then the breakdown of solenoidality which occurs is that sound waves of wavelength comparable with the body size are formed, radiating away at the wave velocity

$$a \doteqdot \sqrt{(7p/5\rho)} \doteqdot \sqrt{(\tfrac{7}{5}RT)}, \tag{8}$$

a significant fraction of the energy of the fluctuations. In terms of a, the condition (7) requires that $\omega l/a$ be small, or that l be small compared with the 'radian wavelength' a/ω, which latter condition is derived also in the theory of sound as the condition that such oscillations of the obstacle radiate negligible energy (Rayleigh 1894, vol. 2, p. 248).

As an example of the above considerations, we may ask: how quickly does a flow have to be started or stopped for the process to differ significantly from that obtaining at constant density? The answer is that if the time taken is t_1, the characteristic frequency ω of the process is t_1^{-1}, and so the difference will be insignificant if $t_1 \gg l/a$. Next, in this problem U_ω may be taken equal to U, since the variation of velocity is equal to the whole velocity. Hence, if t_1 is *not* large compared with l/a, pressures of order $\rho Ul/t_1$ will be found. These are already not small compared with ρUa, the pressure predicted by the theory of sound in an *instantaneously* stopped or started flow. Clearly, such pressures may be very much bigger than those of order ρU^2 produced in steady flow. (That large pressures can occur when a flow pattern is changing rapidly is familiar to anyone who has turned off a tap.) However, the *effect* of such pressures is not necessarily very great; for example, the energy required to start a sphere moving through air impulsively is only double that needed to do the same thing in a time so long (compared with l/a) that no sound waves are generated (Longhorn 1952, Miles 1951).

2.7. *Summary of the conditions for solenoidality*

In steady flow, the condition $U^2 \ll RT$ for solenoidality is usually written in terms of the 'Mach number' $M = U/a$, which is the most useful parameter defining the influence of compressibility on such a flow, particularly since $M = 1$ represents the transition between flows where the upstream influence of an obstacle is unlimited and flows where it is limited.

Written with the velocity of sound a, given by equation (8), used as the velocity standard, our four conditions for solenoidality (Sections 2.4 and 2.6) state that

$$\frac{\omega l}{a}, \quad \frac{U}{a}, \quad \frac{T_w - T_\infty}{T_\infty}, \quad \frac{gl}{a^2} \tag{9}$$

are all small. In words, we must have (i) a slowly varying flow, (ii) a low Mach number, (iii) small temperature difference between obstacle and stream, and (iv) a length scale small compared with the scale height of the atmosphere.

3. Other relevant physical properties of air

3.1. *Viscosity*

We must now discuss the slight departures from the exact equilibrium state which are present in any non-uniform motion. It might have been expected, as noted in Section 1, and from a different point of view in Section 2.2, that such departures could be neglected altogether, yielding, under conditions (9), the perfect-fluid theory. However, the fact that the flows determined by perfect-fluid theory require, in general, a non-zero velocity at the surface of any body, where therefore the departures from equilibrium would locally be large, indicates that the effects of these departures must be considered—at any rate to a first approximation, and in parts of the flow.

Now, the departure from equilibrium of a minute bit of air in motion (say, the 2×10^8 molecules in a cube of side 2 microns) could not depend on conditions farther from the bit than say 1 micron, because, as explained in Section 2.2, any molecules reaching the bit from so far off must have 'forgotten' about their previous state. Hence, it is only very local variations of velocity, pressure, temperature and atmospheric composition, over distances of one or two microns, that affect the character of the departures from equilibrium (Meyer 1899, Chapman and Cowling 1952, Hirschfelder, Curtiss, and Bird 1954). Across such distances, these quantities (which specify the approximate equilibrium state) have to a very close approximation simple linear gradients, and so it is on these gradients alone that departures from equilibrium depend. In addition, because the departures are small, it is reasonable to a first approximation to neglect quadratic terms in their relationship with these gradients. The remaining dependence is simply linear.

We consider first how the *momentum transport* departs from its equilibrium value, p per unit area in all directions. Now, momentum transport cannot be influenced by the gradient of pressure or temperature or humidity. This becomes obvious if we suppose that the directions of all the coordinate axes were reversed. Then a linear multiple of any of these gradients would change sign, while in the momentum transport the sign changes in the momentum transported and in the velocity of transport would cancel out. But this argument does not preclude dependence on velocity gradient, in which the sign changes, in both the velocity and the direction of the gradient, would cancel in such a reversal of axes.

We conclude (with Stokes 1845) that the momentum transport is a linear function of the velocity gradient alone.

The simplest kinetic-theory argument for the form of this relationship applies only in a pure shearing motion, in which, say,

$$v_x = Ay, \qquad v_y = v_z = 0. \tag{10}$$

Then the difference of the momentum transport from its hydrostatic value may be expected to involve the transport of x-momentum (the sole non-uniform component) in the y-direction (the sole direction in which it varies), at a rate (per unit time per unit area) of

$$\{\rho\sqrt{(2\pi^{-1}RT)}\}A\lambda, \tag{11}$$

where the term in curly brackets is the mass per unit time per unit area crossing the plane $y = 0$, the length λ is a 'mean free path' of a molecule between collisions, and molecules crossing the plane from the side $y > 0$

have an average x-velocity $A\lambda$, while those crossing from $y < 0$ have an average x-velocity $-A\lambda$ (see for example Meyer 1899, Lighthill 1956a).

The stress, or momentum transport per unit area per unit time, is therefore

$$\mu A = \mu \, \partial v_x / \partial y, \qquad (12)$$

where the coefficient

$$\mu = \{\rho \sqrt{(2\pi^{-1}RT)}\}\lambda \doteq \tfrac{2}{3}\rho a\lambda \qquad (13)$$

is called the viscosity. In equation (13), the velocity of sound

$$a = \sqrt{(\tfrac{7}{5}RT)}$$

is an increasing function of temperature alone, and so is $\rho\lambda$ (because at a fixed temperature the mean free path varies inversely as the density, but, as the temperature is increased, the average deflexion of a molecule by an encounter gradually falls). We infer that μ is a function of T alone, increasing somewhat faster than $T^{\frac{1}{2}}$.

For the more general type of flow, when all nine components of velocity gradient (not just $\partial v_x / \partial y$) are present, subject only to the solenoidality condition

$$\frac{\partial v_x}{\partial x} + \frac{\partial v_y}{\partial y} + \frac{\partial v_z}{\partial z} = 0, \qquad (14)$$

it can be shown (Chapter III), by some more considerations about the effect of changes in the coordinate axes, that the linear relationship between the different components of stress and of velocity gradient can take only one form; this form involves a single arbitrary coefficient μ, which has the property that in the pure shearing motion (10) the shearing stress takes the value given in equation (12). A simple approach to this result is to show that the local flow is a linear combination of (i) two pure shearing motions, each governed, in appropriate axes, by (10), with (ii) a rigid rotation incapable of producing momentum transport.

The viscous-stress terms, each proportional to μ times some velocity gradient, represent the first-order correction to the equilibrium stress condition (of equal pressure p in all directions). Second-order corrections have been calculated (Chapman and Cowling 1952, pp. 259–72), but this refined theory has never been conclusively matched with experiment, and the first-order correction appears to be amply adequate for all problems with a length scale l large compared with λ.

Now, the most important inference from the above discussion is that fluid flows subject to conditions (9) are completely determined by four conditions: the solenoidality condition (14), and the three conditions that each component of the rate of change of momentum of a fluid element is equal to the corresponding component of force on the element, resulting from the variations of pressure and viscous stress around its boundary. These are four conditions on four unknowns (p, v_x, v_y and v_z), which, with appropriate boundary conditions (which we shall see are present), uniquely determine the development of the flow pattern. They contain two coefficients, the density ρ and the viscosity μ, both of which can be taken as constants throughout the flow under conditions (9), since the temperature, on which μ alone depends, varies negligibly.

Some simple flow patterns (Chapter III), for which the equations can be solved, give excellent opportunities for comparison with experiment, from which it appears that, at densities not large compared with atmospheric, the viscosity μ is very closely a function of temperature alone, and increases with temperature somewhat faster than $T^{\frac{1}{2}}$, as suggested by equation (13). A table of μ against T for air is given in Section 5.3. It is from these experiments that the value of the mean free path

$$\lambda = 1 \cdot 5 \mu / \rho a \qquad (15)$$

is inferred; it is 10^{-5} cm (0·1 micron) at room temperature and pressure.

3.2. *Conditions at a solid surface*

The boundary conditions at a solid surface have been mentioned already. From a thermodynamic point of view, they say that departures from equilibrium are just as small there as in the rest of the fluid, owing (in both places) to the high collision frequency. Accordingly, to a close approximation, air in motion satisfies at a solid surface the *equilibrium* conditions, of zero velocity relative to the surface and temperature equal to that of the surface.

Further, no special study of molecular behaviour at the surface is needed to predict the force with which the air acts on an elementary area of solid surface. This is simply the limit of the force, due to pressure and viscous stress, acting on a parallel elementary area displaced into the fluid, when the distance of displacement is allowed to tend to zero (a result which follows at once from the equation of motion of a cylinder of fluid whose end faces are the two elementary areas).

These very simple considerations are sufficient to fit the boundary conditions into the general thermodynamic picture. On the other hand, the mechanism which so effectively restrains departures from the equilibrium condition at the surface is made clearer by a look at some details of that condition. Air molecules are attracted to a solid surface (see, for example, Brunauer 1944) by the various 'van der Waals' forces of cohesion; and their potential energy drop Q on reaching the surface is from 1 to 3 times the energy of liquefaction in each case (varying from about 3 times for the sites most favourable to adsorption to 1 for adsorption on to an existing adsorbed layer). It follows that, in equilibrium, at least part of the surface is covered by a monomolecular layer of 'adsorbed' air molecules, and that molecular species at a partial pressure not negligible compared with their vapour pressure may locally form layers two or more molecules thick.

The adsorbed layer is by no means static. It partakes of the thermal vibrations of the solid, and when a molecule reaches an energy greater than its potential energy defect Q it escapes from the surface. Its lifetime on the surface is of the order of $\tau = \tau_0 e^{Q/kt}$, where $\tau_0 \backsimeq 10^{-14}$ sec is the period of vibration of the molecule when attached to the surface. At the same time, the population of adsorbed molecules is maintained by the continual bombardment of the surface, at a mass rate per unit area given by half the value of the expression in curly brackets in equation (11). Most molecules striking the surface remain on it for a time of the order of magnitude $\tau_0 e^{Q/kT}$ just mentioned, though obviously this order of magnitude varies greatly with the point of impact as well as with the molecular species, since, as already mentioned, Q itself varies in this way.

In the case of air at room temperature, the lifetime $\tau_0 e^{Q/kT}$ is much greater for H_2O molecules than for N_2 and O_2. Even on a strongly hydrophobic surface the heat of adsorption of H_2O is hardly less than the heat of liquefaction, and Q/k is about 5,000° K. The maximum Q/k that has been observed for N_2 and O_2 is about 2,000° K. On these figures the lifetime of H_2O on the surface would be $e^{3,000/T}$ times that of N_2 and O_2, or 60,000 times at $T = 288°$ K. Therefore, even at quite low absolute humidities, for example, proportions 1:1,000 of H_2O to other molecules in the air, the proportions in the surface layer would be 60:1.

At high relative humidities, still greater quantities of surface water are found, especially since all surfaces are 'rough' on a microscopic scale; thus, condensation of water can occur on portions of surface of high concave curvature, even though the partial pressure is below the vapour pressure, exactly as high convex curvature makes supersaturation possible, and owing in both cases to surface tension (see Section 4.3 below).

To sum up, surfaces exposed to air are often mainly water surfaces, although at low relative humidities substantial portions of the surface at any instant may be dry and without adsorbed gas. The drop in potential energy Q when a molecule strikes the water surface may be fairly near to its heat of solution in water. However, this does not differ greatly from its heat of adsorption on a dry surface (for example, for the heat of solution Q of O_2 in H_2O we have $Q/k = 1,900°$ K).

Now, provided that $e^{Q/kT}$ is a large number, a molecule during its lifetime on the surface (of order $\tau_0 e^{Q/kT}$) reaches thermal equilibrium with the surface, and so will leave the surface in no preferred direction, and in particular with zero momentum parallel to the surface on the average. It is this, combined with the high frequency of collision with the surface of the molecules near it, that maintains so effectively the boundary condition of zero fluid velocity (that is, zero mean molecular momentum) relative to the surface.

Even if, on the average, a fraction β of the momentum of molecules hitting the surface is retained on leaving it, one can show (Lighthill 1956a, p. 262) by arguments similar to those leading to equation (13), that the fluid velocity v relative to the surface is equal to

$$\frac{1+\beta}{1-\beta} \lambda \frac{\partial v}{\partial n} \qquad (16)$$

at the surface, if $\partial/\partial n$ signifies differentiation along the outward normal; there can be no significant addition to equation (16) due to an adsorbed water layer being pulled by shearing stress over the surface, because the viscosity of water is so much greater than that of air. Now, $\lambda \, \partial v/\partial n$ is the change in velocity in one mean free path, and this is a very small velocity indeed at ordinary densities. Also, β is normally a small number, but we see from equation (16) that, even if (at high temperatures, for example) β becomes a substantial fraction, there is little effect provided that the distance in which substantial changes of velocity occur is a really large multiple of the mean free path.

The same mechanism ensures that the fluid at the surface has the temperature of the surface. This is the boundary condition used in the discussion of heat transfer (Section 3.3), but it does not influence the flow itself, since under conditions (9) the variations of temperature cause negligible variations of the density ρ and the viscosity μ. Since this list of two constants influencing the flow has not been lengthened by the present discussion of boundary conditions, we can now conclude that the list is complete. For the consequences of this conclusion see Section 5.1.

3.3. *Heat transfer and evaporation*

The determination of heat transfer between a solid surface and a flow is such an important application of boundary-layer theory that, although it is not to be studied in detail in this book (owing to the substantial treatment in Howarth 1953, pp. 757–853), some brief account is desirable. It uses the combined action of conduction and convection. At the surface itself convection is absent, and so the heat has to traverse a thin layer close to the surface, at a rate dominated principally by conduction, before reaching a region where convection of the heat downstream plays the greater part in controlling the temperature distribution.

The theory of heat conduction in a gas is similar to that of viscosity. The flow of heat (that is, of the energy of the molecules relative to the bulk motion) must to a first approximation, like the momentum transport, depend linearly on the gradients of the quantities which specify the equilibrium state. The velocity gradient, however, cannot affect it, being unchanged (unlike the heat flow) by a reversal of axes. As for gradients of the various scalar quantities, only that of temperature can affect heat flow, since by the second law of thermodynamics no energy exchange between contiguous portions of matter at the same temperature is possible.

It follows that, say, the x-component q_x of the heat flow must be a constant multiple

$$q_x = -k\,\partial T/\partial x \qquad (17)$$

of the x-component of temperature gradient, and similarly with q_y and q_z. To estimate the 'thermal conductivity' k, one may argue that although at any point the internal energy E per unit mass is the average over all molecules, the average over those with positive x-velocity is $E(x-C\lambda, y, z) \doteqdot E - C\lambda\,\partial E/\partial x$, while the average over those with negative x-velocity is $E + C\lambda\,\partial E/\partial x$. Here $C \doteqdot 2$ is a factor included to take into account the fact that molecules with high translational energy are more effective in transport than other molecules (Lighthill 1956a, p. 258). By arguments similar to those leading to equation (11), it follows that

$$q_x = -\{\rho\sqrt{(2\pi^{-1}RT)}\}C\lambda\frac{\partial E}{\partial x} = -C\mu\frac{\partial E}{\partial x} = -C\mu c_v\frac{\partial T}{\partial x}, \qquad (18)$$

and so

$$k = C\mu c_v. \qquad (19)$$

Here, $c_v = \partial E/\partial T \doteqdot \tfrac{5}{2}R$ is the specific heat of air at constant volume. With this value for k, an equation, expressing the balance of heat transfer by convection, conduction and exchange with mechanical energy, can be written down, and used, with the boundary condition on temperature mentioned in Section 3.2, to determine the rate of heat transfer as well as the complete temperature field.

Another important application of boundary-layer theory is the study of evaporation from a wet surface (Owen and Ormerod 1951). In describing this theory we shall speak of the liquid as water, although the theory is the same for other liquids.

The boundary condition at the surface is again that of thermodynamic equilibrium, namely that the partial pressure ph of water vapour is equal to the vapour pressure $p_v(T_w)$ for the temperature T_w of the surface. If the value of this partial pressure is different in the main stream, then diffusion and convection of vapour will take place, with diffusion dominating very near the surface, where the fluid velocity is low, and convection dominating farther out.

At any point the average value of h for molecules with positive x-velocity is $h - B\lambda\, \partial h/\partial x$, where $B = 1\cdot4$ is a factor included to take into account the effect of multiple collisions in which some persistence in the sign of the x-velocities is retained (an effect greater here than in momentum transport, where simultaneous persistence of x-velocity and y-velocity is needed). Similarly, the average value of h for molecules with negative x-velocity is $h + B\lambda\, \partial h/\partial x$, and it follows that the mass flow of vapour in the x-direction is

$$-J\{\rho\sqrt{(2\pi^{-1}RT)}\}B\lambda\frac{\partial h}{\partial x} = -JB\mu\frac{\partial h}{\partial x}, \qquad (20)$$

per unit area, per unit time, if J ($= \tfrac{18}{29}$) is the ratio of the molecular weight of H_2O to that of the average air molecule.

In addition to this term, due to the gradient of the concentration h, small terms in the rate of vapour flow exist, due to the gradients of the pressure p and the temperature T, but can be neglected except in centrifugal or thermal separation apparatus.

By equation (20), the mass rate of evaporation from a wet surface is $-JB\mu\, \partial h/\partial n$, where $\partial/\partial n$ signifies differentiation along the outward normal. Hence the surface loses heat at a rate

$$-LJB\mu\, \partial h/\partial n, \qquad (21)$$

where L is the latent heat of the vapour per unit mass. This process continues until the surface is at a temperature (the 'wet-bulb' temperature) so much below that of the main stream that heat transfer to it by conduction balances the heat loss by evaporation; thus

$$-LJB\mu \frac{\partial h}{\partial n} = k\frac{\partial T}{\partial n} = C\mu c_v \frac{\partial T}{\partial n}. \tag{22}$$

This equation leads, as we shall see in the next section, to an equation determining the wet-bulb temperature T_w, given T_∞ and h_∞, the temperature and humidity in the main stream.

3.4. Diffusivities

In Sections 3.1 and 3.3 we have discussed the diffusion of momentum, heat and vapour by the mechanism which may be described as 'drift between collisions'. A useful measure, for comparing the speeds of diffusion of different quantities like these, is the 'diffusivity' or 'diffusion coefficient'. This is defined as the rate of flow of a quantity down its gradient, per unit area per unit time, divided by the gradient of the volume-density of the quantity. ('Down its gradient' means 'in the direction of its greatest rate of decrease'.)

Thus, for diffusion of momentum in solenoidal flows, the diffusivity is the momentum flow μA, given in equation (12), divided by the gradient ρA of the momentum per unit volume ρv. This fraction, the 'diffusivity of momentum'

$$\nu = \mu/\rho, \tag{23}$$

is commonly called the kinematic viscosity.

For diffusion of heat, at least in steady-flow problems for which (as remarked in Section 2.3) the enthalpy H is the appropriate measure of heat (as well as in unsteady flows when the relative pressure variations are much smaller than the relative temperature variations), the appropriate diffusivity is the heat flow k grad T down the temperature gradient, divided by the gradient of the enthalpy per unit volume ρH. Since grad $H = c_p$ grad T, where $c_p = c_v + R = \frac{7}{2}R$ is the specific heat at constant pressure, the 'diffusivity of heat' (or 'thermometric conductivity') is

$$\kappa = k/\rho c_p. \tag{24}$$

The ratio of the diffusivity of momentum to the diffusivity of heat is called the Prandtl number σ. By equation (19),

$$\sigma = \nu/\kappa = \mu c_p/k = c_p/Cc_v \doteqdot 0\cdot 7, \tag{25}$$

a value experimentally verified to one significant figure for practically all gases (for air, $\sigma = 0\cdot 72$). Thus, heat in gases diffuses significantly faster than momentum.

Thirdly, the diffusivity of vapour, κ_v, is the mass flow of vapour $JB\mu$ grad h (see equation (20)) down its concentration gradient, divided by the gradient of the mass of vapour per unit volume $J\rho h$. Thus,

$$\kappa_v = B\mu/\rho = B\nu \doteq \kappa, \tag{26}$$

since $B = 1\cdot4$.

The fact that the diffusivities of heat and of vapour are approximately equal has some interesting consequences. It means that, in many flows, the processes governing the convection and diffusion of heat and of vapour are identical, so that, on an appropriate scale, the resulting distributions of these quantities are the same. Mathematically speaking, the equations for T and h are

$$\frac{DT}{Dt} = \kappa\nabla^2 T, \qquad \frac{Dh}{Dt} = \kappa_v\nabla^2 h, \tag{27}$$

equations which express a balance between the convection of heat (or vapour), as represented by the D/Dt term (standing for differentiation following an individual bit of air), and their diffusion, represented by the Laplacians on the right (standing for the effect of the heat flow in the x-direction varying with x, etc.); equations (27) are correct if the exchange between heat energy and mechanical energy is negligible, and if the temperature variation is small enough for ρ, κ and κ_v to be regarded as uniform. Now, the equations (27) become identical when $\kappa = \kappa_v$. Hence, if T and h take the values T_∞ and h_∞ in the main stream and T_w and h_w at the surface of the obstacle, we have

$$(T-T_w)/(T_\infty-T_w) = (h-h_w)/(h_\infty-h_w) \tag{28}$$

everywhere, because both sides of equation (28) satisfy the same boundary conditions as well as the same differential equation.

We can take the case of steady flow past a wet obstacle as an example of the use of equation (28). Substituting it in equation (22), we obtain

$$-LJB\mu(h_\infty-h_w) = Cc_v(T_\infty-T_w), \tag{29}$$

an equation which determines h_∞, the humidity of the stream, if T_∞ and T_w are measured (since h_w must be the saturation humidity $p_v(T_w)/p$ at temperature T_w). Conversely, equation (29) can be solved to determine the wet-bulb temperature T_w in terms of T_∞ and h_∞. Numerically, equation (30) gives

$$h_\infty = h_w - 0\cdot0007(T_\infty-T_w), \tag{30}$$

a relation which is verified experimentally provided that the wet-bulb thermometer is kept in a steady airstream (Whipple 1933).

The simplicity of 'analogy' arguments like the one just given make them very attractive, and much work has been done on the analogy between heat and momentum, usually called the Reynolds analogy although Reynolds's use of it was confined to turbulent flow (Howarth 1953, pp. 815–53). However, this latter analogy is of more restricted application, not only because $\nu \neq \kappa$, but still more because momentum is affected by pressure gradients as well as by convection and diffusion. Hence, it is only in a flow with negligible pressure gradients that this analogy can properly be drawn, and even there the fact that $\nu < \kappa$ tends to make heat diffuse farther than momentum.

For numerical estimates of distance of diffusion, note that the dimension of any diffusivity, such as κ, is the square of a length divided by a time. Hence the distance of diffusion in time t is expected from dimensional considerations to be proportional to $\sqrt{(\kappa t)}$. This expectation is borne out by the study of the elementary solutions of equations (28) in hydrostatic conditions (when convection is absent, so that D/Dt is simply $\partial/\partial t$); these all involve terms like $e^{-x^2/4\kappa t}$ (see, for example, Carslaw and Jaeger 1959), which becomes negligibly small only when the space coordinate x is large compared with $\sqrt{(\kappa t)}$.

Since ν, κ, and κ_v are all of the same order of magnitude, the distances of diffusion of momentum, heat, and vapour in time t are all of the order of magnitude $\sqrt{(\nu t)}$. It follows that in steady flow with a velocity of order U, the distance of diffusion while the fluid is being convected through a distance x is of order $\sqrt{(\nu x/U)}$. This will be seen in Chapter II to be one of the main considerations underlying the boundary-layer concept.

4. Analogies with liquid motions

4.1. *Comparison between liquids and gases in equilibrium*

In Sections 2 and 3 we have discussed both the conditions under which the velocity field is solenoidal in external aerodynamics, and, also, the physical properties of air which influence such a velocity field, together with any heat transfer or evaporation, or both, which it may produce. In Section 4 we discuss conditions under which the effect of an obstacle on a uniform stream of *liquid* is of a closely similar character, first in cases when the obstacle is at a distance of many diameters from the free surface, and next when it is near the free surface. As noted at the beginning of Chapter I, any knowledge about these flows is directly applicable to problems of the motion of bodies through liquid at rest.

It is undesirable to go into the physical background in as much detail here as in Sections 2 and 3, partly because we wish to place the main emphasis in this chapter on external aerodynamics, and partly

because knowledge of this background is in fact much less complete
for liquids than for gases. However, we may note the principal similari-
ties and differences between the two phases (see also Guggenheim 1957,
Mayer and Mayer 1940, Hill 1956).

Liquids are like gases in that they possess only one equilibrium state
at a given pressure and temperature—instead of being able, like solids,
to remain in equilibrium while supporting a range of different shear
stresses. Their difference from gases is rather of a quantitative kind
—namely that the forces between molecules, and especially the attractive or cohesive forces, act far more strongly in the denser phase.

For example, in water at 288° K, the part $RT\rho$ of the pressure, which
results from momentum transport by the thermal agitation of the molecules, is about 1,300 atm. Therefore, at ordinary pressures (of a few
atmospheres or less), the resultant of the intermolecular forces acting
across unit area of liquid must be a counterbalancing tension of, again,
about 1,300 atm. Furthermore, these intermolecular forces include
repulsive forces brought into play in very close encounters, so that the
resultant of the attractive forces alone must be even greater.

In both liquids and gases an increase in density requires an increase
in pressure, because the resultant of the attractive forces increases less
rapidly with density than (in a liquid) the resultant of the repulsive
forces or (in a gas) the momentum transport rate. However, at those
temperatures, below the 'critical' temperature (647° K for water), with
which we shall be exclusively concerned, *homogeneous* fluid states with
densities intermediate between the liquid and the gaseous values are
not possible, because a local increase in density in such a fluid would
be accompanied by a *drop* in pressure (dominated by the effect of the
attractive forces), which would encourage the local increase to continue.
Therefore, the fluid would spontaneously separate into phases of higher
and lower density. This is, of course, the explanation of the existence
of a distinct liquid phase, separated in general from some gaseous phase
by a free surface.

4.2. *The liquid-vapour transition*

The minimum pressure at which a homogeneous liquid phase is
possible at a given temperature is not exactly known in most cases,
but at temperatures well below the critical it is certainly negative; the
liquid is then in a state of tension, which may amount even to hundreds
of atmospheres. Between this state and that of the homogeneous vapour
phase at its maximum possible pressure, there lies not only the aforesaid

range of densities for which no homogeneous fluid phase is possible, but also a range of pressures at any of which both the liquid and the vapour phase can exist.

However, at any given pressure, one of these phases is the more stable, in the thermodynamic sense of having a lower free energy: at pressures above the vapour pressure the liquid is more stable; at pressures below it, the vapour. From the statistical point of view, the stable phase is that which has more states available to it, bearing in mind the Maxwell-Boltzmann weighting by the factor $e^{-\epsilon/kT}$, where ϵ is the energy of a state. Only at pressures below the vapour pressure does the greater number of molecular configurations available in the vapour phase outweigh the advantage accruing from this weighting factor to the liquid phase with its negative potential energies due to intermolecular attraction.

The transition to the more stable phase can nevertheless require a time very much greater than the age of the universe, if there are no extraneous surfaces on which the stable phase can grow. To be sure, a supercooled vapour in a container can always condense out on the walls even if no nuclei of condensation are present, and such nuclei have in any case a marked tendency to form spontaneously by chance encounters of molecules (Emmons 1958, pp. 526–73); but a liquid below its vapour pressure, even at a large negative pressure, can persist indefinitely (Plesset 1957, Birkhoff and Zarantonello 1957) if all bubbles of foreign gas and other suitable internal surfaces are first removed (for example, by filtering the liquid and then subjecting it to tension for long enough to make all bubbles grow to a size at which gravity separates them).

On the other hand, in water and other liquids under ordinary conditions, there are gas bubbles with diameters of order, say, 30 microns (these rise under gravity at a speed of only about $\frac{1}{2}$ mm/sec), and such bubbles can grow by evaporation of liquid already at pressures of about 1/10 atm below the vapour pressure. It is this growth, together with the growth of small bubbles attached to dust particles in the liquid, which is observed as 'cavitation' in liquid flows where the absolute pressure falls locally to values in the neighbourhood of zero or below.

4.3. *Surface tension*

Small bubbles like those just discussed, and indeed all liquid surfaces with radius of curvature less than about 1 cm, are strongly influenced by surface tension. At a pressure above the vapour pressure, each molecule in the body of a liquid has a free energy less than it would possess in the vapour phase; however, the free energy of molecules in the free surface cannot be nearly so small, because they are only half-surrounded by attracting neighbours. Hence, the free energy of any portion of liquid includes not only a term proportional to the total mass but also one proportional to the area of free surface. If the surface energy is γ per unit area, γ can be regarded as a 'surface tension', because extending the area by δS requires work $\gamma \delta S$, and therefore an applied tension γ per unit length of curve along which the area increase is made.

The tendency of surface tension is to reduce all free surfaces to minimum area; for example, drops and bubbles are pulled back into spherical shape in this way against forces (e.g. aerodynamic, gravitational) which attempt to deform them (Prandtl 1952, pp. 324–30; Lane and Green 1956). This effect is greatest for very small drops and bubbles, which are those whose area is greatest relative to their volume. This is also why very small bubbles cannot grow, even at pressures below the vapour pressure, although when larger bubbles are present cavitation occurs rather easily.

4.4. *Conditions for solenoidality of liquid flows*

Cavitation alone inhibits the solenoidality of flows due to the presence of a stationary obstacle in a uniform stream of liquid. Changes of density due to changes of pressure and temperature (such as were discussed exhaustively for air in Section 2) are too small, in the absence of phase changes, to produce any significant departure from solenoidality in steady flow.

For example (Washburn 1926, vol. 3, pp. 35–42), a pressure of 200 atm is required to increase the density of water by 1 per cent.; values of the order of 100 atm are also normal for other liquids; and even at the enormous pressures present in the extreme depths of the ocean, the density does not exceed its surface value by more than 5 per cent. Now, a flow would have to have a velocity of 200 m/sec to produce a pressure rise of 200 atm in water; not only are such velocities unattainable, but such flows would be expected to involve also comparable drops of pressure, and so to be dominated by cavitation.

Temperature, again, affects liquid densities only slightly, that of water varying by only 4 per cent. between its melting- and boiling-points, and by only 1 per cent. in the range 0° to 45° C. Further, the rates of change of temperature of elements of liquid are in general small, being due simply to heat conduction (exchange with kinetic energy producing a quite negligible effect, owing to the low fluid velocities which are attainable); the rate of change of density which results (and which if significant would disturb the solenoidality condition) is therefore completely negligible.

It follows that the condition for solenoidality in steady flows is simply a condition for the absence of cavitation. With liquids that have not been specially 'outgassed', this condition, as noted in Section 4.2, is that the pressure p shall not fall by more than a rather small margin below the vapour pressure $p_v(T)$ of the liquid; the margin is usually neglected in the necessarily unrefined study of this difficult subject.

The pressure p can be separated into the hydrostatic pressure p_h (atmospheric pressure plus ρg times the depth below the undisturbed level of the surface) and the dynamic pressure p_d, and so the condition becomes

$$(-p_d)_{\max} < p_h - p_v. \tag{31}$$

The maximum dynamic pressure drop on the left of this inequality will in any given steady flow be proportional (see Section 2.4) to ρU^2, so that in such a flow cavitation will be absent provided (Ackeret 1931, Rouse 1950, Plesset 1957) that the non-dimensional ratio

$$Q = (p_h - p_v)/(\tfrac{1}{2}\rho U^2), \tag{32}$$

usually called the 'cavitation number', exceeds some critical value (of the order of the maximum suction coefficient, $(-p_d)_{\max}/(\tfrac{1}{2}\rho U^2)$, for the particular flow).

For flow near the surface the numerator of Q is about an atmosphere. Then Q will exceed 1 (a typical critical value for bluff shapes) only if $\tfrac{1}{2}\rho U^2$ is less than an atmosphere, that is, if $U < 14$ m/sec. This stringent restriction on velocity will obviously be relaxed somewhat at greater depths. For streamlined shapes at small angles of incidence, again, Q may need only to exceed a smaller number, say 0·4.

This is not the place to discuss the complications which arise when cavitation does occur; it may, however, be noted that vapour bubbles passing into regions of higher pressure collapse catastrophically, and that continued collapse of such bubbles on a solid surface can damage it very severely. This is the principal mechanism of erosion by water, on the grand geographic scale as well as in machinery.

It should also be noted that at quite small cavitation numbers, large cavities are formed which trail behind obstacles (Birkhoff and Zarantonello 1957, Gilbarg 1957). On the other hand, in many flows at large cavitation number, cavitation may occur only very locally, in the middle of such discrete vortices as may be produced in the flow; this cavitation may be unimportant except as a source of sound.

Finally, the presence in unsteady flow of further contributions to the dynamic pressure, those fluctuating with frequency ω being of order $\omega\rho U_\omega l$ (see Section 2.6), should be remembered, as leading to a further possibility of the condition (31) for absence of cavitation being broken, at least at certain phases of the oscillation. At high frequency, again, sound waves can become important; to exclude them, we must add to the conditions for solenoidality, as in Section 2.6, one that $\omega l/a$ be small. However, the speed of sound a is 1·4 km/sec in water, and of the same order of magnitude in other liquids, so that only very high frequencies indeed are hereby excluded.

4.5. *The viscosity of liquids*

When the liquid flow does satisfy the same 'solenoidality' condition as the airflows discussed in Sections 2 and 3, we may ask whether also the relation between stress and velocity gradient takes the same form. If this is so, and also any free surface which is present does not interfere with the flow (conditions for which are discussed in Section 4.8), then the liquid flow must be governed by exactly the same conditions as the airflow, with simply different values for the constants ρ and μ. This will be seen in Section 5 to make the analogy between airflow and liquid motion very close.

Now, although stress in liquids is made up principally of direct forces between molecules rather than momentum transport, the arguments of Section 3.1 for the departure of the stress from its equilibrium value to be a function of velocity gradient alone, and further (because of the expected smallness of departures from equilibrium) to depend linearly on it, are still forceful. Extensive experimentation has, in fact, failed to show departures from this law for homogeneous liquids, other than those with exceptionally long molecules (Hatschek 1928, Hermans 1953).

For example, the discharge of such a liquid through a capillary tube is observed to be closely proportional to the pressure difference producing it, right up to the value at which unsteady 'turbulent' flow sets in (due to instability). This is strong evidence for a constant viscosity coefficient (whose relationship to the ratio of discharge to pressure difference will be inferred in Chapter III) in the law of dependence of shearing stress on velocity gradient. With tubes of narrow bore the condition that instability be avoided does not prevent the attainment of fairly high velocity gradients (for example, 10^6 sec^{-1} with water at 15° C in a tube of diameter 1/10 mm), at which the linear relationship is still observed.

Even suspensions in a homogeneous liquid, of such particles as do not attract one another, are found to show the same linear dependence, although with a viscosity coefficient greater than for the pure liquid. On the other hand, with suspensions of particles which do (for any reason) attract one another in the presence of the liquid, there is a continual tendency of these particles to form into a large-scale structure, a tendency which their slight thermal agitation (the Brownian movement) is normally powerless to resist. When such a structure is present the whole no longer behaves as a liquid; some rigidity is observed, the relationship between stress and strain being a complicated mixture of those appropriate to solids and to liquids. In some cases stirring or other deformation can destroy the structure so that the suspension behaves like a fluid for a time and only later relapses into quasi-solid behaviour; such suspensions are called 'thixotropic'.

With solutions of polymers and other substances with exceptionally long molecules similar 'anomalous' or 'non-Newtonian' behaviour under shearing stress is found, the principal cause being again interactions between molecules, in which a prominent role is played by intertwining. Emulsions (that is, suspensions of droplets of another liquid; for example, milk or mayonnaise) also show this sort of behaviour, the deformability of the droplets being a complicating factor in this case.

However, there remains a wide range, not only of homogeneous liquids but also of solutions, colloids and suspensions, which show the 'Newtonian' linear relationship between shearing stress and velocity gradient. Once the linearity of the relationship is admitted, its form is unique (as discussed in Section 3.1 and more fully in Chapter III), and involves only a single arbitrary constant, the viscosity μ, which may however be a function of the state of the fluid (Section 4.6). As with air, again, there is also a condition of zero relative motion at all boundaries, for the same basic thermodynamic reason that departures from the local equilibrium conditions must be small. The details of these local conditions are again complicated; but the high accuracy of the conclusion is ensured by the high frequency of collisions with the surface.

4.6. *Variation of viscosity with pressure and temperature*

When μ is determined, by substantially the same methods as for gases, its dependence on pressure, as with them, is found to be small

(Hatschek 1928, pp. 79–97; Washburn 1926, vol. 5, pp. 10–52; vol. 7, pp. 211–24): thus, there is a gradual increase with pressure for most liquids (although water between 0° and 30° C shows some initial decrease, which is ascribed to strong chemical association between molecules being broken up as the pressure increases), but a pressure of the order of 1,000 atm is required to double the viscosity. However, the variation of μ with temperature is extremely rapid, much more so than with gases, and is in the opposite sense—as is well known, the viscosity of liquids decreases with increasing temperature, water at its freezing-point being 6·3 times more viscous than at its boiling-point. Liquids which are chemically more normal show the same behaviour in a less marked degree: the ratio of viscosity at 0° to that at 100° C lies between 2 and 4 for a wide range of organic liquids.

A full understanding of the physical mechanism of viscosity and its temperature-dependence in liquids is still wanting, but the presence of larger clusters of mutually interacting molecules at low temperatures, clusters which a shear has in due course to break up, is doubtless important (see, for example, Glasstone, Laidler, and Eyring 1941).

Now, liquid flows will be exactly analogous to the airflows discussed in Sections 2 and 3 only if the viscosity is substantially constant throughout the flow, and we now see that this will require substantially constant temperature. Thus, although the solenoidality condition (Section 4.5) imposed no restriction on temperature variations, the simplicity of flows with constant, uniform viscosity will be absent unless the temperature variations are small; as in Section 2.3, this excludes flows past obstacles whose surface temperature differs significantly from that of the undisturbed stream.

4.7. Heat conduction and diffusion in liquids

There are problems of heat conduction and diffusion in liquids which are closely analogous to those discussed for gases in Section 3.3.

In homogeneous liquids local departures from thermodynamic equilibrium are expected to be small, whence one expects (as shown in Section 3.3) a proportionality between heat flux and temperature gradient. Experimental results on the coefficient of proportionality, that is, the thermal conductivity of liquids, are scanty, but the picture they give is of a quantity which varies far less, both with temperature and (especially) with constitution, than viscosity (Washburn 1926, vol. 5, pp. 226–30). Results typical of the dependence on temperature are these for water: $k = 6 \cdot 0 \times 10^4$ ergs/cm sec °K at 10° C and $6 \cdot 7 \times 10^4$ at

80° C. Dependence on constitution may conveniently be exhibited by comparing values of $\kappa = k/\rho c_p$, the diffusivity of heat, which was shown in Section 3.4 to be the constant governing the temperature distribution in a given flow. (Even for liquids it is worth retaining the distinguishing suffix on the specific heat c_p, since c_v is measurably less, owing to the substantial amount of work which must be done on a liquid after a rise in temperature to compress it to its original volume.) For all non-metallic liquids, κ is close to 10^{-3} cm²/sec, being about $0 \cdot 9 \times 10^{-3}$ for alcohols, oils, etc., and rising exceptionally to $1 \cdot 5 \times 10^{-3}$ for water. The mechanism of heat conduction is direct exchange of translational energy by jostling. No breaking-up of large clusters is required. Migration of individual molecules through the liquid is also unimportant, as is shown by the fact that the diffusivity κ_d of molecules of solute through a solution, or of a particular constituent through a liquid mixture, is found to be of the order of magnitude of 10^{-5} cm²/sec. (It varies more than κ does, but never rises much above this.)

The kinematic viscosity ν, on the other hand, is often much greater for liquids than 10^{-3} (see Table I. 5 in Section 5.3), and so heat transfer in the liquid flows discussed in Section 4, although governed by the same equations as those in gases, differs widely in the relevant value of the Prandtl number $\sigma = \nu/\kappa$, the ratio of diffusivities of momentum and heat. Thus, σ is 7 for water at 15° C (ten times as much as for air), while σ is about 10^4 for many oils, etc.

Diffusion of particular constituents in a liquid mixture, again, although governed (as discussed in Section 3.4) by these same equations in many cases, involves some still larger values of the ratio of the diffusivity of momentum ν to the diffusivity κ_d (of the order of 10^{-5} cm²/sec) of the constituent.

These considerations show that high values of these diffusivity ratios are by far the most important, after the particular value $0 \cdot 7$ noted in Section 3.4 as normal for gases. However, liquid metals are an exception, owing to the very effective transport of heat energy by the free electrons. For example, in Hg at 15° C, $\sigma = 0 \cdot 026$.

4.8. *The effect of a free surface*

Analogies between the effect of an obstacle on uniform streams of liquid and of air respectively may persist even if the liquid has a free surface. This is already fairly obvious in cases when the depth h of the centroid of the obstacle is much greater than its linear dimension l. In such a case the presence of a free surface, in a remote region where disturbances are very small, can affect the flow only very slightly; we may note also that the theory of surface waves demonstrates that waves of length comparable with l will not penetrate as deep as the body if $h \gg l$.

However, even in cases when h is comparable with l, and even when the body protrudes partially from the surface, it is possible for the analogy with a body in an airstream to remain fairly close. This will be so provided that the free surface almost retains its plane shape in the presence of the obstacle. It will then behave like a plane of symmetry in an airstream, so that the flow past an immersed body will be identical with the flow of a homogeneous fluid past a combination of the immersed part of the body with its mirror-image in the free surface.

The condition for such approximate planeness of the free surface is that the dynamic pressures generated on the plane of symmetry in the analogous airflow are so small that the surface rise above that plane, necessary to maintain atmospheric pressure at the surface, is negligible compared with the body dimension l. Since the dynamic pressures are of order ρU^2, the surface rise is of order U^2/g, and the required condition is that

$$U^2/gl \qquad (33)$$

is small. Modern practice defines the 'Froude number' as

$$F = U/\sqrt{(gl)}, \qquad (34)$$

and we see that, provided F is small, its square, (33), will be amply small enough for the free surface to have no effect.

This condition of low Froude number has practical importance, since it ensures that there is a negligible contribution to the resistance associated with the generation of surface waves.

For very small bodies, another condition is necessary if the free surface is to remain effectively plane. This is that the meniscus where the surface meets the obstacle be negligible compared with the size of the obstacle. The size of the meniscus is of order $\sqrt{(\gamma/\rho g)}$, so the required condition is that the 'Bond number'

$$B = \rho g l^2/\gamma \qquad (35)$$

be large. The use of Froude number and Bond number will be further discussed in Section 5.5.

Occasionally another type of free surface is present, one between two liquids of different density; for example, near the mouth of a river there may be a fairly abrupt separation between fresh water (above) and salt water (below). Vertical displacements z of such a free surface produce hydrostatic pressure changes $g(\Delta\rho)z$, where $\Delta\rho$ is the density difference. Therefore, the condition for the interface to remain flat enough to be regarded as a plane of symmetry (both for the upper and for the lower flow) is that values of z of the order of $\rho U^2/g(\Delta\rho)$ (produced by pressure differences between the two flows of order ρU^2) be small compared with the body dimension l. Thus,

$$\frac{\rho}{\Delta\rho}\frac{U^2}{gl} \tag{36}$$

must be small. This is a more stringent condition than (33), and in certain Norwegian fiords it has been observed that ships moving at speeds at which their wave-making resistance would normally be low can experience a strangely high drag, due to the production of large waves on such an unseen interface (Lamb 1916, 1932).

On the other hand, there are obviously values of $\Delta\rho$ so small that the interface will be unimportant for a quite different reason—namely, that (far from remaining plane) it will take up the shape of a stream surface in the flow of a homogeneous fluid past the same obstacle, and that hydrostatic pressure differences set up thereby will be too small to have any dynamic effect. The condition for this is that $g(\Delta\rho)l$ is small compared with ρU^2—in other words, that (36) is *large*. Thus, it is only for an intermediate range of values of (36) 'of order 1', neither small nor large, that an important interaction between the dynamic and hydrostatic pressure fields can occur, or that significant wave motion on the interface is generated.

When the vertical density gradient $\partial\rho/\partial z$ is more gradual, the density change $\Delta\rho$ in a distance of order l is of order $l\,\partial\rho/\partial z$, and so the relevant parameter which replaces (36) is

$$\frac{\rho}{\partial\rho/\partial z}\frac{U^2}{gl^2}. \tag{37}$$

Wave motions will be generated if (37) is of order 1. This is substantially the case, also, in the meteorological problem of the 'lee waves' behind hills (Scorer 1949). In aeronautical problems, however, the value of (37) is too great for the density gradient to have any effect. This is why such buoyancy effects did not need to be considered in the problems of external aerodynamics discussed in Section 3.

PART III

THE MAJOR SIMPLIFYING FEATURE OF THE SUBJECT

5. Dynamical similarity and dimensional analysis

5.1. *Dynamical similarity; Reynolds number*

In Part II we have discussed a wide range of flows, each generated by the presence of an obstacle in a uniform stream, and found conditions for each to be governed, to good approximation, by the same conditions of solenoidality and constant viscosity. In every steady-flow case (that is, when the obstacle is simply held at rest) the motion of the fluid is then dependent only on

   (i) the size and shape of the obstacle;

   (ii) the values of the constants ρ and μ for the fluid in question, and of U, the velocity of the stream.

We now discuss conditions under which, keeping only the shape of the obstacle fixed ('geometrical similarity'), we vary its size (as specified by some 'length-scale' l; for example its 'diameter', the greatest distance between any pair of points on it), and also the three constants ρ, μ and U, to new values l', ρ', μ' and U', and yet the change, in every flow quantity that we can measure, is simply that which would be produced by a change in the fundamental units of length, time, and mass. The flow pattern is then unaltered, and we can speak of the flows as 'dynamically similar'.

Such a change of units (in which, for example, the new unit of length is taken as L cm, that of time as T sec, and that of mass as M gm) must be accompanied by changes in the units of derived quantities (force, density, viscosity, etc.), so as to ensure that the laws defining these quantities, which are those governing our fluid motions, are unaltered. For example, in order that mass times acceleration shall still equal force, the new unit of force must be MLT^{-2} dynes. Similarly, that of density must be ML^{-3} gm cm^{-3}, that of pressure $ML^{-1}T^{-2}$ dyne cm^{-2}, that of viscosity $ML^{-1}T^{-1}$ gm cm^{-1} sec^{-1}, that of surface tension MT^{-2} dyne cm^{-1}, etc.

After such a change of units, the length-scale, stream velocity, density and viscosity would have the values

$$l' = \frac{l}{L}, \quad U' = \frac{U}{LT^{-1}}, \quad \rho' = \frac{\rho}{ML^{-3}}, \quad \mu' = \frac{\mu}{ML^{-1}T^{-1}} \qquad (38)$$

Now, equations (38) imply that

$$\frac{\rho' U' l'}{\mu'} = \frac{\rho U l}{\mu}. \tag{39}$$

Conversely, if for any set of values of ρ', U', l' and μ' equation (39) is satisfied, then the equations (38) must hold provided that the new units L, T and M are taken as

$$L = \frac{l}{l'}, \quad T = \frac{l U'}{l' U}, \quad M = \frac{\rho l^3}{\rho' l'^3}. \tag{40}$$

The result just obtained is by far the most important simplifying feature of our subject. It means that in many cases the use of a scale model of the obstacle, together with a change in the speed of the undisturbed stream, and possibly changes in the pressure, temperature or constitution of the fluid, may make no essential alteration to the flow. Provided only that the single quantity $\rho U l/\mu$ remains unaltered, the change is identical with that produced by simply adopting the new units (40) for length, time and mass (together with the new units for derived quantities implied by these).

The flow pattern is thus a function not of the four variables ρ, U, l and μ but only of the single variable

$$R = \rho U l/\mu. \tag{41}$$

The immense simplification which this produces is well illustrated by the remark of Jeffreys that a good table of a function of one variable may require a page; that of a function of two variables a volume; that of a function of three variables a bookcase; and that of a function of four variables a library.

R is called the 'Reynolds number', because it is a 'pure number', independent of the system of units (as the step from (38) to (39) shows), and because Reynolds (1883) first showed its importance in the particular problem of the onset of turbulence.

5.2. Force coefficients and pressure coefficients

When measurements are made on the steady flow past an obstacle of given shape, it is desirable to express the results in a form dependent only on the Reynolds number $\rho U l/\mu$ and not on the individual values of ρ, U, l and μ used in the experiment; the results can then be applied directly to a flow with different values ρ', U', l' and μ', subject only to the condition (39) of equal Reynolds number. For example, if a force (like the drag D) is measured, it will be convenient to divide it by that combination of ρ, U and l which has the dimensions of force, namely $\rho U^2 l^2$. This yields a pure number, or 'coefficient',

$$k_D = D/(\rho U^2 l^2), \tag{42}$$

whose value must be unaltered by a change of units, or by a change to another flow at equal Reynolds number (which two changes have been shown to be equivalent). In fact, the drag would be changed to

$$D' = \frac{D}{MLT^{-2}} = \frac{D\rho' U'^2 l'^2}{\rho U^2 l^2} \tag{43}$$

by equation (40), whence k_D is the same in the two flows.

In practice, a different drag coefficient C_D is normally used (especially in English-speaking countries), but it differs from k_D by a simple numerical factor for any given obstacle shape, and therefore shares with k_D the property just described. This is (Glauert 1926, Goldstein 1938, Robinson and Laurmann 1956, Thwaites 1960)

$$C_D = D/(\tfrac{1}{2}\rho U^2 S), \tag{44}$$

in which the factor ρU^2 is altered into $\tfrac{1}{2}\rho U^2$, the greatest dynamic pressure normally found on the surface, and the factor l^2 is altered into an area S characteristic of the obstacle; thus, for wings, S is taken as the area of the planform. Drag measurements, or drag predictions from theory, are stated in terms of the dependence of C_D upon R. Similar coefficients are used for other forces; for example, $C_L = L/(\tfrac{1}{2}\rho U^2 S)$, where L is the lift (force at right angles to the undisturbed stream).

Again, the difference p_d between the measured pressure and the hydrostatic pressure (pressure at the same level in the undisturbed fluid) is divided by $\tfrac{1}{2}\rho U^2$ (a combination of ρ and U with the dimensions of pressure) to give a non-dimensional 'pressure coefficient'

$$C_p = p_d/(\tfrac{1}{2}\rho U^2), \tag{45}$$

which must have the same value at corresponding points of different flow fields at the same Reynolds number.

In the same way, every measurement or theoretical prediction about such flows should be reduced to non-dimensional form, so that the stated values shall have the widest possible application. When this can be done in more than one way, one may select that which appears most illuminating.

5.3. *Numerical values of the Reynolds number*

In this section we review typical numerical values of R for different fluids, speeds and length-scales occurring in practice. Now, since

$$R = \rho Ul/\mu = Ul/\nu, \tag{46}$$

the only property of the fluid on which R depends is the 'diffusivity of momentum' or 'kinematic viscosity' ν (see Section 3.4); the latter name was suggested by Maxwell because, as we now see, ν alone (and not μ or ρ separately) influences the flow pattern. We begin by noting some values of ν for different fluids.

TABLE I. 2

Viscosity μ and kinematic viscosity ν, in c.g.s. units, for air at atmospheric pressure, as a function of temperature T

T (°C)	−100	−50	0	50	100	150	200	250	300
$10^6\mu$	116	145	171	195	218	239	258	277	295
ν	0·057	0·091	0·132	0·178	0·230	0·286	0·346	0·410	0·478

For air, μ is effectively a function of temperature alone, which is tabulated in the first column of Table I. 2; in the second column it has been divided by the value of ρ at a pressure of 1 atm to give ν at 1 atm as a function of temperature, whence ν, at other pressures for which gas imperfection can be ignored, is obtained on division by the pressure in atmospheres. Table I. 2 is appropriate whenever the pressure and temperature are known, but for flight studies, when this is not so, one may wish for rough average values of ν and other quantities as a function simply of altitude; these are given by the 'I.C.A.O. Standard Atmosphere' data summarized in Table I. 3.

TABLE I. 3

Viscosity μ and kinematic viscosity ν, in c.g.s. units, as a function of altitude in kilometres, in the International Civil Aviation Organization (1954) Standard Atmosphere

Altitude	0	2·5	5	7·5	10	12·5	15	17·5	20
$10^6\mu$	179	171	163	154	145	142	142	142	142
ν	0·146	0·179	0·221	0·227	0·352	0·493	0·732	1·085	1·610

For water, values of μ and ν as a function of temperature are given in Table I. 4; values are for atmospheric pressure but neither quantity varies significantly with pressure. In the c.g.s. units employed μ and ν remain nearly equal throughout the range, because ρ remains near to 1.

The values of μ are greater for water than for air; but the values of ν are less (at atmospheric pressure). Thus, momentum diffuses faster in air than in water, and, for given U and l, the Reynolds number is smaller in air than in water.

TABLE I. 4

Viscosity μ and kinematic viscosity ν, in c.g.s. units, for water at
atmospheric pressure, as a function of temperature T

T (°C)	0	5	10	15	20	25	30
μ	0·01787	0·01514	0·01304	0·01137	0·01002	0·00891	0·00798
ν	0·01787	0·01514	0·01304	0·01138	0·01004	0·00894	0·00802
T (°C)	40	50	60	70	80	90	100
μ	0·00654	0·00548	0·00467	0·00405	0·00355	0·00316	0·00283
ν	0·00659	0·00554	0·00475	0·00414	0·00366	0·00327	0·00295

To complete the picture of viscosity data Table I. 5 gives μ and ν for a number of substances at 15° C and atmospheric pressure, for comparison with those of air and water. The importance of density in determining kinematic viscosities, and hence flow patterns, is well illustrated by the fact that hydrogen has the same kinemàtic viscosity as olive oil.

We pass now to Reynolds-number values. In air at sea-level, at an aircraft speed such as 100 m/sec, about the highest at which density variations can be regarded as small, the Reynolds number is 7×10^6 'per metre'. (This means that it is 7×10^6 times the value of the length-scale l in metres.) Hence, for a large transport plane (the D.C. 6), the Reynolds number R_b based on the wing span $b = 39$ m is $2·7 \times 10^8$, while R_c, that based on the wing chord, which is more useful in many studies of wing aerodynamics, is 3×10^7. For a light aeroplane (the Miles Gemini) $R_b = 8 \times 10^7$ and $R_c = 1·2 \times 10^7$.

At other altitudes the Reynolds number per metre at 100 m/sec is $10^6/\nu$, with ν as in Table I. 3; thus it is $4·5 \times 10^6$ per m at 5 km, $2·8 \times 10^6$ at 10 km, $1·4 \times 10^6$ at 15 km, and $4·2 \times 10^5$ at 20 km. The values of R_b and R_c just quoted are reduced accordingly.

In wind-tunnels designed to investigate flows in which the density may be regarded as constant, speeds U of the same order of magnitude 100 m/sec are often used, although in many tunnels considerations of cost have caused U to be limited to, say, 30 m/sec (Pankhurst and Holder 1952). Length-scales are usually much smaller than on a large aeroplane. An aircraft model, even in one of the largest wind-tunnels in the world, could hardly have $b > 4$ m or $c > 1·5$ m; hence, at $R = 7 \times 10^6$ per m, $R_b < 3 \times 10^7$ and $R_c < 10^7$.

Thus, to attempt the representation of full-scale sea-level conditions, an increased Reynolds number per m is needed; that is, ν must be reduced. This could in theory be achieved by using refrigerated air or

TABLE I. 5

Viscosity μ and kinematic viscosity ν, in c.g.s. units, for gases and liquids at 15° C and atmospheric pressure

	μ	ν
Air	0·00018	0·15
Nitrogen N_2	0·00017	0·15
Oxygen O_2	0·00020	0·15
Hydrogen H_2	0·00009	1·05
Helium He	0·00020	1·14
Neon Ne	0·00031	0·37
Argon A	0·00022	0·13
Chlorine Cl_2	0·00013	0·043
Methane CH_4	0·00010	0·15
Ethylene C_2H_4	0·00010	0·084
Hydrogen sulphide H_2S . . .	0·00012	0·085
Sulphur dioxide SO_2	0·00012	0·045
Nitrous oxide N_2O	0·00014	0·077
Carbon dioxide CO_2	0·00014	0·077
Carbon monoxide CO . . .	0·00017	0·15
Water H_2O	0·0114	0·0114
Sugar solution $\begin{cases} (20\% \ C_{12}H_{22}O_{11} \text{ by wt.}) \\ (40\%) \\ (60\%) \end{cases}$	0·023 0·075 0·75	0·021 0·064 0·58
Salt solution (22·8% NaCl). . .	0·021	0·018
Bromine Br	0·010	0·0034
Mercury Hg	0·016	0·0012
Sulphuric acid H_2SO_4 . . .	0·30	0·16
Hydrocyanic acid HCN . . .	0·0021	0·0030
Ethyl ether $(C_2H_5)_2O$	0·0025	0·0034
Carbon bisulphide CS_2 . . .	0·0038	0·0029
Chloroform $CHCl_3$	0·0059	0·0039
Carbon tetrachloride CCl_4 . . .	0·0104	0·0066
Methyl alcohol CH_3OH . . .	0·0064	0·0080
Ethyl alcohol C_2H_5OH . . .	0·013	0·017
Propyl alcohol C_3H_7OH . . .	0·026	0·032
Benzene C_6H_6	0·0070	0·0080
Acetic acid CH_3CO_2H . . .	0·013	0·012
Aniline $C_6H_5NH_2$	0·052	0·051
Glycol $CH_2OH.CH_2OH$ . . .	0·19	0·17
Paraffin oil	0·2	0·25
Fish oil	0·7	0·7
Olive oil	1·0	1·0
Glycerine	13	10
Castor oil	15	15
Pitch	$\simeq 10^{10}$	$\simeq 10^{10}$

a gas of higher molecular weight, but the only approach reasonably satisfactory in practice is pressurization. For example, a compressed-air tunnel like that at the N.P.L. may operate at 25 atm, and so increase the Reynolds number per m by a factor of 25 at a given speed.

In spite of all the efforts of wind-tunnel designers there remains a substantial range of full-scale Reynolds numbers which cannot be reproduced in model experiments. Extrapolation to these higher Reynolds numbers is a delicate process, for reasons to be touched on in Chapter II, and it is partly for this reason that flight tests have so often revealed unexpected aerodynamic features.

Still larger values of R are found in ship motions, where although typical speeds are lower (say, 15 m/sec), the kinematic viscosity is less (say, 0·011 at 15° C), giving a Reynolds number of $1·4 \times 10^7$ per m. In addition, length-scales exceed those for aeroplanes; a large liner (the *Queen Elizabeth*) has a length $l = 324$ m and thus a Reynolds number of $4·5 \times 10^9$ under the conditions mentioned.

Passing to more modest values, a moderate wind of 10 m/sec at sea level has a Reynolds number of 7×10^5 per m, so that $R = 1·4 \times 10^7$ when it blows past a house of length-scale 20 m, $R = 1·4 \times 10^6$ for a man of height 2 m, and the Reynolds number based on diameter would be 10^5 for a telegraph pole and 10^3 for a telegraph wire. Again, for solid or liquid spheres of specific gravity 1 falling steadily in air, R is 10,000 for diameter 1 cm, 3,000 for 1 mm, 1,000 for $\frac{1}{10}$ mm, 300 for 10 microns, 50 for 1 micron.

When swimming at their maximum speed in water at 15° C, a blue whale ($l = 27$ m) has $R = 3 \times 10^8$, a shark ($l = 1·5$ m) $R = 8 \times 10^6$, a man ($l = 2$ m) $R = 4 \times 10^6$, a snake ($l = 40$ cm) $R = 10^5$, a nematode ($l = 1$ mm) $R = 0·6$, a spermatozoon ($l = 0·07$ mm) $R = 0·006$.

For many of the highly viscous liquids of Table I. 5, flow patterns totally different from those familiar in air and water are commonly observed, because Reynolds numbers are so much less. Thus, for motion at 1 cm/sec in glycerine, R is 10^{-1} per cm; it follows that $R = 2$ for a steel ball of diameter 1 cm falling through glycerine. It must be emphasized, however, that identical flow patterns are observed in those very-small-scale motions in air or water which have the same Reynolds number.

To end this section with an extreme value, the Reynolds number for a bubble of 1 cm diameter rising through pitch at 15° C is 10^{-17}, corresponding to a speed of 7 mm/year.

5.4. *Dynamical similarity in more general flows*

We now seek conditions for dynamical similarity in flows more general than those studied in Section 5.1. In many cases the flow will depend on more than four quantities, even when the body shape is fixed. However, dimensional analysis can at least reduce by three the effective

number of quantities on which it depends. The quantities that remain
will be non-dimensional; a change in which they are kept constant
will be equivalent to a simple change of units.

First, consider unsteady flows. If the oscillations in position or
attitude of a body in a stream are harmonic with frequency ω, we may
compare the flow with that in which a scale model of the body makes
geometrically similar oscillations with a different frequency ω', the
other quantities ρ, U, l and μ which define the flow being also changed
to ρ', U', l' and μ'.

For the change to be equivalent simply to a change of units, we must
have not only equations (38) but also $\omega' = \omega/T^{-1}$. The first three of
equations (38) then imply the values of L, T and M given in equation
(40); the fourth implies equation (39), constancy of Reynolds number;
and the one just stated implies that

$$\omega'l'/U' = \omega l/U. \tag{47}$$

Thus, the 'frequency parameter' $\lambda = \omega l/U$, as well as the Reynolds
number R, must have the same value in the two flows if they are to
be dynamically similar. It is still a great simplification, however, that
both the flow pattern and any non-dimensional quantity characteristic
of the flow (for example, the amplitude of the oscillations of the lift
coefficient C_L) are functions only of these two variables λ and R,
instead of the five variables ρ, U, l, μ and ω (see, for example, Robinson
and Laurmann 1956, pp. 481–530).

Similar arguments apply when the body oscillates anharmonically.
Then the spectra of such non-dimensional quantities as will specify its
position and attitude (that is, angles of pitch, roll and yaw, and mass-
centre displacements divided by l), plotted as functions not of frequency
but of the frequency *parameter* $\lambda = \omega l/U$, are sufficient, with the
Reynolds number, to fix the non-dimensional value of every flow
quantity, independently of the individual values of ρ, U, l and μ.

Another good illustration is provided by the problems of heat transfer
in solenoidal flows, discussed in Section 3.3 and Section 4.7. The temperature variations there discussed were small enough for the thermal
conductivity to be regarded as a constant, and it was shown (equation
(27)) that they are then controlled only by the velocity field and a single
constant of the fluid, the thermal diffusivity κ.

'Dynamical similarity' (used in a slightly extended sense to include
similarity of the heat-flow pattern) will now involve constancy not only
of Reynolds number but also of some non-dimensional expression

involving κ. An obvious candidate is the Prandtl number $\sigma = \nu/\kappa$, the ratio of the diffusivities of momentum and heat.

If, for example, the body surface is maintained at a temperature T_w slightly different from the temperature T_∞ of the stream, then although the fluid-flow pattern depends only on R, the heat-flow pattern, that is, the distribution of

$$(T-T_w)/(T_\infty-T_w), \tag{48}$$

depends (Howarth 1953, pp. 757–853) both on R and on σ—but not on any further parameters such as T_w and T_∞ since expression (48) satisfies boundary conditions independent of T_w and T_∞ (and the same linear equation as T itself).

Much work has been done both on unsteady flow and on heat transfer in fluid flow, using both experiment and calculation, and in all this work the use of non-dimensional forms has proved invaluable. Our knowledge remains at the end less complete than with steady-flow patterns only because the dependence on two variables (R and λ, or R and σ) in each problem calls for such a much wider coverage of cases.

5.5. *Use of non-dimensional parameters to determine which physical properties may be neglected*

We now observe that non-dimensional parameters have appeared, not only in Part III, where they have been shown to govern dynamical similarity, but also in Part II, wherever conditions for neglect of some particular physical property of the fluid have been studied. Conditions (9) for the neglect of density variation, for example, require four particular non-dimensional parameters to be small.

Of these, the most important is the 'Mach number'

$$M = U/a. \tag{49}$$

The condition that M be small may be interpreted as requiring that the speed of sound a be large compared with the speed U of the flow. Then the fact that disturbances are propagated only at a finite speed can be neglected, and we recover the solenoidal theory, in which (as is well known) changes in the boundary conditions make an instantaneous effect on the whole flow, as if the velocity of sound were infinite. Identical remarks apply to the additional condition in equation (9) that the product of Mach number and frequency parameter,

$$M\lambda = \omega l/a, \tag{50}$$

be small.

It is sometimes suggested that two steady flows, at speeds *not* small compared with the speed of sound, are dynamically similar if the Mach number M as well as the Reynolds number R takes the same value in the two flows. This is very far from the truth, because in flows of this kind temperature variations comparable with the absolute temperature are inevitable, and so the flow does not depend solely on ρ, U, l, μ and a, but on many additional properties of the fluid. These include the equation of state (for relating changes of density to changes of pressure and temperature), specific-heat results (for relating changes of temperature to changes of kinetic energy), and results on thermal conductivity and on the variation of viscosity and thermal conductivity with temperature.

In calculations on high-speed gas flows, these properties are commonly simplified by assuming a perfect gas with constant specific heats c_p and c_v in the ratio γ, constant Prandtl number σ, and variation of viscosity (and hence also of thermal conductivity) as the χth power of the temperature (which for suitable χ, somewhat greater than $\frac{1}{2}$, will represent the observed behaviour reasonably over a fairly substantial temperature range). Dynamical similarity depends then (Howarth 1953) on five non-dimensional parameters R, M, γ, σ and χ, an enormous number; and, even so, the application to high-pressure gas has been excluded by the perfect-gas assumption, and that to high-temperature or polyatomic gas by the assumption of constant specific heats. For all these reasons dynamical similarity, so invaluable for the treatment of the solenoidal flows described in Part II, has proved to be of only restricted value for high-speed flows.

Other conditions proposed in Part II for neglect of particular physical properties also involve non-dimensional parameters. Cavitation can be neglected if the cavitation number

$$Q = (p_h - p_v)/(\tfrac{1}{2}\rho U^2), \tag{51}$$

which compares a typical excess of the hydrostatic pressure over the vapour pressure with a typical dynamic pressure, exceeds a critical value. Again, if a body in water is at a depth h below the surface, the additional non-dimensional parameter h/l must in general affect dynamic similarity, but we can neglect the presence of the surface if h/l is large.

With a body in or near the free surface, quantities determining the flow include the gravitational acceleration g (which appears in the boundary condition at the surface and measures its tendency to return to a flat shape). Dynamical similarity in these problems requires constancy both of Reynolds number and of the Froude number

$F = U/\sqrt{(gl)}$. Of these, F affects mainly the wave-making resistance of the obstacle (Lamb 1932, pp. 415–38) and R the frictional resistance. When F is small, however, gravity is so effective in keeping the surface flat (because g is large compared with that combination of ρ, U and l, namely U^2/l, which has the same dimensions) that it can be effectively equated with a plane of symmetry and so reduced (Section 4.8) to a problem without a free surface, dependent only on R.

Yet another example is given by the condition (Section 4.8) for surface tension γ to be neglected, namely that the Bond number $B = \rho g l^2/\gamma$ be large. Here the effect of surface tension in making a meniscus is being compared with the effect of gravity in keeping the surface flat over length-scales of order l. The condition therefore requires γ to be small compared with the combination of ρ, g and l which has the same dimensions.

The Bond number governs also the shape of sitting drops, drops falling steadily through air under their own weight, the relative importance of gravity and surface tension in water waves of length l, and generally every question dominated by the four parameters ρ, g, l and γ (Prandtl and Tietjens 1934a, pp. 60–65; Lamb 1932, pp. 455–75). On the other hand, the shape of drops flying through the air at speeds U unrelated to their speed of steady fall under gravity is a function of the Weber number $W = \gamma/(\frac{1}{2}\rho U^2 l) = 2/(BF^2)$. These are closely spherical (which implies predominance of surface tension over dynamic pressure forces) if W is large (Prandtl 1952, pp. 324–30; Lane and Green 1956).

All these examples would lead one to expect that in our central problem (Section 5.1) of steady flow about an obstacle, at constant density and viscosity, the Reynolds number $R = \rho U l/\mu$ would provide not only the condition for dynamical similarity, but also a condition for viscosity to be completely negligible—namely when R is sufficiently large. To bear this out we might urge that, in units in which the length-scale, stream velocity, and density are all 1 (these units, by equation (40), are $L = l$, $T = l/U$, $M = \rho l^3$), the viscosity is $1/R$. Hence, if terms in $1/R$ in the equations of motion can be suppressed for large R, then viscosity can be neglected.

This very plausible conjecture, which as stated in Section 1 was widespread in the nineteenth century, would imply that the great majority of the flows listed in Section 5.3, those with large R, would have flow patterns uninfluenced by viscosity, and so independent of R. Experimentally, however, flow patterns with R around 10^2, 10^3, 10^4, 10^5, 10^6 and 10^7 are all markedly different, in ways which have an important

effect on force coefficients and the like. The reason for the failure of
the conjecture, as discussed in Section 1, is the non-existence of solutions
satisfying the boundary conditions if the viscous stresses be neglected
altogether.

Reynolds number, then, is the liveliest of all the non-dimensional
parameters. The flow characteristics do not simply flatten out when
R becomes large or small. They continue to vary, and for many geo-
metries give several big and unexpected 'kicks' as R passes through
values which are quite surprisingly high (Chapter II, Section 4); and
even the variation of the flow as $R \to 0$, though not of such extreme
complexity as that when R becomes large, will be seen in Chapter IV
to be far from simple.

INTRODUCTION. BOUNDARY LAYER THEORY

.1. Vorticity and the development of fluid flows

1.1. *Introduction*

THE object of this chapter is to describe qualitatively the position and significance of boundary layers in fluid flows, as a background to the more detailed and quantitative information given in later chapters.

Prandtl (1904) introduced the boundary-layer theory in the first instance to resolve, for flows in which the Reynolds number is large (which were shown in Section I. 5.3 to include most flows of practical importance), the difficulty referred to in Section I. 1 and at the end of Section I. 5.5—namely, that the 'irrotational' or 'potential' flow solutions derived by neglecting viscosity (that is, putting $R = \infty$) do not satisfy the boundary condition at a solid surface. Rather, they require slip over the surface, which we have seen is impossible.

Prandtl's suggestion was that one might resuscitate such irrotational flows by postulating the existence, between them and the solid surface, of a thin layer of fluid in which the velocity increased steeply from zero at the wall to the theoretical surface value at the edge of the layer. In such a 'boundary layer', where the velocity gradient is high, viscosity would be important (or else, indeed, the layer would appear already in the inviscid theory). Prandtl now asked the question: does the mechanics of such a layer, when viscous effects are included, permit a development in which it remains thin all along the surface? Clearly, if it does, then the irrotational-flow approximation will have considerable value, and the drag coefficient will be small—that is, close to the value 0 given by that approximation. This is the case, as we shall see, for many obstacles, of the kind usually described as 'streamlined'. If, alternatively, the mechanics of the layer indicates development up to a catastrophe, in which fluid retarded by viscous forces breaks right away from the surface, disturbing large areas of the flow field, then clearly the original irrotational flow ceases to have value as an approximation, and new considerations become necessary. The flow is described in this case as 'separated'.

Experimental work has supported the correctness of Prandtl's assumptions; methods to be described in Chapter X have shown, not only that the boundary layer exists, but also that the velocity distribution across it develops in accordance with the mechanics to be discussed below.

They showed, too, under what conditions the steady 'laminar' boundary layer develops instabilities and becomes 'turbulent' (Section 3), and Prandtl (1914, 1927) was again the discoverer of the effects of this transition on the mechanics of the layer—notably, in delaying separation—and on the variation with Reynolds number (Section 4) of the flow patterns around bluff and streamlined bodies.

Now, the desired mechanics of a boundary layer can be very effectively discussed in terms of momentum changes due to convection, viscous diffusion, and the action of pressure gradients. A qualitative view of this theoretical approach, which throws valuable light on the behaviour of a wide variety of particular flows, is given in Section 2.9. On the other hand, both to explain convincingly the existence of boundary layers, and, also, to show what consequences of flow separation (including matters of such practical importance as the effect of trailing-vortex wakes) may be expected, arguments concerning vorticity are needed. In addition, these alone explain (as in the classical inviscid theory) why the flow outside the boundary layer and wake should be irrotational.

We see, then, that, although momentum considerations suffice to explain the local behaviour in a boundary layer, vorticity considerations are needed to place the boundary layer correctly in the flow as a whole. It will also be shown (surprisingly, perhaps) that they illuminate the detailed development of the boundary layer (see Sections 2.1–2.8) just as clearly as do momentum considerations (which are·briefly described in Section 2.9).

Accordingly, this Section 1 is concerned mainly with vorticity and with its relation to the development of fluid flows, in preparation for the discussion of boundary-layer mechanics in Section 2. A simplified treatment is used, to avoid the sometimes forbidding aspect of vorticity theory. (One can of course regard some of these simple arguments as being fully justified only by the more mathematical deductions of Chapter III; see also Lamb 1932, Truesdell 1954.)

1.2. *Vorticity*

The vorticity at any point in a fluid flow is proportional to the instantaneous angular momentum of a spherical particle of fluid centred on the point. One can regard the motion of such a small sphere of fluid as a combination (Fig. II. 1) of three motions:

(i) Uniform translation with the velocity **v** of the centre. All the momentum of the sphere's motion is in this part.

(ii) Rotation, with the angular velocity and the direction of the axis of rotation specified by the vector $\frac{1}{2}\boldsymbol{\omega}$, where $\boldsymbol{\omega} = \operatorname{curl} \mathbf{v}$ is the vorticity. All the angular momentum of the sphere's motion is in this part.

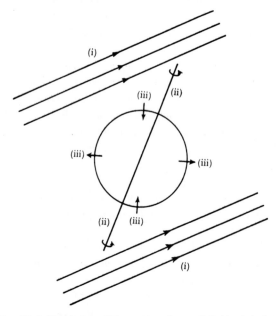

FIG. II. 1. Resolution of the motion of a small fluid sphere into (i) translation, (ii) rotation, (iii) straining.

(iii) A symmetrical squeezing, or 'straining', which is changing the sphere into an ellipsoid (thus elongating it in some directions and fore-shortening it in others). This motion has no net linear or angular momentum.

Note that the motion of a *rigid* sphere is composed simply of (i) and (ii), a translation and a rotation. *Fluid* spheres, however, are in general always changing shape. For a small sphere, the instantaneous rate of change of shape consists always of a uniform elongation process in one direction, a uniform foreshortening process in a second direction, at right angles to the first, and a third process (which may be either elongation or foreshortening) in a third direction at right angles to the first two. These three directions are the axes of the ellipsoid mentioned under heading (iii), and are usually called the 'principal axes of rate-of-strain' of the fluid particle.

If these axes were taken as the coordinate axes, then the rates of elongation in the three directions would be $\partial v_x/\partial x$, $\partial v_y/\partial y$, $\partial v_z/\partial z$. It is of course the solenoidality condition (Section I. 2.5) that ensures, because their sum is zero, that if one of these is positive then at least one other must be negative (indicating a foreshortening), and vice versa.

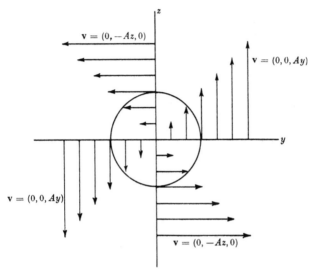

Fig. II. 2. Because the vector sum of the two shear flows shown is a uniform rotation with angular velocity A, in which the angular momentum of the sphere is IA, the angular momentum in one shear flow alone (for example, that with $\partial v_z/\partial y = A$) is $\frac{1}{2}IA$.

The expressions for the components of the vorticity,

$$\boldsymbol{\omega} = \operatorname{curl} \mathbf{v} = \left(\frac{\partial v_z}{\partial y} - \frac{\partial v_y}{\partial z}, \frac{\partial v_x}{\partial z} - \frac{\partial v_z}{\partial x}, \frac{\partial v_y}{\partial x} - \frac{\partial v_x}{\partial y}\right), \tag{1}$$

are easily understood from Fig. II. 2, which shows, for example, that the shear term $\partial v_z/\partial y$ produces an angular momentum $\frac{1}{2}I\,\partial v_z/\partial y$ about the x-axis, where I is the sphere's moment of inertia. The signs of the terms in (1) reflect that a rotation about (say) the x-axis is called positive (in a right-handed system of axes) if it is in the direction of turning of a right-handed screw moving along the positive x-axis, and negative if it is in the opposite direction.

Expressions (1) imply that **ω**, like **v**, satisfies the solenoidality condition

$$\text{div}\,\boldsymbol{\omega} = \frac{\partial \omega_x}{\partial x} + \frac{\partial \omega_y}{\partial y} + \frac{\partial \omega_z}{\partial z} = 0. \tag{2}$$

Geometrically, this means (Section I. 2.5) that the magnitude of the vorticity varies along any 'elementary vortex tube' (thin tube to which

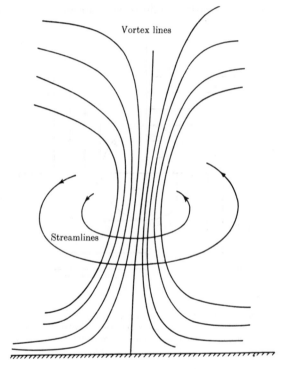

Fig. II. 3. Vortex lines in a whirlwind.

the *vorticity* vector is everywhere tangential) inversely as the cross-sectional area. To represent a vorticity field pictorially, one may imagine it honeycombed with such vortex tubes, each of the same 'strength' (product of cross-sectional area and vorticity magnitude)— the position of each tube being indicated by a 'vortex line' (*curve* to which the vorticity vector is everywhere tangential) threaded centrally down it. Wherever these vortex lines congregate densely, the associated tubes have reduced cross-sectional area and the vorticity is correspondingly great.

Such vortex lines cannot end abruptly in the fluid, whence it is sometimes stated that they either form closed 'vortex loops' *or* end on a solid surface. It is worth noting, however, that the no-slip condition makes the latter alternative impossible (except for isolated vortex lines, similar to 'dividing streamlines' in velocity fields) at any solid surface at rest (or in pure translational motion), where necessarily the normal component of vorticity is zero. Hence, in flows which do not contain rotating bodies, *all* vorticity appears in closed loops. It is usually instructive, in flows where the vortex lines appear to be predominantly in one direction, to consider where they in fact turn round to form closed loops—those in a whirlwind, for example, turning in the boundary layer on the ground and proceeding nearly horizontally until they reach anticyclonic regions where they can rise and join the vortex lines high in the atmosphere which have been making a similar horizontal progress above the region of high wind (Fig. II. 3).

1.3. *Variation of vorticity in an inviscid fluid*

Consider next how the vorticity varies with time, in the first place with viscosity neglected. In this case, the rate of change of angular momentum of the fluid sphere of Section 1.2 must be zero, since the pressure forces at its boundary all act through the centre, and so does the force of gravity (and, indeed, it may be shown more generally that the resultant over a homogeneous sphere of any conservative field of external forces acts through its centre).

This vanishing of the rate of change of angular momentum does not imply conservation of the angular velocity $\frac{1}{2}\boldsymbol{\omega}$ of part (ii) of the sphere's motion, since part (iii) in general is altering its moments of inertia. It means rather that, as the sphere becomes ellipsoidal, the *component* of angular velocity about each of the principal axes of rate-of-strain is changing in *inverse* proportion to the moment of inertia about that axis—which implies variation in *direct* proportion to the length of that axis. Thus, vorticity components about axes that are being elongated are increasing (just as any spinning body spins faster if its girth is reduced by stretching of the axis of rotation); while those about axes that are being foreshortened are decreasing.

To represent this result pictorially (Fig. II. 4), one may draw an arrow in the direction of the vorticity vector $\boldsymbol{\omega}$, and proportional to it in length, both for the initial spherical state of the particle and also an instant later (when it has become ellipsoidal). The results, that the elongation of $A'OA$ is increasing the component of $\boldsymbol{\omega}$ in this direction, in proportion to the increased length of that axis, while the foreshortening of $B'OB$ decreases the component of ω in that direction in proportion to the length $B'OB$, with a third similar result in the $C'OC$ direction (not shown on the figure), mean that the variation of ω can be obtained by applying these elongations and foreshortenings directly to the arrow itself.

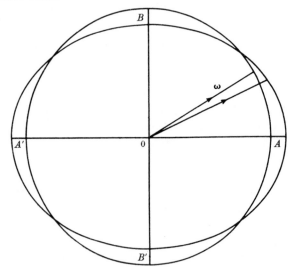

FIG. II. 4. Variation of the vorticity of a fluid particle due to straining.

In other words, the arrow may be thought of as a little arrow-shaped element of fluid—subject, like the whole spherical particle, to precisely these elongations and foreshortenings. The variation of vorticity with time is exhibited both in magnitude and direction by the changes in length, direction and position of this arrow-shaped element. The changes in *position* arise from convection by the translational component (i) of the motion of one small fluid sphere; these are essential to the accuracy of representation, since of course the changes of angular momentum and vorticity discussed above were changes for the particle as it moved about, and not changes at a fixed point of space. The arrow-shaped element would, on the other hand, be unmoved by the rotational component (ii), on whose axis it lies. (It appears paradoxical that the arrow is turned round only by the part (iii) of the motion which is 'without rotation'; but it must be remembered that only the total angular momentum of the sphere is zero for this part of the motion, and not that of individual asymmetrically shaped bits.)

To sum up: if one imagines a fluid flow at any instant as including millions of tiny arrow-shaped elements of fluid, each pointing in the direction of the local vorticity, and of length proportional to its magnitude, then, if viscosity can be neglected, these individual arrow-shaped elements will move so that at all subsequent times they give the same information with equal accuracy.

This is the result stated by Helmholtz in the form 'vortex lines move with the fluid'. Vortex lines, obtained by suitably joining up the arrows, are curves (Section 1.2) to which the vorticity vector is everywhere tangential. Helmholtz's statement by itself shows only how the direction of $\boldsymbol{\omega}$ changes, but if one adds that the magnitude varies in proportion as the vortex line is locally *stretched*, the combined statement becomes equivalent to that just given.

A particular case of the result is Lagrange's theorem, that fluid which at one instant has vanishing vorticity will also have vanishing vorticity at later instants, if viscosity can be neglected. For the fluid motion cannot stretch any arrow by an *infinite* factor, as clearly would be necessary to convert zero vorticity into non-zero vorticity.

1.4. *Variation of vorticity in a viscous fluid*

In a real fluid, the angular momentum of the sphere discussed in Section 1.3 changes, as a result of tangential stresses proportional to the viscosity. This leads to an additional term in the rate of change of vorticity, which can be interpreted as due to diffusion with diffusivity ν. For each term in the expression (1) for $\boldsymbol{\omega}$ is proportional to a momentum gradient, whose change due to viscosity must correspond to diffusion with this diffusivity, simply because this is so for the momentum itself (Section I. 3.4).

The inertial rate of change of $\boldsymbol{\omega}$ for a fluid particle, represented by the turning and stretching of the vortex lines, must accordingly be supplemented by a diffusion term $\nu\nabla^2\boldsymbol{\omega}$. The corresponding contribution of diffusion to the rate of change of the 'total vorticity' in any volume of fluid (integral of vorticity over it) is equivalent to a flow, across unit area of its surface, at a rate ν times the gradient of $\boldsymbol{\omega}$ along the outward normal.

This important idea of vorticity flow across a surface (so closely parallel to that of heat flow) cannot be viewed as diffusion of angular momentum; vorticity is proportional to the angular momentum of a spherical particle about its mass centre, and when it diffuses from one particle to another the relevant angular momentum is about quite a different point. The correct view relates diffusion of vorticity to that of momentum, through that of momentum gradient, as indicated above.

1.5. *Solid boundaries as sources of vorticity*

The last conclusion of Section 1.3, that a particle of fluid with zero vorticity will continue to have zero vorticity, is false in a viscous fluid, since diffusion of vorticity from nearby particles can occur. But diffusion cannot create vorticity out of nothing, so that in external aerodynamics one may reasonably ask: when a uniform stream flows past an obstacle, how is vorticity imparted to the fluid, all of which lacks it initially?

The answer is that the solid boundary is a *distributed source* of vorticity (just as, in some flows, it may be a distributed source of heat). To convince oneself of this, it suffices to examine any of the known exact solutions of the equations of motion (Chapter III), and to observe that at almost all points of the boundary the vorticity has a non-zero gradient along the normal. This gradient, multiplied by $(-\nu)$, represents (Section 1.4) the flow of 'total vorticity' out of the solid surface per unit area per unit time, so that it is the local *strength* of the surface distribution of vorticity sources. A physical explanation of the need for vorticity creation at the boundary is postponed to Section 1.7.

The tangential-vorticity source strength has a simple relation to pressure gradient, at least for flow over a stationary plane surface. If the surface is taken as $z = 0$, the flow of x-vorticity out of it is

$$-\nu \frac{\partial \omega_x}{\partial z} = -\nu \frac{\partial}{\partial z}\left(\frac{\partial v_z}{\partial y} - \frac{\partial v_y}{\partial z}\right) = \nu \frac{\partial^2 v_y}{\partial z^2} = \nu \nabla^2 v_y = \frac{1}{\rho}\frac{\partial p}{\partial y}, \qquad (3)$$

since v_x, v_y, v_z are zero on $z = 0$ (whence all their derivatives with respect to x and y vanish, and hence also $\partial v_z/\partial z = 0$ by the solenoidality condition), and because at a solid surface transfer of momentum by convection is absent, so that transfer by diffusion must exactly balance transfer by pressure gradient.

It follows from (3) that the tangential vorticity created is in the direction of the surface isobars (the sense of rotation being that of a ball rolling down the line of steepest pressure fall), and that the source strength per unit area is of magnitude ρ^{-1} times the pressure gradient. (To see this, take the x-direction first tangent, and then normal, to an isobar.) It is significant that this expression does not vanish if the viscosity is made to tend to zero. On curved surfaces the corresponding result is not exact, but, for high Reynolds number, we shall find that it is still a good approximation. Also, normal-vorticity production is then an effect of smaller order. It is required, in general, to maintain the solenoidality condition (2) on **ω**, which, indeed, relates the normal-vorticity source strength directly to the surface distribution of tangential vorticity, by the equation

$$-\nu \frac{\partial \omega_z}{\partial z} = +\nu\left(\frac{\partial \omega_x}{\partial x} + \frac{\partial \omega_y}{\partial y}\right). \tag{4}$$

In the next two sections it will be seen how the vorticity which is produced at the surface, and carried away from it by diffusion and convection, determines the entire flow, whose development in turn controls the production of vorticity.

1.6. The vorticity distribution as fixing the flow field

A special case of the unique determination of the flow field by the vorticity distribution is the theorem of classical hydrodynamics (Lamb 1932, chapter iii) that, if a body moves through unlimited fluid which far from the body is at rest (which, as observed in Section I. 1, produces motions equivalent to those of external aerodynamics), then one and only one flow, with *zero* vorticity everywhere, satisfies the boundary condition of zero *normal* relative velocity at the solid surface—supposed 'without holes' or, more precisely, such that the region outside it is simply connected. Such an 'irrotational' motion in such a region has necessarily a 'velocity potential' ϕ, with

$$\mathbf{v} = \operatorname{grad}\phi; \quad \text{that is,} \quad v_x = \partial\phi/\partial x, v_y = \partial\phi/\partial y, v_z = \partial\phi/\partial z. \tag{5}$$

The solenoidality condition on **v** becomes Laplace's equation,

$$\nabla^2\phi = 0; \quad \text{that is,} \quad \partial^2\phi/\partial x^2 + \partial^2\phi/\partial y^2 + \partial^2\phi/\partial z^2 = 0. \tag{6}$$

The theorem stated then follows from the fact (Kellogg 1929, chapter xi) that (6), together with the condition $\operatorname{grad}\phi \to 0$ at infinity, and the boundary condition

$$\partial\phi/\partial n = v_{wn} \tag{7}$$

(where the gradient of ϕ along the normal to the surface, $\partial\phi/\partial n$, is the normal component of the fluid velocity, and v_{wn} is the normal velocity component of the solid surface itself), fix ϕ uniquely, except to within an arbitrary constant whose value does not affect the velocity components (5).

A particular case of the theorem says that, at any instant when the body is *not* moving, the fluid must be at rest (if the other assumptions, notably irrotationality, are satisfied). Indeed, one proves this first (by applying the 'divergence theorem' to the vector $\phi\mathbf{v}$), and infers that two solutions of the more general problem are necessarily identical, because by (7) their difference must satisfy $\partial\phi/\partial n = 0$, which is the condition at a stationary surface.

In this chapter we need the still more general result (Lamb 1932, chapter vii) that, for *any* given solenoidal distribution of vorticity $\boldsymbol{\omega}$ outside the body surface (whose motion is again prescribed), one and only one solenoidal velocity field exists, tending to zero at infinity and with zero normal relative velocity at the solid surface. The proof of this result is in two parts. First, we write down a velocity field $\mathbf{v}_0$ which has the given vorticity distribution and tends to zero at infinity. This is given by the Biot–Savart law,

$$\mathbf{v}_0 = \int \frac{\boldsymbol{\omega} \times \mathbf{r}}{4\pi r^3}\, dV, \tag{8}$$

where the integration is over the whole vorticity field and $\mathbf{r}$ is the position vector relative to the volume element dV. The relationship (8) is the same as for the magnetic field $\mathbf{H}$ produced by a steady current distribution of density $\mathbf{i}$ (which in rationalized electromagnetic units equals $\operatorname{curl} \mathbf{H}$). It means that the vorticity $\boldsymbol{\omega}$ in each volume element dV induces a rotation of all the fluid at a distance r from it with angular velocity $\boldsymbol{\omega}\, dV/4\pi r^3$.

In general, $\mathbf{v}_0$ does not satisfy the boundary condition for $\mathbf{v}$. However, the difference $\mathbf{v} - \mathbf{v}_0$ must be irrotational (since $\operatorname{curl} \mathbf{v}_0 = \boldsymbol{\omega}$), and hence equal to $\operatorname{grad} \phi$ for some potential ϕ. On the body surface,

$$\frac{\partial \phi}{\partial n} = v_n - v_{0n} = v_{wn} - v_{0n}, \tag{9}$$

which is fixed, and also $\operatorname{grad} \phi \to 0$ at infinity. As we have seen, just one ϕ (except for an arbitrary additive constant) satisfies these conditions.

This addition $\operatorname{grad} \phi$ to the Biot–Savart velocity field is sometimes described as the field of the image vorticity, since for simple shapes of boundary (planes, circular cylinders, spheres) it can be easily related by the same Biot–Savart formula to a distribution of 'virtual' or 'image' vorticity within the body (Lighthill 1956*b*).

Two notable features of these theorems are the instantaneous response of the flow to changes in the body's movements, and the unique determination of even a rotational flow by the boundary condition on the normal velocity component alone. The first feature is not paradoxical, because of the effective assumption of infinite velocity of the sound waves with which irrotational disturbances are propagated, which is implied by the conditions (I. 9) for solenoidality; the second will be fully discussed in Section 1.7. We note also Kelvin's result (Lamb 1932, p. 47), that the kinetic energy of one of these motions with vorticity is necessarily greater than that of the irrotational flow satisfying the

same boundary conditions, by an amount equal to the kinetic energy
of the flow which would be induced by the vorticity with the boundary
at rest. This means that it is the irrotational flow which least disturbs
the fluid through which the body moves.

1.7. *Flow development*

We now ask the question: how does a body moving through otherwise undisturbed fluid determine the development of the flow around
it ? The answer may be considered given if we can describe how a computing machine of sufficiently large capacity could calculate to sufficient
accuracy how the flow field changes, progressing by suitably small steps
forward in time.

Until recently, such an account would have been of largely theoretical
value, as showing how the conditions (including boundary conditions)
derived in Chapter I determine. uniquely the flows under discussion.
(This is not obvious, particularly since there is no information on the
variation of pressure, except that the effect of pressure-gradient forces
on the velocity field must constantly be such as to keep it solenoidal.)
However, the development of digital computers of really high speed
and capacious memory has given practical value to such considerations;
already two important cases of flow development have been computed
by the method described below (Payne 1956, 1958), and much further
work is planned, while closely analogous methods are being used in
numerical weather forecasting. Alternative methods, attaching cardinal
importance to the pressure or a stream function in place of vorticity,
are inadequate both theoretically and practically, for reasons to be
mentioned at the end of this section.

The results of Section 1.6 show that it is sufficient to study the
development of the vorticity field around the body, because for a given
movement of the body this determines the whole flow—and, indeed,
'over-determines' it, requiring only the boundary condition on the
normal velocity component at the surface to fix the flow uniquely. Thus,
there is only a restricted class of vorticity distributions that correspond to
real flows satisfying also the no-slip condition on the tangential velocity.

For a step-by-step computation of vorticity development, we need
a method of progressing from one vorticity distribution within this
restricted class to the vorticity distribution a short time later. The
results of Sections 1.3 and 1.4 show how this is to be achieved away
from the body surface. The rate of change of vorticity is that generated
by the flow field in convecting and stretching the vortex lines, as

discussed in Section 1.3, plus that produced by viscous diffusion (Section 1.4). To complete our knowledge of the vorticity field at the later instant, we must determine the rate of production of vorticity at the boundary.

Relations between tangential-vorticity source strength and pressure gradient (Section 1.5) are *not* useful here, since the pressure has been eliminated from the problem (rightly, as a variable whose rate of change is unknown) by our concentration on vorticity. Equally, the expression for vorticity source strength $-\nu\,\partial\boldsymbol{\omega}/\partial z$ (where $z = $ normal distance from boundary) is valueless, for diffusion (which, of course, dominates over convection near to the boundary) tends to spread the vorticity created at any instant $t = \tau$ according to a Gaussian distribution

$$e^{-z^2/4\nu(t-\tau)}\{\pi\nu(t-\tau)\}^{-\frac{1}{2}}, \qquad (10)$$

so that the contribution to the expression $-\nu\,\partial\boldsymbol{\omega}/\partial z$ at time t from a source at any previous instant is zero, although the integrated effect up to time t may be shown to be equal to the source strength at time t. This means that the instantaneous source strength *determines* the normal gradient and *not* vice versa. On the other hand, the normal-vorticity source strength is expressible directly in terms of *tangential* gradients of vorticity as in (4), which incidentally ensures that the vorticity field remains solenoidal. Accordingly, it is only the values of the tangential-vorticity source strengths that remain in doubt.

To find these, we first suppose them zero and proceed to the next stage of our problem—determining the velocity field at the later instant from the vorticity field. This, as shown in Section 1.6, requires only a knowledge of the normal velocity at the surface. The resulting tangential velocity at the surface may *not* satisfy the no-slip condition. In this case, we deduce that exactly enough tangential vorticity must have been created at the surface, during the time interval in question, so that the velocity field of that vorticity (which during such a short interval has diffused only a very small distance from the surface) combines with that previously determined to give zero slip.

For example, at a point where the slip-velocity component v_x (the x-direction being tangential to the wall) is calculated as X after the interval δt, we deduce that, during the interval, 'total' y-vorticity X per unit area has been generated. This forms a 'vortex sheet', corresponding to a velocity field falling, from zero beyond a distance which is small of order $\sqrt{(\nu\,\delta t)}$, to $-X$ at the surface. Its distribution, easily derived by simple diffusion theory, is not needed in practical calcula-

tions of vorticity and velocity at the mesh-points of a lattice, since the
time interval δt is always taken so small that this additional velocity
field affects significantly the velocity only at mesh-points on the surface
(reducing the slip to zero); accordingly, the expression for the total
tangential vorticity generated at the surface in time δt is all that is
needed to proceed to the next instant.

To sum up: any flow development is in principle computable by
studying the diffusion of vortex lines, and their convection and stretching by the associated flow, while supposing normal and tangential
vorticity to appear at the surface continuously, in just such measure
as is required to maintain, respectively, the solenoidality of the vorticity
field and the no-slip condition. For practical details of the computation of particular unsteady flows by this method, see Payne (1956,
1958).

The method has many advantages over other approaches. Note that,
even for 'two-dimensional' flows, the employment of a 'stream function' ψ gains nothing, since the equation (III. 38) which governs it
gives the rate of change not of ψ but of $\nabla^2 \psi$, which *is* the vorticity.
Alternatively, the problem might be approached by determining at
each stage what pressure field will maintain solenoidality of the velocity
field everywhere; this involves solving an equation of Poisson's type
for the pressure, before using the momentum equation to derive the
velocity field at the next instant. In a practical problem this introduces
the difficulty of operating in the whole infinite flow field, instead of in
the region of non-zero vorticity, which includes only those portions of
fluid that have passed near the body surface. A second difficulty is
that the fluid velocities respond by large sudden changes to any sudden
alteration in the velocity or angular velocity of the solid surface, while
pressures have enormous peaks (the so-called 'impulsive pressures')
during such changes; on the other hand, the vorticity distribution
varies smoothly, and the method described above operates unaltered
during such changes.

Advantages of thinking in terms of vorticity, the only flow quantity
whose values are not propagated at the enormous speed of sound, become
particularly clear from examples in Section 2, but we may conclude
Section 1 by an even simpler example. When one blows out a candle
some distance away, the airflow during the puff consists of an irrotational 'source' flow in addition to the vorticity-induced flow. However, such irrotational flows fall off rapidly with distance. Accordingly,
the candle does not respond until later, when the lip-generated 'vortex

ring', each portion of which induces a forward motion in the others, has reached the candle. It would be hard to explain this motion by direct consideration of pressure-velocity interactions.

2. Boundary layers and separation

2.1. *The development of a laminar boundary layer*

In Section 2, the study of flow development, including development to a possible steady flow, is pursued, without any discussion of the stability of the motions under the small disturbances which are always present. Some (though not all) of the conclusions will have to be modified in the light of the evidence on flow instability and the effects of turbulence which is presented in Section 3. However, the latter material is understood more easily after a full discussion of the mechanics of 'laminar' flow, that is, of flow in which no such amplification of the effects of small disturbances is supposed to have occurred.

The boundary-layer concept can appropriately be introduced by discussing a flow started up from rest when a stationary body begins suddenly to move through fluid with uniform velocity U_∞. In our discussion of this flow, all velocities will be specified relative to the body, so that we think of the flow of a uniform stream past a body, starting instantaneously at time $t = 0$.

At this instant, no vorticity has been created, and hence the flow around the body is the irrotational one. Immediately, however, as Section 1.7 shows, this creates tangential vorticity at the boundary—concentrated in the form of a 'vortex sheet', which just permits the irrotationally flowing fluid to slip over the fluid at rest in contact with the boundary. All this vorticity then diffuses out from the boundary, in proportion to $(\pi\nu t)^{-\frac{1}{2}}\exp(-z^2/4\nu t)$ (see (10)), the speed of this diffusion in its very earliest stages being much greater than any convection speed, which can therefore be neglected in comparison. The body is then surrounded by a vortex layer 'of uniform thickness'. To speak thus of the 'thickness' of the layer is not absurd, since the exponential falls to zero extremely fast when z increases above about $3\sqrt{(\nu t)}$; but, to get a precise measure of thickness, one may, for example, consider the distance of vortex elements from the surface and evaluate their average δ_1 (which for reasons to appear will be called the 'displacement thickness' of the layer) as

$$\delta_1 \sim 2\sqrt{(\nu t/\pi)} \quad \text{for small } t. \tag{11}$$

In this early stage no normal vorticity is created; expression (4) may be shown to vanish owing to the irrotationality of the external flow.

Further, the influence of the vortex layer is felt almost entirely inside itself, producing a velocity variation across it, from the surface value zero to the non-zero 'surface' value predicted by irrotational-flow theory. Such change as does occur in the irrotational flow outside the vortex layer may be estimated by replacing the layer, to a first approximation, by a concentrated vortex sheet at the mean distance δ_1 of vorticity from the surface (Lighthill 1958). This replacement reduces to rest the flow inside the sheet, while the flow outside it is irrotational and slips freely over it; therefore, by the uniqueness theorem, the latter flow is that around a modified body, with surface displaced outwards into the fluid by the 'displacement thickness' δ_1. Thus, the vortex layer, when thin enough for this approximation to be good, alters the irrotational flow into one around a thickened body.

The simplicity of such a 'boundary layer' of vorticity dominated entirely by diffusion persists for only a very short time. As soon as the body has moved through even a small percentage of its length, convection begins to redistribute the vorticity which has been created. The vortex lines, which may be shown to lie initially along the surface equipotentials of the irrotational flow, are carried around the body, leading to a distribution of vorticity that no longer corresponds to zero slip at the surface. By Section 1.7 this requires the generation of new tangential vorticity, which may be in a quite different (or indeed opposite) direction from that originally created (see Section 2.8 below). This in turn is convected downstream, a redistribution which leads to still further vorticity production at the surface.

We may now ask: will these processes yield ultimately a steady-flow field, and, if so, how and of what kind? Even if the matter of stability be disregarded, we cannot yet give these questions their precise answers, whose immense complication (at least!) is embarrassingly clear from Chapters IV to VIII. However, some essential parts of the answers follow plainly from the above discussion.

2.2. Boundary layers and wakes in steady flow

First, it is possible for convection to prevent the 'boundary layer', that is, the region of vorticity near the surface, from growing beyond a thickness of order $\sqrt{(\nu l/U_\infty)}$, which is much smaller than the scale l of the body provided that $R = U_\infty l/\nu$ is large. For the vorticity in the outer parts of the boundary layer is convected downstream at a speed which is close to that of the irrotational flow outside the layer, and therefore of order U_∞; hence, the time since its generation remains at most of order l/U_∞, during which it can have diffused a distance at most of order $\sqrt{(\nu l/U_\infty)}$ away from the surface. Here, it is assumed that *convection* has not greatly altered its distance from the surface, in other words, that the streamlines near the surface are closely parallel to it; this rule is generally correct, but has important exceptions which will shortly be discussed.

It is, indeed, clear that convection must in time carry some vorticity right away from, or at least right past, the surface. We shall use the word 'wake' to denote the region of vorticity which is not close to the surface. Of this vorticity, the outlying portions are convected downstream at a speed close to U; hence, the wake has a continually increasing length, which prevents the flow as a whole from ever becoming steady. Nevertheless, after a time interval of order $10l/U_\infty$, the further lengthening of the wake, far downstream, has a negligible influence on the flow pattern near the body, which becomes steady as far as changes from this cause are concerned; it is then effectively as if the wake were infinitely long, as in the completely steady flow which we shall principally discuss.

These considerations regarding the two regions of vorticity—boundary layer and wake—indicate the possible existence of a particularly important class of fluid flows. They are what may be called 'thin-wake' flows, in which the boundary-layer thickness remains small, of order $\sqrt{(\nu l/U_\infty)}$, over the whole surface, and the vorticity leaves the surface in a wake of the same order of thickness. Such flows are important largely because, with a thin wake, a body leaves less energy behind in the fluid than with a thick one, and hence its resistance is lower. A second valuable property is that they can be approximately calculated, in three stages (of which just the first two, or even the first alone, may often be regarded as sufficient):

(i) determine the irrotational flow outside the boundary layer and wake, by ignoring the former and replacing the latter by a 'vortex sheet', its mathematical limit as the thickness tends to zero, the total vorticity per unit area remaining unchanged;

(ii) from a knowledge of this external flow, determine the detailed vorticity distribution within the boundary layer, by methods to be described below;

(iii) find the modifications to the irrotational flow due to the calculated 'displacement thickness' of the boundary layer (an effect already explained in a simple special case in Section 2.1).

Although calculations of type (i) are not studied in this book, but rather in the companion volume *Incompressible Aerodynamics*, we may here mention some of the principal kinds. In steady 'two-dimensional' flow (that is, flow around cylinders, with the same velocity field in each plane perpendicular to the generators), the total vorticity per unit area of wake can be shown to vanish, which leaves for calculation a simple irrotational flow without concentrated vorticity. By contrast, in three-dimensional flows, and also in unsteady flows, the solution requires in general the presence of a vortex sheet, like that behind the trailing edge of a straight wing, or that stretching from the leading edge of a 'narrow delta' wing. The appropriate distribution of total vorticity in such cases follows from the condition of 'smooth flow' at the edge, to be explained in Section 2.5.

Actually, diffusion must thicken the vortex wake far behind the body, and other complications, including its 'rolling up' into discrete vortices, are often neglected in the theory, but, as already remarked, the detailed distribution of vorticity far behind the body has little effect on the flow near it, and hence on the aerodynamic forces. These may to good approximation be divided into those present in the irrotational-flow calculation (i) (these include 'lift' and 'induced drag', and are closely related to the distribution of total vorticity in the wake), and those due to the boundary layer, namely, skin-friction forces deducible from calculation (ii), and extra pressure forces, whose calculation in principle requires (iii) as well as (ii), but whose resultant can be inferred from (ii) alone.

We must now ask: under what circumstances do such thin-wake flows occur? This leads to the general question of how boundary layers separate from solid surfaces, and, through it (as we shall see) to the still more general question of how vorticity distributes itself in steady laminar boundary layers. All these questions are now discussed, first in the simple particular case of 'two-dimensional' flow, and then in the general case.

2.3. *Two-dimensional flows; attachment and separation*

The greatest simplifying feature of two-dimensional flow about an infinite cylinder of arbitrary cross-section is that all vortex lines are parallel to the generators of the cylinder at all times; because, physically, any spin must be about this direction, or, mathematically, choosing the y-axis parallel to the generators, we have $v_y = 0$, v_x and v_z independent of y, and hence, by (1), $\omega_x = \omega_z = 0$ and ω_y independent of y. Convection of the vortex lines cannot therefore stretch or rotate them, so that values of ω (where for brevity the suffix y is henceforth dropped) are convected without alteration except that due to diffusion—just like values of (say) temperature.

It must be admitted that this and other simplifying features have tempted theoretical hydrodynamicists into an unwarrantable concentration on two-dimensional flows, leading experimentalists to similar restrictions for the sake of comparison with theory. Actually, reproduction of these flows is not easy, as in a real flow the 'straight parallel vortex lines' must form parts of closed loops (Section 1.2) by turning at their ends—either on the side walls of a wind-tunnel, where they can generate complicated 'secondary flows', or else as trailing vorticity (behind finite cylinders), with power to change the whole velocity field. In the meantime, the huge class of motions that depend crucially on the stretching and rotation of vortex lines have been inadequately studied; accordingly, we must hasten to resume three-dimensional theory after the following preliminary discussion of the two-dimensional case.

The most important question is whether the boundary-layer thickness remains small, of order $\sqrt{(\nu l/U_\infty)}$, or whether this diffusion distance is far exceeded by the effect of convection in separating vorticity from the surface. We must ask, therefore: how parallel to the surface are the neighbouring streamlines? The answer can be given in terms of ω_w, the vorticity at the surface. It is easy to see that, at a very small distance z from the surface, the velocity has components $\omega_w z$ parallel to the surface (in a clockwise direction, if ω, the vorticity, is measured clockwise) and $-\frac{1}{2}\omega'_w z^2$ normal to it (where the prime signifies differentiation along the surface, also in the clockwise direction). Accordingly, the direction of streamlines very close to the surface (that is, where z is very small) is almost parallel to it, unless $\omega_w = 0$. Indeed, along any such streamline,

$$\tfrac{1}{2}\omega_w z^2 = \epsilon, \tag{12}$$

the constant ϵ being the volume flow per unit span between the streamline and the surface. Hence, the distance z from the surface varies like $\omega_w^{-\frac{1}{2}}$, which implies only a moderate variation except where ω_w approaches zero.

Points on the surface where $\omega_w = 0$ and $\omega'_w < 0$ (giving a positive velocity component $-\frac{1}{2}\omega'_w z^2$ normal to the surface) are called points of separation; conversely, points where $\omega_w = 0$ and $\omega'_w > 0$ are called points of attachment. That at such points streamlines come right away from the surface is indicated by the flow direction failing to become tangential as $z \to 0$, as well as by equation (12). However, this equation loses accuracy seriously as $\omega_w \to 0$, and needs to be supplemented with the z^3 term in the expansion of the volume flow in powers of z, giving

$$\tfrac{1}{2}\omega_w z^2 + \frac{1}{6}\left(\frac{p'_w}{\mu} - \kappa\omega_w\right)z^3 = \epsilon, \tag{13}$$

where p_w is the pressure at the surface and κ its curvature. Solutions of equation (13) for z remain small, and close to $\sqrt{(2\epsilon/\omega_w)}$, except near

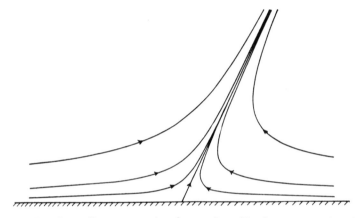

Fig. II. 5. Streamlines near a point of separation. (For those near a point of attachment, reverse all arrows.)

points of attachment or separation, where they cease to be small. The limit as $\epsilon \to 0$ of these solutions is a 'dividing streamline', which at each such point leaves the surface, at an angle (measured clockwise from it) of $\tan^{-1}(3\mu\omega'_w/p'_w)$, the flow thereon being towards the surface at a point of attachment and away from it at a point of separation (Fig. II. 5).

Around the cross-section of the cylinder there must be an even number of points where $\omega_w = 0$, which are alternately points of attachment and of separation. If several points of attachment exist, at most one of the streamlines dividing at them can come from far upstream (since, if two did, then the separation streamline which must lie between them would involve back flow far upstream, which is impossible). Apart from this 'first' point of attachment (of a streamline from far upstream), the others are points of attachment of streamlines that have left the surface at points of separation, enclosing 'bubbles' of various forms (see Fig. II. 6, in which points of attachment and separation are marked A and S respectively). These flows are not thin-wake flows, as vorticity is convected and diffused throughout the bubble in each case. Note that a thin boundary layer exists only between the first attachment point and the two nearest separation points, which accordingly are the points of 'boundary-layer separation'.

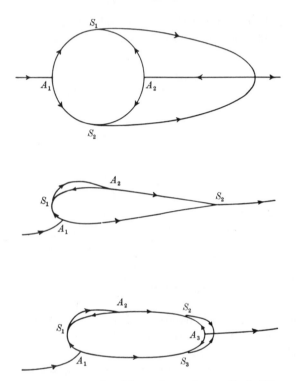

FIG. II. 6. Illustrating different forms of separation bubble.

If, however, there is only one attachment point, and hence only one separation point, then the boundary layer covers the whole surface, from which vorticity is convected away only at the final separation point, where the volume flow of rotational fluid is small, yielding a thin wake. (At the same time, since 'thin' is a relative term, we must admit that a thin wake is possible also if, say, two separation points and a second attachment point are extremely closely clustered together at the rear of the cylinder.) At the end of the next section we study the conditions tending to produce boundary-layer separation, whence can be inferred those for thin-wake flows to exist.

2.4. *Two-dimensional boundary-layer theory*

We discuss now the distribution of vorticity in the boundary layer, beginning at the 'first point of attachment', where a streamline from far upstream joins the surface.

We have noted already a tendency for boundary-layer thickness to increase as the distance from this point increases, since the vorticity in the outer parts of the layer has then been diffusing for a longer time. However, this has not inevitably increased its distance from the surface. For example, near the first point of attachment, diffusion away from the surface is combated by convection towards it, along streamlines which converge in this neighbourhood (as the condition $\omega'_w > 0$ implies). If the surface is smooth at this point (that is, exhibits no sharp edge or angle), the streamline convergence is enough to keep the boundary layer locally of uniform thickness, for the flow outside the boundary layer, because it is an irrotational flow near the point where a dividing streamline joins a smooth surface, satisfies approximately

$$w = -\beta z, \tag{14}$$

where w is the velocity component normal to the surface and β is a constant of order U_∞ / l. This inflow can exactly balance the speed at which vorticity in the outer parts of the layer diffuses outwards (which after diffusion through distance z is of order ν/z), for a value of z of order $\sqrt{(\nu/\beta)}$. Thus, the boundary-layer thickness is of order $\sqrt{(\nu l/U_\infty)}$, even at the first point of attachment; it may grow with distance from that point as the value of $-\partial w/\partial z$ outside the boundary layer falls off, but not change its order of magnitude. (On the other hand, if attachment occurs at a sharp edge or angle, then the layer grows with distance from a much smaller value at the edge.)

The 'displacement thickness' δ_1 at any point of the surface is defined (Section 2.1) as the mean distance, along the normal from the point, of vortex elements. To a first approximation, these behave as if concentrated in a vortex sheet at distance δ_1 from the surface, whence the irrotational flow outside the boundary layer is the same as the irrotational flow over a solid surface in this position. This means, for example, that (14) should really have read $w = -\beta(z-\delta_1)$, but it is easily seen that this would not have altered the conclusion drawn from that equation. Exact calculation (Chapter V) shows, in fact, that $\delta_1 = 0.65\sqrt{(\nu/\beta)}$ in this region.

To proceed farther, it is necessary to consider the actual vorticity source strength per unit area of surface, and to use an approximate relationship between vorticity and velocity in the boundary layer. This relationship, which is equivalent to the 'boundary-layer approximation' introduced by Prandtl, is

$$\omega = \partial u/\partial z, \tag{15}$$

where u is the velocity component parallel to the surface (in a clockwise direction). In Cartesian coordinates x, z, equation (15) neglects the additional term $-\partial w/\partial x$ in ω, but this is permissible since w is much smaller than u near the surface, and, also, gradients in the z-direction (normal to the surface) are much steeper than those in the x-direction (tangential to it). Actually, the definition of z as distance from the, in general, curved surface makes the coordinate system curvilinear, although it is still *orthogonal* if the x-coordinate of a point P is defined as the distance along the surface between the nearest point on the surface to P and (say) the first point of attachment. The curvilinear character of the system adds a term κu to ω, but this also is small compared with (15) provided that the radius of curvature κ^{-1} of the surface is large compared with the boundary-layer thickness.

Now U, defined as the total vorticity per unit area of boundary layer at a given point of the surface, can be written as

$$U = \int_0^\delta \omega \, dz, \tag{16}$$

if δ is a value of z at the outer edge of the boundary layer. Hence, on the approximation (15), U is the velocity at $z = \delta$; for this reason, it may be called the 'external flow' velocity.

To the same approximation, the rate of convection of total vorticity, per unit span, past a given point of the surface is

$$\int_0^\delta u\omega \, dz = \int_0^\delta u(\partial u/\partial z) \, dz = \tfrac{1}{2}U^2 \tag{17}$$

(which shows that the *mean* velocity of convection is $\tfrac{1}{2}U$). The variation of this vorticity-flow rate with x can in steady flow be due only to new vorticity, whose rate of creation at the surface is therefore

$$d(\tfrac{1}{2}U^2)/dx = UU' \tag{18}$$

per unit area. This agrees with the formula $-p'_w/\rho$ for a flat surface which follows from Section 1.5, since Bernoulli's equation gives approximately $p + \tfrac{1}{2}\rho U^2 = $ constant for the external flow, and the pressure varies negligibly across the layer (see Section 2.9). The reason why the finite radius of curvature of the surface makes negligible difference is that it has been supposed large compared with the boundary-layer thickness.

Now, as the external flow velocity U rises from its value 0 at the first point of attachment to the maximum positive value which it takes on the surface, the vorticity source strength (18) remains positive. Since only positive vorticity is being created, it follows that, whatever convection and diffusion occur, ω must be positive throughout this

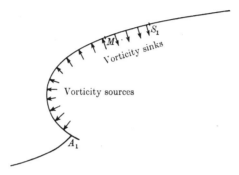

Fig. II. 7. Two-dimensional boundary-layer separation. The vorticity ω is positive (clockwise) throughout the layer in the region of positive vorticity source strength, but, after the strength becomes negative (at M, where the external flow velocity is a maximum), abstraction of vorticity at the surface rapidly reduces the surface value ω_w, which becomes zero at S_1, signifying separation.

part of the layer, where therefore separation (which requires $\omega_w = 0$) is impossible; in fact, ω_w must exceed the values of ω away from the surface, a result which we shall need to remember in Section 3.1. Beyond the maximum of U, however, (18) is negative, so that vorticity is abstracted at the surface (Fig. II. 7). This does not at once bring ω_w down to zero, since reduction of ω_w below the values of ω in the middle of the layer is combated by diffusion in towards the surface. Nevertheless, the surface sink of vorticity succeeds in reducing ω_w to zero when U has fallen to around 95 per cent. of its maximum, so that separation follows fairly hard on the attainment of the maximum external velocity (Chapter VI; the figure quoted is for a typical case, where the negative gradient of U increases continuously beyond the point M; values around 90 per cent. are possible if the gradient is nearly uniform, as this gives inward diffusion more chance).

Where $U' < 0$, the divergence of streamlines in the boundary layer supplements diffusion in producing thickening. Just before separation the thickening becomes particularly marked (Section 2.3), and the boundary-layer approximations then become inadequate; nevertheless, they have led to reasonable agreement with experiment in predictions of the point of separation.

2.5. *Two-dimensional thin-wake flows*

When the two boundary layers stretching out on either side of the first point of attachment separate at points not very close together, there must be a thick wake. The distribution of the external flow velocity U is then strongly influenced by the distribution of vorticity in the wake, and cannot be calculated in advance (even approximately) from irrotational-flow theory.

This would make boundary-layer theory, in which U, as we have seen, is supposed known, of little value, if it were not that the main *practical* requirements from it are a condition for the existence of thin-wake flows and a technique for calculating them. Now, if thin-wake flow is possible, the external flow velocity U is approximately that for irrotational flow around the cylinder. Hence the requirement, that (at least 'till the last moment') separation does not occur, exacts that the surface velocity in that irrotational flow fall only a few per cent. below its maximum.

Conversely, if the irrotational distribution of external flow velocity satisfies this condition for the absence of premature separation, then it is impossible, when the motion is started from rest, that any flow but the thin-wake flow be set up. For, if separation cannot occur in the steady state, then also it cannot earlier, when it is more effectively combated by inward diffusion because the boundary layer is thinner.

Now, the stated condition on the surface velocity distribution in the irrotational flow around the cylinder can be exactly satisfied only if the cylinder ends in a cusped 'trailing edge', where such a flow commonly departs from the surface at a velocity only a little below that of the undisturbed stream (whereas dividing streamlines can leave *smooth* surfaces only at stagnation points). However, this trailing-edge velocity is sufficiently near to the maximum of U only if the dimensions of the cylinder at right angles to the stream are much less than those parallel to it. This indicates the importance of 'aerofoil' sections—thin shapes with cuspidal trailing edges. Even with these, extreme slenderness would be required to satisfy the condition of no premature separation of a laminar boundary layer (for example, the thickness-chord ratio of a 'Joukowsky' aerofoil, even in symmetrical flow, would need to be 5 per cent. or less). Fortunately, the transition to turbulence, which we shall see occurs in all practical aerofoil flows, delays separation sufficiently so that this requirement on slenderness is made considerably less extreme.

A cusped edge is inacceptable in a practical structure, but a thin-wake flow is still attainable with various 'near-cusped' shapes, such as that obtained by rounding off the tip of the cusp. A sharp-angled trailing edge is also acceptable; although irrotational-flow separation

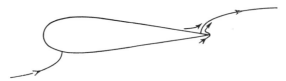

FIG. II. 8. Irrotational flow about an aerofoil.

from it does require it to be a stagnation point, the velocity on that theory falls to zero only very abruptly and 'at the last moment' (like the $\alpha/(2\pi-\alpha)$th power of the distance from the edge, where α is its angle); this may well produce separation only close to the edge, and, in any case, the true variation of the external flow is made less extreme by the displacement effect of the boundary layer.

Clearly, thin-wake flow can occur only if the aerofoil has an appropriate attitude to the oncoming stream. Indeed, irrotational-flow theory tells us that, except in one particular attitude, the dividing streamline does not leave the surface at the trailing edge, but at a stagnation point just ahead of the edge, the velocity at the edge itself being 'infinite' (Fig. II. 8). It is clear that, of the two boundary layers approaching the stagnation point in this case, the one approaching it from behind must separate at a higher value of the external flow speed U, and hence also of the vorticity flow rate (17). Therefore, in the case illustrated in the figure, negative (that is, anticlockwise) vorticity is 'cast off' into the wake.

Now, the presence of such negative vorticity behind the aerofoil alters the flow about it in such a way as to bring the stagnation point nearer the trailing edge. This consideration leads to the Kutta–Joukowsky hypothesis, that such vorticity will continue to be cast off until the flow about the aerofoil in the presence of the wake vorticity leaves the surface 'smoothly' at the trailing edge. The success of the two-dimensional-aerofoil theory for unsteady flows (e.g. with oscillating aerofoils), where one supposes the vorticity in the wake concentrated into a plane vortex sheet, adjusting itself with zero delay time to the requirement

of smooth flow at the trailing edge, indicates that such adjustment is
in fact very rapid.

In steadily maintained flow, the total cast-off vorticity tends in due
course to a limit, say, $-K$, and all this vorticity departs far downstream. Near the body we have, then, a steady flow with no net wake
vorticity but total boundary-layer vorticity $+K$ (because, in two-
dimensional flow, convection and diffusion cannot alter the total vorticity of the fluid). Outside the boundary layer this flow is approximately
the irrotational one around the aerofoil 'with circulation K', whence
K may be determined by the condition of smooth flow at the trailing
edge; more accurately, this condition (with 'smooth flow' interpreted
to mean equal external-flow velocity on both sides of the aerofoil,
yielding zero total vorticity discharge into the wake) should be applied
to the external flow as modified by the boundary-layer displacement
thickness. The 'lift' on the aerofoil per unit span is then close to $\rho U_\infty K$,
attainable values of the lift being limited by the requirement that the
flow with circulation K must be such that premature separation is
avoided.

These matters are discussed further in the companion volume *Incompressible Aerodynamics*, while there will be some further discussion of
two-dimensional flows in general in Section 4.

2.6. *Attachment and separation in three-dimensional flows*

We return now, in the general three-dimensional case, to the question,
'does the boundary-layer thickness remain small, of order $\sqrt{(\nu l/U_\infty)}$?',
which, as we have seen, involves the question, 'how parallel to the surface are the neighbouring streamlines?' Strong indications of the answer
are again given by the distribution of $\boldsymbol{\omega}_w$, the vorticity at the surface
(which in general is a *vector*, tangential to the surface, not as in Section 2.3, where ω stood for the single non-zero component ω_y).

At a very small distance z from the surface, the velocity is approximately
$$\mathbf{v} = \boldsymbol{\epsilon}_w z, \tag{19}$$

where
$$\boldsymbol{\epsilon}_w = \boldsymbol{\omega}_w \times \mathbf{n} = \boldsymbol{\tau}_w/\mu \tag{20}$$

is the vector $\boldsymbol{\omega}_w$ turned through $90°$ (in the negative sense, about the
outward normal $\mathbf{n}$ from the surface), and $\mu\boldsymbol{\epsilon}_w = \boldsymbol{\tau}_w$ is the viscous force
on the surface per unit area, or 'skin friction'. Expression (19) for the
velocity, neglecting terms in z^2, is tangential to the surface, but from
it one can deduce a first approximation, of order z^2, to the normal

component of velocity w. For, by solenoidality, $\partial w/\partial z$ must be minus the two-dimensional divergence of $\boldsymbol{\epsilon}_w z$ for very small z. Hence,

$$w = -\tfrac{1}{2}\Delta z^2, \tag{21}$$

where Δ is div $\boldsymbol{\epsilon}_w$, with $\boldsymbol{\epsilon}_w$ regarded as a two-dimensional vector field; Δ is also related directly to $\boldsymbol{\omega}_w$, being the surface value of the normal component of curl $\boldsymbol{\omega}$.

We see from (19) and (21) that the direction of streamlines as $z \to 0$ becomes parallel to the surface, except where $\boldsymbol{\epsilon}_w = 0$, or, what is the same thing, $\boldsymbol{\omega}_w = 0$. This condition, that both tangential components of vorticity vanish simultaneously, is satisfied in general only at isolated points of the surface, which we call 'points of separation' if $\Delta < 0$ (so that the normal velocity (21) is positive) and 'points of attachment' if $\Delta > 0$ (Legendre 1956). It is only in quite exceptional circumstances, usually owing to some kind of symmetry, that $\boldsymbol{\omega}_w = 0$ all along a line; these include, however, the case of ideal two-dimensional flow (note that when such flow is thought of as 'in two dimensions', we refer to *points* of attachment, etc., but that, when it is seen as a three-dimensional flow around an infinite cylinder, such a 'point' becomes a whole generator of the cylinder, that is, a line of attachment at right angles to the stream). Again, in axisymmetrical flow about a body of revolution, symmetry produces whole lines of separation or attachment, in this case circles coaxial with the body. However, any slight change to either of these situations, such as cropping the cylinder or yawing the body, retrieves the general case, in which $\boldsymbol{\omega}_w = 0$ only at isolated points.

In this general case, the character of the flow near the surface can, to a large extent, be inferred from the surface pattern of 'skin-friction lines' (curves to which $\boldsymbol{\epsilon}_w$ is everywhere tangential, so that the skin-friction vector $\boldsymbol{\tau}_w = \mu\boldsymbol{\epsilon}_w$ also is) and of vortex lines. Both these systems of lines cover the surface completely, crossing each other everywhere at right angles. The pattern of skin-friction lines can often be approximately determined by an experimental technique, described in Chapter X, in which the surface is covered with an oily substance, which leaves permanently visible streaks behind it when the skin-friction force causes it to flow along those lines.

Streamlines very near to the surface lie closely along the skin-friction lines, as (19) indicates (for this reason they are sometimes called 'surface streamlines' or 'limiting streamlines'); however, their distance z from the surface varies, not as ω_w^{-1} (see equation (12)), but as $(\omega_w h)^{-1}$, where h is the distance between two adjacent skin-friction lines. This is because in a streamtube of rectangular section, whose base is the portion of surface between the two skin-friction lines and whose (variable) height is z, we have

$$\tfrac{1}{2}\omega_w z^2 h = \epsilon, \tag{22}$$

where ϵ is the volume flow along the streamtube, and ω_w is the magnitude of $\boldsymbol{\omega}_w$ (and of $\boldsymbol{\epsilon}_w$). It follows that streamlines can increase greatly their distance from the surface, not only where ω_w becomes very small, but also where h does, that is, where skin-friction lines run very close together. These alternative mechanisms of separation need to be borne continuously in mind.

There is just one skin-friction line and one vortex line through each point of the surface, except a point of attachment or separation (where $\boldsymbol{\epsilon}_w = \boldsymbol{\omega}_w = 0$). These last are 'singular points' of the differential equations of both systems of curves (namely, the equations $d\mathbf{r} \| \boldsymbol{\epsilon}_w$ and $d\mathbf{r} \| \boldsymbol{\omega}_w$, respectively, where $d\mathbf{r}$ is the relative position of two adjacent points on a curve). Such singular points are classified by mathematicians into two main types (see, for example, Kaplan 1958, chapter 11), depending on the sign of the 'Jacobian',

$$J = \frac{\partial \omega_x}{\partial x}\frac{\partial \omega_y}{\partial y} - \frac{\partial \omega_x}{\partial y}\frac{\partial \omega_y}{\partial x} = \frac{\partial \epsilon_x}{\partial x}\frac{\partial \epsilon_y}{\partial y} - \frac{\partial \epsilon_x}{\partial y}\frac{\partial \epsilon_y}{\partial x}, \tag{23}$$

where the suffices denote components of $\boldsymbol{\omega}_w$ and $\boldsymbol{\epsilon}_w$ in the x- and y-directions, and x, y, z are Cartesian coordinates with origin O at the singular point and Oz normal to the surface.

A singular point where $J < 0$ is a 'saddle point' (of attachment or separation according as $\Delta > 0$ or $\Delta < 0$). Near a saddle point the pattern of skin-friction and vortex lines is as in Fig. II. 9, where the arrows indicate the direction of $\boldsymbol{\epsilon}_w$, and hence also of streamlines very close to the surface.

A singular point where $J > 0$, however, is a 'nodal point'. Fig. II. 10 indicates a number of possible surface patterns near nodal points of attachment, with arrows meaning the same as before. The inequalities under the patterns give, in terms of J and of

$$\Delta = \operatorname{div} \boldsymbol{\epsilon}_w = \frac{\partial \epsilon_x}{\partial x} + \frac{\partial \epsilon_y}{\partial y} = \frac{\partial \omega_y}{\partial x} - \frac{\partial \omega_x}{\partial y},$$

$$\Omega = \operatorname{div} \boldsymbol{\omega}_w = \frac{\partial \omega_x}{\partial x} + \frac{\partial \omega_y}{\partial y}, \tag{24}$$

the condition for each type to occur; cases of equality, however, are not exhibited, except for the case $\Omega = 0$, which we shall see is of special importance, since it occurs at any nodal point of attachment of a stream-line from far upstream. From each type of nodal point an infinite number of skin-friction lines emerge, either having all (except one) the

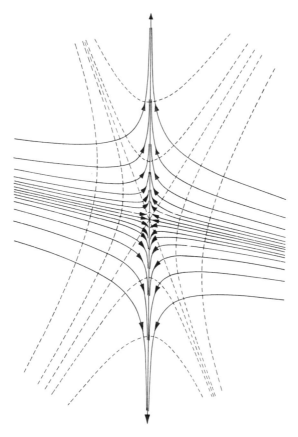

Fig. II. 9. Typical pattern of skin-friction lines (full) and vortex lines (broken) near a saddle point.

same tangent, or else spirally. Spiral attachment occurs principally when either the surface or the external flow is rotating, as, for example, in flows studied in Section III. 20.

The possible local patterns at a nodal point of separation are exactly the same as in Fig. II. 10, but with all the arrows reversed. Spiral separation, however, can occur even in ordinary flows over sweptback wings, when oil is sometimes seen to accumulate at a point and spin around (see Garner and Bryer 1959 and Fig. II. 14 below).

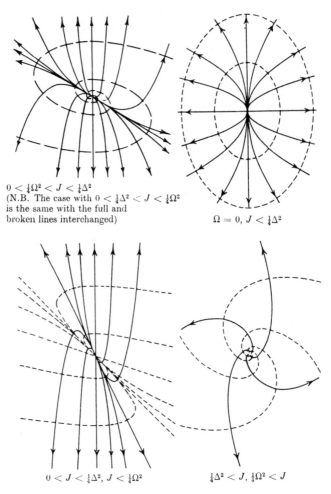

$0 < \tfrac{1}{4}\Omega^2 < J < \tfrac{1}{4}\Delta^2$
(N.B. The case with $0 < \tfrac{1}{4}\Delta^2 < J < \tfrac{1}{4}\Omega^2$
is the same with the full and
broken lines interchanged)

$\Omega = 0, \, J < \tfrac{1}{4}\Delta^2$

$0 < J < \tfrac{1}{4}\Delta^2, \, J < \tfrac{1}{4}\Omega^2$ $\tfrac{1}{4}\Delta^2 < J, \, \tfrac{1}{4}\Omega^2 < J$

Fig. II. 10. Different types of pattern of skin-friction lines (full) and vortex
lines (broken) near a nodal point of attachment ($J > 0, \Delta > 0$).

2.7. *Topography of skin-friction lines and vortex lines*

The range of possible overall patterns of skin-friction and vortex lines
on a smooth surface is subject to a topological law, that the number
of nodal points must exceed the number of saddle points by 2 (see for
example Kaplan 1958, p. 444, or Coddington and Levinson 1955,
chapter 16).

To get a physical 'feel' for this law (whose mathematical proof, from
properties of the Jacobian (23), is not extremely recherché, but would

be out of place here), one may argue that the infinity of skin-friction lines on the surface must begin and end somewhere, which indicates that there is at least one nodal point of attachment and one nodal point of separation. If there are *two* nodal points of attachment, the skin-friction lines from each must somewhere run into one another, and so have to divide at a saddle point. Fig. II. 11 shows that this combina-

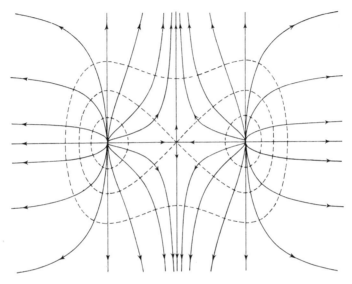

Fig. II. 11. A combination of two nodal points of attachment and one saddle point.

tion, of two nodal points of attachment and a saddle point (whether of attachment or separation), is similar to a single nodal point of attachment in being a simple 'source' of skin-friction lines; the same is true of n nodal points of attachment and $(n-1)$ saddle points. Similarly, m nodal points of separation and $(m-1)$ saddle points behave like a 'sink', into which skin-friction lines issuing from the 'source' can disappear, giving a possible arrangement of such lines with $m+n$ nodal points and $m+n-2$ saddle points. Actually, the most general arrangement is of the form just described, except when $\Delta = 0$ at some nodal points, whose total number, even then, must exceed by 2 that of the saddle points.

A feature of three-dimensional flow is that there can be any number of nodal points of attachment of streamlines from far upstream. This is true even for ideal irrotational flow, in which a body with (say) two protuberances in front has normally a stagnation point on each; these are nodal points of attachment of irrotational-flow streamlines, and somewhere between them is a third stagnation point, which is a saddle point of attachment (such as may occur in practice on a wing leading edge between two engine nacelles). The real flows about bodies of this kind have points of attachment close to those given by irrotational-flow theory, any differences being due mainly to wake-induced flow. Fig. II. 11 shows a typical surface pattern over the front; note that, as no vortex line attaches itself to the surface at these points of attachment of streamlines from far upstream, the surface vortex lines in their neighbourhood are closed (compare Fig. II. 10 for the case with $\Omega = 0$).

At any nodal point of attachment of fluid which has not previously acquired vorticity, the boundary-layer thickness is determined, as in Section 2.4, by a balance between diffusion of vorticity out from the surface and convection inward; the external flow normal to the surface being (as before) of the form $w = -\beta z$, or $w = -\beta(z-\delta_1)$ if the displacement-thickness effect is taken into account. This argument again suggests a thickness of order $\sqrt{(\nu/\beta)}$, and calculation has shown that δ_1 is between $0.65\sqrt{(\nu/\beta)}$ and $0.80\sqrt{(\nu/\beta)}$ for all such nodal points (Howarth 1951c). Calculations have not been made for the full range of saddle points of attachment, but the same arguments apply, however surprising this may seem in view of the far greater stretch of surface which has been traversed by some of the fluid near a saddle point. The reason is that, even if this fluid was formerly in a much thicker boundary layer, it has recently formed part of a layer with $\partial w/\partial z = -\beta$ outside it, for long enough to bring the thickness down to order $\sqrt{(\nu/\beta)}$.

Departure from the surface of the vorticity in a boundary layer, which has originated as just described from one or more points of attachment, occurs commonly at a 'line of separation'. This is defined as a skin-friction line which issues from both sides of a saddle point of separation and, after embracing the body, disappears into a nodal point of separation. A line of separation partitions the surface; only the skin-friction lines ahead of it have originated at the forward points of attachment, while those behind have issued from a nodal point (or points) of attachment at the rear. Note that it may or may not be 'wake fluid' (with previously acquired vorticity) that becomes attached at such a rear point, but that, if it is, then a wider range of surface patterns is possible there than at the nodal points of attachment just mentioned.

The twofold mechanism of separation, referred to in Section 2.6, is clearly exhibited at lines of separation. Streamlines depart from the surface, not only because ω_w falls to zero as either point of separation is approached, but also because the surface topography near a saddle point is such as to make streamlines come close together along the line of separation, whence the h of equation (22) falls greatly as they approach it. The apparently rather extreme case of this running together exhibited in Fig. II. 9 is by no means atypical of surface patterns inferred from oilflow photographs, which have led some writers to speak

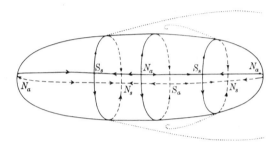

Fig. II. 12. Possible pattern of skin-friction lines on a smooth surface (of which the full and broken lines are on the near and far sides, respectively). N and S signify nodal and saddle points, and subscripts a and s attachment and separation. The dotted lines suggest what happens to fluid separating at the primary and secondary lines of separation.

of skin-friction lines as 'running tangentially into', or 'having cusps on' a line of separation (Maskell 1955). These statements have often very considerable approximate validity, although to go on and call the line of separation an 'envelope' of skin-friction lines is confusingly inaccurate.

The main ingredients of skin-friction-line topography on a smooth surface have now been described. Fig. II. 12 illustrates a further combination of them, in which the backflow towards the line of separation of the boundary layer suffers a 'secondary separation' before reaching it. Note that the law regarding numbers of nodal and saddle points is satisfied.

On surfaces with sharp edges or pointed tips, the topography can be somewhat different. To be sure, the edge or tip is in practice rounded, so that the general theory is correct provided that the detailed pattern in the rounded portion of the surface is included; but such a microscopic view is inconvenient, and one prefers usually to speak of what is left when that small portion of surface is ignored.

The lifting wing with cusped trailing edge is an example whose importance is obvious from Section 2.5 and from practical considerations.

With small enough thickness-chord ratio and angle of incidence, the boundary layer on such a wing may avoid separation altogether, leaving the trailing edge smoothly to form a thin vortex wake. To relate this to the general theory, note that, with a rounded trailing edge, there would be a line of separation around its shoulder, issuing from a saddle point of separation on the lower surface, travelling out to the wing tip,

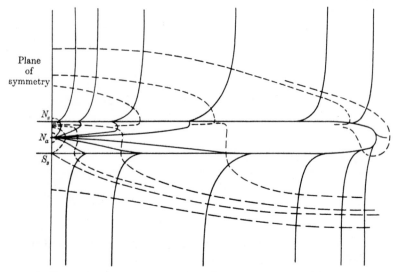

FIG. II. 13. Surface pattern near a rounded trailing edge in thin-wake flow about a lifting wing. (View upstream from behind the trailing edge, with the vertical scale very greatly enlarged.)

and returning along the upper surface to disappear into a nodal point of separation. This contrary motion generates the trailing vorticity, and indeed Fig. II. 13 shows how the surface vortex lines would turn into the downstream direction just before separation.

With other wings or angles of incidence, separation occurs ahead of the trailing edge, and the flow pattern on this smooth part of the surface can show all the features already discussed. Attachment may occur at the trailing edge if there is a line of separation ahead of it. Such attachment would conform to the general theory (taking place at a nodal point, etc.) only if the edge were rounded; if it is cusped, skin-friction lines can become attached all along it.

The line of separation on a stalled wing may lie right along the upper surface of the leading edge, but when only the tips are stalled it issues from a saddle point of separation in a part-span position, whence one branch travels to the tip while the other travels back to the trailing edge, or sometimes to a spiral point of separation, in both cases shedding a 'part-span vortex sheet' (Fig. II. 14).

The needs of supersonic aircraft have given prominence to the slender 'conical' wing shape, in the general sense of a surface generated by any set of straight lines stretching back from an apex. In certain attitudes,

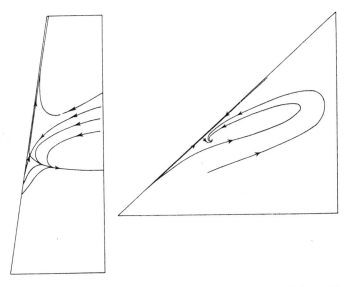

FIG. II. 14. Types of surface pattern for a wing with the tip stalled (straight wing on the left, sweptback wing on the right).

the sharp apex is simply a nodal point of attachment, and the general theory applies; but, at higher angles of incidence, the surface pattern is that generated by two nodal points of attachment and a saddle point of separation which have coalesced at the apex (but would be distinct if the apex were rounded). Such a surface pattern is illustrated in Fig. II. 15. The line of separation S is well marked in oilflow photographs. The almost straight skin-friction line A through the second nodal point of attachment, although less closely defined, has been called a 'line of attachment'. In many such flows the boundary layer is thin enough, except near S, for a thin-wake theory, in which the twirled conical vortex wake which leaves the surface there is suitably approximated, while the flow is regarded as irrotational outside it, to have reached reasonable agreement with experiment (Mangler and Smith 1959). More examples of flow patterns of practical interest are given in Section 26, in Chapter VIII, and in the companion volume *Incompressible Aerodynamics*.

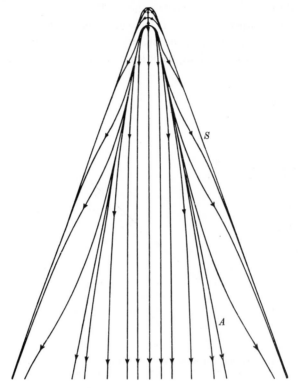

Fig. II. 15. Upper-surface pattern for flow about a 'conical' wing shape at incidence, with apex rounded to show how this splits the singularity there into three.

2.8. *Three-dimensional boundary-layer theory*

The boundary layer in axisymmetrical flow about bodies of revolution has been much investigated. The results are extremely similar to those for two-dimensional flow. This is principally because the vorticity source strength per unit area is the same; modifications to the arguments leading to (18) cancel out, since the additional flow of total vorticity, called for by the additional area (normal to the direction of motion) occupied by vortex elements when they stretch on moving farther from the axis of symmetry, is provided exactly by the dynamical effect of that stretching. Thus, vorticity production and diffusion are unaltered, which, in particular, leaves the condition for separation almost the same as in two-dimensional flow; the quantitative changes in boundary-layer development, due to modified convective processes, are not great, as is shown in Chapter VIII, Part II, which treats also the case when the body rotates about its axis. Axisymmetrical flow has some attractions if precise comparisons with experiment are sought, as being more accurately realizable than two-dimensional flow and equally amenable to calculation.

By contrast, the quantitative theory of general three-dimensional flow in boundary layers is pitifully undeveloped (Chapter VIII, Part III). Accordingly, we are able here to give only a crude qualitative picture of the factors influencing the vorticity distribution, both through the layer and over the surface, of which the latter has been shown (Sections 2.6 and 2.7) to regulate separation. We shall see that, although the *stretching* of vortex lines has just been found to be relatively immaterial, their *rotation* is of the first importance.

As discussed in connexion with equations (15) and (16), vorticity components are to a good approximation gradients normal to the surface of tangential velocity components, and the total vorticity per unit area of boundary layer, namely

$$\int_0^\delta \boldsymbol{\omega}\, dz = \mathbf{n} \times \mathbf{U}, \tag{25}$$

can be regarded as the external flow velocity, say $\mathbf{U}$, turned through $90°$ (in the positive sense, about the outward normal $\mathbf{n}$ from the surface). Thus, the mean vortex lines (averaged across the layer) are perpendicular to the surface streamlines of the external flow, and hence lie along the surface equipotentials of that irrotational motion, as vortex lines were noted in Section 2.1 to do exactly in the initial stage of the motion, before convection begins to operate.

Convection tends to alter this distribution of mean or total vorticity, both in magnitude and in direction. To redress the balance, new vorticity is produced at the surface, not only in the direction of the equipotentials, at the rate UU' (the prime signifying gradient along the streamlines), which has already been discussed in special cases, but also (in general) in the direction at right angles, that of the external streamlines, at the rate $\kappa_s U^2$, where κ_s is the curvature of those streamlines in a plane tangential to the surface.

The simplest physical picture of the generation of this so-called streamwise vorticity comes from the idea (Section 2.4) that the 'average velocity of convection' of vorticity is $\frac{1}{2}U$. In time δt this would advance the vortex lines by $\frac{1}{2}U\,\delta t$, which is *directly* proportional to U; but to lie on an adjacent equipotential, on which the velocity potential is greater by $\delta\phi$, they should have advanced by $U^{-1}\delta\phi$, which is *inversely* proportional to U. Hence, convection makes vortex lines 'lag' most, relative to equipotentials, wherever U is smallest. Fig. II. 16 (which should be read from the bottom upwards) shows this geometrically,

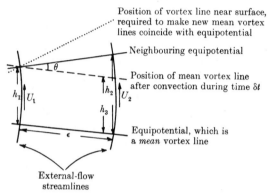

Fig. II. 16. Mechanism of generation of streamwise vorticity. We have $U_1 h_1 = U_2 h_2$, $h_2 = h_1(1 + \kappa_s \epsilon)$, $h_1 = \frac{1}{2}U_1 \delta t$, $h_3 = \frac{1}{2}U_2 \delta t$, and so the angle

$$\theta = \frac{h_2 - h_3}{\epsilon} = \frac{\frac{1}{2}U_1\,\delta t(1 + \kappa_s \epsilon) - \frac{1}{2}U_1\,\delta t(1 + \kappa_s \epsilon)^{-1}}{\epsilon} = \kappa_s U_1\,\delta t.$$

indicating that, after a time δt, a vortex line initially along an equipotential arrives at an angle $U\kappa_s\delta t$ with the local equipotential; it follows that convection produces total streamwise vorticity $U^2\kappa_s$ per unit area per unit time. This is distributed throughout the layer, while, to balance it, equal and opposite streamwise vorticity is created at the surface. This means that the vortex lines near the surface turn still more rapidly than the equipotentials (as the dotted line in Fig. II. 16 indicates). Note that the distribution of streamwise vorticity through the boundary layer is associated with velocity components perpendicular to the external streamlines and towards their centre of curvature.

A more precise account of vorticity balance gives the same result, that cross-stream vorticity is created at the rate UU' and streamwise vorticity at the rate $U^2\kappa_s$. This can also be directly related (Section 2.9) to the result concerning pressure gradient derived in Section 1.5.

These considerations give one some physical feel for how vorticity distributes itself in boundary layers, explaining why the skin-friction lines tend to curve more exaggeratedly than the external streamlines, and why the surface vortex lines tend to slew round into a streamwise direction, as near the saddle point of separation in Fig. II. 9. Points of separation themselves tend to be on streamlines that have not curved much on the average (since both components of vorticity must vanish at such points).

We consider now in the general case the effect of the boundary layer on the external flow, which can again be expressed in terms of a displacement thickness δ_1. By redistributing the total cross-stream vorticity U in a vortex sheet at the mean distance δ_c of cross-stream vorticity from the surface, namely

$$\delta_c = \frac{\int\limits_0^\delta z(\partial u/\partial z)\,dz}{\int\limits_0^\delta (\partial u/\partial z)\,dz} = \frac{\int\limits_0^\delta (U-u)\,dz}{U}, \qquad (26)$$

where u is the velocity component parallel to the external streamlines, we see that the effect of this vorticity on the irrotational flow outside the boundary layer is to change it into the flow around a surface displaced into the fluid through a distance δ_c. However, the effect of the streamwise vorticity on the external flow is not negligible. Because the total streamwise vorticity across the layer is zero, this vorticity can be thought of as a set of little vortex rings whose axes are equipotentials. But, according to potential theory, a vortex ring is equivalent to a doublet perpendicular to the plane of the ring. It follows that the streamwise vorticity has the same effect as a doublet of strength $U\delta_s$ with axis along an equipotential, where $U\delta_s = \int\limits_0^\delta v\,dz$ and v is the cross-stream velocity in the boundary layer. It may be shown (Lighthill 1958) that these doublets alter the effective displacement thickness from δ_c to

$$\delta_1 = \delta_c - \frac{1}{U}\frac{\partial}{\partial c}\int\limits_{\phi_a}^{\phi} \delta_s\,d\phi, \qquad (27)$$

where the integral with respect to the external velocity potential ϕ is along an external streamline from its point of attachment to the surface (namely $\phi = \phi_a$), and where $\partial/\partial c$ signifies differentiation with respect to distance along an equipotential.

We conclude this section by remarking that it is not in every case convenient to resolve the vorticity into the cross-stream and streamwise directions. For example, in the yawed flow past an infinite cylinder,

which is often a valuable idealization of some aspects of the flow over
sweptback wings, it is more convenient to work with the 'spanwise'
and 'chordwise' components. This is especially so because in this flow
the motion of one of the 'arrow-shaped elements of fluid' of Section 1.3
cannot stretch or rotate its spanwise component. (Also, the chordwise
component is merely stretched, not rotated.) It follows that the spanwise vorticity distribution, and so also the chordwise velocity distribution, in the boundary layer are the same as in two-dimensional flow,
which greatly simplifies the calculation of these flows (Section VIII. 22).

2.9. *Pressure in boundary layers*

The key to understanding complete flows, as we have tried to show,
is vorticity theory, which eliminates the pressure as a variable that
needs to be considered. However, some knowledge of its distribution
is obviously necessary, and may be obtained as follows.

In irrotational flow, the force component in any direction on a fluid
element is minus the gradient of the dynamic pressure p_d (Section I. 2.4)
per unit volume. This force component equals the mass, ρ per unit
volume, multiplied by the component of acceleration in that direction,
which may be shown to be the gradient of $\partial\phi/\partial t + \frac{1}{2}v^2$. Hence, the
gradient of

$$p_d + \rho(\partial\phi/\partial t + \tfrac{1}{2}v^2) \tag{28}$$

in any direction is zero throughout an irrotational flow, so that (28)
must have the same value throughout the flow (Lamb 1932, p. 19).
Since the value may vary with time, it is usually written $F(t)$; but for
a body moving through otherwise undisturbed fluid we can always
take $\phi \to 0$ at infinity, in which case (since $p_d \to 0$ there also) the value
of (28) is zero at infinity and so zero everywhere.

Again, in steady flow, with velocity U_∞ at infinity, the uniform value
of (28) (where now $\partial\phi/\partial t = 0$) must clearly be $\frac{1}{2}U_\infty^2$, giving

$$p_d = \tfrac{1}{2}\rho(U_\infty^2 - v^2). \tag{29}$$

Bernoulli's equation (29) encourages the view of p_d in steady flow as
a potential energy per unit volume which on addition of the kinetic
energy $\frac{1}{2}\rho v^2$, is conserved if the flow is irrotational (when the non-
conservative viscous forces vanish). Constant use of (29) must not,
however, seduce one into applying it in unsteady flow without adding
the 'transient pressure' $-\rho\,\partial\phi/\partial t$, which can be large (Section I. 2.6).
Again, in boundary layers and wakes the flow is not irrotational and
(29) cannot be applied, the energy argument suggesting in fact a lower
value of $p_d + \frac{1}{2}\rho v^2$ than $\frac{1}{2}\rho U_\infty^2$, owing to viscous dissipation.

To the 'boundary-layer approximation' (Section 2.4), the pressure is constant across the layer. This is simply because the layer is thin, and the gradient of dynamic pressure across it only moderate—approximately $\kappa\rho u^2$, which is the gradient required to make fluid with velocity u follow a body contour with curvature κ. It follows that the dynamic pressure change across the thickness δ is small compared with the value (29) if $\kappa\delta$ is small (as was assumed already in Section 2.4), and therefore, at any point in the boundary layer,

$$p_d \doteqdot \tfrac{1}{2}\rho(U_\infty^2 - U^2), \qquad (30)$$

where U is the external flow velocity.

In particular, equation (30) gives the pressure at the surface itself, a result which one might hope to use in 'thin-wake' flows, where the whole surface is covered by boundary layer, to calculate the force on the body. However, the approximation is not good enough for this purpose. Errors, due to neglecting either the pressure gradient across the layer, or the displacement-thickness effect on U, produce a resultant pressure force ('form drag') comparable with the whole viscous force on the body ('skin-friction drag'). Accordingly, such errors cannot be neglected, as often no drag is present from other causes, the pressure forces in pure irrotational flow having zero resultant. Again, in wing aerodynamics, although at high lift the induced drag associated with trailing vorticity may be much greater than the drag due to the boundary layer, it is imperative to know also the drag at zero lift, when this latter component predominates. To get round these difficulties, one does not in practice attempt to calculate surface pressure more precisely, but uses a combination of arguments (Chapter X) in which drag is inferred, from conservation of momentum for large masses of fluid, in terms of the state of the boundary layer at the trailing edge.

We conclude the discussion of pressure in boundary layers with some simple physical arguments for which approximation (30) is adequate. These arguments tell us nothing that has not already been derived more rigorously by vorticity arguments, but they are included because it is useful to be able to view a subject from more than one angle.

From (30), the dynamic pressure gradient parallel to the external streamlines is $-\rho U U'$ at all points of a boundary layer. This gradient (which, according to Sections 1.5, 2.4 and 2.8, is associated with generation of cross-stream vorticity at the rate $U U'$) tends to accelerate the fluid in the boundary layer (which, however, is acted on also by viscous forces) when $U' > 0$, and to retard it when $U' < 0$. In the latter case, the fluid near the wall (which already is moving only sluggishly) will tend to be brought to rest, leading to separation of the fluid behind it, and the results quoted in Section 2.4 show that this tendency can be withstood by viscous forces to only a restricted extent. This view of pressure forces as tending to produce the (usually un-wished-for) separation has led to the phrase 'adverse' pressure gradient being used to denote a rise of pressure (which goes with a fall of velocity) along the external streamlines.

Again, the dynamic pressure gradient perpendicular to the external streamlines is $\kappa_s \rho U^2$ away from their centre of curvature (this 'curva-ture', and its magnitude κ_s, being curvature in a tangent plane, as in Section 2.8). This result follows directly from (30) and the irrota-tionality of the external flow, or more simply from considering the centrifugal acceleration of the fluid just outside the boundary layer, and by Sections 1.5 and 2.8 it is associated with generation of stream-wise vorticity at the rate $\kappa_s U^2$. Now, the centrifugal acceleration of the much more slowly moving fluid near the surface fails to balance this normal pressure gradient, whence this fluid tends to acquire a velocity component towards the centre of curvature. This is the cross-stream flow, associated with streamwise vorticity, which has been discussed already in Section 2.8.

3. Instability and turbulence

3.1. *Hydrodynamic instability*

We must now refer to the commonplace observation that the flow around a body does not normally develop in a smooth, orderly fashion to a perfectly steady state, as might be expected from Sections 2.1 and 2.2, but that more or less violent, irregular fluctuations appear, especially in the wake. These are ascribed to 'instability' of the flow, that is, the tendency for small disturbances (due to noise, mechanical vibra-tion, surface roughness, non-uniformity of the oncoming stream, etc.) to be amplified into substantial fluctuations. As a result, the final, 'turbulent', motion is at most 'statistically steady', in the sense that the fluid velocity at each point varies about a constant mean value.

The instability can be viewed as an instability of the vorticity distri-bution, as this fixes the flow field (Section 1.6). We must suppose, therefore, that a very slight displacement of some vorticity, or the creation at the surface of a very little extra vorticity, may induce slight changes in the velocities of convection of existing vortex lines, such that resulting changes in the vorticity pattern a short time later induce alterations in the velocities of convection of that vorticity pattern, such that, etc., etc.,..., the whole altered process of convection, production and diffusion of vorticity tending more and more to depart from what it would have been without the original disturbance. This supposition would explain why the greatest unsteadiness is found in the wake, the boundary layer, and irrotational-flow regions close enough to these to partake strongly of the motions which are induced by their vorticity fluctuations. In fact, although turbulence is observed most frequently in wakes, it was found soon after the discovery of the boundary layer (Prandtl 1914) that parts of it (at least) are turbulent in a wide range of flows.

In this Section 3, the properties of the initial flow instability, of the ultimately resulting turbulent motion, and of the transition between them, are sketched as briefly as will allow us in Section 4 to give a general picture of the variation of flow patterns with Reynolds number. This material is needed in a work on laminar boundary layers, both to show when and how they fit into flows in general (other parts of which may be turbulent), and to relate the theory of their stability (Chapter IX) to the characteristics of observed motions.

Since diffusion by itself is a stable process, the vorticity distribution is necessarily stable when it dominates sufficiently over convection. By comparing a diffusion rate of order $\nu \omega_0 / \delta$, where ω_0 is a typical vorticity and δ the thickness of a layer across which ω varies from 0 to ω_0, with a convection rate of order $U \omega_0$ (both per unit area), we see that stability may be expected if

$$R_\delta = U\delta/\nu \tag{31}$$

is small enough. This gives already a reason why the wake is often observed to be unstable when the boundary layer, or, perhaps, the thinner part of the layer (say, the region of accelerating external flow), is not. However, two effects conspire here; not only is the value of δ less in the region of accelerating external flow, but also, as we shall see, the stability of this part of the layer persists up to considerably higher values of R_δ itself. Meanwhile, we note that the order of magnitude of δ in a boundary layer (Section 2.2) shows that R_δ is of order $\sqrt{(Ul/\nu)} = R^{\frac{1}{2}}$, and, also, that experiment has confirmed the stability of all kinds of flow at sufficiently low Reynolds number.

The stability theory is a mathematical construction of great complexity and beauty, due principally to Tollmien (1929, 1935), although details that help to complete the picture have been contributed by very many workers. In it, one considers small sine-wave disturbances to a simple vortex layer of uniform thickness, and investigates their distribution across the layer, their phase velocity c_r, and their rate of amplification (positive, negative or zero) with time. Note that, as wave theory tells us, even a localized disturbance can be considered as a combination of such sine waves, although the part of the disturbance with wavelength around the value λ will travel along, not at the speed c_r of its individual crests, but at its 'group velocity' $c_r - \lambda \, dc_r/d\lambda$.

The most important results are as follows:

(i) If, as a first approximation, diffusion and the production of new vorticity are neglected (as in inviscid flow theory), then the waves can have positive rate of amplification only if the undisturbed vorticity distribution has a maximum in the midst of the layer (Tollmien 1935; see also Görtler 1940a). On this simplified theory, boundary layers in an accelerating external flow are stable, because in them the maximum vorticity is always at the wall (Section 2.4). On the other hand, boundary layers in retarded flow are unstable, and so are wakes (in which the vorticity must have maxima since it vanishes at the centre); in both these, the rate of amplification is positive for a large band of wavelengths.

(ii) This simplified theory, although making an important distinction, is not accurate enough; in particular, for boundary layers in accelerating flow, the actual predicted wave system (with zero amplification rate) has some seriously unrealistic features, due to the total neglect of the production and diffusion of vorticity. Furthermore, when these are reintroduced, with R_δ finite but still large (slight diffusion), they do not for all wavelengths reduce the amplification rate to negative values; there is, rather, a small band of waves (whose length is a rather large multiple of the layer thickness) the modifications to which cause the amplification rate to become positive (Tollmien 1929, Lin 1945). Accordingly, such a boundary layer is unstable to disturbances of frequencies equal to those of these waves.

(iii) At lower values of R_δ the main effect of diffusion is stabilizing or smoothing, as expected. However, a stronger diffusive effect is necessary to remove the instability (see (i)) of layers with vorticity maxima, which is large and almost independent of R_δ, than to remove the weaker instability (see (ii)) of layers with monotonic vorticity. Accordingly, the 'critical' R_δ (separating values of R_δ at which waves of some lengths are unstable from those at which none are) is lowest for layers with pronounced vorticity maxima; it increases as the vorticity maximum approaches the wall, to take considerably higher values for layers with monotonic vorticity, and continues to rise as the vorticity gradient becomes more precipitous (Schlichting 1940, 1955; Pretsch 1941*b*; Lin 1955).

(iv) Although the above theory is for two-dimensional vortex layers, it can be applied to three-dimensional boundary layers if one considers separately the stability of the 'cross-stream' and 'streamwise' vorticity distributions (Section 2.8). Now, since the total streamwise vorticity (integrated across the layer) is zero, it must have a maximum somewhere. It may happen, therefore, if the external flow is accelerating, that R_δ has a value for which the cross-stream vorticity is stable but the streamwise vorticity unstable, leading to concentration of the latter vorticity in 'streaks' which may be visible on oilflow photographs (Gregory, Stuart, and Walker 1955).

The implications of these four results in the problem of transition to turbulence are discussed in Section 3.2. Meanwhile, some explanatory remarks which help to throw light on the essential facts (i) and (ii) are offered, although any attempt at a complete explanation that omits the mathematical theory is out of the question.

The comparison in Fig. II. 17 of a boundary layer in accelerated flow (*a*) and one in retarded flow (*b*) is at first sight relevant to (i). In (*a*), the slight additional vorticity at P (to whose effect must be added that of its image P') produces 'downwash' ahead, whose convective effect on the undisturbed vorticity distribution (which decreases upwards) is to reduce the vorticity in that region, whither the vortex is moving. This fact appears to give the process positive stiffness; the same is true in (*b*) of a vortex at Q. However, the downwash ahead of the vortex at R convects *increased* vorticity into the region whither it is moving, since the undisturbed vorticity increases upwards. This might be taken to signify negative stiffness, and consequent amplification of disturbances, in (*b*) but not in (*a*).

However, such a conclusion would prove too much, indicating instability also for flows in which the vorticity increases upwards, not to a maximum in the layer, but monotonically until a second wall is reached. Furthermore, any simple mathematical model of a convection process of the kind just described, if it takes into account the fact that the convective increase of vorticity ahead of the vortex is balanced by an equal and opposite decrease behind it, shows that the result is merely to augment the effective *velocity* of convection of the disturbance R (while reducing those of P and Q), without introducing any amplification.

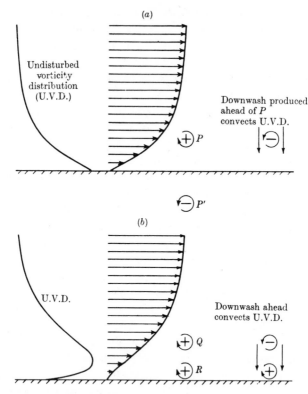

Fig. II. 17. Convective effect of additional vorticity on the undisturbed vorticity distribution, for layers with (a) monotonic vorticity, (b) a vorticity maximum in the midst of the layer.

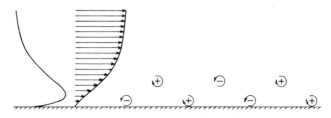

Fig. II. 18. Schematic representation of disturbance to which a layer with a vorticity maximum is unstable.

A mechanism of instability closer to the true one indicated by the mathematical theory is illustrated in Fig. II. 18, where two disturbances are shown, the one above the vorticity maximum having a phase lead over the one below. The possibility of some wave of this general form receiving amplification as it travels along is strongly indicated by two facts: first, that every vortex shown produces such vertical convection of the undisturbed vorticity distribution as tends to augment the disturbances at *both* adjacent vortices; and, secondly, that the above-mentioned increase in the velocity of convection for the lower vortices, and decrease for the upper ones, helps to 'keep them in step'. Together, these facts amount to a physical explanation of the destabilizing effect of the vorticity maximum.

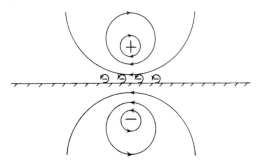

Fig. II. 19. Illustrating how vorticity near the wall causes the generation of vorticity of opposite sign at the wall.

Passing to (ii), all authorities are agreed (see, for example, Lin 1945, p. 291, Taylor 1915, and Lin 1954*b*) that the destabilizing effect of viscosity for certain wavelengths operates in the region very close to the wall. In other words, it results from the diffusion, away from the wall, of vorticity produced there in accordance with the mechanism of Section 1.7. Indeed, Fig. II. 19 shows that additional vorticity of positive sign near the wall causes vorticity of negative sign to be generated at the wall, which for waves of appropriate length must diffuse out as far as the original vortex in time to reinforce the negative phase of the wave when it arrives.

However, the total effect of even a very small amount of diffusion is certainly more complicated than this. The inviscid disturbance theory for boundary layers in accelerating flow is exceptional, in that general disturbances do not show normal longitudinal dispersion into wave packets, each with its own phase velocity and group velocity; rather, a wave system tends to get set up, in which disturbances at every distance from the wall have a phase velocity equal to the local undisturbed velocity. (This possibility corresponds in the mathematical theory to the pole of the vorticity at the 'critical' speed.) Clearly, the resulting interference of waves will be greatly reduced by even the smallest amount of diffusion. These considerations contribute to the complication of the theory from which the result (ii) is finally derived. All the theories are more fully discussed in Chapter IX, together with material on the stability of internal flows, etc.; see also Schlichting (1955) and Lin (1955).

3.2. *Transition to turbulence*

Despite the advance of stability theory, and parallel advances in theoretical and observational knowledge of turbulent flows, the intervening topic, namely the transition between slightly disturbed laminar flow and fully turbulent flow, remains one of the least understood parts of aerodynamics.

Two opposing factors combine to make the value of R_δ at which a vortex layer becomes fully turbulent different from the 'critical' R_δ (Section 3.1) at which instability first appears. The first is that a layer which is stable to small disturbances can be unstable to larger ones. This is well attested for all types of flow, internal and external; the value of R_δ for onset of turbulence can normally be reduced by a factor of 5 or more by deliberate introduction of disturbances, such as involve velocity fluctuations around, say, 3 per cent. of the mean. The main physical feature in the growth of such large disturbances, that is absent from the theory for small disturbances, is self-convection of the disturbance-vorticity distribution (as distinct from its convection by the undisturbed flow, or the convection of undisturbed vorticity by the disturbance). A possible way in which self-convection may help a fluctuating vorticity distribution to grow is by changing the mean vorticity distribution so as to make it more unstable (perhaps introducing a maximum in the midst of the layer); other possibilities are discussed in Chapter IX.

The second factor is that R_δ, at least in external aerodynamics, increases with distance in the direction of motion. Now, under 'smooth' conditions (of low mainstream turbulence, vibration, roughness, etc.), disturbances may be expected to follow the stability theory at least initially, and this has been verified experimentally in certain cases (Schubauer and Skramstad 1947). In particular, they have a certain rate of amplification with time, but also are convected downstream (more precisely, they travel at the appropriate group velocity, with a a certain degree of dispersion, which causes a localized disturbance to grow in size). As they become amplified, the effect of self-convection may increase the amplification rate, at least at first; but disturbances

must have reached regions where R_δ is substantially greater than its
critical value before they attain the 'equilibrium' turbulence level
(Section 3.3). There is then some further delay before different localized disturbances
have grown to fill the whole flow. This occurs in a 'transition region',
which in the much studied boundary layer with uniform external flow
is from a quarter to a half as long as the distance of its front from the
leading edge. It is filled with a random collection of 'turbulent spots',
which grow as they move downstream until spots all over the surface
have merged into one turbulent boundary layer (Emmons 1951, Schubauer and Klebanoff 1955, Hama, Long, and Hegarty 1957, Dhawan
and Narasimha 1958). The velocity variation at a point is found, by
hot-wire measurements (Chapter X), to be almost steady at its laminar-
flow value, except during intermittent 'bursts' of large, turbulent
fluctuations, during which all characteristics of the record, including
mean velocity, are as in a fully turbulent boundary layer. An interesting feature of the spots or bursts is their 'sharp front'. Like the simpler
self-convection processes which can give a sharp front (the 'shock wave')
to high-frequency acoustic pulses, the self-convection of turbulent vorticity shows a tendency (only partially understood) to steepen the vorticity
gradient at the edge of a patch of turbulence; this tendency prevents
its weakening by diffusion, and is responsible also for the sharpness of
image of bullet wakes in spark photographs, such as Fig. II. 20 (Plate).
As the fraction of time occupied by these bursts increases from 0 to 1
through the transition region, all averaged properties (including skin
friction, see Section 3.3) adjust proportionately, from laminar-layer to
turbulent-layer values.

Under 'smooth' conditions, it has been found that transition does
not normally begin before a point, at which small disturbances, of at
least some frequencies, should have been amplified by a factor of order
10^4, according to calculations (Smith 1956a) which allow for the variation of amplification rate as the disturbance passes through parts of
the boundary layer with different undisturbed-vorticity distributions,
but ignore its dependence on amplitude. On the other hand, a much
smaller factor would suffice in rough conditions.

For example, in a layer with uniform external flow, the critical R_{δ_1}
(based on displacement thickness) is 420, which gives 6×10^4 for R_x
(based on the distance x from the point of attachment). But the value
of R_{δ_1} at the beginning of transition is around 3,000 under smooth
conditions (giving $R_x = 3 \times 10^6$), and it falls away as the degree of

disturbance increases, to a minimum around $R_{\delta_1} = 500$ (giving $R_x = 8 \times 10^4$); in this very 'rough' flow, the 'two factors' which were discussed above almost cancel.

If, however, the boundary layer passes into a region of retarded flow, the critical R_{δ_1} quickly falls (say, to around 100), while δ_1 rapidly increases (Section 2.4); this may jerk a laminar boundary layer into turbulence, well before it would have separated, and thus help it, as we shall see, to avoid separation altogether. On the other hand, in the region of accelerating flow near the front stagnation point, the critical R_{δ_1} is around 10^4, while the layer is thin, and transition occurs in this region only at values of R_x exceeding 10^8. Then, as the external-flow gradient U' falls, so does the critical R_{δ_1}, while δ_1 increases, and transition becomes steadily more likely.

Although the above remarks about this difficult subject are based largely on data for two-dimensional boundary layers, they are believed to have substantial general value, except in that, for three-dimensional flows, the instability of the streamwise vorticity distribution (Section 3.1) is an important additional source of transition.

3.3. *The turbulent boundary layer*

We pass now to a subject where enormous volumes of quantitative information exist, but of which a brief qualitative survey will suffice for the purposes of this volume.

Although the rate of amplification of disturbances to a boundary layer may be initially positive, and even increasing with amplitude, it becomes zero by the time the layer is 'fully turbulent', when the ratio of the root-mean-square fluctuation of velocity to the external flow velocity has a maximum of around 10 per cent. (attained, as we shall see, very close to the wall) and shows no further tendency to increase.

One reason for this change is that turbulence redistributes the vorticity in such a way that viscous diffusion becomes more effective in countering the amplification of the disturbances. Especially, it concentrates most of the vorticity much closer to the wall than before, although at the same time allowing some straggling vorticity to wander away from it farther. Fig. II. 21 (derived principally from Schubauer and Klebanoff 1955) shows the vorticity distribution in a two-dimensional laminar layer with uniform external flow, where transition begins, at $R_x = 2 \cdot 3 \times 10^6$, and also the distribution of the mean vorticity $\bar{\omega}$, and of the root-mean-square fluctuation of vorticity $\sigma\{\omega\} = \{\overline{(\omega - \bar{\omega})^2}\}^{\frac{1}{2}}$, in the fully turbulent layer at the rear of the transition region, where

FIG. II 20. Spark photograph of the wake of a bullet. (Ballistics Research Laboratory, Aberdeen Proving Ground, 1958)

$R_x = 3\cdot3 \times 10^6$. During transition some 95 per cent. of the vorticity has moved closer to the wall, much of it very close indeed; the mean vorticity at the wall, $\bar{\omega}_w$ (which is τ_w/μ, where τ_w is the skin friction), has risen to 8 times the laminar value, and $\bar{\omega}$ now falls precipitously away from this maximum. However, the other 5 per cent. of the mean vorticity has moved out much farther than it would have in the normal development of the laminar layer.

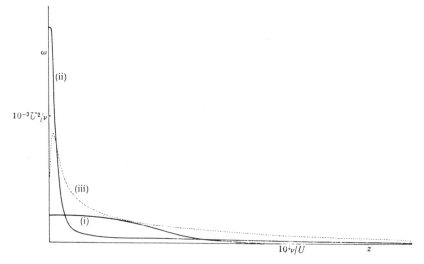

FIG. II. 21. Distribution of mean vorticity in a boundary layer with uniform external flow; (i) at beginning, (ii) at end, of transition. Curve (iii) gives rough values of the root-mean-square fluctuation $\sigma(\omega)$ at the end of transition.

Downstream, the turbulent boundary layer grows principally by extension of this 'tail' of the vorticity distribution (a typical angle between the edge of the boundary layer and the surface being $1°$). By contrast, the mechanism concentrating vorticity close to the wall (which is discussed below) permits that concentration to fall off only very gradually indeed—much more gradually than the boundary-layer thickness increases. Nevertheless, small quantities of vorticity do continually break loose from the region of concentration; and the fluctuations in w (velocity component normal to the surface) which they themselves induce have a statistical tendency to spread that vorticity over a greater and greater area. At any one instant the region of vorticity has an irregular edge, like that of the wake photograph Fig. II. 20 (Plate). The turbulence is measurably intermittent in the outer half of the boundary layer (Dhawan and Narasimha 1958), because the induced velocity fluctuations in the irrotational-flow regions between protruding tongues of vorticity are relatively mild. By contrast, the 'busy' motion at the edges of those tongues (visible clearly in, say, a smoke jet) is continually forming convolutions which 'entrain' irrotational fluid into the region of vorticity, where diffusion quickly makes it rotational.

This mechanism for spreading out the vorticity in, say, the outer four-fifths of a boundary layer (or in the whole of a 'free' turbulent layer, such as a wake) is analogous to the statistical mechanism of diffusion (Section I. 3), except that the random motion is of lumps of vorticity instead of individual molecules. It is commonly referred to as 'turbulent diffusion', and it has been shown that the resulting distributions of mean vorticity and mean velocity in the regions in question behave as if the diffusivity ν (of vorticity or momentum) were increased by the presence of turbulent diffusion to a much higher value ν_T (Townsend 1956). For the turbulent layer of Fig. II. 21, ν_T/ν is about 40, but it increases with the Reynolds number R_δ based on layer thickness. For a wake far behind a cylinder of drag D per unit length, ν_T is about $0\cdot02\,D/\rho U_\infty$. There is evidence in both cases that the effective ν_T falls off in the region of markedly intermittent turbulence.

This statistically uniform churning-up of the outer four-fifths of a boundary layer, by vorticity which has escaped from the region of concentration, is both regulated as regards intensity, and also prevented from acting unchanged in the inner fifth, by a mechanism depending crucially on the presence of the solid surface, although assisted in its operation by the outer vorticity fluctuations.

The main effect of a solid surface on turbulent vorticity close to it is to *correlate inflow towards the surface with lateral stretching*. Note that only the stretching of vortex lines can explain how during transition the mean wall vorticity increases as illustrated in Fig. II. 21; and only a tendency, for vortex lines to stretch as they approach the surface and relax as they move away from it, can explain how the gradient of mean vorticity illustrated in Fig. II. 21 is maintained in spite of viscous diffusion down it—to say nothing of any possible 'turbulent diffusion' down it, which the old 'vorticity transfer' theory supposed should occur. It is relevant to both these points that Fig. II. 21 relates to uniform external flow, which implies zero mean rate of production of vorticity at the surface; but, even in an accelerating flow, the rate of production UU' is too small to explain either.

A simplified illustration of how inflow towards a wall tends to go

with lateral stretching, and outflow with lateral compression, is given
in Fig. II. 22. Doubtless some longitudinal deformation is usually also
present, which reduces the need for lateral deformation (perhaps, on
the average, by half). However, there is evidence (from attempts to
relate different types of theoretical model of a turbulent boundary layer
to observations by hot-wire techniques; see, for example, Townsend

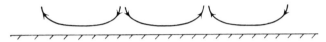

Fig. II. 22. Correlation of inflow with lateral stretching, and outflow with
lateral compression, of vortex lines (the mean flow is normal to the plane of
the paper).

1956) that the larger-scale motions (which push out the 'tongues' of
rotational fluid discussed above) are elongated in the stream direction,
as if their vortex lines had been stretched longitudinally by the mean
shear; in such motions, the correlation between inflow and lateral
stretching illustrated in Fig. II. 22 would be particularly strong. We
may think of them as constantly bringing the major part of the vorticity
in the layer close to the wall, while intensifying it by stretching, and,
doubtless, generating new vorticity at the surface; meanwhile, they
relax the vortex lines which they permit to wander into the outer layer.
Smaller-scale movements take over from these to bring vorticity still
closer to the wall, and so on. Thus, the 'cascade process', which in free
turbulence (see, for example, Batchelor 1953) continually passes the
energy of fluctuations down to modes of shorter and shorter length-
scale—because at high Reynolds numbers motions in a whole range
of scales may be unstable, which implies that motions of smaller scale
can extract energy from them—this cascade process has the additional
effect in a turbulent boundary layer of bringing the fluctuations into
closer and closer contact with the wall, while their vortex lines are more
and more stretched.

Ultimately, they reach a region where gradients have become so
intense that viscous diffusion counteracts the effect of further stretching. A measure, η, of the thickness of the 'viscous sub-layer', where
owing to diffusion the mean vorticity has reached a uniform value
(which is $\bar{\omega}_w$), is obtained by balancing rates of diffusion, of order $\nu\bar{\omega}_w/\eta$,
and of convection, of order $(\bar{\omega}_w\eta)\bar{\omega}_w$, to give

$$\eta = (\nu/\bar{\omega}_w)^{\frac{1}{2}} = \nu(\tau_w/\rho)^{-\frac{1}{2}}. \tag{32}$$

Experimentally, uniformity of $\bar{\omega}$ extends to about $z = 5\eta$ (Townsend

1956; but this is *not* a 'laminar' sub-layer, as supposed in the early literature; the root-mean-square fluctuation of ω is about 30 per cent. of the mean). On the other hand, viscous diffusion ceases to be important compared with convection effects for $z > 30\eta$. We should note the extremely small value of η, as appears from the order of magnitude, 30, of the Reynolds number $U\eta/\nu$.

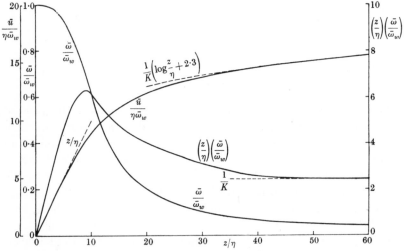

FIG. II. 23. The law of the wall (mean values). A plot of $\bar{\omega}/\bar{\omega}_w$, $(z/\eta)(\bar{\omega}/\bar{\omega}_w)$, and $\bar{u}/\bar{\omega}_w\eta$ against z/η in the equilibrium layer near a solid surface (Laufer 1954).

Experiments on a wide range of turbulent flows (including flow in pipes) have shown that a layer adjacent to the solid surface, of thickness far greater than η, and nearer to a tenth of the thickness of the whole region of vorticity, is approximately identical in structure (statistically speaking) in all such flows, differing only in intensity, as measured, say, by $\bar{\omega}_w$. The violent agitations of such an inner layer maintain its 'equilibrium' of structure, although the fluid in it may have come from a region where $\bar{\omega}_w$ was different, because the downstream convection process is slow by comparison. It follows by dimensional analysis (Section I. 5) that any quantity in this region, when multiplied by a combination of $\bar{\omega}_w$ and the constants ρ and μ to make it non-dimensional, is a function of z/η alone (the 'law of the wall'). This functional relationship, for various means and standard deviations of observed quantities, is given in Figs. II. 23 and 24. The simplifications for $z/\eta > 30$ may be ascribed to the unimportance of viscous diffusion in this region, where the transport of momentum towards the surface, at a rate τ_w

per unit area, to make up for the momentum removed there by skin friction, takes place solely by turbulent convection. In this region, $\bar{\omega}$, for example, depends on τ_w, ρ, and z alone, giving

$$\bar{\omega} = \frac{(\tau_w/\rho)^{\frac{1}{2}}}{Kz} = \frac{\bar{\omega}_w \eta}{Kz}, \tag{33}$$

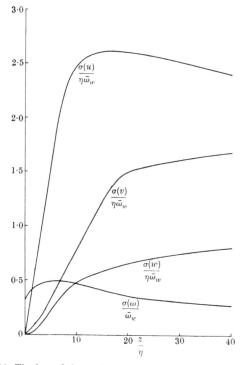

FIG. II. 24. The law of the wall (approximate root-mean-square fluctuations). A plot of $\sigma(\omega)/\bar{\omega}_w$, $\sigma(u)/\bar{\omega}_w \eta$, $\sigma(v)/\bar{\omega}_w \eta$, $\sigma(w)/\bar{\omega}_w \eta$ against z/η in the equilibrium layer.

where K is a constant determined experimentally as 0.40 ± 0.01. Integrating,

$$\bar{u} = \frac{(\tau_w/\rho)^{\frac{1}{2}}}{K}\left\{\log\frac{z}{\eta} + A\right\}, \tag{34}$$

where A is a constant determined experimentally as 2.5 ± 0.2 (Coles 1955). Equations (33) and (34) hold if z exceeds 30η and is less than about a tenth of δ.

It would be out of place here to discuss further details of the inner and outer layers and the interaction between them. We must note, though, how the turbulent layer reacts to removal of vorticity at the wall. Because of the mechanism, which continually concentrates vorticity at the wall, a much more extensive region of negative vorticity-source strength UU' at the surface is required to reduce $\bar{\omega}_w$ to zero than for the laminar layer, a typical required reduction in U being not 5 per cent. but 30 per cent. This is why transition to turbulence may so greatly delay, or even prevent, separation.

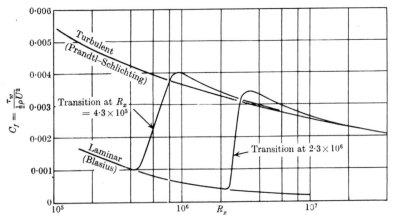

FIG. II. 25. The local skin-friction coefficient C_f plotted against R_x for boundary layers on smooth surfaces with uniform external flow and different values of R_x at transition.

We illustrate also, in Fig. II. 25, the variation of the skin-friction coefficient,

$$C_f = \tau_w/(\tfrac{1}{2}\rho U^2), \tag{35}$$

for uniform external flow over a smooth surface with various values of R_x at transition (Dhawan and Narasimha 1958). These graphs have general illustrative utility, since for the reasons just given τ_w depends less strongly on the distribution of U with x than in a laminar layer. For rough surfaces, the gradual change in C_f, as R_x increases, flattens out to a constant value where the Reynolds number of the flow over a typical roughness element becomes large enough for it to shed a turbulent wake; in the case of a very rough surface, a rather abrupt *rise*, to a value as high as $0\cdot01$, may precede this flattening (Goldstein 1938, p. 380).

4. Variation of flow patterns with Reynolds number

4.1. *Flow around bluff bodies*

To illustrate how knowledge of the properties of vorticity, boundary layers, and turbulence is applied, we end this chapter with some remarks on the variation of the flow pattern with Reynolds number,

$$R = \rho U_\infty l/\mu = U_\infty l/\nu, \tag{36}$$

for the steady flow about a stationary body of length-scale l, and given shape and attitude, under conditions when ρ and μ can be regarded as constant; such flow patterns were shown in Section I. 5.1 to depend on R alone. First, we consider 'bluff bodies', which include most shapes not specifically 'streamlined' for good aerodynamic performance, and which may be defined as those for which 'thin-wake' flow is impossible, however far forward the boundary layer may increase its resistance to separation by transition to turbulence.

When R is very small indeed (say, $R < 1$) a type of flow very different from those discussed earlier in this chapter occurs (see Chapter IV). This is because convection of vorticity is slow, compared even with diffusion over distances of order l. It follows that, in the outer regions of vorticity, convection proceeds at almost the uniform speed U_∞, which, balanced against a speed of order ν/s for diffusion through distance s, gives ν/U_∞ as a measure of the upstream penetration of vorticity, instead of the $\sqrt{(\nu l/U_\infty)}$ for large R which follows from the use of (14). Actually, diffusion makes the vorticity fill an enormous paraboloid of revolution, with focus in the body and vertex a distance of 2 or 3 times ν/U_∞ upstream of it.

Near the body, on the other hand, the scale of the vorticity variations is l, and hence diffusive flow is large compared with convective flow. Accordingly, the separation mechanism, whereby (Section 2.4) convection continually alters the vorticity distribution so as to call for generation, over parts of the surface, of vorticity in the opposite sense, fails to operate; on the contrary, as vorticity diffuses away from the body, its effect in maintaining the no-slip condition at the surface is weakened, requiring the generation of more vorticity in the same sense. Therefore, separation does not occur, or, more precisely, is delayed until a final 'nodal point' at the rear of the body.

In this type of flow, which is treated in detail in Chapter IV, viscous stresses near the body are of order $\mu U_\infty/l$, as also are dynamic pressures, since the usual terms of order ρU_∞^2, needed to make dynamic pressure gradients balance changes of momentum, are small compared with terms of order $\mu U_\infty/l$, needed to make them balance gradients of viscous stress. It follows that the drag is of order $\mu U_\infty l$ for very small R, so that the coefficient C_D (Section I. 5.2) satisfies

$$C_D \sim A/R \quad \text{as} \quad R \to 0, \tag{37}$$

where A is a constant, which is 24 for a sphere of diameter l if its projected area $\frac{1}{4}\pi l^2$ is used in the definition of C_D, equation (I. 44).

Similar arguments hold for two-dimensional flow about an infinite cylinder, but the functional dependence of C_D on R as $R \to 0$ is slightly different, because diffusion at a steady rate from an infinite cylinder makes that which diffuses grow logarithmically with distance from the cylinder, instead of becoming constant; it follows that a distribution of vorticity diffusing to a distance of order ν/U_∞, and producing a total change U_∞ in velocity, must involve changes of order $U_\infty/\log(\nu/U_\infty l)$ over distances of order l. This alters the previous argument, introducing a $\log(R^{-1})$ factor in the denominator of C_D, as in the formula

$$C_D \sim 8\pi/R\log(7\cdot4R^{-1}) \quad \text{as } R \to 0$$

for a circular cylinder of diameter l,

In the region between $R = 1$ and $R = 10$, convection of vorticity near the body begins to assume the role described in Section 2, leading to the formation of a separation line, which moves forward from the rear as R increases above a value R_s in this range. The flow then has a separation bubble and a steady laminar wake, provided that R remains below the value R_t at which the wake becomes unstable. Fig. II. 26 (Plate) illustrates three flows of this kind for the circular cylinder, with $R = 3\cdot9$ (which is near R_s), $R = 18\cdot6$, and $R = 33\cdot5$. The last value is large enough for the arguments of boundary-layer theory to have real value; thus, the displacement thickness at the first point of attachment is only $0\cdot11$ radii.

It is still not known for certain what determines the length of the separation bubble, or whether this would continue to grow with increasing R if the flow did not become unstable above $R = R_t$, which is about 40 for the circular cylinder. Batchelor (1956) argues that l_s/l (where l_s is the length of the separation bubble) would tend to a constant with increasing R, while C_D would tend to zero; but Imai (1957a) argues that l_s/l would increase in proportion to R, while C_D would tend to the value given by the Helmholtz–Kirchhoff discontinuous flow theory.

The mode of redistribution of vorticity which builds up to large amplitude in the wakes of cylinders at Reynolds numbers just above R_t is of the general type illustrated in Fig. II. 18, leading to the staggered parallel rows of vortices known as Kármán's vortex street. Behind a circular cylinder, a regular street like that illustrated in Fig. II. 28 (Plate) occurs for Reynolds numbers between $R_t = 40$ and around 200. Fig. II. 27 (Plate) shows its build-up for five Reynolds numbers

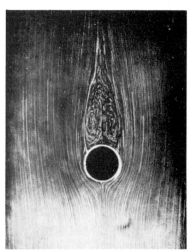
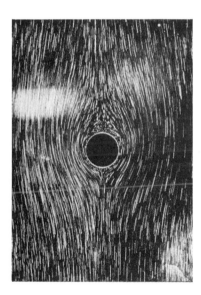

Fig. II. 26. Flow about a circular cylinder at $R = 3 \cdot 9$, $18 \cdot 6$, $33 \cdot 5$.
(Homann 1936a)

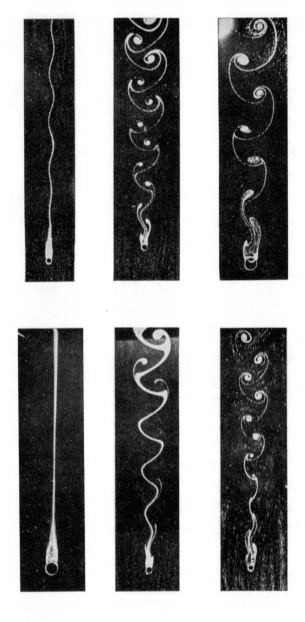

Fig. II. 27. Flow about a circular cylinder at $R = 31\cdot6$, $54\cdot8$, $65\cdot2$, 73, $101\cdot5$, 161. (Homann 1936a)

Fig. II. 28. Kármán vortex street behind a cylinder. (Richards 1933)

in this range, the lowest ($R = 54\cdot8$) being near to the (somewhat increased) value of R_l appropriate to the tunnel width that was used. As R increases still more, other modes become capable of amplification, which, together with the 'cascade process' (Section 3.3), namely the break-up of larger eddies by instability into smaller ones, produces a more and more irregularly turbulent wake. When the vorticity close to the cylinder is fluctuating between large positive and negative values, there is a substantial fluctuating lift on the cylinder (compare Section 2.5), and the equal and opposite reaction on the air generates the sound known as Aeolian tones (Phillips 1956).

There is less information on three-dimensional bluff bodies, such as spheres, in this range of Reynolds numbers, but values of R_l appear to be higher, about 500 for spheres (Schmiedel 1928, Möller 1938), because no mode of vorticity redistribution in their wakes has the very marked instability of rows of staggered parallel vortices. The dominant mode is often a spiral vortex. Similarly, R_s is greater (around 17) for spheres (Jenson 1959).

The configuration of mean streamlines (curves to which the mean of the velocity vector is everywhere tangential) in the turbulent region immediately behind any bluff body is often similar to what it would be in laminar flow with ν increased to a greater value, the 'eddy viscosity' ν_T (compare Section 3.3). The 'effective Reynolds number' $U_\infty d/\nu_T$, based on eddy viscosity, is commonly between 40 and 50 for cylinders (Imai 1957a). Accordingly, the part of C_D due to surface pressures, which depends largely on this mean-streamline pattern, remains approximately constant from $R = R_l$ up to the value $R = R_c$ (of order 10^5) at which boundary-layer transition begins to affect the separation point. At the same time, the part of C_D due to skin friction falls in proportion to $R^{-\frac{1}{2}}$, since the viscous stresses which produce it are of order $\mu U_\infty/\delta$, which in turn is of order $\rho U_\infty^2 R^{-\frac{1}{2}}$ because the boundary-layer thickness δ is of order $(\nu l/U_\infty)^{\frac{1}{2}}$. Fig. II. 29 illustrates these effects for a circular cylinder. For a sphere, the two parts of C_D have not been separately measured, but the variation of C_D with R (Fig. II. 30) is consistent with a pressure contribution of around $0\cdot4$ and a skin-friction contribution of around $7R^{-\frac{1}{2}}$ (compare $1\cdot0$ and $4R^{-\frac{1}{2}}$ for the circular cylinder).

For both shapes there is a striking fall in C_D when R passes through the critical value R_c (defined conventionally for the sphere as the value for which $C_D = 0\cdot3$). At $R = R_c$, transition in the boundary layer begins to precede separation, and therefore to postpone it (Section 3.3).

The fall in C_D, due to the resulting narrowing of the wake region of fluid disturbed by the body, is not quite abrupt because of the inter-mittent character of transition (Section 3.2).

The fact that R_c depends, not only on body shape, but also on less obvious features, such as roughness and the level of turbulence in the wind-tunnel, an increase in either of which tends to reduce R_c (Section

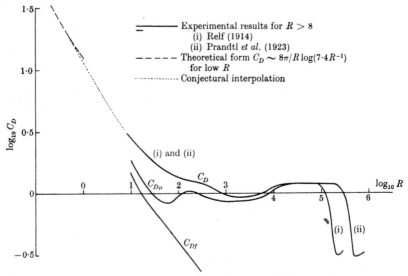

FIG. II. 29. Drag coefficient C_D as a function of R for flow about a circular cylinder, with the separate contributions (obtained by Thom 1928) C_{Dp} (due to normal pressure) and C_{Df} (due to skin friction).

3.2), means that, near $R = 10^5$, such non-dimensional coefficients as C_D are not unique functions of R for a given shape (Figs. II. 29 and 30). This illustrates well (compare Section I. 5.5) the dangers of too simple-minded an approach to dimensional analysis; one might assume from the smallness of non-dimensional parameters formed from the roughness height ϵ, or the root-mean-square velocity fluctuation u' of the undisturbed stream, that these would not affect the flow pattern, but the experimental failure of the resulting similarity law near $R = 10^5$ tells us that in this region such factors do play a part.

Subcritical and supercritical distributions of pressure around a sphere are plotted in Fig. II. 31. The supercritical distribution is close to the theoretical distribution for irrotational flow up to the separation point ($\theta = 140°$); the slight inflexion in the curve is due to the sudden drop in displacement thickness on transition, as vorticity moves in towards the wall (Section 3.2); while, beyond the separation point, we have locally almost hydrostatic conditions. By contrast, the earlier separation in subcritical flow raises the pressure even upstream of it. As R increases beyond R_c the extent of the turbulent boundary layer increases, and there is some resulting rise in C_D (Figs. II. 29 and 30).

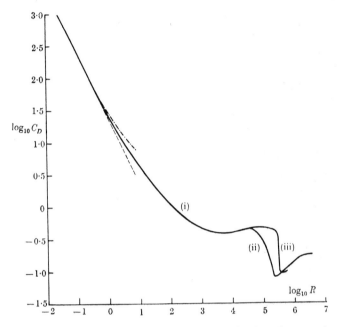

Fig. II. 30. Drag coefficient C_D as a function of R for flow about a sphere. Different observers agree closely on curve (i), but around $R = 10^5$ there are many variations of which curves (ii) (Jacobs and Abbott 1932) and (iii) (Millikan and Klein 1933) represent extremes. The broken line represents the theoretical expression $C_D = 24/R$ for small R. For the dash-dotted line, representing Oseen's theoretical value $C_D = (24/R)(1 + \frac{3}{16}R)$, see Chapter IV.

Prandtl's photographs (Fig. II. 32 (Plate)) of two flows past a sphere, at a Reynolds number which the 'trip wire', present only in the second case, suffices to make supercritical, show the delay in separation and reduction in breadth of wake that boundary-layer transition produces. 'Seam bowlers' in the game of 'cricket' produce a similar effect on one side of the ball only (the yawed 'seam' acting as a trip wire). A new cricket ball is smooth enough for laminar flow to be achieved even at high speeds like 30 m/sec ($R = 1.4 \times 10^5$); the lower pressures (Fig. II. 31), on the side where separation is delayed by the action of the seam, generate a swerving force which at these high speeds can make the ball difficult to hit. A cunning bowler can achieve this condition late in the ball's flight; for example, A. V. Stephens found in unpublished work that, with the seam at $20°$ incidence, the lift became far less at slightly higher speeds, when turbulent separation occurred on both sides.

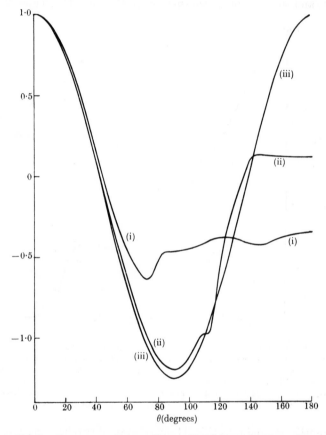

FIG. II. 31. Pressure coefficient $C_p = p_d/(\frac{1}{2}\rho U_\infty^2)$, as function of angular distance θ from front stagnation point, on a sphere in uniform flow: (i) subcritical ($R = 1.57 \times 10^5$), (ii) supercritical ($R = 4.24 \times 10^5$), (iii) irrotational-flow theory. (Fage 1936.)

Popular opinion, that the effect operates best at high relative humidity, could conceivably have foundation in fact if condensation on to areas of high concave curvature (Section I. 3.2) acts to smooth out roughnesses capable of preventing laminar flow.

Bodies with salient edges often have the line of separation fixed at the edge, at least in most attitudes. This is because flow up to the edge

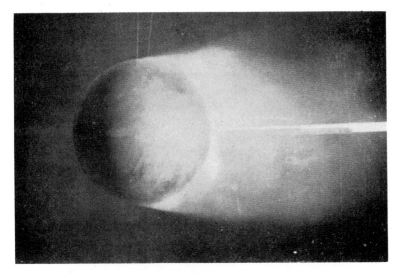

(a)

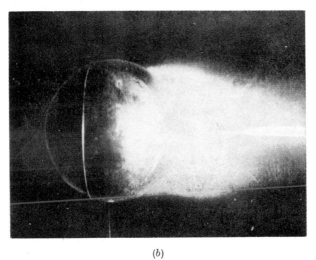

(b)

FIG. II. 32. Flow around a sphere (a) without, and (b) with, a trip wire

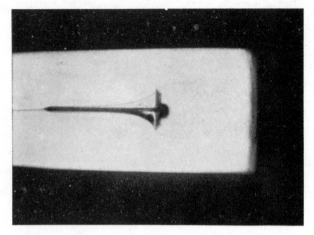

FIG. II. 33. Flow up a step. (Farren 1938)

is accelerating, but flow around it would involve retardations that would separate any boundary layer. For such bodies and attitudes there is no critical Reynolds number; thus, for a long flat strip normal to the stream, C_D (based on the area of the strip) is constant at 2·0 for $R > 1,000$.

On the other hand, separation occurs already *ahead* of any corner which is *concave* to the surface, since this would be a stagnation point of an irrotational external flow. Fig. II. 33 (Plate) illustrates the separation bubble produced in the corner for 'flow up a step', with laminar separation; a turbulent boundary layer, on the other hand, yields a shorter bubble because it can support a greater retardation before separating.

4.2. *Flow over streamlined bodies*

Bodies 'streamlined' to achieve thin-wake flow, with the object of reducing C_D to values small compared with 1, will now be discussed at values of R other than those very low ones at which, because separation is not expected in any case, their behaviour differs insignificantly from that of bluff bodies.

As noted in Section 2.5, it is only extremely slender bodies that can avoid separation of a completely laminar layer. One such is a Joukowsky aerofoil of 5 per cent. thickness-chord ratio, which in symmetrical flow has a laminar, unseparated boundary layer up to a Reynolds number R_c (based on the chord c) of around 5×10^5, with C_D around $3 \cdot 6 R^{-\frac{1}{2}}$ (Fage, Falkner, and Walker 1929; this exceeds the value $2 \cdot 7 R^{-\frac{1}{2}}$ for a flat plate parallel to the stream because of the more rapid thickening of the aerofoil boundary layer in the region of retarded flow). Again, on a suitably designed body of revolution in axisymmetrical flow, an unseparated laminar layer can be achieved above a 'fineness ratio' (length to maximum cross-sectional diameter) of around 7, and the drag is once more slightly above that of a flat plate of the same surface area (Millikan 1932).

As R increases beyond the value at which transition first appears near the trailing edge, the point of transition moves back, but the drag coefficient varies little, because the increase due to the spread of the turbulent layer, and the decrease (like $R^{-\frac{1}{2}}$) in the contribution of the laminar layer (together with a much more gradual decrease in that of the turbulent layer), almost cancel out. Finally, when R is so great that practically the whole layer is turbulent, the drag is almost the same as on a flat plate of the same surface area, since non-uniform external flow affects turbulent layers only slightly; in particular, it decreases gradually with increasing R (Fig. II. 25).

Surface roughness and mainstream turbulence cause transition to begin at a lower value of R, in which case the level of C_D remains higher during transition. In the fully turbulent régime, roughness also causes the fall in C_D to be arrested at a certain value of R, and C_D then levels out to a constant value, sometimes after a preliminary rise (Section 3.3).

Between these results for extremely slender bodies and those discussed in Section 4.1 for bluff bodies (with C_D a function mainly of the position of separation), there is a fine gradation of intermediate cases; in these, there is some postponement of separation as R passes through a critical interval and transition begins to precede it, but with moderately slender bodies the associated drag reduction may be much smaller than in Section 4.1—say, of the same order as the changes associated with dependence of skin friction on Reynolds number in the interval. In such a case the critical value of R may be not at all obvious from the vagaries of the (C_D, R) curve.

For aerofoils at small angles of incidence α to the oncoming stream, cast-off vorticity leads to a flow 'with circulation' (Section 2.5), in which the external flow velocity takes higher values on the upper surface (so that the pressure is lower there and the aerofoil experiences lift). The boundary layer on this surface is then more prone to separation than that on the lower surface (since the velocity on each must fall to the same value at the trailing edge); but, also, it will become turbulent at a lower Reynolds number R_x based on distance x from the leading edge (and so be helped to resist separation). These two facts lead to complicated variations in the lift coefficient C_L, as well as in C_D, as α and R_c vary (see, for example, Thwaites 1960).

The most important moral to be drawn from all these considerations is that already noted at the end of Section I. 5.5, that there is no cessation of dependence on R when R reaches large values—marked variations in non-dimensional quantities being still prominent for R around 10^6. Before this was fully realized, much wind-tunnel work, in which models were tested at Reynolds numbers from 10^5 to 10^6 in the hope of getting information on full-scale flows at Reynolds numbers of about 10^7 or more, was practically useless.

Later, it became accepted that, since at the Reynolds numbers relevant in full-scale aeronautics (Section I. 5.3) almost the whole boundary layer is turbulent, the main aim in model testing should be to ensure this, by combining as high a Reynolds number as could conveniently be achieved with a sufficiently high level of tunnel turbulence or with suitable trip wires or roughness elements on the model (Pankhurst and Holder 1952). By these means the major features of the flow pattern can be correctly reproduced—although, to be sure, the detailed turbulent-boundary-layer characteristics are not identical, and certain features at high angles of incidence (see below), depending on the detailed state of the boundary layer very near the leading edge, are not reproduced well.

At a still later date, the possibility of large increases in the area of laminar flow being achieved, even at the high Reynolds numbers of full-scale flight, which would lead to very important reductions in C_D, began to be extensively studied (Goldstein 1948a). In contrast to the work just described, this requires the use of wind-tunnels of extremely low turbulence (Chapter X). The aerofoil must also be very smooth, and often is specially designed to have accelerated external flow over as large a fraction (say 0·5) of its surface as is compatible with other requirements. In addition, transition may be delayed by 'boundary-layer suction', boundary-layer fluid being sucked away through a suitable porous surface; this helps to stabilize the boundary layer by reducing R_δ, as well as by changing the distribution of vorticity to one of a more stable type, and the power required for such suction is much less than the power saving due to the reduction of C_D. Difficulties arise, however, because the tendency of any roughness elements (say, of height ϵ) to promote transition is increased by the reduction of δ and consequent increase of ϵ/δ; in addition, operational difficulties associated with the practical use of porous or specially smooth surfaces have so far prevented their adoption in aeronautics.

A more widespread form of 'boundary-layer control' uses a variety of devices to prevent local separations. These include the sucking away of the entire boundary layer at a 'slot', on the downstream shoulder of which a completely new boundary layer becomes attached. The aerofoil shape near the slot can be designed so that the external flow downstream of the slot is much slower than that upstream, and in this way a large retardation is achieved without separation (Goldstein 1948a). Alternatively, separation can be avoided by devices such as 'vortex generators', which are tiny vanes whose action increases the mixing in the turbulent boundary layer above its equilibrium level, and so promotes the transport of vorticity towards the wall.

As the angle of incidence α of an aerofoil is increased, the external flow velocity develops a higher and higher peak at the leading edge, which depends on the fact that velocities in irrotational flow must be greatest on the inside of a bend, and builds up most rapidly if the leading-edge radius of curvature is low. Sooner or later, the retardation following this peak produces separation close to the leading edge, followed by an extensive wake region including the whole upper surface of the aerofoil; there is loss of lift, and a very large increase in drag, and the aerofoil is said to be stalled.

Before the stall is reached, there can be a local separation of a laminar layer at the leading edge, followed so closely by transition in the separated layer that reattachment is made possible; this 'short bubble' condition is dangerous, as further increase of α may lead with unpleasant suddenness to complete stalling (Owen and Klanfer 1955). On the other hand, at lower Reynolds numbers (but still greater than 10^6) one may find instead a 'long bubble' extending with increase of incidence to give a gradual, and therefore safer, stall. There are many other complications of stalling behaviour; these sometimes include oscillations of large amplitude in the separation position and wake shape; 'hysteresis' is also common, with the stall ceasing, as α is gradually decreased, at a lower value than that at which it appeared when α was increased (Farren 1935).

Three-dimensional wing aerodynamics will not be discussed here, as the general account of the thin-wake theory and of the varieties of possible surface topography in separated flow (Sections 2.2 and 2.7; note especially the discussion of 'tip stalling') are equally applicable when the boundary layer is wholly or partly turbulent.

On the other hand, we may note the useful comparison that has been made (Allen and Perkins 1951) between flow over slender bodies of revolution at high angle of incidence and the development in time of the flow around a circular cylinder which suddenly begins to move through a field. The basis of this comparison is that, as a large lump of fluid sails past the yawed body, it is confronted with an obstacle of circular cross-section whose position relative to the lump changes at the rate $U_\infty \sin \alpha$. This may cause the lump of fluid to develop a boundary layer of axial vorticity, growing as described in Section 2.1 and then separating, first at the rear and then farther forward, as described in Section 2.2. Next, the wake, left behind the 'cylinder' in its motion relative to the lump, grows to its steady size, becomes unstable and begins to cast off vorticity of alternating sign (Section 4.1). Interpreting this development in time as a development with distance along the body as the lump moves downstream from the nose, we are led to a possible picture of the flow, Fig. II. 34, which experimental studies have confirmed. Such flow has the practical advantage of a substantial lift force centred reasonably far back from the nose, but may have the disadvantage of a fluctuating side force (normal to the plane in which the axis of the body is yawed), due to the first cast-off vortex leaving at some times from one side and at others from the other.

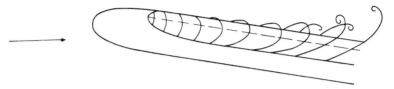

FIG. II. 34. Flow around a yawed body of revolution.

This very brief survey of a variety of complete flows in Section 4 has shown in part how knowledge of boundary layers can be used to illuminate whole flow patterns. To go farther, one must combine this knowledge with a study of the properties of possible external flows. This is the aim of the companion volume, *Incompressible Aerodynamics*.

III

THE NAVIER–STOKES EQUATIONS OF MOTION

PART I

GENERAL THEORY

1. Analysis of the motion of a fluid element

THE motion of a fluid is completely determined when the velocity vector **v** is known as a function of time and position. We now show how the motion of any small element of fluid may be analysed in terms of this function. If the components of **v** at the point $P(x, y, z)$ are (u, v, w), and at a neighbouring point $(x+\delta x, y+\delta y, z+\delta z)$ the velocity components are $(u+\delta u, v+\delta v, w+\delta w)$, then, to the first order of small quantities,

$$\delta u = \tfrac{1}{2}(e_{xx}\delta x + e_{xy}\delta y + e_{xz}\delta z) + \tfrac{1}{2}(\eta\,\delta z - \zeta\,\delta y),$$

$$\delta v = \tfrac{1}{2}(e_{yx}\delta x + e_{yy}\delta y + e_{yz}\delta z) + \tfrac{1}{2}(\zeta\,\delta x - \xi\,\delta z),$$

$$\delta w = \tfrac{1}{2}(e_{zx}\delta x + e_{zy}\delta y + e_{zz}\delta z) + \tfrac{1}{2}(\xi\,\delta y - \eta\,\delta x), \tag{1}$$

where

$$e_{xx} = 2\frac{\partial u}{\partial x}, \qquad e_{yy} = 2\frac{\partial v}{\partial y}, \qquad e_{zz} = 2\frac{\partial w}{\partial z},$$

$$e_{yz} = e_{zy} = \frac{\partial w}{\partial y} + \frac{\partial v}{\partial z}, \qquad e_{zx} = e_{xz} = \frac{\partial u}{\partial z} + \frac{\partial w}{\partial x},$$

$$e_{xy} = e_{yx} = \frac{\partial v}{\partial x} + \frac{\partial u}{\partial y}, \tag{2}$$

and

$$\xi = \frac{\partial w}{\partial y} - \frac{\partial v}{\partial z}, \qquad \eta = \frac{\partial u}{\partial z} - \frac{\partial w}{\partial x}, \qquad \zeta = \frac{\partial v}{\partial x} - \frac{\partial u}{\partial y}. \tag{3}$$

A small element of fluid initially at P has an over-all translational velocity (u, v, w), but as it moves it is distorted and rotated in accordance with the relative velocities given by (1).

The grouping of the terms in (1) corresponds to their different physical interpretations. The terms $\tfrac{1}{2}(\eta\,\delta z - \zeta\,\delta y)$, $\tfrac{1}{2}(\zeta\,\delta x - \xi\,\delta z)$, $\tfrac{1}{2}(\xi\,\delta y - \eta\,\delta x)$, represent a rotation of the fluid element as if it were a rigid body with angular velocity $(\tfrac{1}{2}\xi, \tfrac{1}{2}\eta, \tfrac{1}{2}\zeta)$. The vector $\boldsymbol{\omega} = (\xi, \eta, \zeta)$ defined by (3) is the curl of **v** and is the vorticity of the fluid. The quantities e_{xx}, etc., defined in (2) are called the rate-of-strain components, and they constitute the rate-of-strain tensor. The contribution of each of these components to the motion described by (1) is now considered.

First, suppose that all the components except e_{xx} are zero. Then $\delta u = \tfrac{1}{2} e_{xx} \delta x$, $\delta v = 0$, $\delta w = 0$, which represents an extension of the element at a rate $\tfrac{1}{2} e_{xx}$ per unit length in the x direction. Similarly, $\tfrac{1}{2} e_{yy}$ and $\tfrac{1}{2} e_{zz}$ are the rates of extension of the fluid element in the y- and z-directions. Secondly, if all the components except e_{xy} are zero,

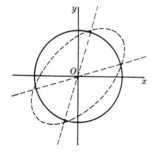

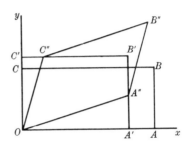

FIG. III. 1. Deformation produced by the rate-of-strain component e_{xy}.

FIG. III. 2. General deformation of a fluid element.

then $\delta u = \tfrac{1}{2} e_{xy} \delta y$, $\delta v = \tfrac{1}{2} e_{xy} \delta x$, $\delta w = 0$. This represents a motion in which the angle between the two lines of particles which lie initially on the x- and y-axes is decreasing at a rate e_{xy}. The position of these two lines of particles after a short time is shown by the broken lines in Fig. III. 1. If, for example, a section of the fluid element is initially circular, it will be deformed into an ellipse under this distortion (see Fig. III. 1). The interpretation of the component e_{xy} may be modified slightly by considering its effect in conjunction with a rigid-body rotation with angular velocity $-\tfrac{1}{2} e_{xy}$ which reduces the line of particles on the x-axis to rest. Then, we have a simple shear flow parallel to the x-axis with rate of shear equal to e_{xy}.

To exemplify the combined effects of the rate-of-strain components, the distortion, in two-dimensional flow, of a fluid element which is initially rectangular in shape, is shown in Fig. III. 2. The original shape $OABC$ is deformed under the rates of extension e_{xx}, e_{yy}, alone into $OA'B'C'$, and the final shape is $OA''B''C''$.

2. Equation of continuity

Throughout the motion the mass of any element of fluid must be conserved; hence, for incompressible flow, the volume of the fluid element must remain constant. This condition yields the equation of continuity which must be satisfied by the rate-of-strain components at all points of the fluid. (The components of vorticity are not involved since a rigid-body rotation leaves the volume unchanged.) If we consider the fluid initially occupying a small rectangular parallelepiped with faces normal to the coordinate axes, it is clear from the interpretations given above that e_{yz}, e_{zx}, e_{xy} have only a second-order effect on the change of the volume of the element in a small time δt. But the lengths of the sides are increased by factors $1+\frac{1}{2}e_{xx}\delta t$, $1+\frac{1}{2}e_{yy}\delta t$, $1+\frac{1}{2}e_{zz}\delta t$. Hence, the rate of increase of volume per unit volume is $\Delta = \frac{1}{2}(e_{xx}+e_{yy}+e_{zz})$. This quantity Δ is called the dilatation, and for incompressible flow it must vanish. Thus, the equation of continuity is

$$\operatorname{div}\mathbf{v} = \frac{\partial u}{\partial x}+\frac{\partial v}{\partial y}+\frac{\partial w}{\partial z} = 0. \tag{4}$$

3. Principal axes of rate of strain

When discussing general properties of the flow, it is often convenient to transform to the special set of rectangular axes for which the components corresponding to e_{yz}, e_{zx}, e_{xy} become zero. The existence of such axes can be shown by appeal to a geometrical argument. If we write

$$\Psi = e_{xx}(\delta x)^2+e_{yy}(\delta y)^2+e_{zz}(\delta z)^2+2e_{yz}\,\delta y\delta z+2e_{zx}\,\delta z\delta x+2e_{xy}\,\delta x\delta y, \tag{5}$$

and regard δx, δy, δz as current coordinates, then $\Psi = $ constant is the equation of a quadric with its centre at P. In any other set of coordinates, (x', y', z') say, if $e_{x'x'}$, $e_{y'z'}$, etc., are defined in terms of the corresponding velocity components (u', v', w') as in (2), Ψ will have exactly the same form as (5) in terms of x', y', z'. This 'invariance' is an essential consequence of the tensor character of the rate-of-strain components. It may be verified directly by going through the coordinate transformation in detail, but it also follows from the following property of the quadric. In the motion described by (1), omitting the rigid-body rotation, the displacements of points on the quadric (5) are normal to the surface of the quadric since δu, δv, δw are proportional to the derivatives of Ψ with respect to $\delta x, \delta y, \delta z$, respectively. This property is independent of the choice of axes, and it follows that for any coordinate system the coefficients in the equation of the quadric have the meanings given by (1), i.e. they are the rate-of-strain components.

Now, the new axes may be chosen along the principal axes of the quadric, and then Ψ becomes

$$e_{x'x'}(\delta x')^2+e_{y'y'}(\delta y')^2+e_{z'z'}(\delta z')^2.$$

Hence, for these axes, $e_{y'z'}$, $e_{z'x'}$, $e_{x'y'}$ vanish. The rates of change of the angles between lines of particles along the axes are zero, and the distortion of the fluid consists entirely of extensions along the principal axes. For example, in Fig. III. 1 the principal axes are at $45°$ to the original axes. Quite generally, a fluid element which is initially spherical will be distorted into an ellipsoid with its axes along the principal axes.

The result used above that the terms in (1) which include the rate-of-strain components are proportional to the derivatives of Ψ, is worth noticing for its own sake, since it shows that this part of the motion may be deduced from a potential function. It also leads to the result that, if Q is any point on the rate-of-strain quadric, the rate of change of $(PQ)^2$ is Ψ. For, the rate of increase of PQ is

$$\frac{1}{4}\left\{\frac{\partial\Psi}{\partial(\delta x)}\frac{\delta x}{PQ}+\frac{\partial\Psi}{\partial(\delta y)}\frac{\delta y}{PQ}+\frac{\partial\Psi}{\partial(\delta z)}\frac{\delta z}{PQ}\right\}=\frac{1}{2}\frac{\Psi}{PQ}.$$

Hence, the rate of extension of any line element through P is inversely proportional to the square of the radius vector drawn to the rate-of-strain quadric in the direction of the element.

Finally, it may be shown from (1) (preferably using principal axes for ease of calculation) that the angular momentum of a small sphere of fluid is the same as if it were rotating as a rigid body with angular velocity $\frac{1}{2}\boldsymbol{\omega}=(\frac{1}{2}\xi,\frac{1}{2}\eta,\frac{1}{2}\zeta)$. Thus, the whole of the rotation is given by the second terms on the right-hand side of (1), and the rotation depends only on the vorticity vector. It should be pointed out, however, that this result does not apply to *any* small portion of the fluid with its mass centre at P; it is true only if the principal axes of rate of strain coincide with the principal axes of inertia of the fluid element.

4. Analysis of stress

Let us consider any small element of surface containing a point $P(x,y,z)$, and let us define the direction of the normal to the element, $\mathbf{n}$, as pointing from one side, called 'negative', to the other, called 'positive'. We then consider the stress exerted *on* the fluid on the negative side, *by* that on the positive side; this will be a vector which depends on $\mathbf{n}$. The components of the resultant stress in the direction of the fixed axes Ox, Oy, Oz, will be denoted by p_{nx}, p_{ny}, p_{nz}, respectively. Thus, when the surface is normal to the x-direction, we denote the components of the stress parallel to the x-, y-, z-axes by p_{xx}, p_{xy}, p_{xz}, respectively. Similarly, the stresses across surfaces normal to the y- and z-axes are denoted by (p_{yx},p_{yy},p_{yz}) and (p_{zx},p_{zy},p_{zz}), respectively.

The stress components p_{xx}, etc., constitute the stress tensor, and the stress across a surface at P with its normal in *any* given direction may be obtained from them. For, consider a small tetrahedron with three of its faces through P and normal to the coordinate axes, and with the fourth face normal to the given direction **n**. The forces exerted across the faces of this tetrahedron are proportional to the areas of the faces; hence, the external body forces and the inertia forces which are proportional to the volume of the tetrahedron are of smaller order. Thus, to this order of approximation, the surface tractions must form a system in equilibrium. Moreover, to the same approximation, the stresses can be taken equal to their values at P. Then, if the stresses across the surface normal to n are (p_{nx}, p_{ny}, p_{nz}), we have by resolving in the x-direction

$$p_{nx}\Delta S_n = p_{xx}\Delta S_x + p_{yx}\Delta S_y + p_{zx}\Delta S_z,$$

using an obvious notation for the areas ΔS of the faces of the tetrahedron. Now

$$\Delta S_x/\Delta S_n = l, \qquad \Delta S_y/\Delta S_n = m, \qquad \Delta S_z/\Delta S_n = n,$$

where (l, m, n) are the direction cosines of the normal **n**. Therefore, we have

$$p_{nx} = l p_{xx} + m p_{yx} + n p_{zx}.$$

Two similar equations are found for p_{ny} and p_{nz}.

The same considerations apply for the equilibrium of the stresses exerted across the faces of a cube centred at P with its faces perpendicular to the axes. Then, taking moments of the forces about P, we have

$$p_{yz} = p_{zy}, \qquad p_{zx} = p_{xz}, \qquad p_{xy} = p_{yx}. \tag{6}$$

In the same way as for the rate-of-strain components we can define a stress quadric which is invariant to change of coordinates. Then, we can say that there exist principal axes Ox', Oy', Oz', such that $p_{x'x'}$, $p_{y'y'}$, $p_{z'z'}$ are the only non-zero components of stress. The planes perpendicular to the principal axes of stress are called principal planes of stress; the stress across each of them is purely normal, and these three normal stresses are called the principal stresses.

5. Relations between the stress and rate-of-strain components

The simplest assumption for the relations between the two sets of components is that they are linear. That is, each stress component may be expressed as a sum of multiples of the six rate-of-strain components plus a quantity independent of them. If the rate-of-strain components were small this would certainly be a natural approximation, but as explained in Chapter I the relations have in fact been verified for many fluids under a very wide range of conditions when the rate-of-strain components are not small. The assumption that the relations are linear is the basic one in deriving the Navier–Stokes equations for incompressible flow.

In an isotropic fluid the principal axes of stress and rate of strain coincide, and the relations between the stress and rate-of-strain components must be symmetric since there is no preferred direction. Therefore, relative to principal axes, we have

$$p_{x'x'} = -p + \mu e_{x'x'},$$
$$p_{y'y'} = -p + \mu e_{y'y'},$$
$$p_{z'z'} = -p + \mu e_{z'z'}, \tag{7}$$

where the quantities p and μ are independent of the rate-of-strain components, but may vary from point to point of the fluid. (For compressible flow, in which $\Delta = \frac{1}{2}(e_{x'x'} + e_{y'y'} + e_{z'z'})$ is not zero, a multiple of Δ is added to each of these equations.) The appropriate relations for any other set of Cartesian coordinates (x, y, z) may then be deduced from (7) together with the transformation equations for the stress and rate-of-strain components. Apart from the term $-p$ in (7), the stress components are equal to the rate-of-strain components multiplied by μ; hence, since the transformation equations for p_{xx}, etc., and e_{xx}, etc., are identical, this is true in any set of axes. Therefore, in general,

$$p_{xx} = -p + \mu e_{xx} = -p + 2\mu \frac{\partial u}{\partial x},$$

$$p_{yy} = -p + \mu e_{yy} = -p + 2\mu \frac{\partial v}{\partial y},$$

$$p_{zz} = -p + \mu e_{zz} = -p + 2\mu \frac{\partial w}{\partial z},$$

$$p_{yz} = \mu e_{yz} = \mu \left(\frac{\partial w}{\partial y} + \frac{\partial v}{\partial z} \right),$$

$$p_{zx} = \mu e_{zx} = \mu \left(\frac{\partial u}{\partial z} + \frac{\partial w}{\partial x} \right),$$

$$p_{xy} = \mu e_{xy} = \mu \left(\frac{\partial v}{\partial x} + \frac{\partial u}{\partial y} \right). \tag{8}$$

Further details of the derivation of these equations are to be found in Lamb (1932, pp. 571–6). A more sophisticated derivation using the full power of the tensor properties is given by Jeffreys (1931, Chapters 7 and 9).

For an incompressible flow it is observed, using the equation of continuity (4), that p is the mean of the normal pressures over three planes mutually at right angles; it is called simply the pressure. It is also seen that in a simple shear flow with $u = u(y)$, $v = w = 0$, we have

$$p_{xy} = \mu \frac{\partial u}{\partial y}. \tag{9}$$

Hence μ is the coefficient of shear viscosity introduced and discussed in Chapter I. For each substance it varies only with temperature, and thus where the temperature is constant, or the temperature variations are small, the coefficient of shear viscosity may be taken to be a constant.

6. The momentum equations

The momentum equations, which must be satisfied by the flow quantities at each point of the fluid, may be deduced by applying Newton's second law of motion to the fluid which occupies a rectangular parallelepiped centred at P with its edges parallel to the coordinate axes. To the second order in the length of its sides, the stresses form a system in equilibrium (as discussed in Section 4). But, we now write down its equation of motion including terms of the third order. The x-component of the net force due to the stresses on the element is

$$\frac{\partial p_{xx}}{\partial x} + \frac{\partial p_{yx}}{\partial y} + \frac{\partial p_{zx}}{\partial z}$$

multiplied by the volume of the element. (This type of result is often required in this chapter; it is deduced as follows: in the distance δx between the two faces normal to the x-axis, p_{xx} increases by $\delta x . \partial p_{xx}/\partial x$; when multiplied by the face area, this gives a contribution $\partial p_{xx}/\partial x$ multiplied by the volume of the element. Similarly, the other stress components contribute the terms proportional to $\partial p_{yx}/\partial y$ and $\partial p_{zx}/\partial z$.) If the extraneous force $\mathbf{F}$ per unit mass has components (X, Y, Z) and the acceleration $\mathbf{f}$ has components (f_x, f_y, f_z), we have

$$\rho f_x = \rho X + \frac{\partial p_{xx}}{\partial x} + \frac{\partial p_{yx}}{\partial y} + \frac{\partial p_{zx}}{\partial z}, \tag{10}$$

with two similar equations for the y- and z-directions.

Now,
$$f_x = \frac{Du}{Dt} = \frac{\partial u}{\partial t} + u \frac{\partial u}{\partial x} + v \frac{\partial u}{\partial y} + w \frac{\partial u}{\partial z}$$

$$= \frac{\partial u}{\partial t} + \frac{\partial}{\partial x} (\tfrac{1}{2}\mathbf{v}^2) - (v\zeta - w\eta), \tag{11}$$

with similar expressions for f_y and f_z. The expression

$$\left(u\,\frac{\partial u}{\partial x} + v\,\frac{\partial u}{\partial y} + w\,\frac{\partial u}{\partial z} \right)$$

represents the contribution to f_x resulting from the change of the position of the fluid element; it, and similar ones, are usually called the 'convection terms'. Substituting (11) in (10) and using the relations (8) together with the continuity equation (4), we find

$$\frac{\partial u}{\partial t} + u\,\frac{\partial u}{\partial x} + v\,\frac{\partial u}{\partial y} + w\,\frac{\partial u}{\partial z} = -\frac{1}{\rho}\,\frac{\partial p}{\partial x} + X + \nu\nabla^2 u,$$

$$\frac{\partial v}{\partial t} + u\,\frac{\partial v}{\partial x} + v\,\frac{\partial v}{\partial y} + w\,\frac{\partial v}{\partial z} = -\frac{1}{\rho}\,\frac{\partial p}{\partial y} + Y + \nu\nabla^2 v,$$

$$\frac{\partial w}{\partial t} + u\,\frac{\partial w}{\partial x} + v\,\frac{\partial w}{\partial y} + w\,\frac{\partial w}{\partial z} = -\frac{1}{\rho}\,\frac{\partial p}{\partial z} + Z + \nu\nabla^2 w, \tag{12}$$

where $\nu = \mu/\rho$, and

$$\nabla^2 u = \operatorname{div\,grad} u = \frac{\partial^2 u}{\partial x^2} + \frac{\partial^2 u}{\partial y^2} + \frac{\partial^2 u}{\partial z^2}, \quad \text{etc.} \tag{13}$$

In vector form the equations may be written

$$\mathbf{f} = \frac{\partial \mathbf{v}}{\partial t} + \operatorname{grad}(\tfrac{1}{2}\mathbf{v}^2) - \mathbf{v}\times\boldsymbol{\omega} = -\frac{1}{\rho}\,\operatorname{grad} p + \mathbf{F} + \nu\nabla^2\mathbf{v}, \tag{14}$$

where $\nabla^2\mathbf{v}$ is the vector whose components in Cartesian coordinates are $(\nabla^2 u, \nabla^2 v, \nabla^2 w)$. Since $\nabla^2\mathbf{v} = \operatorname{grad}(\operatorname{div}\mathbf{v}) - \operatorname{curl\,curl}\mathbf{v}$ and $\operatorname{div}\mathbf{v} = 0$ whilst $\operatorname{curl}\mathbf{v} = \boldsymbol{\omega}$, the term $\nabla^2\mathbf{v}$ may be replaced by $-\operatorname{curl}\boldsymbol{\omega}$. If, in addition, the extraneous field of force is potential so that $\mathbf{F} = -\operatorname{grad}\Omega$, we may then write (14) as

$$\frac{\partial \mathbf{v}}{\partial t} - \mathbf{v}\times\boldsymbol{\omega} = -\operatorname{grad}\left(\frac{p}{\rho} + \Omega + \tfrac{1}{2}\mathbf{v}^2\right) - \nu\operatorname{curl}\boldsymbol{\omega}. \tag{15}$$

The equations of motion (12) were obtained by Navier (1823), Poisson (1831), Saint-Venant (1843), and Stokes (1845), and are usually known as the 'Navier–Stokes equations'. A short account of the various methods and hypotheses adopted by these authors is to be found in Stokes (1846).

7. Equations for the vorticity. The rate of change of circulation

The equation for the rate of change of the vorticity vector is obtained by taking the curl of (14). Assuming again that $\mathbf{F} = -\operatorname{grad}\Omega$, we have

$$\frac{\partial \boldsymbol{\omega}}{\partial t} - \operatorname{curl}(\mathbf{v}\times\boldsymbol{\omega}) = \nu\nabla^2\boldsymbol{\omega}. \tag{16}$$

Now, $\operatorname{div}\boldsymbol{\omega} = 0$ since $\boldsymbol{\omega} = \operatorname{curl}\mathbf{v}$, and $\operatorname{div}\mathbf{v} = 0$ from the equation of continuity; hence, the components of $\operatorname{curl}(\mathbf{v}\times\boldsymbol{\omega})$ are $\boldsymbol{\omega}.\operatorname{grad}u-\mathbf{v}.\operatorname{grad}\xi$ and two similar expressions with v and η, w and ζ, respectively, in place of u and ξ. Therefore, the components of (16) are

$$\frac{D\xi}{Dt} = \boldsymbol{\omega}.\operatorname{grad}u + \nu\nabla^2\xi,$$

$$\frac{D\eta}{Dt} = \boldsymbol{\omega}.\operatorname{grad}v + \nu\nabla^2\eta,$$

$$\frac{D\zeta}{Dt} = \boldsymbol{\omega}.\operatorname{grad}w + \nu\nabla^2\zeta, \qquad (17)$$

and they may be combined in the abbreviated form

$$\frac{D\boldsymbol{\omega}}{Dt} = \boldsymbol{\omega}.\nabla\mathbf{v} + \nu\nabla^2\boldsymbol{\omega}.$$

These extend Helmholtz's equations to viscous flow.

The first terms on the right of (17) have the same interpretation as they have in ideal flow ($\nu = 0$). They represent a stretching of the vortex lines with a consequent increase in the vorticity. To see this, consider first any line element $\delta\mathbf{r}$ which moves with the fluid. Its rate of change $D(\delta\mathbf{r})/Dt$ is the difference of the velocities at its ends. Hence

$$\frac{D}{Dt}\delta\mathbf{r} = \delta\mathbf{r}.\nabla\mathbf{v},$$

and we observe that $\boldsymbol{\omega}$ and $\delta\mathbf{r}$ satisfy the same relation. Now, suppose that $\delta\mathbf{r}$ is part of a vortex line at $t = 0$, with $\delta\mathbf{r} = \epsilon\boldsymbol{\omega}$, say. The equations for $\delta\mathbf{r}$ and $\boldsymbol{\omega}$ give

$$\frac{D}{Dt}(\delta\mathbf{r}-\epsilon\boldsymbol{\omega}) = (\delta\mathbf{r}-\epsilon\boldsymbol{\omega}).\nabla\mathbf{v},$$

and we want to conclude that $\delta\mathbf{r}-\epsilon\boldsymbol{\omega} = 0$ for all time. This is certainly a solution; it is the only solution provided that the derivatives of $\mathbf{v}$ are bounded (and integrable). This appeals to the well-known uniqueness theorem for ordinary differential equations. (The essential requirement is that the right-hand sides should be Lipschitz continuous in the unknowns; in the present case, this is so if the components of $\nabla\mathbf{v}$ are bounded.) The result that $\delta\mathbf{r} = \epsilon\boldsymbol{\omega}$ for all time shows that vortex lines move with the fluid and the vorticity is proportional to the length $|\delta\mathbf{r}|$ of the line element. If we consider a small vortex tube, its cross-sectional area will be inversely proportional to $|\delta\mathbf{r}|$ as it moves with the fluid. Therefore, the 'strength' of the vortex tube, defined as the vorticity multiplied by the cross-sectional area, remains constant. These results constitute Helmholtz's theorem for ideal flow.

Some remarks should be made about the derivation given here, since it is almost the same as Helmholtz's original one and that has been criticized by Lamb and various subsequent writers as being unrigorous. However, the version rightly contested by Lamb uses only the fact that $D(\delta \mathbf{r} - \epsilon \boldsymbol{\omega})/Dt = 0$ at $t = 0$. Clearly, the result cannot follow from this fact alone, since any function behaving like t^2 has this property. But when the full equation is used as above, there is no gap in the argument. (Notice that t^2 satisfies $df/dt = Af$ with $A \propto f^{-\frac{1}{2}}$ which is *unbounded* near $t = 0$.) After pointing out the flaw in Helmholtz's argument, Lamb discards this method instead of correcting it, and goes on to deduce the results from a different approach. This is a pity because, first of all, the corrected argument gives a very direct derivation of Helmholtz's theorem; secondly, it is desirable to have the physical interpretation of the terms in Helmholtz's equation as a stretching of vortex lines without feeling a little uneasy about its soundness; thirdly, when the viscosity terms are added, their interpretation is immediate from (17) (see below) but not from the alternative approaches. Lamb refers to Stokes (1845), who pointed out a similar flaw in a 'proof' of Lagrange's theorem that $\boldsymbol{\omega} = 0$ for all time if it does so initially. But Stokes, in fact, goes on to propose a genuine proof using exactly the argument given above; he starts from $D\boldsymbol{\omega}/Dt = \boldsymbol{\omega} \cdot \nabla \mathbf{v}$ and concludes that $\boldsymbol{\omega} = 0$ for all t if it does so at $t = 0$. This seems to have been overlooked.

The second terms on the right of (17) show the additional variation introduced by the viscosity of the fluid. This variation follows the same law as the variation of temperature in the conduction of heat and represents diffusion of the vorticity.

An alternative approach to the above results uses the expression for the rate of change of circulation round any closed circuit moving with the fluid. By definition the circulation round a closed circuit is

$$\Gamma = \oint \mathbf{v} . d\mathbf{r}, \tag{18}$$

where the integral is taken once completely round the circuit. If the fluid particles making up the circuit are labelled by a parameter σ, the motion of the circuit will be given by a function $\mathbf{r} = \mathbf{r}(\sigma, t)$. Then we may write

$$\Gamma = \oint \mathbf{v} . \frac{\partial \mathbf{r}}{\partial \sigma} \, d\sigma.$$

As the circuit moves with the fluid, the rate of change of circulation is

$$\frac{D\Gamma}{Dt} = \oint \left(\frac{D\mathbf{v}}{Dt} \cdot \frac{\partial \mathbf{r}}{\partial \sigma} + \mathbf{v} \cdot \frac{\partial^2 \mathbf{r}}{\partial \sigma \partial t}\right) d\sigma.$$

Since $D\mathbf{v}/Dt = -\mathrm{grad}(p/\rho + \Omega) - \nu\,\mathrm{curl}\,\boldsymbol{\omega}$ and $\partial \mathbf{r}/\partial t = \mathbf{v}$, this may be written

$$\frac{D\Gamma}{Dt} = -\oint \frac{\partial}{\partial \sigma}\left(\frac{p}{\rho} + \Omega - \tfrac{1}{2}\mathbf{v}^2\right) d\sigma - \nu \oint (\mathrm{curl}\,\boldsymbol{\omega}) . d\mathbf{r}.$$

Assuming that Ω is single valued, we have

$$\frac{D\Gamma}{Dt} = -\nu \oint (\mathrm{curl}\,\boldsymbol{\omega}) . d\mathbf{r}. \tag{19}$$

Thus, in a viscous fluid, the rate of change of circulation in a circuit moving with the fluid depends only on the kinematic viscosity and the space rates of change of the vorticity components at the contour, so that it is small when the viscosity is small, unless the space rates of change of the vorticity components are large.

In an ideal fluid in which ν is taken to be zero, we have Kelvin's theorem that the circulation remains constant. From this result and Stokes's theorem it is possible to give an alternative proof that vortex lines move with the fluid and the strength of a narrow vortex tube remains constant (Lamb 1932, pp. 203–4). In fact, (17) and (19) are equivalent to each other, and either may be deduced directly from the other.

8. The energy equation

In incompressible motion the equations of continuity and momentum (together with appropriate boundary conditions) are sufficient to determine the pressure and the three components of velocity. Essentially, the energy equation is replaced by the assumption $\rho = $ constant. In any real flow there will be small density and temperature variations and these become determinate when the energy equation and an equation of state between p, ρ, and T are introduced. In the approximation of 'incompressible motion', the equations of continuity and momentum are solved first, neglecting the small variations in density, then the values of $\mathbf{v}$ and p obtained from them may be used in the energy equation to determine the temperature distribution in the flow. In liquids, the density changes may be very much smaller than temperature changes, but in gases (to which the 'incompressible' theory applies when the velocities are small compared to the sound speed) they will be comparable. Thus, for the energy equation, changes in ρ must be included; however, their explicit appearance may be eliminated in the final form.

First, the rate of dissipation of energy by the viscous forces will be obtained. We consider again a fluid element which at time t occupies a rectangular parallelepiped centred at $P(x, y, z)$ with edges parallel to the coordinate axes. The net rate at which the stresses are doing work on this element is

$$\frac{\partial}{\partial x}(p_{xx}u+p_{xy}v+p_{xz}w) + \frac{\partial}{\partial y}(p_{yx}u+p_{yy}v+p_{yz}w) + \frac{\partial}{\partial z}(p_{zx}u+p_{zy}v+p_{zz}w) \tag{20}$$

per unit volume, and the rate of working of the extraneous forces is

$$\rho(Xu+Yv+Zw) \tag{21}$$

per unit volume. The kinetic energy of this element is increasing at the rate

$$\rho \frac{D}{Dt}\{\tfrac{1}{2}(u^2+v^2+w^2)\} \tag{22}$$

per unit volume. Using equation (10), it is found that the total rate of working of the forces, which is equal to (20) plus (21), exceeds the rate of increase of the kinetic energy by

$$\tfrac{1}{2}\{p_{xx}e_{xx}+p_{yy}e_{yy}+p_{zz}e_{zz}+2p_{yz}e_{yz}+2p_{zx}e_{zx}+2p_{xy}e_{xy}\}. \tag{23}$$

(It should be noted that the assumption $\rho = $ constant is not made in the derivation of the momentum equation (10).) Introducing the relations between stress and rate-of-strain components given by (8), (23) can be expressed as

$$-p\Delta+\Phi, \tag{24}$$

where

$$\Phi = \tfrac{1}{2}\mu\{e_{xx}^2+e_{yy}^2+e_{zz}^2+2e_{yz}^2+2e_{zx}^2+2e_{xy}^2\}, \tag{25}$$

and Δ is the dilatation $\tfrac{1}{2}(e_{xx}+e_{yy}+e_{zz})$. Although Δ may be set equal to zero as far as the equations of continuity and momentum are concerned, for gases the term $p\Delta$ is not small compared with Φ. Now, $-p\Delta$ represents the rate at which work is done in compressing the element of fluid, since Δ is the rate of increase of volume per unit volume. Hence Φ given by (25) is the rate of dissipation of energy per unit time per unit volume by the viscous forces.

As noted in Section 5, for compressible flow a multiple of Δ is added to the first three equations of (8), and this leads to an additional term proportional to Δ^2 in the expression for Φ (see Howarth 1953). But for 'incompressible' flow, this term can be neglected.

In addition to the work done by the stresses acting on the fluid element, heat energy is being conducted across its boundaries. If the thermal conductivity is k and we neglect its variation with temperature, the net loss of heat by conduction is

$$\frac{\partial}{\partial x}\left(k\frac{\partial T}{\partial x}\right)+\frac{\partial}{\partial y}\left(k\frac{\partial T}{\partial y}\right)+\frac{\partial}{\partial z}\left(k\frac{\partial T}{\partial z}\right)=k\nabla^2 T \tag{26}$$

per unit volume. The difference of (24) and (26) is equal to the rate at which the internal energy is increasing. Thus, if E denotes the internal energy per unit mass,

$$\rho\frac{DE}{Dt}=-p\Delta+\Phi+k\nabla^2 T. \tag{27}$$

Introducing the entropy S and the enthalpy $I=E+p/\rho$, this equation may be written in the alternative forms

$$\rho T\frac{DS}{Dt}=\rho\frac{DI}{Dt}-\frac{Dp}{Dt}=\Phi+k\nabla^2 T. \tag{28}$$

Equation (28) gives explicitly the rate of increase of entropy due to viscosity and heat conduction.

In terms of pressure and temperature, the enthalpy is given by

$$dI=C_p\,dT+\left\{1+\frac{T}{\rho}\left(\frac{\partial\rho}{\partial T}\right)_p\right\}\frac{dp}{\rho};$$

for this and other thermodynamical results introduced here, reference may be made to the discussion given by Howarth (1953, chapter 2). An immediate consequence of the result quoted above is that (28) may be written

$$\rho C_p\frac{DT}{Dt}-\frac{T}{\rho}\left(\frac{\partial\rho}{\partial T}\right)_p\frac{Dp}{Dt}=\Phi+k\nabla^2 T. \tag{29}$$

For liquids, the coefficient of expansion, $-\rho^{-1}(\partial\rho/\partial T)_p$, is usually very small and as a consequence the term in Dp/Dt can be omitted. For a perfect gas, in which $p\propto\rho T$, we have $-T\rho^{-1}(\partial\rho/\partial T)_p=1$. In either case, derivatives of the density do not occur, and in the coefficient of the first term ρ may now be taken as a constant. Thus, when the velocity and pressure have been determined from the equations of continuity and momentum, we have a linear equation for the temperature.

In an important class of problem, the temperature variations are principally due to applied heating (e.g. the wall of a body may be maintained at a given temperature) and the terms involving Dp/Dt and Φ may then be neglected in (29). For liquids the small coefficient of Dp/Dt makes the term negligible in any case, but for gases the coefficient is not small (being unity for a perfect gas) and we must consider the magnitude of Dp/Dt. From the inertia terms in the momentum equations we see that the pressure changes are $O(\rho U_1^2)$, where U_1 is a typical value of the main-stream velocity. Hence, if T_1 is a typical main-stream temperature, Dp/Dt is small compared with $\rho C_p DT/Dt$ if the temperature changes are much greater than U_1^2/C_p. Since $C_p T_1$ is proportional to the square of the sound speed a_1, the condition becomes

$$\frac{T-T_1}{T_1} \gg M_1^2, \tag{30}$$

where M_1 is the Mach number U_1/a_1.

If we estimate the order of magnitude of Φ by the value of $\mu(\partial u/\partial y)^2$ in a boundary layer (where the viscous dissipation is greatest), we see that it is of the order $\mu U_1^2/\delta^2 \approx \rho U_1^3/l$, where δ is the boundary-layer thickness proportional to $(\mu l/\rho U_1)^{\frac{1}{2}}$ and l is a typical length in the stream direction. Thus Φ is also small compared to $\rho C_p DT/Dt$ if the relative temperature changes are large compared to M_1^2. Therefore, when (30) is satisfied, we have both for gases and liquids the approximate equation

$$\frac{DT}{Dt} = \frac{k}{\rho C_p} \nabla^2 T = \frac{\nu}{\sigma} \nabla^2 T, \tag{31}$$

where σ is the Prandtl number $\mu C_p/k$. Of course $(T-T_1)/T_1$ must still be small if we are to neglect density changes in the equations of continuity and momentum and the variation of k with T.

9. Dynamical similarity

It has been shown in Chapter I that, as far as the effects of viscosity are concerned, the determining parameter for geometrically similar flow patterns is the Reynolds number. We may now verify this in detail for equations (4) and (12) which determine $\mathbf{v}$ and p. It is assumed that either the external forces are negligible or they are conservative and have been absorbed into the pressure terms in (12) so that p measures the difference of the pressure from its hydrostatic value $-\rho\Omega$.

We consider the steady flow of a uniform stream parallel to the x-axis with velocity U past a fixed obstacle of given shape and given orientation whose size is specified by a typical length d. Then we introduce non-dimensional variables by the following scheme:

$$\mathrm{u} = u/U, \qquad \mathrm{v} = v/U, \qquad \mathrm{w} = w/U,$$

$$\mathrm{x} = x/d, \qquad \mathrm{y} = y/d, \qquad \mathrm{z} = z/d,$$

$$\mathrm{p} = p/\rho U^2.$$

The equation of continuity takes the same form in the new variables, that is,

$$\frac{\partial \mathrm{U}}{\partial \mathrm{X}} + \frac{\partial \mathrm{V}}{\partial \mathrm{Y}} + \frac{\partial \mathrm{W}}{\partial \mathrm{Z}} = 0, \tag{32}$$

while the momentum equations (12) become.

$$\mathrm{U}\frac{\partial \mathrm{U}}{\partial \mathrm{X}} + \mathrm{V}\frac{\partial \mathrm{U}}{\partial \mathrm{Y}} + \mathrm{W}\frac{\partial \mathrm{U}}{\partial \mathrm{Z}} = -\frac{\partial \mathrm{P}}{\partial \mathrm{X}} + \frac{1}{R}\left(\frac{\partial^2 \mathrm{U}}{\partial \mathrm{X}^2} + \frac{\partial^2 \mathrm{U}}{\partial \mathrm{Y}^2} + \frac{\partial^2 \mathrm{U}}{\partial \mathrm{Z}^2}\right) \tag{33}$$

with two similar equations, where R is the Reynolds number Ud/ν. The boundary conditions $u = U$, $v = 0$, $w = 0$ at infinity, and

$$u = v = w = 0$$

at the boundary of the solid obstacle, become $\mathrm{U} = 1$, $\mathrm{V} = 0$, $\mathrm{W} = 0$ at infinity, and $\mathrm{U} = \mathrm{V} = \mathrm{W} = 0$ at a fixed surface, independent of d, in the $(\mathrm{X},\mathrm{Y},\mathrm{Z})$ space. With these boundary conditions, (32) and the equations of type (33) determine U, V, W, and P. Thus, for fluids of different densities and coefficients of viscosity, for streams of different speeds and obstacles of different sizes, so long as R is the same, u/U, v/U, w/U, and $p/\rho U^2$ will be functions of x/d, y/d, z/d only. Since

$$p_{xx} = -p + 2\mu \frac{\partial u}{\partial x} = \rho U^2\left(-\mathrm{P} + \frac{2}{R}\frac{\partial \mathrm{U}}{\partial \mathrm{X}}\right),$$

$$p_{yz} = \mu\left(\frac{\partial w}{\partial y} + \frac{\partial v}{\partial z}\right) = \rho\frac{U^2}{R}\left(\frac{\partial \mathrm{W}}{\partial \mathrm{Y}} + \frac{\partial \mathrm{V}}{\partial \mathrm{Z}}\right),$$

the same is true for any stress component divided by ρU^2. Any velocity component divided by U, and any stress component divided by ρU^2 is a function of x/d, y/d, z/d, and R only. Again, the component along the axis of x, for example, of the force on the obstacle (apart from the force of buoyancy) is $\int p_{nx}\, dS$, and since, for a given value of R, p_{nx} varies as ρU^2, this force component will vary as $\rho U^2 S$, where S is some representative area associated with the obstacle. The same is true for any other force component; hence, any force component divided by $\rho U^2 S$ is a function of R alone.

When the temperature is determined by (31) it is clear that, in addition to the Reynolds number, the Prandtl number appears as a similarity parameter for the temperature field.

10. The stream function

In two-dimensional flow the equation of continuity is

$$\frac{\partial u}{\partial x} + \frac{\partial w}{\partial z} = 0, \tag{34}$$

and it may be solved by introducing the stream function ψ such that

$$u = \frac{\partial \psi}{\partial z}, \qquad w = -\frac{\partial \psi}{\partial x}. \tag{35}$$

The only non-zero component of vorticity is η, and, in terms of ψ, it becomes

$$\eta = \frac{\partial u}{\partial z} - \frac{\partial w}{\partial x} = \nabla^2 \psi. \tag{36}$$

The equation of motion for ψ may then be established from the appropriate vorticity equation which reduces, since there is no stretching of vortex lines in this case, to

$$\frac{D\eta}{Dt} = \nu \nabla^2 \eta. \tag{37}$$

Thus,

$$\frac{\partial}{\partial t} (\nabla^2 \psi) - \frac{\partial(\psi, \nabla^2 \psi)}{\partial(x, z)} = \nu \nabla^4 \psi. \tag{38}$$

When coordinate systems other than the Cartesian one are considered, the continuity equation both for two-dimensional flow and for axisymmetric flow may still be solved by the introduction of a stream function. The details and the equations corresponding to (36) and (38) are included in the next section.

11. General orthogonal coordinates

The invariant vector form of the equations of motion, that is, equation (15) for the momentum equation and $\operatorname{div} \mathbf{v} = 0$ for the continuity equation, apply for any coordinate system. In order to expand them in component form for any particular system we require the formulae for the gradient of a scalar and the divergence and curl of a vector in that system. Here, we write out these formulae for general orthogonal coordinates, x_1, x_2, x_3.

Let the elements of length at (x_1, x_2, x_3) in the directions of increasing x_1, x_2, and x_3 respectively, be $h_1 dx_1$, $h_2 dx_2$, and $h_3 dx_3$. Let (a_1, a_2, a_3) denote the components of a vector $\mathbf{a}$ in the directions of increasing x_1, x_2, and x_3, respectively. Then (see, for example, Weatherburn (1944), pp. 28–30, or Love (1927), pp. 51–55, but note that the quantities h_1, h_2, h_3 used by Love are the reciprocals of those employed here),

$$\operatorname{div} \mathbf{a} = \frac{1}{h_1 h_2 h_3} \left\{ \frac{\partial}{\partial x_1} (h_2 h_3 a_1) + \frac{\partial}{\partial x_2} (h_3 h_1 a_2) + \frac{\partial}{\partial x_3} (h_1 h_2 a_3) \right\}, \tag{39}$$

and the components of $\mathbf{b} = \operatorname{curl} \mathbf{a}$ are given by

$$b_1 = \frac{1}{h_2 h_3} \left\{ \frac{\partial}{\partial x_2} (h_3 a_3) - \frac{\partial}{\partial x_3} (h_2 a_2) \right\}, \quad \text{etc.} \tag{40}$$

The components of the gradient of a scalar ϕ are

$$\frac{1}{h_1}\frac{\partial\phi}{\partial x_1}, \quad \frac{1}{h_2}\frac{\partial\phi}{\partial x_2}, \quad \frac{1}{h_3}\frac{\partial\phi}{\partial x_3}. \tag{41}$$

With these results the equation of continuity and the three components of (15) may be obtained for any system of orthogonal coordinates. However, since div $\mathbf{v} = 0$ for incompressible flow, there is an indeterminateness in the equations because expressions involving div $\mathbf{v}$ may be added. In fact it is usual to retain the form

$$\nu(\text{grad div } \mathbf{v} - \text{curl } \boldsymbol{\omega})$$

in working out the last term of (15), since this has components $\nabla^2 u$, $\nabla^2 v$, $\nabla^2 w$, in Cartesian coordinates.

It should be noted that in general orthogonal coordinates the components of $\nabla^2 \mathbf{a}$ have terms in addition to $\nabla^2 a_1$, $\nabla^2 a_2$, $\nabla^2 a_3$ (where $\nabla^2 a_1 = \text{div grad } a_1$, etc.); the correct expressions may be obtained using

$$\nabla^2 \mathbf{a} = \text{grad div } \mathbf{a} - \text{curl curl } \mathbf{a}. \tag{42}$$

This must be used, for example, in deriving the appropriate form of the vorticity equations from (16). Similarly, the vector, usually denoted by $(\mathbf{b}.\nabla)\mathbf{a}$, defined by the components

$$(\mathbf{b}.\text{grad } a_x, \ \mathbf{b}.\text{grad } a_y, \ \mathbf{b}.\text{grad } a_z)$$

in Cartesian coordinates, cannot be expressed immediately in general orthogonal coordinates. We do, in fact, avoid using the formulae for this vector, but since they are often useful and do not appear in the usual reference books, we note the results here. The x_1 component is

$$\mathbf{b}.\text{grad } a_1 + \frac{b_1}{h_1}\left\{\frac{a_1}{h_1}\frac{\partial h_1}{\partial x_1} + \frac{a_2}{h_2}\frac{\partial h_1}{\partial x_2} + \frac{a_3}{h_3}\frac{\partial h_1}{\partial x_3}\right\} -$$
$$- \left\{\frac{a_1 b_1}{h_1^2}\frac{\partial h_1}{\partial x_1} + \frac{a_2 b_2}{h_2 h_1}\frac{\partial h_2}{\partial x_1} + \frac{a_3 b_3}{h_3 h_1}\frac{\partial h_3}{\partial x_1}\right\}, \tag{43}$$

and the other components are given by similar expressions.

We now consider the expressions for the rate-of-strain components in general orthogonal coordinates. For Cartesian coordinates with axes in the directions of x_1 increasing, x_2 increasing, and x_3 increasing at P, the rate-of-strain components would be defined exactly as in (2). Thus, even for non-Cartesian orthogonal coordinates, $\frac{1}{2}e_{11}$ is still the rate of extension of a line element in the direction of x_1 increasing, and e_{23} is still the rate of change of the angle between two lines, moving with the fluid, drawn in the directions of x_2 increasing and x_3 increasing. But the directions of x_1 increasing, x_2 increasing, and x_3 increasing are different at (x_1, x_2, x_3) and at any neighbouring point, so that additional terms are introduced when the rate-of-strain components are expressed in terms of the derivatives of the velocity components. These expressions are (Love (1927), pp. 53, 57)

$$\tfrac{1}{2}e_{11} = \frac{1}{h_1}\frac{\partial v_1}{\partial x_1} + \frac{v_2}{h_1 h_2}\frac{\partial h_1}{\partial x_2} + \frac{v_3}{h_3 h_1}\frac{\partial h_1}{\partial x_3},$$

$$e_{23} = \frac{h_3}{h_2}\frac{\partial}{\partial x_2}\!\left(\frac{v_3}{h_3}\right) + \frac{h_2}{h_3}\frac{\partial}{\partial x_3}\!\left(\frac{v_2}{h_2}\right), \tag{44}$$

and the other components are given by similar expressions. The stress components are still given by

$$p_{11} = -p + \mu e_{11}, \qquad p_{23} = p_{32} = \mu e_{23}, \quad \text{etc.}, \tag{45}$$

where p_{23}, for example, is the component in the direction of x_3 increasing of the stress exerted at (x_1, x_2, x_3) across the surface $x_2 = $ constant.

For two-dimensional motion, if x_1 and x_3 are general orthogonal coordinates in the plane of motion, the equation of continuity div $\mathbf{v} = 0$ becomes

$$\frac{\partial}{\partial x_1}(h_3 v_1) + \frac{\partial}{\partial x_3}(h_1 v_3) = 0.$$

Therefore, we can introduce a stream function ψ such that

$$v_1 = \frac{1}{h_3}\frac{\partial \psi}{\partial x_3}, \qquad v_3 = -\frac{1}{h_1}\frac{\partial \psi}{\partial x_1}.$$

The non-zero component of vorticity, ω_2, is then given by

$$\omega_2 = \frac{1}{h_1 h_3}\left[\frac{\partial}{\partial x_1}\!\left(\frac{h_3}{h_1}\frac{\partial \psi}{\partial x_1}\right) + \frac{\partial}{\partial x_3}\!\left(\frac{h_1}{h_3}\frac{\partial \psi}{\partial x_3}\right)\right] = \nabla^2 \psi.$$

Substituting this value in the third component of the vorticity equation (16), we have the equation for ψ:

$$\frac{\partial}{\partial t}(\nabla^2 \psi) - \frac{1}{h_1 h_3}\frac{\partial(\psi, \nabla^2 \psi)}{\partial(x_1, x_3)} = \nu \nabla^4 \psi.$$

For axisymmetric flow, if x_1 and x_3 are general orthogonal coordinates in a meridian plane and x_2 is the azimuthal angle, and if all quantities are supposed independent of x_2, the equation of continuity is

$$\frac{\partial}{\partial x_1}(h_2 h_3 v_1) + \frac{\partial}{\partial x_3}(h_1 h_2 v_3) = 0,$$

where h_2 measures distance from the axis of symmetry. Again a stream function may be introduced and in this case we take

$$h_2 v_1 = \frac{1}{h_3}\frac{\partial \psi}{\partial x_3}, \qquad h_2 v_3 = -\frac{1}{h_1}\frac{\partial \psi}{\partial x_1}.$$

This applies whether the velocity v_2 round the axis is zero or not, so long as it is independent of x_2. If it is not zero, we put $h_2 v_2 = \Omega$. Then

$$\omega_1 = -\frac{1}{h_2 h_3}\frac{\partial \Omega}{\partial x_3}, \qquad \omega_3 = \frac{1}{h_2 h_1}\frac{\partial \Omega}{\partial x_1},$$

$$\omega_2 = \frac{1}{h_1 h_3}\left[\frac{\partial}{\partial x_1}\left(\frac{h_3}{h_2 h_1}\frac{\partial \psi}{\partial x_1}\right) + \frac{\partial}{\partial x_3}\left(\frac{h_1}{h_2 h_3}\frac{\partial \psi}{\partial x_3}\right)\right] = \frac{1}{h_2}D^2\psi,$$

where
$$D^2 = \frac{h_2}{h_1 h_3}\left[\frac{\partial}{\partial x_1}\left(\frac{h_3}{h_2 h_1}\frac{\partial}{\partial x_1}\right) + \frac{\partial}{\partial x_3}\left(\frac{h_1}{h_2 h_3}\frac{\partial}{\partial x_3}\right)\right].$$

The x_2 component of the equation for the vorticity gives

$$\frac{\partial}{\partial t}(D^2\psi) + \frac{2\Omega}{h_1 h_3 h_2^2}\frac{\partial(\Omega, h_2)}{\partial(x_1, x_3)} - \frac{1}{h_1 h_2 h_3}\frac{\partial(\psi, D^2\psi)}{\partial(x_1, x_3)} + \frac{2D^2\psi}{h_1 h_3 h_2^2}\frac{\partial(\psi, h_2)}{\partial(x_1, x_3)} = \nu D^4\psi.$$

If $v_2 = 0$ then $\Omega = 0$ and this is an equation for ψ. Otherwise, we require another equation, which is provided by the second component of the momentum equation. This gives

$$\frac{\partial \Omega}{\partial t} - \frac{1}{h_1 h_2 h_3}\frac{\partial(\psi, \Omega)}{\partial(x_1, x_3)} = \nu D^2\Omega.$$

12. Cylindrical polar coordinates

With cylindrical polar coordinates r, θ, z such that

$$x = r\cos\theta, \qquad y = r\sin\theta,$$

if r, θ, z are taken as x_1, x_2, x_3, respectively, then

$$h_1 = 1, \qquad h_2 = r, \qquad h_3 = 1.$$

Hence, using subscripts r, θ, z for the components of vectors and tensors, we have

$$\operatorname{div}\mathbf{v} = \frac{1}{r}\frac{\partial}{\partial r}(rv_r) + \frac{1}{r}\frac{\partial v_\theta}{\partial \theta} + \frac{\partial v_z}{\partial z}, \tag{46}$$

$$\omega_r = \frac{1}{r}\frac{\partial v_z}{\partial \theta} - \frac{\partial v_\theta}{\partial z}, \qquad \omega_\theta = \frac{\partial v_r}{\partial z} - \frac{\partial v_z}{\partial r}, \qquad \omega_z = \frac{1}{r}\frac{\partial}{\partial r}(rv_\theta) - \frac{1}{r}\frac{\partial v_r}{\partial \theta}, \tag{47}$$

$$\tfrac{1}{2}e_{rr} = \frac{\partial v_r}{\partial r}, \qquad \tfrac{1}{2}e_{\theta\theta} = \frac{1}{r}\frac{\partial v_\theta}{\partial \theta} + \frac{v_r}{r}, \qquad \tfrac{1}{2}e_{zz} = \frac{\partial v_z}{\partial z},$$

$$e_{\theta z} = \frac{1}{r}\frac{\partial v_z}{\partial \theta} + \frac{\partial v_\theta}{\partial z}, \qquad e_{zr} = \frac{\partial v_r}{\partial z} + \frac{\partial v_z}{\partial r}, \qquad e_{r\theta} = r\frac{\partial}{\partial r}\left(\frac{v_\theta}{r}\right) + \frac{1}{r}\frac{\partial v_r}{\partial \theta}, \tag{48}$$

and the momentum equations are

$$\frac{\partial v_r}{\partial t}+v_r\frac{\partial v_r}{\partial r}+\frac{v_\theta}{r}\frac{\partial v_r}{\partial\theta}+v_z\frac{\partial v_r}{\partial z}-\frac{v_\theta^2}{r} = -\frac{1}{\rho}\frac{\partial p}{\partial r}+\nu\left(\nabla^2 v_r-\frac{v_r}{r^2}-\frac{2}{r^2}\frac{\partial v_\theta}{\partial\theta}\right),$$

$$\frac{\partial v_\theta}{\partial t}+v_r\frac{\partial v_\theta}{\partial r}+\frac{v_\theta}{r}\frac{\partial v_\theta}{\partial\theta}+v_z\frac{\partial v_\theta}{\partial z}+\frac{v_r v_\theta}{r} = -\frac{1}{\rho}\frac{\partial p}{r\partial\theta}+\nu\left(\nabla^2 v_\theta+\frac{2}{r^2}\frac{\partial v_r}{\partial\theta}-\frac{v_\theta}{r^2}\right),$$

$$\frac{\partial v_z}{\partial t}+v_r\frac{\partial v_z}{\partial r}+\frac{v_\theta}{r}\frac{\partial v_z}{\partial\theta}+v_z\frac{\partial v_z}{\partial z} = -\frac{1}{\rho}\frac{\partial p}{\partial z}+\nu\nabla^2 v_z, \qquad (49)$$

where
$$\nabla^2 \equiv \frac{\partial^2}{\partial r^2}+\frac{1}{r}\frac{\partial}{\partial r}+\frac{1}{r^2}\frac{\partial^2}{\partial\theta^2}+\frac{\partial^2}{\partial z^2}.$$

13. Spherical polar coordinates

With spherical polar coordinates (r,θ,λ) such that

$$x = r\sin\theta\cos\lambda, \qquad y = r\sin\theta\sin\lambda, \qquad z = r\cos\theta,$$

if r, θ, λ are taken as (x_1, x_2, x_3) respectively, then

$$h_1 = 1, \qquad h_2 = r, \qquad h_3 = r\sin\theta.$$

Hence, using subscripts r, θ, λ for the components of vectors and tensors, we have

$$\text{div}\,\mathbf{v} = \frac{1}{r^2}\frac{\partial}{\partial r}(r^2 v_r)+\frac{1}{r\sin\theta}\frac{\partial}{\partial\theta}(v_\theta\sin\theta)+\frac{1}{r\sin\theta}\frac{\partial v_\lambda}{\partial\lambda}, \qquad (50)$$

$$\omega_r = \frac{1}{r\sin\theta}\left\{\frac{\partial}{\partial\theta}(v_\lambda\sin\theta)-\frac{\partial v_\theta}{\partial\lambda}\right\},$$

$$\omega_\theta = \frac{1}{r\sin\theta}\frac{\partial v_r}{\partial\lambda}-\frac{1}{r}\frac{\partial}{\partial r}(rv_\lambda),$$

$$\omega_\lambda = \frac{1}{r}\frac{\partial}{\partial r}(rv_\theta)-\frac{1}{r}\frac{\partial v_r}{\partial\theta}, \qquad (51)$$

$$\tfrac{1}{2}e_{rr} = \frac{\partial v_r}{\partial r}, \qquad \tfrac{1}{2}e_{\theta\theta} = \frac{1}{r}\frac{\partial v_\theta}{\partial\theta}+\frac{v_r}{r},$$

$$\tfrac{1}{2}e_{\lambda\lambda} = \frac{1}{r\sin\theta}\frac{\partial v_\lambda}{\partial\lambda}+\frac{v_r}{r}+\frac{v_\theta\cot\theta}{r},$$

$$e_{\theta\lambda} = \frac{\sin\theta}{r}\frac{\partial}{\partial\theta}\left(\frac{v_\lambda}{\sin\theta}\right)+\frac{1}{r\sin\theta}\frac{\partial v_\theta}{\partial\lambda},$$

$$e_{\lambda r} = \frac{1}{r\sin\theta}\frac{\partial v_r}{\partial\theta}+r\frac{\partial}{\partial r}\left(\frac{v_\lambda}{r}\right),$$

$$e_{r\theta} = r\frac{\partial}{\partial r}\left(\frac{v_\theta}{r}\right)+\frac{1}{r}\frac{\partial v_r}{\partial\theta}. \qquad (52)$$

and the momentum equations are

$$\frac{\partial v_r}{\partial t} + v_r \frac{\partial v_r}{\partial r} + \frac{v_\theta}{r}\frac{\partial v_r}{\partial \theta} + \frac{v_\lambda}{r\sin\theta}\frac{\partial v_r}{\partial \lambda} - \frac{v_\theta^2 + v_\lambda^2}{r}$$

$$= -\frac{1}{\rho}\frac{\partial p}{\partial r} + \nu\left(\nabla^2 v_r - \frac{2v_r}{r^2} - \frac{2}{r^2}\frac{\partial v_\theta}{\partial \theta} - \frac{2v_\theta \cot\theta}{r^2} - \frac{2}{r^2\sin\theta}\frac{\partial v_\lambda}{\partial \lambda}\right),$$

$$\frac{\partial v_\theta}{\partial t} + v_r \frac{\partial v_\theta}{\partial r} + \frac{v_\theta}{r}\frac{\partial v_\theta}{\partial \theta} + \frac{v_\lambda}{r\sin\theta}\frac{\partial v_\theta}{\partial \lambda} + \frac{v_r v_\theta}{r} - \frac{v_\lambda^2 \cot\theta}{r}$$

$$= -\frac{1}{\rho}\frac{\partial p}{r\partial \theta} + \nu\left(\nabla^2 v_\theta + \frac{2}{r^2}\frac{\partial v_r}{\partial \theta} - \frac{v_\theta}{r^2\sin^2\theta} - \frac{2\cos\theta}{r^2\sin^2\theta}\frac{\partial v_\lambda}{\partial \lambda}\right),$$

$$\frac{\partial v_\lambda}{\partial t} + v_r \frac{\partial v_\lambda}{\partial r} + \frac{v_\theta}{r}\frac{\partial v_\lambda}{\partial \theta} + \frac{v_\lambda}{r\sin\theta}\frac{\partial v_\lambda}{\partial \lambda} + \frac{v_\lambda v_r}{r} + \frac{v_\theta v_\lambda \cot\theta}{r}$$

$$= -\frac{1}{\rho}\frac{1}{r\sin\theta}\frac{\partial p}{\partial \lambda} + \nu\left(\nabla^2 v_\lambda - \frac{v_\lambda}{r^2\sin^2\theta} + \frac{2}{r^2\sin\theta}\frac{\partial v_r}{\partial \lambda} + \frac{2\cos\theta}{r^2\sin^2\theta}\frac{\partial v_\theta}{\partial \lambda}\right),$$

$$\tag{53}$$

where $\quad \nabla^2 \equiv \dfrac{1}{r^2}\dfrac{\partial}{\partial r}\left(r^2\dfrac{\partial}{\partial r}\right) + \dfrac{1}{r^2\sin\theta}\dfrac{\partial}{\partial \theta}\left(\sin\theta\dfrac{\partial}{\partial \theta}\right) + \dfrac{1}{r^2\sin^2\theta}\dfrac{\partial^2}{\partial \lambda^2}.$

PART II

SOME EXACT SOLUTIONS

14. Solutions for which the convection terms vanish

The fundamental difficulty in solving the Navier–Stokes equations (either exactly or approximately) is the non-linearity introduced by the convection terms in the momentum equations (12). There exist, however, non-trivial flows in which the convection terms vanish, and these provide the simplest class of solutions of the equations of motion.

For the equations in Cartesian form, such solutions are obtained by taking all except one of the velocity components equal to zero. If we take $v = w = 0$, an immediate consequence of the continuity equation is that u is independent of x, and it then follows that all the convection terms in (12) vanish. Assuming, as in the remainder of this chapter, that any external field of force may be accounted for by measuring p

from its hydrostatic value, as in Section 9, the equations become

$$\frac{\partial u}{\partial t} = -\frac{1}{\rho}\frac{\partial p}{\partial x} + \nu\left(\frac{\partial^2 u}{\partial y^2} + \frac{\partial^2 u}{\partial z^2}\right), \tag{54}$$

$$\frac{\partial p}{\partial y} = 0, \qquad \frac{\partial p}{\partial z} = 0. \tag{55}$$

Since u is independent of x, we see that $\partial p/\partial x$ must be a function of t alone. This pressure gradient may be prescribed as an arbitrary function of t, then $u(y, z, t)$ is determined by solving the *linear* equation (54). It should be noted that (54) is identical with the equation for heat conduction in two dimensions if the term $-\rho^{-1}\partial p/\partial x$ is interpreted as a uniform distribution of heat sources. Thus, known solutions in the theory of heat conduction may be taken over directly and interpreted as fluid flows.

It is clear that the flows to which this theory applies are parallel to cylindrical surfaces whose generators are in the x-direction. There are two main problems: (i) steady flows through pipes of uniform cross-section with constant pressure gradient, and (ii) unsteady flows produced by the motion of a solid boundary in the x-direction.

In problem (i), $u(y, z)$ satisfies Poisson's equation,

$$\frac{\partial^2 u}{\partial y^2} + \frac{\partial^2 u}{\partial z^2} = \frac{1}{\mu}\frac{dp}{dx}, \tag{56}$$

and the boundary condition $u = 0$ at the walls of the pipe. It is clear that in all cases u may be expressed as $-f(y, z)\mu^{-1}dp/dx$, where $f(y, z)$ depends only on the cross-sectional shape; similarly, the volume flux takes the form $-C\mu^{-1}dp/dx$. The problem can be solved analytically for several special shapes of cross-section, and for a detailed account of these, reference may be made to Love (1927, chapter xiv), where the analogous problem of the torsion of bars of various cross-sections is considered. Here, we note the results for the more important cases.

(a) Two-dimensional channel $-c \leqslant z \leqslant c$:

$$f = \tfrac{1}{2}(c^2 - z^2), \qquad C = \tfrac{2}{3}c^3.$$

(In this case, of course, C corresponds to the volume flux per unit width.)

(b) Circular section of radius c:

$$f = \tfrac{1}{4}(c^2 - r^2), \qquad C = \tfrac{1}{8}\pi c^4,$$

where $r^2 = y^2 + z^2$.

(c) Annular section $b \leqslant r \leqslant c$:

$$f = \frac{1}{4}\left(b^2 - r^2 + \frac{c^2 - b^2}{\log c/b}\log\frac{r}{b}\right), \qquad C = \frac{1}{8}\pi\left\{c^4 - b^4 - \frac{(c^2 - b^2)^2}{\log c/b}\right\}.$$

(d) Elliptic section $y^2/b^2 + z^2/c^2 \leqslant 1$:

$$f = \frac{b^2 c^2}{2(b^2 + c^2)}\left(1 - \frac{y^2}{b^2} - \frac{z^2}{c^2}\right), \qquad C = \frac{1}{4}\pi\frac{b^3 c^3}{b^2 + c^2}.$$

(e) Rectangular section $-b \leqslant y \leqslant b$, $-c \leqslant z \leqslant c$:

$$f = \frac{1}{2}b^2 - \frac{1}{2}y^2 - 2b^2\left(\frac{2}{\pi}\right)^3 \sum_0^\infty \frac{(-1)^n}{(2n+1)^3}\frac{\cosh(2n+1)(\pi z/2b)}{\cosh(2n+1)(\pi c/2b)}\cos(2n+1)\frac{\pi y}{2b},$$

$$C = \frac{4}{3}cb^3 - 8b^4\left(\frac{2}{\pi}\right)^5\sum_0^\infty \frac{1}{(2n+1)^5}\tanh(2n+1)\frac{\pi c}{2b}.$$

When $b = c$, $C = 0.5623b^4$; when $c > 3b$,

$$C \sim cb^3\left(\frac{4}{3} - 0.840\frac{b}{c}\right).$$

When the cross-section is not one of the special shapes for which an analytic solution can be found, the required results may be obtained by making certain measurements on soap films. For, if a soap film is stretched across a hole of the given shape and has a small excess pressure p on one side of it, then the displacement $X(y, z)$ satisfies

$$2T\left(\frac{\partial^2 X}{\partial y^2} + \frac{\partial^2 X}{\partial z^2}\right) + p = 0$$

(where T is the surface tension), together with the boundary condition $X = 0$ on the edges of the hole. Therefore,

$$X = \frac{p}{2T}f(y, z)$$

and is proportional to u. Thus, the velocity distribution can be deduced from measurements of the displacement X. The volume flux is proportional to $\iint X \, dydz$ and this is found by measuring the total volume under the soap film. These measurements are much more easily made than direct measurements of the velocity in the fluid-flow problem or of the displacement in the torsion problem. The experimental technique is described by G. I. Taylor (1937a).

Perhaps the simplest case of problem (ii) is that of an infinite plate which, starting at $t = 0$, is moved in its own plane with constant velocity U through fluid initially at rest. If the plate lies in the plane

$z = 0$, $u(z, t)$ satisfies

$$\frac{\partial u}{\partial t} = \nu \frac{\partial^2 u}{\partial z^2},$$

and the appropriate boundary and initial conditions are $u(0, t) = U$ $(t > 0)$, and $u(z, 0) = 0$. The analogous problem in the theory of heat conduction is well known and the solution is (Carslaw and Jaeger 1947, p. 43)

$$u = U\left(1 - \operatorname{erf}\frac{z}{2\sqrt{(\nu t)}}\right), \tag{57}$$

where

$$\operatorname{erf}\zeta = \frac{2}{\sqrt\pi}\int_0^\zeta e^{-\lambda^2}\,d\lambda. \tag{58}$$

In diffusion problems there is, of course, no true propagation speed, but if the boundary-layer thickness is defined as the distance in which u drops to a given small fraction of U, we may determine its rate of growth. From (57) we see that this boundary-layer thickness is proportional to $\sqrt{(\nu t)}$, and it grows at a rate proportional to $\sqrt{(\nu/t)}$.

Rayleigh (1911) suggested that this comparatively simple solution could be used to give an approximate solution to the problem of steady flow along a semi-infinite flat plate, the flow direction being perpendicular to the edge of the plate. The basic idea is that the disturbance due to the plate spreads out into the stream at the rate given by the unsteady problem, but at the same time it is swept downstream with the fluid. As a rough approximation, it is assumed that the disturbance is convected downstream with the main stream velocity U. Thus, at a distance x along the plate from the leading edge, the boundary-layer thickness and velocity distribution can be found by identifying t in (57) with x/U. Modifying (57) so that u measures downstream velocity relative to the plate, this gives

$$u = U\operatorname{erf}\tfrac12 z\sqrt{\left(\frac{U}{x\nu}\right)}. \tag{59}$$

Therefore, the boundary-layer thickness is proportional to $\sqrt{(\nu x/U)}$, and the skin friction is

$$\tau = \mu\left(\frac{\partial u}{\partial z}\right)_{z=0} = \frac{\rho U^2}{\sqrt\pi}\sqrt{\left(\frac{\nu}{xU}\right)}. \tag{60}$$

Actually, the momentum equation for the x-direction in the steady flow past a flat plate is

$$u\frac{\partial u}{\partial x} + w\frac{\partial u}{\partial z} = \nu\left(\frac{\partial^2 u}{\partial x^2} + \frac{\partial^2 u}{\partial z^2}\right),$$

and the physical argument given above is equivalent mathematically to the following approximations in this equation. Firstly, the convection terms on the left are replaced by the approximation $U \, \partial u/\partial x$, and, secondly, the term $\nu \, \partial^2 u/\partial x^2$ is neglected in the viscous terms on the right. In this way, we obtain the diffusion equation for u with t replaced by x/U. The boundary-layer approximation retains the convection terms in full and makes only the second simplification.

The Rayleigh approximation obviously overestimates the convection effects; hence, its prediction of the boundary-layer thickness will be too small and the value of τ too great. As later investigations show (see Section V. 12), the accurate value for τ, obtained from boundary-layer theory, is $0 \cdot 332 \rho U^2 \sqrt{(\nu/xU)}$, which corresponds to identifying t with $x/(0 \cdot 346 U)$. But, in spite of its approximate nature, this so-called 'Rayleigh analogy' offers a method of estimating the skin friction in steady problems for which the accurate formulation proves intractable. As examples of unsteady problems which have been used for this purpose, we may mention the flows resulting from the impulsive motions of a semi-infinite plate parallel to its edge (Howarth 1950), a wedge parallel to its edge (Hasimoto ·1951, Sowerby and Cooke 1953), and cylinders of finite cross-section parallel to their generators (Batchelor 1954a). These will be discussed in Chapter VII, and again in Chapter VIII where the steady-flow 'analogies' are required.

For the motion of the infinite plate, the solution can be obtained for any prescribed variation of the velocity of the plate with time. One case of special interest arises when the plate oscillates periodically, that is, $u = A \cos \omega t$ at $z = 0$. The solution satisfying this boundary condition is

$$u = Ae^{-kz}\cos(\omega t - kz), \qquad k = \sqrt{(\omega/2\nu)}. \qquad (61)$$

It represents waves spreading out from the plate with velocity

$$\omega/k = \sqrt{(2\nu\omega)}$$

and amplitude decaying exponentially with z. When ν is small the damping is heavy and the disturbance is then confined mainly to a thin boundary layer near the plate with thickness of order $\sqrt{(\nu/\omega)}$.

There are, of course, many other solutions of the heat equation which may be applied to fluid flows, but we do not attempt a complete survey here. (Additional examples are given in Schlichting (1955), chapter v.) However, it should be pointed out that the solutions are not confined to the Cartesian form of the equations. For example, in cylindrical polar coordinates (Section 12), we may take $v_r = v_z = 0$, $v_\theta = v_\theta(r, t)$,

$p = \text{constant}$. Then v_θ satisfies

$$\frac{\partial v_\theta}{\partial t} = \nu\left(\frac{\partial^2 v_\theta}{\partial r^2} + \frac{1}{r}\frac{\partial v_\theta}{\partial r} - \frac{v_\theta}{r^2}\right),$$

and the vorticity, $\omega_z = \frac{1}{r}\frac{\partial}{\partial r}(rv_\theta)$,

satisfies the diffusion equation

$$\frac{\partial \omega_z}{\partial t} = \nu\left(\frac{\partial^2 \omega_z}{\partial r^2} + \frac{1}{r}\frac{\partial \omega_z}{\partial r}\right). \tag{62}$$

A well-known solution of this equation is

$$\omega_z = \frac{\Gamma}{4\pi\nu t}e^{-r^2/4\nu t};$$

in the application to fluid flow it describes the dissolution of a vortex filament which is concentrated at the origin at $t = 0$, and Γ is the initial value of the circulation about the origin.

Another application of (62) is to the motion of fluid contained in or surrounding an infinite cylinder which starts to rotate. Equation (62) may be used to determine how the vorticity, which is initially concentrated at the surface of the cylinder, spreads out into the fluid. Outside the cylinder, $\omega_z \to 0$ as $t \to \infty$ and then $v_\theta \propto 1/r$; inside the cylinder, ω_z tends to a constant value equal to twice the angular velocity of the cylinder, and the fluid rotates like a solid body.

In concluding this section we may refer briefly to a solution which comes under the heading of this section, although it is quite different from the above solutions. It was derived by Taylor (1923a) in the following way. In two-dimensional flow the equation for the vorticity η is (Section 10)

$$\frac{\partial \eta}{\partial t} + \frac{\partial \psi}{\partial z}\frac{\partial \eta}{\partial x} - \frac{\partial \psi}{\partial x}\frac{\partial \eta}{\partial z} = \nu\nabla^2\eta, \tag{63}$$

and η is given in terms of the stream function ψ by $\eta = \nabla^2\psi$. Now the convection terms in (63) vanish when η is a function of ψ. As a special case we take $\eta = -k\psi$; then (63) is satisfied if

$$\frac{\partial \psi}{\partial t} = -k\nu\psi, \qquad \nabla^2\psi = -k\psi.$$

Therefore $\psi = \psi_1(x, z)e^{-k\nu t}$, where $\nabla^2\psi_1 = -k\psi_1$. This equation for ψ_1 arises in the mechanical problem of the vibrating membrane, and we have the useful analogy that the streamlines $\psi_1 = \text{constant}$ are given by the contours of the membrane. A particular example is

$$\psi = A\cos\frac{\pi x}{d}\cos\frac{\pi z}{d}\exp\left\{-\frac{2\pi^2\nu t}{d}\right\}, \tag{64}$$

and this flow may be interpreted as a double array of vortices (as shown in Fig. III. 3) which decay exponentially with time.

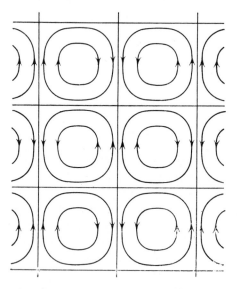

Fig. III. 3. Streamlines of the flow given by equation (64).

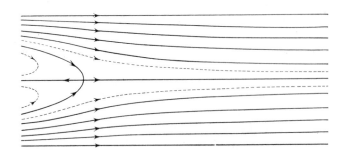

Fig. III. 4. Streamlines of the flow given by equation (65).

Kovasznay (1948) has obtained a steady-flow solution in a similar manner by assuming that η is proportional to $\psi - Uz$, U being the mainstream velocity in the x-direction. The stream function in that case is given by

$$\psi = Uz - A \sin \frac{2\pi z}{d} \exp\left\{\frac{x}{2d}\left(R - \sqrt{(R^2 + 16\pi^2)}\right)\right\}, \tag{65}$$

where $R = Ud/\nu$. The flow is periodic in the z-direction, and the stream-lines for one period are shown for $R = 40$ in Fig. III. 4; Kovasznay suggests that this may be used to describe the flow downstream of a two-dimensional grid.

15. Examples of flows with suction

Even if the convection terms do not vanish, they will not introduce serious complications provided that they are linear in the unknown variables. Such is the case in the following problems of flows with suction.

(a) Asymptotic suction profile

A surprisingly simple solution, which is nevertheless important, describes steady flow parallel to an infinite plane surface on which the normal component of velocity takes a given non-zero value. This solution represents the steady flow far downstream of the leading edge of a semi-infinite flat plate. Without suction the boundary layer would grow indefinitely downstream so that, at any finite distance from the plate, the velocity ultimately tends to zero. But with suction this is not the case; the boundary-layer growth is eventually subdued, and we have the 'asymptotic suction profile'.

If x and z are measured along and perpendicular to the plate, the velocity components u, w, and the pressure are independent of x. Hence, from the continuity equation (4), w remains constant and equal to its value, $-W$ say, at the wall; from (12),

$$-W\,du/dz = \nu\,d^2u/dz^2 \tag{66}$$

and the pressure remains constant throughout the flow. Since $u = 0$ at $z = 0$ and tends to the main-stream value U as $z \to \infty$, the appropriate solution of (66) is

$$u = U(1 - e^{-zW/\nu}). \tag{67}$$

As $\nu \to 0$, the disturbance to the main stream becomes more and more concentrated in a 'boundary layer' at the plate, and in fact (67) is also the solution of the approximate boundary-layer equations (see Section V. 19).

(b) Circulatory flow about a rotating circular cylinder with suction

As noted in the previous section, if an infinite cylinder immersed in fluid at rest is suddenly rotated about its axis with constant angular velocity, the vorticity $\omega_z = r^{-1}\partial(rv_\theta)/\partial r$, which is initially concentrated at the surface of the cylinder, diffuses out until $\omega_z = 0$ everywhere. In this final steady state $v_\theta = \Gamma_1/2\pi r$, where Γ_1 is the circulation around the cylinder. However, if there is suction through the surface of the cylinder, the vorticity may ultimately settle down to a steady-state distribution in which the outward diffusion is balanced by the convection of vorticity towards the cylinder. Such solutions were first obtained by Hamel (1917) and have been discussed more recently by Preston (1950a). If r_0 is the radius of the cylinder and the suction velocity normal to the surface of the cylinder is $-V$, the radial velocity in the fluid must be given by

$$v_r = -\frac{Vr_0}{r},$$

in order to satisfy the continuity equation. The rate at which vorticity diffuses across a circle $r = $ constant is $-2\pi r \nu\, \partial\omega_z/\partial r$, and the rate of convection is $2\pi r v_r \omega_z$; therefore, a balance is achieved when

$$\frac{\partial\omega_z}{\partial r} + R\frac{\omega_z}{r} = 0,$$

where $R = r_0 V/\nu$.

The solution for ω_z is

$$\omega_z = \frac{1}{r}\frac{\partial}{\partial r}(rv_\theta) = A\left(\frac{r_0}{r}\right)^R, \tag{68}$$

where A is the value of ω_z at the cylinder. This example is of particular importance in considering the possibility of using suction to maintain different values for the circulation at the cylinder and at infinity (see Preston 1950a, Thwaites 1950), and it is useful, therefore, to quote the expression for the circulation $\Gamma = 2\pi r v_\theta$. We have, from (68),

$$\Gamma = \Gamma_1 - \frac{2\pi r_0^2}{R-2}A\left(\frac{r_0}{r}\right)^{R-2} \quad (R \neq 2),$$

$$\Gamma = \Gamma_1 + 2\pi r_0^2 A\log\frac{r}{r_0} \quad (R = 2). \tag{69}$$

We see that if $R \leqslant 2$, the only solution with finite circulation at infinity is $\Gamma = \Gamma_1$, $\omega_z = 0$, $v_\theta = \Gamma_1/2\pi r$, but if $R > 2$, Γ_1 is the value of the circulation at infinity and A can be adjusted to give any circulation at the cylinder. Thus to maintain different values of the circulation at the cylinder and at infinity, it is necessary for the suction velocity V to exceed $2\nu/r_0$.

16. Similarity solutions

Apart from types of solutions described in the previous sections, in which linear equations are obtained, all exact solutions known to the present writer are similarity solutions. The dependent variables are functions of only two coordinates and, moreover, they can be so chosen that they are functions of a *single* elementary function of the coordinates. Then the unknowns satisfy *ordinary* differential equations, and the solution of such equations (numerically, if necessary) is a simple matter compared with the solution of the original partial differential equations. If we consider equations for two variables $u(x, y)$ and $v(x, y)$, typical examples of similarity solutions are $u = x^m U(\eta)$ and $v = x^n V(\eta)$, where η is a given function of x and y. In fact the similarity solutions in this chapter all belong to the simple case where η is y itself (at least when the most suitable coordinate system is used), but the more general type arises in connexion with the approximate boundary-layer equations.

As will be illustrated below, the existence of similarity solutions is often recognized by physical considerations, and in particular from deductions as to the forms of solution which are possible dimensionally when the physical parameters in the problem do not provide both a fundamental length and a fundamental time. The emphasis is on these two units since, if such quantities appear, the unit of mass can always be derived from the density.

There is also a rather general method of testing for similarity solutions; it is most conveniently demonstrated by an example, and for the general theory reference may be made to Birkhoff (1950) and Morgan (1952). If we consider the equations for steady two-dimensional flow (equations (4) and (12) with $w = 0$), then, in applying this method, we look for a one-parameter transformation of the variables x, y, u, v, $p - p_0$ under which the equations are invariant (since only derivatives of p occur in the equations of motion, p_0 may be any constant value of the pressure). A particularly useful transformation is

$$x' = \lambda^a x, \qquad y' = \lambda^b y,$$

$$u' = \lambda^\alpha u, \qquad v' = \lambda^\beta v, \qquad p' - p_0' = \lambda^\gamma (p - p_0), \qquad (70)$$

where λ is the parameter, and it is easily found that the equations are invariant provided that $\alpha = \beta = -a = -b$, $\gamma = -2a$. Then, we can say that there exists a solution in which ux, vx, $(p - p_0)x^2$ are functions of y/x, since each of these quantities is invariant in the transformation. Of course it is now clear that for this solution polar coordinates are more appropriate; then, rv_r, rv_θ, $r^2(p - p_0)$ are functions of θ alone.

The final step, having deduced a form of solution by this transformation method, is to check that the relevant boundary conditions can be satisfied. The example given here describes flow between inclined plane walls, and it is discussed in detail in the next section.

17. Two-dimensional flow between non-parallel plane walls

Although the form of solution for this problem has been found as an example of the 'transformation method', the following dimensional argument, which leads immediately to the required form, is more satisfactory. The only physical parameters involved in the problem are the kinematic viscosity ν and the volume flux Q per unit distance perpendicular to the flow plane. But Q and ν both have dimensions L^2/T. Hence, the velocity components v_r, v_θ and the distance r can appear only in the combinations rv_r and rv_θ which have dimensions L^2/T. Thus rv_r/ν and rv_θ/ν must be functions of θ and Q/ν alone. The equation of continuity then shows that $v_\theta r$ is constant, and since $v_\theta = 0$ at the walls the constant must be zero; therefore, the flow is radial. Using a similar dimensional argument to establish the form of the pressure difference $p - p_0$, we have

$$v_r = \frac{\nu F(\theta)}{r}, \qquad \frac{p - p_0}{\rho} = \frac{\nu^2 P(\theta)}{r^2}. \tag{71}$$

These expressions and the equations for F given below were first obtained and studied by Jeffery (1915) and Hamel (1917). Subsequently, many writers (Harrison 1919, Kármán 1924, Tollmien 1931, Noether 1931, Dean 1934) worked on special aspects of the problem but the most comprehensive treatments have been given by Rosenhead (1940) and Millsaps and Pohlhausen (1953); we shall refer in detail to the last two investigations.

When v_r and p given by (71) are substituted in (49), we find $P = -\frac{1}{2}(F^2 + F'')$, $P' = 2F'$; hence $P = 2F + C$, where C is an arbitrary constant, and

$$F'' + F^2 + 4F + 2C = 0. \tag{72}$$

On multiplication by F', the equation for F can be integrated to

$$\tfrac{1}{2}F'^2 + \tfrac{1}{3}F^3 + 2F^2 + 2CF = \text{constant.}$$

It is convenient to write

$$\tfrac{1}{2}F'^2 - \tfrac{1}{3}(a - F)(F - b)(F - c) = 0, \tag{73}$$

where only two of the constants a, b, c are independent since they satisfy

$$a + b + c = -6. \tag{74}$$

Now v_r must vanish at the walls, $\theta = \pm\alpha$, say, so that (73) must be solved subject to the conditions $F(\pm\alpha) = 0$. The integration can be carried out in terms of elliptic functions and the values of α and $Q/\nu = \int_{-\alpha}^{\alpha} F(\theta)\, d\theta$ for the possible range of values of a, b, and c may then be deduced. But appeal to the theory of elliptic functions can with advantage be postponed, and reduced to a minimum, by making use of a dynamical interpretation. If we consider a particle of unit mass moving along a straight line, with its displacement at time θ measured

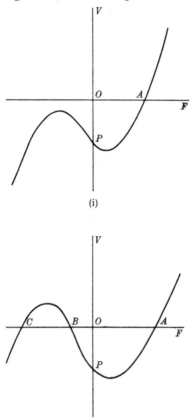

(i)

(ii)

Fig. III. 5. Sketches of the two possible forms for the potential energy $V(F)$.

by $F(\theta)$, equation (73) is the energy equation for a motion in which the potential energy of the particle is given by

$$V(F) = -\tfrac{1}{3}(a-F)(F-b)(F-c),$$

and the total energy is zero. Since $V < 0$ in the motion and the particle starts at $F = 0$ for $\theta = -\alpha$ and returns to $F = 0$ for $\theta = \alpha$, it is clear that there are only two cases to consider. If a is real and b and c are complex conjugates, $V(F)$ must be as in Fig. III. 5 (i) with $a > 0$; if

a, b, c are all real ($a > b > c$), $V(F)$ must be as shown in Fig. III. 5 (ii) with $a > 0$, $b < 0$, $c < 0$. In case (i) the particle starts at O with finite velocity and moves to A and back to O; the representative point on the curve of $V(F)$ starts at P, moves up to A, and back to P. (The subsequent motion does not concern us since the particle cannot return to O.) For the fluid motion this represents 'pure outflow', since $F > 0$ throughout, and the flow is symmetric. But in case (ii) the fluid motion may be 'pure outflow' OAO, or 'pure inflow' OBO, or it may be composed of a number of alternate outflow and inflow regions represented by the particle oscillating between A and B; indeed, if α is too large multiple oscillations cannot be avoided. Thus, in case (ii) there are several possible values of α and Q/ν for each set of constants a, b, c. However, they can all be deduced from the appropriate combinations of the values for the two basic motions: outflow OAO and inflow OBO.

Definite integrals for α and Q are easily written down from (73) and they can be transformed into expressions involving only elliptic functions, for which tables are available. We see from the above interpretation that there may be several solutions, corresponding to different numbers of outflow and inflow regions, which lead to the same values of α and Q/ν. In fact, Rosenhead (1940) finds that there is an infinite number of solutions for each α and Q/ν and that for each *type* of solution (i.e. number of outflow and inflow regions) there is, for given α, a critical value of Q/ν above which that particular solution becomes impossible. For $\alpha < \frac{1}{2}\pi$, the critical values of Q/ν are all positive, the smallest being for pure outflow, but for $\pi > \alpha > \frac{1}{2}\pi$ pure inflow is also limited. For practical purposes, the critical curve for pure outflow and pure inflow is of particular importance and it is shown in Fig. III. 6; as $\alpha \to 0$, $(Q/\nu)_{\text{crit}} \sim 9 \cdot 424/\alpha$.

In pure outflow the flow becomes more and more concentrated in the centre of the channel as Q/ν increases, until at the critical value the velocity gradient at the wall drops to zero; for greater values of Q/ν, inflow regions must appear. But for pure inflow, as $|Q|/\nu$ increases the velocity profile becomes flatter with nearly uniform flow across the channel except for thin boundary layers at the walls. Velocity profiles for a channel with $\alpha = 5°$ are shown in Fig. III. 7, which is taken from Millsaps and Pohlhausen (1953). These authors use, in place of Q/ν, a Reynolds number based on maximum outward or inward velocity and distance r; thus, for outflow the Reynolds number is a, and for inflow it is $-b$. (This certainly simplifies the mathematical analysis, since Q is given by a somewhat complicated expression involving the Jacobian

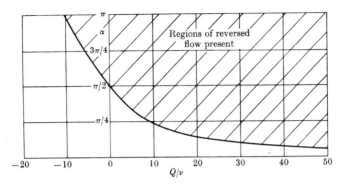

FIG. III. 6. Critical values of Q/ν for pure outflow and pure inflow.

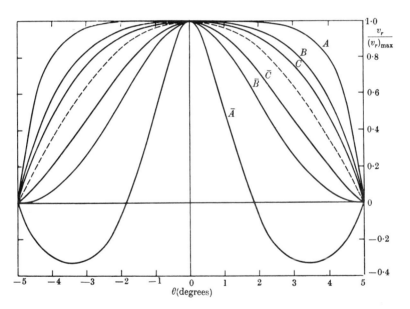

FIG. III. 7. Velocity profiles for a channel with $\alpha = 5°$. The broken line is the Poiseuille parabola. A, B, C are inflows with $|b| = 5,000$, $|b| = 1,342$, and $|b| = 684$, respectively. $\bar{A}$, $\bar{B}$, $\bar{C}$ are outflows with $a = 5,000$, $a = 1,342$, and $a = 684$, respectively, $a = 1,342$ being the critical value for this channel.

zeta function.) For fixed α, the variations of pure outflow with increasing a and of pure inflow with increasing $-b$ are similar to the variations with increasing $|Q|/\nu$. There is again a critical value of a above which pure outflow is impossible. The relation between the critical values of a and α is given below, in equation (83); for large values of a,

$$\alpha \sim 3 \cdot 211 a^{-\frac{1}{2}}. \tag{75}$$

The graph of α against a is given in Fig. III. 8.

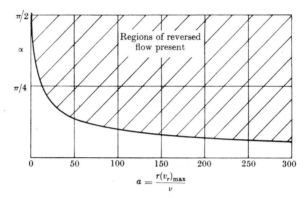

$$a = \frac{r(v_r)_{\max}}{\nu}$$

Fig. III. 8. Critical values of a for pure outflow.

On the question of which Reynolds number to use, it may be remarked that in some ways the Reynolds number $R = a\alpha$, based on maximum velocity and channel semi-width, is most significant. This is so, for example, in comparing the present results with those for flow in non-uniform channels in general. In terms of R we see from (75) that pure outflow becomes impossible when $\alpha \simeq 10 \cdot 31/R$. This is very close to the results found for the critical value of the divergence in the approximate theories for general channels of small variation. Thus Abramowitz (1949), improving on the work of Blasius (1910), finds that the critical divergence is $9 \cdot 24/R$, where R is based on maximum velocity and channel semi-width. (The value obtained by Blasius was $13 \cdot 125/R$.)

It is perhaps worth noting the main analytical results for pure outflow and inflow; the results for the more complicated flows may be deduced from the appropriate combination of these. For outflow, since $F = a$ when $\theta = 0$, we have from (73)

$$\theta = \sqrt{\tfrac{3}{2}} \int_F^a \frac{dF}{\sqrt{\{(a-F)(F-b)(F-c)\}}}; \tag{76}$$

for the inflow regions, the integration is from b to F. Reducing these by the use of standard transformations (see, for example, Jeffreys and Jeffreys 1950, p. 685), we have:

(i) If a is real and b and c are complex conjugates, only pure outflow is possible and it is given by

$$F(\theta) = a - \frac{3M^2}{2} \frac{1 - \operatorname{cn}(M\theta, \kappa)}{1 + \operatorname{cn}(M\theta, \kappa)},\tag{77}$$

$$M^2 = \tfrac{2}{3}\{(a-b)(a-c)\}^{\frac{1}{2}}, \qquad \kappa^2 = \tfrac{1}{2} + \frac{a+2}{2M^2}.\tag{78}$$

(ii) If a, b, c are real, then for outflow

$$F = a - 6k^2m^2 \operatorname{sn}^2(m\theta, k),\tag{79}$$

and for inflow

$$F = a - 6k^2m^2 \operatorname{sn}^2(K - m\theta, k) = b + 6k^2m^2 \operatorname{cn}^2(K - m\theta, k),\tag{80}$$

where $\qquad m^2 = \tfrac{1}{6}(a-c), \qquad k^2 = \dfrac{a-b}{a-c},$ $\qquad\qquad(81)$

and $K(k^2)$ is the first complete elliptic integral.

The values of α are found by setting $F = 0$ in (76) and the corresponding integral for inflow; the values of Q are found by integrating the appropriate expressions for $F(\theta)$ from $-\alpha$ to α. The relation between α and a for the limiting condition in pure outflow may be deduced by noting that pure outflow becomes impossible when $F'(\theta)$ drops just to zero at the walls, and therefore $b = 0$. Then from (74), $c = -6 - a$; hence, from (76),

$$\alpha = \sqrt{\tfrac{3}{2}} \int_0^a \frac{dF}{\sqrt{\{F(a-F)(F+a+6)\}}},$$

$$= \sqrt{\frac{3}{2a}} \int_0^1 \frac{dt}{\sqrt{[t(1-t)\{1+(1+6/a)t\}]}}.\tag{82}$$

This result may also be written

$$\alpha = \left(\frac{3}{3+a}\right)^{\frac{1}{2}} K\left\{\frac{1}{2}\left(\frac{a}{3+a}\right)\right\},\tag{83}$$

and could be deduced directly from (79), since in the critical conditions $m\alpha = K(k^2)$ and

$$m^2 = \frac{3+a}{3}, \qquad k^2 = \frac{1}{2}\left(\frac{a}{3+a}\right).\tag{84}$$

For large values of a, $\alpha a^{\frac{1}{2}} \to \sqrt{3}\, K(\tfrac{1}{2}) = 3\cdot211$. The critical flux is

$$\frac{Q}{\nu} = 2 \int_0^\alpha (a - 6k^2m^2 \operatorname{sn}^2 m\theta)\, d\theta = \frac{12k^2}{\sqrt{(1-2k^2)}} \int_0^K \operatorname{cn}^2\chi\, d\chi,$$

from (84). Hence

$$\frac{Q}{\nu} = \frac{12}{\sqrt{(1-2k^2)}}\{E - (1-k^2)K\},$$

where $E(k^2)$ is the second complete elliptic integral; for large values of a, $k^2 \sim \frac{1}{2} - \frac{3}{2}a^{-1}$, and therefore

$$Q/\nu \sim (a/3)^{\frac{1}{2}} \, 12\{E(\tfrac{1}{2}) - \tfrac{1}{2}K(\tfrac{1}{2})\} = 2 \cdot 934 a^{\frac{1}{2}}.$$

In pure inflow, as the Reynolds number, $-b$, becomes larger, the tendency for the flow to become uniform, except for boundary layers near the walls, is easily shown analytically from (80). Since α is given and m is large, we see from (80) that K must be large; hence, $k \sim 1$. But, when $k = 1$ the function $\operatorname{sn} t$ becomes $\tanh t$, and $c = b$, $a = -6 - 2b \sim -2b$; therefore,

$$F = b\{3 \tanh^2[(-\tfrac{1}{2}b)^{\frac{1}{2}}(\alpha - \theta) + \beta] - 2\}, \tag{85}$$

where $\beta = \tanh^{-1}\sqrt{(\tfrac{2}{3})} = 1 \cdot 146$. Thus F is approximately equal to b except in the boundary layer of thickness proportional to $(-b)^{-\frac{1}{2}}$. We see then that in this case the boundary-layer assumptions are borne out, and in fact (85) is exactly the solution which is obtained by solving the approximate boundary-layer equations (see Section V. 17).

Millsaps and Pohlhausen (1953) also obtain the temperature distributions in these flows for the case when the walls are maintained at constant temperature; for the details, reference should be made to their paper.

Hamel (1917) discussed the flow between non-parallel plane walls as a special case of flow in which the streamlines are equiangular spirals, which he showed to be the only possible form if, for a two-dimensional motion, they are to coincide with the streamlines of a potential flow without the actual motion itself being irrotational. When the more general spiral motion takes place between solid walls, the results are similar to those obtained above. Hamel's results have formed the starting-point for a number of researches by other authors (Olsson and Faxen 1927, Oseen 1927b); a general review of this work is given by Rosenblatt (1933).

18. Round jets

In axisymmetric flow there is an analogue of the plane flow described in the previous section. But it is not flow through a cone, as might have been expected; it is found to be the flow in a round jet. The reason for this becomes clear if we consider the dimensional quantities involved. For flow through a cone the volume flux has dimensions L^3T^{-1}, so that with ν, both a fundamental length and a fundamental time can be formed. Hence there is no reason why the dependence of velocities, etc., on r and θ should take a simple form. But if, instead of a source of mass at the origin, we consider a source of momentum, the rate of transfer M of the appropriate component of momentum across a sphere of radius r gives a parameter M/ρ whose dimensions are L^4T^{-2}. Since ν has dimensions L^2T^{-1}, flows in which M/ρ and ν are the only given parameters take a simple form as in Section 17, because the problem has no fundamental length or time. Clearly the application of these flows is to jets, although more accurately we may say that they describe the flow resulting from the continuous application of a force of magnitude M at the origin.

From dimensional considerations, the flow quantities must be given, using spherical polar coordinates, by

$$v_r = \frac{\nu F(\eta)}{r}, \qquad v_\theta = \frac{\nu G(\eta)}{r},$$

$$\frac{p-p_0}{\rho} = \frac{\nu^2 P(\eta)}{r^2}, \tag{86}$$

where $\eta = \cos\theta$ and F, G, P are functions of η and $M/\rho\nu^2$ alone. (The existence of such a solution of the equations of motion may also be deduced by the transformation method described at the end of Section 16.)

The equation of continuity is satisfied by taking

$$F(\eta) = -f'(\eta), \qquad G(\eta) = -\frac{f(\eta)}{\sqrt{(1-\eta^2)}}, \tag{87}$$

corresponding to the stream function $\psi = \nu r f(\eta)$. Then the momentum equations (53) give

$$P = -\frac{f^2}{2(1-\eta^2)} - \frac{1}{2}\frac{d}{d\eta}\{ff' - (1-\eta^2)f''\},$$

$$P' = -\frac{d}{d\eta}\left\{\frac{f^2}{2(1-\eta^2)}\right\} - f''.$$

Therefore
$$P = -\frac{f^2}{2(1-\eta^2)} - f' - \tfrac{1}{2}c_1, \tag{88}$$

and
$$2ff' = 2(1-\eta^2)f'' + 4f + 2c_1\eta + c_2, \tag{89}$$

where c_1 and c_2 are arbitrary constants of integration. Equation (89) can be integrated immediately to give

$$f^2 = 2(1-\eta^2)f' + 4\eta f + \Sigma(\eta), \tag{90}$$

where $\Sigma(\eta) = c_1\eta^2 + c_2\eta + c_3$, c_3 being a third constant of integration. This equation for f was first obtained by Slezkin (1934) and the solution which applies to the round jet (equation (93) below) was discussed by

Landau (1944a). Yatseyev (1950) has since obtained the general solution of (90) and Squire (1951) has given a detailed discussion of the round jet. Squire also obtains the temperature field for a heated jet, and makes further applications (Squire 1952, 1955) of the general solution. Morgan (1956) notes that these solutions can be interpreted as flows inside cones, if the condition of zero slip or the condition of zero normal velocity is relaxed. But the interpretation as jet flows is the fundamental one.

Before discussing the applications to jet flows, we may note in advance that $\Sigma(\eta) = K(1-\eta)^2$ is the *only* choice of $\Sigma(\eta)$ which does not lead to singularities of the flow quantities on the axis, $\eta = 1$. For, if v_θ is finite at $\eta = 1$, $f(1)$ must be zero; hence, if v_r is also finite at $\eta = 1$, with $f'(1) = -A$, say, we must have $f \sim A(1-\eta)$. But (90) then shows that $\Sigma(\eta) \sim K(1-\eta)^2$; therefore, since $\Sigma(\eta)$ is a quadratic it must be *equal* to $K(1-\eta)^2$.

Equation (90) is of the Riccati type and can be transformed into a second-order linear equation by the substitution

$$f = -2(1-\eta^2)g'/g. \tag{91}$$

Then g satisfies a form of the hypergeometric equation, but in the special case $\Sigma(\eta) = K(1-\eta)^2$ its solutions are simply

$$g = (1+\eta)^\lambda, \qquad \lambda = \tfrac{1}{2}\{1 \pm \sqrt{(1+K)}\}. \tag{92}$$

For the round jet, $\Sigma(\eta) = 0$, that is, $K = 0$, and the general solution for f becomes

$$f = \frac{2(1-\eta^2)}{a+1-\eta}, \tag{93}$$

where a is an arbitrary constant. It is found after some calculation that the rate of transfer of the x component of momentum (including the contributions of pressures and viscous stresses) across a sphere of radius r is given by

$$\frac{M}{2\pi\rho\nu^2} = \frac{32(1+a)}{3a(2+a)} + 8(1+a) - 4(1+a)^2 \log\left(\frac{2+a}{a}\right), \tag{94}$$

and we see that large values of the parameter $M/\rho\nu^2$ correspond to small values of a. The streamlines of the flow are shown in Fig. III. 9 for the case $a = 10^{-2}$, $M/\rho\nu^2 = 3,282$. Squire (1951) has also shown that the appropriate solution of (31) for a heated jet is

$$T - T_0 = \frac{(2\sigma+1)Q}{8\pi\rho C_p \nu r}\left(\frac{a}{a+1-\eta}\right)^{2\sigma}, \tag{95}$$

where σ is the Prandtl number and Q is the strength of the heat source at the origin. The temperature contours for the case $a = 10^{-2}$, $\sigma = 0.72$, $(2\sigma+1)Q/8\pi\rho C_p \nu = 10$, are shown in Fig. III. 10.

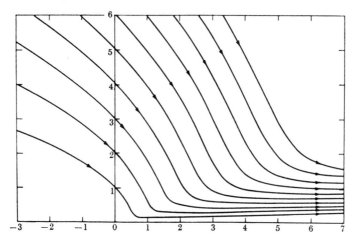

FIG. III. 9. Streamlines of round jet: $a = 10^{-2}$; $M/\rho\nu^2 = 3{,}282$.

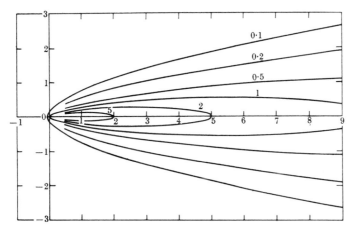

FIG. III. 10. Temperature contours of heated round jet: $a = 10^{-2}$, $\sigma = 0.72$, $(2\sigma+1)Q/8\pi\rho C_p \nu = 10$. The numbers on the curves indicate values of $T-T_0$.

The unit of length can be chosen arbitrarily in Figs. III. 9, III. 10, and III. 11, but then the unit of temperature in Fig. III. 10 is fixed by the requirement that $(2\sigma+1)Q/8\pi\rho C_p \nu$, which has the dimensions of length multiplied by temperature, should have the value 10 in these units.

For small values of a the jet becomes concentrated near the axis and its velocity increases. In this case, $f \simeq 2(1+\eta)$ except near the axis $\eta = 1$. Thus away from the axis, that is outside the jet, there is a radial velocity $v_r = -2\nu/r$ which provides the fluid (with volume flux $8\pi\nu r$) which is entrained by the jet. Near $\eta = 1$, that is, in the jet, we may approximate f by

$$f \simeq \frac{(2/a)\theta^2}{1+\tfrac14\{(2/a)\theta^2\}}.$$

From (94), $2/a \sim 3M/(16\pi\rho\nu^2)$; hence,

$$f \simeq \frac{\xi^2}{1+\tfrac14\xi^2}, \qquad \xi = \frac{1}{4\nu}\left(\frac{3}{\pi}\frac{M}{\rho}\right)^{\tfrac12}\theta. \tag{96}$$

This is precisely the solution obtained by Schlichting (1933a) directly from the approximate boundary-layer equations (see Section VIII. 17).

As a second application Squire (1952) uses (91), (92) with $K \neq 0$, to describe a jet emerging from a small hole in a plane wall. However, the boundary conditions $v_r = v_\theta = 0$ at the wall are not both satisfied; only the normal velocity component V_θ vanishes there. If K is set equal to $-(4b^2+1)$, $\lambda = \tfrac12 \pm ib$ in (92), and the solution for f is

$$f = (1-\eta)\left\{-1+2b\frac{1-c\cot[b\log(1+\eta)]}{c+\cot[b\log(1+\eta)]}\right\}, \tag{97}$$

where c is a second arbitrary constant. Since $v_\theta = 0$ for $\eta = 0$, we require $f(0) = 0$, which leads to

$$1+2bc = 0. \tag{98}$$

With this value for c,

$$f = \frac{(1+4b^2)(1-\eta)}{2b\cot[b\log(1+\eta)]-1}. \tag{99}$$

Narrow high-speed jets correspond to small values of the denominator in (99), and thus to values of b near to the root of

$$2b\cot[b\log 2] = 1.$$

The significant root is $b = 1.8937$, and it is found that as b approaches this value, $M/\rho\nu^2 \to \infty$. The streamlines of the flow in the case $b = 1.88$, $M/\rho\nu^2 = 3.8\times10^3$, are shown in Fig. III. 11.

Finally, we may note that the theoretical results for the round laminar jet agree well with the experimental results for the *turbulent* jet. For the turbulent jet ν must be interpreted as an eddy viscosity, and the agreement of the results suggests that in this flow it is a good approximation to assume that the eddy viscosity is constant. Using a dimensional argument again, we can see that there is no variation of eddy viscosity in the longitudinal direction, since $M^{\tfrac14}$, the only quantity of the same dimensions, is constant along the jet. But the eddy viscosity may vary with θ across the jet, and, indeed, experiments indicate some decrease near the boundary of the jet. Detailed comparison between theory and experiment is to be found in Hinze and van der Hegge Zijnen (1949). The value of a is chosen in order to give the observed rate of spread

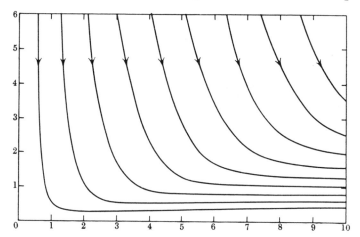

FIG. III. 11. Streamlines of jet emerging from hole in wall: $b = 1\cdot88$, $M/\rho\nu^2 = 3\cdot8 \times 10^3$.

of the jet and M is equated to the thrust of the jet; a value of ν can then be deduced. In applying the results, the origin in the theoretical solution is taken at a suitable distance upstream from the orifice of the jet. The calculated and experimental velocity distributions are compared and found to be in good agreement.

19. Stagnation point flows

(a) Two-dimensional flow

For an ideal fluid the flow against an infinite flat plate in the plane $z = 0$ is given by

$$u = kx, \qquad w = -kz, \tag{100}$$

where k is a constant. In the case of a general bluff body equation (100) applies to the flow in the neighbourhood of the stagnation point, $x = z = 0$, where x and z are small compared to the radius of curvature of the nose of the body. When viscosity is included, it must still be true that u is proportional to x, for small x and *all* z. Thus, for small x, at least, we may take $u = xF(z)$; the equation of continuity then gives $\partial w/\partial z = -F(z)$. However, it is found that the solution of this form is exact and in the case of the flat plate it applies for all x.

Introducing non-dimensional variables, we take

$$u = kxf'(\zeta), \qquad w = -(\nu k)^{\frac{1}{2}}f(\zeta), \qquad \zeta = z(k/\nu)^{\frac{1}{2}}. \tag{101}$$

These satisfy the momentum equations (12) if

$$\frac{p_0-p}{\rho} = \tfrac{1}{2}k^2x^2 + k\nu f'(\zeta) + \tfrac{1}{2}k\nu f^2, \tag{102}$$

and the function f is a solution of

$$f''' + ff'' - f'^2 + 1 = 0. \tag{103}$$

The boundary conditions for f are

$$f(0) = f'(0) = 0, \qquad f'(\infty) = 1, \tag{104}$$

and the appropriate solution has been calculated numerically (Hiemenz 1911, Howarth 1934). The values of f, f', f'' are given later in Table V. 2.

When the viscosity is small, we see that the disturbance to the 'main stream' (100) is limited to a boundary layer whose thickness is proportional to $\sqrt{(\nu/k)}$. The boundary layer is of *constant* thickness so that the thinning of the layer due to the accelerating main stream, $u = kx$, is just sufficient to balance the thickening due to the diffusion of shear. Moreover, we may notice that the exact solution is also a solution of the approximate boundary-layer equations. For $-\rho^{-1}\partial p/\partial x$ takes the value k^2x which it has in the main stream and $\partial^2u/\partial x^2 = 0$ throughout; as will be seen in detail in Chapter V, these are precisely the approximations which are made in the boundary-layer theory.

(b) Axisymmetric flow

The analogous solution for axisymmetric flow against a flat plate (Homann 1936b) is obtained by taking (in cylindrical polar coordinates),

$$v_r = krf'(\zeta), \qquad v_z = -2(k\nu)^{\frac{1}{2}}f(\zeta), \qquad \zeta = z(k/\nu)^{\frac{1}{2}}. \tag{105}$$

The equation for f differs from (103) only in that the term ff'' has a factor 2, and the boundary conditions are the same as (104). It is sometimes convenient to modify (105) slightly and take $v_r = krf'(\zeta)$, $v_z = -(2k\nu)^{\frac{1}{2}}f(\zeta)$, $\zeta = z(2k/\nu)^{\frac{1}{2}}$. This alternative form will be used in Chapters V and VIII. Values of the functions f, f', f'' using these modified variables are given in Table V. 3.

(c) Three-dimensional flow

The flow at a general three-dimensional stagnation point also yields an exact solution of the equations of motion: details are given in Section VIII. 21.

20. Flow due to rotating disks

The solution given by the substitutions (105) may be generalized by including a rotation of the fluid about the axis with angular velocity depending on z. It is convenient to take the velocity components as

$$v_r = Krf'(\zeta), \qquad v_\theta = \Omega rg(\zeta), \qquad v_z = -2(K\nu)^{\frac{1}{2}}f(\zeta),$$

$$\zeta = z(K/\nu)^{\frac{1}{2}}, \tag{106}$$

where K and Ω are constants having dimension T^{-1}. When the expressions are substituted in the momentum equations (49), it is found that the pressure is given by

$$(p-p_0)/\rho = \tfrac{1}{2}\lambda K^2 r^2 - 2\nu K(f^2 + f'), \tag{107}$$

where λ is an arbitrary constant, and the functions f and g satisfy

$$f'^2 - 2ff'' - g^2(\Omega/K)^2 - f''' = -\lambda, \tag{108}$$

$$2(f'g - fg') = g''. \tag{109}$$

Kármán (1921) first pointed out the existence of a solution of the form (106), and he considered its application to the flow produced by the rotation of an infinite plane disk. For this problem we take $K = \Omega$ where Ω is the angular velocity of the disk. Assuming that the disk lies in the plane $z = 0$, the appropriate boundary conditions on f and g are

$$f(0) = f'(0) = 0, \qquad g(0) = 1, \tag{110}$$

$$f' \to 0, \quad g \to 0 \quad \text{as} \quad \zeta \to \infty; \tag{111}$$

in addition, since the pressure approaches a constant value at infinity, $\lambda = 0$. These conditions determine the solution uniquely so that the value of v_z at infinity cannot be arbitrarily imposed; it is determinate in terms of Ω and ν. This is to be expected on physical grounds, for in the absence of a radial pressure gradient the fluid near the disk moves radially outwards under the influence of centrifugal force, and therefore an axial inflow at infinity is required by continuity.

An approximate solution to the problem was obtained by Kármán using momentum integral methods, and later an accurate solution was found numerically by Cochran (1934). Cochran uses expansions in powers of ζ for the flow near the disk and an expansion in powers of $e^{-c\zeta}$ for large ζ, where $c = 2f(\infty)$; by making a suitable join of these solutions at an intermediate value of ζ, the arbitrary constants in them, including the value of c, are determined. It is found that $c = 0\cdot886$, so that the axial inflow at infinity is

$$-0\!\cdot\!886(\Omega\nu)^{\frac{1}{2}}. \tag{112}$$

Graphs of the functions $2f(\zeta)$, $f'(\zeta)$, $g(\zeta)$ are shown in Fig. III. 12 and the values of these functions are given in detail in Table III. 1.

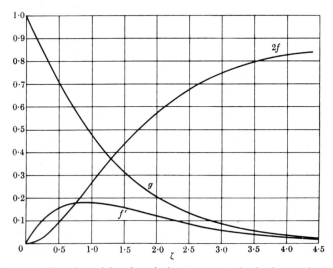

FIG. III. 12. Functions giving the velocity components in the flow produced by a rotating disk.

Again we may notice the boundary-layer character of the solution for small viscosity. The functions f, f', g are within a given percentage of their values at infinity for some finite value of $\zeta = z(\Omega/\nu)^{\frac{1}{2}}$; hence, the flow is approximately uniform except in a boundary layer of thickness $(\nu/\Omega)^{\frac{1}{2}}$. We may also note that, as in Section 19, the exact solution discussed here also satisfies the boundary-layer equations since the terms neglected in boundary-layer theory are identically zero.

Although the solution applies strictly to an infinite disk it may be used to find an approximate value for the frictional moment on a finite disk of radius a, provided that the Reynolds number $a^2\Omega/\nu$ is large. The shearing stress at the disk is

$$p_{z\theta} = \rho\nu\!\left(\frac{\partial v_\theta}{dz}\right)_{z=0} = \rho(\nu\Omega^3)^{\frac{1}{2}}g'(0)r,$$

so that the moment for both sides of the disk becomes

$$M = -2\int_0^a 2\pi r^2 p_{z\theta}\,dr = -\pi a^4\rho(\nu\Omega^3)^{\frac{1}{2}}g'(0).$$

TABLE III. 1

The functions $f(\zeta)$, $f'(\zeta)$, and $g(\zeta)$ for the flow due to a rotating disk (see equations (108)–(111) and Fig. III. 12)

With the exception of the two starred entries this Table is quoted directly from Cochran (1934). The starred entries incorporate minor corrections derived by smoothing differences.

ζ	f'	g	$2f$
0	0	1	0
0·1	0·046	0·939	0·005
0·2	·084	·878	·018
0·3	·114	·819	·038
0·4	·136	·762	·063
0·5	·154	·708	·092
0·6	0·166	0·656	0·124
0·7	·174	·607	·158
0·8	·179	·561	·193
0·9	·181	·517	·230
1·0	·180	·477*	·266
1·1	0·177	0·439	0·301
1·2	·173	·404	·336
1·3	·168	·371	·371
1·4	·162	·341	·404
1·5	·156	·313	·435
1·6	0·148	0·288	0·466
1·7	·141	·264	·495
1·8	·133	·242	·522
1·9	·126	·222	·548
2·0	·118	·203	·572
2·1	0·111	0·186	0·596
2·2	·104	·171	·617
2·3	·097	·156	·637
2·4	·091	·143	·656
2·5	·084	·131	·674
2·6	0·078	0·120	0·690
2·8	·068	·101	·721
3·0	·058	·085*	·746
3·2	·050	·071	·768
3·4	·042	·059	·786
3·6	0·036	0·050	0·802
3·8	·031	·042	·815
4·0	·026	·035	·826
4·2	·022	·029	·836
4·4	·018	·024	·844
∞	0	0	·886

Introducing a non-dimensional moment coefficient C_M and the Reynolds number $R = a^2\Omega/\nu$, we have

$$C_M = \frac{M}{\frac{1}{2}\rho(a\Omega)^2.\pi a^2.a} = -\frac{2g'(0)}{R^{\frac{1}{2}}} = \frac{1\cdot232}{R^{\frac{1}{2}}}. \tag{113}$$

For values of R less than about 10^5, this formula gives values in close agreement with experimental results, but for greater values of R, the flow becomes turbulent and the laminar theory ceases to apply.

Further applications of (106) may be made in which equations (108) and (109) have to be solved under different boundary conditions. The most straightforward of these is to include in the Kármán problem a uniform suction through the disk; this has been investigated by Stuart (1954a). The conditions at infinity (111) remain the same and $\lambda = 0$, but in (110) we now have

$$f(0) = \tfrac{1}{2}\alpha, \qquad f'(0) = 0, \qquad g(0) = 1 \tag{114}$$

where α is the suction parameter corresponding to the suction velocity $v_z = -(\nu\Omega)^{\frac{1}{2}}\alpha$. Stuart computed the solution by Cochran's method in the case $\alpha = 1 \cdot 0$, and obtained a series solution in descending powers of α, which is used when $\alpha > 2$. For the details reference should be made to the paper cited.

Miss D. M. Hannah (1947) considers the problem of forced flow against a rotating disk. This is a combination of the Kármán problem and the stagnation point flow described in Section 19. The boundary conditions at the disk remain as in (110), but at infinity the flow is required to approach the potential flow

$$v_r = kr, \qquad v_\theta = 0, \qquad v_z = -2kz,$$

$$\frac{p-p_0}{\rho} = -\tfrac{1}{2}k^2r^2 - 2k^2z^2. \tag{115}$$

In this case K is taken as $(k^2+\Omega^2)^{\frac{1}{2}}$, and the conditions at infinity become

$$f \sim \frac{\zeta}{(1+\mu^2)^{\frac{1}{2}}}, \qquad g \to 0, \tag{116}$$

where $\mu = \Omega/k$. From the form of the pressure at infinity, or by substitution from (116) in (108), we have

$$\lambda = -(1+\mu^2)^{-1}.$$

The special cases $\mu = 0$ and $\mu = \infty$ correspond to the Homann and Kármán flows, respectively, and Miss Hannah calculated the solution for $\mu = 0 \cdot 5, 1, 2$. Unaware of this work, Schlichting and Truckenbrodt (1952) applied Kármán's approximate method to this problem, and later Tifford and Chu (1952) solved the equations numerically for a range of values of μ.

Finally, we refer to the two related problems of the flow over a rotating disk with a prescribed rotation of the fluid at infinity and the flow between two rotating disks. In the first problem, if the angular velocity of the disk at $z = 0$ is Ω_0 and the angular velocity of the fluid as $z \to \infty$ is Ω_∞, we may choose $\Omega = K = (\Omega_0^2 + \Omega_\infty^2)^{\frac{1}{2}}$ in (106) and then equations (108) and (109) must be solved subject to the boundary conditions

$$f(0) = f'(0) = 0, \qquad g(0) = \Omega_0/\Omega,$$

$$f' \to 0, \quad g \to \Omega_\infty/\Omega \quad \text{as} \quad \zeta \to \infty; \qquad (117)$$

the boundary conditions at infinity show that the constant λ in (108) takes the value $\Omega_0^2/(\Omega_0^2 + \Omega_\infty^2)$. Bödewadt (1940) obtained a numerical solution to this problem in the case of a fixed disk ($\Omega_0 = 0$) and more accurate calculations have been carried out by Browning (unpublished) whose results are given in Schlichting (1955, p. 158). Fettis (1956) describes a new method for performing these and similar calculations and obtains results for a range of values of Ω_0/Ω_∞. The velocity components for the case $\Omega_0 = 0$ are given in Table III. 2; the oscillation in the velocities should be noted.

TABLE III. 2

The velocity distribution in the rotating flow over a fixed plane

ζ	f'	g	$-2f$
0	0	0	0
0·5	−0·343	0·382	0·190
1·0	−0·468	0·731	0·614
1·5	−0·437	1·004	1·076
2·0	−0·318	1·175	1·460
2·5	−0·171	1·246	1·704
3·0	−0·038	1·242	1·800
3·5	0·056	1·192	1·784
4·0	0·106	1·123	1·702
4·5	0·117	1·056	1·590
5·0	0·103	1·003	1·478
5·5	0·074	0·969	1·390
6·0	0·041	0·954	1·332
6·5	0·013	0·953	1·308
7·0	−0·010	0·959	1·304
7·5	−0·020	0·975	1·320
8·0	−0·023	0·990	1·340
8·5	−0·020	1·000	1·364
9·0	−0·013	1·007	1·382
9·5	−0·006	1·010	1·390
10·0	0·000	1·009	1·390
10·5	0·003	1·007	1·386
11·0	0·004	1·005	1·382
11·5	0·003	1·002	1·380
12·0	0·001	1·000	1·380
12·5	0·000	1·000	1·380
∞	0·000	1·000	1·380

In the case of two rotating disks at $z = 0$, $z = d$, say with angular velocities Ω_0 and Ω_d, respectively, if we choose $\Omega = K = (\Omega_0^2 + \Omega_d^2)^{\frac{1}{2}}$, the boundary conditions are

$$f = f' = 0, \quad g = \Omega_0/\Omega \quad \text{at} \quad \zeta = 0,$$
$$f = f' = 0, \quad g = \Omega_d/\Omega \quad \text{at} \quad \zeta = d(\Omega/\nu)^{\frac{1}{2}}; \tag{118}$$

the constant λ must be determined in the course of the solution in order to satisfy these conditions. The solution has not yet been calculated but qualitative aspects of it have been discussed by Batchelor (1951) and Stewartson (1953).

IV

FLOW AT SMALL REYNOLDS NUMBER

1. Introduction

In Chapter III the Navier–Stokes equations of flow for a viscous incompressible fluid were introduced, and some exact solutions, valid for all Reynolds numbers, were discussed; none of them, however, deals with flow past a finite body. At present there appear to be no exact solutions of the flow past bodies of finite size, and, consequently, in order to discuss such flows, it is necessary to derive approximate solutions. These may be either numerical solutions of the exact Navier–Stokes equations, or solutions—analytical or numerical—of approximate equations. Whichever type of solution is involved it is first necessary to specify the value of the Reynolds number R, in some cases precisely, in others approximately, because the character of the flow depends critically upon it. For extreme values of R the Navier–Stokes equations can be replaced by approximate forms which are more tractable. For large R the exact equations reduce to Euler's equations of inviscid flow, except in the comparatively narrow regions in which transverse velocity gradients are large, where they reduce to Prandtl's boundary-layer equations. The study of flows obeying Prandtl's equations is the main concern of this book. For small R, by which we shall usually mean R less than 1, the exact equations are replaced by Oseen's equations, except in regions near fixed surfaces, where they reduce to Stokes's equations. This chapter is concerned with flows obeying either Oseen's or Stokes's equations, as appropriate.

In passing it may be mentioned that in the intermediate range, where R takes values between the very small and the very large, there are only a few solutions of the Navier–Stokes equations, and these are numerical. They deal, chiefly, with flow past a circular cylinder or a sphere. For example, the circular cylinder has been investigated by Thom (1933) for R (based on diameter) = 10 and 20, and by Allen and Southwell (1955) for $R = 0$, 1, 10, 100, and 1,000. (The last two cases, as the authors observe, are physically unrealistic since the flow becomes unstable in practice when R reaches a critical value of about 40.) Jenson (1959) has treated the sphere for $R = 5, 10, 20$, and 40. Also, in a series of papers, Kawaguti (1956, and references cited therein) has used different numerical techniques for both the circular cylinder and the sphere. His work on the former is for several values of R up to 40, and on the latter for values up to 70. Apelt (1958) has calculated the flow past a circular cylinder at $R = 40$ and 44, and he confirms Kawaguti's (1953) results. A prominent feature of the flow at intermediate Reynolds numbers is the existence of a pair of eddies behind the cylinder, whose extension downstream increases with R, until the flow becomes unstable. Apelt and, independently, Kawaguti (1959) show that experimental results and theoretical calculations are in good agreement about the growth of the eddies, except that Allen and Southwell's results for $R = 100$ and 1,000 are anomalous, probably due to the use of too coarse a mesh in the (relaxation) calculation of the flow.

The Reynolds number may be small because the velocity, or the length, or the density, is small, or because the viscosity is large. Flow at small Reynolds number therefore includes not only slow 'creeping' motions but also the motion of very small objects such as particles in a Brownian motion, or minute swimming organisms. As further examples we may mention the coalescence of fine water drops during cloud formation, the motion of electrically charged particles in colloids, and the slow motion of fluids carrying solid particles in filtration processes. If one supposes that R is small primarily because the velocity is small, it seems reasonable to neglect those terms in the Navier–Stokes equations that involve the squares of velocities; this leads to Stokes's equations, which will be considered in Section 3. If, on the other hand, it is the representative length that is particularly small, say for streaming past a fixed obstacle, one may argue that the obstacle is too small to affect the main flow very much, and so the inertia terms should correspond to convection with the free-stream velocity; this point of view results in Oseen's equations, which will be discussed in Section 5.

There is a strong analogy between the theory of flow at small Reynolds number and boundary-layer theory. This analogy was first clearly recognized by Kaplun, and it has been discussed in papers by Lagerstrom and his colleagues (Lagerstrom, to be published; Lagerstrom and Cole 1955; Kaplun 1957; Kaplun and Lagerstrom 1957). Consider the flow near a fixed obstacle; we may term this the inner flow. This must satisfy the no-slip condition, and so the velocities in it will be small. To a first approximation, then, the inner flow will obey Stokes's equations, and if, in addition, it tends to the undisturbed free stream at infinity (which is not always possible) it will be referred to as a Stokes flow. Here the free stream corresponds to the Euler (main-stream) flow in boundary-layer theory, and the Stokes flow to the Prandtl (boundary-layer) flow. Conventional boundary-layer theory may be regarded as the second stage in an iterative process, following the initial step of determining the Euler flow past the body concerned in the absence of viscosity. The third step is to redetermine the Euler flow allowing for a virtual change in the surface of the body due to boundary-layer thickness. The corresponding third stage for small Reynolds number is to improve upon the free stream as a representation of the outer flow far from the obstacle. In its second approximate form the outer flow will obey Oseen's equations; in addition, it must reduce to the free stream at infinity and, following the analogy with boundary-layer theory, it should 'match' the Stokes flow near the obstacle. (Two expressions will be said to 'match' in a region if, in that region, they are equivalent to the order of accuracy considered (see Section 6).) If, instead, the outer flow is made to satisfy the no-slip condition at the surface, it will be referred to as an Oseen flow (see Section 5). For the purpose of obtaining the drag, as will be seen later, the Oseen flow can be used instead of the second approximation to the outer flow.

The broad intention in this chapter is to review Stokes and Oseen flows in turn, and then to consider how they fit into a composite picture of the flow that can be built up by matching the outer and inner flows. However, it may be helpful to start with a short account of the historical development of the subject. The theory of slow flow based on Stokes's equations, as applied to the motion of isolated bodies, was largely developed during the second half of the nineteenth century. The theory embraced streaming and non-streaming motions in both two and three dimensions, and was founded on Stokes's (1851) paper on the effect of viscosity on the motion of pendulums. Stokes's primary object in this investigation was to determine the non-streaming motion produced by small rectilinear oscillations of a sphere or circular cylinder in a fluid at rest, and in particular to calculate the force exerted on the body. He then solved the equations for streaming past a sphere, giving his well-known drag law for a sphere. For flow past a circular cylinder, however, Stokes showed that there is no solution of his equations that matches the free stream at infinity (see Section 3); this formed a serious obstacle to the theory of streaming flow in two dimensions. The further application of the theory to the motion of small liquid drops falling under gravity led to investigations of the flow past liquid spheres, involving internal fluid motion as well, and of the flow produced by a sphere accelerating through a fluid at rest.

The case of a sphere falling with constant velocity, as a result of its weight being balanced by the viscous drag, became prominent in physical applications. One example was the development of the viscometer in which the velocity of a solid sphere falling steadily in a liquid is measured, and the viscosity of the liquid is determined from Stokes's drag law. In a second example, falling oildrops carrying ions were used in a series of experiments, conducted during the period from 1897 to 1910 approximately, to measure the charge on an electron (see Millikan 1947). In such experiments the falling particles are not isolated; they move near other particles and near the walls of the apparatus. It was, in fact, during this period that attention was first directed to the influence of neighbouring boundaries on the steady motion of spheres. Moreover, when the boundaries limited the extent of the fluid sufficiently, as in the case of flow between parallel walls, it was possible to reconsider two-dimensional flows because the difficulty of satisfying the conditions at infinity was removed. This research on Stokes flow, involving non-isolated bodies, was actively developed from about 1897 until about 1925, and still continues.

Meanwhile, in this same period, Stokes's equations were also used to study the small motions of small spherical and ellipsoidal particles suspended in a liquid. In such cases there is no streaming motion because the particles are carried along with the surrounding fluid, but the particles may well produce a non-streaming motion by virtue of their spin. One object of these investigations was to determine the effective viscosity of the liquid containing such particles (Einstein 1906, 1911).

After 1910, when Oseen proposed his equations to meet the objection that Stokes's equations are invalid in the distant field of flow, the way was open to reconsider some of the previous investigations on streaming motions on the basis of Oseen's equations. Consequently, during the next fifteen years or so, the steady Oseen flows past spheres, ellipsoids, and circular cylinders were studied both with and without the effects of nearby boundaries. A full account of this work is given in Oseen's book (1927a).

The development of the whole subject up to about 1930 is well covered by Lamb's *Hydrodynamics* (1932), in which references can be found to all the aspects mentioned above, and also to a number of cases of unsteady flow. There is a useful review of this part of the subject, with more emphasis on physical applications than Lamb provides, in Dryden, Murnaghan, and Bateman (1932).

Since 1932 the main contributions to the subject have been concerned with steady streaming motions past isolated bodies and, as it is the intention here to concentrate on the main developments during the last twenty-five years, matters such as unsteady flow, the influence of boundaries, and non-streaming motions will be largely ignored in what follows.

2. The Stokes and Oseen variables

When there are no external forces the Navier–Stokes equations, from which we start, may be written in the vector form

$$\nabla . \mathbf{v} = 0, \tag{1}$$

$$\partial \mathbf{v}/\partial t + \nabla(\tfrac{1}{2}\mathbf{v}^2) - \mathbf{v} \times \boldsymbol{\omega} = -\rho^{-1}\nabla p - \nu \nabla \times \boldsymbol{\omega}, \tag{2}$$

where
$$\boldsymbol{\omega} = \nabla \times \mathbf{v} \tag{3}$$
is the vorticity.

If the motion is so slow that squares of velocities can be neglected in comparison with the other terms, the second and third terms on the left-hand side of (2) can be omitted, thereby reducing (1) and (2) to Stokes's equations. For streaming past a fixed obstacle the error involved in this approximation is greatest in the distant parts of the flow field. If, in this case, the free stream U is uniform, and the x-axis is chosen to lie in the direction of U, the velocity in the outer flow is $U\mathbf{i}$ to a first approximation, where $\mathbf{i}$ is the unit vector in the fixed x-direction. Hence the left-hand side of (2), which is equivalent to $\partial \mathbf{v}/\partial t + (\mathbf{v}.\nabla)\mathbf{v}$ (see equation (III.11)), reduces to the approximate form $(\partial/\partial t + U \partial/\partial x)\mathbf{v}$ in the equations governing the second approximation to the outer flow. This change reduces (1) and (2) to Oseen's equations.

It will also be instructive to derive the equations for flow at small R by the more formal process of rendering (1) and (2) non-dimensional in a suitable manner and then letting R tend to zero. A similar procedure is often used in presenting the boundary-layer equations (Section V. 1), but in the present context it appears to have been first adopted by Lagerstrom (see Lagerstrom, to be published). The advantages of the formal method are that it not only exhibits the appropriate non-dimensional variables, but that it also indicates the relative importance of the various terms in the Navier–Stokes equations, a point which must be considered when the question of higher approximation arises (see Section 6).

If R tends to zero in the non-dimensional form, given by equations (III.32) and (III.33), of the Navier–Stokes equations, the pressure disappears from the equations, leaving four scalar equations to be satisfied by the three unknown velocity components, and in general this is impossible. To avoid this, one is led to formulate the following scheme for the non-dimensional time, space coordinates, velocity vector, and pressure, respectively:

$$\bar{t} = \omega t, \quad \bar{\mathbf{r}} = \mathbf{r}/l, \quad \bar{\mathbf{v}} = \mathbf{v}/U, \quad \bar{p} = R[(p-p_\infty)/\rho U^2], \qquad (4)$$

where $R = Ul/\nu$. Here ω is a representative frequency, $\mathbf{r}$ the vector coordinate, l the representative length, and U and p_∞ the velocity and pressure of the free stream. In terms of non-dimensional quantities, (1) and (2) become

$$\bar{\nabla}.\bar{\mathbf{v}} = 0, \qquad (5)$$

and

$$R[(\omega l/U)\partial\bar{\mathbf{v}}/\partial\bar{t}+\bar{\nabla}(\tfrac{1}{2}\bar{\mathbf{v}}^2)-\bar{\mathbf{v}}\times\bar{\boldsymbol{\omega}}] = -\bar{\nabla}\bar{p}-\bar{\nabla}\times\bar{\boldsymbol{\omega}}, \qquad (6)$$

where $\bar{\nabla}$ represents the gradient operator corresponding to the coordinate $\bar{\mathbf{r}}$, and $\bar{\boldsymbol{\omega}} = \bar{\nabla}\times\bar{\mathbf{v}}$. Provided that $\omega l/U$ and the non-dimensional variables remain finite, (5) and (6) reduce to Stokes's equations for steady flow as $R \to 0$. Indeed the unsteady term $\partial\mathbf{v}/\partial t$ will survive in Stokes's equations only if $\omega l^2/\nu = O(1)$. We shall refer to $\bar{t}$, $\bar{\mathbf{r}}$, $\bar{\mathbf{v}}$, and $\bar{p}$ as Stokes variables.

In order to obtain Oseen's equations the factor R must not appear in the inertia terms in (6), and this can be arranged by multiplying the Stokes variable $\bar{\mathbf{r}}$ by R to give the Oseen variable $\hat{\mathbf{r}}$. The complete set of Oseen variables is

$$\hat{t} = R\omega t, \quad \hat{\mathbf{r}} = R\mathbf{r}/l, \quad \hat{\mathbf{v}} = \mathbf{v}/U, \quad \hat{p} = (p-p_\infty)/\rho U^2, \qquad (7)$$

and when these are introduced (1) and (2) become

$$\hat{\nabla}.\hat{\mathbf{v}} = 0, \qquad (8)$$

$$(\omega l/U)\partial\hat{\mathbf{v}}/\partial t+\hat{\nabla}(\tfrac{1}{2}\hat{\mathbf{v}}^2)-\hat{\mathbf{v}}\times\hat{\boldsymbol{\omega}} = -\hat{\nabla}\hat{p}-\hat{\nabla}\times\hat{\boldsymbol{\omega}}. \qquad (9)$$

As $R \to 0$ the equations are not at first changed, but the apparent size of the obstacle is reduced. If the surface is given by the equation $f(\mathbf{r}/l) = 0$ in natural coordinates, it becomes $f(\hat{\mathbf{r}}/R) = 0$ in Oseen coordinates, so that as $R \to 0$ the obstacle appears to shrink to the origin in Oseen coordinates. For this reason the Oseen flow may be regarded as a combination of the free stream with non-dimensional velocity $\mathbf{i}$ and a small perturbation $\hat{\mathbf{v}}-\mathbf{i}$, and so the inertia terms in (9) reduce to the Oseen form $(\omega l/U)\partial\hat{\mathbf{v}}/\partial\hat{t}+\partial\hat{\mathbf{v}}/\partial\hat{x}$.

The Stokes and Oseen variables introduced here will turn out to be particularly useful in Section 6.

3. Stokes flow

In this section we shall use Stokes's equations in the form

$$\nabla.\mathbf{v} = 0, \tag{10}$$

$$\nabla \times \boldsymbol{\omega} = -\mu^{-1}\nabla p. \tag{11}$$

As we have already noticed, these equations are also valid for unsteady flow if the frequency is such that $\omega l^2/\nu = o(1)$. It follows immediately from (11) that

$$\nabla^2 p = 0, \tag{12}$$

and

$$\nabla \times (\nabla \times \boldsymbol{\omega}) = 0. \tag{13}$$

Equation (12) shows that p is a harmonic function, and this result is the starting-point for solving Stokes's equations in terms of spherical harmonic functions. Thus Lamb (1932, pp. 595–7) shows that if

$$p = \sum p_n \tag{14}$$

where the sum is taken over all positive and negative integers n (except -1, for which the formulae are not valid) of harmonics p_n, where the suffix denotes the degree, then the velocity may be written as

$$\mathbf{v} = \sum \left[\nabla\phi_{n+1} + \mathbf{r} \times \nabla\chi_n + \frac{1}{\mu}\frac{1}{2n(2n+1)} \times \right.$$
$$\left. \times \{(n+2)r^2\nabla p_{n-1} - 2(n-1)p_{n-1}\mathbf{r}\} \right], \tag{15}$$

in which ϕ_n and χ_n are harmonic functions. The corresponding vorticity is

$$\boldsymbol{\omega} = \sum [-(n+1)\nabla\chi_n + (\mu n)^{-1}\mathbf{r} \times \nabla p_{n-1}]. \tag{16}$$

In the particular case of a body of revolution fixed at zero incidence in a uniform stream, the vorticity can have no components in a meridian plane and so the terms involving χ_n are absent. The no-slip condition (requiring both velocity components in a meridian plane to vanish at the surface) is sufficient to determine the unknown constants that occur in the negative harmonics, p_n and ϕ_n, involved in the disturbance to the free stream. In fact, Lamb obtains the Stokes flow past a sphere by this means.

There is a general solution (Lamb 1932, pp. 632–7), corresponding to (14), (15), and (16), in terms of spherical harmonics and Bessel functions, that applies to oscillatory non-streaming flows involving spherical boundaries. This is a solution, not of (10) and (11), but of (1) and (2) without the terms involving squares of velocities. The representative velocity in this case is ωh, where ω is the frequency and h the representative amplitude of the oscillation. Reference to (6), with U equal to ωh, indicates that the solution is valid if the Reynolds number $\omega hl/\nu$ is $o(1)$, and $\omega l^2/\nu$ is $O(1)$; these conditions, of course, imply that h/l

must be $o(1)$. The solution can be used to give Stokes's (1851) solution for an oscillating sphere. We shall not pursue the matter further here, but it will be taken up again in Section VII. 12.

3.1. *Flow past a sphere*

Returning to steady streaming motions we shall now describe the Stokes flow past a fixed sphere of radius a in terms of the Stokes stream function ψ. In spherical polar coordinates r, θ, λ, with the axis $\theta = 0$ chosen to lie in the direction of the free stream U, the equation of continuity (10) is satisfied if the velocity components are given in terms of ψ by

$$v_r = \frac{1}{r^2 \sin\theta}\frac{\partial\psi}{\partial\theta}, \qquad v_\theta = -\frac{1}{r\sin\theta}\frac{\partial\psi}{\partial r}. \tag{17}$$

In the absence of swirling, $v_\lambda = 0$ and the only component of vorticity is

$$\omega_\lambda = -(r\sin\theta)^{-1}D^2\psi, \tag{18}$$

where D^2 represents the differential operator $\partial^2/\partial r^2 + r^{-2}(1-c^2)\partial^2/\partial c^2$, in which $c = \cos\theta$. Equation (13) reduces to

$$D^4\psi = 0, \tag{19}$$

and the required solution of this equation giving zero velocity at the surface $r = a$, and the velocity $U\mathbf{i}$ at infinity, is

$$\psi = \tfrac{1}{2}Ua^2\sin^2\theta\left(\frac{r}{a}-1\right)^2\left(1+\frac{1}{2}\frac{a}{r}\right). \tag{20}$$

It follows that

$$\omega_\lambda = -\tfrac{3}{2}Uar^{-2}\sin\theta, \tag{21}$$

and then it is easy to establish from (11) that

$$p = p_\infty - \tfrac{3}{2}\mu Uar^{-2}\cos\theta. \tag{22}$$

Since ψ is symmetrical about the plane $\theta = \tfrac{1}{2}\pi$, the streamline distribution is symmetrical fore and aft and therefore shows no wake. This defect in the Stokes solution arises because the convection of vorticity was eliminated from the problem when the inertia terms were discarded.

Now (20) can be separated into two parts. The first,

$$\psi = \tfrac{1}{2}Ur^2\sin^2\theta[1+\tfrac{1}{2}(a/r)^3],$$

represents irrotational flow past a doublet of moment $2\pi Ua^3\mathbf{i}$ situated at the origin in the free stream $U\mathbf{i}$; this makes no contribution to the total force on the sphere. The second part, $\psi = -\tfrac{3}{4}Uar\sin^2\theta$, represents rotational flow with radial and transverse velocity components equal to $-\tfrac{3}{2}U(a/r)\cos\theta$ and $\tfrac{3}{4}U(a/r)\sin\theta$ respectively, and involves a singularity at $r = 0$ that has been called a Stokeslet (Hancock 1953). The stress on the surface of the sphere has components p_∞ radially inwards

and $\frac{3}{2}\mu U/a$ downstream, and so the action of viscosity is to produce a drag
$$D = 6\pi\mu Ua. \tag{23}$$
This drag is entirely associated with the flow due to the Stokeslet, and it follows that a Stokeslet may be interpreted physically as a force applied to the fluid at a point. We shall specify Stokeslets by the forces they experience. For example, the Stokeslet **i** experiences unit drag, and has the stream function $-r\sin^2\theta/(8\pi\mu)$; it corresponds to a force $-$**i** applied to the fluid at the origin. For the sphere the drag coefficient is
$$C_D = D/(\tfrac{1}{2}\rho U^2.\pi a^2) = 24/R, \tag{24}$$
when the Reynolds number is based on diameter. Actually, the skin friction is responsible for two-thirds of the drag, and the viscous component of the normal stress for the remaining one-third. It can be seen from Fig. II. 30 that formula (24) agrees well with experimental measurements of the drag of spheres for $R < 1$, but that it begins to underestimate the drag when R reaches 1.

The drag formula corresponding to (23) has been found by Oberbeck (1876) for an ellipsoid with one of its principal axes parallel to the free stream, and is quoted by Lamb (1932).

3.2. *Flow past a circular cylinder*

In two-dimensional flow parallel to the x, z plane, the vorticity η is given in terms of the Lagrangian stream function ψ by the relation $\eta = \nabla^2\psi$, and (13) becomes
$$\nabla^4\psi = 0. \tag{25}$$
For flow past a circular cylinder $r = a$, the stream function representing the free stream at infinity is $Ur\sin\theta$ in plane polar coordinates r, θ, and so we seek a solution of (25) in the form $\psi = f(r)\sin\theta$. It then appears that the general value of $f(r)$ is $A_1 r^3 + A_2 r\ln r + A_3 r + A_4 r^{-1}$, and the first two terms would have to be omitted, and A_3 put equal to U, in order to match the free stream at infinity. This would leave only A_4 to be determined, and it would be impossible for both v_r and v_θ to vanish at $r = a$. The solution which satisfies the no-slip condition and tends to infinity most slowly as $r \to \infty$ is, in fact,
$$\psi = A\sin\theta\left[\left(\frac{r}{a}\right)\ln\left(\frac{r}{a}\right) - \frac{1}{2}\frac{r}{a} + \frac{1}{2}\frac{a}{r}\right], \tag{26}$$
obtained by discarding only the term involving r^3. This expression for ψ leads to a definite formula for the drag, namely $4\pi\mu A/a$, and the expression is valid at points not too far from the cylinder, but of course the solution suffers from the defect that it does not determine the value

of the constant A. However, the appropriate value of A will be found in Section 6 for which (26) represents the first approximation to the inner flow past the circular cylinder.

The expression for ψ corresponding to (26) for flow past an elliptic cylinder, with one of its principal axes parallel to the free stream, has been given in terms of elliptic coordinates by Berry and Swain (1923).

In neither of the above cases is the solution a Stokes flow as defined in Section 1, and so further discussion of them would be out of place here.

4. Swimming of microscopic organisms

A development in the application of Stokes's equations to non-streaming motions concerns the swimming of self-propelling objects. The hydrodynamics of the self-propulsion of ships and fishes depends almost entirely on the inertia of the surrounding fluid. A fish, for example, creates backward momentum of the fluid by sending lateral waves down its body from head to tail, and thereby gains a forward thrust to overcome the resistance to its forward motion. There are also much smaller creatures with tails, such as tadpoles and, on an even smaller scale, spermatozoa, that *appear* to swim like fishes, but the hydrodynamics of their motions must be different, because the inertia involved is negligible. For example, whereas the Reynolds number for a fish is measured in thousands, it is about 100 for a tadpole, and of the order of 10^{-3} for a spermatozoon in water. Moreover, the frequency of the flagellations of a spermatozoon is about 100 sec^{-1}, making $\omega l^2/\nu$ of the order of 10^{-6}, and so the steady-flow equation (11) is certainly applicable. Since inertia forces are therefore completely negligible, the question arises whether the swimming of microscopic organisms can be explained by the action of viscous forces only.

Attention was first drawn to this new problem in fluid dynamics by Taylor (1951). In the first place he considered the two-dimensional motion generated in a viscous fluid in the x, z plane by the waving of an inextensible sheet about its mean position $z = 0$. The displacement of the sheet was assumed to be

$$z = h \sin k(x - Ut), \tag{27}$$

representing a progressive transverse wave of small amplitude h, and wavelength $2\pi/k$, travelling along the sheet with velocity U in the x-direction. By using Stokes's equations (10) and (11) and the no-slip condition on the sheet, Taylor showed that the sheet moved with velocity

$$\tfrac{1}{2}(kh)^2 U + O[(kh)^4] \tag{28}$$

in the negative x-direction. Since the fluid at infinity (large $|z|$) is at rest, this is the velocity of propulsion and it is seen to be a quantity of the second order; there is no propulsion according to a first order theory (which retains only terms of order kh).

In a second paper Taylor (1952) discussed the same problem for transverse progressive waves (in the x, z plane) moving along an infinite filament with a circular cross-section of radius a, which lies along the x-axis in its undisturbed position. To the same approximation as before, the velocity of propulsion is

$$\tfrac{1}{2}(kh)^2 U \frac{K_0 - \tfrac{1}{2}kaK_1 + \tfrac{1}{2}kaK_0^2/K_1}{kaK_1(\tfrac{1}{2} + \tfrac{1}{2}K_0/K_2 - K_0^2/K_1^2) + K_0}, \tag{29}$$

where the K_n are Bessel functions (Watson 1944) with argument ka.

In some cases the observed values of kh are greater than those for which Taylor's formulae are valid, but Hancock (1953) investigated the motion of a filament for arbitrary values of kh. He represented the flow field by means of distributions of Stokeslets and doublets (see Section 3) along the centre line of the filament. He determined the appropriate strengths of the two distributions by (i) satisfying the no-slip condition at the surface of the filament and (ii) observing the condition that the total energy per unit length of filament of the induced velocity field must be finite. Since the velocity components due to a Stokeslet at the origin are proportional to r^{-1}, the velocity field of a *single* Stokeslet has infinite energy, and so the energy condition introduces certain restrictions on the distribution of Stokeslets. Hancock found that the no-slip condition could be satisfied for small ka, and his results for the velocity of propulsion of an infinite filament are summarized in Table IV. 1. In addition, Hancock showed that the velocity of a finite filament consisting of one wave is the same as for an infinite

TABLE IV. 1

Velocity of propulsion of an infinite filament

	kh		
$ka/2\pi$	*small*	1	π
o	$\tfrac{1}{2}U\dfrac{(kh)^2}{1 + (kh)^2}$		
small	$\tfrac{1}{2}(kh)^2 U\dfrac{\ln(kh) + 0\cdot384}{\ln(kh) - 0\cdot616}$	..	..
0·01	..	0·20U	0·28U
0·02	..	0·17U	0·22U

filament when $ka = 0$ and is almost the same (slightly less) when ka is small.

Lighthill (1952) investigated the swimming of a tailless object, by considering the squirming motion of a flexible sphere. The analysis involved is an extension of the work of Section 3, and the general axisymmetric solution of (19) that is regular at $\theta = 0$ and π, and yields velocities vanishing at infinity, is

$$\psi/Ua^2 = A_0 \cos\theta + \sin\theta \sum_1^\infty [A_n(a/r)^{n-2} + B_n(a/r)^n] V_n. \qquad (30)$$

In this equation the representative velocity U, and the mean radius a, have been inserted so that the constants A_n, B_n are non-dimensional, and

$$V_n = \frac{2}{\sin\theta} \int_c^1 P_n(\alpha)\, d\alpha, \qquad (31)$$

in which $P_n(\alpha)$ is the Legendre polynomial in α. It is necessary that $A_1 = 0$ in order to avoid infinite energy in the flow.

The deformation from the natural spherical shape is assumed to be small and axisymmetric, and the ring of points on the surface with coordinates (a, θ) in the undeformed position are assumed to have the coordinates

$$a\left[1 + \sum_0^\infty \alpha_n(t)P_n\right] \quad \text{and} \quad \theta + \sum_1^\infty \beta_n(t)V_n \qquad (32)$$

at time t. The origin of coordinates is chosen to coincide with the centroid of the deformed sphere, and one of the main objects of the investigation is to determine the velocity U of the centroid. (The acceleration associated with such a moving origin is too small to invalidate the *steady* flow equation (19) used in this problem.) With this choice of origin, $\alpha_1 = 0$ and the radial and transverse velocities of the moving surface are

$$UP_1 + a\sum_0^\infty \dot\alpha_n P_n \quad \text{and} \quad -UV_1 + a\left(1 + \sum_0^\infty \alpha_n P_n\right)\sum_1^\infty \dot\beta_n V_n \qquad (33)$$

respectively. By equating these expressions to the velocity components evaluated from (30), the velocity U can be determined. If only first order quantities are retained, $U = \tfrac{2}{3}a\dot\beta_1$, and since, in a squirming motion, β_1 will be a periodic function of t, the body will simply oscillate about a stationary mean position. Therefore, as in Taylor's theory, the rate of progression of the sphere must depend on squares of deformations. Of the types of deformation in which only two of the α_n and β_n are present, the α_2, β_3 mode appears to be the most efficient, when efficiency is measured by the ratio of the mean power expended by the body to the power required to propel the undeformed sphere with a constant velocity equal to the mean velocity $\overline{U}$. However, this involves backward tangential motion of the front and rear, combined with forward motion of the central zone, and it is difficult to believe that this type of motion will occur in practice. The β_1, β_2 mode is physically more likely, since it consists of forward motion at the rear, succeeded by forward motion at the front, then retraction at the rear, and finally retraction at the front; for this mode $U = 2a(3\beta_1\dot{\beta}_2 - \dot{\beta}_1\beta_2)/15$.

5. Oseen flow

The limitations of Stokes flow in providing descriptions of streaming motions have already been mentioned, and they may be recognized again by noticing that $\mathbf{v} \times \boldsymbol{\omega}$, a typical inertia term neglected, has a magnitude $Ur/\nu = Rr/l$ compared with $\nu\nabla \times \boldsymbol{\omega}$, the viscous stress retained in Stokes's equations. Hence, no matter how small R may be, the assumptions underlying Stokes's equations are not valid at sufficiently large distances r from the obstacle. To avoid this difficulty Oseen (1910) proposed that the inertia terms should be retained in the far field where the velocity is approximately equal to $U\mathbf{i}$. These inertia terms are of order R near the obstacle, where it is permissible to neglect them altogether, and so we find that in three-dimensional flow Stokes's and Oseen's equations both yield the same terms of order 1, and only differ in the terms of order R as can be seen, for example, from equations (20) and (54).

We start with Oseen's equations for steady flow in the form

$$\nabla \cdot \mathbf{v} = 0, \tag{34}$$

$$U(\partial\mathbf{v}/\partial x) = -\rho^{-1}\nabla p - \nu\nabla \times \boldsymbol{\omega} = -\rho^{-1}\nabla p + \nu\nabla^2\mathbf{v}. \tag{35}$$

We may observe here that there do not yet appear to be any solutions of Oseen's equations for unsteady flow, such as one might expect, for example, with a variable free stream. By taking the divergence of (35) we find that

$$\nabla^2 p = 0, \tag{36}$$

and, by taking the curl, that

$$\left(\nabla^2 - 2k\frac{\partial}{\partial x}\right)\boldsymbol{\omega} = 0, \tag{37}$$

where $k = U/2\nu$. It follows from (36) that p can be expressed by

$$p - p_\infty = -\rho U\left(\frac{\partial\phi}{\partial x} - U\right), \tag{38}$$

where ϕ satisfies $\nabla^2\phi = 0.$ (39)

It then follows that $\qquad \mathbf{v} = \nabla\phi + \dfrac{1}{2k}\nabla\chi - \chi\mathbf{i},$ $\qquad\qquad$ (40)

provided that $\qquad\qquad \left(\nabla^2 - 2k\dfrac{\partial}{\partial x}\right)\chi = 0.$ $\qquad\qquad$ (41)

The flow field is seen to consist of two components, an irrotational flow with velocity $\mathbf{v}_1 = \nabla\phi$ satisfying

$$\nabla\cdot\mathbf{v}_1 = 0, \qquad U(\partial\mathbf{v}_1/\partial x) = -\rho^{-1}\nabla p, \qquad (42)$$

and a rotational flow $\mathbf{v}_2 = (1/2k)\nabla\chi - \chi\mathbf{i}$ satisfying

$$\nabla\cdot\mathbf{v}_2 = 0, \qquad U(\partial\mathbf{v}_2/\partial x) = \nu\nabla\times\boldsymbol{\omega} = \nu\nabla^2\mathbf{v}_2. \qquad (43)$$

Thus the pressure is entirely associated with the irrotational flow, while the vorticity in the rotational flow is given by

$$\boldsymbol{\omega} = -\nabla\times(\chi\mathbf{i}). \qquad (44)$$

The representation of the flow in the manner of (38) and (40) is due to Lamb (1911), and it will now be exemplified in the particular cases of flow past a sphere and a circular cylinder.

5.1. *Flow past a sphere*

With r, θ denoting plane polar coordinates in any meridian plane of the sphere, the general solution of (39) valid outside the sphere is

$$\phi = Ua\left[\frac{r}{a}P_1(c) + \sum_0^\infty A_n\left(\frac{a}{r}\right)^{n+1}P_n(c)\right], \qquad (45)$$

and the appropriate general solution of (41) is given by

$$\chi = Ue^{\xi c}\sum_0^\infty B_m\chi_m(\xi)P_m(c), \qquad (46)$$

where $\xi = kr = \frac{1}{4}R(r/a)$, which is clearly an Oseen coordinate, and

$$\chi_m(\xi) = (2m+1)(\pi/2\xi)^{\frac{1}{2}}K_{m+\frac{1}{2}}(\xi). \qquad (47)$$

In Lamb's solution for the sphere (quoted in Lamb 1932), only the constants A_0, A_1, and B_0 are retained. Using the complete expressions (45) and (46), Goldstein (1929b) showed that the no-slip condition $v_r = v_\theta = 0$ on the surface of the sphere, $\xi = ka$, leads to the set of simultaneous equations

$$\sum_{m=0}^\infty B_m\lambda_{mn}(ka) = \begin{cases} -6 & (n=1) \\ 0 & (n=0,2,3,...) \end{cases} \qquad (48)$$

for the constants B_m. Here the λ_{mn} are rather complicated linear combinations of functions of the type $K_{p+\frac{1}{2}}(\xi)I_{q+\frac{1}{2}}(\xi)$ which are quoted by Goldstein (1929b) and by Tomotika and Aoi (1950).

The pressure drag is

$$D_1 = -2\pi a^2 \int_0^\pi p \sin\theta \cos\theta \, d\theta = -\tfrac{4}{3}\pi\rho U^2 a^2 A_0, \qquad (49)$$

as can be easily verified from (38) and (45). Furthermore, it will be shown in Section 8 that the total drag D is $m\rho U$, where m is the strength of the source in the irrotational flow (in this case $-4\pi U a^2 A_0$) and so the drag due to skin friction is

$$D_2 = -\tfrac{8}{3}\pi\rho U^2 a^2 A_0 = 2D_1. \qquad (50)$$

Now one of the equations emerging from the condition $v_r = 0$ at $\xi = ka$ is

$$A_0 = -\tfrac{1}{4}\pi(ka)^{-2} \sum_0^\infty (2m+1)B_m, \qquad (51)$$

and so

$$C_D = \frac{D}{\tfrac{1}{2}\rho U^2 . \pi a^2} = \frac{32\pi}{R^2} \sum_0^\infty (2m+1)B_m. \qquad (52)$$

When all the B_m are ignored except B_0, it follows from (48) and (52) that $B_0 = (3R/4\pi)(1+\tfrac{3}{16}R)$ and

$$C_D = \frac{24}{R}[1 + \tfrac{3}{16}R + O(R^2)], \qquad (53)$$

in which the term $\tfrac{3}{16}R$ is Oseen's correction to the Stokes drag coefficient. If B_1 is also retained, the next two terms in the series, $-\tfrac{19}{1280}R^2 + \tfrac{71}{20480}R^3$, can be calculated. In fact Goldstein retained B_0, B_1, and B_2, and thereby developed the series as far as the term in R^5. Although such additional terms increase the accuracy of the solution of Oseen's equations they do not significantly improve the formula (53) for the drag coefficient for small R. This is because equally important terms, like $R^2 \ln R$, are introduced when solutions of the Navier–Stokes equations more accurate than Oseen's are determined (see Section 6). Oseen's drag coefficient, like Stokes's, agrees with the experimental results for $R < 1$, but it begins to overestimate the drag when R reaches the value of about 1 (see Fig. II. 30).

The flow pattern, as well as the drag, is of interest. Photographs of the flow behind bluff bodies (Fig. II. 26 (Plate) and Fig. II. 27 (Plate)) show remarkable changes in the wake as the Reynolds number is progressively increased, of which one of the first developments is the formation of a vortex behind the body.

Theoretical flow patterns will be shown in Figs. IV. 1 and 2; we may observe now that theories based on Oseen's equations predict a clearly defined wake, but that they show no evidence of an incipient vortex at sufficiently small Reynolds numbers, say $R < 1$.

Tomotika and Aoi (1950) obtained the formal solution for the Stokes stream function ψ corresponding to the general expressions (45) and (46), and in constructing the streamlines near the sphere they used an approximate expression for ψ which neglects terms $O(R^2)$. Their formula, however, does not appear to include contributions from the terms involving B_1 and B_2, and, in order to quote ψ for Oseen flow near the sphere correct to $O(R)$, it is necessary to use all the terms retained by Goldstein, which yield

$$\psi = \tfrac{1}{2}Ua^2(1-c^2)\left(\frac{r}{a}-1\right)^2\left[(1+\tfrac{3}{16}R)\left(1+\frac{1}{2}\frac{a}{r}\right)-\tfrac{3}{16}R\left(1+\frac{a}{r}\right)^2 c\right]. \quad (54)$$

Oseen's solution which omits B_1, B_2, etc., in (46) can only give ψ near the sphere correct to $O(1)$, and in this respect it is just equivalent to Stokes's solution, for equation (54) without the terms in R is the same as (20). The improved value of ψ given in (54) is an important by-product of Goldstein's solution of Oseen's equations. We may also notice, in passing, that we cannot be sure of the numerical value of Oseen's correction to Stokes's drag formula until it has been confirmed by a solution such as Goldstein's, which shows that it is permissible to ignore B_1, B_2, etc., in obtaining B_0 from (48).

In the far field it is undoubtedly correct to discard B_1, B_2, etc., in (46) because $B_1/B_0 = O(R^2)$, $B_2/B_0 = O(R^4)$, while

$$\chi \sim \tfrac{1}{2}\pi U\xi^{-1}e^{-\xi(1-c)}\sum_0^\infty (2m+1)B_m P_m(c)$$

for large ξ. It follows that

$$\psi \sim \tfrac{1}{2}Ua^2\left[(1-c^2)\left(\frac{r}{a}\right)^2-\frac{6}{R}(1+\tfrac{3}{16}R)(1+c)[1-\exp\{-\tfrac{1}{4}R(r/a)(1-c)\}]\right] \quad (55)$$

as r tends to infinity. Here the first term represents the uniform stream U. The second term, excluding the exponential, represents the potential flow due to a point source of strength

$$m = 12\pi Ua^2 R^{-1}(1+\tfrac{3}{16}R),$$

and the exponential part of the second term represents a rotational flow which is negligible except in the region W within the paraboloidal boundary $R(r/a)(1-c) = O(1)$. In other words the flow at infinity outside W is the potential flow due to a source m in a uniform stream $U\mathbf{i}$, and the vorticity is confined to the region W which is the wake of the sphere. It is not difficult to deduce from (55) that the rotational part of the flow provides an inflow of m units of volume per unit time across any surface spanning W at great distance from the sphere, and this inflow exactly compensates the uniform outflow at infinity produced by the source m. This is illustrated in Fig. IV. 1 which refers to the flow produced by a sphere moving steadily from right to left through a fluid at rest; the figure shows the streamline pattern, valid for large r, as it would instantaneously appear (in a meridian plane) to a fixed

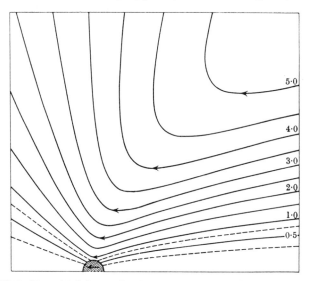

Fig. IV. 1. Flow at infinity produced by a sphere moving through fluid at rest, at $R = 1$. The streamlines correspond to constant values of

$$\tfrac{5}{16}\tfrac{7}{16}(1 + \cos\theta)[1 - \{\exp - \tfrac{1}{4}(r/a)(1 - \cos\theta)\}],$$

the second term (with reversed sign) of the asymptotic expression (55) for ψ/Ua^2, and they are so numbered.

observer. The fluid particles are dragged along in the wake behind the sphere, but elsewhere they are pushed out in all directions as from a source.

5.2. Flow past a circular cylinder

For a circular cylinder the appropriate expressions for ϕ and χ are

$$\phi = Ua\left[\left(\frac{r}{a}\right)\cos\theta + A_0\ln\left(\frac{r}{a}\right) + \sum_{1}^{\infty} A_n\left(\frac{a}{r}\right)^n \cos n\theta\right], \tag{56}$$

and

$$\chi = Ue^{\xi\cos\theta}\sum_{0}^{\infty} B_m K_m(\xi)\cos m\theta. \tag{57}$$

It is easy to establish that the drag coefficient is given by

$$C_D = \frac{D}{\tfrac{1}{2}\rho U^2 . 2a} = \frac{4\pi}{R}\sum_{0}^{\infty} B_m. \tag{58}$$

Tomotika and Aoi (1951), following Goldstein's method of procedure, show that $B_1/B_0 = O(R^2\ln R)$, $B_2/B_0 = O[(R^2\ln R)^2]$ and that

$$C_D = \frac{8\pi}{RS}\left[1 - \frac{1}{32}\left(\frac{5}{16S} - \frac{1}{2} + S\right)R^2 + O\{(R^2\ln R)^2\}\right], \qquad (59)$$

where $S = \frac{1}{2} - \gamma + \ln(8R^{-1})$, in which γ is Euler's constant. The leading term in (59) was originally given by Lamb (1911). We shall find, in Section 6, that the first term, $8\pi/RS$, in (59) is multiplied by a factor $1 + O(S^{-2})$ in a more accurate solution of the Navier–Stokes equations. For values of R between 0 and 1 (and, indeed, up to about 10) the second term of the series in (59) is therefore less important than the correction to the first term.

Near the cylinder the Lagrangian stream function is given approximately by

$$\psi = Ua\sin\theta\left[\frac{1}{2S}\left\{\frac{r}{a}\left(2\ln\frac{r}{a} - 1\right) + \frac{a}{r}\right\} + \right.$$
$$\left. + R\left\{\frac{1}{8S}\left(\frac{r}{a}\right)^2\ln\frac{r}{a} - \frac{1}{8}\left(\frac{r}{a}\right)^2 - \left(\frac{1}{16S} - \frac{1}{4}\right) + \left(\frac{1}{16S} - \frac{1}{8}\right)\left(\frac{a}{r}\right)^2\right\}\cos\theta\right]. \quad (60)$$

In deriving this formula it is necessary to retain B_1 as well as B_0, although if only the first term is required, it is sufficient to use Lamb's solution which retains only B_0.

At large distances from the cylinder

$$\psi \sim Ua\left[\frac{r}{a}\sin\theta + \frac{4}{RS}\sin\theta - \frac{1}{S}\left(\frac{2\pi}{R}\frac{r}{a}\right)^{\frac{1}{2}}\int_0^\theta (1 + \cos\alpha)\times\right.$$
$$\left. \times\exp\{-\tfrac{1}{4}R(r/a)(1 - \cos\alpha)\}\,d\alpha\right], \quad (61)$$

in which the three terms represent respectively the uniform stream U, the potential flow due to a line source of strength $m = 8\pi Ua/RS$ per unit length, and the rotational flow in the wake. The influx (per unit length) taken at infinity in the wake is m, and the wake is confined to the region behind the cylinder within the parabola

$$R(r/a)(1 - \cos\theta) = O(1).$$

5.3. *Flow past a flat plate*

The problem of the flow past a semi-infinite flat plate is a basic one in boundary-layer theory. In this problem there is no fundamental length, and so the appropriate Reynolds number, R_x, is a local one, defined in terms of the distance x from the leading edge of the plate. Near the leading edge, where R_x is small, Stokes's equations are valid, but along the plate, where R_x is large, they are replaced by Prandtl's equations. The matching of the solutions of these equations was discussed by Carrier and Lin (1948) in order to describe the flow near $x = 0$ (see Section V. 13). Following this work, Lewis and Carrier (1949) calculated the Oseen flow past a flat plate, but without introducing the boundary-layer flow. A simpler version of their solution is given by Kaplun (1954) as follows.

The velocity components in two-dimensional flow in the x, z plane may be expressed in terms of a stream function ψ as

$$u = \partial\psi/\partial z, \qquad w = -\partial\psi/\partial x, \tag{62}$$

and the vorticity η is given by

$$\eta = \nabla^2\psi. \tag{63}$$

It follows from (37) that

$$[\nabla^2 - 2k(\partial/\partial x)]\nabla^2\psi = 0. \tag{64}$$

It is convenient to introduce the real and imaginary parts of $[2k(x+iz)]^{\frac{1}{2}}$ as parabolic coordinates $(2\xi)^{\frac{1}{2}} \cos\frac{1}{2}\theta$, $(2\xi)^{\frac{1}{2}} \sin\frac{1}{2}\theta$, and then (64) is satisfied if

$$\psi = 2\nu(2\xi)^{\frac{1}{2}} \cos\tfrac{1}{2}\theta F[(2\xi)^{\frac{1}{2}} \sin\tfrac{1}{2}\theta], \tag{65}$$

where $F(\alpha) = \alpha \operatorname{erf}\alpha - \pi^{-\frac{1}{2}}(1-e^{-\alpha^2})$. Since $F(0) = F'(0) = 0$, it follows that ψ and $\partial\psi/\partial\theta$ both vanish on $\theta = 0$, and the no-slip condition at the plate is therefore satisfied. Also, since $F(\alpha) \sim \alpha$ as $\alpha \to \infty$, it is clear that as $r \to \infty$, except on $\theta = 0$, $\psi \sim 2\nu . 2\xi \cos\frac{1}{2}\theta \sin\frac{1}{2}\theta$; this is $Ur\sin\theta$, the stream function in the uniform stream. Thus, all the boundary conditions are satisfied by (65). It is interesting to notice that Oseen's equations, when modified according to boundary-layer theory, reduce to

$$\left(\frac{\partial^2}{\partial z^2} - 2k\frac{\partial}{\partial x}\right)\frac{\partial^2\psi}{\partial z^2} = 0, \tag{66}$$

and that the appropriate solution of this equation is

$$\psi = 2\nu(2\xi \cos\theta)^{\frac{1}{2}} F[(\xi/2 \cos\theta)^{\frac{1}{2}} \sin\theta], \tag{67}$$

which satisfies all the boundary conditions just as before. If, for fixed z, the coordinate x is allowed to become very large, $\theta \to 0$ and both (65) and (67) have the same form $2\nu(2\xi)^{\frac{1}{2}} F[(\frac{1}{2}\xi)^{\frac{1}{2}}\theta]$. Thus, as $\xi \to \infty$ and $\theta \to 0$, the Oseen flow reduces to the corresponding boundary-layer flow.

5.4. Oseen's fundamental solutions

Having considered one or two particular Oseen flows, we shall now refer to solutions given by Oseen (1927a) that open up the possibility of dealing with more general flow problems.

Oseen uses Green's theorem as applied to his equations in order to express **v**, p at any point in the fluid in terms of the values of these quantities on the surface S bounding the fluid. This had already been done by Lorentz (1896a) for solutions of Stokes's equations. Actually it is possible to go farther with Stokes's equations and find a Green's function which will enable one to express **v**, p in terms of the surface values of **v** alone, when S is a spherical surface for example. The Green's function, which is quite complicated, is quoted by Oseen (1927a).

In developing his theory, Oseen introduces the symmetric tensor

$$t_{ij} = \delta_{ij} \nabla^2 f - \frac{\partial^2 f}{\partial x_i \, \partial x_j}, \tag{68}$$

and the vector
$$p_j = -\mu \frac{\partial}{\partial x_j}\left(\nabla^2 f - 2k \frac{\partial f}{\partial x_1}\right), \tag{69}$$

where the x_i are Cartesian coordinates with the axis 1 in the direction of the stream U, and $f(x_i)$ is a scalar function satisfying

$$[\nabla^2 - 2k(\partial/\partial x_1)]\nabla^2 f = 0. \tag{70}$$

When j has a particular value (1, 2, or 3), the velocity t_{ij} and the pressure p_j satisfy Oseen's equations (34) and (35).

A simple solution of (70) in the case of axisymmetric flow is

$$f = A \int_0^{k(r-x)} (1 - e^{-\alpha})\alpha^{-1} \, d\alpha, \tag{71}$$

where the coordinates x, y, z are identical with x_1, x_2, x_3. If, in particular, we choose the suffix j equal to 1, and take the constant A equal to $-m/4\pi$, we obtain, for the vector t_{i1},

$$\mathbf{t}_1 = -\frac{m}{4\pi}\left[\nabla \frac{1 - e^{-k(r-x)}}{r} + 2k \frac{e^{-k(r-x)}}{r}\mathbf{i}\right] \tag{72}$$

and, for the scalar p_1,
$$p_1 = \frac{m\rho U}{4\pi}\frac{\partial}{\partial x}\left(\frac{1}{r}\right). \tag{73}$$

Equations (72) and (73) are very much like the perturbation velocity and pressure due to a sphere fixed in the stream U. In fact they are derived from the potential source, the term involving A_0 in (45), and the first term, involving B_0, in (47). If the potential doublet, the term involving A_1 in (45), had also been included, we should have obtained Oseen's solution for the perturbation due to a fixed sphere. As it is, (72) and (73) give the potential flow outside the wake due to a source m, and rotational flow within the wake that shows an influx m at infinity. The singularity at the origin that induces this flow will be called an Oseenlet, since, like a Stokeslet in Stokes flow, it corresponds to a force concentrated at a point. It will be specified by the force it experiences, which is $m\rho U\mathbf{i}$ in the present case, as we shall verify in Section 8.

The choice of j equal to 3 and the constant A equal to $\Gamma/4\pi$ yields an Oseenlet which experiences a lift $\Gamma\rho U$ in the z-direction. The potential flow associated with this Oseenlet is that due to a horseshoe vortex, for which the product of the infinitesimal span and the strength of the line vortex is Γ.

In an investigation on Oseen flow past a circular disk held broadside to the stream, Hocking (1959) has used a distribution of dragging Oseenlets over the two sides of the disk to represent the disturbance to the incident stream.

In two-dimensional flow, in the x_1, x_3 (i.e. x, z) plane, an appropriate solution of (70) is obtained by taking

$$\partial f/\partial x = A[\ln r + e^{kx}K_0(kr)], \qquad \nabla^2 f = 2kAe^{kx}K_0(kr). \qquad (74)$$

Then, with the suffix j equal to 1, and with $A = -m/2\pi$ we obtain

$$\mathbf{t}_1 = \frac{m}{2\pi}[\nabla\{\ln r + e^{kx}K_0(kr)\} - 2ke^{kx}K_0(kr)\mathbf{i}], \qquad (75)$$

$$p_1 = -\frac{m}{2\pi}\rho U \frac{\partial}{\partial x}(\ln r), \qquad (76)$$

representing a line Oseenlet with an associated drag $m\rho U$ per unit length. Finally, with j equal to 3, and with $A = -\gamma/2\pi$, we obtain a line Oseenlet which experiences a lift in the z-direction of amount $\gamma\rho U$ per unit length. The potential flows involved in these two cases are those due to a line source m and a line vortex γ respectively.

These two fundamental solutions offer the possibility of representing plane Oseen flow past a cylinder by means of an equivalent distribution of dragging and lifting line Oseenlets, as in the analogous case of potential flow past a thin aerofoil, for example, where a distribution of line sources and line vortices may be used to represent the disturbance to the incident stream. This procedure was used by Bairstow, Cave, and Lang (1923) in calculating the drag of a circular cylinder at various Reynolds numbers and in obtaining a formula for the drag of an elliptic cylinder held with one of its principal axes parallel to the stream. They also used it in calculating the drag of a finite flat plate at zero incidence for one Reynolds number, and subsequently Piercy and Winny (1933), using the same technique, determined the analytical formula for the drag of a flat plate, valid for all sufficiently small Reynolds numbers.

5.5. *Imai's method for plane flow*

We have just alluded to aerofoil theory, and it will be recalled that as an alternative to source and vortex distributions, the complex variable and conformal mapping afford a very powerful method of solving plane potential flow problems. Imai (1954) has extended this method to the solution of Oseen's equations.

In considering flow in the x, z plane, Imai uses the complex variable $\mathfrak{z} = x + iz$ and its conjugate $\bar{\mathfrak{z}}$ as independent variables instead of x and z. The (conjugate) complex velocity $W = u - iw$ is then given by

$$W = 2i(\partial \psi/\partial \mathfrak{z}) \qquad (77)$$

and the vorticity η by

$$\partial W/\partial \bar{\mathfrak{z}} = \tfrac{1}{2} i \eta. \qquad (78)$$

Equation (37) shows that

$$[\nabla^2 - 2k(\partial/\partial x)]\eta = 0, \qquad (79)$$

and the appropriate solution of this equation, vanishing at infinity, is

$$\eta = e^{kx} \mathscr{R} \sum_0^\infty C_n K_n(kr) e^{in\theta} \qquad (80)$$

where the C_n are complex constants. By integrating (78) and using the condition that W should be a single-valued function, Imai finds that the complex velocity can be written in the general form

$$W = \frac{i}{2k} e^{kx} \Big[A_1 K_0(kr) + \sum_1^\infty (A_{n+1} e^{in\theta} - \bar{A}_n e^{-in\theta}) K_n(kr) \Big] + f'(\mathfrak{z}), \qquad (81)$$

where $A_n = - \sum_{p=0}^\infty C_{n+p}$, and $f(\mathfrak{z})$ is an arbitrary analytic function. The first term in (81) represents the rotational part of the flow, which is negligible outside the wake, and the second term represents the potential part of the flow, for which $f(\mathfrak{z})$ is the complex potential. The problem now is to apply the boundary conditions on the cylinder C and at infinity in order to determine the A_n and the function $f(\mathfrak{z})$.

Near C, where $kr = O(R)$, we can use the expansions of $K_n(kr)$ for small values of the argument, and this gives, with $O(R^4)$ neglected,

$$W = f'(\mathfrak{z}) - \frac{i e^{kx}}{2k} \Big[\frac{8}{k^3} g''(\mathfrak{z}) + \frac{4}{k^2} \bar{g}'(\bar{\mathfrak{z}}) + \frac{2}{k} \mathfrak{z} g'(\mathfrak{z}) + \mathfrak{z} \bar{g}(\bar{\mathfrak{z}}) -$$

$$- \frac{k^3}{32} \bar{A}_1 \mathfrak{z} \bar{\mathfrak{z}}^2 (\ln \bar{\mathfrak{z}} - 2Q - \tfrac{3}{2}) - \frac{k}{4} A_2 \mathfrak{z} (\ln \mathfrak{z} - 2Q - 1) \Big], \qquad (82)$$

where $Q = \ln(2k^{-1}) - \gamma$, and

$$g(\mathfrak{z}) = \tfrac{1}{32}k^3 A_1[\mathfrak{z}^2\ln\mathfrak{z} - \tfrac{1}{2}\mathfrak{z}^2 - (2Q+1)\mathfrak{z}^2] + \tfrac{1}{8}k^2\bar{A}_1\mathfrak{z}(\ln\mathfrak{z} - 1) -$$

$$- \tfrac{1}{4}k\bar{A}_2\ln\mathfrak{z} + \tfrac{1}{4}k\sum_3^\infty (n-3)!\,\bar{A}_n(\tfrac{1}{2}k\mathfrak{z})^{2-n}. \quad (83)$$

Since we are expanding in powers of R, we may suppose that

$$\bar{A}_1 = k\sum_0^\infty a_n k^n, \qquad \bar{A}_2 = k^2\sum_0^\infty b_n k^n,$$

$$f(\mathfrak{z}) = k^{-1}\sum_0^\infty f_n(\mathfrak{z})k^n, \qquad g(\mathfrak{z}) = k^3\sum_0^\infty g_n(\mathfrak{z})k^n. \quad (84)$$

Then, because $e^{-kx}W = 0$ on C, it follows that

$$f_0'(\mathfrak{z}) = 4ig_0''(\mathfrak{z}), \quad (85)$$

$$f_1'(\mathfrak{z}) = \tfrac{1}{2}(\mathfrak{z}+\bar{\mathfrak{z}})f_0'(\mathfrak{z}) + 4ig_1''(\mathfrak{z}) + 2i\bar{g}_0'(\bar{\mathfrak{z}}), \quad (86)$$

etc., on C.

At infinity, according to Imai (1951),

$$f(\mathfrak{z}) = U\mathfrak{z} + \frac{m+i\gamma}{2\pi}\ln\mathfrak{z} - \frac{ik^{\frac12}m^2}{4\pi^{\frac12}U}\frac{1}{\mathfrak{z}^{\frac12}} + O\!\left(\frac{1}{\mathfrak{z}}\right), \quad (87)$$

where the drag and lift of the cylinder are $m\rho U$, $\gamma\rho U$ per unit length. Also

$$g_0''(\mathfrak{z}) = \frac{a_0}{8\mathfrak{z}} + \frac{b_0}{4\mathfrak{z}^2} + O\!\left(\frac{1}{\mathfrak{z}^3}\right), \quad (88)$$

$$g_n''(\mathfrak{z}) = \frac{a_{n-1}}{16}(\ln\mathfrak{z} - 2Q) + \frac{a_n}{8\mathfrak{z}} + \frac{b_n}{4\mathfrak{z}^2} + O\!\left(\frac{1}{\mathfrak{z}^3}\right), \quad (89)$$

for $n \geqslant 1$.

By referring to (87) and (88) we see that (85) holds at infinity, as well as on the cylinder, and so it is valid everywhere in the flow field. We then write (86) in the form

$$F_1(\mathfrak{z}) = G_0(\mathfrak{z},\bar{\mathfrak{z}}), \quad (90)$$

where

$$F_1(\mathfrak{z}) = f_1'(\mathfrak{z}) - 4ig_1''(\mathfrak{z}), \quad \text{and} \quad G_0(\mathfrak{z},\bar{\mathfrak{z}}) = 2i(\mathfrak{z}+\bar{\mathfrak{z}})g_0''(\mathfrak{z}) + 2i\bar{g}_0'(\bar{\mathfrak{z}}). \quad (91)$$

Finally, if the outside of C is mapped conformally onto the outside of the unit circle $\mathfrak{z}' = e^{i\theta'}$ in the $\mathfrak{z}'$-plane by means of the transformation $\mathfrak{z} = M(\mathfrak{z}')$, then

$$F_1[M(e^{i\theta'})] = G_0[M(e^{i\theta'}), \bar{M}(e^{-i\theta'})].$$

But from (87) and (89)

$$F_1[M(e^{i\theta'})] = U - \tfrac{1}{4}i\bar{a}_0[\ln M(e^{i\theta'}) - 2Q] + P(e^{-i\theta'}),$$

where $P(\mathfrak{z}')$ is a power series in $\mathfrak{z}'$ devoid of a constant term. It now follows by integrating this expression round the unit circle that

$$\int_0^{2\pi} \frac{G_0[M(e^{i\theta'}), \bar{M}(e^{-i\theta'})]+\tfrac14 i\bar{a}_0 \ln M(e^{i\theta'})}{e^{i\theta'}-\mathfrak{z}'} ie^{i\theta'}\,d\theta' = 2\pi i(U+\tfrac12 i\bar{a}_0\,Q). \quad (92)$$

This is regarded as an equation for the unknown function $g_0'(\mathfrak{z})$ which occurs, with its derivative, in the integrand. The functions $g_1'(\mathfrak{z})$ and $g_2'(\mathfrak{z})$ can be obtained by a similar procedure, and when these have all been determined, the functions $f_0'(\mathfrak{z})$, $f_1'(\mathfrak{z})$, $f_2'(\mathfrak{z})$ are known from (85), (86), etc., and the quantities m and γ, occurring in (87), can be calculated.

To illustrate the application of this method, Imai considers the particular case of an elliptic cylinder with semi-axes $a = 1+\sigma^2$, $b = 1-\sigma^2$, and with its major axis inclined at a positive angle of incidence α to the uniform stream. For this cylinder

$$M(\mathfrak{z}') = e^{-i\alpha}(\mathfrak{z}'+\sigma^2/\mathfrak{z}')$$

and $f_n(\mathfrak{z})$, $g_n(\mathfrak{z})$ turn out to be simple functions of $\mathfrak{z}$ with rather complicated coefficients. This example is a comprehensive one which includes several special cases previously treated by other authors (circular cylinder, finite flat plate at zero incidence and broadside on), and Imai's final results are therefore quoted below:

$$C_D = \frac{16\pi}{R}\frac{2S-(2+\sigma^2\cos 2\alpha)}{D} - \frac{\pi R}{(1+\sigma^2)^2 D}\left[S^2+c_1 S+c_2+\frac{1}{D}(c_3 S+c_4)\right],$$
$$(93)$$

and

$$C_L = \frac{16\pi}{R}\frac{\sigma^2\sin 2\alpha}{D} - \frac{\pi R\sigma^2\sin 2\alpha}{(1+\sigma^2)^2 D}\left[2S^2+d_1 S+d_2+\frac{1}{D}(d_3 S+d_4)\right], \quad (94)$$

where $\qquad\qquad D = 4S^2-4S-(\sigma^4+2\sigma^2\cos 2\alpha)$
and $\qquad\qquad S = \tfrac12-\gamma+\ln[8(1+\sigma^2)R^{-1}]$ $\qquad(95)$

in which $R = 2Ua/\nu$. Imai gives the expressions for the coefficients c_i and d_i, which are functions of σ and α. However, the significance of the second parts of the expressions for C_D and C_L is jeopardized by the corrections to the first parts which would result, as in the case of a circular cylinder, from a more accurate solution of the Navier–Stokes equations.

6. An improved theory of flow at small Reynolds number

Whitehead (1889) tried to improve Stokes's formula for the drag of a sphere by using Stokes's solution to calculate the neglected inertia terms, which were then reintroduced into the equations of motion. This yielded inhomogeneous equations of the Stokes type, namely (10) and (11) with the known inertia terms added, to be solved for the second approximation to the flow. The method failed because it was not possible to match the resulting velocity with the uniform stream at infinity. An important development in the theory of flow at small Reynolds number which leads to improvements in the drag formulae has been initiated by Kaplun and his associates (Lagerstrom and Cole 1955; Kaplun and Lagerstrom 1957; Kaplun 1957), and taken up by Proudman and Pearson (1957). They distinguish between the inner flow in the region near the obstacle, where the Stokes variable $\bar{r}$ ($= r/l$) is $O(1)$, and the outer flow where the Oseen variable $\hat{r}$ ($= R\bar{r}$) is $O(1)$. The outer flow is represented by expressions for the velocity and pressure in the forms

$$\left.\begin{array}{l} \mathbf{v}/U = \sum\limits_{0}^{\infty} \epsilon_n \mathbf{f}_n(\hat{\mathbf{r}}) \\[2mm] (p-p_\infty)/\rho U^2 = \sum\limits_{0}^{\infty} \epsilon_n p_n(\hat{\mathbf{r}}) \end{array}\right\} \tag{96}$$

where the ϵ_n are functions of R such that $\epsilon_0 = 1$ and $\epsilon_{n+1}/\epsilon_n \to 0$ as $R \to 0$. The inner flow is similarly represented by

$$\left.\begin{array}{l} \mathbf{v}/U = \sum\limits_{0}^{\infty} \epsilon_n \mathbf{h}_n(\bar{\mathbf{r}}) \\[2mm] R(p-p_\infty)/\rho U^2 = \sum\limits_{0}^{\infty} \epsilon_n r_n(\bar{\mathbf{r}}) \end{array}\right\} \tag{97}$$

The equations satisfied by $\mathbf{f}_n$, p_n and $\mathbf{h}_n$, r_n are obtained by inserting the expansions (96) and (97) in the Navier–Stokes equations, written in terms of Oseen and Stokes variables respectively, and picking out coefficients of the ϵ_n. For example, $\mathbf{f}_0 = \mathbf{i}$, $p_0 = 0$, and $\mathbf{f}_1$, p_1 satisfy Oseen's equations. Henceforward it will not again be necessary to mention the pressure functions p_n, r_n explicitly. The velocity functions must satisfy the boundary conditions $\mathbf{f}_n \to 0$ ($n \geqslant 1$) as $\hat{r} \to \infty$, and $\mathbf{h}_n = 0$ on the body, but the inner condition on $\mathbf{f}_n$ and the outer one on $\mathbf{h}_n$ are still to be determined. This is done by matching the inner and outer expansions.

Kaplun connects the two expansions by introducing certain intermediate expansions to bridge the gap. Intermediate variables are introduced which, for the sake of illustration, we shall take to be given by $\mathbf{r}^* = R^\alpha \bar{\mathbf{r}}$, $\mathbf{v}^* = \bar{\mathbf{v}}$, and $p^* = R^{-\alpha}\bar{p}$, where $0 < \alpha < 1$. (It will be noticed that $\alpha = 0$ corresponds to Stokes variables, and $\alpha = 1$ to

Oseen variables.) The intermediate expansion for the velocity is

$$\mathbf{v}/U = \sum_{0}^{\infty} \epsilon_n \, \mathbf{g}_n(\mathbf{r}^*). \tag{98}$$

If the Navier–Stokes equations are written in terms of the intermediate variables, and R is then allowed to tend to 0, Stokes's equations are obtained. This means that if $\mathbf{g}_0$ is taken to be a solution of Stokes's equations, obeying the no-slip condition at the body, it will represent $\mathbf{v}/U$ to order 1 for all α in $0 \leqslant \alpha < 1$. Kaplun next shows that $\mathbf{v}/U$ is equal to $\mathbf{i}$ to order 1 for some intermediate variables as well as for the Oseen variables. It then follows that for such variables

$$\lim_{R \to 0} (\mathbf{g}_0 - \mathbf{i}) = 0. \tag{99}$$

More generally, Kaplun's arguments establish that there are intermediate variables for which the intermediate and Oseen expansions are equal, i.e.

$$\lim_{R \to 0} \frac{1}{\epsilon_m} \sum_{0}^{m} \epsilon_n(\mathbf{f}_n - \mathbf{g}_n) = 0 \tag{100}$$

for all m, when the $\mathbf{f}_n$ as well as the $\mathbf{g}_n$ are expressed in terms of the relevant intermediate variable. For a sphere, $\mathbf{g}_n = \mathbf{h}_n$, and for a circular cylinder $\mathbf{g}_n$ is proportional to $\mathbf{h}_1$, and so (100) provides the connexion between the inner and outer expansions that serves to determine the inner boundary condition on $\mathbf{f}_n$ and the outer one on $\mathbf{h}_n$.

Kaplun and Lagerstrom (1957) apply this procedure to the case of flow past a sphere, and Kaplun (1957) similarly considers the application to a circular cylinder. The most thorough application of Kaplun's method to flow past a sphere has been given by Proudman and Pearson (1957), and their work will be outlined in Section 6.1.

6.1. *Flow past a sphere*

The radius a of the sphere is used as the representative length so that the Stokes variable $\bar{r}$ is equal to r/a, but the Reynolds number is $2Ua/\nu$ as on previous occasions. The Stokes stream function ψ may be expressed as an Oseen expansion

$$\psi R^2/Ua^2 = \hat{\psi} = \sum_{0}^{\infty} \epsilon_n \hat{\psi}_n(\hat{\mathbf{r}}) \tag{101}$$

in the outer flow, and by a Stokes expansion

$$\psi/Ua^2 = \bar{\psi} = \sum_{0}^{\infty} \epsilon_n \bar{\psi}_n(\bar{\mathbf{r}}) \tag{102}$$

in the inner flow. There is no need to introduce intermediate variables explicitly in this case, and the matching is effected by identifying $\hat{\psi}(\hat{\mathbf{r}})$ for small $\hat{\mathbf{r}}$ with $R^2\bar{\psi}(\bar{\mathbf{r}})$ for large $\bar{\mathbf{r}}$.

As already mentioned above $\epsilon_0 = 1$, and indeed we know that

$$\hat{\psi}_0 = \tfrac{1}{2}\hat{r}^2(1-c^2) \tag{103}$$

because the leading term in (101) must represent the undisturbed stream $U\mathbf{i}$. The matching condition requires that $\bar{\psi}_0 \sim \tfrac{1}{2}\bar{r}^2(1-c^2)$ as $\bar{r} \to \infty$, and the required solution of Stokes's equations satisfying this condition and the no-slip condition at $\bar{r} = 1$ is, from equation (20) of Section 3,

$$\bar{\psi}_0 = \tfrac{1}{4}(2\bar{r}^2 - 3\bar{r} + \bar{r}^{-1})(1-c^2). \tag{104}$$

When the expansion (101) for ψ is substituted into the Navier–Stokes equations written in Oseen variables, the terms involving ϵ_1 show that $\hat{\psi}_1$ satisfies Oseen's equation

$$\left(\hat{D}^2 - \frac{c}{2}\frac{\partial}{\partial\hat{r}} - \frac{1-c^2}{2\hat{r}}\frac{\partial}{\partial c}\right)\hat{D}^2\hat{\psi}_1 = 0, \tag{105}$$

where $\hat{D}^2 = \partial^2/\partial\hat{r}^2 + \hat{r}^{-2}(1-c^2)\partial^2/\partial c^2$. This equation is solved by substituting $\hat{D}^2\hat{\psi} = e^{\frac{1}{4}\hat{r}c}f(\hat{r})g(c)$ and observing that dg/dc satisfies Legendre's equation. The required solution, which must vanish as $\hat{r} \to \infty$ and at $c = \pm 1$ (because $\hat{D}^2\hat{\psi} \propto \sin\theta$ according to equation (18)), is

$$\hat{D}^2\hat{\psi}_1 = e^{\frac{1}{4}\hat{r}c}(\tfrac{1}{4}\hat{r})^{\frac{1}{2}} \sum_1^\infty A_n K_{n+\frac{1}{2}}(\tfrac{1}{4}\hat{r}) \int_c^1 P_n(\alpha)\,d\alpha. \tag{106}$$

Since $\hat{D}^2\hat{\psi} = \bar{D}^2\bar{\psi}$, both being equal to $D^2\psi/U$ in natural coordinates, it follows that (106) multiplied by ϵ_1 must be equal to $\tfrac{3}{2}\bar{r}^{-1}(1-c^2)$+smaller terms. This implies that $\epsilon_1 = R$, $A_1 = \tfrac{3}{2}(2\pi)^{-\frac{1}{2}}$, $A_n = 0$ $(n \geqslant 2)$. Equation (106) is now a simple equation for $\hat{\psi}_1$, and the solution that gives a vanishing velocity as $\hat{r} \to \infty$ and matches the Stokes expansion is

$$\hat{\psi}_1 = -3(1+c)[1-\exp\{-\tfrac{1}{4}\hat{r}(1-c)\}]. \tag{107}$$

The second term, $\epsilon_1\bar{\psi}_1$, in the Stokes expansion satisfies the inhomogeneous Stokes equation

$$\bar{D}^4\bar{\psi}_1 = -\tfrac{9}{8}(2\bar{r}^{-2} - 3\bar{r}^{-3} + \bar{r}^{-5})c(1-c^2). \tag{108}$$

The general solution of this equation vanishing at $c = \pm 1$ and satisfying the no-slip condition at $\bar{r} = 1$ is

$$\bar{\psi}_1 = -\tfrac{3}{64}(2\bar{r}^2 - 3\bar{r} + 1 - \bar{r}^{-1} + \bar{r}^{-2})c(1-c^2) +$$

$$+ \sum_1^\infty [A_n\{(2n-1)\bar{r}^{n+3} - (2n+1)\bar{r}^{n+1} + 2\bar{r}^{-n+2}\} +$$

$$+ B_n\{2\bar{r}^{n+1} - (2n+1)\bar{r}^{-n+2} + (2n-1)\bar{r}^{-n}\}] \int_c^1 P_n(\alpha)\,d\alpha. \tag{109}$$

When this is expressed in terms of $\hat{r}$ and multiplied by R (in order to compare it with $\hat{\psi}$) it must not then contain any term of order greater than 1, and so all the A_n and B_n must be zero except B_1. Moreover, by matching the terms that are $O(1)$ with the expansion of (107) for small $\hat{r}$, we find that $B_1 = \frac{3}{32}$, and so

$$\bar{\psi}_1 = \tfrac{3}{64}(\bar{r}-1)^2(1-c^2)[(2+\bar{r}^{-1})-c(2+\bar{r}^{-1}+\bar{r}^{-2})]. \tag{110}$$

Observing the expression in square brackets, we may regard $\bar{\psi}_1$ as the difference of two expressions of which the second term has arisen from the right-hand side of (108) and so represents the effect of the inertia terms on the inner flow. Since this second term is an odd function of c, it makes no contribution to the drag on the sphere. Since the first term is $\frac{3}{16}\bar{\psi}_0$, the drag to the second approximation is $(1+\frac{3}{16}R)$ times Stokes's estimate of the drag.

The third term, $\epsilon_2\bar{\psi}_2$, in equation (102) can be found as follows. After some analysis it emerges that $\epsilon_2 = R^2\ln R$, and hence that $\bar{\psi}_2$, which satisfies $\bar{D}^4\bar{\psi}_2 = 0$, must be of the form $C\bar{\psi}_0$. In order to determine the constant C it is necessary to introduce $R^2\bar{\psi}_3$, but it is not necessary to determine $\bar{\psi}_3$ completely. In fact, by considering that part of $\bar{\psi}_3$ which contains the factor $(1-c^2)$, and by noticing that $R^2\ln R$ cannot occur in the Oseen expansion, we find that C is equal to $\frac{9}{160}$. It follows that

$$C_D = \frac{24}{R}[1+\tfrac{3}{16}R+\tfrac{9}{160}R^2\ln R+O(R^2)]. \tag{111}$$

This result is also obtained if the Navier–Stokes equations are solved iteratively by using Oseen's solution to calculate the neglected inertia terms and thereby obtaining inhomogeneous Oseen equations for the second approximation to the flow.

An example of the inner flow pattern is shown in Fig. IV. 2, which shows some streamlines (lines of constant $\bar{\psi}_0+R\bar{\psi}_1$), for the case $R = 1$. These streamlines are, of course, only approximate, because they are based on an incomplete expression for $\bar{\psi}$.

6.2. *Flow past a circular cylinder*

When the Lagrangian stream function ψ is expressed in non-dimensional form by the relations $\psi = Ua\hat{\psi}/R = Ua\bar{\psi}$, the first term in the Oseen expansion is

$$\hat{\psi}_0 = \hat{r}\sin\theta. \tag{112}$$

The leading term in the Stokes expansion must (i) satisfy Stokes's equation $\bar{\nabla}^4\bar{\psi}_0 = 0$, (ii) contain the factor $\sin\theta$, and (iii) satisfy the no-slip condition at $\bar{r} = 1$. In fact, as can be seen from equation (26), the

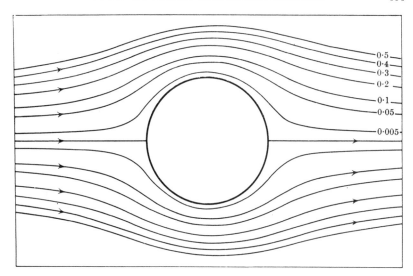

FIG. IV. 2. Inner flow past a sphere at $R = 1$. Lines of constant $\bar{\psi}_0 + R\bar{\psi}_1$.
(The streamlines are wider apart behind the sphere than in front.)

appropriate expression for it is

$$\bar{\psi}_0 = \epsilon(\bar{r}\ln\bar{r} - \tfrac{1}{2}\bar{r} + \tfrac{1}{2}\bar{r}^{-1})\sin\theta, \tag{113}$$

where ϵ is a function of R such that $\epsilon\ln R^{-1} \to 1$ as $R \to 0$. This condition is necessary in order to match the Oseen expansion.

The second term, $\epsilon_1\hat{\psi}_1$, in the Oseen expansion satisfies Oseen's equation

$$\left(\hat{\nabla}^2 - \frac{c}{2}\frac{\partial}{\partial\hat{r}} - \frac{1-c^2}{2\hat{r}}\frac{\partial}{\partial c}\right)\hat{\nabla}^2\hat{\psi}_1 = 0, \tag{114}$$

and the general solution for $\hat{\nabla}^2\hat{\psi}_1$ odd in θ and vanishing at infinity is

$$\hat{\nabla}^2\hat{\psi}_1 = e^{\frac{1}{4}\hat{r}\cos\theta}\sum_{1}^{\infty} A_n K_n(\tfrac{1}{4}\hat{r})\sin n\theta. \tag{115}$$

By expanding for small $\hat{r}$ both sides of the relation $\bar{\nabla}^2\bar{\psi} = R\hat{\nabla}^2\hat{\psi}$, which is obtained by expressing $\nabla^2\psi$ in both Stokes and Oseen variables, we find that $2\epsilon_1 A_1 = \epsilon$, $A_n = 0$ $(n \geqslant 2)$. Without loss of generality we choose $\epsilon_1 = \epsilon$, and the required solution of (115) is then

$$\hat{\psi}_1 = -\sum_{0}^{\infty} [2K_1(\tfrac{1}{4}\hat{r})I_n(\tfrac{1}{4}\hat{r}) + K_0(\tfrac{1}{4}\hat{r})\{I_{n-1}(\tfrac{1}{4}\hat{r}) + I_{n+1}(\tfrac{1}{4}\hat{r})\}]\hat{r}\sin n\theta/n. \tag{116}$$

There is no harmonic complementary function $\sum B_n \hat{r}^{-n}\sin n\theta$ because B_n must be 0 in order to match $\hat{\psi}$ and $R\bar{\psi}$.

The Stokes expansion turns out to be of the form $\sum_{0}^{\infty} \epsilon_n\bar{\psi}_n$, where the

$\bar\psi_n$ satisfy Stokes's equation and are therefore proportional to $\bar\psi_0$. In fact,

$$\bar\psi = \epsilon\Big(1+ \sum_1^\infty a_n \epsilon^n\Big)(\bar r \ln \bar r-\tfrac12\bar r+\tfrac12\bar r^{-1})\sin \theta. \tag{117}$$

For small $\hat r$, (116) yields

$$\hat\psi = \hat r \sin \theta+\epsilon[\ln(\hat r/8)+\gamma-1]\hat r \sin \theta+\dots . \tag{118}$$

If we let $\epsilon = S^{-1}$, as suggested by comparing (117) and (60), it follows that $\epsilon \ln R^{-1} = 1+(\gamma-\tfrac12-\ln 8)\epsilon$ and we find that (117) and (118) agree in the terms $\hat r$ and $\hat r \ln \hat r$ to $O(\epsilon)$ if $a_1 = 0$. Reference to (59) and (117) shows that the drag coefficient is then given by

$$C_D = \frac{8\pi}{RS}\Big(1+ \sum_2^\infty \frac{a_n}{S^n}\Big) \tag{119}$$

when terms $O(R^2)$ are neglected. The constant a_2, by the matching procedure, must be equal to the coefficient of $\hat r \sin \theta$ in the expansion of $\hat\psi_2$ for small $\hat r$, while $\hat\psi_2$ must satisfy the inhomogeneous Oseen equation

$$\Big(\bar\nabla^2-\frac{c}{2}\frac{\partial}{\partial \hat r}-\frac{1-c^2}{2\hat r}\frac{\partial}{\partial c}\Big)\bar\nabla^2\hat\psi_2 = -\frac{1}{2\hat r}\frac{\partial(\hat\psi_1,\bar\nabla^2\hat\psi_1)}{\partial(\hat r, \theta)},$$

and vanish at infinity.

Actually the value of a_2, equal to $-0\cdot87$, was determined by Kaplun (1957) rather differently. He expressed the velocity components in terms of Oseen's fundamental solutions, and carefully discussed the matching procedure, which is more complicated for a circular cylinder than it is for a sphere.

7. Heat transfer

The question of heat transfer between an obstacle and a stream at small Reynolds number is not without interest, particularly in connexion with the hot-wire technique of measuring turbulent velocities, in which the Reynolds number may be as small as $0\cdot05$ for each 1 ft/sec of velocity. In this case the free-stream velocity is a fluctuating one, and the temperature difference between the wire and the stream is large, so that strictly we ought to start with the Navier–Stokes equations (including the energy equation) for unsteady compressible flow and reduce them to either the Stokes or the Oseen form. To introduce compressibility would, however, take us outside the province of this book, and so we shall consider only the heat transfer when the temperature T_w of the obstacle is nearly equal to the temperature T_∞ of the free stream. In such cases the temperature equation (III. 31) is valid, and for steady flow at small Reynolds number the Oseen form of this equation is

$$U\frac{\partial T}{\partial x} = \frac{\nu}{\sigma}\nabla^2 T, \qquad (120)$$

which is similar to equation (37) for the vorticity. The same type of equation is satisfied by the spanwise component of velocity when an infinite cylinder is set obliquely to a stream (Tomotika, Aoi, and Yosinabu 1953). It can be readily solved, and indeed it is also a straight-forward matter to solve the corresponding equation when the free stream fluctuates.

7.1. *Circular cylinder*

The example of the hot-wire anemometer leads us first to consider heat transfer from a warm circular cylinder, and if we write

$$T = T_\infty + (T_w - T_\infty)f, \qquad (121)$$

the appropriate solution of (120) is given by

$$f = e^{\sigma\xi\cos\theta}\sum_0^\infty C_m K_m(\sigma\xi)\cos m\theta \qquad (122)$$

subject to the boundary condition, at the surface $r = a$,

$$\sum_0^\infty C_m K_m(\sigma ka)\cos m\theta = e^{-\sigma ka\cos\theta}, \qquad (123)$$

which determines the constants C_m.

The heat transfer may be expressed in terms of a Nusselt number N, defined by

$$N = -\frac{\int_0^{2\pi}\lambda(\partial T/\partial r)_{r=a}\, a\, d\theta}{2\pi a[\lambda(T_w - T_\infty)/2a]},$$

which gives

$$N = 2\left[\frac{I_0(\tfrac{1}{4}\sigma R)}{K_0(\tfrac{1}{4}\sigma R)} + 2\sum_1^\infty (-1)^m \frac{I_m(\tfrac{1}{4}\sigma R)}{K_m(\tfrac{1}{4}\sigma R)}\right]. \qquad (124)$$

For small R, the Prandtl number σ being assumed to be $O(1)$, equation (124) can be expanded in the form

$$N = A - B, \qquad (125)$$

when $O[(\sigma R/8)^4]$ is ignored, where

$$A = 2[\ln(8/\sigma R) - \gamma]^{-1}, \quad \text{and} \quad B = (\sigma R/8)^2(8 + \tfrac{1}{2}A^2).$$

We may note in passing that the solution of Stokes's temperature equation cannot satisfy the boundary conditions in this case.

Some values of N for air ($\sigma = 0.72$) calculated from (125) are compared with the empirical formula

$$N = 0.32 + 0.43 R^{0.52} \qquad (126)$$

for heat transfer from a circular cylinder (McAdams 1951, p. 220) in Table IV. 2.

TABLE IV. 2

Heat transfer from a circular cylinder

R	A	B	N from equation (125)	N from equation (126)
0·1	0·484	0·001	0·483	0·456
0·2	0·581	0·003	0·578	0·512
0·4	0·728	0·011	0·717	0·592
0·6	0·854	0·024	0·830	0·653
0·8	0·974	0·044	0·930	0·705
1·0	1·092	0·070	1·022	0·750

7.2. *Sphere*

For a sphere, (122) and (123) are valid when the K_m and $\cos m\theta$ are replaced by $\chi_m(\sigma\xi)$ and $P_m(c)$ respectively. The Nusselt number in this case is

$$N = -\frac{2\pi a^2 \int_{-1}^{1} \lambda(\partial T/\partial r)_{r=a}\, dc}{4\pi a^2[\lambda(T_w - T_\infty)/2a]} = \frac{4\pi}{\sigma R} \sum_{0}^{\infty} (-1)^m (2m+1) \frac{I_{m+\frac12}(\tfrac14 \sigma R)}{K_{m+\frac12}(\tfrac14 \sigma R)}, \qquad (127)$$

which can be expanded as

$$N = 2 + \tfrac12 \sigma R - \tfrac{1}{24}(\sigma R)^2 + \tfrac{1}{96}(\sigma R)^3 - \dots \qquad (128)$$

for small R. The first term in this series is the value which would be obtained from Stokes's temperature equation.

8. The flow at large distances from an obstacle

The flow at large distances from an obstacle differs only slightly from the free stream, with velocity $U\mathbf{i}$ and pressure p_∞, and so, whatever the Reynolds number, it satisfies Oseen's equations, which result when the squares of perturbations to the free stream are omitted from the Navier–Stokes equations. Moreover, the flow at infinity has a special significance because the system of forces acting on the obstacle can be deduced from it when the laws of conservation of linear and angular momentum are applied to the fluid between the obstacle and a surrounding closed surface at infinity.

We shall refer, in the first instance, to plane flow past a cylinder. By considering linear momentum, Filon (1926) showed that the force

X, Z per unit span of cylinder is given by

$$X = - \oint_C [l(p-p_\infty)+\rho u(lu+nw)-\mu n\eta]\,ds, \qquad (129)$$

$$Z = - \oint_C [n(p-p_\infty)+\rho w(lu+nw)+\mu l\eta]\,ds, \qquad (130)$$

where C is a closed curve at infinity, to which the outward normal has direction cosines l, n. The pressure p and velocity $\mathbf{v}$ are given by (38) and (40) in terms of ϕ and χ, for which the general expressions are

$$\phi = Ur\cos\theta + A_0\ln r + \sum_1^\infty r^{-n}(A_n\cos n\theta + B_n\sin n\theta), \qquad (131)$$

$$\chi = e^{\xi\cos\theta}\sum_0^\infty K_m(\xi)(C_m\cos m\theta + D_m\sin m\theta). \qquad (132)$$

Since $K_m(\xi) \sim (\pi/2\xi)^{\frac{1}{2}}e^{-\xi}$ for large ξ, (132) shows that χ is negligible at infinity except in the wake W which occupies the parabolic region $kr(1-\cos\theta) = O(1)$. Here $\theta = O[(kr)^{-\frac{1}{2}}]$, and so $z = O(r^{\frac{1}{2}})$. In W, $\chi = O(r^{-\frac{1}{2}})$ and so the vorticity η, which is $-\partial\chi/\partial z$, is $O(r^{-1})$. In the irrotational flow, $\mathbf{v} = U\mathbf{i}+O(r^{-1})$, but in W, $\mathbf{v} = (U-\chi)\mathbf{i}+O(r^{-1})$. These results, concerning orders of magnitude, immediately yield from (129) that $X = \rho U \int_{C_w} l\chi\,ds$, where C_w is the part of C, of length $O(r^{\frac{1}{2}})$, lying in W. Also, since there can be no net outflow across C,

$$\oint_C \left(l\frac{\partial\phi}{\partial x}+n\frac{\partial\phi}{\partial z}\right) ds - \int_{C_w} l\chi\,ds = 0. \qquad (133)$$

The first of these integrals is the efflux $2\pi A_0$ from the potential source, and the second is the compensating influx along the wake. It therefore follows that the drag per unit span is given by

$$X = m\rho U, \qquad (134)$$

where m is the strength of the potential source. This is a result which we have already used in Section 5. Similarly, when the negligible terms have been discarded from (130), the result is

$$Z = \rho U \oint_C [n(\partial\phi/\partial x)-lw]\,ds,$$

which is the same as $\rho U \oint_C (nu-lw)\,ds$, provided that C is chosen to cross W at right angles, so that $\oint_{C_w} n\chi\,ds = 0$. This implies that the lift per unit span is given by

$$Z = \gamma\rho U, \qquad (135)$$

where γ is the (clockwise) circulation round C.

By considering angular momentum, Filon (1928) showed that the clockwise torque per unit span on the cylinder is

$$M = -2\mu\gamma - \oint_C [(lz-nx)(p-p_\infty)-\mu(lx+nz)\eta +$$
$$+\rho(lu+nw)(zu-xw)]\,ds, \quad (136)$$

which reduces to

$$M = -2\mu\gamma + \int_0^{2\pi} (\mu\eta+v_r\,v_\theta)r^2\,d\theta \quad (137)$$

when C is taken to be a circle of radius r. In applying (137) to calculate M, Filon (1928) used the second approximation to the solution of Oseen's equations and found that M was apparently logarithmically infinite when there was a circulation round the cylinder. Filon argued that this paradox could not be avoided by proceeding to the next approximation, and that the Oseen equations do not provide a satisfactory basis for developing successive approximations to the Navier–Stokes equations. However, Imai (1951) reconsidered this problem and reversed these conclusions of Filon.

Imai starts from the Helmholtz equation (Section III. 10)

$$\nabla^2\eta = -\frac{1}{\nu}\frac{\partial(\psi,\eta)}{\partial(x,z)}. \quad (138)$$

Writing $\psi = Uz+\psi_1+\psi_2+\psi_3+...$ for the stream function at large distances from the cylinder, where ψ_1, ψ_2, ψ_3, etc., represent successive approximations, he obtains the first approximation to (138) in the Oseen form

$$[\nabla^2-2k(\partial/\partial x)]\eta_1 = 0, \qquad \eta_1 = \nabla^2\psi_1. \quad (139)$$

Introducing parabolic coordinates $\alpha = (2\xi)^{\frac{1}{2}}\cos\frac{1}{2}\theta$, $\beta = (2\xi)^{\frac{1}{2}}\sin\frac{1}{2}\theta$, Imai obtains

$$\psi_1 = (\gamma/2\pi)\ln r - \tfrac{1}{2}m(\mathrm{erf}\,\beta - \theta/\pi). \quad (140)$$

Outside the wake the flow is irrotational, and (140) reduces to

$$\psi_1 = \mathscr{I}\left(\frac{m+i\gamma}{2\pi}\ln\mathfrak{z}\right), \quad (141)$$

where $\mathfrak{z} = x+iz$.

The second approximation satisfies

$$\left(\nabla^2-2k\frac{\partial}{\partial x}\right)\eta_2 = -\frac{1}{\nu}\frac{\partial(\psi_1,\eta_1)}{\partial(x,z)}, \qquad \eta_2 = \nabla^2\psi_2, \quad (142)$$

and then

$$\psi_2 = -\frac{km^2}{4\pi^{1/2}U\alpha}[\sqrt{2}\,\mathrm{erf}(\beta\sqrt{2})-e^{-\beta^2}\mathrm{erf}\,\beta]-\frac{km\gamma}{\pi^{3/2}U}\left(\frac{\ln\alpha}{\alpha}\right)e^{-\beta^2}+\frac{A}{\alpha}e^{-\beta^2},$$
$$(143)$$

where A is an arbitrary constant; outside the wake this reduces to

$$\psi_2 = \mathscr{I}\left(-\frac{ik^{\frac{1}{2}}m^2}{4\pi^{\frac{1}{2}}U_3^{\frac{1}{2}}}\right). \tag{144}$$

Filon's difficulty arose because the term involving $\ln \alpha$ in ψ_2 introduces a term $\ln r$ into the expression for M. Imai shows that this is cancelled by the contribution from a term involving $\ln_3$ that occurs in the expression for ψ_3.

In three dimensions, the question of the flow at large distances from the obstacle is more difficult to handle in general terms. Goldstein (1929a) established the result $X = m\rho U$ for a finite body of revolution, and in a later paper (1931a) he confirmed the result for an arbitrary finite body. In the latter paper he showed that the transverse force on the body in the y-direction, say, is given by

$$Y = -\rho U \int_{\Sigma} (lv - mu) \, dS \tag{145}$$

over some large surface Σ surrounding the body. If Σ is chosen to be a right cylinder with its generators parallel to the z-axis, the transverse force is given by

$$Y = \rho U \int_{-\infty}^{\infty} \gamma(z) \, dz, \tag{146}$$

where $\gamma(z)$ is the clockwise circulation round the cylinder at the station z. Garstang (1937) formulated the general solution of Oseen's equations in three dimensions in terms of series, and identified $\int_{-\infty}^{\infty} \gamma(z) \, dz$ with one of the coefficients in the series. The system of couples acting on a three-dimensional body does not, however, appear to have been studied in this connexion.

V

TWO-DIMENSIONAL BOUNDARY LAYERS

PART I

EQUATIONS OF MOTION

1. Derivation of the boundary-layer equations for flow along a flat surface

WHEN a fluid of any viscosity flows along a fixed impermeable wall, or past the rigid surface of an immersed body, an essential condition is that the velocity at any point on the wall or other fixed surface is zero. The extent to which this condition modifies the general character of the flow depends upon the value of the viscosity, as is illustrated by some of the solutions of the two previous chapters. If the body is of streamlined shape and if the viscosity is small without being negligible, the modifying effect appears to be confined within narrow regions adjacent to the solid surfaces; these are called *boundary layers* (German, *Grenzschichten* or *Reibungsschichten*; French, *couches limites*; Russian, пограничные слои or *pogranichnye sloi*, transliterated). Within such layers the fluid velocity changes rapidly from zero to its main-stream value, and this may imply a steep gradient of shearing stress; as a consequence, not all the viscous terms in the equations of motion will be negligible, even though the viscosity, which they contain as a factor, is itself very small.

A more precise criterion for the existence of a well-defined laminar boundary layer is that the Reynolds number should be large, though not so large as to imply a breakdown of the laminar flow. It is one of the important features of the exact solutions of Chapter III that, for large values of R, they actually exhibit regions of steep velocity gradient, boundary layers in the sense already defined. To this theoretical evidence may be added the results of much experimental observation, which shows that these boundary layers occur in practice.

In developing a mathematical theory of boundary layers, the first step is to show the existence, as the Reynolds number R tends to infinity, or the kinematic viscosity ν tends to zero, of a limiting form of the equations of motion, different from that obtained by putting $\nu = 0$ in the first place. A solution of these limiting equations may then reasonably be expected to describe approximately the flow in a laminar boundary layer for which R is large but not infinite. This is the basis of the classical theory of laminar boundary layers; a few later developments have been in the direction of estimating the error of applying such an *asymptotic* solution to a situation in which R is really finite.

The full equations of motion for two-dimensional flow are:

$$\frac{\partial u}{\partial t} + u\frac{\partial u}{\partial x} + w\frac{\partial u}{\partial z} = -\frac{1}{\rho}\frac{\partial p}{\partial x} + \nu\left(\frac{\partial^2 u}{\partial x^2} + \frac{\partial^2 u}{\partial z^2}\right), \tag{1}$$

$$\frac{\partial w}{\partial t} + u\frac{\partial w}{\partial x} + w\frac{\partial w}{\partial z} = -\frac{1}{\rho}\frac{\partial p}{\partial z} + \nu\left(\frac{\partial^2 w}{\partial x^2} + \frac{\partial^2 w}{\partial z^2}\right), \tag{2}$$

$$\frac{\partial u}{\partial x} + \frac{\partial w}{\partial z} = 0. \tag{3}$$

The xz-plane is taken as the plane of the boundary-layer flow, with the axis of x along, and that of z perpendicular to, the plane wall; thus $u = w = 0$ on $z = 0$.

The equation of conservation of mass (3) implies the existence of a stream function $\psi(x, z, t)$ such that

$$u = \partial\psi/\partial z, \qquad w = -\partial\psi/\partial x, \tag{4}$$

and a fourth-order equation for ψ may be obtained by eliminating the pressure p from equations (1) and (2), and using (4). With

$$\nabla^2\psi \equiv \partial^2\psi/\partial x^2 + \partial^2\psi/\partial z^2,$$

this may be written

$$\frac{\partial}{\partial t}(\nabla^2\psi) + \frac{\partial\psi}{\partial z}\frac{\partial}{\partial x}(\nabla^2\psi) - \frac{\partial\psi}{\partial x}\frac{\partial}{\partial z}(\nabla^2\psi) = \nu\nabla^2(\nabla^2\psi). \tag{5}$$

Since the only component of vorticity is $\eta = \partial u/\partial z - \partial w/\partial x = \nabla^2\psi$, (5) may also be written in the form

$$\frac{\partial\eta}{\partial t} + \frac{\partial\psi}{\partial z}\frac{\partial\eta}{\partial x} - \frac{\partial\psi}{\partial x}\frac{\partial\eta}{\partial z} = \nu\nabla^2\eta. \tag{6}$$

In order to derive the limiting form referred to earlier, a non-dimensional form of the equations is convenient. If l is a typical length, U a typical speed, and $R = lU/\nu$ the corresponding Reynolds number for the flow as a whole, the following choice of variables is made:

$$\begin{aligned} \text{x} &= x/l, & \text{z} &= R^{\frac12}z/l, & \text{т} &= Ut/l, \\ \text{u} &= u/U, & \text{w} &= R^{\frac12}w/U, & \text{p} &= p/\rho U^2. \end{aligned} \tag{7}$$

Equations (1) to (3) become

$$\frac{\partial u}{\partial \tau} + u\frac{\partial u}{\partial x} + w\frac{\partial u}{\partial z} = -\frac{\partial p}{\partial x} + \frac{1}{R}\frac{\partial^2 u}{\partial x^2} + \frac{\partial^2 u}{\partial z^2}, \tag{8}$$

$$\frac{1}{R}\left(\frac{\partial w}{\partial \tau} + u\frac{\partial w}{\partial x} + w\frac{\partial w}{\partial z}\right) = -\frac{\partial p}{\partial z} + \frac{1}{R^2}\frac{\partial^2 w}{\partial x^2} + \frac{1}{R}\frac{\partial^2 w}{\partial z^2}, \tag{9}$$

$$\frac{\partial u}{\partial x} + \frac{\partial w}{\partial z} = 0, \tag{10}$$

in which quantities denoted by small capital letters are non-dimensional. On the assumption that all the derivatives in these equations are of the same order of magnitude for large values of R, their limiting forms are

$$\frac{\partial u}{\partial \tau} + u\frac{\partial u}{\partial x} + w\frac{\partial u}{\partial z} = -\frac{\partial p}{\partial x} + \frac{\partial^2 u}{\partial z^2}, \tag{11}$$

$$0 = -\frac{\partial p}{\partial z}, \tag{12}$$

$$\frac{\partial u}{\partial x} + \frac{\partial w}{\partial z} = 0. \tag{13}$$

Equations (11) to (13) are the boundary-layer equations in non-dimensional form.

The original method of deriving the boundary-layer equations, due to Prandtl (1904) and Blasius (1908), is based on a consideration of approximate orders of magnitude. It is less precise than the argument already given, but may be physically easier to understand. Suppose that l is a typical length, and U a typical speed, along the boundary layer; and that δ is a typical length, and W a typical speed, across the layer. In some sense δ is the *thickness* of the boundary layer. Then in equation (3) the terms $\partial u/\partial x$ and $\partial w/\partial z$ are respectively of order U/l and W/δ. Consequently $W/U = O(\delta/l)$, and the ratio δ/l is supposed small compared with unity.

In equation (1), the inertia terms $u\,\partial u/\partial x$ and $w\,\partial u/\partial z$ are now seen to be both of order U^2/l. Of the two viscous terms on the right-hand side, $\nu\,\partial^2 u/\partial z^2$, being of order $\nu U/\delta^2$, is greater than $\nu\,\partial^2 u/\partial x^2$ by a factor $(l/\delta)^2$, and so the latter term may be neglected. If the surviving viscous term is now required to have the *same order of magnitude as the inertia terms*, it follows that $(\delta/l)^2$ is of the same order as ν/Ul, or

$$\delta/l = O(R^{-\frac{1}{2}}). \tag{14}$$

On the further assumption that the time derivative $\partial u/\partial t$ is of no

greater order than the other terms, equation (1) may be simplified
slightly to

$$\frac{\partial u}{\partial t}+u\frac{\partial u}{\partial x}+w\frac{\partial u}{\partial z} = -\frac{1}{\rho}\frac{\partial p}{\partial x}+\nu\frac{\partial^2 u}{\partial z^2}, \tag{15}$$

and this is formally equivalent to (11).

In equation (2), each term which involves a velocity component is, by comparison with the corresponding term of (1), of lesser order by a factor δ/l; hence $\partial p/\partial z$ may be neglected by comparison with $\partial p/\partial x$. This means that the pressure is almost constant through the thickness of the boundary layer, and its value at any point is therefore determined by the corresponding main-stream conditions. If $U(x,t)$ now denotes the main-stream velocity, so that $-\rho^{-1}\partial p/\partial x = \partial U/\partial t+U\,\partial U/\partial x$, elimination of the pressure from (15) gives

$$\frac{\partial u}{\partial t}+u\frac{\partial u}{\partial x}+w\frac{\partial u}{\partial z}-\nu\frac{\partial^2 u}{\partial z^2} = f(x,t) = \frac{\partial U}{\partial t}+U\frac{\partial U}{\partial x}. \tag{16}$$

This equation was derived by Kármán (1921) by seeking a solution of (5) in the form $\psi = \nu^{\frac{1}{2}}\Psi(x, z\nu^{-\frac{1}{2}}, t)$. It may be seen to be of third order when written in terms of the stream function, and this is an important mathematical difference from the full equation (5), leading to certain anomalies which are discussed in later sections.

2. Boundary-layer equations for flow along a curved surface

When the surface at which the boundary layer forms is curved, the method used in Section 1 must be modified to take account of the curvature. The general equations of the two-dimensional motion of a viscous fluid referred to an orthogonal curvilinear coordinate system are (see Section III. 11):

$$\frac{\partial v_1}{\partial t}+v_3\,\omega_2 = -\frac{1}{h_1}\frac{\partial}{\partial x_1}\left(\frac{p}{\rho}+\tfrac{1}{2}v_1^2+\tfrac{1}{2}v_3^2\right)+\frac{\nu}{h_3}\frac{\partial\omega_2}{\partial x_3}, \tag{17}$$

$$\frac{\partial v_3}{\partial t}-v_1\,\omega_2 = -\frac{1}{h_3}\frac{\partial}{\partial x_3}\left(\frac{p}{\rho}+\tfrac{1}{2}v_1^2+\tfrac{1}{2}v_3^2\right)-\frac{\nu}{h_1}\frac{\partial\omega_2}{\partial x_1}, \tag{18}$$

$$\frac{\partial}{\partial x_1}(h_3\,v_1)+\frac{\partial}{\partial x_3}(h_1\,v_3) = 0, \tag{19}$$

where
$$\omega_2 = \frac{1}{h_1 h_3}\left\{\frac{\partial}{\partial x_3}(h_1\,v_1)-\frac{\partial}{\partial x_1}(h_3\,v_3)\right\} \tag{20}$$

is the only component of vorticity present.

The coordinates x, z of Section 1 are now defined as distances measured along the wall and at right angles to the wall, so that these form a set of orthogonal curvilinear coordinates. The corresponding components of velocity are then u, w respectively. These coordinates and velocity components are then made dimensionless as in Section 1, by introducing the variables x, z, u, w. When x, z are taken for the variables x_1, x_3 used in equations (17) to (20),

$$h_1 = l(1+\kappa l R^{-\frac{1}{2}}\mathrm{z}) = l\mathrm{H}, \qquad h_3 = lR^{-\frac{1}{2}}, \qquad (21)$$

where κ is the curvature of the wall, reckoned positive in the case of Fig. V. 1, in which the centre of curvature is on the side $z < 0$.

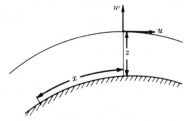

FIG. V. 1. Coordinates for boundary-layer flow along
a curved surface.

In terms of these non-dimensional variables, equations (17) to (19) become

$$\mathrm{H}\frac{\partial \mathrm{U}}{\partial \mathrm{T}}+\mathrm{U}\frac{\partial \mathrm{U}}{\partial \mathrm{X}}+\mathrm{W}\frac{\partial(\mathrm{H}\mathrm{U})}{\partial \mathrm{Z}} = -\frac{\partial \mathrm{P}}{\partial \mathrm{X}}+\mathrm{H}\frac{\partial}{\partial \mathrm{Z}}\left\{\frac{1}{\mathrm{H}}\frac{\partial(\mathrm{H}\mathrm{U})}{\partial \mathrm{Z}}-\frac{1}{R}\frac{1}{\mathrm{H}}\frac{\partial \mathrm{W}}{\partial \mathrm{X}}\right\}, \quad (22)$$

$$\frac{1}{R}\left(\frac{\partial \mathrm{W}}{\partial \mathrm{T}}+\frac{\mathrm{U}}{\mathrm{H}}\frac{\partial \mathrm{W}}{\partial \mathrm{X}}+\mathrm{W}\frac{\partial \mathrm{W}}{\partial \mathrm{Z}}\right)-\frac{\mathrm{U}^2}{\mathrm{H}}\frac{\partial \mathrm{H}}{\partial \mathrm{Z}} = -\frac{\partial \mathrm{P}}{\partial \mathrm{Z}}+\frac{1}{\mathrm{H}}\frac{\partial}{\partial \mathrm{X}}\left(\frac{1}{R^2}\frac{1}{\mathrm{H}}\frac{\partial \mathrm{W}}{\partial \mathrm{X}}-\frac{1}{R}\frac{1}{\mathrm{H}}\frac{\partial(\mathrm{H}\mathrm{U})}{\partial \mathrm{Z}}\right),$$
$$(23)$$

$$\frac{\partial \mathrm{U}}{\partial \mathrm{X}}+\frac{\partial(\mathrm{H}\mathrm{W})}{\partial \mathrm{Z}} = 0. \qquad (24)$$

Now from (21), as $\nu \to 0$, so that $R \to \infty$, H tends to 1 and $\partial \mathrm{H}/\partial \mathrm{X}$, $\partial \mathrm{H}/\partial \mathrm{Z}$ both tend to 0. Then the limiting forms of (22) to (24) as $\nu \to 0$ may be seen to be identical with the equations (11), (12), (13) obtained in the case of flow over a plane surface. Thus when R is large the equations of motion reduce to the boundary-layer equations

$$\frac{\partial u}{\partial t}+u\frac{\partial u}{\partial x}+w\frac{\partial u}{\partial z} = \frac{\partial U}{\partial t}+U\frac{\partial U}{\partial x}+\nu\frac{\partial^2 u}{\partial z^2}, \qquad (25)$$

$$\frac{\partial u}{\partial x}+\frac{\partial w}{\partial z} = 0, \qquad (26)$$

which have the same form for flow over a curved surface as for flow past a plane wall. It is, however, necessary that $\partial \mathrm{H}/\partial \mathrm{X}$ and $\partial \mathrm{H}/\partial \mathrm{Z}$ shall be small compared with 1, so that $\kappa\delta$ and $\delta l\, d\kappa/dx$ must be small, where

δ is a measure of boundary-layer thickness as in Section 1. The pressure gradient across the layer is given by (23) and (21) as approximately $\partial P/\partial z = \kappa l R^{-\frac{1}{4}} U^2$ or

$$\partial p/\partial z = \kappa \rho u^2. \tag{27}$$

This is just the gradient of pressure required to balance the centrifugal effect of the flow round the curved surface.

3. Boundary conditions for steady flow

If the surface at which the boundary layer forms is fixed and impermeable the conditions to be satisfied by the velocity are $u = w = 0$ at $z = 0$. It follows that the derivatives $\partial u/\partial x$ and $\partial w/\partial x$ are zero at the surface; so also is $\partial w/\partial z$, by the equation of continuity. However, $\partial u/\partial z$, which is proportional to the skin friction, is not in general zero except at a point of separation (see Section 11). If the surface is permeable there may be normal suction or blowing, in which case the conditions are

$$u = 0, \qquad w = \mp w_s(x) \quad \text{at } z = 0 \tag{28}$$

where $w_s(x)$ is assumed to be prescribed. There may be oblique suction or blowing, and then neither u nor w is zero at the surface.

A boundary layer may also occur in the form of a narrow jet (see Section 23) or a thin wake (see Section VI. 9), in which cases the line $z = 0$ is the central axis and the conditions there are $\partial u/\partial z = 0$, $w = 0$ by the symmetry of the flow.

At the other extreme, the boundary layer must join smoothly to the main flow. The form of the solutions to the boundary-layer equations is, however, such that the main stream must be regarded as being 'at infinity'. Thus

$$u \rightarrow U(x) \quad \text{as } z \rightarrow \infty \tag{29}$$

for each value of x. Although no formal proof is available, it seems likely that the condition (29) need be applied at only one value of x, and that for positions downstream of this point it will automatically be satisfied (Rheinboldt 1955). The reason for this is that the boundary-layer equation itself contains information about the velocity of the main stream.

Finally, the velocity profile $u(z)$ must be specified at an initial section, say at $x = 0$.

It will be noticed that no explicit restrictions are placed on w either at $x = 0$ or at $z = \infty$, as would be necessary if a solution of the full viscous equations were being sought. Boundary-layer solutions may not, in fact, give realistic values of w at points away from the surface. The main reason is that the boundary-layer approximation reduces the equations of motion from fourth order to third order, so that some reduction of the minimum essential boundary conditions is inevitable. It is not, however, impossible for boundary-layer solutions to exhibit the correct physical behaviour at all limits (see Section 18).

Even if the conditions set out above ensure the existence of a solution of the boundary-layer equations, they may not guarantee its uniqueness; in some problems (see Section 21) the contrary is, in fact, known to be the case.

4. Vorticity, stress, and energy dissipation in boundary layers

In a two-dimensional flow there is only one component of vorticity, namely that at right angles to the plane of flow. In Cartesian coordinates,

$$\eta = \frac{\partial u}{\partial z} - \frac{\partial w}{\partial x}. \tag{30}$$

The same expression is approximately true if x and z are orthogonal curvilinear coordinates (see Section 2), provided that $\kappa\delta$ is small.

At an ordinary point of a boundary layer, $\partial w/\partial x$ is expected to be of smaller order than $\partial u/\partial z$ by a factor R^{-1}, hence it is usual to adopt for the vorticity the simplified formula $\eta = \partial u/\partial z$. When $\partial u/\partial z$ is itself very small, as in the immediate neighbourhood of a point of separation (see Section 11), the two derivatives $\partial w/\partial x$ and $\partial u/\partial z$ may be of the same order of magnitude, and it would be better to retain the exact expression (30).

The normal components of stress perpendicular and parallel to a straight wall may be derived from Section III. 5. Expressed non-dimensionally they are as follows:

$$\frac{p_{xx}}{\rho U^2} = -\frac{p}{\rho U^2} + 2\frac{\nu}{U^2}\frac{\partial u}{\partial x}, \tag{31}$$

$$\frac{p_{zz}}{\rho U^2} = -\frac{p}{\rho U^2} + 2\frac{\nu}{U^2}\frac{\partial w}{\partial z}. \tag{32}$$

The last term in each of these equations is of order R^{-1}, and so is negligible; the boundary-layer approximation thus gives

$$p_{xx} = p_{zz} = -p.$$

The shearing stress over surfaces parallel to the wall is

$$p_{zx} = \mu\left(\frac{\partial u}{\partial z} + \frac{\partial w}{\partial x}\right) \tag{33}$$

and, like the vorticity, this is approximately

$$p_{zx} = \mu\,\partial u/\partial z \tag{34}$$

except when it happens to be very small. It should be noted, however, that (33) and (34) are identical at points on a fixed impermeable wall, where $w = 0$ and $\partial w/\partial x \equiv 0$. If the wall is curved, subject to the same restriction as before, the formulae (31) to (34) are still valid.

The rate of dissipation of energy per unit volume per unit time in a boundary layer is, from Section III. 8, approximately equal to $\mu(\partial u/\partial z)^2$, and this has a finite limit when $R \to \infty$. The order of magnitude of the boundary-layer thickness could have been determined by imposing this condition.

PART II

PROPERTIES OF THE EQUATIONS AND THEIR SOLUTIONS

5. Boundary-layer thicknesses, skin friction, and energy dissipation

In most physical problems the solutions of the boundary-layer equations (25) and (26) are such that the velocity component u attains its main-stream value U only asymptotically as $R^{\frac{1}{2}}z/l \to \infty$. The thickness of the layer is therefore indefinite, as there is always some departure from the asymptotic value at any finite distance z from the surface. In practice the approach to the limit is rapid and a point is soon reached beyond which the influence of viscosity is imperceptible. It would therefore be possible to regard the boundary-layer thickness as the distance δ from the surface beyond which $u/U > 0.99$, for example, but this is not sufficiently precise (since $\partial u/\partial z$ is small there) for experimental work, and is not of theoretical significance.

The scale of the boundary-layer thickness can, however, be specified adequately by certain lengths capable of precise definition, both for experimental measurement and for theoretical study. These measures of boundary-layer thickness are defined as follows:

Displacement thickness δ_1:

$$\delta_1 = \int_0^\infty \left(1 - \frac{u}{U}\right) dz. \tag{35}$$

Momentum thickness δ_2:

$$\delta_2 = \int_0^\infty \frac{u}{U}\left(1 - \frac{u}{U}\right) dz. \tag{36}$$

Energy thickness δ_3:

$$\delta_3 = \int_0^\infty \frac{u}{U}\left(1 - \frac{u^2}{U^2}\right) dz. \tag{37}$$

The upper limit of integration is taken as infinity owing to the asymptotic approach of u/U to 1, but in practice the upper limit is the point beyond which the integrand is negligible.

$U\delta_1$ is the diminution, due to the boundary layer, of the volume flux across a normal to the surface; the streamlines of the outer flow are thus displaced away from the surface through a distance δ_1. Similarly, $\rho U^2\delta_2$ is the flux of the defect of momentum, and $\frac{1}{2}\rho U^3\delta_3$ is the flux of the defect of kinetic energy.

Two other quantities related to these boundary-layer thicknesses are the *skin friction* τ_w and the *dissipation integral* D. The skin friction is defined as the shearing stress exerted by the fluid on the surface over which it flows, and is therefore the value of p_{zx} at $z = 0$, which by (34) is

$$\tau_w = \mu\left(\frac{\partial u}{\partial z}\right)_{z=0} \tag{38}$$

The rate at which energy is dissipated by the action of viscosity has been shown (in Section 4) to be $\mu(\partial u/\partial z)^2$ per unit time per unit volume, and D is the integral of this across the layer:

$$D = \int_0^\infty \mu\left(\frac{\partial u}{\partial z}\right)^2 dz. \tag{39}$$

Consequently D is the total dissipation in a cylinder of small cross-section with axis normal to the layer per unit time per unit area of cross-section.

6. Momentum and energy equations

The skin friction and dissipation are connected with the boundary-layer thicknesses by two equations which represent the balance of momentum and of energy within a small section of the boundary layer, and are due respectively to Kármán (1921) and to Leibenson (1935). The energy equation was also derived by Wieghardt (1946, 1948).

Momentum integral

The equation is most simply obtained, as shown by Pohlhausen (1921), by integration from the boundary-layer equations (25) and (26). These may be written as

$$-\nu\frac{\partial^2 u}{\partial z^2} = \frac{\partial}{\partial t}(U-u) + U\frac{\partial U}{\partial x} - u\frac{\partial u}{\partial x} - w\frac{\partial u}{\partial z},$$

$$0 = (U-u)\frac{\partial u}{\partial x} + (U-u)\frac{\partial w}{\partial z},$$

where (26) has been multiplied by $(U-u)$. By addition of these,

$$-\nu \frac{\partial^2 u}{\partial z^2} = \frac{\partial}{\partial t}(U-u) + \frac{\partial}{\partial x}(Uu-u^2) + (U-u)\frac{\partial U}{\partial x} + \frac{\partial}{\partial z}(wU-wu).$$

On integration with respect to z from 0 to ∞ this yields, since $\partial u/\partial z$ and $w(U-u)$ tend to 0 as $z \to \infty$,

$$\nu\left(\frac{\partial u}{\partial z}\right)_{z=0} = \frac{\partial}{\partial t}\int_0^\infty (U-u)\,dz + \frac{\partial}{\partial x}\int_0^\infty (Uu-u^2)\,dz + \frac{\partial U}{\partial x}\int_0^\infty (U-u)\,dz + w_s U, \tag{40}$$

where $w_s = w_s(x) = -w(x, 0)$ is the velocity of suction. When the integrals are expressed in terms of the boundary-layer thicknesses, this becomes

$$\frac{\tau_w}{\rho} = \frac{\partial}{\partial t}(U\delta_1) + \frac{\partial}{\partial x}(U^2\delta_2) + U\frac{\partial U}{\partial x}\delta_1 + w_s U, \tag{41}$$

or, in non-dimensional form,

$$\frac{\tau_w}{\rho U^2} = \frac{1}{U^2}\frac{\partial}{\partial t}(U\delta_1) + \frac{\partial\delta_2}{\partial x} + \frac{\delta_1 + 2\delta_2}{U}\frac{\partial U}{\partial x} + \frac{w_s}{U}. \tag{42}$$

The original derivation by Kármán was based on momentum considerations. It is simpler, however, to interpret equation (40), multiplied by $\rho\,\delta x$, as an equation for the rate of change of 'momentum defect', $\rho(U-u)$ per unit volume, for the small slice of boundary layer between the planes x and $x+\delta x$. On the right-hand side of (40) the first term represents the local rate of change of this momentum defect, the second is the rate of change due to convection across the planes x and $x+\delta x$, and the last term represents convection across the porous surface $z = 0$. Since there is no convection at the edge of the layer, where the momentum defect is zero, the total rate of change is equal to the opposing frictional force, which gives the term on the left-hand side, together with two terms which cancel outside the boundary layer. One of these is the opposing pressure force

$$\partial p/\partial x = -\rho(\partial U/\partial t + U\,\partial U/\partial x)$$

per unit volume, and the other is the rate of change of the main-stream momentum ρU associated with any particle of fluid in the boundary layer, namely $\rho(\partial U/\partial t + u\,\partial U/\partial x)$. The net effect of these two is a term

$$-\partial U/\partial x \int_0^\infty (U-u)\,dz$$

on the left-hand side of (40), which appears as the third term on the right-hand side with the opposite sign.

Energy integral

Equations (25) and (26), multiplied by $2u$ and (U^2-u^2) respectively, are

$$-2\nu u\frac{\partial^2 u}{\partial z^2} = 2u\frac{\partial}{\partial t}(U-u)+2uU\frac{\partial U}{\partial x}-2u^2\frac{\partial u}{\partial x}-2wu\frac{\partial u}{\partial z},$$

$$0 = (U^2-u^2)\frac{\partial u}{\partial x}+(U^2-u^2)\frac{\partial w}{\partial z},$$

and by addition they imply

$$2\nu\left(\frac{\partial u}{\partial z}\right)^2-2\nu\frac{\partial}{\partial z}\left(u\frac{\partial u}{\partial z}\right)$$

$$= \frac{\partial}{\partial t}(Uu-u^2)+U^2\frac{\partial}{\partial t}\left(1-\frac{u}{U}\right)+\frac{\partial}{\partial x}(U^2u-u^3)+\frac{\partial}{\partial z}(wU^2-wu^2).$$

Since $w(U^2-u^2)$ and $\partial u/\partial z$ both tend to 0 as z tends to ∞, this equation gives on integration with respect to z from 0 to ∞,

$$\frac{2D}{\rho} = \frac{\partial}{\partial t}(U^2\delta_2)+U^2\frac{\partial\delta_1}{\partial t}+\frac{\partial}{\partial x}(U^3\delta_3)+w_s U^2. \tag{43}$$

This may be written non-dimensionally as

$$\frac{2D}{\rho U^3} = \frac{1}{U}\frac{\partial}{\partial t}(\delta_1+\delta_2)+\frac{2\delta_2}{U^2}\frac{\partial U}{\partial t}+\frac{1}{U^3}\frac{\partial}{\partial x}(U^3\delta_3)+\frac{w_s}{U}. \tag{44}$$

The energy integral may also be regarded as an equation for the 'kinetic energy defect' $\frac{1}{2}\rho(U^2-u^2)$ per unit volume, namely

$$\frac{\partial}{\partial t}\int_0^\infty \frac{1}{2}\rho(U^2-u^2)\,dz+\frac{\partial}{\partial x}\int_0^\infty \frac{1}{2}\rho(U^2-u^2)u\,dz+\frac{1}{2}\rho U^2 w_s$$

$$= D+\rho\frac{\partial U}{\partial t}\int_0^\infty (U-u)dz. \tag{45}$$

In this equation the left-hand side represents the sum of the local and convective rates of change of kinetic energy defect. On the right-hand side the first term is the contribution of viscous dissipation. The second is the sum of (i) the rate of energy loss due to pressure gradient forces, which is

$$u\,\partial p/\partial x = -\rho u(\partial U/\partial t+U\,\partial U/\partial x)$$

per unit volume, and (ii) the rate of change of the main-stream kinetic energy $\frac{1}{2}\rho U^2$ associated with a particle of fluid in the boundary layer, namely $\partial(\frac{1}{2}\rho U^2)/\partial t+u\partial(\frac{1}{2}\rho U^2)/\partial x$ per unit volume. As before, these balance outside the boundary layer, but in it have the net effect given by the last term in equation (45).

7. Behaviour of the solutions of the boundary-layer equations and conditions for separation

If a fixed obstacle in a steady stream is a cylinder of suitable shape, the pressure at its surface will fall from the stagnation value at the leading edge over the forward part, and rise again at the rear. The conditions $u = w = 0$ at $z = 0$, combined with (15), imply that

$$\nu\left(\frac{\partial^2 u}{\partial z^2}\right)_{z=0} = \frac{1}{\rho}\frac{dp}{dx}, \tag{46}$$

while, if $u \to U$ from below as $z \to \infty$, $\partial^2 u/\partial z^2$ is negative for large values of z. Hence, when $dp/dx < 0$ it may be expected, as is found in practice,

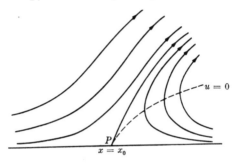

FIG. V. 2. Streamlines near separation.

that $\partial^2 u/\partial z^2$ is negative right across the layer and the 'boundary-layer profile', the graph of u plotted against z for fixed x, is concave towards the z-axis. This is typical of the behaviour of a boundary layer in a favourable pressure gradient, and $\partial u/\partial z$ has its greatest value at $z = 0$. If $dp/dx > 0$, on the other hand, (46) shows that $\partial^2 u/\partial z^2$ must change sign within the layer, and so the profile has an inflexion. It is also found that $(\partial u/\partial z)_{z=0}$, which is proportional to the skin friction τ_w, decreases with increasing x in the region of rising pressure, and may eventually vanish, at $x = x_0$ say. (See Section VI. 25 for some further discussion of velocity profiles.)

When separation of the flow occurs at a point P there is a reverse flow beyond P close to the surface, and so $(\partial u/\partial z)_{z=0}$ changes sign at P (see Fig. V. 2). Consequently any solution of the boundary-layer equations in which $(\partial u/\partial z)_{z=0}$ vanishes at some point $x = x_0$ in the region of adverse pressure gradient indicates the occurrence of separation. Calculations based on observed pressures indicate, moreover, an approximate agreement between theory and experiment in the position of the separation point (see Sections VI. 10 and VI. 26). However, the solutions of the boundary-layer equations may be anomalous in the sense that they exhibit singular behaviour at $x = x_0$, whereas the corresponding solutions of the Navier–Stokes equations are presumably regular (Dean 1950). Too much importance should not, therefore, be

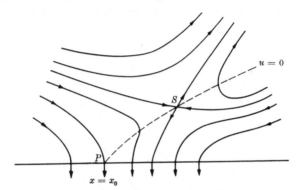

FIG. V. 3. Streamlines near separation with suction.

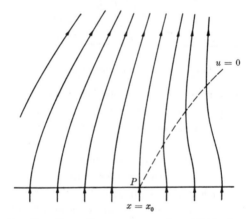

FIG. V. 4. Streamlines near separation with blowing.

attached to the numerical value of x_0, as determined by the boundary-layer equations together with the condition

$$(\partial u/\partial z)_{z=0} = 0 \quad \text{at } x = x_0.$$

When the boundary layer is formed at a porous surface through which suction or blowing is applied, the condition for determining the point of separation is even less clear (see Figs. V. 3 and V. 4). With suction applied the separation appears to start from a stagnation point S within the fluid farther downstream than P, where $(\partial u/\partial z)_{z=0} = 0$.

This may lead to an instability of the flow at S. In the case of blowing the actual position of separation is not definite, though it is in the neighbourhood of P. The region of reverse flow in Figs. V. 2, V. 3, V. 4 is bounded by the curve $u = 0$ marked with a broken line, which passes through S in Fig. V. 3.

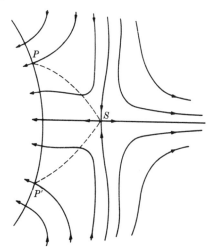

FIG. V. 5. Streamlines near a rear stagnation point.

For flow with suction or blowing (46) must be modified to

$$\nu\left(\frac{\partial^2 u}{\partial z^2}\right)_{z=0} = \frac{1}{\rho}\frac{dp}{dx} - w_s\left(\frac{\partial u}{\partial z}\right)_{z=0}, \qquad (47)$$

where $w_s = -w(x, 0)$ is the suction velocity. Thus, while $(\partial u/\partial z)_{z=0} > 0$ suction has the effect of opposing an adverse pressure gradient by making the boundary-layer profile more concave. This becomes less effective towards the rear stagnation point, since $(\partial u/\partial z)_{z=0}$ is expected to decrease as U decreases, and it is probable that the skin friction will in fact become negative before the rear stagnation point is reached. Owing to the effect previously mentioned, separation may be delayed so much as to be non-existent in this case, as illustrated in Fig. V. 5, where P, P' are the points at which $(\partial u/\partial z)_{z=0}$ changes sign, and are the limits of the region of reverse flow. It is known that the flow may be unstable at the stagnation point S within the fluid.

8. The transposition theorem of Prandtl

Prandtl (1938) observed that from any solution $u(x, z, t)$, $w(x, z, t)$, of the boundary-layer equations (25) and (26) further solutions can be

derived by writing
$$u^*(x, z, t) = u(x, z+f(x), t),$$ (48)
where $f(x)$ is arbitrary. The stream function is then
$$\psi^*(x, z, t) = \psi(x, z+f(x), t),$$ (49)
and hence
$$w^*(x, z, t) = w(x, z+f(x), t)-f'(x)u(x, z+f(x), t).$$ (50)

Restricting attention to steady flow, for convenience, the boundary conditions for u and w at $z = 0$ may be transferred to $z = -f(x)$ for u^*, w^*, and the condition at infinity (29) holds for u^* as well as for u. In particular, since $\psi(x, z) - Uz \to -U\delta_1(x)$ as $z \to \infty$, the choice $f(x) = \delta_1(x)$ leads to the conditions
$$\psi^*(x, z) - Uz \to 0 \quad \text{as } z \to \infty,$$
$$\psi^* = \frac{\partial \psi^*}{\partial z} = 0 \quad \text{at } z = -\delta_1(x),$$ (51)
which serve to determine both $\psi^*(x, z)$ and $\delta_1(x)$.

Also, if $u(x, z)$ represents a motion with back flow, so that $u(x, z) = 0$ both at $z = 0$ and $z = f(x)$, the derived solution satisfies the conditions
$$u^*(x, 0) = 0, \qquad w^*(x, 0) = w(x, f(x)),$$
$$u^* \to U \quad \text{as } z \to \infty.$$

Thus there is a new solution of the boundary-layer equations with a certain distribution of suction or blowing. Examples of such related solutions are found among the 'similar' solutions discussed in Section 21. For a generalization of the theorem to three-dimensional flow, with applications, see Glauert (1957).

9. Transformations of the equations of steady motion

The equations of motion for steady flow in a boundary layer are
$$u\frac{\partial u}{\partial x} + w\frac{\partial u}{\partial z} = U\frac{dU}{dx} + \nu\frac{\partial^2 u}{\partial z^2},$$
$$u = \partial\psi/\partial z, \qquad w = -\partial\psi/\partial x.$$ (52)
If $z = 0$ represents a fixed impermeable wall, the associated boundary conditions are $u = w = 0$, and $\psi = 0$. As z and ψ tend to infinity, $u \to U(x)$.

There are two transformations of these equations which are useful not only in revealing their essential mathematical nature, but also in providing a basis for approximate methods, which will be discussed later. The first of these transformations (Mises 1927) takes as independent variables x and ψ instead of x and z, and uses a dependent variable $\chi = U^2 - u^2$ instead of u. The result, obtained by routine methods, is as follows:

$$\frac{\partial \chi}{\partial x} = \nu (U^2 - \chi)^{\frac{1}{2}} \frac{\partial^2 \chi}{\partial \psi^2},$$

$$\psi = 0, \quad \chi = U^2; \qquad \psi = \infty, \quad \chi = 0. \qquad (53)$$

The original variable z is recovered from the relation

$$z = \int_0^{\psi} d\psi / u = \int_0^{\psi} (U^2 - \chi)^{-\frac{1}{2}} d\psi,$$

and the components of velocity may be determined from

$$u = (U^2 - \chi)^{\frac{1}{2}}, \qquad w = u \int_0^{\psi} \frac{\partial}{\partial x} \left(\frac{1}{u} \right) d\psi,$$

at least formally. The shear stress is $\tau = \mu u (\partial u / \partial \psi) = -\frac{1}{2} \mu (\partial \chi / \partial \psi)$ and a point of zero skin friction is therefore characterized by the condition $\partial \chi / \partial \psi = 0$ at $\psi = 0$.

Equation (53) is a fairly simple example of a partial differential equation of *parabolic type* in its normal form, not unlike the simpler equations of heat conduction and material diffusion, which are linear. The equation has only one set of characteristics, the lines $x = $ constant, and it is only necessary to give one boundary condition along any such line, in order to determine the solution elsewhere. Thus if χ is given as a function of ψ for any value of x, equation (53) implies that $\partial \chi / \partial x$ (and hence higher x-derivatives) is automatically known, and $\chi(\psi)$ for a neighbouring value of x can, in principle, be calculated. This is equivalent to saying that one *velocity profile* $u(z)$ at a certain value of x, together with a complete knowledge of $U(x)$, the main-stream velocity, is sufficient to determine conditions downstream, as far as the boundary layer adheres to the wall and remains laminar. Numerical calculations on this principle are, however, affected by the singularity possessed by equation (53) where $\chi = U^2$, that is, at any point on the wall (Mitchell and Thomson 1958).

The quantity χ is closely connected with the total head: thus

$$\tfrac{1}{2} \chi = -\left(\frac{p}{\rho} + \tfrac{1}{2} u^2 \right) + \left(\frac{p}{\rho} + \tfrac{1}{2} U^2 \right),$$

where the second bracket is constant. Equation (53) may therefore be seen as an equation for the diffusion of total head.

The second transformation is a restricted form of one due to Crocco

(1939), originally intended for compressible boundary layers. The equation of motion is first written in the form

$$\rho\left(u\frac{\partial u}{\partial x}+w\frac{\partial u}{\partial z}\right)=-\frac{dp}{dx}+\frac{\partial\tau}{\partial z},$$

in which τ is the shear stress. Then x and u are adopted as independent variables, with τ as a dependent variable. Thus

$$\tau=\mu/(\partial z/\partial u)\quad\text{and}\quad z=\mu\int_0^{} du/\tau.$$

After a straightforward calculation, the following equation is obtained:

$$\mu\rho u\frac{\partial}{\partial x}\left(\frac{1}{\tau}\right)+\frac{\partial^2\tau}{\partial u^2}-\mu\frac{dp}{dx}\frac{\partial}{\partial u}\left(\frac{1}{\tau}\right)=0. \tag{54}$$

In the special case of a uniform main stream, $dp/dx=0$ and (54) simplifies to

$$\frac{\mu\rho}{\tau^2}\frac{\partial\tau}{\partial x}=\frac{1}{u}\frac{\partial^2\tau}{\partial u^2}, \tag{55}$$

again exhibiting clearly the parabolic character of the differential equation. The associated boundary conditions are

$$u=0,\quad \partial\tau/\partial u=0;\qquad u=U,\quad \tau=0.$$

10. The analogy with heat conduction for the steady boundary layer

It was shown in the previous section that the equation of a steady boundary layer could be put in a form similar to that of the equation of heat conduction; the analogy is not exact since the boundary-layer equation is non-linear. However, in the outer regions of a boundary layer, where the velocity component u does not change too rapidly, equation (53) is approximately linear, and the mathematical theory of heat conduction may be invoked to give an asymptotic solution appropriate to such a region. Although in boundary-layer theory most interest is attached to conditions immediately adjacent to an impermeable wall (in particular, to the skin friction and the tendency to separation), there is some value in considering independently this asymptotic solution, especially since it is of a general character.

Kármán and Millikan (1934) appear to have been the first to exploit the analogy in this way. They first introduced a velocity potential of the main stream,

$$\phi=\int_0^{} U(x)\,dx,$$

and apart from differences of notation obtained (53) in the form

$$\frac{\partial \chi}{\partial \phi} = \nu \frac{u}{U} \frac{\partial^2 \chi}{\partial \psi^2} = \nu \left(1 - \frac{\chi}{U^2}\right)^{\frac{1}{2}} \frac{\partial^2 \chi}{\partial \psi^2}. \tag{56}$$

Where χ is small, that is, in the outer layers, this equation may be replaced by the approximate one

$$\frac{\partial \chi}{\partial \phi} = \nu \frac{\partial^2 \chi}{\partial \psi^2}, \tag{57}$$

this being equivalent to exaggerating the viscous term of (52) in the ratio U/u.

The boundary conditions adopted by Kármán and Millikan were

$$\psi = 0, \quad \chi = U^2; \qquad \psi = \infty, \quad \chi = 0 \quad (\text{all } \phi > 0),$$

$$\phi = 0, \quad \chi = 0 \quad (\text{all } \psi > 0), \tag{58}$$

so that there is an analogy with the conduction of heat in a semi-infinite rod initially at zero temperature, and with a thermometric conductivity equal to ν, the ends being respectively at temperatures U^2 and zero.

The following objection may be raised concerning the boundary conditions (58). The approximate equation (57) is meant to apply only to the outer regions of the boundary layer, hence it is not formally necessary either that $\psi = 0$ should represent the wall or that the value of χ at $\psi = 0$ should equal U^2. In fact, the adoption of the first of the boundary conditions (58) introduces an error into the solution which partly offsets the advantage of having linearized the differential equation. A better procedure, adopted by Tollmien (1946), is to apply a boundary condition $\psi = 0$, $\chi = F_0(\phi)$, where F_0 is an unknown function, unless it is determined by the use of an 'inner solution'. Tollmien wrote the relevant solution of (57) in the form

$$\chi(\phi, \psi) = \frac{1}{2\sqrt{\pi}} \int_0^\phi F_0(\xi) \frac{\psi/\nu^{1/2}}{(\phi-\xi)^{3/2}} \exp\left\{\frac{-\psi^2/\nu}{4(\phi-\xi)}\right\} d\xi, \tag{59}$$

and, in seeking an asymptotic relation for large values of $\psi/\sqrt{(\nu\phi)}$, made a change of variable to $\theta = \frac{1}{2}\psi/\sqrt{\{\nu(\phi-\xi)\}}$. Equation (59) becomes

$$\chi = (2/\sqrt{\pi}) \int_a^\infty F_0[\{1-(a^2/\theta^2)\}\phi]\exp(-\theta^2)\,d\theta, \tag{60}$$

where

$$a = \frac{1}{2}\psi/\sqrt{(\nu\phi)}. \tag{61}$$

By two partial integrations, assuming F_0' and F_0'' to exist, Tollmien deduces the following result, distinguishing two cases:

$$\text{(i) if } F_0(0) \neq 0, \quad \chi \sim (1/a\sqrt{\pi})F_0(0)\exp(-a^2), \tag{62}$$

$$\text{(ii) if } F_0(0) = 0, \quad \chi \sim (1/a^3\sqrt{\pi})F_0'(0)\phi\exp(-a^2). \tag{63}$$

Case (i) corresponds with the existence of a singularity at a leading edge, as in the flow past a flat plate; in case (ii), the point $\phi = \psi = 0$ is a stagnation point, as for instance in the flow past a cylindrical obstacle. These results may be generalized in the following way.

Assume $F_0(\phi) = \phi^m g(\phi)$, where $m \geqslant 0$ and $g'(\phi)$ is bounded, and let

$$I_m(x) = \int\limits_x^\infty (1-x^2/t^2)^m \exp(-t^2)\, dt,$$

$$= 2^{m-\frac{1}{2}}\Gamma(m+1)\exp(-\tfrac{1}{2}x^2)U(2m+\tfrac{1}{2}, x\sqrt{2}),$$

where $U(a,x)$ is the Weber function (see Appendix to this chapter). Hence, or otherwise,

$$I_m(x) \sim \tfrac{1}{2}\Gamma(m+1)x^{-2m-1}\exp(-x^2)$$

as $x \to \infty$.

Now from (60), with an integration by parts,

$$\chi = \frac{2}{\sqrt{\pi}} \int\limits_a^\infty \phi^m\left(1-\frac{a^2}{\theta^2}\right)^m g\left\{\phi\left(1-\frac{a^2}{\theta^2}\right)\right\}\exp(-\theta^2)\, d\theta$$

$$= \frac{2}{\sqrt{\pi}}\phi^m\left[\left\{-\int\limits_\theta^\infty \left(1-\frac{a^2}{t^2}\right)^m \exp(-t^2)\, dt\right\}.g\left\{\phi\left(1-\frac{a^2}{\theta^2}\right)\right\}\right]_{\theta=a}^{\theta=\infty} -$$

$$- \frac{2}{\sqrt{\pi}}\phi^m \int\limits_a^\infty \left\{\int\limits_\theta^\infty \left(1-\frac{a^2}{t^2}\right)^m \exp(-t^2)\, dt\right\}.g'\left\{\phi\left(1-\frac{a^2}{\theta^2}\right)\right\}\frac{2a^2\phi}{\theta^3}\, d\theta.$$

Of the two terms on the right-hand side, the first predominates (provided that g' is bounded). Thus

$$\chi \sim \frac{2}{\sqrt{\pi}}\phi^m g(0)I_m(a) \sim \frac{1}{\sqrt{\pi}}\Gamma(m+1)g(0)\phi^m a^{-2m-1}\exp(-a^2) \tag{64}$$

as $a \to \infty$. The special cases $m = 0, 1$ may be seen to correspond with Tollmien's results (62) and (63). See also Betz (1955).

A certain fundamental property of boundary layers may be inferred from (61) and (64), namely that *the vorticity is exponentially small for large z*. This is because the vorticity is proportional to $\partial\chi/\partial\psi$ and, for given x and large z, the variables a, ψ, and z are themselves proportional.

11. Algebraic singularities in boundary-layer solutions ; conditions at a point of separation

It was shown in Section 9 that, because of the parabolic nature of the boundary-layer equation, a knowledge of the velocity profile $u(z)$ at one section, together with the complete distribution of main-stream velocity $U(x)$, is sufficient to determine conditions downstream (or for that matter upstream) of the section, as far as the boundary layer extends and remains laminar. On the basis of this principle, a numerical method may be envisaged whereby velocity profiles at a succession of closely-spaced values of x are constructed step-by-step as far as desired, the values of u in each calculated profile being used as initial data for the following step. The success of such a method is not, however, guaranteed by the validity of the principle because algebraic singularities can occur in the mathematical solutions, making numerical work difficult in their neighbourhoods.

Goldstein (1930) considered the conditions for the *absence* of such singularities, taking the steady boundary-layer equations in a non-dimensional form (see equations (11) to (13)):

$$\mathrm{U}\frac{\partial \mathrm{U}}{\partial \mathrm{X}}+\mathrm{W}\frac{\partial \mathrm{U}}{\partial \mathrm{Z}} = -\frac{d\mathrm{P}}{d\mathrm{X}}+\frac{\partial^2 \mathrm{U}}{\partial \mathrm{Z}^2}, \tag{65}$$

$$\frac{\partial \mathrm{U}}{\partial \mathrm{X}}+\frac{\partial \mathrm{W}}{\partial \mathrm{Z}} = 0. \tag{66}$$

The pressure in the main stream is such that

$$-d\mathrm{P}/d\mathrm{X} = p_0+p_1\mathrm{X}+p_2\mathrm{X}^2+\ldots, \tag{67}$$

and the velocity profile at $\mathrm{X} = 0$ is

$$\mathrm{U} = a_0+a_1\mathrm{Z}+a_2\mathrm{Z}^2+\ldots. \tag{68}$$

The origin of X is at an arbitrary section of the boundary layer at which the profile (68) is specified; it does not denote any special point such as the leading edge of a plate. For flow along a fixed surface, $a_0 = 0$ and, in general, $a_1 \neq 0$. At a point of zero skin friction, however, $a_1 = 0$. For the flow in a two-dimensional wake (see Section VI. 9), $a_0 \neq 0$.

When a singularity is present at $\mathrm{X} = \mathrm{Z} = 0$, the solution in its neighbourhood appears to depend on a stream function Ψ such that

$$\Psi = \xi^{n-1}f(\xi,\eta), \qquad \xi = \mathrm{X}^{1/n}, \quad \eta = \mathrm{Z}\mathrm{X}^{-1/n}, \tag{69}$$

and if $a_0 \neq 0$, $n = 2$; if $a_0 = 0$, $a_1 \neq 0$, $n = 3$; if $a_0 = a_1 = 0$, $a_2 \neq 0$, $n = 4$. If, on the other hand, there is no singularity at the origin, certain relations between the coefficients in (67) and (68) must be satisfied.

(i) *The case $a_0 = 0$, $a_1 \neq 0$.* The left-hand side of (65) is zero when $u = w = 0$ at a fixed wall; at $x = 0$, the right-hand side is $p_0 + 2a_2 + 6a_3 z + \ldots$, and by putting $z = 0$ in this the condition

$$2a_2 + p_0 = 0 \qquad (70)$$

is obtained. This is necessary for the absence of a singularity at $x = z = 0$. Further conditions are obtainable by successive differentiation of (65), using (66) where necessary, and are as follows:

$$a_3 = 0,$$
$$5! \, a_5 + 2a_1 p_1 = 0,$$
$$6! \, a_6 - 2p_0 p_1 = 0, \quad \text{etc.} \qquad (71)$$

The constants $a_1, a_4, a_7, \ldots$, are left undetermined and will depend on the special circumstances. The exact solutions presented in Part III of this chapter exemplify the above set of conditions at all ordinary points of the boundaries.

The numerical method already envisaged will not be easy to operate unless the distributions of pressure and velocity corresponding to (67) and (68), but given numerically, satisfy at least some of the conditions (70), (71). This was found necessary by Hartree (1939a), in an investigation which is referred to later in this section; at the same time, if a velocity profile satisfying (70) was taken as the initial datum, the corresponding profile at the end of the next step also obeyed the condition, so that a continuous calculation was feasible.

(ii) *The case $a_0 = a_1 = 0$, $a_2 \neq 0$.* No exact analytical solution is known for a complete boundary-layer flow involving separation, and such tentative conclusions as are available rest upon a comparison of numerical solutions with formulae derived from the transformation (69). The exact solutions of Sections 12 to 21 are unhelpful because they have the property that velocity profiles at different sections of the boundary layer are similar. In a flow with separation, however, the progressive distortion of the profile is of primary importance. Thus, from (46),

$$\mu(\partial^2 u/\partial z^2)_{z=0} = dp/dx. \qquad (72)$$

Now, as a point of separation is approached, the pressure increases, so that $dp/dx > 0$; the skin friction $\mu(\partial u/\partial z)_0$, although diminishing, is still positive. Since $\partial u/\partial z \to 0$ as $z \to \infty$ in any case, the derivative $\partial^2 u/\partial z^2$ must change from positive to negative at some point of the profile, which therefore has an inflexion.

Published work on the problem of separation is linked mainly to a main-stream velocity which diminishes linearly with distance downstream, conveniently written in a non-dimensional form

$$U = 1 - (x/8).$$ (73)

This was first studied by Kármán and Millikan (1934), partly for reasons connected with a certain type of aerofoil, but subsequent writers have followed the example for the sake of comparison. Howarth (1938) used a series solution to obtain an estimate of the position of the separation point (see Section VI. 3) and found $x_s = 0.96$ approximately; he also calculated a velocity profile at separation. Hartree (1939a), by a direct numerical process, was able to confirm and improve Howarth's estimates. He showed also that there was a strong suggestion of the existence of a singularity at the point of separation, both because of the form of the skin friction in its neighbourhood, and because of a breakdown of the numerical process if an attempt was made to pass beyond the separation point. These conclusions were confirmed by Leigh (1955) who repeated Hartree's calculation for the same velocity distribution, using an automatic computor and working to a greater number of significant figures. Leigh found $x_s = 0.9585$. Meanwhile, Goldstein (1948b) had published a study of the problem revealed by Hartree, constructing an asymptotic solution for the immediate neighbourhood of the separation point; because of certain peculiarities of this solution it was not, however, clear that the latter was valid. Nevertheless, a numerical comparison (Jones 1948) of the solutions of Goldstein, Hartree, and Howarth, as regards both skin friction and velocity profiles, indicated no serious discrepancies, and this conclusion has since been reinforced by Leigh. Stewartson (1958) resolved the difficulties found by Goldstein and his modification to the theoretical solution is mentioned below. Terrill (1960) extended Stewartson's work to include suction, and also gave a numerical solution for $U = \sin x$ which again suggested the presence of a singularity.

To study the singularity at separation (assuming its existence), let x_s, U_s, and U'_s be the values of x, U, and dU/dx at separation, so that $U_s > 0$, $U'_s < 0$. As representative length and Reynolds number take $l = -U_s/U'_s$, $R = U_s l/\nu$, and define $x_1 = (x_s - x)/l$, $z_1 = R^{\frac{1}{2}}z/l$. If $p_1 = p/\rho U_s^2$, the equation corresponding to (67) is

$$-dp_1/dx_1 = 1 + c_1 x_1 + c_2 x_1^2 + ...,$$ (74)

and for the linear velocity distribution,

$$c_1 = 1, \qquad c_2 = c_3 = ... = 0,$$ (75)

so that, in this particular case, the coefficients do not depend on the position of separation.

In order that the solution should fit the numerical calculation (which depends on the condition (70) being satisfied), the theoretical velocity profile at separation was assumed by Goldstein to be of the form

$$u/U_s = \mathrm{u}_1 = \tfrac{1}{2}\mathrm{z}_1^2 + a_3\,\mathrm{z}_1^3 + a_4\,\mathrm{z}_1^4 + ..., \tag{76}$$

and the motion upstream was described by writing

$$\xi = \mathrm{x}_1^{1/4}, \qquad \eta = \mathrm{z}_1/2^{1/2}\mathrm{x}_1^{1/4},$$
$$\Psi_1 = 2^{3/2}\xi^3[f_0(\eta) + \xi f_1(\eta) + \xi^2 f_2(\eta) + ...],$$
$$\mathrm{u}_1 = \partial\Psi_1/\partial\mathrm{z}_1, \qquad \mathrm{w}_1 = \partial\Psi_1/\partial\mathrm{x}_1. \tag{77}$$

The non-dimensional shearing stress at the wall was then

$$2^{3/2}(\alpha_1\,\mathrm{x}_1^{1/2} + \alpha_2\,\mathrm{x}_1^{3/4} + \alpha_3\,\mathrm{x}_1 + \alpha_4\,\mathrm{x}_1^{5/4} + ...) \tag{78}$$

where α_1, α_2,..., are constants. It was found that

$$f_0(\eta) = \eta^3/6, \quad f_1(\eta) = \alpha_1\,\eta^2, \quad f_2(\eta) = \alpha_2\,\eta^2 - \alpha_1^2\,\eta^5/15,$$

while $f_3(\eta)$, $f_4(\eta)$, and $f_5(\eta)$ were obtained as infinite series involving α_3, α_4, and α_5 respectively. The constants α_2, α_3, and α_4 could be expressed in terms of α_1; also $a_3 = 0$, $a_4 = -\alpha_1^2/6$, and the solution as far as the terms derived from $f_4(\eta)$ involved the single arbitrary constant α_1. The latter has been estimated by fitting the theoretical solution to the numerical results obtained by Hartree and Leigh, comparing either (i) skin friction, or (ii) the velocity profile a short distance upstream of separation. The estimate made by Leigh is $\alpha_1 = 0\cdot492\pm0\cdot002$.

The non-dimensional variables used by Hartree and Goldstein are related in the following way:

$$\xi = \left(\frac{\mathrm{x}_s-\mathrm{x}}{8-\mathrm{x}_s}\right)^{1/4}, \qquad \eta = \frac{1}{4}\left(\frac{8-\mathrm{x}_s}{\mathrm{x}_s-\mathrm{x}}\right)^{1/4}\mathrm{z},$$

and
$$\mathrm{u} = (1-\tfrac{1}{8}\mathrm{x}_s)\mathrm{u}_1 = 0\cdot8802\mathrm{u}_1.$$
Thus, using (77),

$$\mathrm{u} = \tfrac{1}{4}\{(\mathrm{x}_s-\mathrm{x})(8-\mathrm{x}_s)\}^{1/2}[f_0' + \xi f_1' + \xi^2 f_2' + ...]. \tag{79}$$

The functions f_0, f_1, f_2,..., being known, it is possible to express the shearing stress at the wall $(\partial\mathrm{u}/\partial\mathrm{z})_0$ in terms of the constants α_1, α_2,..., and the non-dimensional distances x, x_s, which correspond with the original definition of the main-stream velocity (73). The result is

$$\frac{100(\partial\mathrm{u}/\partial\mathrm{z})_0}{\{100(\mathrm{x}_s-\mathrm{x})\}^{1/2}} = 3\cdot317[\alpha_1 + 0\cdot3453\{100(\mathrm{x}_s-\mathrm{x})\}^{1/4}\alpha_1^2 +$$
$$+\,0\cdot1248\{100(\mathrm{x}_s-\mathrm{x})\}^{1/2}\alpha_1^3 + 0\cdot0524\{100(\mathrm{x}_s-\mathrm{x})\}^{3/4}\alpha_1^4 + ...] \tag{80}$$

(Jones 1948), where, following Hartree, certain numerical factors are inserted for convenience.

Stewartson (1958) has shown that logarithmic terms should be admitted to the solution (77) for Ψ_1, and corresponding terms added to (78). The term of lowest order which could occur in (77) would be $\xi^8 \ln \xi F_5(\eta)$, so that for the purpose of the above-mentioned comparison the solution is not altered. But the presence of these new terms obviates the need to satisfy certain integral conditions inherent in the Goldstein solution. On the other hand, some of the added terms become infinite at $x = x_s$, $z \neq 0$ and the velocity profile at separation can no longer be assumed to have the simple form (76). Moreover, the solution now contains an infinite number of arbitrary constants α_1, α_5, α_9,..., and it is not clear how these are determined from boundary conditions. Terrill (1960) has confirmed the need for the logarithmic terms.

These investigations need careful evaluation. The only evidence of a singularity at separation comes from the numerical solutions based on special main-stream velocity distributions. It is possible that the occurrence of a singularity is restricted to special cases, and that experimental pressure distributions might be such that singularities are avoided (see Section VI. 12). One of the mathematical consequences of the solution (77), which applies only to the flow upstream of the separation point, is that no formal solution *of the same type* exists for the flow downstream, except when $\alpha_1 = 0$, in which case all singularities are absent (as are the new logarithmic terms). Stewartson (1958) suggests that, if a boundary layer is to continue downstream of separation into a region of reversed flow, the main stream must adjust itself so that, in fact, no singularity occurs.

On the other hand, if it is accepted that a singularity does exist at a separation point of a boundary-layer solution with practical significance, there are certain important consequences. The solution (77) indicates that, at $x_1 = 0$, w_1 and $\partial u_1 / \partial x_1$ become infinite like $x_1^{-\frac{1}{2}}$. The basic assumptions of boundary-layer theory therefore do not hold near a separation point of a solution, and large transverse velocities may be expected: existing experimental observations are insufficient to settle this point. Theoretically, a reversion to the full Navier–Stokes equations near separation is probably needed.

An interesting discussion on flow near a separation point is given by Landau and Lifshitz (1959, pp. 151–6). Finally, it must be pointed out that, in the above account, the word 'separation' is used conventionally to denote merely a point of zero skin friction.

PART III

SPECIAL EXACT SOLUTIONS

12. Flow along a flat plate at zero incidence in a uniform stream

The physical problem considered in this section gave rise to one of the original, and now classical, solutions of the equations of boundary-layer theory (Blasius 1908). The mathematical formulation presented below differs slightly from the original one in order that the solution shall be a special case of a later, more general, solution. Some additional mathematical analysis of the Blasius equation is also included, as are suitably revised tables of the solution.

A thin flat plate is immersed at zero incidence in a uniform stream, which flows with speed U_0, and is assumed not to be affected by the presence of the plate, except in the boundary layer. The fluid is supposed unlimited in extent, and the origin of coordinates is taken at the leading edge, with x measured downstream along the plate and z perpendicular to it. In the absence of a pressure gradient, the equations of steady motion in the boundary layer reduce to

$$u\frac{\partial u}{\partial x} + w\frac{\partial u}{\partial z} = \nu\frac{\partial^2 u}{\partial z^2}, \tag{81}$$

$$u = \frac{\partial \psi}{\partial z}, \qquad w = -\frac{\partial \psi}{\partial x}, \tag{82}$$

and the appropriate boundary conditions are

$$z = 0, \ x > 0: \quad u = w = 0,$$

$$z = \infty, \text{ all } x: \quad u = U_0,$$

$$x = 0: \qquad u = U_0.$$

The fact that these conditions demand an infinite gradient in speed at the leading edge $x = z = 0$ implies a singularity in the mathematical solution there. However, the assumptions implicit in the boundary-layer approximation break down for the region of slow flow around the leading edge, and the solution to be derived here must be taken to apply only from a short distance downstream of $x = 0$.

Blasius's solution for the stream function is of the form

$$\psi = (2\nu U_0 x)^{\frac{1}{2}} f(\eta) \tag{83}$$

where

$$\eta = (U_0/2\nu x)^{\frac{1}{2}} z, \tag{84}$$

although each of these expressions differs by a factor $\sqrt{2}$ from its original definition. By differentiation, the velocity components are obtained as

$$u = U_0 f'(\eta), \qquad w = (\nu U_0/2x)^{\frac{1}{2}}\{\eta f'(\eta) - f(\eta)\},$$

and equation (81) reduces to

$$f''' + ff'' = 0. \tag{85}$$

The boundary conditions become $f(0) = f'(0) = 0$; $f'(\infty) = 1$. The shear stress is given by

$$\tau = \mu(U_0^3/2\nu x)^{\frac{1}{2}} f''(\eta). \tag{86}$$

Equation (85) is non-linear, and the boundary conditions are given at more than one point. The existence of the desired solution is therefore not guaranteed, and its numerical tabulation would not be particularly straightforward, except for the special circumstance that $f(0) = 0$. For, if $F(\eta)$ is any solution of (85), so also is $f = aF(a\eta)$ with a an arbitrary 'constant of homology'. Then

$$\lim_{\eta\to\infty} f'(\eta) = a^2 \lim_{\eta\to\infty} F'(a\eta) = a^2 \lim_{\eta\to\infty} F'(\eta)$$

and so, if $f'(\infty) = 1$, the constant a may be determined by the relation

$$a = \left\{ \lim_{\eta\to\infty} F'(\eta) \right\}^{-\frac{1}{2}}.$$

If, in addition, it is arranged that $F(0) = F'(0) = 0$, all three boundary conditions will be satisfied by taking $f = aF(a\eta)$ as the solution. Finally, since $f''(0) = a^3 F''(0)$, it is convenient to prescribe $F''(0) = 1$ and to obtain the relation

$$f''(0) = \{F'(\infty)\}^{-3/2}. \tag{87}$$

A numerical calculation of Blasius's solution may therefore be carried out in two stages: first, the step-by-step tabulation of $F(\eta)$, starting with the initial values $F(0) = F'(0) = 0$; $F''(0) = 1$, and carrying enough figures to give $f''(0)$ with sufficient accuracy from (87); secondly, a direct tabulation of $f(\eta)$, using the value of $f''(0)$ so found. It happens that this numerical process is stable, and there is no significant accumulation of error.

Table V. 1 gives f, f', and f'' and some associated quantities. Earlier numerical solutions were published by Blasius (1908), Töpfer (1912), Goldstein (1930), and Howarth (1938).

The value of $f''(0)$ is needed in order to obtain the shearing stress at the surface of the plate, which by (86) is

$$\tau_w = \mu(U_0^3/2\nu x)^{\frac{1}{2}} f''(0) = \rho U_0^2 (2R_x)^{-\frac{1}{2}} f''(0), \tag{88}$$

TABLE V. 1

Solution of equation (85)

$$f'''+ff'' = 0 \quad \text{with} \quad f(0) = f'(0) = 0, \quad f'(\infty) = 1$$

η	f	f′	f″
0·0	0·0000 000	0·0000 00	0·4696 00
0·1	·0023 480	·0469 59	·4695 63
0·2	·0093 914	·0939 05	·4693 06
0·3	·0211 275	·1408 06	·4686 09
0·4	·0375 492	·1876 05	·4672 54
0·5	·0586 427	·2342 27	·4650 30
0·6	·0843 856	·2805 75	·4617 34
0·7	·1147 447	·3265 32	·4571 77
0·8	·1496 745	·3719 63	·4511 90
0·9	·1891 148	·4167 18	·4436 28
1·0	0·2329 900	0·4606 32	0·4343 79
1·1	·2812 075	·5035 35	·4233 68
1·2	·3336 572	·5452 46	·4105 65
1·3	·3902 111	·5855 88	·3959 84
1·4	·4507 234	·6243 86	·3796 92
1·5	·5150 312	·6614 73	·3618 04
1·6	·5829 560	·6966 99	·3424 87
1·7	·6543 045	·7299 30	·3219 50
1·8	·7288 718	·7610 57	·3004 45
1·9	·8064 429	·7899 96	·2782 51
2·0	0·8867 962	0·8166 94	0·2556 69
2·2	1·0549 463	·8633 03	·2105 80
2·4	·2315 267	·9010 65	·1675 61
2·6	·4148 231	·9306 01	·1286 13
2·8	·6032 823	·9528 75	·0951 14
3·0	·7955 666	·9690 54	·0677 11
3·2	1·9905 796	·9803 65	·0463 70
3·4	2·1874 658	·9879 70	·0305 35
3·6	·3855 888	·9928 88	·0193 29
3·8	·5844 972	·9959 44	·0117 59
4·0	2·7838 848	0·9977 70	0·0068 74
4·2	2·9835 535	·9988 18	·0038 61
4·4	3·1833 808	·9993 96	·0020 84
4·6	·3832 941	·9997 03	·0010 81
4·8	·5832 520	·9998 59	·0005 39
5·0	·7832 324	·9999 36	·0002 58
5·2	3·9832 236	·9999 71	·0001 19
5·4	4·1832 197	·9999 88	·0000 52
5·6	·3832 181	·9999 95	·0000 22
5·8	·5832 173	·9999 98	·0000 09
6·0	4·7832 170	0·9999 99	0·0000 03

$$f' \sim 1-0·331 \int_{\zeta}^{\infty} \exp(-\tfrac{1}{2}\zeta^2)\,d\zeta \sim 1-0·331(\zeta^{-1}-\zeta^{-3}+3\zeta^{-5}...)\exp(-\tfrac{1}{2}\zeta^2).$$

$$\zeta = \eta-1·21678; \qquad \int_{0}^{\infty}(1-f')\,d\eta = 1·21678,$$

$$\int_{0}^{\infty} f'(1-f')\,d\eta = 0·46960, \qquad \int_{0}^{\infty} f'(1-f'^2)\,d\eta = 0·73849$$

where $R_x = xU_0/\nu$. Numerically, $\tau_w/\rho U_0^2 = 0.33206(\nu/U_0 x)^{\frac{1}{2}}$. The drag on one side of a plate of length l and unit breadth is then

$$D = \int_0^l \tau_w \, dx = \rho(\tfrac{1}{2}\nu U_0^3)^{\frac{1}{2}} f''(0) \int_0^l x^{-\frac{1}{2}} \, dx = 2^{\frac{1}{2}}\rho U_0^2 l \cdot f''(0) \cdot (U_0 l/\nu)^{-\frac{1}{2}},$$

and the drag coefficient is

$$C_D = D/(\tfrac{1}{2}\rho l U_0^2) = 2^{3/2} f''(0) R^{-1/2} = 1.3282 R^{-1/2}, \tag{89}$$

where $R = lU_0/\nu$. It should be noted here that the solution is used from $x = 0$, although a slight error may thereby be introduced.

The displacement thickness is, without approximation,

$$\begin{aligned}
\delta_1 &= \int_0^\infty \left(1 - \frac{u}{U_0}\right) dz = (2\nu x/U_0)^{\frac{1}{2}} \int_0^\infty (1 - f') \, d\eta \\
&= (2\nu x/U_0)^{\frac{1}{2}} \lim_{\eta \to \infty} (\eta - f) \\
&= 1.7208(\nu x/U_0)^{\frac{1}{2}}. \tag{90}
\end{aligned}$$

Then if $R_x = xU_0/\nu$ and $R_\delta = \delta_1 U_0/\nu$, it follows that $R_\delta = 1.7208 R_x^{\frac{1}{2}}$, which is an exact verification of a relationship whose form is easily found by simpler, but less precise, methods (Prandtl 1952). Also, the momentum thickness is

$$\delta_2 = (2\nu x/U_0)^{\frac{1}{2}} f''(0) = 0.6641(\nu x/U_0)^{\frac{1}{2}}, \tag{91}$$

this being derived either from (36) or from (41) and (88).

The value of η corresponding with $z = \delta_1$ is the same for all x, and from (84) and (90) is

$$\eta_1 = 1.2168. \tag{92}$$

The variable η is, in fact, an appropriate non-dimensional coordinate for distances across the boundary layer. Since the motion at a distance x from the leading edge is unaffected by that farther downstream, it cannot depend on the length of the plate, and the appropriate Reynolds number is R_x; the natural unit of distance away from the plate is therefore $xR_x^{-\frac{1}{2}}$, and the definition of η in (84) is seen to be in accordance with the general non-dimensional theory in Section 1.

It remains to consider the approximate form of $f(\eta)$ for small and large values of η respectively. The series in ascending powers of η is

$$f(\eta) = \sum_0^\infty (-1)^n C_n \eta^{3n+2}, \tag{93}$$

where (Weyl 1942a),

$$(3n+2)(3n+1)3nC_n = \sum_0^{n-1} (3i+2)(3i+1)C_i C_{n-1-i}, \tag{94}$$

and $C_0 = \frac{1}{2}f''(0)$. The first few coefficients in the series are

$$C_1 = (1/5!)(2C_0)^2, \qquad C_2 = (11/8!)(2C_0)^3, \qquad C_3 = (375/11!)(2C_0)^4,$$
$$C_4 = (27897/14!)(2C_0)^5, \qquad C_5 = (3817137/17!)(2C_0)^6.$$

This series is useful in starting a numerical integration from $\eta = 0$. As Weyl has pointed out, the radius of convergence of the series is finite, and it should therefore be used only for small values of η. For the case in which $f''(0) = 1$, Shanks (1953) claims to have shown that the radius of convergence is $3 \cdot 12735$. For the actual Blasius solution, he also obtains by a continued fraction a result equivalent to

$$f''(0) = 0 \cdot 469600.$$

An asymptotic formula valid for large values of η may be found as follows: in equation (85), substitute $f(\eta) = \eta - \beta + \phi(\eta)$, where $\phi(\eta)$ is small. If the product $\phi\phi''$ is neglected, an approximate linear equation for $\phi(\eta)$ is obtained:

$$\phi''' + (\eta - \beta)\phi'' = 0. \qquad (95)$$

Hence, writing $\zeta = \eta - \beta$, it follows that $\phi'' \sim A \exp(-\frac{1}{2}\zeta^2)$, and that

$$\phi \sim A\zeta^{-2}\exp(-\tfrac{1}{2}\zeta^2). \qquad (96)$$

The constant β has already been used, in the formula for displacement thickness (90), where

$$\beta = \lim_{\eta \to \infty} (\eta - f) = 1 \cdot 21678 \qquad (97)$$

and, from (92), $\beta = \eta_1$. Thus an approximate formula for $f(\eta)$, valid for large η, is

$$f(\eta) \sim \eta - \eta_1 + A(\eta - \eta_1)^{-2}\exp\{-\tfrac{1}{2}(\eta - \eta_1)^2\}. \qquad (98)$$

An immediate consequence of this result is that the transverse velocity component w is given by the asymptotic formula

$$w/U_0 \sim \eta_1(2R_x)^{-\frac{1}{2}}. \qquad (99)$$

Thus w does not tend to zero, and this is one of the characteristic features of boundary-layer solutions.

13. Limitations of the boundary-layer solution for a flat plate ; better approximations near the leading edge

The original theory of the boundary layer was based on two assumptions:

(i) In the equations of motion certain derivatives are of a smaller order of magnitude than others, and so may be neglected.

(ii) The main stream is supposed unaffected by the presence of the boundary layer, and the boundary-layer solution is constructed to correspond with the undisturbed main stream; in particular, the pressure at any point in the boundary layer is that of the main stream at the same section. The first of these assumptions is accurate only if the Reynolds number is large enough. It has been indicated that the appropriate definition of the Reynolds number for a flat plate in a uniform stream is $R_x = U_0 x/\nu$, where x is the distance from the leading edge. Consequently, R_x is not large near the leading edge, and assumption (i) is inaccurate. On the other hand, as x increases, the boundary-layer solution may be expected to be an increasingly accurate description of the flow farther downstream, so long as the flow remains laminar.

Assumption (ii) may be violated in more than one way. The presence of the boundary layer in any case implies a displacement of the streamlines of the main flow by the amount δ_1. But also, if there is an adverse pressure gradient along the plate, the boundary layer may *separate*, and modify the main stream to a much greater extent.

Quite apart from these considerations, the approximate solution given by boundary-layer theory depends on the system of coordinates which is used when assumption (i) is applied to the full equations of viscous flow. Thus, the conventional solution for a flat plate contains a mathematical singularity on the line $x = 0$; this, however, may be eliminated by a different choice of coordinates (see later in this section) and hence the singularity has no particular physical significance. The role of coordinate systems in boundary-layer theory is treated in a general way in Section 18.

A second approximation to the laminar boundary-layer flow over a flat plate in a uniform stream has been attempted by Alden (1948). He starts with the accurate equation for the stream function in the form

$$\frac{\partial \psi}{\partial z} \frac{\partial}{\partial x}(\nabla^2 \psi) - \frac{\partial \psi}{\partial x} \frac{\partial}{\partial z}(\nabla^2 \psi) = \nu \nabla^2(\nabla^2 \psi) \tag{100}$$

(see (5)), but first transforms to parabolic coordinates σ, τ defined by the relations

$$x + iz = re^{i\theta} = (\sigma + i\tau)^2. \tag{101}$$

If $\nabla^2 \psi$ now denotes $(\partial^2 \psi/\partial \sigma^2) + (\partial^2 \psi/\partial \tau^2)$, equation (100) becomes

$$(\sigma^2 + \tau^2)\left\{\frac{\partial \psi}{\partial \tau} \frac{\partial}{\partial \sigma}(\nabla^2 \psi) - \frac{\partial \psi}{\partial \sigma} \frac{\partial}{\partial \tau}(\nabla^2 \psi)\right\} - 2\left(\sigma \frac{\partial \psi}{\partial \tau} - \tau \frac{\partial \psi}{\partial \sigma}\right)\nabla^2 \psi$$

$$= \nu\left[4\nabla^2 \psi - 4\left\{\sigma \frac{\partial}{\partial \sigma}(\nabla^2 \psi) + \tau \frac{\partial}{\partial \tau}(\nabla^2 \psi)\right\} + (\sigma^2 + \tau^2)\nabla^2(\nabla^2 \psi)\right], \tag{102}$$

after a routine process of transformation.

The solution investigated by Alden is based on a suitable generalization of the quantities used in the Blasius solution. With minor changes from Alden's definitions, this is as follows. In the boundary layer θ is small so that, from (101), τ is small compared with σ. Now $x = \sigma^2 - \tau^2$, $z = 2\sigma\tau$, and hence $x = \sigma^2$, approximately. The variable η defined in (84) is thus nearly equal to the new variable $\xi = (2U_0/\nu)^{\frac{1}{2}}\tau$. Also, the effective Reynolds number $R_x = U_0 x/\nu$ is approximately $R_\sigma = U_0 \sigma^2/\nu$. Alden's solution is then a generalization of (83) which involves an expansion in inverse powers of R_σ, namely

$$\psi = (2\nu U_0)^{\frac{1}{2}}\sigma\{f_0(\xi) + (\nu/U_0\sigma^2)f_1(\xi) + ...\}, \tag{103}$$

and only the first two functions f_0, f_1 are considered. The boundary condition on the velocity at the surface of the plate, $\tau = 0$, leads to the conditions

$$f_0(0) = f_0'(0) = f_1(0) = f_1'(0) = 0. \tag{104}$$

Conditions to be satisfied at infinity are

$$u \to U_0, \; w \to 0 \quad \text{as } \tau \to \infty, \; \sigma \text{ fixed and } \sigma \to \infty, \; \tau \text{ fixed}, \tag{105}$$

but these are not sufficient to determine f_1.

The function f_0 is the Blasius function expressed in terms of the new variable ξ, and $f_0 \sim \xi - \beta_0$. Goldstein (1960, pp. 136–44) has pointed out that the corresponding form of f_1 for large ξ is

$$f_1(\xi) \sim k\xi - \beta_1 + ag_1(\xi) + bh_1(\xi),$$

in which a and b are constants and the approximate asymptotic forms of g_1 and h_1 are

$$g_1(\xi) \sim (\xi - \beta_0)^{-1} + (\xi - \beta_0)^{-3} + ...,$$
$$h_1(\xi) \sim \exp\{-\tfrac{1}{2}(\xi - \beta_0)^2\}.$$

The boundary conditions (105) do not determine any of the constants k, β_1, a and b. Alden arbitrarily eliminates k and β_1, but leaves a multiple of $g_1(\xi)$ in his solution. In order that vorticity shall decay exponentially (see Section 10), however, $g_1(\xi)$ should be absent; in any case, the excluded terms $k\xi$ and β_1 affect ψ to a higher order of magnitude. To determine f_1, and later functions in the series (103), the asymptotic form of ψ for large ξ and σ should be merged with a potential flow—a solution of (102) without its right-hand side—which itself must tend to a uniform stream as $\tau \to \infty$. But even when the correct forms of functions in the series (103) have thus been decided, there still remain arbitrary constants which can be determined only by reference to a solution valid near the leading edge. Goldstein further suggests, for reasons connected with the possibility of singularities in the potential flow, that the expansion (103) is not sufficiently general for this problem.

Imai (1957b) has reconsidered the series solution of (102), introducing terms of order $R_\sigma^{-1/2}$, $R_\sigma^{-3/2}$,..., also logarithmic terms, and replacing (105) by the condition that vorticity shall decay exponentially. He finds that f_1 must be replaced by an expression (involving $\log \sigma$) which can be written explicitly in terms of f_0, except for an arbitrary constant, C_1. The resulting formula for the skin friction is

$$\tau_w = \rho U_0^2 (2R_x)^{-\frac{1}{2}} f_0''(0)[1 + R_x^{-1}(C_1 + 0.83 \log R_x)],$$

a generalization of (88). Imai next determines the potential flow induced by the distribution of vorticity in the boundary layer (Imai 1951) and determines the drag by the momentum theorem, finding the following extension of (89):

$$C_D = \frac{2^{3/2} f_0''(0)}{R_x^{1/2}} + \frac{\frac{1}{2}\pi\beta_0^2}{R_x} - \frac{2^{3/2} f_0''(0)}{R_x^{3/2}}[C_1 + 1.659(1 + \tfrac{1}{2}\log R_x)] + O(R_x^{-2}).$$

$$(106)$$

$$= 1.328 R_x^{-1/2} + 2.326 R_x^{-1} + \dots. \qquad (107)$$

Another investigation which seeks to extend the Blasius solution is that of Kuo (1953) for a flat plate of infinite width and *finite* chord length l, situated athwart a stream whose undisturbed speed is U_∞. The Reynolds number $R = lU_\infty/\nu$ gives a small parameter $\epsilon = R^{-\frac{1}{2}}$; both the stream function and the pressure are expanded in a series of integral powers of ϵ, and are then substituted into the exact equations (8) to (10). The first-order perturbation of the pressure is found to be independent of z, and is therefore expressible in terms of the first-order perturbation of the velocity at the outer edge of the boundary layer—which, in its turn, is estimated from the asymptotic form of the Blasius solution (99). Kuo, in fact, formulates a potential problem with the boundary conditions on $z = 0$:

$$w/U_\infty = \begin{cases} 0 & (x < 0), \\ \beta\epsilon(2x)^{-\frac{1}{2}} & (0 \leqslant x \leqslant 1), \\ 0 & (x > 1), \end{cases}$$

(the slow spread of the wake being ignored). The partial differential equation for the first-order perturbation of ψ can then be solved in a series of functions of $\eta = z/(2x)^{\frac{1}{2}}$, which leads to a drag coefficient

$$C_D = 1.328 R^{-\frac{1}{2}} + 4.12 R^{-1}. \qquad (108)$$

The first two terms in the ϵ-series for ψ—the Blasius solution and the first-order perturbation—each contribute to the integrand of the drag integral a term of order $x^{-\frac{1}{2}}$. Later terms would make the integral divergent, as Alden noted. Kuo therefore seeks instead a coordinate transformation which removes the singularity on x = 0, and ensures that the second-order perturbations of ψ and the pressure shall be free from the higher singularities of the original solution. The transformation is

$$x = x' + \epsilon^2 g(\eta') + ..., \qquad z = z',$$

where $\eta' = z'/(2x')^{\frac{1}{2}}$ and $g(\eta')$ is a function approximately equal to $-\frac{1}{2}\eta'^2$ both for large and small η'. The parabolas $\eta' = $ const. correspond in the x, z plane with parabolas whose vertices are spaced along the negative x-axis, upstream of the plate. If the ϵ-series for ψ and the pressure are now expressed in terms of the new coordinates the resulting solution is physically more realistic, in so far as it includes a diffusive effect upstream of the leading edge, and is, moreover, 'uniformly valid'—reducing to a potential flow away from the plate and to Stokes flow near the leading edge. Whether the variables η' and x' (or z) are 'optimal' in the sense of Section 18 is not clear.

Carrier and Lin (1948) have given an analysis of the flow near the leading edge, constructing by an iterative process a series

$$\psi = \psi_0 + \psi_1 + ...$$

Each term is regarded as a function of $\zeta = re^{i\theta}$ and its conjugate $\bar{\zeta}$. Velocity components are given by $u + iw = -2i\,\partial\psi/\partial\bar{\zeta}$, and the boundary conditions on ψ are

$$\theta = 0 \text{ and } 2\pi, \qquad \partial\psi/\partial\bar{\zeta} = 0.$$

The solution is intended to be appropriate to a limited region around the leading edge, where the Reynolds number is small, and it is really an example of the Stokes type of solution discussed in Chapter IV. Since the region of validity is finite, and actually quite small, there are no boundary conditions at infinity, and arbitrary constants must be determined by fitting with other kinds of solution. Thus Carrier and Lin give

$$\psi_0 = Ar^{3/2}(\cos\tfrac{1}{2}\theta - \cos\tfrac{3}{2}\theta), \tag{109}$$

and so

$$\psi_0 = \tfrac{1}{2}A(\zeta\bar{\zeta}^{1/2} + \zeta^{1/2}\bar{\zeta} - \zeta^{3/2} - \bar{\zeta}^{3/2}), \tag{110}$$

$$\mathscr{R}(-2i\,\partial\psi_0/\partial\bar{\zeta}) = \tfrac{1}{2}Ar^{1/2}(5\sin\tfrac{1}{2}\theta + \sin\tfrac{3}{2}\theta). \tag{111}$$

If the velocity component u is now imagined to be developed in a power series involving r and θ, the leading term is, from (110), $2Ar^{\frac{1}{2}}\theta$. Now in the original Blasius solution,

$$u/U_0 = f'(\eta) = f''(0)\eta + ...$$
$$= f''(0)(U_0/2\nu x)^{\frac{1}{2}}z + ...$$
$$= 0.3321(U_0 r/\nu)^{\frac{1}{2}}\theta + ...$$

if $x+iz = re^{i\theta}$. Thus the two solutions may be matched in their first terms, and the constant A found. The solutions, however, differ in higher-order terms, since the Stokes type of solution involves logarithmic terms which are not present in the Blasius solution. Goldstein has also expressed doubt as to whether the solution of Carrier and Lin is sufficiently general. There may be a regular solution with leading terms of order $r^{5/2}$.

14. Steady flow in the boundary layer along a cylinder near the forward stagnation point

Consider a two-dimensional flow around a cylindrical obstacle, with a boundary layer extending from the front stagnation point in both directions around the cylinder. There is no great curvature of the surface and so the standard equations (52) are valid, with x measured along the surface from the stagnation point, and z normal to the surface. Sufficiently near $x = 0$, the velocity U just outside the boundary layer may be represented by the formula $U = U_1 x/l$, and a more extended series for U would have this as its first term (see Section VI. 2).

This problem was also dealt with by Blasius (1908). Physically, it is complementary to the previous problem: the flat plate represents the extreme case of a slender body in two-dimensional flow, the neighbourhood of a stagnation point the extreme case of a bluff body. In fact, the boundary-layer solution now to be discussed has the same form as that for two-dimensional viscous flow against a flat plate held perpendicular to its original direction (Section III. 19).

The boundary conditions needed here are:

$$z = 0,\ u = w = 0;\quad x = 0,\ u = 0;\quad z = \infty,\ u = U_1 x/l.$$

There is no reason to introduce a singularity at $x = 0$, as was done for the flat plate, and the appropriate solution, expressed in terms of the variable

$$\eta = (U_1/\nu l)^{\frac{1}{2}} z = R^{\frac{1}{2}}(z/l),$$

is

$$\psi = (\nu U_1/l)^{\frac{1}{2}} x f(\eta),$$

$$f''' + ff'' - f'^2 + 1 = 0, \tag{112}$$

$$f(0) = f'(0) = 0,\qquad f'(\infty) = 1,$$

$$u = (U_1 x/l)f'(\eta) = Uf'(\eta),\qquad w = -(\nu U_1/l)^{\frac{1}{2}}f(\eta).$$

Equation (112) has been discussed by Hiemenz (1911), Howarth (1934), and Bickley (unpublished). Table V. 2 is based on Bickley's results.

The significance of this solution is enhanced by the fact that it satisfies the *exact* equations of viscous flow in two dimensions, and not

TABLE V. 2

Solution of equation (112)

$$f''' + ff'' + 1 - f'^2 = 0 \quad \text{with} \quad f(0) = f'(0) = 0, f'(\infty) = 1$$

η	f	f'	f''
0·0	0·0000 0000	0·0000 000	1·2325 88
0·1	·0059 9640	·1182 649	·1328 31
0·2	·0233 2226	·2266 124	1·0344 54
0·3	·0509 9480	·3252 411	0·9386 31
0·4	·0880 5659	·4144 561	·8463 25
0·5	0·1335 8522	0·4946 493	0·7583 07
0·6	·1867 0100	·5662 805	·6751 71
0·7	·2465 7292	·6298 609	·5973 50
0·8	·3124 2302	·6859 375	·5251 31
0·9	·3835 2925	·7350 793	·4586 72
1·0	0·4592 2702	0·7778 653	0·3980 13
1·1	·5389 0971	·8148 734	·3430 96
1·2	·6220 2803	·8466 711	·2937 76
1·3	·7080 8860	·8738 080	·2498 36
1·4	·7966 5179	·8968 086	·2110 03
1·5	0·8873 2900	0·9161 682	0·1769 58
1·6	0·9797 7949	·9323 482	·1473 51
1·7	1·0737 0688	·9457 741	·1218 13
1·8	·1688 5548	·9568 338	·0999 64
1·9	·2650 0648	·9658 772	·0814 25
2·0	1·3619 7417	0·9732 167	0·0658 25
2·2	·5577 6033	·9838 534	·0420 40
2·4	·7552 5389	·9905 494	·0260 20
2·6	1·9538 0683	·9946 336	·0155 97
2·8	2·1529 9652	·9970 457	·0090 49
3·0	2·3525 5669	0·9984 242	0·0050 78
3·2	·5523 2542	·9991 861	·0027 55
3·4	·7522 0768	·9995 931	·0014 44
3·6	2·9521 4968	·9998 032	·0007 31
3·8	3·1521 2205	·9999 080	·0003 57
4·0	3·3521 0931	0·9999 584	0·0001 69
4·2	·5521 0365	·9999 819	·0000 77
4·4	·7521 0121	·9999 923	·0000 34
4·6	3·9521 0020	·9999 969	·0000 14
4·8	4·1520 9979	·9999 988	·0000 06
5·0	4·3520 9964	0·9999 995	0·0000 02

$$f' \sim 1 - 0·645(\zeta^{-3} - 6\zeta^{-5} + 45\zeta^{-7} + \ldots)\exp(-\tfrac{1}{2}\zeta^2)$$
$$\zeta = \eta - 0·64790$$

merely the boundary-layer approximation, when x and z are interpreted as Cartesian coordinates. In this case, the flow is against a plane surface represented by $z = 0$, and the original direction of flow is along lines $xz =$ constant. (See Section III. 19.)

15. Weyl's theory of the simpler boundary-layer equations

An alternative approach to some of the equations occurring in boundary-layer theory has been described by Weyl (1941, 1942a, b). He is not concerned with the equations of motion as such but with ordinary differential equations derived from them in the manner illustrated by the two previous sections. These derived equations he replaces by integral equations, incorporating the appropriate boundary conditions, and constructs an iterative process which at least establishes the *existence* of the desired solutions, and may even provide an efficient numerical method of obtaining approximations to them. In connexion with the latter see Section VI. 12.

The equation of Blasius for the flat plate in a uniform stream,

$$f'''+ff'' = 0, \tag{113}$$

together with the boundary conditions

$$f(0) = f'(0) = 0; \qquad f''(0) = 1, \tag{114}$$

has a solution which has already been denoted by $F(\eta)$. With

$$g(\eta) = F''(\eta)$$

the following integral equation is equivalent to (113) and (114):

$$g(\eta) = \exp\left\{-\tfrac{1}{2} \int\limits_0^\eta (\eta - \zeta)^2 g(\zeta)\, d\zeta\right\}. \tag{115}$$

If it is written in the form $g = \Phi(g)$, where Φ is a kind of operator, an iterative process is suggested in which a sequence of functions $g_n(\eta)$ defined by $g_{n+1} = \Phi(g_n)$ is constructed, starting with $g_0(\eta) = 0$. It is readily shown that this process converges to a limit, thus guaranteeing the existence of the desired solution.

The same method is applied by Weyl to the equation found by Goldstein (1930) for the wake behind a flat plate,

$$f'''+2ff''-f'^2 = 0 \tag{116}$$

(see Section VI. 9), and also to the equation of Homann (1936b) for boundary-layer flow near a point of stagnation at the front of a body of revolution,

$$f'''+2ff''-f'^2+1 = 0 \tag{117}$$

(see Section VIII. 5).

For the equation of the corresponding two-dimensional flow, (112), a similar process proves more difficult to justify, and Weyl treats this equation and its generalization, the 'equation of similar profiles'

$$f''' + ff'' + \beta(1 - f'^2) = 0 \tag{118}$$

(see Section 21), by a more complicated method.

16. Steady flow in the boundary layer along a wedge; the solution of Falkner and Skan

The inviscid potential flow past a wedge placed symmetrically in a stream may be specified in terms of a complex potential as follows:

$$\mathfrak{w} = \phi + i\psi = \frac{1}{n+1} U_{-1} e^{-in\pi} \mathfrak{z}^{n+1}$$

where
$$\mathfrak{z} = re^{i\theta}, \qquad n = \alpha/(\pi - \alpha) > 0.$$

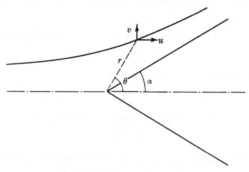

FIG. V. 6. Flow past a wedge.

The velocity is given by

$$\frac{d\mathfrak{w}}{d\mathfrak{z}} = u - iv = U_{-1} e^{-in\pi} \mathfrak{z}^n = U_{-1} r^n e^{-in(\pi - \theta)},$$

so that the components of velocity along and perpendicular to the axis of symmetry are

$$u = U_{-1} r^n \cos n(\pi - \theta), \qquad v = U_{-1} r^n \sin n(\pi - \theta).$$

The constant U_{-1} may now be recognized as the speed at $\mathfrak{z} = -1$, on the axis. The components of velocity at points on the wedge $\theta = \alpha$ are respectively $U_{-1} r^n \cos \alpha$ and $U_{-1} r^n \sin \alpha$, and the speed at the wedge is thus equal to $U_{-1} r^n$. This must be the 'main-stream velocity' for the corresponding two-dimensional boundary-layer problem.

Reverting now to the usual notation for boundary layers,

$$U = U_{-1}(x/l)^n \tag{119}$$

where l is a typical length, and x is measured along the surface of the wedge from its vertex. The special cases of the flat plate ($n = 0$) and the flow near a stagnation point ($n = 1$) are obviously included in this formula, and have already been discussed.

A formally similar problem was solved by Falkner and Skan (1930), though in a different context, in which negative values of n were not excluded. Their analysis and equations were slightly modified by Hartree (1937a), whose work in this connexion is discussed later (Section 21). A more general application of Hartree's solution is given in Section VI. 12. Attention here is confined to the solution in its relevance to flow past a wedge, and Hartree's form of the equations is adopted. If

$$\eta = \left(\frac{n+1}{2}\right)^{\frac{1}{2}}\left(\frac{U}{\nu x}\right)^{\frac{1}{2}} z = \left\{\frac{(n+1)U_{-1}}{2\nu l}\right\}^{\frac{1}{2}} (x/l)^{\frac{1}{2}(n-1)} z \tag{120}$$

and

$$\psi = \left(\frac{2}{n+1}\right)^{\frac{1}{2}} (U\nu x)^{\frac{1}{2}} f(\eta) = \left(\frac{2U_{-1}\nu l}{n+1}\right)^{\frac{1}{2}} (x/l)^{\frac{1}{2}(n+1)} f(\eta), \tag{121}$$

the function $f(\eta)$ satisfies the equation

$$f''' + ff'' + \beta(1 - f'^2) = 0 \tag{122}$$

where $\beta = 2n/(n+1)$. The boundary conditions are

$$f(0) = f'(0) = 0; \qquad f'(\infty) = 1.$$

When $n = 0$, $\beta = 0$ and (122) reduces to the Blasius equation for the flat plate; when $n = \beta = 1$, equation (112), for stagnation-point flow, is recovered.

In applying the solution to the boundary layer along the wedge, it is useful to note the relations $n = \alpha/(\pi - \alpha) = \beta/(2 - \beta)$ and $\alpha = \frac{1}{2}\pi\beta$. From (120) and (121), $u = Uf'(\eta)$, and

$$\frac{\partial u}{\partial z} = \left(\frac{n+1}{2}\right)^{\frac{1}{2}}\left(\frac{U}{\nu x}\right)^{\frac{1}{2}} Uf''(\eta).$$

Hence the displacement thickness is given by

$$\delta_1 = \left(\frac{2}{n+1}\right)^{\frac{1}{2}}\left(\frac{\nu x}{U}\right)^{\frac{1}{2}} \int_0^\infty (1 - f')\,d\eta \tag{123}$$

and the shearing stress at the wedge by

$$\tau_w = \mu\left(\frac{n+1}{2}\right)^{\frac{1}{2}}\left(\frac{U^3}{\nu x}\right)^{\frac{1}{2}} f''(0). \tag{124}$$

It will be seen that

$$\delta_1 \propto (2-\beta)^{-\frac{1}{2}} x^{(1-\beta)/(2-\beta)}, \qquad \tau_w \propto (2-\beta)^{\frac{1}{2}} x^{(2\beta-1)/(2-\beta)};$$

and thus $\beta = \frac{1}{2}$ gives a constant skin friction, whilst $\beta = 1$ gives a constant displacement thickness.

Tables V. 1, V. 2, and V. 3 give some properties of the solutions of (122) for three values of β. See also Section 21.

17. Flow in a converging channel between intersecting planes

The flow outside the boundary layer for convergent radial motion between intersecting planes is given by

$$U = -U_0 l/x, \tag{125}$$

where x is the distance from the line of intersection of the planes, and U_0 is the speed where $x = l$. The negative sign indicates that the motion is towards the line of intersection. The boundary-layer motion due to the outer flow (125) was discussed by Pohlhausen (1921), from whose solution the following treatment is adapted. If

$$u = Ug(\eta), \qquad \eta = (U_0 l/\nu)^{\frac{1}{2}}(z/x),$$

the continuity equation (26) becomes

$$\frac{\partial w}{\partial z} = -\frac{U_0 l}{x^2}(g + \eta g'),$$

of which an integral is

$$w = -\frac{(U_0 l\nu)^{\frac{1}{2}}}{x}\eta g(\eta). \tag{126}$$

The equation of momentum (25), together with the boundary conditions $u = w = 0$ at $z = 0$, $u \to U$ as $z \to \infty$, then give

$$g'' + 1 - g^2 = 0,$$

$$g(0) = 0, \qquad g(\infty) = 1, \tag{127}$$

the condition on w being satisfied automatically by (126).

The solution of (127) is

$$g(\eta) = 3\tanh^2(\xi_0 + \eta/\sqrt{2}) - 2, \tag{128}$$

where ξ_0, which is given by the condition $g(0) = 0$, is $\pm\tanh^{-1}\sqrt{(2/3)}$. In order to have a motion without back flow the positive sign must be taken; thus

$$\xi_0 = \tanh^{-1}\sqrt{(2/3)} = \ln(\sqrt{2} + \sqrt{3}) = 1\cdot146216.$$

In Table V. 4, g (called f') is given as a function of η in the column $\alpha = 0$, $\beta = 1$.

The solution given above is the limiting form, for large Reynolds number, of an exact solution of the Navier–Stokes equations of viscous flow, details of which are given in Section III. 17. The corresponding problem for divergent flow, where (125) is replaced by $U = U_0 l/x$, leads

TABLE V. 3

Solution of equation (VIII. 37)

$$f''' + ff'' + \tfrac{1}{2}(1-f'^2) = 0 \quad \text{with} \quad f(0) = f'(0) = 0, f'(\infty) = 1$$

η	f	f'	f''
0·0	0·0000	0·0000	0·9278
0·1	·0046	·0903	·8777
0·2	·0179	·1756	·8278
0·3	·0395	·2559	·7779
0·4	·0689	·3311	·7282
0·5	0·1056	0·4015	0·6788
0·6	·1490	·4669	·6300
0·7	·1988	·5275	·5819
0·8	·2544	·5833	·5347
0·9	·3153	·6344	·4888
1·0	0·3811	0·6811	0·4442
1·1	·4514	·7234	·4014
1·2	·5256	·7614	·3604
1·3	·6035	·7955	·3215
1·4	·6846	·8258	·2850
1·5	0·7686	0·8526	0·2508
1·6	·8550	·8761	·2192
1·7	0·9437	·8965	·1902
1·8	1·0342	·9142	·1637
1·9	·1264	·9294	·1399
2·0	1·2200	0·9422	0·1185
2·2	·4106	·9623	·0831
2·4	·6045	·9761	·0564
2·6	·8007	·9853	·0370
2·8	1·9984	·9913	·0234
3·0	2·1971	0·9950	0·0143
3·2	·3963	·9972	·0085
3·4	·5959	·9985	·0048
3·6	·7957	·9992	·0026
3·8	2·9955	·9995	·0014
4·0	3·1955	0·9998	0·0007
4·2	·3954	0·9999	·0003
4·4	·5954	1·0000	·0001

$$f' \sim 1 - 0.393(\zeta^{-2} - 3\zeta^{-4} + 15\zeta^{-6}\ldots)\exp(-\tfrac{1}{2}\zeta^2)$$

$$\zeta = \eta - 0.8046$$

to a differential equation which is incompatible with the boundary conditions in (127), so that no boundary-layer motion of this type is possible.

18. The role of coordinate systems in boundary-layer theory

For given boundary conditions, the approximate solution derived from boundary-layer theory depends upon the system of coordinates, and the conventional Cartesian system is not necessarily the best. Thus the solution of Blasius for flow past a flat plate (Section 12) is invalidated by a singularity along the line $x = 0$, which is not found if the boundary-layer solution is instead derived in parabolic coordinates (Section 13). The latter are presumably more appropriate for that problem. The importance of the choice of coordinates depends on the use to which the boundary-layer theory is to be put in any special case. For instance, if only the skin friction is required, different systems of coordinates give the same result, as will be shown. But if the boundary-layer solution forms part of a calculation of the whole field of flow, its dependence on the coordinate system may actually be exploited, as Kaplun (1954) has shown.

It is customary to divide the field of flow, apart from the wake, into two regions; in one of these, the Eulerian equations of inviscid motion are used to obtain an 'external flow', which may perhaps be corrected for the displacement effect of the boundary layer, which occupies the 'inner region'. A dividing line between the two regions is then, in principle, found by a smooth join of the two solutions, but since the boundary-layer solution in unsuitable coordinates behaves incorrectly away the solid wall (for example, along $x = 0$ in the case of the flat plate), this process of 'matching' may be difficult. If, however, a certain system of optimal coordinates is chosen for the boundary-layer solution the problem of 'matching' is not only eased, but eliminated, since the inner solution in this case can be arranged to *contain* the external flow.

The above considerations were presented by Kaplun (1954) in a systematic study of the relation between solutions in different coordinates for incompressible steady two-dimensional flow without separation. He denotes by $\zeta \equiv (\xi, \eta)$ a set of arbitrary curvilinear coordinates, and by $\chi \equiv (\rho, \sigma)$ another set, where required. Velocity components are derived from a stream function ψ by the relations

$$u = \partial\psi/\partial\eta, \qquad v = -\partial\psi/\partial\xi.$$

The coordinates are not necessarily orthogonal, the only restriction on

them being that $\eta = 0$, or $\sigma = 0$, corresponds with the solid boundary where $u = v = 0$. The theory also depends on a small parameter ϵ defined so that
$$\lim_{\epsilon \to 0} (\nu/\epsilon^2) = \text{constant} \neq 0.$$

Following Weyl (1942b) and others, Kaplun introduces two limiting processes:

(i) Let $f(\zeta, \nu)$ be a function of position and viscosity. In the first process, ξ and η are held fixed while ν tends to zero: the result is denoted by $\lim_1 f(\zeta, \nu)$. If this process is applied to an exact solution ψ of the equations of viscous flow, the resulting function ψ_e satisfies the Eulerian equations and represents an 'external flow'.

(ii) In the second process ξ remains fixed, but η varies so that the ratio η/ϵ is constant as $\epsilon \to 0$. This limit depends upon the coordinate system as well as on the function f, and the result is denoted by $\lim_\zeta f$, or $f_\zeta(\xi, \eta/\epsilon)$. If this process is applied to the equations of viscous flow it gives the boundary-layer equations for the coordinate system ζ. The stream function and velocity components in the corresponding boundary-layer solution are
$$\psi_\zeta = \epsilon \lim_\zeta(\psi/\epsilon), \qquad u_\zeta = \lim_\zeta u, \qquad v_\zeta = \epsilon \lim_\zeta(v/\epsilon),$$
and these equations are defined wherever the ζ coordinates are defined, so that a field of flow is given formally for the region outside the boundary layer.

Since $\eta = 0$ at the wall, the first and second limit processes are identical there, and limiting values obtained by either process do not depend upon the particular coordinate system used. Thus the *skin-friction* calculated by boundary-layer theory is independent of the choice of coordinates. Kaplun embodies his results in two theorems, the first of which deals with two boundary-layer approximations to the same exact solution, based on ζ and χ respectively:

THEOREM I. *If $\psi_\zeta = \epsilon f(\xi, \eta/\epsilon)$ is given, as representing one solution, the other may be found by the substitutions*
$$\psi_\chi = \epsilon f(\xi_\chi, \eta_\chi/\epsilon),$$
$$\xi_\chi = \lim_\chi \xi = \xi(\rho, 0),$$
$$\eta_\chi = \epsilon \lim_\chi(\eta/\epsilon) = \sigma(\partial\eta/\partial\sigma)_{\sigma=0}.$$

The two solutions will thus be identical if and only if the systems ζ and χ are connected by the relations
$$\xi(\rho, \sigma) = \xi(\rho, 0), \qquad \eta(\rho, \sigma) = \sigma(\partial\eta/\partial\sigma)_{\sigma=0},$$

which are equivalent to the simpler statements

$$\xi = f_1(\rho), \qquad \eta = \sigma f_2(\rho),$$

where f_1, f_2 are arbitrary functions.

The second theorem relates the boundary-layer approximation for any system of coordinates, specified by ψ_ζ, to the external flow given by ψ_e, and shows that with a suitable choice of ζ the former may contain the latter. The external flow, however, has first to be corrected for the presence of the boundary layer, by adding a small perturbation $\epsilon\psi_e'$; this may formally be derived by the first limiting process as $\epsilon \lim_1(\psi - \psi_e)/\epsilon$, where ψ is imagined known and $\psi_e = \lim_1 \psi$. If the same limiting process is now applied to the *boundary-layer approximation*, it gives $\psi_{\zeta e} = \lim_1 \psi_\zeta$, together with a corresponding perturbation $\epsilon\psi_{\zeta e}' = \epsilon \lim_1(\psi_\zeta - \psi_{\zeta e})/\epsilon$. The boundary-layer solution will therefore contain the external flow (corrected for displacement thickness) if

$$\psi_{\zeta e} = \psi_e, \qquad \psi_{\zeta e}' = \psi_e',$$

and a system of coordinates yielding this result is called *optimal*.

THEOREM II *states that* $\zeta \equiv (\xi, \eta)$ *is a particular optimal system if*

$$\xi = \psi_e', \qquad \eta = \psi_e$$

and that any other system $\chi \equiv (\rho, \sigma)$ *is optimal if and only if it is related to* ζ *by*

$$\rho = f_1(\xi), \qquad \sigma = f_2(\xi)\eta.$$

The field of flow given by the boundary-layer approximation is the same for all optimal systems, but different for any other.

As examples of the application of these ideas, Kaplun discusses three special problems.

EXAMPLE 1. *Flow towards a flat plate*

The exact solution of viscous flow in this case has already been given, in Section 14, as $\psi = (\nu U_1/l)^{\frac12}xf(\eta)$, where $\eta = (U_1/\nu l)^{\frac12}z$. Since $f(\eta) \sim \eta$ for large values of η,

$$\psi_e = \lim_1 \psi = (U_1/l)xz.$$

Choosing the parameter ϵ equal to $(\nu/lU_1)^{\frac12}$, the second limit process is seen to involve $\epsilon \to 0$ with x and η constant. Thus the boundary-layer approximation is

$$\psi_\zeta = \epsilon \lim_\zeta(\psi/\epsilon) = \epsilon \lim_\zeta U_1 xf(\eta) = \epsilon U_1 xf(\eta)$$
$$= (\nu U_1/l)^{\frac12}xf(\eta),$$

being thus identical with the full solution. Without further calculation it can therefore be seen that the coordinates x, z are optimal, and a calculation of $\psi_e' = \lim_1(\psi - \psi_e)/\epsilon$ confirms this.

EXAMPLE 2. *Oseen flow past a semi-infinite flat plate*

In this example, the linearized Oseen equations are regarded as the 'exact' equations of the flow, and are treated in the same way as were the Navier–Stokes equations previously. The solution of the Oseen equations for this problem is known (Lewis and Carrier 1949; see also Section IV. 5.3), and the point of interest is that the boundary-layer approximation, when expressed in parabolic coordinates (which are optimal in this case), is identical with the 'exact' solution. On the other hand, if the usual Cartesian coordinates x, z are employed, the boundary-layer approximation exhibits all the anomalies of the Blasius solution.

EXAMPLE 3. *Flow against a wedge*

The starting-point in this case must be the potential flow with $\nu = 0$, which is given in Section 16 as a complex potential $\mathfrak{w} = \phi + i\psi$. The imaginary part is then ψ_e. Also, the boundary-layer solution is known. Optimal coordinates prove to be $\xi = \mathscr{R}\mathfrak{w}^{\frac{1}{2}}$, $\eta = \mathscr{I}\mathfrak{w}^{\frac{1}{2}}$, which are conformal, and are called 'stream-line parabolic' by Kaplun. The optimal coordinates in Examples 1 and 2 are special cases of these, when the angle of the wedge is $180°$ or 0, but it is only in the former case that the optimal boundary-layer solution happens to be an exact solution of the Navier–Stokes equations.

19. The asymptotic suction profile

The simplest example of the flow of a viscous fluid which involves suction through a porous surface is that of a uniform stream which passes over an infinite plane through which the fluid is being withdrawn by suction at a constant rate. Since the conditions are independent of x and t a solution is sought in which u and w are functions of z only. This solution was found by Griffith and Meredith (1936) and is an exact solution of the Navier–Stokes equations (see Section III. 15).

If w_s is the given constant velocity of suction and U_0 the uniform speed of the stream, the solution for the velocity components is

$$u = U_0\{1 - \exp(-w_s z/\nu)\}, \qquad w = -w_s. \tag{129}$$

It is assumed that the suction is everywhere normal to the surface and, since w is constant, the pressure is the same throughout the flow.

The velocity profile (129) has been called the 'asymptotic suction profile' since it is expected that, for flow over a large but finite plate with constant suction, the velocity distribution will approximate to (129) at points far enough from the leading edge. Pretsch (1944a, b) showed that (129) is also the limiting form of the velocity distribution for an arbitrary boundary-layer flow when the rate of suction tends to infinity, even when U and w_s are functions of x (Section VI. 32).

20. Solutions for boundary-layer flow with suction derived from those without suction: flat-plate and stagnation-point flows

Schlichting and Bussmann (1943) showed that it was possible to generalize the solutions of Blasius (Sections 12 and 14) for uniform flow past a semi-infinite plate and for flow near a stagnation point, by altering one of the boundary conditions for the appropriate ordinary differential equation, so as to take into account certain distributions of normal suction or blowing at the surface. The same considerations were brought forward by Preston (1946).

In each case the modification consists of applying the boundary condition

$$f(0) = K, \qquad (130)$$

instead of $f(0) = 0$, to the differential equations (85) and (112) respectively. The remaining conditions $f'(0) = 0$ and $f'(\infty) = 1$ remain unchanged. In the case of the flat plate, the normal component of velocity is given by

$$w = (\nu U_0/2x)^{\frac{1}{2}}\{\eta f'(\eta) - f(\eta)\},$$

where $f(\eta)$ is the appropriate solution of (85); thus, on the plate,

$$w = -K(\nu U_0/2x)^{\frac{1}{2}} \qquad (131)$$

and (130) implies a distribution of suction ($K > 0$) or blowing ($K < 0$) proportional to $x^{-\frac{1}{2}}$.

Solutions of (85) with the above conditions can be found for all values of $K > K_0$, where $K_0 \simeq -0.87574$ (Iglisch and Grohne 1945). Numerical solutions for various values of K have been given by Schlichting and Bussmann, and by Thwaites (1946a), in both cases with $f'(\infty) = 2$. The most extensive calculations are those of Emmons and Leigh (1953), again with $f'(\infty) = 2$, and from these the above value of K_0 has been derived. The variation with K of the quantities $(\tau_w/\rho U_0)(x/U_0\nu)^{\frac{1}{2}}$, $\delta_1(U_0/\nu x)^{\frac{1}{2}}$, $\delta_2(U_0/\nu x)^{\frac{1}{2}}$, and of $H = \delta_1/\delta_2$, $T = \tau_w \delta_2/\mu U_0$, is shown in Fig. V. 7.

In the case of the stagnation-point flow

$$w = -(\nu U_1/l)^{\frac{1}{2}}f(\eta),$$

where $f(\eta)$ is the appropriate solution of (112). The condition (130) leads to a constant normal velocity at the wall,

$$w = -K(\nu U_1/l)^{\frac{1}{2}}. \qquad (132)$$

It appears that (112) can be solved with the above boundary conditions for any value of K. Schlichting and Bussmann gave several solutions, some with suction and some with blowing, which were obtained by integrating (112) backwards from infinity, using a false origin and an approximate boundary condition at infinity, until the true origin was

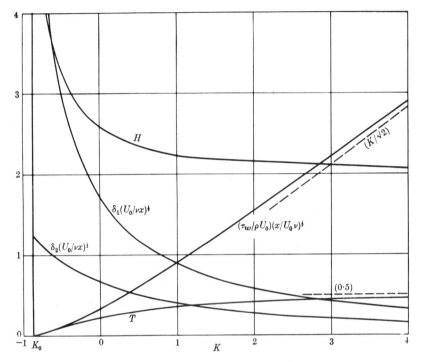

Fig. V. 7. Boundary-layer parameters for flow with suction along a flat plate.

found by the vanishing of $f'(\eta)$. Then K was the corresponding value of $f(\eta)$. Fig. V. 8 shows the variation with K of the quantities $(\tau_w/\rho U)(l/U_1\nu)^{\frac{1}{2}}$, $\delta_1(U_1/l\nu)^{\frac{1}{2}}$, $\delta_2(U_1/l\nu)^{\frac{1}{2}}$, $H = \delta_1/\delta_2$, and $T = \tau_w \delta_2/\mu U$, as found by Schlichting and Bussmann.

21. Solutions with similar velocity profiles

The solutions of the steady two-dimensional boundary-layer equations given in the preceding sections are 'similarity solutions' in the sense that the velocity component u has the same shape of profile across any transverse section of the layer. More precisely,

$$u = U(x)f'(\eta), \tag{133}$$

where

$$\eta = z/g(x) \tag{134}$$

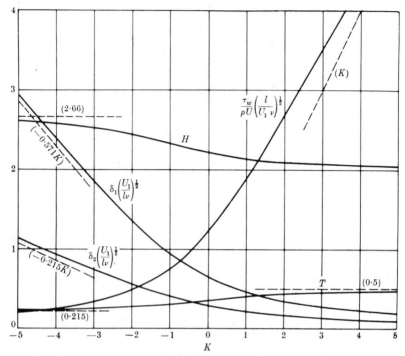

FIG. V. 8. Boundary-layer parameters for flow with suction near a forward stagnation point.

and $g(x)$ represents the variation of boundary-layer thickness. It will now be shown, following Goldstein (1939) and Mangler (1943, 1944a), that this type of solution is possible only for a limited choice of the main stream $U(x)$, with the corresponding forms of $g(x)$ and the suction velocity $w_s(x)$, if present. It will be assumed that the positive x-direction is that of the main stream, so that $U(x) > 0$, and also that $g(x) > 0$.

Since $u = \partial\psi/\partial z$, (133) implies that the stream function is of the form

$$\psi = U(x)g(x)f(\eta)+\psi_0(x), \qquad (135)$$

and the transverse velocity component is then

$$w = -\partial\psi/\partial x = -(Ug)'f+Ug'\eta f'-\psi_0', \qquad (136)$$

where the appropriate arguments of the functions are omitted. Thus $w_s(x) = \psi_0'(x)$. Substitution of (133) and (136) for u and w in the equation of motion now leads to

$$\nu f'''+g(Ug)'ff''+g^2U'(1-f'^2)+w_s gf'' = 0.$$

This, it can be shown, must be an ordinary differential equation for $f(\eta)$, so that

$$f''' + \alpha f f'' + \beta(1 - f'^2) + \gamma f'' = 0, \qquad (137)$$

where

$$\alpha = g(Ug)'/\nu, \qquad \beta = g^2 U'/\nu, \qquad \gamma = w_s g/\nu \qquad (138)$$

are constants.

It follows from (138) that $(g^2 U)' = (2\alpha - \beta)\nu$. Hence when $\beta \neq 2\alpha$ the general solution of equations (138) is of the form

$$\left. \begin{aligned} U(x) &= U_0(|x - x_0|/l)^n \\ g(x) &= [(2\alpha - \beta)(x - x_0)\nu/U(x)]^{\frac{1}{2}} \\ w_s(x) &= \gamma[U(x)\nu/(2\alpha - \beta)(x - x_0)]^{\frac{1}{2}} \end{aligned} \right\} . \qquad (139)$$

where
$$n = \beta/(2\alpha - \beta)$$
and
$$(2\alpha - \beta)(x - x_0) > 0$$

In the case when $\beta = 2\alpha$ the solution is

$$\left. \begin{aligned} U(x) &= U_0 e^{2\alpha x/l} \\ g(x) &= (\nu l/U_0)^{\frac{1}{2}} e^{-\alpha x/l} \\ w_s(x) &= \gamma(\nu U_0/l)^{\frac{1}{2}} e^{\alpha x/l} \end{aligned} \right\} . \qquad (140)$$

The general solution of equations (138) contains two arbitrary constants, which are x_0 and $U_0 l^{-n}$ in (139), and U_0 and l in (140).

Examples of the main-stream flows given by (139) include the following:

(i) Semi-infinite flat plate. $\alpha = 1$, $\beta = 0$; $U = U_0$ $(x > 0)$.
(Section 12)

(ii) Forward stagnation point. $\alpha = \beta = 1$; $U = U_0 x/l$ $(x > 0)$.
(Section 14)

(iii) Wedge flow. $\alpha = 1$, $0 < \beta < 2$; $U = U_0(x/l)^n$ $(x > 0)$.
(Section 16)

(iv) Convergent channel. $\alpha = 0$, $\beta = 1$; $U = -U_0 l/x$ $(x < 0)$.
(Section 17)

(v) Divergent channel. $\alpha = 0$, $\beta = -1$; $U = U_0 l/x$ $(x > 0)$.

(vi) Rear stagnation point. $\alpha = \beta = -1$; $U = -U_0 x/l$ $(x < 0)$.

(vii) Asymptotic suction profile. $\alpha = \beta = 0$, $\gamma > 0$; $U = U_0$, w_s constant.
(Section 19)

It will appear that the example (v) can be realized only with a sufficiently great amount of suction, and that example (vi) cannot lead to a boundary-layer flow. The outer flows given by (139) and (140) form a continuous family depending on the ratio of β to α and on their signs. Some examples are shown in Fig. V. 9.

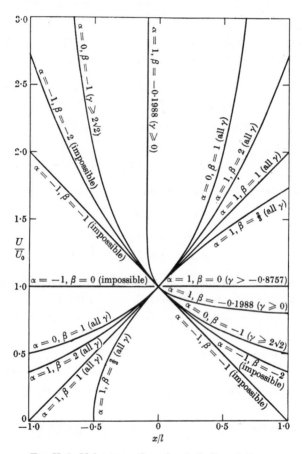

Fig. V. 9. Main-stream flows for similarity solutions.

The equation (137) for $f(\eta)$ is called the 'equation of similar profiles'. Since the shape of the velocity profile is unaffected by a change of scale of η, it follows that the profile (α, β, γ) is equivalent to $(\lambda^2\alpha, \lambda^2\beta, \lambda\gamma)$ for any $\lambda > 0$. Thus if $\alpha \neq 0$ the equation may be normalized so that $\alpha = \pm 1$, and if $\alpha = 0$ it may be normalized so that $\beta = \pm 1$ or 0. The boundary conditions for equation (137) are

$$f(0) = f'(0) = 0, \qquad f'(\infty) = 1. \tag{141}$$

If $\alpha \neq 0$, the term $\gamma f''$ in (137) can be absorbed into the term $\alpha f f''$, so that

$$f''' + \alpha f f'' + \beta(1 - f'^2) = 0,$$
$$f(0) = \gamma/\alpha, \quad f'(0) = 0, \quad f'(\infty) = 1 \left.\right\}.$$

(142)

Although the general conditions on the main stream $U(x)$ are provided by equations (139) and (140), these do not suffice to ensure the existence, or uniqueness, of a corresponding boundary-layer flow. Such questions require a study of the differential equation (137). Some important results may be conjectured from the possible behaviour of the solutions for large values of η. As $\eta \to \infty$, $f' \to 1$ and

$$\eta - f \to \Delta_1 = \int_0^\infty (1 - f')\, d\eta,$$

which must be finite if the displacement thickness of the boundary layer is finite. Hence, when η is large the equation for $q(\eta) = 1 - f'(\eta)$ approximates to

$$q'' + \{\alpha(\eta - \Delta_1) + \gamma\}q' - 2\beta q = 0.$$

(143)

When $\alpha \neq 0$, equation (143) may be solved in terms of parabolic cylinder functions and, from the asymptotic expansions of these functions (see Appendix to this chapter), it may be shown that as $\eta \to +\infty$ the general solution of (143) has the approximate forms

$$q(\eta) \sim A e^{-\frac{1}{2}\zeta^2} \zeta^{-(2\beta+\alpha)/\alpha} + B\zeta^{2\beta/\alpha} \quad (\alpha > 0)$$
$$q(\eta) \sim A \zeta^{2\beta/\alpha} + B e^{\frac{1}{2}\zeta^2} \zeta^{-(2\beta+\alpha)/\alpha} \quad (\alpha < 0) \left.\right\},$$

(144)

where
$$\zeta = (\eta - \Delta_1 + \gamma/\alpha)\sqrt{|\alpha|}$$

and A, B are constants. Thus if $\alpha > 0$, $\beta \geqslant 0$, the condition $q(\infty) = 0$ requires $B = 0$, and then $q \to 0$ with exponential rapidity. If $\alpha > 0$, $\beta < 0$, however, there is no immediate restriction on B, so that there may be a whole family of integrals of (137) satisfying the conditions (141). For this reason Hartree (1937a) added the extra condition that, as $\eta \to \infty$, $f'(\eta)$ shall tend to 1 as rapidly as possible, in order to make $B = 0$. The approach is then exponential. When $\alpha < 0$, the condition $q(\infty) = 0$ requires both $B = 0$ and $\beta > 0$, and then $q(\eta) = O(\eta^{2\beta/\alpha})$. If $\alpha < 0$ and $\beta \leqslant 0$ there is no solution satisfying the condition at infinity.

The case $\alpha = 0$ is simpler, since the solution of (143) is now

$$q(\eta) = A e^{-\lambda_1 \eta} + B e^{-\lambda_2 \eta}$$
$$\lambda_{1,2} = \tfrac{1}{2}[\gamma \pm \sqrt{(\gamma^2 + 8\beta)}] \left.\right\}.$$

(145)

where

If $\beta > 0$, $\lambda_1 > 0 > \lambda_2$, so that $B = 0$. If $\beta < 0$, λ_1 and λ_2 are complex if $\gamma^2 < -8\beta$, and hence any solution oscillates about $q = 0$. When $\gamma > \sqrt{(-8\beta)}$, λ_1 and λ_2 are both positive, but the condition of most rapid approach again makes $B = 0$. A slight modification is needed when $\gamma = \sqrt{(-8\beta)}$, and $\lambda_1 = \lambda_2$.

The results obtained by this heuristic method may be proved by rigorous arguments. It is generally desirable on physical grounds to exclude flows with supervelocities ($f' > 1$), or back flow ($f' < 0$), though small amounts of back flow may be appropriate when conditions after separation are considered (Stewartson 1954). For this reason Iglisch (1953, 1954) introduced the further condition

$$0 < f' < 1 \quad \text{for} \quad 0 < \eta < \infty. \tag{146}$$

(1) $\alpha = 1$, $\beta \geqslant 0$. Weyl (1942a) proved the existence of solutions of (137) and (141) with $\gamma = 0$ (no suction); see Section 15. Iglisch (1953, 1954) proved the existence and uniqueness of the solution for general values of γ with the extra condition (146). The suction parameter γ may have any value if $\beta > 0$, but when $\beta = 0$ the solution exists only when $\gamma > K_0 = -0.87574$. Iglisch had earlier shown the necessity of the condition $f' > 0$ for uniqueness. Coppel (1960) gave a classification of solutions of (137), complete for $0 \leqslant \beta \leqslant \frac{1}{2}$.

Numerical integrations of equation (137) were made by Hartree (1937a) for $\beta = 0\,(\cdot 1)\,0 \cdot 6\,(\cdot 2)\,1 \cdot 2\,(\cdot 4)\,2 \cdot 4$ with $\gamma = 0$, and some of these results are quoted in Table V. 4. More recent computations were made by Smith (1954). Calculations for flow with suction or blowing have been made by Schlichting and Bussmann (1943) for $\beta = 0$ and 1 (Section 20), by Schaefer (1943) for $\beta = 0 \cdot 2$, and by Brown and Donoughe (1951).

(2) $\alpha = 1$, $\beta < 0$. Iglisch and Kemnitz (1955) showed that solutions of (137), subject to (141) and (146), exist only for $\gamma \geqslant \gamma_0(\beta)$, where $\gamma_0(\beta)$ is a function which increases with $|\beta|$. When $\gamma = \gamma_0(\beta)$ there is only one such solution, which has $f''(0) = 0$ and so gives a separation profile. When $\gamma > \gamma_0(\beta)$ there is a solution in which $f' \to 1$ more rapidly than in any other, thus satisfying Hartree's criterion. A graph of $\gamma_0(\beta)$, based largely on calculations by Terrill (1960), is shown in Fig. V. 10.

Hartree's (1937a) numerical solutions were carried out with $\gamma = 0$ for various values of β down to $\beta_0 = -0.1988$, where $f''(0) = 0$. This represented the lower limit of significance since, as Stewartson (1954) proved, any solution of (137) with $\beta < \beta_0$, $\gamma = 0$, satisfying the conditions (141), has $f' > 1$ for some values of $\eta > 0$. These solutions with supervelocities are rejected as being physically unacceptable.

Stewartson (1954) also introduced an alternative form of the boundary condition at infinity. Let $f_a(\eta)$ be a solution of (137) which satisfies the conditions $f_a(0) = f'_a(0) = 0, f'_a(a) = 1$. Then the solutions appropriate to boundary-layer theory are defined to be those of the form $\lim_{a \to \infty} f_a(\eta)$. When this criterion is applied in the range $\beta_0 < \beta < 0$, $\gamma = 0$, with $f''(0) > 0$, the solutions chosen by Hartree are obtained.

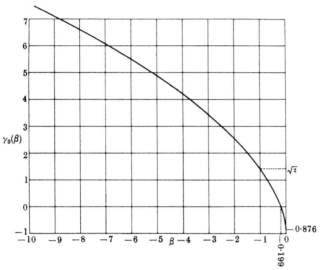

FIG. V. 10. Graph of the function $\gamma_0(\beta)$.

However, another family of solutions with $f''(0) < 0$, and so containing regions of back flow, may also be constructed in this way. These were not considered by Hartree, but have some relevance in the context of Stewartson's paper, namely the theory of flow downstream of a point of separation of a boundary layer from a surface. In the new solutions $f' \to 1$ exponentially from below (as in Hartree's solutions) and the length of the region of reversed flow increases from zero at $\beta = \beta_0$ to infinity as $\beta \to 0$. The existence of solutions with back flow had earlier been noticed by Mangler (1944a) in the general case with suction.

When $\alpha = 1, \beta = -1$, equation (137) can be integrated twice to yield a first-order equation of Riccati type. In this way Thwaites (1948, 1955) showed that the solution that satisfies the Hartree condition at infinity has $f''(0) = \sqrt{(\gamma^2-2)}$, and thus solved the equation analytically in terms of error functions. It follows that $\gamma_0(-1) = \sqrt{2}$.

Some of Hartree's numerical solutions, including $\beta = -0.1988$, are

TABLE V. 4

Solutions of the equation of similar profiles (137), $f''' + \alpha f f'' + \beta(1-f'^2) = 0,\ f(0) = f'(0) = 0,\ f'(\infty) = 1$

$\alpha =$	1	1	1	1	1	1	1	1	1	0	−1	−1
$\beta =$	−0·15	−0·18	−0·1988	−0·18	−0·15	0	0·5	1	2	1	4	1
$f''(0) =$	−0·132	−0·097	0	0·1285	0·2161	0·4696	0·928	1·233	1·687	1·1547	2·273	1·086
η	f'	f'	f'	f'	f'	f'	f'	f'	f'	f'	f'	f'
0	0	0	0	0	0	0	0	0	0	0	0	0
0·1			0·001	0·014	0·022	0·047	0·090	0·118	0·159	0·110	0·207	0·104
0·2			·004	·029	·046	·094	·176	·227	·298	·211	·377	·197
0·3			·009	·047	·072	·141	·256	·325	·419	·302	·513	·282
0·4	−0·041	−0·024	·016	·066	·098	·188	·331	·414	·522	·384	·620	·357
0·5			0·025	0·087	0·125	0·234	0·402	0·495	0·610	0·458	0·705	0·425
0·6			·036	·109	·156	·281	·467	·566	·683	·523	·770	·485
0·7			·049	·134	·187	·327	·528	·630	·745	·582	·821	·538
0·8	−0·058	−0·020	·064	·160	·220	·372	·583	·686	·786	·633	·860	·585
0·9			·080	·188	·253	·417	·634	·735	·838	·679	·891	·627
1·0			0·099	0·217	0·287	0·461	0·681	0·778	0·872	0·719	0·914	0·664
1·2	−0·050	+0·013	·142	·279	·359	·545	·761	·847	·921	·786	·947	·726
1·4			·193	·346	·433	·624	·826	·897	·953	·837	·967	·774
1·6	−0·019	0·076	·250	·417	·507	·697	·876	·932	·973	·876	·979	·813
1·8			·313	·490	·581	·761	·914	·957	·985	·906	·986	·843
2·0	+0·035	0·167	0·380	0·562	0·651	0·817	0·942	0·973	0·991	0·929	0·991	0·868
2·4	·119	·283	·523	·700	·776	·901	·976	·991	·998	·960	·996	·904
2·8	·226	·419	·664	·815	·872	·953	·991	·997	·999	·977	·998	·928
3·2	·354	·563	·786	·899	·936	·980	·997	·999	1·000	·987	·999	·944
3·6	·493	·699	·879	·952	·972	·993	·999	1·000		·993	1·000	·956
4·0	0·633	0·814	0·940	0·980	0·989	0·998	1·000			0·996		0·965
4·4	·759	·898	·974	·993	·997	·999				·998		·971
4·8	·858	·951	·990	·998	·999	1·000				·999		·976
5·2	·926	·979	·997	·999	1·000					·999		·980
5·6	·966	·992	·999	1·000						1·000		·983
6·0	0·986	0·997	1·000									0·985
6·4	·995	·999										·986
6·8	·999	1·000										

given in Table V. 4, together with two of Stewartson's back-flow solutions. In the latter, if the origin for each solution is shifted to the
second point where $f' = 0$, the solution from there onward may be
regarded as a velocity profile for a flow with a distribution of blowing
proportional to $(x-x_0)^{(\beta-1)/(2-\beta)}$. This is a simple example of the trans-
position theorem of Section 8. Some computations for flows with suction or blowing were given by Thwaites (1949a) and Brown and
Donoughe (1951).

(3) $\alpha = -1$, $\beta > 0$. It may be shown by methods similar to those
of Iglisch (1953, 1954) that for any value of γ there is a unique solution
of equation (137) subject to the conditions (141) and (146). The solutions with $\beta \leqslant \frac{1}{2}$ have infinite displacement thickness, and so are
physically unimportant. The case $\alpha = -1$, $\beta = 1$ leads to a Riccati
equation after double integration. The solution may thus be obtained
as

$$f(\eta) = \gamma - 2 \frac{U'(a, \eta - A)}{U(a, \eta - A)}, \tag{147}$$

in the notation of the Appendix to this chapter, where $a = \frac{1}{4}(\gamma^2 - A^2)$
and where A, which equals $f''(0)$, is found from the condition $f(0) = 0$.

Numerical solutions of (137), due to R. M. Terrill, with $\alpha = -1$,
$\beta = 1$ and 4, $\gamma = 0$ are given in Table V. 4. Earlier calculations were
made by Wieghardt and Mangler (Mangler 1948a). The case $\beta = 4$ is
appropriate to the flow towards a small hole in the bottom of a tank
(Section VIII. 9).

(4) $\alpha = -1$, $\beta \leqslant 0$. It was conjectured by Goldstein (1939) and
proved by Hardy (1939) that equation (137) with $\alpha = -1$, $\beta = -2$
has no solution in which $f' \to 1$ as $\eta \to \infty$, except $f' = 1$. This case
corresponds to $U = U_0 e^{-x/l}$. Hardy's method, or an adaptation of that
of Iglisch (1953), also proves the same result for any $\beta < 0$ when
$\alpha = -1$. The case $\beta = 0$ is easily disposed of.

(5) $\alpha = 0$, $\beta = 1$. By a method similar to that of Iglisch it may be
proved that the solution of (137), subject to (141) and (146), exists and
is unique for all values of γ. The main-stream flow (139) in this case
is that in a convergent channel, and the Pohlhausen (1921) solution
for the case $\gamma = 0$ is given in Section 17 and Table V. 4. Numerical
solutions with suction and blowing were given by Holstein (1943), who
showed that the equation is soluble by elliptic functions when $\gamma = 5/\sqrt{3}$.
A solution equivalent to the case $\gamma = -3$ was computed by Hartree
(1937b). If $\gamma = -5/\sqrt{3}$, there is an elementary solution with

$$f'(\eta) = 2[1 + (\sqrt{2} - 1)\exp(-\eta/\sqrt{3})]^{-2} - 1. \tag{148}$$

(6) $\alpha = 0, \beta = -1$. In this case, it may be shown, a solution of (137) satisfying (141) and (146) exists only when $\gamma \geqslant \sqrt{8}$, and a definite solution may then be chosen by Hartree's condition. The main-stream flow now corresponds to a divergent channel, and numerical solutions have been given by Holstein (1943) and Thwaites (1949a, 1955). The solution is again expressible in terms of elliptic functions when $\gamma = 5/\sqrt{3}$.

(7) $\gamma \rightarrow \pm\infty$. The behaviour of the solutions of the equation of similar profiles (137) with boundary conditions (141) was studied by Pretsch (1944a) in the limiting cases $\gamma \rightarrow \pm\infty$. For large positive values of γ there is a strong suction velocity, and the boundary layer is thin. The leading terms of (137) are therefore $f''' + \gamma f'' = 0$, so that the velocity profile becomes the asymptotic suction profile $f' = 1 - \exp(-\gamma\eta)$. Higher approximations were found by Pretsch (1944a) and Watson (1947) (see Section VI. 32). The results thus obtained agree well with the available numerical solutions.

When there is a strong blowing velocity, so that $\gamma \rightarrow -\infty$, solutions exist only for $\beta > 0$. The boundary layer is very thick and the viscous effects (which appear in the term f''') are therefore small. The limiting form of (137) is now

$$\alpha ff'' + \beta(1 - f'^2) + \gamma f'' = 0, \tag{149}$$

and the condition at infinity is abandoned. Pretsch showed that the appropriate solution of (149) is given by

$$\left.\begin{array}{l} \eta/|\gamma| = \beta^{-1} \displaystyle\int_0^{f'} (1-t^2)^{(\alpha-2\beta)/2\beta} \, dt \\[2mm] f'^2 = 1 - (1 - \alpha f/|\gamma|)^{2\beta/\alpha} \quad (\alpha \neq 0) \\[2mm] = 1 - \exp(-2\beta f/|\gamma|) \quad (\alpha = 0) \end{array}\right\}, \tag{150}$$

and gave several examples of (150) with higher approximations in a few cases. Again, good agreement with numerical solutions was found.

22. The boundary layer between parallel streams

Lessen (1949) discussed the stability of the laminar boundary layer formed when a uniform stream of fluid passes over a layer of the same fluid at rest, and obtained the velocity distribution in the course of his method. This velocity distribution had already been obtained by Keulegan (1944) using an approximate method. Lock (1951) extended the work of Lessen by considering two parallel uniform streams of different fluids, moving horizontally in the same direction, which come into contact at the line $x = 0$. Görtler (1942) treated the corresponding problem for turbulent flow (with only one fluid), assuming constant eddy viscosity, and obtained similar results.

Let U_1, U_2 be the speeds of the two streams, and ρ_1, ρ_2 the densities, ν_1, ν_2 the kinematic viscosities, of the two fluids, where the suffix 1 refers to the upper fluid and 2 to the lower. The x-axis is drawn horizontally in the direction of motion and the z-axis vertically upwards. At $x = 0$ the fluids come into contact and have different speeds, so that a boundary layer will form at the surface of contact, extending into both fluids. The boundary-layer equations of momentum are

$$u\frac{\partial u}{\partial x} + w\frac{\partial u}{\partial z} = \nu_1\frac{\partial^2 u}{\partial z^2} \tag{151}$$

for the upper fluid, and

$$u\frac{\partial u}{\partial x} + w\frac{\partial u}{\partial z} = \nu_2\frac{\partial^2 u}{\partial z^2} \tag{152}$$

for the lower, since there is no pressure gradient. By continuity a stream function ψ may be introduced, as in (82).

One of the streams may perhaps be at rest, so let $U_1 > 0$, $U_2 \geqslant 0$. Then a solution of the equations analogous to that of Section 12 can be found by the following substitutions. For the upper fluid let

$$\eta_1 = (U_1/2\nu_1 x)^{\frac{1}{2}}z, \qquad \psi = (2\nu_1 U_1 x)^{\frac{1}{2}}f_1(\eta_1), \tag{153}$$

so that

$$u = U_1 f_1'(\eta_1), \qquad w = (\nu_1 U_1/2x)^{\frac{1}{2}}\{\eta_1 f_1'(\eta_1) - f_1(\eta_1)\}, \tag{154}$$

and, as in Section 12, equation (151) reduces to

$$f_1''' + f_1 f_1'' = 0. \tag{155}$$

For the lower fluid the substitutions are

$$\eta_2 = (U_1/2\nu_2 x)^{\frac{1}{2}}z, \qquad \psi = (2\nu_2 U_1 x)^{\frac{1}{2}}f_2(\eta_2), \tag{156}$$

and then

$$u = U_1 f_2'(\eta_2), \qquad w = (\nu_2 U_1/2x)^{\frac{1}{2}}\{\eta_2 f_2'(\eta_2) - f_2(\eta_2)\}, \tag{157}$$

whence equation (152) reduces to

$$f_2''' + f_2 f_2'' = 0. \tag{158}$$

Thus f_1, considered as a function of η_1, and f_2, considered as a function of η_2, both satisfy the differential equation (85) obtained by Blasius for flow past a flat plate.

The boundary conditions require that u shall tend to U_1 and U_2 as $\eta_1 \to +\infty$ and $\eta_2 \to -\infty$, respectively, and that the components of velocity and stress shall be continuous at the interface between the fluids. Hence, from (154) and (157), $f_1'(+\infty) = 1$, $f_2'(-\infty) = U_2/U_1$.

If the surface of contact is

$$\eta_1 = \eta_1^*, \qquad \eta_2 = \eta_2^*, \qquad \eta_2^* = (\nu_1/\nu_2)^{\frac{1}{2}}\eta_1^*,$$

the continuity of u and w is achieved by taking

$$f_1(\eta_1^*) = f_2(\eta_2^*) = 0, \qquad f_1'(\eta_1^*) = f_2'(\eta_2^*).$$

The tangential stress is $\mu(\partial u/\partial z)$ on the boundary-layer approximation, so that this is continuous provided

$$\rho_1 \nu_1^{\frac{1}{2}} f_1''(\eta_1^*) = \rho_2 \nu_2^{\frac{1}{2}} f_2''(\eta_2^*). \tag{159}$$

The normal stress is $p_{zz} = -p + 2\mu(\partial w/\partial z)$, and $\mu(\partial w/\partial z)$ is continuous by (159), so that p must also be continuous. This requires that $\eta_1^* = \eta_2^* = 0$, unless $\rho_1 = \rho_2$. In this case the position of the interface is arbitrary unless further conditions are given, but the substitution

$$f_1(\eta_1) = g_1(\eta_1 - \eta_1^*), \qquad f_2(\eta_2) = g_2(\eta_2 - \eta_2^*)$$

allows the contact conditions to be taken at $\eta_1 = \eta_2 = 0$.

Thus the boundary conditions for equations (155), (158) may be taken as

$$f_1(0) = f_2(0) = 0, \qquad f_1'(0) = f_2'(0),$$

$$f_1''(0) = k^{\frac{1}{2}} f_2''(0), \qquad f_1'(+\infty) = 1, \qquad f_2'(-\infty) = \lambda, \tag{160}$$

where $k = \rho_2 \mu_2/\rho_1 \mu_1$ depends only on the nature of the fluids and $\lambda = U_2/U_1 \geqslant 0$.

Lock found approximate solutions for various values of k, λ by methods involving the use of the momentum equation analogous to those described in Section VI. 13, and also calculated accurate numerical solutions of the problem for $\lambda = 0$ with $k = 5 \cdot 965 \times 10^4$ (corresponding to air over water at $10°$ C), 100, 10, and 1, and for $\lambda = 0 \cdot 501$ with $k = 1$. The case $\lambda = 0$, $k = 1$ (which is that taken by Lessen) leads to the solution of the Blasius equation (85) with the boundary conditions

$$f'(\infty) = 1, \qquad f'(-\infty) = 0, \qquad f(0) = 0.$$

From Lock's calculations it follows that in this case

$$K_0 = f(-\infty) = -0 \cdot 87574,$$

where K_0 is the constant referred to in Sections 20 and 21.

23. The two-dimensional jet

Schlichting (1933a) applied the boundary-layer approximations to the steady flow produced by a fine jet emerging into fluid at rest, assuming the motion to be laminar. The following treatment of the two-dimensional case is based on Bickley's (1937) analytical solution.

The axis of the jet is taken as the x-axis, with origin at the orifice, which is supposed very small. The boundary-layer equation of momentum (15) is

$$u\frac{\partial u}{\partial x} + w\frac{\partial u}{\partial z} = \nu\frac{\partial^2 u}{\partial z^2} \tag{161}$$

in the present case, since the pressure is constant, and u, w are given in terms of the stream function by $u = \partial\psi/\partial z$, $w = -\partial\psi/\partial x$. The boundary conditions are that $u \to 0$ as $z \to \pm\infty$ and, since the motion is symmetrical about the x-axis, $w = 0$ at $z = 0$.

Since no solid boundary is present and the pressure is constant, the rate of flow of momentum across any plane normal to the x-axis must be the same, and thus

$$M = 2\rho \int_0^\infty u^2 \, dz \tag{162}$$

is a constant.

A solution of (161) which satisfies (162) can be obtained by writing

$$\psi = 6\nu x^{1/3} f(\eta), \qquad \eta = zx^{-2/3}. \tag{163}$$

Then

$$u = 6\nu x^{-1/3} f'(\eta), \qquad w = 2\nu x^{-2/3}(2\eta f' - f), \tag{164}$$

and (161) reduces to

$$f''' + 2ff'' + 2f'^2 = 0, \tag{165}$$

while the boundary conditions and (162) become

$$f'(\pm\infty) = f(0) = 0, \qquad M = 72\nu^2\rho \int_0^\infty f'^2(\eta) \, d\eta. \tag{166}$$

The required solution of (165) is readily obtained as

$$f(\eta) = \alpha \tanh \alpha\eta, \tag{167}$$

where α is a constant given by

$$M = 72\nu^2\rho\alpha^3 \int_0^\infty \operatorname{sech}^4\xi \, d\xi = 48\nu^2\rho\alpha^3. \tag{168}$$

Hence

$$\psi = 3(M\nu x/6\rho)^{1/3} \tanh \xi = 1\cdot6510(M\nu x/\rho)^{1/3} \tanh \xi,$$

$$u = \tfrac{1}{4}(6M^2/\nu\rho^2 x)^{1/3} \operatorname{sech}^2\xi = 0\cdot4543(M^2/\nu\rho^2 x)^{1/3} \operatorname{sech}^2\xi,$$

$$w = (M\nu/6\rho x^2)^{1/3}(2\xi\operatorname{sech}^2\xi - \tanh \xi)$$

$$= 0\cdot5503(M\nu/\rho x^2)^{1/3}(2\xi\operatorname{sech}^2\xi - \tanh \xi),$$

where

$$\xi = \alpha\eta = \tfrac{1}{2}(M/6\nu^2\rho x^2)^{1/3}z = 0\cdot2752(M/\nu^2\rho)^{1/3}zx^{-2/3}.$$

The mass flowing across a plane at a distance x from the orifice normal to the jet is

$$Q = 2\rho \int_0^\infty u \, dz = 2\rho[\psi]_{z=0}^{z=\infty} = (36M\nu\rho^2 x)^{1/3} = 3{\cdot}3019(M\nu\rho^2 x)^{1/3} \tag{169}$$

per unit time.

The results obtained satisfy the hypotheses of the boundary layer provided $(Mx/\rho\nu^2)$ is large, which is not true close to the orifice of the jet. According to (169), $Q = 0$ when $x = 0$, so that the actual flow from the jet cannot be found from this solution, which only involves the momentum flux M produced by the jet.

APPENDIX TO CHAPTER V

Parabolic cylinder functions

The equation for the parabolic cylinder functions, otherwise known as Weber's equation, occurs in boundary-layer theory mainly in approximate solutions valid in the outer regions of a boundary layer. It may also occur in an exact solution. Examples are given in Section 21. A standard form of the equation is

$$\frac{d^2 y}{dx^2} - (\tfrac{1}{4}x^2 + a)y = 0, \tag{170}$$

and for a definitive account reference should be made to Miller (1955).

Whether a is positive or negative, the solutions of (170) are of 'exponential' type for large x; if a is negative there is an 'oscillatory' region, for which

$$-2(-a)^{\frac{1}{2}} < x < 2(-a)^{\frac{1}{2}},$$

but this will not be relevant to the boundary-layer application. There is just one solution which is bounded as $x \to +\infty$, and this is identified by its asymptotic behaviour:

$$U(a,x) \sim \exp(-\tfrac{1}{4}x^2)x^{-a-\frac{1}{2}}\left\{1 - \frac{(a+\frac{1}{2})(a+\frac{3}{2})}{2x^2} + \frac{(a+\frac{1}{2})(a+\frac{3}{2})(a+\frac{5}{2})(a+\frac{7}{2})}{2.4x^4} - \cdots\right\}. \tag{171}$$

A second solution which is linearly independent is

$$V(a,x) = \pi^{-1}\Gamma(\tfrac{1}{2}+a)\{\sin\pi a. \, U(a,x) + U(a,-x)\}, \tag{172}$$

and it may be noted that

$$U\frac{dV}{dx} - V\frac{dU}{dx} = \sqrt{\left(\frac{2}{\pi}\right)}.$$

The appropriate asymptotic development of $V(a,x)$ is

$$\left(\frac{2}{\pi}\right)^{\frac{1}{2}}\exp(\tfrac{1}{4}x^2)x^{a-\frac{1}{2}}\left\{1 + \frac{(a-\frac{1}{2})(a-\frac{3}{2})}{2x^2} + \frac{(a-\frac{1}{2})(a-\frac{3}{2})(a-\frac{5}{2})(a-\frac{7}{2})}{2.4x^4} + \cdots\right\}, \tag{173}$$

and both (171) and (173) are valid when x, but not a, is large.

These solutions are connected with other functions which, in some cases, are better known. For instance, $U(a,x)$ may be identified with Whittaker's function

$D_n(x)$, if $a = -n - \frac{1}{2}$. If n is a positive integer, a connexion may be set up with the Hermite polynomials

$$h_n(x) = (-)^n \exp(\tfrac{1}{2}x^2)\left(\frac{d}{dx}\right)^n \exp(-\tfrac{1}{2}x^2)$$

and

$$h_n^*(x) = (-i)^n h_n(ix) = \exp(-\tfrac{1}{2}x^2)\left(\frac{d}{dx}\right)^n \exp(\tfrac{1}{2}x^2).$$

Thus

$$U(-n-\tfrac{1}{2}, x) = \exp(-\tfrac{1}{4}x^2)h_n(x), \tag{174}$$

$$V(n+\tfrac{1}{2}, x) = (-)^n\left(\frac{2}{\pi}\right)^{\frac{1}{2}} \exp(\tfrac{1}{4}x^2)h_n^*(x). \tag{175}$$

Also, there is a connexion with the probability integrals. If the repeated integrals of the error function are $Hh_n(x)$, so that $Hh_{-1}(x) = \exp(-\tfrac{1}{2}x^2)$ and

$$Hh_n(x) = \int_x^\infty Hh_{n-1}(t)\, dt = \frac{1}{n!}\int_x^\infty (t-x)^n \exp(-\tfrac{1}{2}t^2)\, dt,$$

then

$$U(n+\tfrac{1}{2}, x) = \exp(\tfrac{1}{4}x^2)Hh_n(x) \tag{176}$$

if $n \geqslant -1$.

VI

APPROXIMATE METHODS OF SOLUTION

1. Introduction

THE subject of this chapter is the solution of the boundary-layer equations for the steady two-dimensional flow of a viscous fluid over a plane or curved surface. These equations, whose derivation is given in Sections V. 1 and V. 2, may be written as

$$u\frac{\partial u}{\partial x}+w\frac{\partial u}{\partial z} = U\frac{dU}{dx}+\nu\frac{\partial^2 u}{\partial z^2}, \tag{1}$$

$$\frac{\partial u}{\partial x}+\frac{\partial w}{\partial z} = 0. \tag{2}$$

In these equations x and z denote distances measured along and normal to the surface, u and w are the corresponding components of velocity, ν is the kinematic viscosity of the fluid, and U is the velocity at the edge of the boundary layer.

It will usually be assumed in this chapter that the boundary layer forms at a fixed impermeable rigid surface; however, in Part V of the chapter suction or blowing of the fluid through a porous surface will be considered and flow in a laminar wake is treated in Sections 9 and 12. It is supposed that $U = U(x)$ is given as a function of x, either from theory or from experiment, by means of a suitable analytical expression or by numerical data. The main problem is then to find values of the velocity components $u(x, z)$ and $w(x, z)$ which will satisfy the equations (1) and (2) and the appropriate boundary conditions, namely

$$u = w = 0 \quad \text{at } z = 0, \qquad u \to U(x) \quad \text{as } z \to \infty, \tag{3}$$

which were obtained in Section V. 3.

Solutions of this problem have already been given in Chapter V for certain special forms of $U(x)$. These are not enough to cover all the practically important cases, and so methods of general application will be given in this chapter, in order that a wide variety of velocity distributions $U(x)$ may be treated.

A secondary problem is to find the variation with x of the skin friction τ_w and the displacement and momentum thicknesses δ_1, δ_2, defined by equations (V.35), (V.36), and (V.38). These can, of course, be calculated once $u(x, z)$ is known, but they are of interest in themselves. The skin friction is especially important since it vanishes at a point of separation of the flow (Section V. 7). Many of the approximate methods described in this chapter are therefore designed to give these quantities directly, without producing the velocity distribution at an intermediate step.

The methods discussed in this chapter are of two main types. In the first the boundary-layer equations (1) and (2) and the boundary conditions (3) are satisfied as closely as is practicable. The accuracy of these methods is limited, in principle, only by the amount of labour available and the accuracy with which $U(x)$ is known. In methods of the second type the equations are simplified to begin with, or are replaced by integral forms such as the momentum and energy equations (V.42) and (V.43). Methods of this type are generally easier to apply, but capable of less accuracy, than those of the first type. They may, however, give better results when only a limited amount of effort is available, but the errors involved are difficult to estimate. Some information may be obtained by comparing results found by these methods in particular cases with those derived by the more accurate methods of the first type. Such comparisons are made in Section 26, where an attempt is made to assess the relative merits of the approximate methods.

When discussing the accuracy of any approximate solution, one should bear in mind the end for which this solution is required. An engineer may wish only to predict with sufficient ease and accuracy the features which interest him most—the position of separation, the distribution of skin friction, and the variation of the displacement and momentum thicknesses of the boundary layer. The experimental scientist is more concerned with any light which the methods may throw on the physical processes of boundary-layer flow. A mathematician may regard the methods as examples of the numerical solution of differential equations. This last point of view may lead to standards of accuracy which are inappropriate for comparison with experimental results. It is very difficult to achieve experimentally the types of flow considered in theoretical solutions: in particular it is difficult to ensure that the flow is strictly two-dimensional. Moreover, the accurate determination of the experimental position of separation is no easy matter. Thus a simple approximation may have greater practical value than a more accurate but laborious method of calculation.

PART I

ACCURATE SOLUTIONS AND APPROXIMATE METHODS BASED ON THEM

2. Solutions in series: method of Blasius and Howarth

In the neighbourhood of the forward stagnation point on a cylinder with a rounded leading edge the outer flow may be represented approximately by a polynomial, or a power series, of the form

$$U = U_1(x/l)[1+a_1(x/l)+a_2(x/l)^2+...], \qquad (4)$$

where U_1 and l are some appropriate velocity and length. If the higher powers of x/l are neglected, the external velocity close to the stagnation point is $U = U_1 x/l$, and the corresponding solution of the boundary-layer equations is given in Section V. 14. This solution was generalized by Blasius (1908), Hiemenz (1911), and Howarth (1934) to cover the outer velocity distribution (4). The following treatment is adapted from that of Howarth.

By virtue of the continuity equation (2) a stream function ψ is introduced such that

$$u = \partial\psi/\partial z, \qquad w = -\partial\psi/\partial x. \qquad (5)$$

This stream function may be reduced to non-dimensional form by writing

$$\psi = (U_1\nu l)^{\frac{1}{2}}f(\xi,\eta), \qquad (6)$$

where

$$\xi = x/l, \qquad \eta = (U_1/\nu l)^{\frac{1}{2}}z. \qquad (7)$$

Then from (5) the velocity components are

$$u = U_1\frac{\partial f}{\partial \eta}, \qquad w = -(U_1\nu/l)^{\frac{1}{2}}\frac{\partial f}{\partial \xi}. \qquad (8)$$

The boundary-layer equation (1) in terms of these non-dimensional variables is

$$\frac{\partial^3 f}{\partial \eta^3}+\frac{\partial f}{\partial \xi}\frac{\partial^2 f}{\partial \eta^2}-\frac{\partial^2 f}{\partial \xi\partial \eta}\frac{\partial f}{\partial \eta}+F(\xi)F'(\xi) = 0, \qquad (9)$$

where

$$F(\xi) = U/U_1 = \xi[1+a_1\xi+a_2\xi^2+...]. \qquad (10)$$

The boundary conditions (3) become

$$f = \frac{\partial f}{\partial \eta} = 0 \quad \text{at } \eta = 0, \qquad \frac{\partial f}{\partial \eta} \to F(\xi) \quad \text{as } \eta \to \infty. \qquad (11)$$

When $a_1 = a_2 =. \quad = 0$, equations (9) and (11) are satisfied by

$$f(\xi,\eta) = f_0(\eta)\xi, \qquad (12)$$

where

$$f_0'''+f_0f_0''+1-f_0'^2 = 0, \qquad (13)$$

$$f_0(0) = f_0'(0) = 0, \qquad f_0'(\infty) = 1. \qquad (14)$$

This is the solution given in Section V. 14, and it is now generalized by writing

$$f(\xi,\eta) = f_0(\eta)\xi + a_1 f_1(\eta)\xi^2 + \{a_2 f_2(\eta) + a_1^2 f_{11}(\eta)\}\xi^3 +$$
$$+ \{a_3 f_3(\eta) + a_2 a_1 f_{21}(\eta) + a_1^3 f_{111}(\eta)\}\xi^4 + \ldots \quad (15)$$

Here $f_{ijk\ldots}(\eta)$ is the coefficient of $a_i a_j a_k \ldots \xi^{1+i+j+k+\cdots}$ in $f(\xi,\eta)$, and is a function of η alone. Once these functions have been tabulated the boundary-layer flow near $\xi = 0$ can be computed from (15) by inserting the appropriate values of U_1, a_1, a_2,.... By substituting (10) and (15) into (9) it is found that f_0 is given by (13) and (14), and the next few functions by the equations

$$f_1''' + f_0 f_1'' - 3f_0' f_1' + 2f_0'' f_1 = -3$$
$$f_2''' + f_0 f_2'' - 4f_0' f_2' + 3f_0'' f_2 = -4$$
$$f_{11}''' + f_0 f_{11}'' - 4f_0' f_{11}' + 3f_0'' f_{11} = -2 + 2f_1'^2 - 2f_1 f_1'' \quad (16)$$
$$\cdots$$

with the boundary conditions

$$f_1(0) = f_1'(0) = f_2(0) = f_2'(0) = f_{11}(0) = f_{11}'(0) = \ldots = 0$$
$$f_1'(\infty) = f_2'(\infty) = f_3'(\infty) = \ldots = 1 \quad (17)$$
$$f_{11}'(\infty) = f_{21}'(\infty) = f_{111}'(\infty) = \ldots = 0$$

These differential equations may be solved in turn, using the values of f_0 given in Table V. 2, and tables of the derivatives of some of the functions are given in Table VI. 1. Then, by (8), the velocity distribution within the layer is given by

$$u = U_1[f_0'(\eta)\xi + a_1 f_1'(\eta)\xi^2 + \{a_2 f_2'(\eta) + a_1^2 f_{11}'(\eta)\}\xi^3 + \ldots], \quad (18)$$

and the skin friction by

$$\frac{\tau_w}{\rho U_1^2}\left(\frac{U_1 l}{\nu}\right)^{\frac{1}{2}} = f_0''(0)\xi + f_1''(0)a_1\xi^2 + \{f_2''(0)a_2 + f_{11}''(0)a_1^2\}\xi^3 + \ldots \quad (19)$$

When the outer flow is symmetrical about $\xi = 0$, $F(\xi)$ is an odd function of ξ, and so $a_1 = a_3 = a_5 = \ldots = 0$. Thus

$$F(\xi) = \xi(1 + a_2\xi^2 + a_4\xi^4 + \ldots), \quad (20)$$
$$f(\xi,\eta) = f_0(\eta)\xi + a_2 f_2(\eta)\xi^3 + \{a_4 f_4(\eta) + a_2^2 f_{22}(\eta)\}\xi^5 +$$
$$+ \{a_6 f_6(\eta) + a_4 a_2 f_{42}(\eta) + a_2^3 f_{222}(\eta)\}\xi^7 + \ldots, \quad (21)$$

where the form of (21) is analogous to that of (15).

The number of functions involved in the coefficient of ξ^n increases rapidly with n. Earlier calculations are due to Howarth (1934), Frössling (1940), Ulrich (1943, 1949), and Tifford (1954).

TABLE

η	f_0'	f_1'	f_2'	f_{11}'	f_4'	f_{22}'	f_6'
0·0	0	0	0	0	0	0	0
·1	0·11826	0·2247	0·2698	0·056	0·3509	0·057	0·424
·2	·22661	·4198	·5004	·092	·6433	·085	0·769
·3	·32524	·5865	·6935	·111	0·8804	·088	1·043
·4	·41446	·7264	·8515	·115	1·0669	·070	·251
0·5	0·49465	0·8415	0·9777	0·106	1·2082	+0·037	1·401
·6	·56628	0·9341	1·0752	·088	·3103	−0·006	·503
·7	·62986	1·0066	·1478	·063	·3789	·055	·565
·8	·68594	·0615	·1989	·034	·4199	·106	·595
·9	·73508	·1012	·2319	+0·004	·4385	·155	·599
1·0	0·77787	1·1281	1·2500	−0·026	1·4394	−0·198	1·594
·2	·84667	·1521	·2531	·079	·4049	·265	·517
·4	·89681	·1488	·2281	·117	·3434	·299	·426
·6	·93235	·1305	·1898	·136	·2736	·302	·332
·8	·95683	·1060	·1485	·138	·2069	·281	·246
2·0	0·97322	1·0809	1·1102	−0·128	1·1495	−0·244	1·175
·2	·98385	·0585	·0780	·110	·1035	·199	·120
·4	·99055	·0404	·0529	·089	·0689	·154	·079
·6	·99463	·0267	·0344	·068	·0441	·113	·050
·8	·99705	·0168	·0214	·049	·0271	·080	·031
3·0	0·99842	1·0102	1·0129	−0·034	1·0161	−0·053	1·018
·2	·99919	·0060	·0074	·022	·0092	·034	·010
·4	·99959	·0033	·0041	·014	·0051	·021	·006
·6	·99980	·0018	·0022	·008	·0027	·012	·003
·8	·99991	·0009	·0011	·005	·0014	·007	·002
4·0	0·99996	1·0005	1·0006	−0·003	1·0007	−0·004	1·001
·2	·99998	·0002	·0003	·001	·0003	·002	·000
·4	0·99999	·0001	·0001	·001	·0001	·001	·000
·6	1·00000	·0000	·0001	·000	·0001	·000	·000
·8	·00000	·0000	·0000	·000	·0000	·000	·000
5·0	1·00000	1·0000	1·0000	−0·000	1·0000	−0·000	1·000
$f''(0)$	1·23259	2·3962	2·8978	0·656	3·8082	0·715	4·634
$\lim_{\eta\to\infty}(\eta-f)$	0·64790	0·0813	−0·1139	..	−0·4201	..	−0·659
$f(\infty)$	..	..	..	−0·138	..	−0·443	..

VI. 1

f'_{42}	f'_{222}	f'_8	f'_{62}	f'_{44}	f'_{422}	f'_{2222}	η
o	o	o	o	o	o	o	o·o
0·107	0·006	0·490	0·103	0·032	0·061	−0·031	·1
·139	·013	0·884	·112	+0·019	·125	·062	·2
·106	·022	1·188	+0·045	−0·033	·199	·093	·3
+0·024	·035	·413	−0·079	·112	·288	·124	·4
−0·093	0·053	1·569	−0·240	−0·208	0·396	−0·156	0·5
·229	·076	·669	·417	·311	·525	·190	·6
·372	·106	·722	·595	·411	·672	·225	·7
·510	·139	·740	·760	·501	0·833	·262	·8
·634	·177	·730	−0·903	·578	1·002	·301	·9
−0·740	0·217	1·700	−1·019	−0·639	1·171	−0·341	1·0
·882	·295	·604	·157	·704	·480	·423	·2
·928	·361	·489	·176	·703	·710	·502	·4
·892	·405	·375	−1·101	·649	·829	·567	·6
·797	·420	·276	−0·965	·562	·827	·610	·8
−0·671	0·408	1·195	−0·798	−0·460	1·718	−0·625	2·0
·535	·373	·132	·628	·359	·528	·610	·2
·406	·322	·087	·470	·267	·290	·568	·4
·294	·264	·055	·337	·190	1·037	·504	·6
·203	·206	·033	·231	·129	0·795	·426	·8
−0·135	0·153	1·020	−0·152	−0·085	0·581	−0·344	3·0
·085	·108	·011	·096	·053	·406	·265	·2
·052	·073	·006	·058	·032	·271	·195	·4
·030	·047	·003	·034	·019	·173	·137	·6
·017	·029	·002	·019	·010	·106	·092	·8
−0·009	0·017	1·001	−0·010	−0·006	0·062	−0·059	4·0
·005	·010	·000	·005	·003	·035	·036	·2
·002	·005	·000	·003	·001	·018	·021	·4
·001	·003	·000	·001	·001	·009	·011	·6
·001	·001	·000	·001	·000	·004	·006	·8
−0·000	0·000	1·000	−0·000	−0·000	0·001	−0·002	5·0
1·464	0·061	5·399	1·520	0·572	0·607	−0·308	$f''(o)$
··	··	−0·857	··	··	··	··	$\lim_{\eta \to \infty} (\eta - f)$
−1·447	0·796	··	−1·876	−1·153	3·567	−1·397	$f(\infty)$

These series developments are only of use when ξ is small, since only the first few terms of the series are available, and nothing is really known about the convergence of the series. Görtler (1939, 1949) has discussed the accuracy obtained when the series (15) or (21) is cut short at a given term so as to give a polynomial in ξ. Görtler observed that a useful criterion is given by comparing the two sides of the equation $(\partial^3 f/\partial \eta^3)_{\eta=0} = -F(\xi)F'(\xi)$, which results from (9). This will be closely satisfied for small values of ξ, but after the error becomes appreciable (according to the accuracy required) the polynomial abbreviation will be unreliable. Consequently, some other procedure will be needed for larger values of ξ, such as a method for step-by-step continuation.

Hiemenz (1911) applied the series method to his experimental observations on the flow of a uniform stream past a circular cylinder. Here l (diameter of cylinder) $= 9 \cdot 75$ cm, U_∞ (speed of stream) $= 19 \cdot 2$ cm/sec, $\nu = 0 \cdot 01$ cm²/sec, $R = U_\infty l/\nu = 1 \cdot 9 \times 10^4$, and the main-stream flow was represented by

$$U(x) = 7 \cdot 151x - 0 \cdot 04497x^3 - 0 \cdot 0003300x^5 \quad (0 \leqslant x \leqslant 7),$$

where x is measured in cm and $U(x)$ in cm/sec. Hiemenz calculated the coefficients in (19), and found that this indicated a separation point in the region (80° to 82° from the forward stagnation point, or $6 \cdot 80 < x < 6 \cdot 98$) where separation was observed. Later calculations (Section 10) confirm this, but show that the velocity profile is not given accurately by the series method after about $x = 6 \cdot 5$.

The method described applies only to flow over a cylinder with a rounded leading edge, near which U is proportional to x. It could be modified to deal with a wedge-shaped leading edge, where U varies like x^n, if (10) and (15) were replaced by

$$F(\xi) = U/U_1 = \xi^n[1 + a_1\xi + a_2\xi^2 + ...], \tag{22}$$

$$f(\xi, \eta) = \xi^{\frac{1}{2}(n+1)}[f_0(\eta) + a_1 f_1(\eta)\xi + \{a_2 f_2(\eta) + a_1^2 f_{11}(\eta)\}\xi^2 + ...], \tag{23}$$

where now $\xi = x/l, \qquad \eta = (U_1\xi^{n-1}/\nu l)^{\frac{1}{2}}z. \tag{24}$

This would demand a different set of functions $f_0, f_1,...$ for every n.

3. Solutions in series : Howarth's method for an adverse velocity gradient

Several authors have discussed the boundary-layer flow corresponding to an external velocity distribution of the form

$$U = U_0(1 - \xi), \qquad \xi = x/l, \tag{25}$$

where U_0, l are a velocity and a length respectively. It is assumed that the boundary layer starts at $\xi = 0$, where its thickness is zero, so that it might be realized experimentally when a flat plate is placed edge on in a retarded stream of fluid. Howarth (1938) solved this problem by a series expansion in powers of ξ, and the following description is adapted from his treatment.

The flow (25) corresponds to the case $n = 0, a_1 = -1, a_2 = a_3 = \ldots = 0$, of (22), so that a solution of the boundary-layer equations may be achieved by writing

$$\psi = (2U_0 \nu x)^{\frac{1}{2}} f(\xi, \eta), \tag{26}$$

where

$$\eta = (U_0/2\nu x)^{\frac{1}{2}} z. \tag{27}$$

Then

$$u = U_0 \frac{\partial f}{\partial \eta}, \qquad w = -\left(\frac{U_0 \nu}{2x}\right)^{\frac{1}{2}} \left[f + 2\xi \frac{\partial f}{\partial \xi} - \eta \frac{\partial f}{\partial \eta} \right], \tag{28}$$

the boundary-layer equation (1) reduces to

$$\frac{\partial^3 f}{\partial \eta^3} + f \frac{\partial^2 f}{\partial \eta^2} + 2\xi \left[\frac{\partial f}{\partial \xi} \frac{\partial^2 f}{\partial \eta^2} - \frac{\partial^2 f}{\partial \xi \partial \eta} \frac{\partial f}{\partial \eta} \right] = 2\xi - 2\xi^2, \tag{29}$$

and the boundary conditions become

$$f = \frac{\partial f}{\partial \eta} = 0 \quad \text{at } \eta = 0, \qquad \frac{\partial f}{\partial \eta} \to 1 - \xi \quad \text{as } \eta \to \infty. \tag{30}$$

Howarth solved equation (29) by means of a series

$$f(\xi, \eta) = f_0(\eta) + \xi f_1(\eta) + \xi^2 f_2(\eta) + \ldots, \tag{31}$$

and differential equations and boundary conditions for the functions $f_0, f_1, f_2, \ldots$, are obtained by substituting (31) in (29) and (30), and equating coefficients of powers of ξ.

Thus $f_0(\eta)$ is found to be the Blasius function tabulated in Table V. 1, and the succeeding functions may be calculated in turn. From (28) the velocity distribution is

$$u = U_0[f_0'(\eta) + \xi f_1'(\eta) + \xi^2 f_2'(\eta) + \ldots], \tag{32}$$

and the skin friction is given by

$$\frac{\tau_w}{\rho U_0^2} \left(\frac{2U_0 x}{\nu}\right)^{\frac{1}{2}} = f_0''(0) + f_1''(0)\xi + f_2''(0)\xi^2 + \ldots . \tag{33}$$

Howarth estimated that the skin friction would vanish at $\xi = 0\cdot120$, but found that the series fails to converge at about the same place, probably because of a singularity at separation, which is discussed in Section V. 11. Howarth's estimate has been checked by Hartree (1939a) and Leigh (1955), using a step-by-step solution (see Section 10). According to Leigh separation occurs where $8\xi = 0\cdot9585$.

The solution for the linearly retarded main stream (25) was extended by Howarth (1938) to cover approximately a general retarded flow. He assumed that the graph of $U(x)$ could be replaced by a polygon, and that the boundary-layer flow corresponding to each side of the polygon could be taken from the basic solution, with an appropriate variation of ξ (now regarded as a parameter) in terms of x. The parameter ξ has a discontinuity at each vertex of the polygon so as to keep the momentum thickness δ_2 continuous. Finally, the sides of the polygon are made to tend to zero, and then ξ becomes a continuous function of x, specified by a certain differential equation.

This derivation is not given in detail here, since the method is equivalent to the use of the momentum equation as in Pohlhausen's method (Section 13), when the family of velocity profiles is assumed to be that found by Howarth for the case $U = U_0(1-\xi)$. Accordingly, Howarth's equation may be put in the general form (166). This use of Howarth's profiles was actually proposed by Walz (see Section 17).

Tani (1949) generalized (25) to

$$U = U_0(1-\xi^n), \qquad \xi = x/l. \tag{34}$$

The boundary-layer equation (1) now becomes

$$\frac{\partial^3 f}{\partial \eta^3} + f\frac{\partial^2 f}{\partial \eta^2} + 2\xi\left[\frac{\partial f}{\partial \xi}\frac{\partial^2 f}{\partial \eta^2} - \frac{\partial^2 f}{\partial \xi \partial \eta}\frac{\partial f}{\partial \eta}\right] = 2n\xi^n(1-\xi^n), \tag{35}$$

and (35) has a solution in the form

$$f(\xi, \eta) = f_0(\eta) + \xi^n f_1(\eta) + \xi^{2n} f_2(\eta) + \dots. \tag{36}$$

Here f_0 is again the Blasius function, but $f_1, f_2, \dots$ depend on the index n. Tani considered the cases $n = 2, 4, 8$, and estimated the separation points as $\xi = 0\cdot271, 0\cdot462, 0\cdot640$ respectively.

4. Solutions in series: Falkner's transformation

Falkner (1937) has developed a method of solution of the boundary-layer equations by means of a transformation followed by a series expansion. This transformation is suggested by that used by Falkner and Skan (1930) to obtain the 'similar' solutions (see Section V. 16).

Let

$$\psi = (U\nu x)^{\frac{1}{2}} f(\xi, \eta), \tag{37}$$

where

$$\xi = x/l, \qquad \eta = (U/\nu x)^{\frac{1}{2}} z, \tag{38}$$

and the boundary layer starts at $x = 0$. Then

$$u = U\frac{\partial f}{\partial \eta}, \qquad w = -\frac{1}{2}\left(\frac{U\nu}{x}\right)^{\frac{1}{2}}\left[(\chi+1)f + 2\xi\frac{\partial f}{\partial \xi} + (\chi-1)\eta\frac{\partial f}{\partial \eta}\right], \tag{39}$$

where

$$\chi = \chi(\xi) = xU'(x)/U(x). \tag{40}$$

This transformation puts the boundary-layer equation (1) into the form

$$\frac{\partial^3 f}{\partial \eta^3} + \tfrac{1}{2}(\chi+1)f\frac{\partial^2 f}{\partial \eta^2} + \chi\left[1-\left(\frac{\partial f}{\partial \eta}\right)^2\right] + \xi\left[\frac{\partial f}{\partial \xi}\frac{\partial^2 f}{\partial \eta^2} - \frac{\partial^2 f}{\partial \xi \partial \eta}\frac{\partial f}{\partial \eta}\right] = 0, \quad (41)$$

and the boundary conditions (3) become

$$f = \frac{\partial f}{\partial \eta} = 0 \quad \text{at } \eta = 0, \qquad \frac{\partial f}{\partial \eta} \to 1 \quad \text{as } \eta \to \infty. \quad (42)$$

When $U = U_0(x/l)^n$, where U_0 and n are constants, χ is equal to n, and so is independent of ξ; in this case (41) has a solution which is a function of η only. This is one of the similar solutions of the boundary-layer equations (Section V. 21). If U is of the form

$$U = U_0 \xi^n[1+a_1\xi+a_2\xi^2+\dots] \quad (43)$$

near $\xi = 0$, $\chi(\xi)$ has an expansion of the form

$$\chi = n+\chi_1\xi+\chi_2\xi^2+\dots, \quad (44)$$

where

$$\chi_1 = a_1, \qquad \chi_2 = 2a_2-a_1^2, \qquad \chi_3 = 3a_3-3a_2a_1+a_1^3,\dots . \quad (45)$$

As in Section 2, equation (41) may be solved by a series of the type

$$f(\xi,\eta) = f_0(\eta)+\chi_1 f_1(\eta)\xi+\{\chi_2 f_2(\eta)+\chi_1^2 f_{11}(\eta)\}\xi^2+$$
$$+\{\chi_3 f_3(\eta)+\chi_2\chi_1 f_{21}(\eta)+\chi_1^3 f_{111}(\eta)\}\xi^3+\dots, \quad (46)$$

and the differential equations and boundary conditions for $f_0, f_1,\dots,$ are obtained when (46) is substituted in equations (41) and (42). The equation for f_0 can be reduced to the form (V. 122) used by Hartree (1937a). Thus f_0 can be found from Hartree's tabulated solutions, and used in the solution of the remaining equations, which are linear. Falkner gave the results of numerical calculations of the first few functions for $n = 0(\tfrac{1}{4})1, 2$ and applied them to the special cases when $\chi_2 = \chi_3 = \dots = 0$ and χ_1 is negative, so that $U = U_0\xi^n e^{\chi_1\xi}$. Falkner found that for each of these cases there was separation at a definite value of $-\chi_1\xi$, which he estimated, and made the results the basis of an approximate method of calculating the skin friction for a general distribution of U (see Section 5).

5. Falkner's approximate methods

Falkner (1937) applied to more general cases his series solutions (given in Section 4) for the boundary layers corresponding to the outer flows

$$U = U_0 x^n e^{-kx}, \quad (47)$$

where U_0, n, k are constants. The method aims particularly at finding the skin friction, which appears in the dimensionless form

$$\phi(x) = \frac{\tau_w}{\rho U^2}\left(\frac{Ux}{\nu}\right)^{\frac{1}{2}}. \tag{48}$$

In the case (47) the function $\chi(x) = xU'/U$, which is introduced in the series method, reduces to

$$\chi(x) = n - kx, \tag{49}$$

and, for each n, $\phi(x)$ is then a function of kx. Since $\phi(x)$ is found to vanish for a certain positive kx, there is a separation point $x = x_s$ when

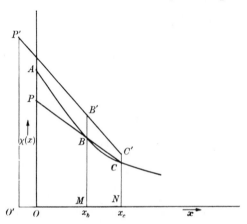

FIG. VI. 1. Graph of $\chi(x)$ and the approximating linear relation (49).

$k > 0$. Falkner gave a table of $\phi^2(x)/\phi^2(0)$ against x/x_s for different values of n, and also tables of $\phi^2(0)$ and kx_s against n, so that $\phi(x)$ can be calculated for a wide range of n and kx.

Let ABC (Fig. VI. 1) be the graph of $\chi(x)$ for a general outer flow $U(x)$. This can be replaced approximately by a polygon, of which BC is a typical side, meeting the χ axis in P. If $U(x)$ is given its correct value at $x = x_b$, the abscissa of B, the values of U, U', and U'' will be approximately correct throughout the interval $x_b \leqslant x \leqslant x_c$, corresponding to BC, when the curve BC is replaced by the straight line BC. The effect of this is to replace the true main stream $U(x)$ by one of the form (47) where $n = OP$ and $kx_b = OP - MB$. Since it is only necessary to have U'/U, that is χ/x, correct at $x = x_b$ and $x = x_c$, any line $P'B'C'$ may be used instead of PBC, with the false origin O', provided that $O'M/OM = MB'/MB$, $O'N/ON = NC'/NC$. The skin friction at $x = x_b$ can be computed from Falkner's tables, using

$n = O'P'$ and $kx = O'P'-MB'$, and the position of O' must be varied
by trial and error until the skin friction agrees with that found in the
previous step. A further application of the tables then gives τ_w at
$x = x_c$. The details of the calculation were illustrated by Falkner for
the case
$$U(x) = U_0\left(1-\frac{1}{8}\frac{x}{l}\right) \qquad (50)$$

in which separation was found at $x = 0\cdot959l$, agreeing with Hartree's
(1939a) result. The boundary-layer flow over an elliptic cylinder was

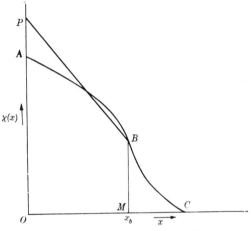

FIG. VI. 2. Graph of $\chi(x)$ and the approximating linear relation (49).

also computed, using Schubauer's (1935) observed pressure distribution,
and good agreement found with Hartree's (1939b) calculations.

In a later report (1941) Falkner gave a simpler approximate method
for computing the skin friction and also methods for finding the displacement and momentum thicknesses. If ABC (Fig. VI. 2) is the
graph of $\chi(x)$, the idea of this method is to replace the portion AB of
the graph by a straight line PB in order to find $\phi(x_b)$ and hence the
skin friction at $x = x_b$, the abscissa of B. Falkner assumed that a
satisfactory straight line PB would be found by requiring the areas
$ABMO$ and $PBMO$ below the graph and the equivalent line to have
equal moments about OA. In this case $\phi(x_b)$ is given by the tables
appropriate to the linear relation (49) with

$$n = \frac{6}{x_b^2}\int_0^{x_b} x\chi(x)\,dx - 2\chi(x_b), \qquad kx = n - \chi(x_b). \qquad (51)$$

This method was applied by Falkner to the same two examples. For
Schubauer's ellipse the approximate skin friction deviated appreciably
from the accurate values only in the retarded region, and not greatly
there, while for the linearly falling main-stream velocity (50) exact
agreement was found up to $x = 0\cdot90l$ with separation occurring at
$x = 0\cdot966l$.

Falkner (1941) also gave a method of integrating the momentum
equation (V.42) approximately to find the momentum thickness δ_2.
In the present notation the momentum equation

$$\frac{\tau_w}{\rho U^2} = \frac{d\delta_2}{dx} + (\delta_1 + 2\delta_2)\frac{U'}{U}$$

becomes $\phi(x) = x\,d\theta/dx + \{(H + \tfrac{3}{2})\chi(x) + \tfrac{1}{2}\}\theta,$ (52)

where $\theta = (\delta_2/x)(Ux/\nu)^{\frac{1}{2}},\qquad H = \delta_1/\delta_2.$ (53)

When $\phi(x)$ has been calculated, (52) is a differential equation for θ
involving the further unknown function H. Falkner assumed that H
can be regarded as a universal function of ϕ, which can be obtained
from the similar solutions $\chi = $ constant. In this way Falkner constructed a table of the approximate momentum thickness function θ
for the case (49) in which χ varies linearly with x. This table can be
used directly in conjunction with equations (51) in a general case,
instead of integrating equation (52) numerically.

An alternative approximate method for calculating θ is to assume
that θ depends only on the function

$$\frac{1}{xU^6(x)} \int\limits_0^x U^6(x')\,dx',$$

the functional relation again being taken from the similar solutions
$\chi = $ constant. The idea of using such an integral was due to Young
and Winterbottom (1940) and similar methods are described later
(Section 18). The skin friction can be deduced satisfactorily from the
momentum equation (52) in the region of accelerated flow, using an
estimated value of H, but the error increases in the retarded region.

6. Solutions in series: Görtler's expansion

Another transformation of the basic equations (1) and (2) is due to
Görtler (1952a, 1955a). If $x = 0$ at the forward stagnation point, or
leading edge, of the surface the velocity potential of the outer flow is

$$\phi = \int\limits_0^x U(x')\,dx',$$ (54)

and the independent variables may be taken as

$$\xi = \phi/U_0 l, \qquad \eta = Uz/(2\nu\phi)^{\frac{1}{2}}, \tag{55}$$

where U_0 and l are a suitable reference velocity and length. The stream function ψ is put in the form

$$\psi = (2\nu\phi)^{\frac{1}{2}}f(\xi, \eta), \tag{56}$$

and the velocity components are then

$$u = U\frac{\partial f}{\partial \eta}, \qquad w = -\left(\frac{\nu}{2\phi}\right)^{\frac{1}{2}}U\left[f + 2\xi\frac{\partial f}{\partial \xi} + (\beta-1)\eta\frac{\partial f}{\partial \eta}\right], \tag{57}$$

where

$$\beta = \beta(\xi) = 2\phi U'(x)/U^2(x). \tag{58}$$

When these velocity components are substituted in equation (1) it becomes ·

$$\frac{\partial^3 f}{\partial \eta^3} + f\frac{\partial^2 f}{\partial \eta^2} + \beta(\xi)\left[1 - \left(\frac{\partial f}{\partial \eta}\right)^2\right] = 2\xi\left[\frac{\partial^2 f}{\partial \xi \partial \eta}\frac{\partial f}{\partial \eta} - \frac{\partial f}{\partial \xi}\frac{\partial^2 f}{\partial \eta^2}\right], \tag{59}$$

and the boundary conditions (3) now become

$$f = \frac{\partial f}{\partial \eta} = 0 \quad \text{at } \eta = 0, \qquad \frac{\partial f}{\partial \eta} \to 1 \quad \text{as } \eta \to \infty. \tag{60}$$

Equations equivalent to (59) have also been obtained by Piercy, Whitehead, and Tyler (see Section 8), and by Meksyn (see Section 12). These authors worked with the velocity potential and stream function of the inviscid flow, but Görtler's approach shows that of this flow the only property needed is the speed $U(x)$ at the edge of the boundary layer.

Görtler (1955a) treats (59) by means of expansions in powers of ξ. When the function $\beta(\xi)$, which describes the outer flow, is given by a series

$$\beta(\xi) = \beta_0 + \beta_1\xi + \beta_2\xi^2 + ..., \tag{61}$$

the function $f(\xi, \eta)$ can be expressed as

$$f(\xi, \eta) = f_0(\eta) + \beta_1 f_1(\eta)\xi + \{\beta_2 f_2(\eta) + \beta_1^2 f_{11}(\eta)\}\xi^2 + ..., \tag{62}$$

where $f_0, f_1, f_2, f_{11}, ...,$ are universal functions of η for the given value of β_0. An extension of (61) is the series

$$\beta(\xi) = \beta_0 + \beta_{\frac{1}{2}}\xi^{1/2} + \beta_1\xi + \beta_{\frac{3}{2}}\xi^{3/2} + ..., \tag{63}$$

in which case

$$f(\xi, \eta) = f_0(\eta) + \beta_{\frac{1}{2}}f_{\frac{1}{2}}(\eta)\xi^{1/2} + \{\beta_1 f_1(\eta) + \beta_{\frac{1}{2}}^2 f_{\frac{1}{2}\frac{1}{2}}(\eta)\}\xi + ..., \tag{64}$$

which involves the additional functions $f_{\frac{1}{2}}, f_{\frac{1}{2}\frac{1}{2}}, f_{\frac{3}{2}}, ...$. In (62) and (64) the first function $f_0(\eta)$ satisfies Hartree's equation (V. 122) with $\beta = \beta_0$, that is

$$f_0''' + f_0 f_0'' + \beta_0(1 - f_0'^2) = 0, \tag{65}$$

with $\qquad f_0(0) = f_0'(0) = 0, \qquad f_0'(\infty) = 1,$ $\qquad\qquad$ (66)

and the subsequent functions are given by linear equations, each involving functions of lower order and f_0.

When the outer flow is represented by a series expansion

$$U(x) = U_0[1 + a_1(x/l) + a_2(x/l)^2 + ...], \qquad\qquad (67)$$

or $\qquad U(x) = U_0(x/l)[1 + b_2(x/l)^2 + b_4(x/l)^4 + ...], \qquad (68)$

$\beta(\xi)$ is given by (61), in which the coefficients are

$$\beta_0 = 0, \quad \beta_1 = 2a_1, \quad \beta_2 = 4a_2 - 4a_1^2, \quad \beta_3 = 6a_3 - 14a_2a_1 + 8a_1^3, \quad ...,$$

in the case (67), and in the case (68)

$$\beta_0 = 1, \quad \beta_1 = 3b_2, \quad \beta_2 = \tfrac{40}{3}b_4 - 13b_2^2, \quad \beta_3 = 42b_6 - 96b_4b_2 + 54b_2^3, \quad ....$$

These velocity distributions correspond respectively to flow over a plate with a sharp leading edge and to symmetrical flow over a cylinder with a rounded leading edge. The case of unsymmetrical flow over a surface with a rounded leading edge, for which

$$U(x) = U_0(x/l)[1 + b_1(x/l) + b_2(x/l)^2 + ...], \qquad\qquad (69)$$

leads to (63) with

$$\beta_0 = 1, \qquad \beta_{\frac{1}{2}} = \tfrac{2}{3}\sqrt{2}\,b_1, \qquad \beta_1 = 3b_2 - \tfrac{22}{9}b_1^2,$$
$$\beta_{\frac{3}{2}} = 2\sqrt{2}(\tfrac{12}{5}b_3 - \tfrac{9}{2}b_2b_1 + \tfrac{59}{27}b_1^3), \qquad ....$$

Tables of Görtler's functions were made at the Computation Laboratory of Harvard University. They are given in a supplement to his report (1955a) and have been published separately (1957b). They extend as far as the terms in ξ^5 in (62) for $\beta_0 = 0$ and $\beta_0 = 1$, corresponding to (67) and (68), and as far as the terms in ξ^2 in (64) for $\beta_0 = 1$, corresponding to (69). Görtler also applied his series to the spanwise flow on a yawed cylinder (see Section VIII. 22) and the supplement to his report includes tables of the appropriate functions for the case (61) with $\beta_0 = 1$.

The numerical applications made by Görtler cover a wide range of problems. Comparisons with the results of other methods indicated that in many cases the tabulated functions enabled the series to be used up to a short distance before the separation point, and the solutions were completed by the difference method of step-by-step continuation developed by Görtler (1946, 1948a) and Witting (1953b): see Section 10.

7. Methods of iteration: the method of Piercy and Preston and its extensions

In discussing the problem of forced convection of heat from a flat plate in a uniform stream, Piercy and Preston (1936) used an iterative method whereby the boundary-layer equation of motion,

$$u\frac{\partial u}{\partial x} + w\frac{\partial u}{\partial z} = \nu\frac{\partial^2 u}{\partial z^2}, \tag{70}$$

was replaced by $$u_{n-1}\frac{\partial u_n}{\partial x} + w_{n-1}\frac{\partial u_n}{\partial z} = \nu\frac{\partial^2 u_n}{\partial z^2}. \tag{71}$$

In this, (u_{n-1}, w_{n-1}) and (u_n, w_n) are successive approximations to the velocity field, each satisfying the equation of continuity exactly. It was noticed that (71), which is an equation for u_n, is identical in form with the equation for the temperature field,

$$u\frac{\partial T}{\partial x} + w\frac{\partial T}{\partial z} = \kappa\frac{\partial^2 T}{\partial z^2}, \tag{72}$$

although the boundary conditions are different.

Starting with the inviscid flow $u_1 = U_0$, $w_1 = 0$, Piercy and Preston carried out the iterative process, but made a further approximation at each stage, and their final result for the skin friction,

$$\frac{\tau_w}{\rho U_0^2}\left(\frac{U_0 x}{\nu}\right)^{1/2} = \frac{1}{2\sqrt{3}}\{\Gamma(\tfrac{4}{3})\}^{-3/2} = 0\cdot 342, \tag{73}$$

differs slightly from the accurate value $0\cdot 332$ (Section V. 12).

This iterative method was extended to a general boundary-layer flow by Piercy, Preston, and Whitehead (1938), who used a coordinate system based on the equipotentials and streamlines of the corresponding inviscid flow. If $\mathfrak{w} = \phi + i\chi$ is the complex potential, with $\mathfrak{w} = 0$ at the forward stagnation point, the boundary-layer equations referred to the orthogonal curvilinear coordinates (ϕ, χ) may be derived from equations (V.17) to (V.20).

In these equations, when $x_1 = \phi$ and $x_3 = \chi$, $h_1 = h_3 = U^{-1}$, where $U = |d\mathfrak{w}/d\mathfrak{z}|$ is the speed of the potential flow. The velocity components in the x_1, x_3 directions are written as

$$v_1 = U\mathfrak{u}, \qquad v_3 = U\mathfrak{v}. \tag{74}$$

On making the usual boundary-layer assumptions, the equations for steady flow simplify to

$$\mathfrak{u}\frac{\partial \mathfrak{u}}{\partial \phi} + \mathfrak{v}\frac{\partial \mathfrak{u}}{\partial \chi} = (1-\mathfrak{u}^2)\left(\frac{1}{U}\frac{\partial U}{\partial \phi}\right)_{\chi=0} + \nu\frac{\partial^2 \mathfrak{u}}{\partial \chi^2}, \tag{75}$$

$$\frac{\partial \mathfrak{u}}{\partial \phi} + \frac{\partial \mathfrak{v}}{\partial \chi} = 0, \tag{76}$$

and the boundary conditions for these equations are

$$\text{U} = \text{V} = 0 \quad \text{at } \chi = 0, \qquad \text{U} \to 1 \quad \text{as } \chi \to \infty. \tag{77}$$

$U(\phi, 0)$ is now the speed at the edge of the boundary layer.

Equations (75) and (76) may further be transformed, by elimination of v and the substitution

$$\xi = \phi/U_\infty l, \qquad \eta = \chi/\sqrt{(2\nu\phi)}, \qquad \text{U} = 1 + \text{U}' \tag{78}$$

(where U_∞ and l are the representative velocity and length), into

$$\frac{\partial^2 \text{U}'}{\partial \eta^2} + \eta \frac{\partial \text{U}'}{\partial \eta} = f(\xi, \eta), \tag{79}$$

where

$$f(\xi, \eta) = 2\xi(1+\text{U}')\frac{\partial \text{U}'}{\partial \xi} - \frac{\partial \text{U}'}{\partial \eta}\int_0^\eta \left(\text{U}' + 2\xi\frac{\partial \text{U}'}{\partial \xi}\right)d\eta + (2\text{U}' + \text{U}'^2)\beta(\xi), \tag{80}$$

$$\beta(\xi) = \left(\frac{2\phi}{U}\frac{\partial U}{\partial \phi}\right)_{\chi=0} \tag{81}$$

It may be noted that within the boundary layer $\chi = Uz$, and therefore the variable η defined in (78) agrees with Görtler's η, given by (55). Further, the functions $\beta(\xi)$ defined by (58) and (81) are identical, so that equation (79) is closely related to Görtler's equation (59).

When $f(\xi, \eta)$ is given, the appropriate solution of equation (79) is

$$\text{U} = 1 + \text{U}' = A\sqrt{(\tfrac{1}{2}\pi)}\text{erf}(\eta/\sqrt{2}) + \int_0^\eta e^{-\frac{1}{2}\eta^2}\left(\int_0^\eta e^{\frac{1}{2}\eta^2}f(\xi, \eta)\,d\eta\right)d\eta, \tag{82}$$

where $A = (\partial \text{U}/\partial \eta)_{\eta=0}$ is determined by the condition $\text{U} \to 1$ as $\eta \to \infty$. When U_{n-1}, the $(n-1)$th approximation to U, is used to calculate $f(\xi, \eta)$ by (80), the nth approximation U_n and A_n may be found from (82). Thus if $\text{U}_1 = 1$, corresponding to the inviscid flow, it follows that $\text{U}_2 = \text{erf}(\eta/\sqrt{2})$, $A_2 = \sqrt{(2/\pi)}$. Piercy, Preston, and Whitehead obtained the approximation A_4 in terms of $\beta(\xi)$ and $\beta'(\xi)$, and used it to estimate the skin-friction distribution and separation point since

$$\tau_w = A\mu U^2/\sqrt{(2\nu\phi)}. \tag{83}$$

An extension of the Piercy and Preston method was made by Schuh (1947) to the problem of forced convection from a flat plate in a viscous compressible fluid whose properties vary with temperature.

Another iterative method was given by Mangler (1941). He showed that the original boundary-layer equations (1) and (2) may be transformed into an inhomogeneous equation of the heat conduction type. The substitutions

$$\xi = \phi/U_\infty l, \qquad \eta = Uz/(U_\infty l\nu)^{\frac{1}{2}}$$
$$\psi = Uz - (U_\infty l\nu)^{\frac{1}{2}}(U_\infty/U)^2\zeta(\xi,\eta)$$

(84)

lead to $u/U = \{\bar{a}(\xi) - \partial\zeta/\partial\eta\}/\bar{a}(\xi),$ (85)

where $\bar{a}(\xi) = U^2/U_\infty^2.$ (86)

Equations (1) and (2) then reduce to

$$\frac{\partial^3\zeta}{\partial\eta^3} - \frac{\partial^2\zeta}{\partial\xi\partial\eta} = \frac{\partial^2\zeta}{\partial\eta^2}\frac{\partial}{\partial\xi}\left(\frac{\zeta}{\bar{a}}\right) - \frac{\partial\zeta}{\partial\eta}\left[\frac{\partial^2}{\partial\xi\partial\eta}\left(\frac{\zeta}{\bar{a}}\right) + \frac{\bar{a}'}{2\bar{a}}\frac{\partial}{\partial\eta}\left(\frac{\zeta}{\bar{a}}\right)\right],$$

(87)

and the boundary conditions for ζ are

$$\zeta = 0, \quad \partial\zeta/\partial\eta = \bar{a}(\xi) \quad \text{at } \eta = 0, \qquad \partial\zeta/\partial\eta \to 0 \quad \text{as } \eta \to \infty. \quad (88)$$

Mangler gives details of an iterative process based on solving (87) at each stage with an approximate right-hand side calculated from the previous step. It is tractable only if $\bar{a}(\xi)$ is a polynomial, but even then numerical integration is called for. However, the method is successfully applied to the boundary layer on a circular cylinder, using the potential flow velocity distribution $U/U_\infty = 2\sin\pi x/l$, which leads to

$$\bar{a}(\xi) = 4\pi\xi - \pi^2\xi^2.$$

The velocity profile at the position of minimum pressure, calculated in three iterative steps, is compared with a Blasius 'flat plate' profile for the appropriate value of U, and with a profile calculated by Pohlhausen's method (see Section 13). All three are in excellent agreement. The suggestion is made that, for most of the boundary layer, the profile is largely unaffected by the trend of the pressure up to that point; but another comparison of profiles near separation suggests that it is necessary there to take into account more than just the local pressure gradient.

Mangler also shows the relationship between his variables and those involved in the transformation of von Mises (Section V. 9). For another transformation of boundary-layer equations to the type for heat conduction see Feinsilber (1946).

8. The method of Piercy, Whitehead, and Tyler

The objectives of the method described here are (i) to construct a solution in series of greater scope than those of Sections 2 to 4, at any rate for symmetrical flows around bodies with a stagnation point at the nose; (ii) to develop from this an approximate solution, extending the range of usefulness even further, so as to cover the whole boundary layer between stagnation and separation with a single closed analytical expression. In the following account, the theory is restated in a notation different from that used by Piercy, Whitehead, and Tyler (1948), and Piercy and Whitehead (1949).

The method is a development of the work of Piercy, Preston, and Whitehead described in Section 7. The equations (75) and (76) are transformed by use of the variables ξ, η defined in (78). Elimination of v then gives

$$\frac{\partial^2 u}{\partial \eta^2} + \frac{\partial u}{\partial \eta} \int u \, d\eta + \beta(\xi)(1-u^2) + 2\xi\left(\frac{\partial u}{\partial \eta} \int \frac{\partial u}{\partial \xi} \, d\eta - u\frac{\partial u}{\partial \xi}\right) = 0, \quad (89)$$

where $\beta(\xi)$ is defined by equation (81). On putting $u = \partial f/\partial \eta$, (89) becomes identical with Görtler's equation (59). If β replaces ξ as an independent variable,

$$\frac{\partial^2 u}{\partial \eta^2} + \frac{\partial u}{\partial \eta} \int u \, d\eta + \beta(1-u^2) + 2\xi\frac{d\beta}{d\xi}\left(\frac{\partial u}{\partial \eta} \int \frac{\partial u}{\partial \beta} \, d\eta - u\frac{\partial u}{\partial \beta}\right) = 0. \quad (90)$$

The series expansions of Piercy, Whitehead, and Tyler are of the form

$$u = F_0(\eta) + (1-\beta)F_1(\eta) + (1-\beta)^2 F_2(\eta) + ..., \quad (91)$$

$$\xi \, d\beta/d\xi = a_1(1-\beta) + a_2(1-\beta)^2 + a_3(1-\beta)^3 + ..., \quad (92)$$

where F_0, F_1, F_2,... are functions of η involving the constants a_1, a_2,.... The form of (92) is shown to embrace many familiar boundary-layer problems. A particularly simple case occurs when $U = U_0(x/l)^n$, for then β is constant, $\xi \, d\beta/d\xi = 0$, and (90) reduces to the ordinary differential equation (V. 122) for similar profiles.

On insertion of the series (91) and (92) into equation (90), a set of differential equations is obtained for F_0, F_1, F_2,.... After calculating a few of the functions, Piercy, Whitehead, and Tyler construct a formula equivalent to

$$2^{\frac{1}{2}}\left(\frac{\partial u}{\partial \eta}\right)_{\eta=0}$$
$$= 1\cdot 7431 - 2(1-\beta)(0\cdot 3795 + 0\cdot 0385a_1 + 0\cdot 0109a_1^2 + 0\cdot 0041a_1^3 + ...) -$$
$$-4(1-\beta)^2(0\cdot 0403 + 0\cdot 0227a_1 + 0\cdot 0192a_2 + 0\cdot 0172a_1^2 +$$
$$+0\cdot 0163a_1 a_2 + ...) -$$
$$-8(1-\beta)^3(0\cdot 0085 + 0\cdot 0122a_1 + 0\cdot 0113a_2 + 0\cdot 0096a_3 + ...) -$$
$$-16(1-\beta)^4(0\cdot 0022 + ...) - .... \quad (93)$$

This gives a measure of the skin friction, since

$$\tau_w = \{\mu U^2/\sqrt{(2\nu\phi)}\}(\partial u/\partial \eta)_{\eta=0}.$$

It may be noted that when $\beta = 1$, in the neighbourhood of the stagnation point, $\partial \mathrm{u}/\partial \eta = f''$, where f is the function defined in Section V. 14. The value $f''(0) = 1\cdot23259 = 2^{-\frac{1}{2}} \times 1\cdot74314$ affords a check of the first term of (93).

Piercy, Whitehead, and Tyler show that (93), when evaluated for flow past a circular cylinder, for Schubauer's ellipse, and for Falkner's flow $U/U_0 = (x/l)\exp(-x/l)$, agrees well with previous methods, but extends farther than other solutions in series based on the forward stagnation point.

The approximate solution which they proceed to construct is based on the observation that the functions $F_2(\eta)$, $F_3(\eta)$,... resemble one another closely and have the same values at $\eta = 0$ and $\eta \to \infty$. They are therefore replaced by a closed expression, thus:

$$\mathrm{u} = F_0(\eta) + (1-\beta)F_1(\eta) + G_1(\xi)g_1(\eta) + G_2(\xi)g_2(\eta). \qquad (94)$$

The functions $g_1(\eta)$ and $g_2(\eta)$ are chosen so that the solution is exactly correct in two cases of the wedge flow $U = U_0(x/l)^n$; in such cases the solution depends only on η, and G_1, G_2 take suitable constant values. The two values of n selected are $n = 0$ (Blasius flow) and $n = -0\cdot085$, the latter being near to the limiting case of zero skin friction for which $\beta = -0\cdot1988$, $n = -0\cdot0904$ (Section V. 21).

With $g_1(\eta)$ and $g_2(\eta)$ so chosen, the functions $G_1(\xi)$ and $G_2(\xi)$ are determined from differential equations obtained by substituting (94) into suitable forms of the boundary-layer equations. The momentum integral equation (Section 13) and Whitehead's double-integral equation (Section 22) were used.

In another paper, Piercy and Whitehead (1949) describe a simplification of the approximate method, in which $G_2(\xi)$ is arbitrarily taken equal to $\{G_1(\xi)\}^2$. In either case, the formula for the skin friction corresponding with (93) is

$$2^{\frac{1}{2}}(\partial \mathrm{u}/\partial \eta)_{\eta=0} = 1\cdot7431 - 0\cdot7589(1-\beta) - 0\cdot3643G_1 + 0\cdot0442G_2. \qquad (95)$$

It is evident from a few applications that the approximate method in either form extends considerably the range that can be covered by a single formula; (94) may be used to continue from where (91) ceases to be accurate, or it may be applied to the whole boundary layer. For the linearly retarded flow (V.73), with a separation point at $\mathrm{x} = 0\cdot96$, the approximate method extends accurately about as far as $\mathrm{x} = 0\cdot85$, but does not place the separation point very accurately. An application to the boundary layer on a wavy surface shows how a small favourable pressure gradient delays separation by a complete wavelength in the particular case selected.

9. Methods of continuation: Goldstein's expansion at a singularity: the wake behind a flat plate

The methods of series expansion described in some of the preceding sections, though useful near the front of a body, become unsatisfactory as a separation point is approached. This may be accounted for by the presence of a singularity at the separation point, as discussed in Section V. 11. The series solution will probably become inadequate at some point $x = x_0$ before the separation point $x = x_s$ is reached. It is then necessary to extend the solution over the interval $x_0 \leqslant x \leqslant x_s$ and to estimate the position of the separation point $x = x_s$. For this purpose a step-by-step method of continuation is required. The series expansion may itself be regarded as a method of continuation from the leading edge $x = 0$ as far as $x = x_0$. The possibility of continuing the solution in this direction before separation occurs is indicated by the parabolic character of the boundary-layer equations (see Section V. 9) since $u \geqslant 0$ for $x \leqslant x_s$. After separation the continuation method cannot be expected to work unchanged since there is now present fluid which has come from farther downstream.

In any continuation method it is therefore required to find a solution of the boundary-layer equations (1) and (2) in a region $x_0 \leqslant x \leqslant x_1$ so as to satisfy the boundary conditions (3) and the initial condition

$$u(x_0, z) = u_0(z), \tag{96}$$

where $u_0(z)$ is the previously calculated velocity distribution at $x = x_0$. The next step will then start from $x = x_1$, and many of the methods aim directly at producing the velocity distribution at $x = x_1$.

As mentioned in Section V. 11, Goldstein (1930) showed that there will in general be an algebraic singularity in the solution at $x = x_0$ unless the initial profile $u_0(z)$ satisfies certain conditions. In terms of the dimensionless variables

$$\mathrm{x} = (x-x_0)/l, \qquad \mathrm{z} = R^{\frac{1}{2}}z/l, \qquad R = U_0 l/\nu,$$
$$\mathrm{u} = u/U_0, \qquad \mathrm{w} = R^{\frac{1}{2}}w/U_0, \qquad \mathrm{P} = p/\rho U_0^2, \tag{97}$$

the boundary-layer equations are (V.65) and (V.66), namely

$$\mathrm{u}\frac{\partial \mathrm{u}}{\partial \mathrm{x}} + \mathrm{w}\frac{\partial \mathrm{u}}{\partial \mathrm{z}} = -\frac{d\mathrm{P}}{dx} + \frac{\partial^2 \mathrm{u}}{\partial \mathrm{z}^2}, \qquad \frac{\partial \mathrm{u}}{\partial \mathrm{x}} + \frac{\partial \mathrm{w}}{\partial \mathrm{z}} = 0. \tag{98}$$

The initial condition is now

$$\mathrm{u}(0, \mathrm{z}) = \mathrm{u}_0(\mathrm{z}) = a_1 \mathrm{z} + a_2 \mathrm{z}^2 + a_3 \mathrm{z}^3 + \dots. \tag{99}$$

If the pressure gradient is

$$-d\mathrm{P}/d\mathrm{x} = p_0 + p_1 \mathrm{x} + p_2 \mathrm{x}^2 + \dots, \tag{100}$$

the conditions for the absence of singularities are

$$2a_2 + p_0 = 0, \qquad a_3 = 0, \qquad 5!\,a_5 + 2a_1 p_1 = 0,$$
$$6!\,a_6 - 2p_0 p_1 = 0, \qquad \ldots, \tag{101}$$

and if $a_1 \neq 0$, only a_1, a_4, a_7,..., are disposable. If these conditions are satisfied,

$$\frac{\tau_w}{\rho U_0^2} R^{\frac{1}{2}} = \left(\frac{\partial \mathrm{U}}{\partial \mathrm{z}}\right)_{\mathrm{z}=0} = a_1 + \frac{4!\,a_4}{a_1}\mathrm{x} + \frac{7!\,a_1 a_7 + (4!\,a_4)^2}{4a_1^3}\mathrm{x}^2 + \ldots \tag{102}$$

The conditions (101) will usually hold if the velocity $U(x)$ of the outer flow is an analytic function, and they can be derived by putting $\mathrm{z} = 0$ in the boundary-layer equations (98) and their derivatives with respect to z. The early conditions are of great importance in several of the continuation methods to be described, and also in many of the approximate methods of Part II of this chapter.

Goldstein (1930) investigated the singular solution which is required when the conditions (101) are not satisfied. If $a_1 \neq 0$ the transformation

$$\mathrm{x} = \xi^3, \qquad \mathrm{z} = 3\xi\eta, \qquad \Psi = \xi^2 f(\xi, \eta) \tag{103}$$

is applied, where Ψ is the non-dimensional stream function. Then

$$\mathrm{u} = \frac{\partial \Psi}{\partial \mathrm{z}} = \frac{1}{3}\xi\frac{\partial f}{\partial \eta}, \qquad \mathrm{w} = -\frac{\partial \Psi}{\partial \mathrm{x}} = -\frac{1}{3\xi}\left[2f + \xi\frac{\partial f}{\partial \xi} - \eta\frac{\partial f}{\partial \eta}\right], \tag{104}$$

and equations (98) become

$$\frac{\partial^3 f}{\partial \eta^3} + 2f\frac{\partial^2 f}{\partial \eta^2} - \left(\frac{\partial f}{\partial \eta}\right)^2 + \xi\left[\frac{\partial f}{\partial \xi}\frac{\partial^2 f}{\partial \eta^2} - \frac{\partial^2 f}{\partial \xi\partial \eta}\frac{\partial f}{\partial \eta}\right] = -27\xi(p_0 + p_1\xi^3 + \ldots). \tag{105}$$

The boundary conditions are

$$f = \frac{\partial f}{\partial \eta} = 0 \quad \text{at } \eta = 0, \qquad \frac{1}{3}\xi\frac{\partial f}{\partial \eta} \sim a_1(3\xi\eta) + a_2(3\xi\eta)^2 + \ldots \tag{106}$$

for large values of η, but small values of ξ. The solution of (105) can be developed in a series

$$f(\xi, \eta) = f_0(\eta) + f_1(\eta)\xi + f_2(\eta)\xi^2 + \ldots. \tag{107}$$

Here $f_0(\eta) = \frac{9}{2}a_1\eta^2$, and explicit formulae can be obtained for $f_1(\eta)$ and $f_2(\eta)$.

For large values of η a more convenient series may be found in the form

$$\Psi(\mathrm{x}, \mathrm{z}) = \psi_0(\mathrm{z}) + \psi_2(\mathrm{z})\xi^2 + \psi_3(\mathrm{z})\xi^3 + \bar{\psi}_3(\mathrm{z})\xi^3 \log \xi + \psi_4(\mathrm{z})\xi^4 + \ldots. \tag{108}$$

This does not satisfy the boundary conditions at $\mathrm{z} = 0$, but is chosen so as to agree with the asymptotic expansions of $f_0, f_1, f_2,\ldots$, for large η.

Then ψ_0, ψ_2, ψ_3, $\bar{\psi}_3$ can be found explicitly from the initial profile $U_0(z)$ and the known asymptotic expansions of f_0, f_1, and f_2.

Goldstein (1930) also considered briefly the case $a_1 = 0$, $a_2 \neq 0$, and the case when $U_0(z)$ starts with a constant term $a_0 \neq 0$, but these do not lend themselves conveniently to analytical treatment.

The method was adapted by Goldstein to investigate the wake behind a flat plate placed parallel to a uniform stream. The length l can then be taken to be the length of the plate and U_0 to be the speed of the stream. The initial profile is that of Blasius, given by the analysis of Section V. 12, namely

$$U_0(z) = a_1 z + a_4 z^4 + a_7 z^7 + ...,$$

where

$$a_1 = 0\cdot 33206, \qquad a_4 = -a_1^2/2.4!, \qquad a_7 = 11a_1^3/2^2.7!, \quad ....$$

Here $d\mathrm{P}/d\mathrm{x} = 0$, but the boundary conditions at $z = 0$ must be modified to $\partial U/\partial z = w = 0$.

The required expansion of $f(\xi, \eta)$ is

$$f(\xi, \eta) = f_0(\eta) + f_3(\eta)\xi^3 + f_6(\eta)\xi^6 + ..., \tag{109}$$

and f_0 has to be determined numerically from the equation

$$f_0''' + 2f_0 f_0'' - f_0'^2 = 0 \tag{110}$$

with $f_0(0) = f_0''(0) = 0$, $f_0'(\eta) \sim 9a_1\eta$ as $\eta \to \infty$. Equation (110) has the same property of homology as has Blasius's equation (V.85) and a similar device can be used for its solution. Goldstein calculated f_0, f_3, and f_6 numerically, and from their asymptotic expansions determined the coefficients as far as $\psi_8'(z)$ in the series

$$U = \partial \Psi/\partial z = \psi_0'(z) + \psi_1'(z)\xi + \psi_2'(z)\xi^2 + ..., \tag{111}$$

which is the analogue of (108). From the series Goldstein was able to compute the velocity distribution in the wake up to $x = \frac{1}{2}$.

This analysis was supplemented by Tollmien (1931), Goldstein (1933), and Stewartson (1957a), who considered the approach of the wake to uniform flow far downstream. Then if $U = 1 - U'$, and U' and w are assumed to be small, the first approximation to the boundary-layer equations is

$$\frac{\partial U'}{\partial x} = \frac{\partial^2 U'}{\partial z^2}, \qquad \frac{\partial U'}{\partial x} = \frac{\partial w}{\partial z}. \tag{112}$$

The required solution of equations (112) is

$$U' = A(x+c)^{-1/2} \exp\{-z^2/4(x+c)\},$$
$$w = -\tfrac{1}{2}Az(x+c)^{-3/2} \exp\{-z^2/4(x+c)\}, \tag{113}$$

where A and c are constants. Considerations of momentum show that the drag on both sides of the plate is given by

$$D = \rho U_0 \int_{-\infty}^{\infty} (U_0 - u)\, dz = 2\rho U_0^2 l R^{-\frac{1}{2}} \int_0^{\infty} \text{U}'\, dz.$$

But from Section V. 12, $D = 4a_1 \rho U_0^2 l R^{-\frac{1}{2}}$ so that $A = 2a_1/\sqrt{\pi}$.

Goldstein (1933) also determined a second approximation to the solution when x is large and showed that the two solutions could be joined satisfactorily if $c = 0.52$. Further approximations were investigated by Stewartson (1957a). In particular, when x is large the second approximation to the velocity on the centre line $z = 0$ is

$$\text{U}(\text{x}, 0) = 1 - A(\text{x} + c)^{-\frac{1}{2}} - \tfrac{1}{2}A^2(\text{x} + c)^{-1}. \tag{114}$$

The problem was also investigated by Luckert (1934) on the basis of von Mises's form (V. 53) of the boundary-layer equations, and the results obtained by Goldstein and Luckert were further examined, and compared with one another, by Rosenhead and Simpson (1936), who concluded that Goldstein's results were probably more satisfactory than Luckert's.

The solution (113) illustrates the broadening of the wake at a considerable distance downstream. Near the trailing edge of the plate, x = 0, the wake does not broaden perceptibly. In an appendix to Goldstein's (1933) paper Fage reports experimental measurements in the wake behind a flat plate which are in good agreement with Goldstein's calculations at x = 0.02, but differ greatly at x = 0.512, at which section he suggests that the motion is no longer laminar.

10. Numerical step-by-step methods

The methods of this section are based on the replacement of the derivative $\partial u/\partial x$ in the boundary-layer equations by a finite-difference approximation. For example, if $u_1(z)$, $u_2(z)$ are the velocity profiles at $x = x_1$, $x = x_2$ respectively, where $\Delta x = x_2 - x_1$ is small, then

$$u_2(z) = u_1(z) + (\partial u/\partial x)_{x=x_1} \Delta x \tag{115}$$

approximately, with an error in which the leading term is $\tfrac{1}{2}(\partial^2 u/\partial x^2)(\Delta x)^2$. If a mean derivative $\overline{\partial u/\partial x}$ at $x = x_1 + \tfrac{1}{2}\Delta x$ can be evaluated or estimated, a better formula is

$$u_2(z) = u_1(z) + (\overline{\partial u/\partial x}) \Delta x \tag{116}$$

with a leading error term $-\tfrac{1}{24}(\partial^3 u/\partial x^3)(\Delta x)^3$.

If the velocity profile $u_1(z)$ is known, formulae such as these can be used to construct $u_2(z)$. The methods are of two types—'explicit' methods in which the values of $u_2(z)$ are given directly in terms of $u_1(z)$, and 'implicit' methods in which $u_2(z)$ has to be found by solving an ordinary differential equation. The explicit methods are simpler to carry out, but are liable to be numerically unstable, especially in regions of adverse pressure gradient.

One explicit method, due to Prandtl (1938) and Görtler (1939), is based on the formal solution

$$\frac{\partial u}{\partial x} = -\frac{\partial w}{\partial z} = \frac{\partial}{\partial z}\left[u\int_{z_0}^{z}\frac{1}{u^2}\left(U\frac{dU}{dx}+\nu\frac{\partial^2 u}{\partial z^2}\right)dz -u\phi(x)\right], \qquad (117)$$

where $\phi(x) = w(x,z_0)/u(x,z_0)$. Usually $z_0 = 0$, and if there is neither suction nor blowing $\phi(x) = 0$. In suitable circumstances the right-hand side of (117) may be evaluated from a knowledge of $u_1(z)$ and $U(x)$, and $u_2(z)$ may then be calculated from (115), and used in its turn as the basis for the next step.

The method of Hartree (1939a) is an example of the implicit type. In this method derivatives in the x-direction are replaced by differences, but all other quantities by averages between the two profiles. Thus equations (1) and (2) give

$$\tfrac{1}{2}(u_1+u_2)(u_2-u_1)/\Delta x-\tfrac{1}{2}(u_1'+u_2')\int_{0}^{z}[(u_2-u_1)/\Delta x]\,dz$$

$$=\frac{1}{2}\left[\left(U\frac{dU}{dx}\right)_1+\left(U\frac{dU}{dx}\right)_2\right]+\tfrac{1}{2}\nu(u_1''+u_2''), \quad (118)$$

where dashes imply differentiation with respect to z. Equation (118) is now regarded as a *differential equation* for $u_2(z)$, with $u_1(z)$ and its derivatives known.

The discussion in some of the preceding sections, particularly Section 9, provides the theory underlying a numerical step-by-step process of this kind. In particular, it shows that the initial profile $u_1(z)$ cannot be chosen arbitrarily: unless it satisfies the conditions (101) the calculations will be vitiated by singularities. Exactly how many of these conditions need be applied depends, of course, on the number of significant figures in the calculation. But each derived profile will need checking, and perhaps smoothing, to ensure that it constitutes a suitable initial profile for the following step.

Görtler (1939) applied his technique, based on (117), to the observations of Hiemenz (1911) on the boundary layer on a circular cylinder (see Section 2). The series solution of Hiemenz was used to give an initial profile at 4·5 cm (about 53°) from the forward stagnation point. The minimum pressure occurs at about 6 cm (71°) and. separation at

about 6·9 cm (81°). Görtler found that by about 6·5 cm (76°) from the
forward stagnation point there was a marked discrepancy between his
velocity profile and that calculated from the series solution, even though
the values of the skin friction agreed well.

Hartree's (1939a) first application of his method was to the boundary-
layer flow with linearly decreasing main-stream velocity (50); see Section
V. 11. The integration of (118), with two-point boundary conditions,
calls for a considerable amount of judgement, being very sensitive to
the precise initial conditions at $z = 0$, and being more sensitive for
smaller Δx. For this reason Leigh (1955), using an automatic computer,
was obliged to construct other ways of solving (118). Leigh's method
has been modified by Terrill (1960), who has included the case
of suction. Hartree (1939b) also applied his method to Schubauer's
(1935) observations of the flow over an elliptic cylinder (see Section 26).

Another process has been developed by Gadd (1952), based on the
transformation of the boundary-layer equations by Crocco (1939); see
Section V. 9. The main features of Gadd's method are as follows: (i) it
uses independent variables x and u/U, and a dependent variable
$q = x\tau^2/\rho\mu U_0^3$, where U_0 is the velocity (assumed to be non-zero) at the
leading edge and τ is the shear stress; (ii) the choice of q eliminates
singularities both at the leading edge, where $\tau \propto x^{-\frac{1}{2}}$, and at the separation point, where $\tau \propto (x_s-x)^{\frac{1}{2}}$; (iii) because of the absence of singularities
fairly large steps in x are possible; (iv) the method applies also to compressible boundary layers with or without heat transfer at the surface,
and gives, for example, the result that separation occurs much less
readily when the surface is cooled to the free-stream temperature than
when it is thermally insulated.

A convenient numerical step-by-step method of solution of the
boundary-layer equations was devised by Görtler (1946, 1948a), who
replaced the x and y derivatives in the dimensionless equations (98)
by suitable difference quotients. A rectangular lattice of points (x_i, z_j)
is used, where

$$x_i = x_0 + ih, \quad z_j = jk \quad (i, j = 0, 1, 2, ...), \tag{119}$$

and h, k are the dimensions of the mesh of the lattice. The velocity
components are

$$u(x_i, z_j) = u_{i,j}, \qquad w(x_i, z_j) = w_{i,j},$$

and the approximations made are

$$\frac{\partial u}{\partial x}(x_i, z_j) = \frac{1}{2h}\Delta_{i,j}, \qquad \frac{\partial u}{\partial z}(x_i, z_j) = \frac{1}{2k}\nabla_{i,j}, \qquad \frac{\partial^2 u}{\partial z^2}(x_i, z_j) = \frac{1}{4k^2}\nabla_{i,j}^2,$$

$$\tag{120}$$

where $\Delta_{i,j} = \mathrm{U}_{i+1,j} - \mathrm{U}_{i-1,j}, \qquad \nabla_{i,j} = \mathrm{U}_{i,j+1} - \mathrm{U}_{i,j-1},$

$$\nabla^2_{i,j} = \nabla_{i,j+1} - \nabla_{i,j-1}. \qquad (121)$$

From the continuity equation,

$$\mathrm{w}_{i,j} = - \int_0^{z_j} \frac{\partial \mathrm{U}}{\partial \mathrm{X}}(\mathrm{x}_i, \mathrm{z})\, d\mathrm{z}.$$

The trapezium rule and the approximation (120) give

$$\mathrm{w}_{i,j} = -(k/2h)(S_{i,j} + \tfrac{1}{2}\Delta_{i,j}), \qquad (122)$$

where $S_{i,j} = \sum_{n=1}^{j-1} \Delta_{i,n}.$

Thus the dimensionless boundary-layer equations (98) become approximately

$$\mathrm{U}_{i,j}\frac{\Delta_{i,j}}{2h} - \frac{k}{2h}(S_{i,j} + \tfrac{1}{2}\Delta_{i,j})\frac{\nabla_{i,j}}{2k} = -\mathrm{P}_i + \frac{\nabla^2_{i,j}}{4k^2}, \qquad (123)$$

where $\mathrm{P}_i = \mathrm{P}'(\mathrm{x}_i)$, and hence

$$\Delta_{i,j} = (-4h\mathrm{P}_i + (h/k^2)\nabla^2_{i,j} + \nabla_{i,j}S_{i,j})/(2\mathrm{U}_{i,j} - \tfrac{1}{2}\nabla_{i,j}). \qquad (124)$$

When the velocity profile at $\mathrm{x} = \mathrm{x}_i$ is known, so that the values $\mathrm{U}_{i,j}$ are given for each $j \geqslant 0$, the differences $\nabla_{i,j}$, $\nabla^2_{i,j}$ can be calculated except for $\nabla_{i,0}$, $\nabla^2_{i,0}$, $\nabla^2_{i,1}$. The conditions (101) for the absence of singularities give

$$\frac{\partial^2 \mathrm{U}}{\partial \mathrm{z}^2}(\mathrm{x}_i, 0) = \mathrm{P}_i, \qquad \frac{\partial^3 \mathrm{U}}{\partial \mathrm{z}^3}(\mathrm{x}_i, 0) = 0.$$

Consequently an interpolation polynomial of the form

$$\frac{\partial^2 \mathrm{U}}{\partial \mathrm{z}^2}(\mathrm{x}_i, \mathrm{z}) = \mathrm{P}_i + c_i \mathrm{z}^2 + d_i \mathrm{z}^3$$

may be assumed. The approximation (120) then gives

$$\nabla^2_{i,0} = 4k^2 \mathrm{P}_i, \qquad \nabla^2_{i,1} = \tfrac{11}{18}\nabla^2_{i,0} + \tfrac{1}{2}\nabla^2_{i,2} - \tfrac{1}{9}\nabla^2_{i,3},$$

whence follows $\nabla_{i,0}$, and so the skin friction.

From (124) the values of $\Delta_{i,j}$ can now be computed successively from $j = 1$ onwards, and the velocity profile at $\mathrm{x} = \mathrm{x}_{i+1}$ is then obtained from

$$\mathrm{U}_{i+1,j} = \mathrm{U}_{i-1,j} + \Delta_{i,j}. \qquad (125)$$

Two consecutive profiles, at x_0 and x_1, are required to start this calculation, and must be found by some other method, such as a series expansion. Görtler recommends that about fifteen points z_j should be taken across the boundary layer. The method is liable to develop an oscillatory error, in which consecutive profiles err by excess and defect alternately, and the solution tends to split into two parts, one for odd values of i and the other for even values. A smoothing technique is therefore required in order to prevent this oscillation from growing too large.

Another numerical difference method was devised by Schröder (1943, 1951), who applied a preliminary transformation to the boundary-layer equations. Let U_0 and l be the reference velocity and length, and let

$$\xi = \int\limits_{x_0}^{x} \frac{U_0}{U(x')} \frac{dx'}{l}, \qquad \eta = (U_0/l\nu)^{\frac{1}{2}}z,$$

$$U = U_0 F(\xi), \qquad \textsc{u}^* = (u-U)/U_0 = \textsc{u}-F(\xi). \qquad (126)$$

The boundary-layer equations then reduce to the form

$$\frac{\partial \textsc{u}^*}{\partial \xi} - \frac{\partial^2 \textsc{u}^*}{\partial \eta^2} = \frac{1}{F(\xi)} \frac{\partial \textsc{u}}{\partial \eta} \int\limits_{0}^{\eta} \frac{\partial \textsc{u}}{\partial \xi} d\eta - \frac{\textsc{u}^*}{F(\xi)} \frac{\partial \textsc{u}}{\partial \xi} = f(\xi, \eta). \qquad (127)$$

If $f(\xi, \eta)$ is known, (127) is an inhomogeneous form of the heat-conduction equation, and Schröder gave a finite difference method for its solution. Since $f(\xi, \eta)$ actually involves the unknown function $\textsc{u}^*$, an iterative process must be employed at each step.

These two numerical difference methods were compared by Witting (1953a), who concluded that they give equal accuracy, but that Görtler's method requires less time. In another paper Witting (1953b) modified Görtler's method so as to give a more accurate solution near the surface $z = 0$, which is especially desirable near the separation point.

These continuation methods have been applied to the external velocity distribution

$$U/U_0 = 7{\cdot}151\textsc{x} - 0{\cdot}04497\textsc{x}^3 - 0{\cdot}0003300\textsc{x}^5 \qquad (128)$$

which (with $U_0 = 1$ cm/sec and $l = 1$ cm) represents the observations of Hiemenz (1911) on the flow past a circular cylinder (Section 2). The series solution was used as far as $\textsc{x} = 4{\cdot}5$ and the separation points estimated by different methods were:

Görtler (1939)	$\textsc{x} = 6{\cdot}77$,
Görtler (1946, 1948a)	$\textsc{x} = 6{\cdot}80$,
Schröder (1943, 1951)	$\textsc{x} = 6{\cdot}87$,
Witting (1953b)	$\textsc{x} = 6{\cdot}80$,
Hiemenz (1911) (observation)	$6{\cdot}80 < \textsc{x} < 6{\cdot}98$.

Other finite difference methods have been described by Rouleau and Osterle (1955), who used them to study flow with suction (see Section 31). Mitchell and Thomson (1958) developed a method based on the equation of von Mises (V. 53) and applied it to Howarth's flow (25).

11. Methods of expansion near the wall

Green (1930) developed a method for the solution of the boundary-layer equations by an expansion in powers of z, the distance from the wall. This expansion is, in general, valid only near the wall, and Green had to extrapolate to reach large values of z. It might be more accurate, as Howarth (1934) suggested, to join Green's solution to an outer solution, valid near the edge of the boundary layer.

If the velocity profile is given by a series of the form

$$u = f_1(x)z + f_2(x)(z^2/2!) + f_3(x)(z^3/3!) + ..., \tag{129}$$

w can be found from the continuity equation (2), and substitution in equation (1) then leads to the relations

$$\nu f_2 = -UU', \quad \nu f_3 = 0, \quad \nu f_4 = f_1 f_1', \quad \nu f_5 = 2f_1 f_2', \quad \nu f_6 = 2f_2 f_2', \quad ..., \tag{130}$$

which are equivalent to equations (101) and (102). Thus the functions $f_2, f_3, f_4, ...,$ are expressible in terms of $U(x)$, $f_1(x)$ and their derivatives. The function $f_1(x)$, which gives the skin friction, must be found from the outer boundary condition, $u \to U(x)$ as $z \to \infty$.

Green used a step-by-step process to calculate the values of $f_1(x)$. He applied his method to the pressure distribution which he had observed on a circular cylinder in a uniform stream at the Reynolds number $9 \cdot 43 \times 10^4$. Separation took place $73°$ from the forward stagnation point of the cylinder. For the region close to the separation point Green used a method of continuation resembling that of Görtler (1939) (see Section 10) and obtained satisfactory agreement with observation. A modification of Green's method was given by Gupta (1938). The series (129) may be of use to find the velocity distribution in the boundary layer when the skin friction $\tau_w = \mu f_1(x)$ has been determined by some other method.

A similar method was devised by Trilling (1950) for flow with suction, though it may also be of use when suction is absent. It is based on Crocco's equation (V.54), namely

$$\mu \rho u \frac{\partial \tau}{\partial x} - \mu p'(x) \frac{\partial \tau}{\partial u} = \tau^2 \frac{\partial^2 \tau}{\partial u^2}, \tag{131}$$

where $p(x)$ is the pressure and $\tau = \mu \, \partial u / \partial z$ the shearing stress. The boundary conditions are

$$\partial \tau / \partial u = \mu p'(x)/\tau - \rho w_s(x) \quad \text{at } u = 0, \qquad \tau = 0 \quad \text{at } u = U(x), \tag{132}$$

where $w_s(x) = -w(x, 0)$ is the suction velocity through the surface.

Trilling assumed a series expansion

$$\tau(x, u) = \tau_0(x) + \tau_1(x)u + \tau_2(x)u^2 + \ldots, \tag{133}$$

where $\tau_0(x)$ is the skin friction $\tau_w(x)$. Substitution in (131) and (132) enables $\tau_1, \tau_2, \ldots$ to be expressed in terms of $p'(x)$, $w_s(x)$, $\tau_0(x)$, and their derivatives. The condition $\tau\{x, U(x)\} = 0$ then serves to determine $\tau_0(x)$. For this purpose Trilling used the terms up to $\tau_6 u^6$ in (133).

The method was applied by Trilling to the boundary-layer flow over the upper surface of an aerofoil. He showed that if the rate of suction was so distributed that $(\partial^2 u/\partial z^2)_{z=0}$ had a small constant negative value, then a stable boundary layer could be maintained to the trailing edge without an excessive skin-friction drag.

Another method related to Green's method is that of Ringleb (1952), who assumed a velocity profile of the form

$$u/U = 1 - \exp(-az - bz^2 - cz^3 - dz^4), \tag{134}$$

where a, b, c, d are functions of x. This form satisfies the boundary conditions on u if $d > 0$. The functions a, b, c, d are determined by the following relations, which generalize the first four of (130) by including suction. At $z = 0$,

$$\nu \frac{\partial^2 u}{\partial z^2} = -UU' - w_s \frac{\partial u}{\partial z}, \qquad \nu \frac{\partial^3 u}{\partial z^3} = -w_s \frac{\partial^2 u}{\partial z^2},$$

$$\nu \frac{\partial^4 u}{\partial z^4} = \frac{\partial u}{\partial z}\frac{\partial^2 u}{\partial x \partial z} - w_s \frac{\partial^3 u}{\partial z^3}, \qquad \nu \frac{\partial^5 u}{\partial z^5} = 2\frac{\partial u}{\partial z}\frac{\partial^3 u}{\partial x \partial z^2} - w_s \frac{\partial^4 u}{\partial z^4}. \tag{135}$$

The first three conditions of (135) enable b, c, d to be expressed in terms of a, and the fourth then leads to a first-order differential equation for a, namely

$$\frac{2aU}{\nu}\frac{d}{dx}(w_s a + U') + \left(\frac{w_s}{\nu} - 5a\right)Uaa' + (w_s a + U')^2\left(\frac{10w_s}{\nu^2} - \frac{28a}{\nu}\right) +$$

$$+ (w_s a + U')\left(-\frac{w_s^3}{\nu^3} + 5\frac{w_s^2 a}{\nu^2} - 21\frac{w_s a^2}{\nu} + 55a^3\right) - \frac{w_s^2 a^3}{\nu} +$$

$$+ 5w_s a^4 - 24a^5\nu = 0. \tag{136}$$

In the case of flow without suction, equation (136) can be simplified, by the substitution $5\nu a^2 = 4U' + f(x)$, to the Riccati equation

$$25Uf' = 32U'^2 + 166U'f - 48f^2. \tag{137}$$

This is equivalent to the second-order linear equation

$$g'' - 5 \cdot 64(U'/U)g' - 2 \cdot 4576(U'/U)^2 g = 0,$$

where $f = 25Ug'/48g$.

Ringleb applied his method to the case of uniform flow over a flat plate with constant suction, and showed that his results agreed well with those of Iglisch (1944)—see Section 31. The method had earlier been suggested by Betz (1950) for the approximate representation of the similar solutions of the boundary-layer equations. For instance, if $U = U_0$ is constant in (137), representing uniform flow over a flat plate, $f = 25U_0/48x$ with $x = 0$ at the leading edge of the plate. Hence $\tau_w/\rho U_0^2 = va/U_0 = 0 \cdot 323(v/U_0 x)^{\frac{1}{2}}$, where the accurate value of the numerical factor is $0 \cdot 332$ (Section V. 12).

12. The work of Meksyn

In his book, Meksyn (1961) describes the methods developed in several earlier papers for the solution of the boundary-layer equations. These papers are concerned with the construction of good approximations obtained with a moderate amount of calculation, and with a comparison between these approximations and various experimental results. Meksyn (1948a) derived a form of the boundary-layer equations with independent variables based on the velocity potential ϕ and stream function χ of the inviscid flow (see Sections 7 and 8). If ψ is the stream function for the boundary-layer flow, the substitutions

$$\psi = (2v\phi)^{\frac{1}{2}}f(\xi, \eta), \qquad \xi = \phi/U_\infty l, \qquad \eta = \chi/\sqrt{(2v\phi)} \qquad (138)$$

lead, as in Sections 7 and 8, to the boundary-layer equation

$$\frac{\partial^3 f}{\partial \eta^3} + f\frac{\partial^2 f}{\partial \eta^2} + \beta(\xi)\left[1 - \left(\frac{\partial f}{\partial \eta}\right)^2\right] = 2\xi\left[\frac{\partial f}{\partial \eta}\frac{\partial^2 f}{\partial \xi \partial \eta} - \frac{\partial f}{\partial \xi}\frac{\partial^2 f}{\partial \eta^2}\right], \qquad (139)$$

where
$$\beta(\xi) = \left(\frac{2\phi}{U}\frac{\partial U}{\partial \phi}\right)_{\chi=0} = \frac{2\phi}{U^2}\frac{dU}{dx}, \qquad (140)$$

and U is the speed of the inviscid flow. Equation (139) is identical with Görtler's equation (59), and equivalent to the Piercy, Whitehead, and Tyler equation (89). The appropriate boundary conditions are

$$f = \partial f/\partial \eta = 0 \quad \text{at } \eta = 0, \qquad \partial f/\partial \eta \to 1 \quad \text{as } \eta \to \infty. \qquad (141)$$

In Meksyn's earlier work, a process of approximation is used to obtain various solutions of equation (139). When the right-hand side is neglected—which is often possible in the forward part of the boundary layer—equation (139) reduces to the ordinary equation of similar profiles

$$f''' + ff'' + \beta(1 - f'^2) = 0, \qquad (142)$$

where β is now the local value of $\beta(\xi)$. If f and f' are regarded as known, (142) is an equation for f'' whose solution is

$$f''(\eta) = e^{-F}\left[a-\beta\int_0^\eta e^F(1-f'^2)\,d\eta\right],\qquad(143)$$

where

$$F(\eta) = \int_0^\eta f(\eta)\,d\eta \quad\text{and}\quad a = f''(0).$$

By using the first few terms of the series

$$f(\eta) = \tfrac{1}{2}a\eta^2-\tfrac{1}{6}\beta\eta^3+\tfrac{1}{60}a^2(\beta-\tfrac{1}{2})\eta^5+...,\qquad(144)$$

the right-hand side of (143) may be evaluated, and then a is given by the equation $f'(\infty) = \int_0^\infty f''(\eta)\,d\eta = 1$. Thus if $\beta = 0$, and only the first term of (144) is retained, $f''(\eta) = a\exp(-\tfrac{1}{6}a\eta^3)$. Hence

$$a = 6^{-1/2}\{\Gamma(\tfrac{4}{3})\}^{-3/2} = 0{\cdot}484,\qquad(145)$$

equivalent to Piercy and Preston's result (73). Meksyn also considers higher approximations.

The general equation (139) was treated in a similar manner, the condition on $a(\xi)$ now being a differential equation. Meksyn (1950a) discussed Schubauer's (1935) observations on an elliptic cylinder, and also (1950b) the linearly decreasing main-stream flow $U = U_0(1-x/l)$. Another application (1951) was to the motion in the wake of a flat plate (see Section 9). Here $\beta = 0$, $\xi = x/l$, and the boundary conditions are modified to

$$f = \partial^2 f/\partial\eta^2 = 0 \quad\text{at }\eta = 0,\qquad \partial f/\partial\eta \to 1 \quad\text{as }\eta\to\infty.\qquad(146)$$

The appropriate series for $f(x,\eta)$ is now

$$f = \alpha\eta+\tfrac{1}{3}x\alpha\alpha'\eta^3+\tfrac{1}{30}x^2\alpha^2\alpha''\eta^5+...,$$

where $\alpha = \alpha(x)$ is the dimensionless speed on the centre line $\eta = 0$. When this is used on the right-hand side of the equation

$$\frac{\partial^2 f}{\partial\eta^2} = 2x\,e^{-F(x,\eta)}\int_0^\eta\left[\frac{\partial f}{\partial\eta}\frac{\partial^2 f}{\partial x\partial\eta}-\frac{\partial f}{\partial x}\frac{\partial^2 f}{\partial\eta^2}\right]e^{F(x,\eta)}\,d\eta,$$

which corresponds to (143), the condition $\int_0^\infty(\partial^2 f/\partial\eta^2)\,d\eta = 1-\alpha$ gives a differential equation for $\alpha(x)$. The first approximation to this is $2x\alpha\alpha' = 1-\alpha$, whence $\alpha = 1-kx^{-\frac{1}{2}}+...$, and

$$\partial f/\partial\eta = 1-kx^{-\frac{1}{2}}\exp(-\tfrac{1}{2}\alpha\eta^2)+...,$$

where k is a constant of integration which is determined by momentum considerations, as in Section 9. Meksyn also constructs a second approximation and obtains

$$\alpha = 1 - kx^{-\frac{1}{2}} - 0\cdot048k^2x^{-1} + ..., \tag{147}$$

which may be compared with Goldstein's result (114).

In a later paper (1956) Meksyn adopts a slightly different approach, inspired by the method of steepest descent. It is most clearly illustrated by the Blasius equation $f''' + ff'' = 0$. This leads to

$$f''(\eta) = ae^{-F(\eta)}, \qquad F(\eta) = \int_0^\eta f(\eta)\,d\eta,$$

and hence
$$\int_0^\infty ae^{-F(\eta)}\,d\eta = f'(\infty) = 1.$$

Meksyn now takes F as the variable of integration. From equation (V.93),

$$F(\eta) = \frac{a\eta^3}{3!} - \frac{a^2\eta^6}{6!} + \frac{11a^3\eta^9}{9!} - \frac{375a^4\eta^{12}}{12!} + ...,$$

so that
$$\eta = \left(\frac{6F}{a}\right)^{1/3}\left[1 + \frac{F}{60} - \frac{F^2}{1260} + \frac{23F^3}{891000} + ...\right].$$

Thus
$$(6a^2)^{1/3}\int_0^\infty \tfrac{1}{3}F^{-2/3}\left[1 + \frac{F}{15} - \frac{F^2}{180} + \frac{23F^3}{89100} + ...\right]e^{-F}\,dF = 1,$$

and term-by-term integration gives

$$(6a^2)^{1/3}\Gamma(\tfrac{4}{3})\left[1 + \frac{1}{45} - \frac{1}{405} + \frac{161}{601425} + ...\right] = 1. \tag{148}$$

If the first term alone of the series (148) is used, the result (145) is obtained. The four terms given lead to $a = 0\cdot4696$, in agreement with the accurate value. However, the series in (148) is probably not convergent.

In the general case, equation (139), Meksyn writes

$$\frac{\partial^2 f}{\partial \eta^2} = e^{-F(\xi,\eta)}g(\xi,\eta), \qquad F(\xi,\eta) = \int_0^\eta f(\xi,\eta)\,d\eta. \tag{149}$$

The expansions for $F(\xi,\eta)$, $g(\xi,\eta)$ in powers of η are obtained by direct calculation from (139) and (149), and Meksyn gives details of a general method of inverting the power series for F. In this way it may be shown that

$$\frac{\partial f}{\partial \eta} = \int_0^F e^{-F}g(\xi,\eta)\frac{\partial \eta}{\partial F}\,dF = \int_0^F e^{-F}\sum_0^\infty d_m F^{(m-2)/3}\,dF, \tag{150}$$

where the first few coefficients d_m are given in terms of $a(\xi)$, $\beta(\xi)$, and their derivatives by

$$d_0 = \tfrac{1}{3}(6a^2)^{1/3}, \qquad d_1 = -(6/a)^{2/3}(5\beta/18), \qquad d_2 = -3\beta^2/8a^2,$$

$$d_3 = \left(\frac{6}{a}\right)^{1/3}\left[\frac{(28\beta+1)a+28\xi a'}{45} - \frac{91\beta^3}{648a^3}\right]$$

$$d_4 = \left(\frac{6}{a}\right)^{2/3}\left[-\frac{41\beta+68\beta^2+120\xi\beta'}{378} + \frac{8\xi\beta a'}{27a} - \frac{935\beta^4}{15552a^4}\right]$$

$$d_5 = \frac{3}{a^2}\left[-\frac{17\beta^2+6\beta^3+60\xi\beta\beta'}{280} + \frac{3\beta^2\xi a'}{10a} - \frac{7\beta^5}{128a^4}\right]$$

$$d_6 = \left(\frac{6}{a}\right)^{1/3}\left[\frac{(-1+133\beta+98\beta^2)a}{540} + \frac{7\xi\beta'a}{27} + \frac{(154+63\beta)\xi a'}{270} - \right.$$
$$\left. -\frac{28\xi^2 a'^2}{135a} + \frac{7\xi^2 a''}{27} + \frac{65\beta^4-286\beta^3}{3888a^3} - \frac{65\xi\beta^2\beta'}{216a^3} + \frac{455\xi\beta^3 a'}{972a^4} - \frac{43225\beta^6}{559872a^7}\right]$$

(151)

Thus $a(\xi)$ is given by the condition

$$\sum_0^\infty d_m \Gamma\left(\frac{m+1}{3}\right) = 1. \tag{152}$$

Meksyn (1956) first treated the case of similar velocity profiles, equation (142), where $\beta(\xi)$ and $a(\xi)$ are constants. Since the series (152) is not convergent, he applied Euler's transformation

$$\sum_0^\infty (-1)^n a_n = \sum_0^\infty 2^{-(n+1)}\Delta^n a_0,$$

where $\Delta a_n = a_{n+1}-a_n$, $\Delta^2 a_n = \Delta a_{n+1}-\Delta a_n$,.... The process was repeated when necessary, and Meksyn was able to verify Hartree's (1937a) numerical results.

Another application was to the measurements of Schubauer (1935) on an elliptic cylinder. The calculations were simplified by the fact that a' does not appear in d_0, d_1, or d_2, and its influence on the series (152) is comparatively small. Meksyn found good agreement with Hartree's (1939b) calculations, except where a is small, near separation.

In his study of separation Meksyn assumed that in practice the pressure distribution near separation is such as to avoid the singularity in the boundary-layer solution, discussed in Section V. 11. By using the independent variable $G = F-\tfrac{1}{6}a\eta^3 = -\tfrac{1}{24}\beta\eta^4+...$, Meksyn obtained an equation

$$\frac{\partial f}{\partial \eta} = \int_0^G e^{-G} \sum_0^\infty e_m G^{(m-3)/4} \, dG, \tag{153}$$

which he used to find the separation point, and the slow back flow farther downstream. If $\lambda = -\beta$, and terms $O(a^2)$ are neglected,

$$\left.\begin{aligned}
&e_0 = \tfrac{1}{4}(24/\lambda)^{1/4}a, \quad e_1 = \tfrac{1}{4}(24\lambda)^{1/2}, \quad e_2 = 0, \quad e_3 = 8\xi aa'/5\lambda \\
&e_4 = (24/\lambda)^{1/4}(-66\lambda - 141\lambda^2 + 94\xi\lambda')a/112\lambda \\
&e_5 = (24/\lambda)^{1/2}(4\lambda - 15\lambda^2 + 10\xi\lambda')/56 \\
&e_6 = -119(24/\lambda)^{3/4}\xi^2 aa'^2/3600\lambda \\
&e_7 = \frac{8\xi aa'}{525\lambda^2}(118\lambda - 75\lambda^2 - 139\xi\lambda') + \frac{24\xi^2(a'^2 + aa'')}{25\lambda}
\end{aligned}\right\}. \quad (154)$$

The equation for a is now $\sum\limits_0^\infty e_m \Gamma\left(\dfrac{m+1}{4}\right) = 0$. Meksyn compared the velocity profiles so obtained with those given by Schubauer in the region beyond separation.

In a later paper Meksyn (1958) extended his method to include compressible flow, and also showed how to find a' from (152) and so to integrate this equation for a.

PART II

APPROXIMATE METHODS BASED ON INTEGRATED FORMS OF THE BOUNDARY-LAYER EQUATIONS

13. Methods based on the momentum equation: Pohlhausen's method

One of the earliest and, until recently, most widely used approximate methods for the solution of the boundary-layer equation is that developed by Pohlhausen (1921). This method is based on the momentum equation of Kármán (1921), which is obtained by integrating the boundary-layer equation (1) across the layer, as shown in Section V. 6. In the case of steady flow over an impermeable surface, to which attention will be confined at present, it reduces to

$$\frac{\tau_w}{\rho U^2} = \frac{d\delta_2}{dx} + \frac{2\delta_2 + \delta_1}{U}\frac{dU}{dx}, \quad (155)$$

where $\tau_w = \mu(\partial u/\partial z)_{z=0}$ is the skin friction, $\delta_1 = \int\limits_0^\infty (1 - u/U)\,dz$ is the displacement thickness, and $\delta_2 = \int\limits_0^\infty (u/U)(1 - u/U)\,dz$ is the momentum thickness of the boundary layer.

From the boundary-layer equations (1), (2) and their derivatives with respect to z, a set of conditions on u can be derived with the aid of the boundary conditions (3). These conditions are

$$z = 0: \quad u = 0, \quad \frac{\partial^2 u}{\partial z^2} = -\frac{U}{\nu}\frac{dU}{dx}, \quad \frac{\partial^3 u}{\partial z^3} = 0,$$

$$\frac{\partial^4 u}{\partial z^4} = \frac{1}{\nu}\frac{\partial u}{\partial z}\frac{\partial^2 u}{\partial x \partial z}, \quad ...;$$

$$z \to \infty: \quad u \to U, \quad \frac{\partial u}{\partial z} \to 0, \quad ..., \quad \frac{\partial^n u}{\partial z^n} \to 0, \quad .... \tag{156}$$

The conditions at $z = 0$ are equivalent to the relations (130).

In Pohlhausen's method, and similar methods dealt with in the next few sections, a form for the velocity profile $u(x,z)$ is sought which satisfies the momentum equation (155) and some of the boundary conditions (156). It is hoped that this form will approximate to the exact profile, which satisfies all the conditions (156) as well as (155). The form assumed is

$$u/U = f(\eta), \qquad \eta = z/\delta(x), \tag{157}$$

where $\delta(x)$ is the effective total thickness of the boundary layer. The function f may also depend on x through certain coefficients which are chosen so as to satisfy some of the conditions (156). Although strictly the conditions at infinity are only approached asymptotically, it is assumed that these conditions can be transferred from infinity to $z = \delta$ without appreciable error. Thus equations (156) become

$$f(0) = 0, \qquad f''(0) = -\Lambda, \qquad f'''(0) = 0,$$

$$f^{iv}(0) = \frac{\delta^3}{\nu}f'(0)\frac{d}{dx}\left(\frac{Uf'(0)}{\delta}\right), \quad ...;$$

$$f(1) = 1, \qquad f'(1) = f''(1) = f'''(1) = ... = 0, \tag{158}$$

where primes denote differentiation with respect to η and

$$\Lambda = -\frac{\delta^2}{\mu U}\frac{dp}{dx} = \frac{\delta^2}{\nu}\frac{dU}{dx}. \tag{159}$$

For the assumed velocity profile (157),

$$\frac{\tau_w}{\rho U^2} = \frac{\nu}{U\delta}f'(0), \qquad \delta_1 = \delta\int_0^1 (1-f)\,d\eta, \qquad \delta_2 = \delta\int_0^1 (f-f^2)\,d\eta. \tag{160}$$

If the form assumed for $f(\eta)$ involves m unknown coefficients, these can be specified by using m of the boundary conditions (158), and the remaining unknown δ can be determined from the momentum equation (155). Also, if not more than the first three of the conditions (158) at $z = 0$ are considered, $\tau_w\delta/\mu U$, δ_1/δ, and δ_2/δ are functions of Λ alone.

In this case, substitution of the relations (160) into (155) leads to an equation of the form

$$Z' = U^{-1}g(\Lambda) + U''h(\Lambda)Z^2, \tag{161}$$

where $Z = \delta^2/\nu = \Lambda/U'$, and primes denote differentiation with respect to x.

The solution of (161) requires rather laborious step-by-step methods. Furthermore, the presence of U'' may be inconvenient if U is given only numerically in terms of x. However, it was discovered by Holstein and Bohlen (1940) and Walz (1941) that if δ_2, instead of δ, is regarded as the unknown function, a simpler equation, not involving U'', is obtained. Equation (161) may therefore be regarded as obsolete, and the improved version of the method is as follows.

A parameter λ is defined, by analogy with (159), as

$$\lambda = \frac{\delta_2^2}{\nu}\frac{dU}{dx} = \frac{\delta_2^2}{\delta^2}\Lambda = -\frac{\delta_2^2}{U}\left(\frac{\partial^2 u}{\partial z^2}\right)_{z=0} \tag{162}$$

Since δ_2/δ is known to be a function of Λ, there is a functional relation between Λ and λ. Hence T and H, where

$$T = \tau_w\delta_2/\mu U, \qquad H = \delta_1/\delta_2, \tag{163}$$

are functions of λ. Equation (155), multiplied by $2U\delta_2/\nu$, may be written as

$$UY' = 2T - 2\lambda(H+2), \tag{164}$$

where

$$Y = \delta_2^2/\nu = \lambda/U'. \tag{165}$$

Thus, since T and H are functions of λ, the momentum equation reduces to

$$Y' = F(\lambda)/U, \tag{166}$$

where

$$F(\lambda) = 2T(\lambda) - 2\lambda\{H(\lambda)+2\}. \tag{167}$$

Pohlhausen (1921) used a family of velocity profiles given by the quartic polynomial

$$u/U = f(\eta) = 2\eta - 2\eta^3 + \eta^4 + \tfrac{1}{6}\Lambda\eta(1-\eta)^3, \tag{168}$$

chosen to satisfy the boundary conditions

$$f(0) = 0, \quad f''(0) = -\Lambda, \quad f(1) = 1, \quad f'(1) = f''(1) = 0. \tag{169}$$

For the family (168), equations (160) lead to

$$\left.\begin{aligned}
(\lambda/\Lambda)^{\tfrac{1}{2}} &= (37 - \tfrac{1}{3}\Lambda - \tfrac{5}{144}\Lambda^2)/315 \\
H(\lambda) &= (\tfrac{3}{10} - \tfrac{1}{120}\Lambda)(\lambda/\Lambda)^{-\tfrac{1}{2}}, \qquad T(\lambda) = (2 + \tfrac{1}{6}\Lambda)(\lambda/\Lambda)^{\tfrac{1}{2}}
\end{aligned}\right\}. \tag{170}$$

Fig. VI. 3 shows some of the velocity profiles (168); the functions $\Lambda(\lambda)$, $H(\lambda)$, $T(\lambda)$, $F(\lambda)$ are tabulated in Table VI. 2 and are plotted graphically in Fig. VI. 4.

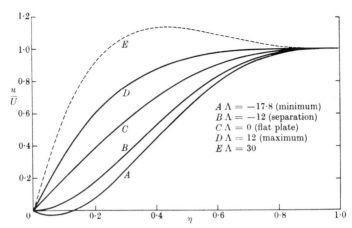

FIG. VI. 3. Shapes of the velocity profiles (168) for the method of Pohlhausen.

Legend (within figure):

$A\ \Lambda = -17 \cdot 8$ (minimum)
$B\ \Lambda = -12$ (separation)
$C\ \Lambda = 0$ (flat plate)
$D\ \Lambda = 12$ (maximum)
$E\ \Lambda = 30$

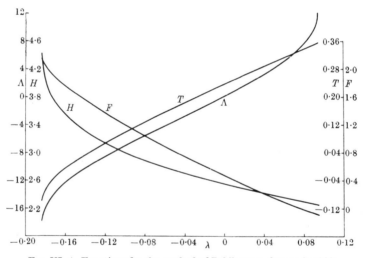

FIG. VI. 4. Functions for the method of Pohlhausen, for use in (166).

The range of tabulation is chosen so as to include the case $\lambda = \Lambda = 0$, corresponding to the boundary layer on a flat plate with zero pressure gradient. From (168) it follows that values of Λ greater than 12 must be excluded, since for such values u would exceed U within the boundary layer, which is physically unreasonable (see Fig. VI. 3). Moreover, it follows from (170) that a maximum value of λ occurs when $\Lambda = 12$ and $\lambda = 0 \cdot 0948$, and since $F \neq 0$ for this value of λ, the integration of (166) normally becomes impossible at this point. There is similarly a

TABLE VI. 2

Functions for the method of Pohlhausen, for use with (166)

λ	Λ	H	T	F	$dH/d\lambda$
0·0948	12	2·25	0·356	−0·095	−3·83
·0941	11	2·25	0·354	−0·091	−3·59
·0919	10	2·26	0·351	−0·081	−3·39
0·0882	9	2·27	0·346	−0·061	−3·27
·0831	8	2·29	0·340	−0·033	−3·18
·0770	7·052	2·31	0·332	0	−3·12
·0767	7	2·31	0·331	+0·002	−3·11
·0689	6	2·33	0·321	0·046	−3·08
·0599	5	2·36	0·310	0·098	−3·07
0·0497	4	2·39	0·297	0·158	−3·10
·0385	3	2·43	0·283	0·226	−3·15
·0264	2	2·47	0·268	0·300	−3·22
·0135	1	2·51	0·252	0·382	−3·33
0	0	2·55	0·235	0·470	−3·47
−0·0140	−1	2·60	0·217	0·563	−3·65
·0284	−2	2·66	0·199	0·662	−3·88
·0429	−3	2·72	0·179	0·764	−4·15
·0575	−4	2·78	0·160	0·870	−4·49
−0·0720	−5	2·85	0·140	0·978	−4·91
·0862	−6	2·92	0·119	1·085	−5·43
·0999	−7	3·00	0·100	1·198	−6·09
·1130	−8	3·08	0·079	1·308	−6·91
·1254	−9	3·18	0·059	1·417	−7·98
−0·1369	−10	3·28	0·039	1·523	−9·38
·1474	−11	3·38	0·019	1·625	−11·30
·1567	−12	3·50	0	1·724	−13·96
·1648	−13	3·63	−0·019	1·816	
·1715	−14	3·77	−0·037	1·902	
−0·1767	−15	3·92	−0·054	1·982	
·1803	−16	4·08	−0·071	2·044	
·1824	−17	4·26	−0·086	2·111	
·1829	−17·76	4·41	−0·097	2·152	

minimum value of λ when $\Lambda = -17 \cdot 76$ and $\lambda = -0 \cdot 1829$, which has accordingly been taken as the lower bound for λ. It can be seen from (170) that $\tau_w = 0$ when $\Lambda = -12$, so that values of Λ less than -12 correspond to conditions beyond the separation point. Such conditions are not usually considered, on the grounds that the boundary-layer equations are not applicable. However, it may sometimes be desirable to use Pohlhausen's method as a very rough guide to conditions beyond the separation point, and for this reason values of Λ less than -12 have been included in the table

If the process of integrating (166) leads to values of λ outside the range of tabulation, the method fails. The assumed quartic profile (168) does not then represent the true velocity profile sufficiently closely, and one of the other methods presented later, depending on different assumptions, should be used.

A singularity occurs in the differential equation (166) at a front stagnation point, where $U = 0$, so that to avoid an infinity in Y', F must be 0 there. Within the range of tabulation the only zero of F occurs at $\lambda = 0.0770$. From equation (166) the corresponding value of Y' is

$$(dF/d\lambda)(\lambda'/U') = (dF/d\lambda)(Y'U'+YU'')/U'$$

since $\lambda = YU'$. Hence

$$Y' = \frac{\lambda \, dF/d\lambda}{1-dF/d\lambda} \frac{U''}{U'^2}.$$

Accordingly the starting values at a forward stagnation point are

$$\lambda = 0.0770, \qquad Y = 0.0770/U', \qquad Y' = -0.0652U''/U'^2.$$

Equation (166) can now be integrated numerically, in conjunction with Table VI. 2, for boundary layers with arbitrary pressure distributions. The solutions give directly those properties of the boundary layer which are of practical importance, namely the skin friction and the thicknesses δ, δ_1, and δ_2. The solutions are, of course, identical with those obtained more laboriously by the use of Pohlhausen's original equation.

14. Methods based on the momentum equation: alternative polynomial forms

In attempts to secure improved accuracy various methods similar to Pohlhausen's have been proposed employing velocity profiles which satisfy more boundary conditions than the simple form (168). Thus Mangler (1944b) suggested the more complicated polynomial

$$u/U = f(\eta) = 1-(1-\eta)^n(1+a_1\eta+a_2\eta^2). \qquad (171)$$

This automatically satisfies n of the conditions (158) at $\eta = 1$. If the coefficient a_2 is assumed to be zero, only the first two boundary conditions at the wall, $f(0) = 0$ and $f''(0) = -\Lambda$, are used, but if a_2 is not assumed to be zero, the third boundary condition, $f'''(0) = 0$, is used as well. The boundary conditions thus determine a_1 and a_2, and hence the functions $H(\lambda)$, $T(\lambda)$, and $F(\lambda)$. The momentum equation, in the form (166), can be integrated as in Pohlhausen's method. The solutions will depend on the value of n and on whether or not a_2 is assumed to be zero, and the choice of these constants can be made to give good agreement with known exact solutions. Mangler found that conditions near a leading-edge stagnation point are best represented by the poly-nomial (171) when $n = 12$, $a_2 \neq 0$, though Pohlhausen's quartic form (168), which is the same as (171) with $n = 3$, $a_2 = 0$, is only a little less accurate. Pohlhausen's quartic profile also represents the boundary layer with zero pressure gradient quite well, but a better representation is obtained with $n = 4$, $a_2 \neq 0$. This latter form of profile had been suggested independently by Schlichting and Ulrich (1940), but it has the disadvantage of failing in the neighbourhood of a leading-edge stagnation point. This is because with this profile F is never zero for real values of λ whereas, from (166), F vanishes at a stagnation point if Y' is finite. In fact, no relation of the form (171) represents the velocity profile satisfactorily over the whole range of interest. This is true of all methods which assume H, T, and F to be functions of the single parameter λ, leaving λ to be determined from the momentum equation.

15. Methods based on the momentum equation: Timman's family of profiles

Timman (1949) put forward a method which satisfies the boundary conditions more adequately than (171) and is probably as accurate a method of this type as can be derived without reference to previously calculated exact solutions. Timman assumes, in place of (168) or (171), a velocity profile of the form

$$\frac{u}{U} = f(\eta) = 1 - \int_{\eta}^{\infty} \exp(-\eta^2)(a + c\eta^2 + \ldots)\, d\eta - \exp(-\eta^2)(b + d\eta^2 + \ldots),$$

$$(172)$$

where $\eta = z/\delta$. It follows from (172) that $f \to 1$ as $z \to \infty$. Therefore, of the boundary conditions (158), only those at the wall $\eta = 0$ need be considered and, if terms of higher order than the c and d terms are omitted, the first four of these conditions are

$$f(0) = 1 - b - \tfrac{1}{2}\sqrt{\pi}(a + \tfrac{1}{2}c) = 0,$$

$$f''(0) = 2(b - d) = -\Lambda,$$

$$f'''(0) = 2(c - a) = 0, \qquad\qquad (173)$$

$$f^{\mathrm{iv}}(0) = 12(2d - b) = \frac{U\delta^2}{\nu} a\left[\frac{da}{dx} + a\left(\frac{1}{U}\frac{dU}{dx} - \frac{1}{\delta}\frac{d\delta}{dx}\right)\right]. \qquad (174)$$

From (173), $a = c = 4(1 - b)/3\sqrt{\pi}$. Hence equations (160) enable $(\lambda/\Lambda)^{\frac{1}{2}}$, H, and T to be expressed as functions of b and d. Thus if b and d can be determined as functions of Λ only, the momentum equation may again be integrated in the form (166). However, the condition

TABLE VI. 3

Functions for the method of Timman, for use with (166)

λ	Λ	H	T	F
0·271	4·53	1·83	0·601	−0·876
·266	4·00	1·87	0·582	−0·896
·254	3·50	1·92	0·557	−0·878
·230	3·00	1·99	0·521	−0·794
·202	2·50	2·06	0·480	−0·682
0·1669	2·00	2·14	0·435	−0·513
·1517	1·80	2·18	0·415	−0·437
·1359	1·60	2·22	0·395	−0·356
·1196	1·40	2·25	0·374	−0·267
·1029	1·20	2·29	0·352	−0·179
0·0858	1·00	2·33	0·331	−0·084
·0712	0·83	2·37	0·311	0
·0686	0·80	2·38	0·308	+0·015
·0513	0·60	2·43	0·286	0·117
·0340	0·40	2·48	0·263	0·221
·0169	0·20	2·54	0·241	0·328
0	0	2·60	0·218	0·435
−0·0088	−0·10	2·66	0·201	0·484
·0183	−0·20	2·72	0·182	0·537
·0282	−0·30	2·80	0·161	0·594
·0383	−0·40	2·89	0·140	0·654
·0483	−0·50	2·99	0·117	0·716
−0·0579	−0·60	3·11	0·093	0·778
·0668	−0·70	3·24	0·070	0·839
·0748	−0·80	3·39	0·046	0·898
·0816	−0·90	3·56	0·023	0·953
·0871	−1·00	3·75	0	1·002
−0·0909	−1·10	3·98	−0·022	1·044
·0931	−1·20	4·23	−0·042	1·076
·0933	−1·27	4·43	−0·054	1·092

(174) for $f^{\text{iv}}(0)$ cannot then be satisfied. Instead it is assumed that $f^{\text{iv}}(0) = 0$ in regions of rising pressure, where $\lambda < 0$. This assumption is reasonable near separation, since $f'(0) = a = 0$ at the separation point and so, from (174), $f^{\text{iv}}(0) = 0$ at separation provided that the expression in square brackets remains finite. This condition is satisfied in Timman's method, though $df'(0)/dx$ may become infinite for accurate solutions of the boundary-layer equations. When $f^{\text{iv}}(0) = 0$, it follows from (173) and (174) that $b = 2d = -\Lambda$, so that the functions $H(\lambda)$, $T(\lambda)$, and $F(\lambda)$ can be computed.

Unfortunately the function $F(\lambda)$ so obtained is not zero for any real value of λ, whereas it has been shown in Section 13 that F must vanish

at a forward stagnation point. Hence Timman abandons the condition
(174) for $f^{iv}(0)$ in regions of falling pressure ($\lambda > 0$). He assumes instead
that $d = 0$, so that H, T, and F can be computed as functions of λ;
$F(\lambda) = 0$ now when $\lambda = 0.0712$. At the stagnation point the argument
used before gives the starting values

$$\lambda = 0.0712, \qquad Y = 0.0712/U', \qquad Y' = -0.0616U''/U'^2.$$

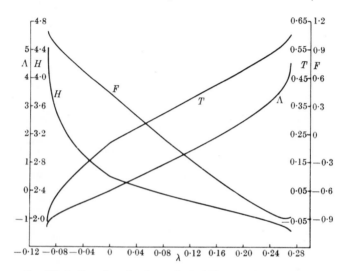

Fig. VI. 5. Functions for the method of Timman, for use in (166).

The assumptions $d = 0$ ($\lambda \geqslant 0$), $b = 2d$ ($\lambda \leqslant 0$) agree when $\lambda = 0$,
so that the velocity profiles and the functions Λ, H, T, F vary continuously with λ through the value $\lambda = 0$. These functions are tabulated in Table VI. 3 and are plotted against λ in Fig. VI. 5. As in
Table VI. 2 the range of tabulation is limited by the minimum and
maximum values of λ; values of λ less than -0.0871 correspond to
boundary-layer profiles beyond the separation point. The slopes of the
graphs in Fig. VI. 5 are discontinuous at $\lambda = 0$, so that on Timman's
method the gradients of the skin friction and displacement thickness
are discontinuous at the pressure minimum.

16. Methods based on the momentum equation: a method of Thwaites

The velocity profiles proposed by Pohlhausen and Mangler indicate
values of u greater than U for sufficiently large positive values of λ.
It is physically unreasonable for u anywhere to exceed U, and in cases

where the pressure decreases with distance from the leading edge the methods of Pohlhausen and Mangler may fail, since λ may reach the critical values. Timman's method is not limited in this way because with his profiles (unlike those of Pohlhausen or Mangler) the maximum value of λ is attained at a lower value of Λ than that for which $\partial u/\partial z$ first becomes zero within the profile. Also, the maximum value of λ is greater in Timman's method than in the others, so that Timman's method is less likely to fail in practical cases. Nevertheless, it is worth mentioning briefly a way suggested by Thwaites (1946b, c, 1947) of specifying the velocity profiles so that u can never be greater than U. Instead of writing $u/U = f(\eta)$, $\eta = z/\delta$, Thwaites writes

$$z/\delta_2 = g(t), \qquad t = u/U, \tag{175}$$

where t is now restricted to the range $0 \leqslant t \leqslant 1$, thus preventing u from exceeding U. However, the difficulty is now introduced of ensuring that $g(t)$ increases monotonically with t, so that there can be only one value of u for a given value of z. The function $g(t)$ must satisfy the equation

$$\int_0^1 (2t-1)g(t)\,dt = 1,$$

which follows from the definition of momentum thickness, and then

$$H = \int_0^1 g(t)\,dt, \qquad T = 1/g'(0), \qquad \lambda = \{g''(0)\}/\{g'(0)\}^3.$$

Thwaites used this method for investigations of boundary-layer flow with suction, which are referred to in Sections 29 and 31.

17. Methods based on the momentum equation: the family of 'similar' profiles

Walz (1941) suggested that the velocity profiles used with the momentum equations should be taken as those found in the 'similar' solutions of the boundary-layer equations. In such a solution the shape of the velocity profile is independent of x, though the boundary-layer thickness varies. These solutions are discussed in Section V. 21, where it is shown that, in the absence of suction, the profiles are given by

$$u = U(x)f'(\eta), \qquad \eta = z/g(x), \tag{176}$$

where
$$\left. \begin{array}{l} f'''+\alpha ff''+\beta(1-f'^2) = 0 \\ f(0) = f'(0) = 0, \qquad f'(\infty) = 1 \end{array} \right\}. \tag{177}$$

Here α and β are constants, and the corresponding main-stream flows are

$$U(x) = U_0(|x-x_0|/l)^n, \qquad n = \beta/(2\alpha-\beta)$$
$$(2\alpha-\beta)(x-x_0) > 0, \quad \text{provided } 2\alpha \neq \beta$$
or $$U(x) = U_0 e^{2\alpha x/l} \quad \text{when } 2\alpha = \beta$$

$$(178)$$

The velocity profiles (176) and the main-stream flows (178) form continuous one-parameter families depending on the ratio of β to α and on the signs of α and β. Some of the profiles are given in Table V. 4, and the main-stream flows are shown in Fig. V. 9.

In Walz's method the profiles are taken in the form (176) for a general external flow $U(x)$. If $U(x)$ is of the type (178) the momentum equation will give the exact solution, but in general only an approximate result will be obtained. From the numerical solutions of (177), which are referred to in Section V. 21, the quantities λ, T, H, and F may be calculated from the equations

$$\lambda = \beta\Delta_2^2, \quad T = f''(0)\Delta_2, \quad H = \Delta_1/\Delta_2, \quad F = 2(\alpha-\beta)\Delta_2^2, \quad (179)$$

where $\Delta_1 \equiv \int_0^\infty (1-f')\,d\eta$, $\Delta_2 \equiv \int_0^\infty f'(1-f')\,d\eta$. Values of the functions (179) are given in Table VI. 4 and are shown in Fig. VI. 6.

TABLE VI. 4

Functions for the method of Walz (1941), for use with (166)

α	β	λ	H	T	F	n	$x-x_0$
-1	1	$0\cdot384$	$1\cdot75$	$0\cdot674$	$-1\cdot532$	$-1/3$	—
-1	4	$0\cdot170$	$2\cdot01$	$0\cdot468$	$-0\cdot424$	$-2/3$	—
0	1	$0\cdot1415$	$2\cdot07$	$0\cdot435$	$-0\cdot284$	-1	—
$+1$	$2\cdot4$	$0\cdot1107$	$2\cdot14$	$0\cdot395$	$-0\cdot128$	-6	—
1	2	$0\cdot1063$	$2\cdot16$	$0\cdot389$	$-0\cdot106$	$*$	$*$
1	$1\cdot6$	$0\cdot1000$	$2\cdot17$	$0\cdot381$	$-0\cdot075$	$+4$	$+$
1	1	$0\cdot0855$	$2\cdot22$	$0\cdot360$	0	1	$+$
1	$0\cdot5$	$0\cdot0611$	$2\cdot30$	$0\cdot325$	$+0\cdot122$	$1/3$	$+$
1	$0\cdot2$	$0\cdot0333$	$2\cdot41$	$0\cdot280$	$0\cdot267$	$1/9$	$+$
1	0	0	$2\cdot59$	$0\cdot221$	$0\cdot441$	0	$+$
1	$-0\cdot1$	$-0\cdot0266$	$2\cdot80$	$0\cdot164$	$0\cdot584$	$-1/21$	$+$
1	$-0\cdot16$	$-0\cdot0488$	$3\cdot09$	$0\cdot105$	$0\cdot708$	$-2/27$	$+$
1	$-0\cdot199$	$-0\cdot0682$	$4\cdot03$	0	$0\cdot824$	$-0\cdot09$	$+$

* The case $\beta = 2\alpha$ corresponds to the external velocity distribution
$$U = U_0 \exp(x/l).$$

This method, like that of Timman, has the advantage that it can be used in regions of very sharp pressure drop, since λ can take large positive values. A closely related method was described by Smith (1956b), who approximated to $U(x)$ in an interval $x_i < x < x_{i+1}$ by a distribution of the type (178), and applied the corresponding similarity solution (176). The constants U_0 and x_0 in (178) were chosen so that δ_2 remains continuous at $x = x_i$. Smith's method becomes identical with that of Walz when the intervals (x_i, x_{i+1}) become infinitesimal, but has the advantage that U' is not required.

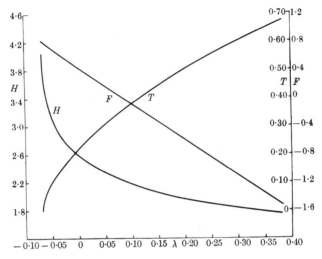

FIG. VI. 6. Functions for the method of Walz (1941).

Walz (1941) also considered the use, with the momentum equation, of Howarth's profiles for the flow $U = U_0(1-\xi)$, $\xi = x/l$, discussed in Section 3. It was observed in that section that this method is equivalent to one suggested by Howarth for use in retarded flow. Walz permitted negative values of ξ, which correspond to accelerated flow.

18. Approximate integration of the momentum equation: relations proposed by Thwaites

The methods hitherto discussed employ the momentum equation in the form (166), which must in general be integrated numerically. An explicit formula can, however, be obtained if $F(\lambda)$ may be treated as a linear function of λ. If

$$F(\lambda) = a - b\lambda, \tag{180}$$

where a and b are constants, equation (166) becomes

$$Y' = \frac{d}{dx}\left(\frac{\delta_2^2}{\nu}\right) = \frac{a-b\lambda}{U} = \frac{a-bYU'}{U},$$

of which the solution is

$$Y = \frac{\delta_2^2}{\nu} = aU^{-b}\left[\int_{x_0}^{x} U^{b-1}\,dx + C\right].$$

If $x_0 = 0$, corresponding to the leading edge of the body, the constant C is zero, since δ_2 is finite at a front stagnation point (see also Section 19). Hence

$$\lambda = \frac{\delta_2^2 U'}{\nu} = aU'U^{-b}\int_0^x U^{b-1}\,dx. \tag{181}$$

The functions $T(\lambda)$ and $H(\lambda)$ then enable the skin friction and displacement thickness to be calculated.

All the methods described above do in fact indicate that $F(\lambda)$ differs little from a linear function, as can be seen from Figs. VI. 4, VI. 5, VI. 6. For any one method there is some freedom of choice of the constants a and b in (180), depending on the range of λ considered. If, for instance, equation (180) is made to hold exactly in the two cases of zero pressure gradient ($\lambda = 0$) and stagnation-point flow ($F = 0$), the following results are obtained:

Method	a	b
Pohlhausen	0·470	6·10
Timman	0·435	6·11
Walz	0·441	5·15

The approximate solution (181) was suggested by Walz (1941) for his own method, by Hudimoto (1941) and Tani (1941) for Pohlhausen's method, and by Zaat (1950) for Timman's method. No one-parameter family of velocity profiles is valid generally, and there is no reason to suppose that (181) is less accurate than (166). Also, it is easier to use the integral formula (181) than to solve the differential equation (166) numerically. Since the values of a and b for the three methods are not very different, the corresponding results for δ_2 will not differ greatly for most pressure distributions.

The momentum equation was first reduced to the simple formula (181) by Young and Winterbottom (1940), who made the drastic assumptions

$$H = \text{constant} = 2\cdot56, \qquad \delta/\delta_2 = \text{constant} = 8\cdot51.$$

These are the values given by Pohlhausen's method for the boundary layer with zero pressure gradient. They assumed further that, as in Pohlhausen's method—see equations (160) and (168)—

$$\frac{\tau_w}{\rho U^2} = \frac{\nu}{U\delta}\left(2 + \frac{1}{6}\frac{\delta^2}{\nu}\frac{dU}{dx}\right).$$

These assumptions imply that $F(\lambda) = 0\cdot470 - 6\cdot28\lambda$, so that the values of a and b to be used in (181) are $0\cdot470$ and $6\cdot28$ respectively, again not very different from the values given previously.

The wide range of validity of the relation (180) was demonstrated convincingly by Thwaites (1949b). Thwaites analysed as many exact solutions, accurate computations, and approximate methods as were

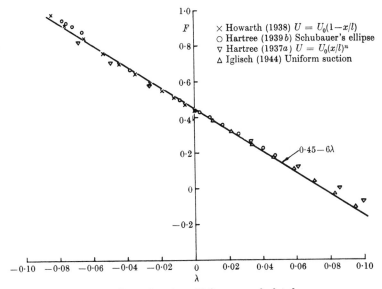

FIG. VI. 7. F as a function of λ for some calculated cases.

known to him, and showed that in no case does $F(\lambda)$ depart far from the linear function $0\cdot45 - 6\lambda$: the comparison for numerical solutions of the boundary-layer equations is shown in Fig. VI. 7 (see also Figs. VI. 4, VI. 5 for approximate methods). Fig. VI. 7 includes data from the calculations of Iglisch (1944) for a flat plate with uniform suction. Here λ is defined by $\lambda = -(\delta_2^2/U)(\partial^2 u/\partial z^2)_{z=0}$, which is equal to $\delta_2^2 U'/\nu$ when there is no suction. It is interesting that in Fig. VI. 7 Iglisch's results should lie close to the others, which are for flow without suction.

Thwaites's choice of the approximation $F(\lambda) = 0\cdot45 - 6\lambda$ implies that the relation for λ corresponding to (181) is

$$\lambda = \frac{\delta_2^2\, U'}{\nu} = 0\cdot45 U' U^{-6} \int_0^x U^5\, dx. \qquad (182)$$

This, since it represents an average of many methods, is probably the most suitable relation to use. Moreover, since all methods lead to results fairly close to (182), it may be expected that this relation will be satisfactory for most cases.

TABLE VI. 5

Functions for the method of Thwaites (1949 b) for use with (182)

λ	H	T	λ	H	T
0·25	2·00	0·500	−0·074	3·30	0·076
·20	2·07	·463	·076	3·38	·067
·14	2·18	·404	·078	3·47	·055
·12	2·23	·382	·079	3·52	·049
·10	2·28	·359	·080	3·58	·039
0·080	2·34	0·333	−0·0804	3·59	0·035
·064	2·39	·313	·0808	3·61	·030
·048	2·44	·291	·0812	3·63	·024
·032	2·49	·268	·0816	3·66	·016
·016	2·55	·244	·0818	3·69	·011
0·000	2·61	0·220	−0·082	3·70	0·000
−0·008	2·64	·208			
·016	2·67	·195	*Modified values of Curle and Skan*		
·024	2·71	·182	(λ < −0·06)		
·032	2·75	·168	λ	H	T
−0·040	2·81	0·153	−0·060	2·99	0·113
·048	2·87	·138	·064	3·04	·104
·052	2·90	·130	·068	3·09	·095
·056	2·94	·122	·072	3·15	·085
·060	2·99	·113	·076	3·22	·072
−0·064	3·05	0·104	−0·080	3·30	0·056
·068	3·13	·094	·084	3·39	·038
·070	3·17	·089	·086	3·44	·027
·072	3·23	·083	·088	3·49	·015
·074	3·30	·076	·090	3·55	·000

Thwaites also suggested relations, given in Table VI. 5 and Fig. VI. 8, between λ, T (the skin-friction parameter), and H (the profile-shape parameter). His relations were based on those given by the various accurate and approximate solutions, but can hardly be said to represent an average of them since they diverge widely where the pressure gradient is adverse, as can be seen from Figs. VI. 4, VI. 5, VI. 9. Thwaites chose $T(\lambda)$ so that, with λ calculated from (182), the predicted separation point for the case $U = U_0(1-x/l)$ is close to the position found by Howarth (1938). If, therefore, one is considering a case in which the velocity gradient is roughly linear, the use of Thwaites's relations should lead to values of τ_w, H, and δ_2 which are approximately correct; if the velocity distribution is of a very different type the errors in τ_w and H may be considerably larger, though the predicted momentum thickness δ_2 should not be far wrong. Curle and Skan (1957) have suggested modifications to Thwaites's functions $T(\lambda)$, $H(\lambda)$ in the region near the separation point. These modifications led to better agreement

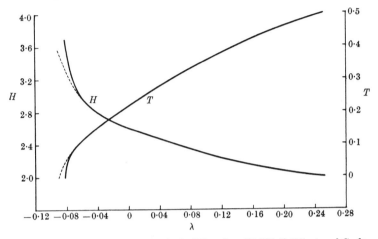

FIG. VI. 8. Functions for the method of Thwaites (1949b) (full line) and Curle and Skan's modifications (broken line), for use with (182).

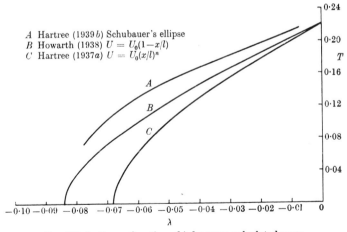

A Hartree (1939b) Schubauer's ellipse
B Howarth (1938) $U = U_0(1-x/l)$
C Hartree (1937a) $U = U_0(x/l)^n$

FIG. VI. 9. T as a function of λ for some calculated cases.

with the solutions of Görtler (1955a), obtained by the method of Section 6, than the original functions. Both sets of functions are presented in Table VI. 5 and Fig. VI. 8. However, Curle and Skan's improved version of Thwaites's method cannot be said with complete generality to be more accurate than the other single-parameter methods described above, because the skin-friction function T does not in fact depend only on λ. This can be seen from the comparison made in Fig. VI. 9 between the results for Howarth's (1938) linear velocity gradient case, for Hartree's (1939b) computation of the case of Schubauer's ellipse, and for the velocity distributions $U = U_0(x/l)^n$. It might, for instance, be possible to find an external velocity distribution such that Pohlhausen's method, often criticized as 'inaccurate', gave the most accurate results for the skin friction. All that one can say is that, for the types of outer velocity distribution most often considered in practice, Thwaites's method is much better than that of Pohlhausen.

19. Application of the energy equation

The main conclusions that emerge from the foregoing analysis are (i) that (182) is, in most circumstances, a fairly accurate relation for the momentum thickness; and (ii) that the skin friction and the shape parameter H will not be very accurately predicted in a region of adverse pressure gradient unless the assumptions made regarding the velocity profiles are close to the truth. These conclusions can be reached more readily if, in addition to the momentum integral equation, the energy integral equation is considered, as follows.

This equation, due originally to Leibenson (1935), represents the balance of mechanical energy within a small section of the boundary layer, and is derived in Section V. 6. For steady flow and an impermeable wall it reduces to

$$d(U^3\delta_3)/dx = 2D/\rho, \tag{183}$$

where $\delta_3 = \int_0^\infty (u/U)(1-u^2/U^2)\,dz$ is the energy thickness, and

$$D = \int_0^\infty \mu(\partial u/\partial z)^2\,dz$$

is the dissipation integral. If

$$K = \frac{\delta_3}{\delta_2}, \qquad L = \frac{\delta_2 D}{\mu U^2} = \int_0^\infty \left(\frac{\partial(u/U)}{\partial(z/\delta_2)}\right)^2 d\left(\frac{z}{\delta_2}\right), \tag{184}$$

equation (183) becomes, when multiplied by $2U^3\delta_3$,

$$d(K^2U^6\delta_2^2)/dx = 4\nu U^5 KL. \tag{185}$$

Hence $\delta_2^2 = (4\nu/K^2U^6)\left(\int_{x_0}^x U^5 KL\,dx + C\right)$. If the lower limit of integration is taken as $x_0 = 0$, the leading edge, the constant of integration C is zero. This is because δ_3 is proportional to $(\nu x/U)^{\frac{1}{2}}$ when the main-stream flow is of the type $U = U_0(x/l)^n$ $(U_0 > 0, n > -0.0904)$, for small x. Hence $K^2U^6\delta_2^2 = U^6\delta_3^2$ varies like x^{5n+1} near $x = 0$, and vanishes at $x = 0$. Consequently

$$\delta_2^2 = \frac{\lambda\nu}{U'} = \frac{4\nu}{K^2U^6} \int_0^x U^5KL\,dx. \tag{186}$$

The energy equation can be combined with the momentum equation (164) to yield a relation for the skin friction. Thus, from equations (164), (165), and (185),

$$T = \lambda(H-1)+2L/K-\lambda UK'/U'K, \tag{187}$$

where T and H, defined by (163), are not assumed now to be functions only of λ.

No approximation has been made in deriving (186) and (187) from the boundary-layer equations. If, following Truckenbrodt (1952b), it is now assumed that K and L can be treated as constants, equation (186) simplifies to

$$\delta_2^2 = \frac{4L}{K}\frac{\nu}{U^6} \int_0^x U^5\,dx.$$

If L and K are given the values appropriate to the Blasius boundary-layer profile for the flat plate this equation becomes

$$\delta_2^2 = \frac{\lambda\nu}{U'} = 0.44\frac{\nu}{U^6} \int_0^x U^5\,dx, \tag{188}$$

which is almost identical with Thwaites's result (182). The justification for this procedure is that the integral in (186) is not very sensitive to local variations of K and L, and that they do not vary greatly, even for a wide range of profile shapes.

In Fig. VI. 10 profiles of u/U, computed by Howarth (1938), are plotted against z/δ_2 for (a) the leading edge and (b) the separation point for the outer flow $U = U_0(1-x/l)$. The shapes of the outer parts of the profiles are much the same in the two cases, as Tollmien's theory (Section V. 10) indicates, though the inner profiles are very different. Below the profiles are plotted the functions

$$\frac{u}{U}\left(1-\frac{u}{U}\right), \quad \frac{u}{U}\left(1-\frac{u^2}{U^2}\right), \quad \text{and} \quad \left(\frac{\partial(u/U)}{\partial(z/\delta_2)}\right)^2,$$

whose integrals are 1, K, and L. The integrands are all small near the wall ($z = 0$) for the separation profile (b), so that at separation the main contributions to K and L come from the outer part of the profile,

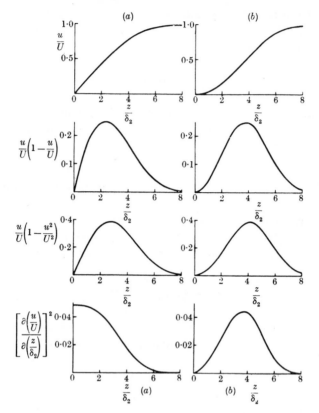

Fig. VI. 10. Functions of the velocity profiles (a) at the leading edge, and (b) at separation, for the case $U = U_0(1-x/l)$.

whose shape differs little from the outer part of the leading-edge profile (a). At the leading edge the inner part of the profile is more important for L than for K, and so L varies more than K between the two positions. Nevertheless neither varies greatly and the actual values are:

	K	L
Leading edge	1·57	0·173
Separation	1·52	0·157

Values for other families of profiles are given in Tables VI. 6 and VI. 7 (Section 21). The approximate constancy of K and L is a consequence of the general shape of the boundary-layer profiles, and all profiles reasonably close to the boundary-layer type, not merely those computed by Howarth, would give nearly the same results.

If now K is assumed to be constant in (187) it follows that

$$T = \lambda(H-1)+2L/K. \tag{189}$$

Hence if L and T are assumed to be functions only of H, equation (189) gives H, and hence T and L, as functions of λ. As has been seen previously, T is far from being a function only of λ in regions of adverse pressure gradient, so if high accuracy is required in such regions it is evidently not justifiable to make the above simplifying assumptions for K, L, and T.

At first sight it may be surprising that such assumptions should not be valid for (187) in situations when similar assumptions (indeed more restrictive, since L is also assumed constant) give the acceptable result (188) when applied to (186). However, the reason is that whereas the proportional errors made in computing δ_2 from (188) are typically only of the same order as the proportional errors made in the assumed value of K, small errors in the terms on the right-hand side of (187) can lead to large proportional errors in T near separation, where T is small.

20. Wieghardt's two-parameter method

In the foregoing section the energy integral equation has been used to confirm results already obtained more laboriously from the momentum integral equation alone. It can, however, be used with the momentum integral equation to form the basis of a more accurate method. Assumed forms for the boundary-layer velocity profiles can be found which satisfy both the energy integral equation (185) and the momentum integral equation (164), or the derived equations (186) and (187), together with certain of the boundary conditions (156). It is hoped that these profiles will approximate to the accurate solution, which satisfies these integral equations and *all* the conditions (156). Sutton (1937) was the first to use the momentum and energy integral equations in this way: he considered the simple problem of the boundary layer with zero pressure gradient and obtained good agreement with the exact solution. Wieghardt (1946, 1948) considered the general case with an arbitrary pressure distribution. In his method it is assumed that the velocity profiles can be represented by a relation of the form

$$u/U = f(\eta) = 1-(1-\eta)^8(1+A_1\eta+A_2\eta^2+A_3\eta^3), \tag{190}$$

where $\eta = z/\delta$. Thus eight of the boundary conditions (158) at $z = \delta$ are satisfied automatically and, of those at the wall, the conditions $f(0) = 0, f''(0) = -\Lambda = -(\delta/\delta_2)^2\lambda$, and $f'''(0) = 0$ are imposed. Since

$f'(0) = (\delta/U)(\partial u/\partial z)_{z=0} = (\delta/\delta_2)T$, the relation (190) becomes

$$u/U = f_1(\eta) + a f_2(\eta) + b f_3(\eta), \tag{191}$$

where
$$f_1(\eta) = 1 - (1-\eta)^8(1 + 8\eta + 36\eta^2 + 120\eta^3),$$
$$f_2(\eta) = (1-\eta)^8 \eta(1 + 8\eta + 36\eta^2),$$
$$f_3(\eta) = -(1-\eta)^8 \eta^2(1 + 8\eta),$$

and
$$a = (\delta/\delta_2)T, \qquad b = (\delta^2/2\delta_2^2)\lambda.$$

From (160), δ_2/δ can be expressed as a function of a and b, and this enables a and b to be determined as functions of the two parameters T and λ only. The functions H, K, and L, which appear in the energy and momentum integral equations (185) and (164), can therefore be expressed as functions of T and λ, and since $\delta_2^2 = \lambda\nu/U'$, T and λ can be determined as functions of x for any given pressure distribution by simultaneous step-by-step integration of (185) and (164).

The profiles (191), though applicable at a forward stagnation point, may become inadequate in regions of sharply falling pressure as $f(\eta)$ may exceed 1 in the range $0 < \eta < 1$. However, Wieghardt proposed to use the momentum integral equation method of Walz (Section 17) in regions of falling pressure, where sufficient accuracy can be attained without the added complication of the two-parameter method, whose application is therefore best started at or after the pressure minimum.

An alternative two-parameter family of velocity profiles was devised by Head (1957a) and intended primarily for flow with suction, though it may also be used for flow over an impermeable surface. A fuller description, with applications involving suction, is given in Section 29. Among the examples without suction treated by Head are the case of Schubauer's (1935) ellipse and the linearly retarded flow of Howarth (1938). The method yields good results without excessive labour.

21. Simplifications of Wieghardt's method

The two-parameter methods described in the preceding section are probably the most accurate, except for those which treat the boundary-layer equations directly, but they require the solution of two simultaneous differential equations. Consequently various workers have proposed to simplify Wieghardt's method by reverting to a one-parameter set of profiles, though retaining the energy equation. They assume that T, K, and L may be regarded as functions of H, but that the relation between H and λ depends on the particular pressure distribution. In fact, of course, T, K, and L are not functions of H only. Nevertheless, they are much more nearly functions of H than of λ only.

This is because the parameter H determines the shape of any profile of the boundary-layer type within broad limits, but not precisely, and so any given value of H is compatible with a much wider variation of λ (proportional to the second derivative of u at the wall) than of T (proportional to the first derivative). Figs. VI. 9 and VI. 11 confirm this, showing T plotted against λ and against H in three cases which

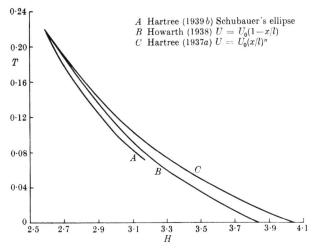

A Hartree (1939b) Schubauer's ellipse
B Howarth (1938) $U = U_0(1-x/l)$
C Hartree (1937a) $U = U_0(x/l)^n$

FIG. VI. 11. T as a function of H for some calculated cases.

have been computed numerically. Accordingly, the methods of the present section, which assume T, K, and L to depend on H, but not on λ, should give better results than those discussed earlier which are based on the momentum equation alone, and assume T and H to be functions of λ.

The present methods determine λ and H from the momentum and energy integral equations (164) and (185), or the derived equations (186) and (187). Walz (1946, 1948) first suggested simplifying Wieghardt's two-parameter method in this way, and proposed to solve (164) and (185) by simultaneous integration. This is less convenient than the methods of Truckenbrodt (1952a, b) and Tani (1954), who make use of the fact that the energy integral equation approximates to (188).

Tani determines λ as a function of x from (188), and then finds H from (187). The relations between T, L, K, and H are assumed to be the same as those holding for Pohlhausen's family of profiles (168). However, Λ in (168) is treated simply as a parameter and is not related to the pressure distribution by (159). Thus the boundary condition

$\mu(\partial^2 u/\partial z^2)_{z=0} = dp/dx$ is not imposed. Tani's relations between T, L, K, and H are tabulated in Table VI. 6. Any reasonable assumed family of profiles would give roughly the same relations, and given these relations (187) can be solved by a method of successive approximation for H (and therefore T, L, and K) as functions of λ and hence of x.

TABLE VI. 6

Functions for the method of Tani, for use with (187) and (188)

H	T	K	L	λ
3·50	0	1·53	0·157	−0·082
3·33	0·029	1·53	0·157	−0·079
3·18	0·059	1·54	0·158	−0·068
3·04	0·089	1·54	0·159	−0·058
2·92	0·120	1·54	0·161	−0·046
2·81	0·150	1·55	0·164	−0·034
2·72	0·180	1·56	0·167	−0·020
2·63	0·210	1·56	0·170	−0·005
2·55	0·235	1·57	0·174	+0·008
2·49	0·260	1·58	0·179	0·022
2·43	0·283	1·59	0·184	0·036
2·33	0·322	1·60	0·193	0·061
2·27	0·347	1·61	0·200	0·078
2·25	0·356	1·62	0·203	0·084

The first approximation ignores the last term on the right-hand side of (187), that is, it replaces (187) by (189). According to this first approximation, therefore, H, T, K, and L are functions of λ alone, and the values of λ appropriate to (189) are included in Table VI. 6. From the first approximation to K the neglected term in (187) can be estimated, and so second approximations may be found to H, T, K, and L. The process of successive approximation is continued until sufficient accuracy has been attained. The final solutions for K and L can be substituted into (186) to obtain more accurate values of λ, but Tani notes that this is not really necessary since it usually leads to results very little different from those given by (188).

Truckenbrodt (1952*a*, *b*) makes use of (188) to determine λ, but finds the variation in the shape parameter from (187) by a different method. Equation (187) may be written

$$\frac{K'}{K(H-1)} = \frac{U'}{U} + \frac{(2L/K-T)U'}{(H-1)\lambda U}. \tag{192}$$

Hence if

$$\int_{K_0}^{K} \frac{dK}{K(H-1)} = P, \tag{193}$$

where K_0 is the value of K for the profile for which $2L/K = T$, and if

$$\frac{2L/K - T}{H - 1} = -Q(P), \tag{194}$$

so that $Q = 0$ when $P = 0$, then (192) becomes

$$P' + (U'/\lambda U)Q(P) = U'/U. \tag{195}$$

Truckenbrodt treats P as the shape parameter to be determined from this equation, and assumes that the relations between H, T, K, L, Q, and P are the same as those which hold for the family of similar profiles (Section 17). The values are tabulated in Table VI. 7.

TABLE VI. 7

Functions for the method of Truckenbrodt, for use with (197) or (198)

P	H	T	K	L	Q
−0·018	4·04	0	1·52	0·157	−0·068
−0·015	3·20	0·095	1·53	0·159	−0·052
−0·010	2·88	0·149	1·55	0·163	−0·032
·0	2·59	0·220	1·57	0·173	0
0·010	2·43	0·277	1·59	0·185	0·030
0·020	2·32	0·320	1·62	0·197	0·058
0·030	2·24	0·357	1·63	0·208	0·083
0·040	2·16	0·390	1·66	0·219	0·111

It is found that a good approximation to $Q(P)$, defined by equations (193) and (194), is $Q = 2·87P$ when $P > 0$ (which is usually in regions of falling pressure) and $Q = 3·53P$ when $P < 0$ (usually in regions of rising pressure). If $Q = cP$, where c is constant, equation (195) can be transformed into

$$\frac{d}{dx}\left[P \exp\left(\int_{x_1}^{x} \frac{cU'}{\lambda U} dx \right) \right] = \frac{U'}{U} \exp\left(\int_{x_1}^{x} \frac{cU'}{\lambda U} dx \right).$$

But λ is given by (188), so that

$$\exp\left(\int_{x_1}^{x} \frac{cU'}{\lambda U} dx \right) = \left[\left(\int_{0}^{x} U^5 dx \right) \Big/ \left(\int_{0}^{x_1} U^5 dx \right) \right]^{d},$$

where $d = c/0·44 = 6·5 \ (P > 0)$

$$= 8·0 \ (P < 0).$$

Hence if x is replaced as independent variable by

$$\xi = \left(\int_0^x U^5 \, dx \right)^d, \tag{196}$$

$$P(\xi) = \frac{\xi_1}{\xi} \left[P(\xi_1) + \log \frac{U(\xi)}{U(\xi_1)} \right] - \frac{1}{\xi} \int_{\xi_1}^{\xi} \log \frac{U(\xi')}{U(\xi)} \, d\xi', \tag{197}$$

where ξ_1 is some datum position. If this is taken as the leading edge, where $\xi = 0$, equation (197) reduces to

$$P(\xi) = -\frac{1}{\xi} \int_0^{\xi} \log \frac{U(\xi')}{U(\xi)} \, d\xi'. \tag{198}$$

This equation can be used as long as P does not change sign, so that the index d does not change from one value to the other. If P changes sign at $x = x_1$ the two values of d will, from (196), lead to an 'upstream' and a 'downstream' value of ξ at $x = x_1$. Beyond $x = x_1$ the values of ξ are calculated by (196), using the downstream value of d. Then P is obtained from (197) with ξ_1 as the downstream value of ξ at $x = x_1$, so that $P(\xi_1) = 0$. The calculation of ξ is easily performed since the integral in equation (196) will already have been computed in determining λ from (188). Hence P, and therefore H, T, etc., can readily be found from (198) or (197).

It is worth noting that, according to (198), $P = 1/6d = 0.026$ at a front stagnation point, and hence from Table VI. 7, $T = 0.342$, $H = 2.27$. The actual values are $T = 0.360$, $H = 2.22$, so Truckenbrodt's solution is not exact at a stagnation point, even though his assumed family of velocity profiles includes the exact stagnation-point profile.

For ease of computation there is probably little to choose between the methods of Truckenbrodt and Tani. Both are more laborious than that of Thwaites (1949b) but not unduly so. They are in fact considerably less laborious than the original form of Pohlhausen's method. In regions of adverse pressure gradient the methods of Truckenbrodt and Tani predict the skin friction τ_w and shape parameter H more accurately than Thwaites's method, and much more accurately than Pohlhausen's, in most cases. The family of profiles assumed by Truckenbrodt—the family of similar solutions—is more satisfactory than Tani's polynomial family in regions of sharply falling pressure, since the polynomial form might then indicate values of u greater than U within the boundary layer. It would, of course, be possible to use Truckenbrodt's profiles with Tani's method and conversely. Further differences which may influence the choice of method are that Tani's original paper extends his method to compressible boundary layers, while Truckenbrodt's paper deals with axisymmetric flow and turbulent boundary layers.

22. Methods of Loitsianskii and Whitehead

Loitsianskii (1949) proposed a different type of approximate method in some ways related to the energy integral equation methods. However, the method uses, not the energy integral equation, but the 'first and second moment' integral equations obtained by multiplying the boundary-layer momentum equation (1) by z and z^2 and integrating from the wall to infinity. The ordinary momentum integral equation is used as well. It is assumed that the variation in profile shape has no effect on those integrals whose integrands are small near the wall, where the principal variations in profile shape occur. Thus the integral

$$U^2 \int\limits_0^\infty z \frac{u}{U}\left(1 - \frac{u}{U}\right) dz$$

occurs in the equations, and is replaced by $H_1 U^2 \delta_2^2$, where H_1 is a dimensionless constant evaluated by substituting the Blasius zero pressure gradient profile for u/U in the integral. The only parameters not assumed to be insensitive to profile shape are T, H, and λ as defined in (162) and (163). Loitsianskii's three integral equations give the following relations for these parameters:

$$H = 2 \cdot 59 - 7 \cdot 55\lambda, \qquad T = 0 \cdot 22 + 1 \cdot 85\lambda - 7 \cdot 55\lambda^2,$$

$$\lambda = \frac{0 \cdot 44 U'}{U^{5 \cdot 5}} \int\limits_0^x U^{4 \cdot 5}\, dx. \tag{199}$$

These relations are broadly similar to those proposed by Thwaites (1949b). However, the results (199) are obtained by arguments which, it should be noted, do not require to postulate a form for the velocity profiles except in the evaluation of those terms assumed not to vary with profile shape.

A related method has been proposed by Whitehead (1949). He uses the equation obtained by integrating equation (1) first from 0 to z and then from 0 to δ, where δ is the effective total thickness of the boundary layer. Since

$$\int_0^\delta \left[\int_0^z f(z)\, dz \right] dz = \delta \int_0^\delta f(z)\, dz - \int_0^\delta z f(z)\, dz,$$

Whitehead's repeated integral is a combination of the ordinary Kármán momentum integral and Loitsianskii's first moment integral. Whitehead suggests two ways of using the repeated integral equation. The first is similar to Pohlhausen's method, except that the quartic velocity profile (168) is used in conjunction with the double integral equation instead of the momentum equation. Whitehead claims that his method predicts the skin friction more accurately than Pohlhausen's. However, Whitehead's derivation leads to an equation of the same form as (161), involving U'', so that it is as inconvenient as the original version of Pohlhausen's method. A second, more accurate, method proposed by Whitehead is to use both the ordinary momentum equation and the double integral equation in conjunction with Pohlhausen's velocity profiles (168). As in Tani's and Truckenbrodt's methods, the condition $\mu(\partial^2 u/\partial z^2)_{z=0} = dp/dx$ is not satisfied. Whitehead's second method probably gives the same sort of accuracy as Tani's method. It is, however, much less convenient because it involves the simultaneous integration of two equations, and also because Whitehead's equations involve U''.

PART III

APPROXIMATE METHODS BASED ON OUTER
AND INNER SOLUTIONS

23. Method of Kármán and Millikan

The approximate solutions now to be considered are based on a division of the boundary layer into two parts, one towards the outer edge of the layer, and the other adjacent to the wall. Two approximate methods have been devised for obtaining the complete boundary-layer flow by joining the 'outer' and 'inner' solutions appropriate to these regions. These are due to Kármán and Millikan (1934), and to Stratford (1954), whose method is described in Section 25.

The outer solution of Kármán and Millikan is derived from equation (V.57), namely

$$\partial \chi/\partial \phi = \nu \partial^2 \chi/\partial \psi^2, \tag{200}$$

where $\chi = U^2 - u^2$, $\phi = \int_0^x U\, dx$, and ψ is the stream function. It was shown in Section V. 10 that (200) is an approximation to the von Mises equation, (V.53) or (V.56), valid when χ is small compared with U^2. The boundary conditions used by Kármán and Millikan were

$$\chi = U^2 = F(\phi) \quad \text{at } \psi = 0, \qquad \chi \to 0 \quad \text{as } \psi \to \infty,$$

$$\chi = 0 \quad \text{at } \phi = 0, \qquad \qquad (201)$$

where $\psi = 0$ represents the wall.

Equation (200) has the form of the heat-conduction equation, and many methods are available for its solution. Thus (compare equation V. 60) a general solution satisfying the conditions (201) is

$$\chi(\phi, \psi) = (2/\sqrt{\pi}) \int_a^\infty F[(1-a^2/\theta^2)\phi]\exp(-\theta^2)\,d\theta, \qquad (202)$$

where $a = \psi/2\sqrt{(\nu\phi)}$. If U^2 is a polynomial, or power series, in ϕ, so that

$$U^2 = F(\phi) = \sum_0^\infty c_n \phi^n,$$

then from (202) $\chi = (2/\sqrt{\pi}) \sum_0^\infty c_n \phi^n I_n(a),$

where $I_n(a) = 2^{n-\frac{1}{2}}n!\exp(-\tfrac{1}{2}a^2)U(2n+\tfrac{1}{2}, a\sqrt{2}),$

as in Section V. 10. A similar expression may be developed when U^2 is represented by different polynomials in two ranges of ϕ.

Kármán and Millikan's choice of the condition at $\psi = 0$, though the most convenient, is not necessarily the most accurate when the outer part of the layer is considered. However, it leads to a fairly good representation of a large fraction of the profile, even though (200) is a good approximation only near the outer edge of the boundary layer.

Since $\partial^2 u/\partial z^2 = -\frac{1}{2}u\partial^2\chi/\partial\psi^2$, the approximate profiles derived from (200) all have inflexions at the wall $\psi = 0$, whereas this is so for the accurate profiles only where $U' = 0$. Both true and approximate profiles necessarily have an inflexion within the boundary layer if $U' < 0$, though not if $U' > 0$. When $U' \geqslant 0$ the inflexion introduced at the wall does not seriously affect the general shape of the profile, so Kármán and Millikan took the outer solution as their approximation for the whole boundary layer when $U' \geqslant 0$.

In regions of adverse pressure gradient, where $U' < 0$, the velocity profile derived from the outer solution may differ considerably from the true profile, as illustrated in Fig. VI. 12. It was pointed out above that in this case both profiles have inflexions within the boundary layer. Beyond the inflexions the two profiles agree reasonably well in shape, and the approximate profile can be made to agree closely with the true one by an appropriate displacement away from the wall. Kármán and Millikan therefore assumed that the outer solution could be applied beyond the inflexion, and determined the required displacement from an inner solution, which they joined to the outer solution at the point of inflexion. The position of the point of inflexion would probably be sensitive to small changes in the inner boundary condition (201). Since,

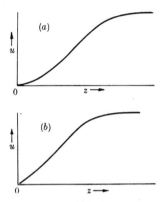

Fig. VI. 12. (a) Accurate and (b) approximate velocity profiles in a region of adverse pressure gradient.

as noted above, the choice of this condition is somewhat arbitrary, this is an unsatisfactory feature of the method.

Let the suffix j denote conditions at the junction of the inner and outer solutions. The velocity distribution for the outer solution is given by

$$u = (U^2 - \chi)^{\frac{1}{2}}, \qquad z = z_j + \int_{\psi_j}^{\psi} \frac{d\psi}{(U^2 - \chi)^{\frac{1}{2}}}, \qquad (203)$$

where $\chi = \chi(\phi, \psi)$ satisfies equation (200) and the conditions (201), and ψ_j is given by $\partial^2\chi/\partial\psi^2 = 0$ at $\psi = \psi_j$. The value of z_j in (203) must be found from the inner solution, which is required to satisfy the conditions

$$z = z_j: \qquad u = u_j = [U^2 - \chi(\phi, \psi_j)]^{\frac{1}{2}},$$

$$\frac{\partial u}{\partial z} = \left(\frac{\partial u}{\partial z}\right)_j = -\frac{1}{2}\left(\frac{\partial \chi}{\partial \psi}\right)_{\psi = \psi_j}, \qquad \frac{\partial^2 u}{\partial z^2} = 0;$$

$$z = 0: \qquad u = 0, \qquad \nu \frac{\partial^2 u}{\partial z^2} = -UU'.$$

These conditions are satisfied by Kármán and Millikan's inner profile

$$u = u_j(1 - \cos Kz) + A \sin Kz \qquad (0 < z < z_j), \qquad (204)$$

where

$$K = \left(-\frac{UU'}{\nu u_j}\right)^{\frac12}, \qquad A = \left[\frac{1}{K^2}\left(\frac{\partial u}{\partial z}\right)_j^2 - u_j^2\right]^{\frac12}, \qquad \tan K z_j = \frac{u_j}{A}.$$

This completes the boundary-layer profile when $U' < 0$, as illustrated in Fig. VI. 13.

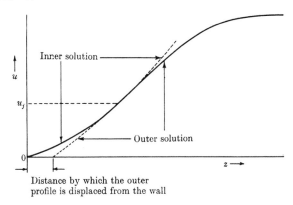

Inner solution

u

u_j

Outer solution

0

$z \longrightarrow$

Distance by which the outer
profile is displaced from the wall

FIG. VI. 13. Boundary-layer profile for adverse pressure gradients approximately represented by outer and inner solutions in Kármán and Millikan's method.

Kármán and Millikan's method, when applied to the few suitable test cases (see Section 26), predicts the position of separation with moderate accuracy, but it is difficult to say how good it would be in an arbitrary case. Kármán and Millikan proposed to obtain a more accurate outer solution from the equation

$$\frac{\partial \chi}{\partial \phi} - \nu \frac{\partial^2 \chi}{\partial \psi^2} = \nu \frac{\partial^2 \chi_0}{\partial \psi^2}\left[\left(1 - \frac{\chi_0}{U^2}\right)^{\frac12} - 1\right]$$

with the boundary conditions (201), where χ_0 is the first approximation derived from (200). Jones (1948) suggested as an alternative second approximation the solution of

$$\frac{\partial \chi}{\partial \phi} = \nu \left(1 - \frac{1}{2}\frac{\chi}{U^2}\right)\frac{\partial^2 \chi}{\partial \psi^2}$$

with the same boundary conditions (201). Either of these should give u_j and $(\partial u/\partial z)_j$ more accurately than the first approximation, but the solutions are laborious.

The inner solution (204) was chosen arbitrarily, since the joining conditions could have been satisfied by other relations, such as polynomials of the form $u = az+bz^2+cz^m$ $(m > 2)$. However, if the inner solution does not extend over too large a proportion of the whole boundary layer, the results for the skin friction should not depend critically on the choice of inner solution, provided that this choice is plausible. This point is further discussed in connexion with Stratford's method; see Section 25.

24. Doenhoff's method for the separation point

From the Kármán and Millikan method Doenhoff (1938) developed a method which enables the position of the separation point to be estimated rapidly for a variety of pressure distributions. He considered a main stream in which

$$U = U_0 \qquad\qquad (0 < x < x_0),$$
$$= U_0[1-F(x-x_0)/x_0] \quad (x > x_0), \qquad\qquad (205)$$

where F is a constant.

In the corresponding boundary layer the proportionate fall of the main-stream velocity $(\Delta U_s/U_0)$ at separation depends only on F, and Doenhoff determined the relationship by Kármán and Millikan's method. The case of an adverse velocity gradient starting from the leading edge corresponds to $F = 0$ since $F = -(x_0/U_0)(dU/dx)$ $(x > x_0)$. Doenhoff's results are presented in Fig. VI. 14, and it will be noted that they make $\Delta U_s/U_0$ vanish when F is about 0·25. Any steeper velocity gradient would cause immediate separation. This point will be considered again in Section 25.

The results of Fig. VI. 14 can be applied to cases where the velocity distribution differs from (205) if the actual main-stream velocity can be replaced by an equivalent one of the type (205). Fig. VI. 15 shows a velocity distribution typical of that on the forward part of an aerofoil, and the equivalent distribution ABC which is to replace it. The constant velocity portion AM should be chosen so as to produce at M, the velocity maximum, a boundary-layer profile approximately the same as that actually produced by the distribution LM. Doenhoff suggested that the length x_1 of the portion AM should be computed from the equation

$$x_1 = \int_0^{x_m} \left(\frac{U}{U_0}\right)^{8·17} dx.$$

This was derived from the momentum equation by assuming that the boundary-layer profile between L and M had the same shape as in the

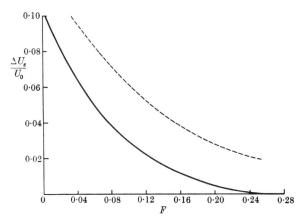

FIG. VI. 14. Relationship between $\Delta U_s/U_0$ and F: full line, Doenhoff's relation; broken line, according to equation (217).

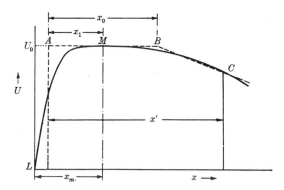

FIG. VI. 15. Approximation of actual velocity distribution LMC by the form ABC for use with Doenhoff's method.

case of constant velocity. Thwaites's results in Section 18 indicate, however, that the formula

$$x_1 = \int_0^{x_m} \left(\frac{U}{U_0}\right)^5 dx \qquad (206)$$

should be more satisfactory. The remaining part MBC of the equivalent velocity distribution is chosen so as to give a reasonable fit to the original curve as far as the estimated separation point. From the length $x_0 = AB$ and the slope of the line BC, the parameter F can be calculated, and hence from Fig. VI. 14 the separation point can be found. Doenhoff's method is useful practically; it is even simpler to apply than

Thwaites's and gives a convenient alternative estimate of the position of separation.

25. Stratford's method

Stratford (1954) has developed another method in which outer and inner solutions are joined. Stratford's outer solution is simpler than that of Kármán and Millikan, and the joining condition is less arbitrary. The method is designed for cases in which the pressure remains constant

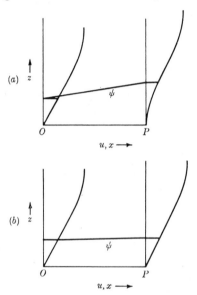

Fig. VI. 16. Velocity profiles (a) with increasing pressure, and (b) at constant pressure.

from the leading edge for a distance x_0 to the point O, after which the pressure rises steeply. In practice, however, the method can be applied satisfactorily under wider conditions.

Equation (200) shows that at a point P, a short distance downstream of O, the outer part of the velocity profile has a curvature of the same order as that at O (see Fig. VI. 16). Hence when $x > x_0$, the pressure gradient term in the equation of motion (1),

$$u\frac{\partial u}{\partial x} + w\frac{\partial u}{\partial z} = -\frac{1}{\rho}\frac{dp}{dx} + \nu\frac{\partial^2 u}{\partial z^2},$$

dominates the viscous term in the outer part of the layer. If the effect of viscosity were ignored completely, Bernoulli's theorem for inviscid flow, namely $p + \frac{1}{2}\rho u^2 =$ constant along a streamline, could be applied in the outer part of the boundary layer; here $\frac{1}{2}\rho w^2$ has been neglected in comparison with $\frac{1}{2}\rho u^2$. In fact, viscosity is not altogether negligible, and any fluid element suffers a loss of total head between O and P. If there were no pressure rise the velocity profile at P would, like that at O, be of the Blasius type for a flat plate (Section V. 12), and the loss of total head could be calculated in this case. In equation (1) the viscous term $\nu(\partial^2 u/\partial z^2)$ does not change very rapidly along a streamline in the outer part of the layer, and so is approximately the same as if the pressure had remained constant. Stratford therefore assumes that the loss of total head along any particular streamline is independent of the pressure rise, and is the same as for the corresponding streamline in the Blasius case, where the pressure remains constant.

Let $u(x,\psi)$ be the velocity distribution in the boundary layer at the point P, whose distance from the leading edge is x, and let ψ denote the stream function. If the pressure had remained constant the velocity distribution at P would be given by $u = u_b(x,\psi)$, where $u_b(x,\psi)$ is the Blasius distribution as in Fig. VI. 16 (b). Then Stratford's assumption is that in the outer part of the boundary layer

$$p + \tfrac{1}{2}\rho u^2(x,\psi) = p_0 + \tfrac{1}{2}\rho u_b^2(x,\psi),$$

so that
$$u^2(x,\psi) = u_b^2(x,\psi) - 2(p-p_0)/\rho. \tag{207}$$

From (207), since p depends only on x,

$$2u(x,\psi)\frac{\partial u}{\partial \psi}(x,\psi) = 2u_b(x,\psi)\frac{\partial u_b}{\partial \psi}(x,\psi).$$

But
$$\frac{\partial u}{\partial z} = \frac{\partial u}{\partial \psi}\frac{\partial \psi}{\partial z} = u\frac{\partial u}{\partial \psi}, \qquad \frac{\partial u_b}{\partial z} = \frac{\partial u_b}{\partial \psi}\left(\frac{\partial \psi}{\partial z}\right)_b = u_b\frac{\partial u_b}{\partial \psi},$$

and therefore
$$\frac{\partial u}{\partial z}(x,\psi) = \frac{\partial u_b}{\partial z}(x,\psi). \tag{208}$$

Similarly, by a further differentiation,

$$\frac{1}{u(x,\psi)}\frac{\partial^2 u}{\partial z^2}(x,\psi) = \frac{1}{u_b(x,\psi)}\frac{\partial^2 u_b}{\partial z^2}(x,\psi). \tag{209}$$

Equations (207) to (209) determine the shape of the outer profile.

An inner solution has to be joined to this outer solution. For the inner flow, the arguments of the two preceding paragraphs do not apply. If the pressure gradient is large, as it is assumed to be, the velocity profile must be sharply curved at the wall, where

$$\mu \partial^2 u/\partial z^2 = dp/dx.$$

However, this sharp curvature can extend only over a limited region near the wall, and the curvature farther out must be much less. Hence in the outer part of the flow the pressure gradient forces are primarily balanced by the slowing up of the fluid, whereas in the inner flow the viscous forces must always be comparable with those due to the pressure gradient, however sharp the latter may be.

The inner solution for the region near the wall must be joined smoothly to the outer solution (207) at a suitable point. Stratford makes the inner solution satisfy the conditions

$$z = 0: \quad u = 0, \quad \mu \frac{\partial^2 u}{\partial z^2} = \frac{dp}{dx};$$

$$z = z_j: \quad \psi = \psi_j, \quad u = u_j, \quad \frac{\partial u}{\partial z} = \left(\frac{\partial u}{\partial z}\right)_j, \quad \frac{\partial^2 u}{\partial z^2} = \left(\frac{\partial^2 u}{\partial z^2}\right)_j. \quad (210)$$

Here z_j is the distance of the junction from the wall, and ψ_j, u_j,... denote the values of ψ, u,... at the junction, where they must agree with the outer solution. The value of z_j is determined by the inner solution, and it completes the specification of the outer solution.

It is assumed that the inner solution extends over only a small part of the total boundary-layer thickness, and this requires that the pressure rise $(p-p_0)$ shall be small. In this case ψ_j is small, and in the range concerned the Blasius velocity u_b is almost linear in z (see Fig. VI. 16). Hence from (208) and (209)

$$\left(\frac{\partial u}{\partial z}\right)_j = \frac{\partial u_b}{\partial z}(x,\psi_j) = \frac{\tau_{wb}(x)}{\mu}, \qquad \left(\frac{\partial^2 u}{\partial z^2}\right)_j = \frac{u_j}{u_b(x,\psi_j)} \frac{\partial^2 u_b}{\partial z^2}(x,\psi_j) = 0,$$

approximately, where $\tau_{wb}(x)$ is the skin friction for the Blasius profile. Similarly
$$\psi_j = \mu u_b^2(x,\psi_j)/2\tau_{wb}(x).$$

But from (207) $$u_j^2 = u_b^2(x,\psi_j) - 2(p-p_0)/\rho,$$

and hence $$\psi_j = \frac{\mu}{\tau_{wb}(x)}\left(\frac{p-p_0}{\rho} + \tfrac{1}{2}u_j^2\right).$$

The conditions (210) therefore become, assuming that z_j is small,

$$z = 0: \quad u = 0, \quad \frac{\partial^2 u}{\partial z^2} = \frac{1}{\mu}\frac{dp}{dx};$$

$$z = z_j: \quad \psi = \frac{\mu}{\tau_{wb}(x)}\left(\frac{p-p_0}{\rho} + \tfrac{1}{2}u^2\right), \quad \frac{\partial u}{\partial z} = \frac{\tau_{wb}(x)}{\mu}, \quad \frac{\partial^2 u}{\partial z^2} = 0. \quad (211)$$

A convenient form for the inner profile is

$$u = az + bz^2 + cz^3, \quad (212)$$

and the conditions (211) then determine a, b, c, and z_j so that the complete boundary-layer profile can be found. At separation the inner profile (212) becomes

$$u = bz^2 + cz^3.$$ (213)

From the conditions (211) it follows that at separation

$$\frac{p-p_0}{\rho}\left(\frac{dp}{dx}\right)^2 = \frac{\tau_{wb}^4(x)}{9\mu^2}.$$ (214)

The Blasius solution for boundary-layer flow over a flat plate with constant pressure, given in Section V. 12, leads to

$$\tau_{wb}(x) = 0 \cdot 33206 \rho U_0^2 (\nu/U_0 x)^{\frac{1}{2}},$$ (215)

where U_0 is the constant external velocity for $x < x_0$. Hence, if the pressure coefficient C_p is defined by

$$C_p = (p-p_0)/\tfrac{1}{2}\rho U_0^2 = 1 - U^2/U_0^2,$$ (216)

then $$[x^2 C_p (dC_p/dx)^2]_s = 0 \cdot 0108,$$ (217)

where the suffix s denotes the value at the separation point.

This solution is based on the assumption that z_j is small, and so the Blasius profile can be regarded as linear in the appropriate range. A necessary requirement for this to be valid is $u_j \ll U_0$. From (213) and (214),

$$\frac{u_j}{U_0} = \frac{4}{3}\frac{\tau_{wb}^2(x)}{\mu U_0(dp/dx)} = \frac{4}{U_0}\left(\frac{p-p_0}{\rho}\right)^{\frac{1}{2}}$$

at separation. Hence $(u_j/U_0)_s = (8C_{ps})^{\frac{1}{2}}$. Thus the condition for the method to be applicable is

$$C_{ps} \ll \tfrac{1}{8}.$$ (218)

The condition (218) will be fulfilled if the pressure rises sufficiently steeply from its initial constant value. As the pressure gradient increases C_{ps} decreases, as shown by (217), but remains greater than zero if the pressure gradient is finite. By contrast, Kármán and Millikan's method predicts, as shown by Doenhoff (1938) and noted in Section 24, that C_{ps} vanishes for a finite value of the pressure gradient, and approximate methods of the Pohlhausen type lead to the same conclusion. In Fig. VI. 14 the results of Stratford's method, given by equation (217), are compared with those of Doenhoff, using Kármán and Millikan's method. If results were obtained accurately from the boundary-layer equations and plotted in this figure, it is likely that they would agree more closely with Stratford's results than with Doenhoff's, since the accuracy of Stratford's method should improve as the pressure gradient increases. However, the assumptions of boundary-layer theory may not be fulfilled if the pressure rises too sharply.

The inner solution is not defined uniquely by the conditions (211). In place of (212), Kármán and Millikan's inner solution (204) could be used, or different polynomials of the type

$$u = az + bz^2 + cz^m \quad (m > 2).$$

Any such form of inner profile leads to a separation condition of the type

$$[x^2 C_p (dC_p/dx)^2]_s = K, \tag{219}$$

where K is a constant depending on the particular form of the inner solution. When $m = 3$, equation (217) gives $K = 0.0108$. Stratford, in his original paper, considered the cases $m = 4$ and $m = 6$, for which K is 0.0065 and 0.0049 respectively. Stratford also showed, by numerical integration, that if the external velocity distribution is of Doenhoff's type, K approaches the limit 0.0076 when F is very large in (205). He proposed that this value of K should be used in general applications of his method. However, Curle and Skan (1957) have shown that it is better to give K the value 0.0104, since the resulting equation

$$[x^2 C_p (dC_p/dx)^2]_s = 0.0104 \tag{220}$$

agrees well with all the known accurate computations for flow with separation. However, in most of these cases the assumptions of Stratford's theory are violated. For example, in Howarth's (1938) flow $U = U_0(1 - x/l)$ the velocity falls from the leading edge, unlike the distribution postulated in the theory, and $C_{ps} = 0.23$, contrary to (218): nevertheless $[x^2 C_p (dC_p/dx)^2]_s = 0.0101$, very close to (220).

Curle (1960) has extended Stratford's method to predict the variation of skin friction as well as the separation point, including the effect of suction. When there is no suction, Curle's result is

$$x^2 C_p (dC_p/dx)^2 = 0.0104(1 - \tau_w/\tau_{wb})^3(1 + 2.02\tau_w/\tau_{wb}), \tag{221}$$

where $\tau_{wb}(x)$ is the skin friction in the Blasius flow, given by (215).

Stratford's method has the advantage that its assumptions correspond clearly to physical reality, in dividing the boundary layer into an inner flow where viscosity is important and an outer flow where it is not. These solutions correspond in fact to the two series solutions (107) and (108) of Goldstein's (1930) method for the continuation of a boundary-layer solution at a singularity. The method can be used for velocity distributions of the type shown in Fig. VI. 15 if the initial portion LM, where the pressure gradient is favourable, is replaced, as in Doenhoff's method, by a section AM at constant pressure, where the length x_1 of AM is given by equation (206). In the results (219), (220), (221), etc., x must be replaced by x', the distance from the equivalent leading edge A, and C_{ps} and τ_{irb} must be defined, as in equations (216) and (215), with reference to the external velocity at M. Finally it should be noticed that the method, when suitably modified, can be applied to compressible flow, as Gadd (1957) has shown.

PART IV

COMPARISON OF APPROXIMATE SOLUTIONS OF THE BOUNDARY-LAYER EQUATIONS

26. The accuracy and relative merits of different methods of solution

It is convenient now to survey the methods of solution presented above. Some of these methods, included because of their historical or theoretical interest, are much less suitable than others for practical use. For a method to be suitable it should be reasonably accurate, though (as pointed out in Section 1) too much stress should not be laid on this. To compare the accuracy of different methods one should present side by side the estimates given by these methods for (say) the position of separation in a number of different cases where accurate numerical solutions are available. However, suitable comparison cases are few. As regards experimental results, the principal ones with two-dimensional laminar boundary layers subject to pressure gradients in the direction of flow are those of:

   (a) Hiemenz (1911) and Fage and Falkner (1931) on circular cylinders,
   (b) Wright and Bailey (1939) on a flat plate,
   (c) Schubauer (1935) on an elliptic cylinder.

The pressure gradients near separation on the circular cylinders are steep, and both approximate and accurate solutions give separation positions which agree well with the observations—see Section 10. Hence this case does not provide a very discriminating test of any method, at least as regards the *position* of separation. The *pressure* at separation would give a much more sensitive criterion, but this is not known very accurately from the experiments. The results of Wright and Bailey differ considerably from most theoretical predictions and have usually been regarded as unreliable. Hartree (1939b) integrated the boundary-layer equations numerically using Schubauer's observed pressure distribution, but his results did not indicate separation. Hartree found, however, that a slight modification of the pressure distribution would lead to a separation point in close agreement with Schubauer's observation. Hartree's calculations for the modified pressure distribution, together with accurate numerical solutions for certain theoretical pressure distributions, are used as the standards of comparison for testing approximate solutions given by different methods.

In Table VI. 8 values of C_{ps}, the pressure coefficient at separation, determined by various approximate solutions, are compared with the accurate values, obtained by numerical integration of the boundary-layer equations. Here $C_{ps} = (p_s-p_0)/\frac{1}{2}\rho U_0^2 = 1-(U_s/U_0)^2$, where p_0, U_0 are the minimum pressure and maximum velocity of the outer flow, and p_s, U_s are the pressure and external velocity at separation. The cases considered are:

(1) Hartree's (1939b) modified pressure distribution on Schubauer's ellipse;

(2) Howarth's (1938) linear adverse velocity gradient

$$U = U_0(1-x/l);$$

(3)
(4) } Tani's (1949) extensions of Howarth's flow
(5) } $U = U_0(1-x^n/l^n)$ for $n = 2, 4, 8;$

(6) Curle's (1958a) distribution $U = \frac{3}{2}\sqrt{3}\, U_0(x/l-x^3/l^3);$

(7) Terrill's (1960) case $U = U_0\sin(x/l).$

The linear approximation for $F(\lambda)$, discussed in Section 18, was used to compute the results for methods of the Pohlhausen type. Many of the methods discussed in the preceding sections are not represented in the table because of the labour required to compute the results. However, the table gives an indication of the range of scatter to be expected. Even the least accurate results presented are good enough for many practical purposes.

If reasonable accuracy is attainable, the principal factors which determine the relative merits of different methods are (i) ease of computation, (ii) realism of physical assumptions, (iii) clarity of theory. In cases where the pressure rises sharply Stratford's method (Section 25) satisfies the second criterion, in its division of the boundary layer into an inner region where viscosity is important and an outer one where it is not. In Section 19 Thwaites's formula (182) for the momentum thickness was shown to have a clear theoretical basis and, since it provides satisfactory accuracy with little computation, his method is very suitable for general use.

It is doubtful whether any new approximate method will throw much further light on the physical nature of laminar boundary-layer flow.

TABLE VI. 8

Pressure coefficients at separation estimated by various methods

Case	*1*	*2*	*3*	*4*	*5*	*6*	*7*
Method							
Accurate	0·082	0·226	0·142	0·089	0·056	0·056	0·062
A	..	0·305	0·192	0·118	0·067	..	..
B	0·072	0·230	0·140	0·080	0·043	..	..
C	0·049	0·204	0·119	0·067	0·035	..	..
D	0·063	0·217	0·133	0·074	0·040	0·041	0·046
E	0·069	0·231	0·138	0·080	0·047	0·047	0·051
F	..	0·225	0·142	0·088	0·057	..	..
G	..	0·215	..	..	..	..	..
H	..	0·236	0·141	0·080	0·044	0·066	..
I	0·069	0·194	..	..	..	..	..
J	0·067	0·194	0·135	0·071	0·051	..	..
K	0·074	0·204	0·125	0·078	0·050	0·048	..
L	0·088	0·227	0·141	0·088	0·055	0·062	0·068

KEY

Case	Mainstream flow
1	Hartree–Schubauer ellipse　Hartree (1939b)
2	$U = U_0(1-x/l)$　Howarth (1938)
3	$U = U_0(1-x^2/l^2)$　Tani (1949)
4	$U = U_0(1-x^4/l^4)$　,,　,,
5	$U = U_0(1-x^8/l^8)$　,,　,,
6	$U = \frac{3}{2}\sqrt{3}\, U_0(x/l - x^3/l^3)$　Curle (1958a)
7	$U = U_0 \sin(x/l)$　Terrill (1960)

Method	
A	Pohlhausen (1921)
B	Timman (1949)
C	Walz (1941)
D	Thwaites (1949b)
E	Curle and Skan (Thwaites modification) (1957)
F	Tani (1954)
G	Truckenbrodt (1952a, b)
H	Loitsianskii (1949)
I	Kármán and Millikan (1934)
J	Doenhoff (1938)
K	Stratford (1954) (equation (219); $K = 0·0076$)
L	Curle and Skan (Stratford modification) (1957) and Curle (1960) $(K = 0·0104)$

This is fairly well understood, and it depends only on the balance of momentum, according to Newton's laws of motion, under the action of pressure and viscous forces. Satisfactory estimates of the separation position, skin friction, and boundary-layer thickness can be obtained quite easily by Curle and Skan's modifications of Thwaites's method. If the boundary-layer thicknesses are not required, Curle's modified and extended version of Stratford's method normally gives remarkably small errors for the skin friction and point of separation.

PART V

BOUNDARY LAYERS ON POROUS SURFACES WITH SUCTION OR BLOWING

27. Boundary-layer problems involving suction or blowing

Many recent developments in boundary-layer theory have been concerned with the flow over a permeable surface through which fluid is withdrawn or expelled. This effect is produced when a difference in pressure is maintained across the surface. The resultant flow through the surface is assumed to be wholly normal, since the pressure gradient through the surface is usually large. The boundary conditions (3) for the boundary-layer equations (1) and (2) are therefore altered to

$$u = 0, \qquad w = -w_s(x) \quad \text{at } z = 0,$$
$$u \to U \quad \text{as } z \to \infty. \tag{222}$$

Here $w_s(x)$ is the velocity of suction, which is regarded as given: it depends on the pressure difference across the porous surface and on the resistance of this surface. In accordance with the usual boundary-layer assumptions $w_s(x)$ is assumed to be small, of order $U_0 R^{-\frac{1}{2}}$, where U_0 is a representative velocity for the outer flow and R is the Reynolds number. In the present notation $w_s(x)$ is regarded as positive for suction, negative for blowing, because suction is of greater importance than blowing, and the value of the stream function at the surface is then given by

$$\psi = \int w_s(x)\, dx \quad \text{at } z = 0.$$

Since the velocity of suction is small, its 'sink effect' on the main flow outside the boundary layer can be neglected. In practice, alterations of the position of separation, due to suction, may have a considerable effect on the main flow, but this effect is much more difficult to take into account.

The chief reasons why boundary-layer suction is of interest are that it causes separation to be delayed, and that it exerts a stabilizing influence on laminar flow; see Section IX. 5.2. These effects are connected with the fact that at $z = 0$ the boundary-layer equation (1) reduces to

$$\nu \frac{\partial^2 u}{\partial z^2} = -U \frac{dU}{dx} - w_s \frac{\partial u}{\partial z}.$$

Consequently, as noted in Section V. 7, suction opposes an adverse pressure gradient, and makes the velocity profile more concave to the z-axis. This leads also to a reduction in the boundary-layer thickness.

It is natural to inquire how far separation is delayed in particular cases by means of suction, and how much suction would be required to suppress separation completely. Answers to these questions may be sought from the boundary-layer equations. Most of the methods for their solution described earlier in this chapter can be adapted, without great difficulty, in order to deal with problems involving suction. Attention will therefore be directed mainly to methods which have actually been used for the solution of suction problems, and to the results obtained from these methods.

Some discussion was given in Section V. 7 of conditions near separation when suction is applied at a porous surface. It was pointed out that the separation appears to start from a stagnation point within the fluid farther downstream than the point P, where $(\partial u/\partial z)_{z=0} = 0$ (see Fig. V. 3). It is likely, however, that the solution of the boundary-layer equations cannot be extended farther than P, since beyond P there is present fluid that has been influenced by conditions farther downstream. Investigators of boundary-layer flow with suction have taken $(\partial u/\partial z)_{z=0} = 0$ as the condition for separation, and it should therefore be remembered that this condition is now only approximate.

If suction begins some distance from the forward stagnation point there will be a length of surface over which the boundary layer accommodates itself to the new conditions. If the suction velocity is sufficiently great this process will be practically complete before the pressure gradients produce any noticeable effect. This 'entry-flow' problem is most easily studied in the case of a uniform stream parallel to a flat plate with constant suction, where there is no pressure gradient. This adjustment of the boundary layer is necessary even when suction begins at the leading edge of the plate, since there the boundary-layer profile is the same as when suction is absent. At a great distance from the leading edge the velocity profile is the asymptotic suction profile $u/U = 1 - \exp(-w_s z/\nu)$. This is also the limiting form of the velocity distribution in a general flow when w_s is large.

The effects of blowing are less interesting since they oppose the stability of the boundary layer and the attachment of the layer to the surface. The boundary layer is thickened and blown out from the surface. Blowing is therefore mentioned in only a few places.

28. Solutions in series: potential flow past a circular cylinder

Thwaites (1949a) extended the series solution of Blasius and Howarth (Section 2) to include a general distribution of suction. The notation of Section 2 will be used, with the addition of the expansion

$$w_s = (U_1 \nu/l)^{\frac{1}{2}}[K + b_1 \xi + b_2 \xi^2 + ...] \tag{223}$$

for the suction velocity. The dimensionless stream function $f(\xi, \eta)$ again satisfies equation (9), but the boundary conditions (11) are modified to

$$f = K\xi + \tfrac{1}{2}b_1\xi^2 + \tfrac{1}{3}b_2\xi^3 + ..., \qquad \partial f/\partial \eta = 0 \quad \text{at } \eta = 0,$$
$$\partial f/\partial \eta \to F(\xi) \quad \text{as } \eta \to \infty. \tag{224}$$

The appropriate expansion for $f(\xi, \eta)$ is now

$$f(\xi, \eta) = f_0\xi + (a_1 f_{1,0} + b_1 f_{0,1})\xi^2 +$$
$$+ (a_2 f_{2,0} + a_1^2 f_{11,0} + a_1 b_1 f_{1,1} + b_2 f_{0,2} + b_1^2 f_{0,11})\xi^3 + ..., \tag{225}$$

where $f_0, f_{1,0}, f_{0,1}, ...$ are functions of η alone. The differential equations and boundary conditions for these functions are readily obtained by substitution of (225) in (9) and (224). In particular, f_0 depends on K since

$$f_0''' + f_0 f_0'' + 1 - f_0'^2 = 0,$$
$$f_0(0) = K, \qquad f_0'(0) = 0, \qquad f_0'(\infty) = 1. \tag{226}$$

The first term $f_0(\eta)\xi$ of (225) represents the stagnation-point flow with suction, discussed by Schlichting and Bussmann (1943), who gave equations (226) (see Section V. 20). Since f_0 appears in the equations for the later functions, the whole system of equations must be solved anew for every different value of K considered. In general, many more functions are involved in the ξ^n term than when suction is absent. The most interesting special case is when $b_1 = b_2 = ... = 0$, so that the suction velocity $w_s = K(U_1 \nu/l)^{\frac{1}{2}}$ is constant, and then the number of functions is the same as when there is no suction.

Bussmann and Ulrich (1944) considered the case of symmetrical flow with constant suction, where $a_1 = a_3 = a_5 = ... = 0$, and solved the equations numerically for the terms up to ξ^9 in (225) in the case $K = 0.5$. They applied their results to the potential flow about a circular cylinder in a uniform stream, for which $U = 2U_\infty \sin 2\xi$, where U_∞ is the stream velocity, and l is the diameter of the cylinder. Then $U_1 = 4U_\infty$, $a_{2r} = (-4)^r/(2r+1)!$, $a_{2r+1} = 0$ and, when $K = 0.5$, $w_s = U_\infty(U_\infty l/\nu)^{-\frac{1}{2}}$. Bussmann and Ulrich found the distributions of skin friction, displacement, and momentum thickness, and estimated that separation would take place at a distance of $120.9°$ from the forward stagnation point. This compares with the value $110°$ found by Ulrich (1943) for flow without suction, also using terms up to ξ^9. The calculations were tested by the momentum equation, and satisfactory agreement was not found within about $30°$ of the estimated separation points. Later calculations by Terrill (1960), using a step-by-step method, led to separation at 104·4° without suction, and at 114·6° in Bussmann and Ulrich's case. Bussmann and Ulrich also computed the terms up to ξ^5 when $K = -3·1905$, a case of blowing, and those up to ξ^3 in the suction case $K = 3$. For $K = -3·1905$, separation was estimated at 70° from the forward stagnation point, but again the momentum equation showed that the solution was unsatisfactory before separation was reached.

Görtler (1957a) has made a similar extension of the series solution given in Section 6.

29. Methods based on the momentum and energy equations

The momentum and energy integral equations were derived in Section V. 6, including the effects of suction. For steady motion they are

$$\frac{\tau_w}{\rho U^2} = \frac{d\delta_2}{dx} + \frac{\delta_1 + 2\delta_2}{U}\frac{dU}{dx} + \frac{w_s}{U}, \tag{227}$$

$$2D/\rho = d(U^3\delta_3)/dx + w_s U^2, \tag{228}$$

in the usual notation. It is convenient to put these equations in forms corresponding to those of Section 19. The momentum equation (227) becomes

$$dY/dx = F/U, \tag{229}$$

where

$$Y = \delta_2^2/\nu, \qquad F = 2\{T - \lambda(H+2) - \sigma\}, \qquad T = \tau_w\delta_2/\mu U,$$

$$\lambda = \delta_2^2 U'/\nu = YU', \qquad H = \delta_1/\delta_2, \qquad \sigma = w_s\delta_2/\nu, \tag{230}$$

and the energy equation (228) becomes

$$d(U^6 K^2 Y)/dx = U^5 K(4L - 2\sigma), \tag{231}$$

where, as in (184), $K = \delta_3/\delta_2$, $L = \delta_2 D/\mu U^2$. Equations (229) and (231) may be combined to give

$$K' = (YU)^{-1}[2L + K\{\lambda(H-1) - T + \sigma\} - \sigma]. \tag{232}$$

The methods used to derive approximate solutions of the boundary-layer equations with suction from the momentum and energy equations are similar to those described in Part II of the present chapter. A suitable form for the velocity profile is assumed, and boundary conditions are imposed at $z = 0$ and as $z \to \infty$. These conditions, which generalize equations (156), are

$$z = 0: \qquad u = 0, \qquad \nu\frac{\partial^2 u}{\partial z^2} = -w_s\frac{\partial u}{\partial z} - UU',$$

$$\nu\frac{\partial^3 u}{\partial z^3} = -w_s\frac{\partial^2 u}{\partial z^2}, \qquad \nu\frac{\partial^4 u}{\partial z^4} = \frac{\partial u}{\partial z}\frac{\partial^2 u}{\partial x\partial z} - w_s\frac{\partial^3 u}{\partial z^3}, \qquad \dots;$$

$$\dot{z} \to \infty: \qquad u \to U, \qquad \partial^n u/\partial z^n \to 0 \quad (n = 1, 2, 3, \dots). \tag{233}$$

These conditions relate the parameters of the profile to λ and σ.

Several methods of solution have been devised on these principles. One of the first methods proposed for general use is that of Schlichting (1943), based on the family of velocity profiles

$$u/U = (1-k)f_1(\eta)+kf_2(\eta), \qquad \eta = z/\delta, \qquad (234)$$

where $\qquad f_1(\eta) = 1-e^{-\eta}, \qquad f_2(\eta) = \sin(\pi\eta/6) \quad (\eta \leqslant 3),$

$$= 1 \qquad\qquad (\eta \geqslant 3). \qquad (235)$$

Then $k = 0$ gives the asymptotic suction profile, and $k = 1$ gives an approximation to the Blasius flat plate profile. The conditions (233) as $z \to \infty$ are satisfied (though $\partial^2 u/\partial z^2$ is discontinuous at $\eta = 3$), and the condition

$$\nu\frac{\partial^2 u}{\partial z^2} = -w_s\frac{\partial u}{\partial z} - UU' \qquad (236)$$

at $z = 0$ leads to

$$g^2(k)(k-1)+\sigma g(k)\{1-k(1-\tfrac{1}{6}\pi)\}+\lambda = 0, \qquad (237)$$

where $g(k) = \delta_2/\delta$ is a quadratic function of k. Since H and T are functions of k only, (237) enables F to be calculated as a function of λ and σ. Equation (229) can then be integrated numerically for any particular distribution of U and w_s.

In order to start the integration the initial values of λ and σ at a stagnation point must be known. The equation $F = 0$ is one relation between λ and σ, and the given initial value of $w_s/\sqrt{(U'\nu)} = \sigma/\sqrt{\lambda}$ provides another. The initial values so obtained agree fairly well with those calculated by Schlichting and Bussmann (1943). Schlichting (1943) applied his method to the entry flow on a flat plate with constant suction (see Section 31), and to the potential flow past a circular cylinder, and a Joukowsky aerofoil, both with constant suction. Schlichting's results agreed fairly well with those of Bussmann and Ulrich (1944) for the circular cylinder, except near the separation point. It should be noted that the separation condition used by Schlichting was $\lambda = -0 \cdot 0682$, which is correct for the flow $U = U_0(x/l)^n$ without suction. The condition $T = 0$ is satisfied when $\lambda = -0 \cdot 0721$, but in general the method breaks down before T can vanish. This is because Schlichting's family of velocity profiles is such that for σ given, T, H, and F are not single-valued functions of λ when λ is near $-0 \cdot 0721$.

In Schlichting's method the shapes of the velocity profiles depend on the single parameter k, though k is a function of λ and σ. No one-parameter method of this sort is likely to give the separation point very accurately in general, even if T, H, and F are single-valued functions of λ. For (236) leads to

$$m = (\delta_2^2/U)(\partial^2 u/\partial z^2)_{z=0} = -\sigma T - \lambda, \tag{238}$$

and since the condition $T = 0$ at separation fixes the profile parameter, (238) requires λ, as well as the profile shape, to be independent of suction conditions at the separation point. In reality suction is likely to have a bigger effect on separation, and better approximate solutions may be found by using a two-parameter family, for which λ and σ may be taken as the parameters. Mangler (1948b) suggested the use of the family of similar profiles with suction, thus extending the work of Walz (Section 17). The only changes required are that (177) must be replaced by the general equation (V. 137) of similar profiles, containing the extra term $\gamma f''$, and that $\sigma = \gamma\Delta_2$ must be included with equations (179). Then H, T, F can be regarded as functions of the two parameters λ and σ, and the separation condition $T = 0$ is a functional relation between λ and σ. Useful charts of these functions are given by Spalding and Evans (1961).

Thwaites (1949a) constructed a method on this principle using numerical solutions of equation (V. 137) obtained by relaxation methods. The function F was represented approximately by the simple formula

$$F = 0.45 - 6\lambda - 1.28\sigma + 0.76\sigma^2. \tag{239}$$

When $\sigma = 0$ this reduces to Thwaites's approximation for flow without suction, discussed in Section 18. The momentum equation (229) can then be integrated in the form

$$\delta_2^2 = \nu U^{-6} \int_0^x U^5(0.45 - 1.28\sigma + 0.76\sigma^2)\, dx. \tag{240}$$

This is an integral equation for δ_2, since σ depends on δ_2 by (230). Thwaites observed that an easy method for the solution of (240) can be developed with the aid of a formula for numerical integration, such as Simpson's rule. If δ_2 has been calculated at the points $x = x_0, x_0+h,...,$ x_0+nh, the numerical integration formula yields a quadratic equation for δ_2 at $x = x_0+(n+1)h$.

Thwaites applied his method to the flat plate with constant suction (Section 31), and chose the numbers in (239) to get agreement with the calculations of Iglisch (1944). Thwaites also considered the case of constant suction with Howarth's (1938) external velocity distribution $U = U_0(1-x/l)$. When $w_s = 0$, separation takes place when $x/l = 0.120$ (Section 3). Thwaites assumed that when

$$\sigma/\surd(-\lambda) = w_s/\surd(-U'\nu) > 4 \tag{241}$$

separation would be completely suppressed, and devised a relation between σ and λ for his separation criterion, such that it agreed with Howarth's result when $\sigma = 0$, and also with (241). The condition (241) is of doubtful validity, however, and the possibility of suppressing separation by suction will be discussed further in Section 30.

Pohlhausen's method (Section 13) was generalized by Torda (1952) so as to include suction. The immediate extension of Pohlhausen's conditions (169) is to replace $f''(0) = -\Lambda$ by $f''(0)+\Sigma f'(0) = -\Lambda$, where $\Sigma = w_s \delta/\nu$, $\Lambda = \delta^2 U'/\nu$. In this case the separation profile ($f'(0) = 0$) is the same as when $\Sigma = 0$, and is given by $\Lambda = -12$, independent of Σ. To avoid this Torda dropped one condition at $\eta = 1$ and added another at $\eta = 0$, so that

$$f(0) = 0, \qquad f''(0)+\Sigma f'(0) = -\Lambda, \qquad f'''(0)+\Sigma f''(0) = 0,$$
$$f(1) = 1, \qquad f'(1) = 0. \qquad (242)$$

The separation condition is now $(6-\Sigma)\Lambda+24 = 0$. Torda's presentation of his method suffers from the disadvantage that U'' appears explicitly in the differential equation as in the original form of Pohlhausen's method, since δ is used as the unknown variable instead of δ_2. Torda applied his method to determine the distribution of suction velocity on an aerofoil which will maintain a constant boundary-layer thickness.

Thwaites (1946c) used the method of Section 16 to investigate the effect of a constant suction velocity on the flow $U = U_0(1-x/l)$. The assumed form of velocity profile is complicated and the application of the method is restricted to comparatively small velocities of suction, but the predicted delay of separation is similar to that obtained later by Thwaites (1949a), as far as the calculations extend.

Reference has already been made in Section 20 to Head's (1957a) two-parameter method, which uses the momentum and energy equations in the forms (229), (232). For his assumed family of profiles, Head represents H, K, and L as functions of T and m by charts giving contour lines in the T, m plane, where m is defined by (238). Equations (229) and (232) can then be integrated step by step. If the values of Y, T, m are known at the beginning of a step Y' and K' can be computed and so the values of Y and K at the end of the step can be found. The known values of U', w_s then give the values of λ and σ, and for these values equation (238) represents a straight line in the T, m plane. The intersection of this line with the appropriate contour on the K chart determines the values of T and m at the end of the step. Each step takes about 7 to 15 minutes in the general case where U' and w_s are not zero. Head applied his method to several cases with and without suction and obtained results agreeing satisfactorily with accurate numerical solutions: the cases with suction included the flat plate with constant suction and the family of similar solutions of the boundary-layer equations. Head also considered the stability of his boundary-layer profiles, using the approximate formula (IX. 95) of Lin (1945), and constructed a chart giving contours of the critical value of $U\delta_2/\nu$ in the T, m plane. It was shown by Head (1957b) that suction, suitably distributed over the porous surface of an aerofoil, would improve the stability of the boundary layer as well as prevent separation.

30. The prevention of separation by means of suction

Prandtl (1935) used the Pohlhausen method to investigate the velocity of suction required to prevent separation of the flow in a region of adverse pressure gradient. Prandtl's argument, slightly generalized, can be stated as follows in the notation of Section 29.

Let the suction velocity w_s be just sufficient to prevent separation, so that the skin friction is everywhere zero. Then $T = 0$, and the momentum equation (229) becomes

$$U d(\lambda/U')/dx = -2\lambda(H+2) - 2\sigma. \tag{243}$$

If a definite shape of profile is assumed, H and m, defined by equations (230) and (238), take the constant values H_1 and m_1. From equation (238) $\lambda = -m_1$, and so (243) becomes

$$\sigma = m_1\{H_1 + 2 - \tfrac{1}{2}(UU''/U'^2)\}.$$

But from (230) $\sigma = w_s(\lambda/\nu U')^{\frac{1}{2}} = w_s(m_1/-\nu U')^{\frac{1}{2}}$. Hence

$$w_s/\sqrt{(-\nu U')} = m_1^{\frac{1}{2}}\{H_1 + 2 - \tfrac{1}{2}(UU''/U'^2)\}. \tag{244}$$

If U'' is neglected (244) reduces to

$$w_s/\sqrt{(-\nu U')} = m_1^{\frac{1}{2}}(H_1 + 2), \tag{245}$$

which is also the form of (244) at a rear stagnation point.

Prandtl used the profile given by Pohlhausen's method at separation. In this case $m_1 = 0.1567$ and $H_1 = 3.5$, so that (245) becomes

$$w_s = 2.18\sqrt{(-\nu U')}. \tag{246}$$

Preston (1946) made a similar calculation, assuming that the profile was that found by Howarth (1938) at separation for the case $U = U_0(1 - x/l)$ without suction. For this profile $m_1 = 0.0841$, $H_1 = 3.83$, and (245) becomes

$$w_s = 1.69\sqrt{(-\nu U')}. \tag{247}$$

As an example, consider the potential flow of a uniform stream about a circular cylinder (Goldstein 1938, p. 534). Then $U = 2U_\infty \sin(2x/l)$, where U_∞ is the stream velocity and l the diameter of the cylinder. At the rear stagnation point $U' = -4U_\infty/l$, so that Prandtl's result (246) requires a suction velocity $w_s = 4{\cdot}35(\nu U_\infty/l)^{\frac{1}{2}}$. If this is applied over the *whole* cylinder the quantity coefficient is

$$C_Q = w_s \pi l/U_\infty l = 4{\cdot}35\pi R^{-\frac{1}{2}},$$

where R is the Reynolds number. From Preston's result (247) the coefficient would be $C_Q = 3{\cdot}38\pi R^{-\frac{1}{2}}$.

Prandtl's calculation of the suction velocity required to prevent separation may be criticized since it assumes a constant form of velocity profile. This is only possible if the flow leads to one of the similar solutions of the boundary-layer equations discussed in Section V.21. In this type of flow equation (244) is satisfied exactly when $T = 0$, but (244) would not in general reduce to (245). It might be expected, however, that (245) would be valid near a rear stagnation point, where the velocity profile might at first sight be supposed to be of constant shape, with the boundary-layer thickness remaining finite. In this case, if $x = 0$ is the stagnation point, and $U = -U_1 x/l$ ($x < 0$), a solution may be sought in the form

$$\psi = -(U_1 \nu/l)^{\frac{1}{2}} x f(\eta), \qquad \eta = (U_1/\nu l)^{\frac{1}{2}} z, \tag{248}$$

so that $u = U f'(\eta)$, $w = (U_1 \nu/l)^{\frac{1}{2}} f(\eta)$. These relations, when substituted either into the boundary-layer equations or into the full Navier-Stokes equations, lead to

$$f''' - f f'' - 1 + f'^2 = 0, \tag{249}$$

where $f(0) = -C$, $f'(0) = 0$, $f'(\infty) = 1$, and $w_s = C(U_1 \nu/l)^{\frac{1}{2}}$. Thus the analysis is formally very similar to that for a forward stagnation point (see Sections III. 19 and V. 14). However, the only solution of (249) satisfying the boundary condition at infinity is $f = \eta + \text{constant}$ (Section V. 21), and this violates the condition of no slip at the wall, whatever the value of C may be. Evidently it is impossible to find a solution in the form (248). If solutions did exist, and one had $f''(0) = 0$, the corresponding value of C would give

$$w_s = C\sqrt{(-\nu U')} \tag{250}$$

as the correct form of (246) and (247). Consequently it would seem that no relation of the type (250) can be valid in general as a criterion for avoiding separation, and that separation could not be prevented from occurring upstream of a rear stagnation point, however much suction was used.

This appears to contradict the experimental observation that it is possible to suppress separation of the flow from the rear of a circular cylinder by means of suction. However, the argument indicates only that the boundary-layer equations do not determine how much suction is necessary to prevent separation. It may be supposed that the required suction velocity could be found from the Navier-Stokes equations, though the result might depend on the flow as a whole, not merely on conditions at the rear of the cylinder. The flow conditions at the rear are discussed further in Section V. 7.

In cases without a rear stagnation point, such as the flow over an aerofoil with a cusped trailing edge, it is probable that, as found by Head (Section 29) and Trilling (Section 11), suction can maintain positive skin friction and a stable boundary-layer flow. The required suction velocity probably increases rapidly towards the rear when the trailing-edge velocity is low compared with the maximum velocity on the aerofoil.

Curle (1960) has extended Stratford's method (Section 25) to study the effect of suction in delaying separation. In the case $U = U_0(1-x/l)$, with constant suction velocity w_s, Curle's method suggests that separation would not occur if

$$w_s/\surd(-\nu U') > 1 \cdot 55.$$

31. Uniform flow over a flat plate with constant suction

The flow of a uniform stream over a flat plate with a constant suction velocity has been studied extensively by means of theory and experiment. At a great distance downstream conditions may be regarded as independent of x, and the continuity equation shows that $w = -w_s$, where w_s is the constant velocity of suction. Hence, as in Section III. 15,

$$u = U_0\{1-\exp(-w_s z/\nu)\}, \tag{251}$$

where U_0 is the speed of the main stream. This solution was first obtained by Griffith and Meredith (1936), and the velocity profile is usually called the 'asymptotic suction profile' (see also Section V. 19).

If suction begins at the leading edge of the plate, $x = 0$, the initial velocity profile is that found by Blasius for the plate without suction (Section V. 12). This was most clearly shown by Thwaites (1946d), who transformed the variables in order to study conditions near the leading edge. Let

$$\psi = (2U_0\nu x)^{\frac{1}{2}}f(\xi, \eta), \qquad \xi = w_s(x/2U_0\nu)^{\frac{1}{2}}, \qquad \eta = (U_0/2\nu x)^{\frac{1}{2}}z. \tag{252}$$

Then
$$u = U_0 \frac{\partial f}{\partial \eta}, \qquad w = -\left(\frac{U_0 \nu}{2x}\right)^{\frac{1}{2}} \left[f + \xi \frac{\partial f}{\partial \xi} - \eta \frac{\partial f}{\partial \eta}\right],$$

and
$$\frac{\partial^3 f}{\partial \eta^3} + f \frac{\partial^2 f}{\partial \eta^2} + \xi \left[\frac{\partial f}{\partial \xi} \frac{\partial^2 f}{\partial \eta^2} - \frac{\partial^2 f}{\partial \xi \partial \eta} \frac{\partial f}{\partial \eta}\right] = 0. \tag{253}$$

The boundary conditions are

$$f = \xi, \qquad \partial f/\partial \eta = 0 \quad \text{at} \ \eta = 0, \qquad \partial f/\partial \eta \to 1 \quad \text{as} \ \eta \to \infty. \tag{254}$$

When ξ is small a solution of (253) may be found by an expansion in powers of ξ. If

$$f(\xi, \eta) = f_0(\eta) + \xi f_1(\eta) + \xi^2 f_2(\eta) + \dots, \tag{255}$$

the function $f_0(\eta)$ is found to be the Blasius function of Section V. 12. The functions $f_1, f_2, \dots$, are then given by linear equations which can be solved in succession. The expansion (255) was generalized by Thwaites (1949a) to include distributions of stream velocity and suction velocity which vary with x.

Iglisch (1944) obtained a complete numerical solution for the flow with suction starting at the leading edge of the plate. The variables used by Iglisch are connected with those appearing in the equation (V. 53) of von Mises by the relations

$$\sigma = 2\xi = w_s(2x/U_0\nu)^{\frac{1}{2}}, \qquad \psi - w_s x = (U_0\nu/2w_s)\sigma\tau^2,$$
$$V = 4u^2/U_0^2, \qquad \chi = U_0^2(1 - \tfrac{1}{4}V). \tag{256}$$

The substitutions (256) then lead to the equation

$$\sqrt{V} \frac{\partial^2 V}{\partial \tau^2} + \left(2\sigma\tau + \tau^3 - \frac{\sqrt{V}}{\tau}\right) \frac{\partial V}{\partial \tau} = 2\sigma\tau^2 \frac{\partial V}{\partial \sigma}, \tag{257}$$

and the boundary conditions for (257) are

$$V = 0 \quad \text{at} \ \tau = 0, \qquad V \to 4 \quad \text{as} \ \tau \to \infty. \tag{258}$$

Iglisch showed that when σ is small the solution of (257) can be expressed as a series $V(\sigma, \tau) = V_0(\tau) + \sigma V_1(\tau) + \sigma^2 V_2(\tau) + \dots$, where $V_0(\tau)$ corresponds to the Blasius function $f_0(\eta)$ in Thwaites's expansion (255). The numerical solution of (257) was computed by a step-by-step process, from small values of σ to larger ones, and Iglisch presented his results in terms of the variables

$$\mathrm{x} = \frac{w_s^2 x}{U_0 \nu} = \tfrac{1}{2}\sigma^2, \qquad \mathrm{z} = \frac{w_s z}{\nu} = 2\sigma \int_0^\tau \frac{\tau \, d\tau}{\sqrt{V(\sigma, \tau)}}. \tag{259}$$

Fig. VI. 17 shows the variation of the displacement thickness along the plate, as computed by Iglisch.

The approach of the boundary layer to the asymptotic suction profile was studied by Stewartson (1957a). From his results

$$w_s \delta_1/\nu = 1 - C\mathrm{x}^{-3/2}\exp(-\mathrm{x}/4) + O\{\mathrm{x}^{-5/2}\exp(-\mathrm{x}/4)\} \qquad (260)$$

as $\mathrm{x} \to \infty$, where C is a constant estimated at 1·2 from Iglisch's calculations.

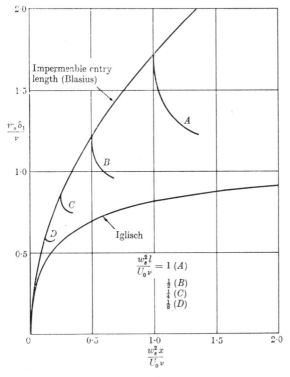

Fig. VI. 17. Variation of displacement thickness along a flat plate in a uniform stream with constant suction, and with various impermeable entry lengths.

If the plate has an impermeable entry length, $0 < x < l$, and uniform suction begins at $x = l$, the boundary layer has a definite thickness where the suction starts. The solution of this problem was derived by Rheinboldt (1956), who generalized the expansion of Goldstein (1930) at a singularity (see Section 9) by the inclusion of suction and extended the solution downstream by the difference method of Görtler (Section 10). Another finite-difference method was used by Rouleau and Osterle (1955) but, since they took $w_s^2 l/U_0\nu = 1/320$, their case differs very little from that of Iglisch. Fig. VI. 17, which is equivalent to one given by Head (1951), shows the variation of displacement thickness with x for a constant suction velocity w_s and various entry lengths l. The distribution of skin friction for various constant velocities of suction and blowing, with a fixed entry length l, is shown in Fig. VI. 18.

Several approximate solutions have been given for the entry flow with suction. Reference has already been made in Sections 29 and 11 to

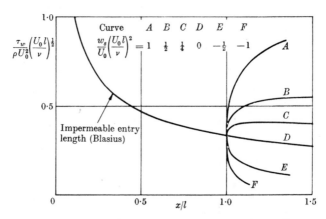

FIG. VI. 18. Distribution of skin friction on a flat plate in a uniform stream with various constant velocities of suction and blowing, and with a fixed impermeable entry length.

the solutions of Schlichting (1943), Thwaites (1949a), and Ringleb (1952). The most interesting of the other solutions are those in which the velocity profile at any station on the plate is assumed to be a linear combination of the initial and final profiles. Schaefer (1944) and Preston (1946) took the velocity profile in the form

$$u/U = f(\eta) = (1-k)B(\eta) + kA(\eta), \qquad \eta = z/\delta_1, \qquad (261)$$

where k is a parameter, δ_1 the displacement thickness, and $A(\eta)$, $B(\eta)$ represent the asymptotic suction profile and the Blasius profile respectively. Then $k = 0$ at the leading edge, and $k \to 1$ as $x \to \infty$. The momentum equation was used to determine the variation of k with x, and hence to find the boundary-layer characteristics. Preston also applied his method to the case where there is an entry length l without suction, but this leads to a discontinuity in the velocity profile and in δ_1 and τ_w at $x = l$, which is not satisfactory. Thwaites (1946b) used the method of Section 16 and took the boundary-layer profile in the form

$$z/\delta_2 = g(t) = (1-k)b(t) + ka(t), \qquad t = u/U, \qquad (262)$$

where k is a parameter, δ_2 the momentum thickness, and $a(t)$, $b(t)$ represent the asymptotic and Blasius profiles.

Experimental investigations have been made by Kay (1948), Head (1951), and Libby, Kaufman, and Harrington (1952). Kay gives graphs of the distribution of δ_1 and δ_2 in the case of suction with $w_s^2 l/U_0 \nu = 1 \cdot 1$. These are broadly similar to the theoretical results illustrated in Fig. VI. 17. Head's observations were made in flight on a specially designed aerofoil, and were extended to include pressure gradients in the main stream. In these experiments the influence of the impermeable section at the leading edge was negligible, and the velocity distributions were found to agree fairly well with those of Iglisch (1944).

The case of uniform blowing was treated numerically by Catherall (unpublished), whose calculations indicate that the flow separates near $x = 0 \cdot 73$.

32. Boundary-layer flow with strong suction and blowing

It was shown by Pretsch (1944a, b) that when the velocity of suction is sufficiently great the boundary-layer profile approximates to the asymptotic suction profile (251). This is true for arbitrary distributions of $U(x)$ and $w_s(x)$. If

$$\psi = \int w_s(x)\,dx + \frac{\nu U(x)}{w_s(x)} f(x, \zeta), \qquad \zeta = w_s z/\nu, \tag{263}$$

the velocity components are

$$u = U \frac{\partial f}{\partial \zeta}, \qquad w = -w_s - \left(\frac{\nu}{w_s^2}\right)\left[U' w_s f + U w_s \frac{\partial f}{\partial x} + U w_s'\left(\zeta \frac{\partial f}{\partial \zeta} - f\right)\right], \tag{264}$$

where the primes denote differentiation with respect to x. The equation of motion of the boundary layer then becomes

$$\frac{\partial^3 f}{\partial \zeta^3} + \frac{\partial^2 f}{\partial \zeta^2} + \left(\frac{\nu}{w_s^3}\right)\left[U' w_s\left\{1 - \left(\frac{\partial f}{\partial \zeta}\right)^2 + f \frac{\partial^2 f}{\partial \zeta^2}\right\} + \right.$$
$$\left. + U w_s\left\{\frac{\partial f}{\partial x} \frac{\partial^2 f}{\partial \zeta^2} - \frac{\partial^2 f}{\partial x \partial \zeta} \frac{\partial f}{\partial \zeta}\right\} - U w_s' f \frac{\partial^2 f}{\partial \zeta^2}\right] = 0, \tag{265}$$

and the boundary conditions for $f(x, \zeta)$ are

$$f = \frac{\partial f}{\partial \zeta} = 0 \quad \text{at } \zeta = 0, \qquad \frac{\partial f}{\partial \zeta} \to 1 \quad \text{as } \zeta \to \infty. \tag{266}$$

When w_s is very great equation (265) reduces to

$$\frac{\partial^3 f}{\partial \zeta^3} + \frac{\partial^2 f}{\partial \zeta^2} = 0,$$

and the solution which satisfies the condition (266) is

$$\partial f/\partial \zeta = 1 - e^{-\zeta}.$$

Hence the limiting form of the velocity distribution within the boundary layer is (251). In particular, the boundary-layer thickness is inversely proportional to $w_s(x)$, and independent of $U(x)$, provided that w_s is sufficiently large.

This argument was extended by Watson (1947) to derive an asymptotic expansion for the velocity distribution when w_s is large. The appropriate form of this expansion is

$$f(x, \zeta) = f_0 + (\nu/w_s^3)(U' w_s f_{1,0} + U w_s' f_{0,1}) +$$
$$+ (\nu^2/w_s^6)(U U'' w_s^2 f_{2,0} + U'^2 w_s^2 f_{11,0} + U U' w_s w_s' f_{1,1} +$$
$$+ U^2 w_s w_s'' f_{0,2} + U^2 w_s'^2 f_{0,11}) + ..., \quad (267)$$

where $f_0, f_{1,0}, f_{0,1}, ...$ are functions of ζ. When this is substituted in equation (265) and conditions (266) the functions $f_0, f_{1,0}, f_{0,1}, ...$ can be calculated in succession. The velocity distribution is given by

$$u/U = f_0' + (\nu/w_s^3)(U' w_s f_{1,0}' + U w_s' f_{0,1}') +$$
$$+ (\nu^2/w_s^6)(U U'' w_s^2 f_{2,0}' + U'^2 w_s^2 f_{11,0}' + U U' w_s w_s' f_{1,1}' +$$
$$+ U^2 w_s w_s'' f_{0,2}' + U^2 w_s'^2 f_{0,11}') + ..., \quad (268)$$

where

$$f_0' = 1 - e^{-\zeta},$$

$$f_{1,0}' = (\tfrac{1}{2}\zeta^2 + 2\zeta)e^{-\zeta},$$

$$f_{0,1}' = -(\tfrac{1}{2}\zeta^2 + \tfrac{1}{2})e^{-\zeta} + \tfrac{1}{2}e^{-2\zeta},$$

$$f_{2,0}' = -(\tfrac{1}{6}\zeta^3 + \tfrac{3}{2}\zeta^2 + \tfrac{9}{4})e^{-\zeta} + (\tfrac{1}{2}\zeta + \tfrac{9}{4})e^{-2\zeta},$$

$$f_{11,0}' = -(\tfrac{1}{8}\zeta^4 + \zeta^3 + \tfrac{7}{2}\zeta^2 + 6\zeta + \tfrac{1}{2})e^{-\zeta} + \tfrac{1}{2}e^{-2\zeta},$$

$$f_{1,1}' = (\tfrac{1}{4}\zeta^4 + \tfrac{3}{2}\zeta^3 + \tfrac{23}{4}\zeta^2 + 3\zeta + \tfrac{21}{2})e^{-\zeta} - (\tfrac{1}{2}\zeta^2 + \tfrac{9}{2}\zeta + \tfrac{21}{2})e^{-2\zeta},$$

$$f_{0,2}' = (\tfrac{1}{6}\zeta^3 + \tfrac{1}{2}\zeta^2 + \tfrac{1}{4}\zeta + \tfrac{25}{24})e^{-\zeta} - (\tfrac{1}{2}\zeta + 1)e^{-2\zeta} - \tfrac{1}{24}e^{-3\zeta},$$

$$f_{0,11}' = -(\tfrac{1}{8}\zeta^4 + \tfrac{1}{2}\zeta^3 + \tfrac{9}{4}\zeta^2 + \tfrac{1}{2}\zeta + \tfrac{65}{12})e^{-\zeta} + (\tfrac{1}{2}\zeta^2 + \tfrac{5}{2}\zeta + \tfrac{11}{2})e^{-2\zeta} - \tfrac{1}{12}e^{-3\zeta}. \quad (269)$$

The characteristics of the boundary layer can be derived from the series (268). In particular, the skin friction τ_w is given by

$$\tau_w/\rho U w_s = 1 + (\nu/w_s^3)(2U' w_s - \tfrac{1}{2}U w_s') +$$
$$+ (\nu^2/w_s^6)(-\tfrac{7}{4}U U'' w_s^2 - \tfrac{13}{2}U'^2 w_s^2 + 9 U U' w_s w_s' +$$
$$+ \tfrac{5}{6}U^2 w_s w_s'' - \tfrac{10}{3}U^2 w_s'^2) + ..., \quad (270)$$

the displacement thickness δ_1 by

$$w_s\delta_1/\nu = 1+(\nu/w_s^3)(-3U'w_s+\tfrac{5}{4}Uw_s')+$$
$$+(\nu^2/w_s^6)(5UU''w_s^2+\tfrac{89}{4}U'^2w_s^2-\tfrac{67}{2}UU'w_sw_s'-$$
$$-\tfrac{191}{72}U^2w_sw_s''+\tfrac{233}{18}U^2w_s'^2)+..., \quad (271)$$

and the momentum thickness δ_2 by

$$w_s\delta_2/\nu = \tfrac{1}{2}+(\nu/w_s^3)(-\tfrac{7}{4}U'w_s+\tfrac{5}{6}Uw_s')+$$
$$+(\nu^2/w_s^6)(\tfrac{251}{72}UU''w_s^2+\tfrac{347}{24}U'^2w_s^2-\tfrac{569}{24}UU'w_sw_s'-$$
$$-\tfrac{275}{144}U^2w_sw_s''+\tfrac{1375}{144}U^2w_s'^2)+.... \quad (272)$$

Corresponding results may be obtained for the similar solutions of the boundary-layer equations (see Section V. 21).

The asymptotic expansions were applied by Watson to the potential flow over a circular cylinder in a uniform stream with constant suction, a problem previously treated by Bussmann and Ulrich (1944) using a series development (Section 28). The method of asymptotic expansion is only suitable for quite large suction velocities, for which there is no danger of separation, and the smallest rate of suction considered by Watson was $w_s = 5\sqrt{2}\, U_\infty(U_\infty l/\nu)^{-\frac{1}{2}}$, where l is the diameter of the cylinder and U_∞ the speed of the stream. This is $(5\sqrt{2})$ times the velocity of suction considered by Bussmann and Ulrich. As noted in Section 30, it is difficult to predict the amount of suction required to prevent separation, and the estimates made by Watson from the series (270) are of doubtful value. An application was also made to suction over the nose of an aerofoil at a high lift.

Pretsch (1944 a, b) also showed that for strong blowing the influence of viscosity becomes negligible, and the flow is influenced only by the pressure gradient. This must be favourable if the flow does not separate. Since viscosity is negligible the flow satisfies Bernoulli's equation and thus, neglecting w^2,

$$U^2(x)-u^2 = f(\psi) = U^2(x_0) \quad (273)$$

if the streamline ψ meets the porous surface $z = 0$ at $x = x_0$, so that

$$\psi = \int_0^{x_0} w_s(x)\,dx. \quad (274)$$

Since $\partial\psi/\partial z = u$,

$$z = \int_{\psi(x,0)}^{\psi(x,z)} \frac{d\psi}{u} = \int_{x_0}^{x} \frac{-w_s(x_1)\,dx_1}{\sqrt{[U^2(x)-U^2(x_1)]}} \quad (275)$$

from (273) and (274). Equations (273) and (275) enable the velocity profile to be found in terms of the parameter x_0. It will be noted that

$U(x)$ must be greater than $U(x_1)$ for $x_1 < x$, so that a favourable pressure gradient is required. For example, the case of the stagnation-point flow with uniform blowing,

$$U(x) = U_1 x/l, \qquad w_s = -K(U_1 \nu/l)^{\frac{1}{2}},$$

leads to the velocity distribution

$$u = U \sin(U'z/|w_s|),$$

which agrees with the case $\alpha = \beta = 1$ of the similar solutions, given by equation (V. 150).

VII

UNSTEADY BOUNDARY LAYERS

1. General introduction

In this chapter we shall mainly consider two categories of boundary
layer which depend on time. They are (i) boundary layers which are
created when a body starts from rest either impulsively or with acceleration (considered in Part I) and (ii) boundary layers which are periodic
due to fluctuations of the stream or oscillations of the body (considered
in Part II). We shall neglect compressibility, an approximation that
entails $\omega d/c \ll 1$ (Section I. 2.6), where ω is a frequency, d a length,
and c the sound speed.

A general description of the nature of the unsteady flow of a viscous
fluid can be built up if the kinematic viscosity is used as a fundamental
parameter underlying what is basically a phenomenon of diffusion.
It is known that this parameter can be used to give a measure of the
rate of diffusion of vorticity and momentum by molecular transport.
In fact it is known that the time for any bulk property of the fluid, such
as vorticity or momentum, to diffuse through a distance δ is of the
order of δ^2/ν (we can conveniently call this the 'diffusion time'), where
ν is the coefficient of kinematic viscosity. The concept of diffusion time
is useful for determining which dimensionless parameters are likely to
be important in the analysis of unsteady viscous flow.

Let us first of all consider a body moving from rest; at first the flow
relative to the body is entirely irrotational but, since the fluid adjacent
to the boundary is at rest relative to it, a region forms in which the
velocity gradient in a direction normal to the surface is very high, and
vorticity is formed there. This vorticity is simultaneously diffused
away from the surface by molecular action and convected by the flow
relative to the body. Consequently a thin layer of vorticity, or boundary
layer, is formed on the surface. After a time t from the commencement
of motion, let us suppose that vorticity is present within a distance δ,
say, from the boundary. Since the diffusion time is of order δ^2/ν, which
clearly must be of the same order as t, it follows that the thickness, δ,
of the boundary layer must be of order $\sqrt{(\nu t)}$. At least for small times,
therefore, the boundary-layer thickness is proportional to the square
root of the time. If z is the distance normal to the boundary, it follows

that $z/\sqrt{(\nu t)}$, the appropriate dimensionless distance, is likely to be one of the important variables which will occur in the mathematical description of the motion.

Let us now consider which dimensionless parameters are likely to occur in an analysis of the differential equations for motion from rest. We first define x_0 to be a reference length in the direction of flow, U_0 to be a reference speed, and t_0 to be a reference time. From these three quantities and the kinematic viscosity it is clearly possible to obtain two independent parameters which will affect the kinematics of the motion. In fact, the analysis given later shows that the two basic parameters at small times are $\nu t_0/x_0^2$ and $U_0 t_0/x_0$, whereas at large times they are $U_0 x_0/\nu$ and $U_0 t_0/x_0$.

Using the concept of diffusion discussed above, we can now express the meaning of each of these parameters in physical terms, as follows. Let us first of all consider the case of 'small times'. Because in this case the boundary-layer thickness, δ, is of order $\sqrt{(\nu t_0)}$ it follows that $\nu t_0/x_0^2$ may be written

$$\frac{\nu t_0}{x_0^2} = \frac{\nu/x_0^2}{\nu/\delta^2} = \frac{\text{rate of diffusion through a distance } x_0}{\text{rate of diffusion through a distance } \delta}.$$

It is also equal to $(\delta/x_0)^2$ and, if it is small, gradients of velocity in the direction of flow are small compared with gradients normal to the boundary, a situation to which boundary-layer theory is applicable. On the other hand, the second basic parameter at small times, namely $U_0 t_0/x_0$, may be written

$$\frac{U_0 t_0}{x_0} = \frac{U_0/x_0}{1/t_0} = \frac{U_0/x_0}{\nu/\delta^2} = \frac{\text{rate of convection by } U_0 \text{ through a distance } x_0}{\text{rate of diffusion through a distance } \delta}.$$

It is worth mentioning here that in steady flow these two rates, represented symbolically by U_0/x_0 and ν/δ^2, must balance, with the result that δ is of order $\sqrt{(\nu x_0/U_0)}$. In the unsteady case boundary-layer *growth* invalidates this conclusion. In particular, if $U_0 t_0/x_0$ is small, diffusion outweighs convection and δ is of order $\sqrt{(\nu t_0)}$ as derived earlier. Consequently, the effects of convection may be neglected compared with those of diffusion, and the resulting differential equations are linear. To a better approximation a solution can be developed in powers of $U_0 t_0/x_0$; moreover if $\nu t_0/x_0^2$ is small enough, we can ignore terms proportional to $\nu t_0/x_0^2$ [or $(\nu t_0/x_0^2)^{\frac{1}{2}}$ if surface curvature of order x_0^{-1} is present] compared with terms in the series like $(U_0 t_0/x_0)^m$, but only up to a certain value of m, beyond which the boundary-layer approximation (neglect of $\nu t_0/x_0^2$) becomes invalid. The use of such a series implies that the Reynolds number $U_0 x_0/\nu$ is large. Cases may arise, however, in which $\nu t_0/x_0^2$ is of the same order as, or is greater than, $U_0 t_0/x_0$, and then the Reynolds number $U_0 x_0/\nu$ is low. If $U_0 t_0/x_0$ is small enough a solution may still be developed in powers of $U_0 t_0/x_0$.

The appearance in the Navier–Stokes equations of the parameters discussed in the preceding paragraph may be demonstrated as follows. We consider the simplest possible case, that of equations expressed in Cartesian coordinates, and consequently neglect effects of curvature; x denotes the coordinate in the direction of flow, z the coordinate normal to the surface, u and w the corresponding velocity components, and U the velocity at the edge of the boundary layer. It is convenient to take axes fixed in the body. Thus with

$$\text{z} = z/\sqrt{(\nu t_0)}, \qquad \text{T} = t/t_0, \qquad \text{X} = x/x_0,$$

$$\text{U} = u/U_0, \qquad \text{W} = (w/U_0)\sqrt{(x_0^2/\nu t_0)},$$

$$F = U/U_0, \qquad \text{P} = pt_0/\rho x_0 U_0 \tag{1}$$

the Navier–Stokes and continuity equations ((III. 4) and (III. 12) in two dimensions) become

$$\frac{\partial \text{U}}{\partial \text{T}} + \frac{U_0 t_0}{x_0}\left(\text{U}\frac{\partial \text{U}}{\partial \text{X}} + \text{W}\frac{\partial \text{U}}{\partial \text{Z}}\right) = -\frac{\partial \text{P}}{\partial \text{X}} + \frac{\nu t_0}{x_0^2}\frac{\partial^2 \text{U}}{\partial \text{X}^2} + \frac{\partial^2 \text{U}}{\partial \text{Z}^2}, \tag{2}$$

$$\frac{\partial \text{W}}{\partial \text{T}} + \frac{U_0 t_0}{x_0}\left(\text{U}\frac{\partial \text{W}}{\partial \text{X}} + \text{W}\frac{\partial \text{W}}{\partial \text{Z}}\right) = -\frac{x_0^2}{\nu t_0}\frac{\partial \text{P}}{\partial \text{Z}} + \frac{\nu t_0}{x_0^2}\frac{\partial^2 \text{W}}{\partial \text{X}^2} + \frac{\partial^2 \text{W}}{\partial \text{Z}^2}, \tag{3}$$

$$\frac{\partial \text{U}}{\partial \text{X}} + \frac{\partial \text{W}}{\partial \text{Z}} = 0. \tag{4}$$

For the case we now consider, that of $U_0 t_0/x_0$ large compared with $\nu t_0/x_0^2$ and $\nu t_0/x_0^2$ small compared with unity, it can be seen from equation (3) that the pressure gradient term is of order $x_0^2/\nu t_0$ times the largest of the other terms of that equation, so that we must have $\partial \text{P}/\partial \text{Z} = 0$ to a first approximation. Thus $\partial \text{P}/\partial \text{X}$ may be replaced by its value at the edge of the boundary layer, namely

$$-\frac{\partial \text{P}}{\partial \text{X}} = \frac{\partial F}{\partial \text{T}} + \frac{U_0 t_0}{x_0}F\frac{\partial F}{\partial \text{X}},$$

and equation (2) becomes

$$\frac{\partial \text{U}}{\partial \text{T}} - \frac{\partial^2 \text{U}}{\partial \text{Z}^2} - \frac{\partial F}{\partial \text{T}} = \frac{U_0 t_0}{x_0}\left(F\frac{\partial F}{\partial \text{X}} - \text{U}\frac{\partial \text{U}}{\partial \text{X}} - \text{W}\frac{\partial \text{U}}{\partial \text{Z}}\right), \tag{5}$$

where terms proportional to $\nu t_0/x_0^2$ are neglected. A solution may now be developed in powers of $U_0 t_0/x_0$, within the limitation (dependent on the order of $\nu t_0/x_0^2$) discussed above. The first approximation is given by

$$\frac{\partial \mathrm{U}}{\partial \mathrm{T}} - \frac{\partial^2 \mathrm{U}}{\partial \mathrm{z}^2} - \frac{\partial F}{\partial \mathrm{T}} = 0. \tag{6}$$

On the other hand if $\nu t_0/x_0^2$ is of the same order as, or greater than, unity the first approximation (for small values of $U_0 t_0/x_0$) involves solution of the slow-motion equations of Section IV. 2.

Let us turn now to the meaning of the parameters which are relevant at 'large times' from the start of the motion. The first of these, the Reynolds number, may be written

$$\frac{U_0 x_0}{\nu} = \frac{U_0/x_0}{\nu/x_0^2} = \frac{\text{rate of convection by } U_0 \text{ through a distance } x_0}{\text{rate of diffusion through a distance } x_0}$$

$$= \frac{\nu/\delta^2}{\nu/x_0^2} = \frac{\text{rate of diffusion through a distance } \delta}{\text{rate of diffusion through a distance } x_0}.$$

The second of these two ratios follows from the first because at large times from the start of the motion we can expect the flow to become steady for the case in which the velocity is changed impulsively from zero to its final value, or to become quasi-steady in the case of accelerated flow; the result in either case is that the rate of diffusion, ν/δ^2, balances the rate of convection, U_0/x_0, as mentioned earlier. The Reynolds number is also equal to $(x_0/\delta)^2$ and, if it is large, gradients of velocity in the direction of flow are small compared with gradients normal to the boundary, a situation to which boundary-layer theory is applicable. The second basic parameter to be considered is $U_0 t_0/x_0$, which may be written

$$\frac{U_0 t_0}{x_0} = \frac{U_0/x_0}{1/t_0} = \frac{\text{rate of convection by } U_0 \text{ through a distance } x_0}{\text{characteristic time rate of change}}.$$

At sufficiently large times from the start of the motion the characteristic time will be such that $U_0 t_0/x_0 \gg 1$. Moreover, if $U_0 x_0/\nu \gg U_0 t_0/x_0$ when there is no surface curvature [or $(U_0 x_0/\nu)^{\frac{1}{2}} \gg U_0 t_0/x_0$ if the curvature has order x_0^{-1}] we can neglect terms proportional to $\nu/U_0 x_0$ [or $(\nu/U_0 x_0)^{\frac{1}{2}}$], which is a boundary-layer approximation. Such a solution clearly requires $x_0^2/\nu t_0 \gg 1$. As $t_0 \to \infty$, however, $x_0^2/\nu t_0$ becomes of order of, and less than unity. Thus ultimately, at large times, the boundary-layer approximation is not strictly valid for calculating the trend of the solution to a steady or quasi-steady state. This situation arises because terms neglected in boundary-layer theory, namely those proportional to $\nu/U_0 x_0$, are of the same order as some of those retained, namely those proportional to $x_0/U_0 t_0$. Consequently it is strictly necessary to retain terms of both types and not to apply the boundary-layer approximation.

The appearance of these parameters in the Navier–Stokes equations can be demonstrated as follows. We write

$$z = z\sqrt{(U_0/\nu x_0)}, \qquad T = t/t_0, \qquad X = x/x_0,$$
$$U = u/U_0, \qquad\qquad W = w\sqrt{(x_0/\nu U_0)},$$
$$F = U/U_0, \qquad\qquad P = p/\rho U_0^2, \tag{7}$$

and the Navier–Stokes equations and equation of continuity in cartesian coordinates then become

$$\frac{x_0}{U_0 t_0}\frac{\partial U}{\partial T} + U\frac{\partial U}{\partial X} + W\frac{\partial U}{\partial Z} = -\frac{\partial P}{\partial X} + \frac{\nu}{U_0 x_0}\frac{\partial^2 U}{\partial X^2} + \frac{\partial^2 U}{\partial Z^2}, \tag{8}$$

$$\frac{x_0}{U_0 t_0}\frac{\partial W}{\partial T} + U\frac{\partial W}{\partial X} + W\frac{\partial W}{\partial Z} = -\frac{U_0 x_0}{\nu}\frac{\partial P}{\partial Z} + \frac{\nu}{U_0 x_0}\frac{\partial^2 W}{\partial X^2} + \frac{\partial^2 W}{\partial Z^2}, \tag{9}$$

$$\frac{\partial U}{\partial X} + \frac{\partial W}{\partial Z} = 0. \tag{10}$$

For the case we now consider, that of $U_0 x_0/\nu$ large compared with $U_0 t_0/x_0$ and large compared with unity, it can be seen that the pressure term in equation (9) is of order $U_0 x_0/\nu$ times the largest of the other terms. Consequently $\partial P/\partial Z$ may be taken to be zero to a first approximation. Thus $\partial P/\partial X$ may be replaced by its value at the edge of the layer, namely

$$-\frac{\partial P}{\partial X} = \frac{x_0}{U_0 t_0}\frac{\partial F}{\partial T} + F\frac{\partial F}{\partial X},$$

and equation (8) becomes

$$U\frac{\partial U}{\partial X} + W\frac{\partial U}{\partial Z} - \frac{\partial^2 U}{\partial Z^2} - F\frac{\partial F}{\partial X} = \frac{x_0}{U_0 t_0}\left(\frac{\partial F}{\partial T} - \frac{\partial U}{\partial T}\right), \tag{11}$$

where terms proportional to $\nu/U_0 x_0$ are neglected. In the particular case when $F = T^n f(X)$ we may define

$$U = T^n U', \qquad Z = Z'/T^{n/2}, \qquad W = T^{n/2} W',$$

in accord with the powers of U_0 indicated by the transformation (7); then, neglecting terms proportional to $x_0/U_0 t_0$, we obtain

$$U'\frac{\partial U'}{\partial X} + W'\frac{\partial U'}{\partial Z'} - \frac{\partial^2 U'}{\partial Z'^2} - f\frac{\partial f}{\partial X} = 0. \tag{12}$$

This equation is analogous to the steady boundary-layer equation with a velocity $U_0 \tau^n f(\mathrm{x})$ at the edge of the layer. It suggests that at large times the flow becomes quasi-steady, in the sense that it behaves like a *steady* flow of boundary-layer theory with the instantaneous free-stream speed.

Another case of boundary-layer flow which is related to the case of boundary-layer flow from rest is that in which the external stream velocity changes suddenly from one value to another. The major part of the original boundary layer reacts as though it were inviscid, because viscosity has insufficient time to counter the increase in velocity. However, very close to the wall the fluid which was originally almost at rest now attains a finite velocity. Thus at the wall there appears a thin secondary boundary layer of the type which appears when a body of fluid is brought impulsively from rest to a finite velocity. This secondary layer grows in thickness and ultimately interacts in a non-linear way with the steady, primary boundary layer, and the whole field of flow proceeds to grow into a new steady state. Work on this and related aspects of unsteady flow is a comparatively recent development and is referred to only briefly in this chapter, in Section 13.

Let us now examine the situation obtaining in cases of periodic boundary-layer flow. There are two main subdivisions to consider, on the one hand periodic boundary layers in the absence of an imposed mean flow, and on the other hand periodic boundary layers with an imposed mean flow. (The word 'imposed' is used here because the non-linear Reynolds stresses associated with most periodic flows often produce a mean flow, with respect to a time-average, if there is not one already present. For a discussion of the concept of Reynolds stress the reader is referred to the Appendix to Chapter IX.)

It can be shown that the equations which arise in the theory of periodic boundary layers in the absence of an imposed mean flow are analogous to those of the theory of boundary-layer motion from rest, when the time from the start of the motion is small. Firstly, we note that the time, δ^2/ν, for vorticity to diffuse outwards from the boundary through a distance, δ, representative of the boundary-layer thickness, must be of the order of ω^{-1}, where ω is the frequency of the periodic motion. Consequently, the boundary-layer thickness is proportional to $\sqrt{(\nu/\omega)}$. Furthermore, if z is the distance normal to the surface then the appropriate dimensionless distance, which will appear in the equations, is clearly $z\sqrt{(\omega/\nu)}$. If we regard ω^{-1} as a typical time, t_0, for the system, then, by an argument similar to that given earlier for flow from rest, it can be deduced that the two important parameters for the flow are $\omega x_0^2/\nu$ and $\omega x_0/U_0$, where x_0 is again a typical length, and U_0 is a speed typical of the amplitude of the velocity fluctuations. These two parameters are the inverses of the corresponding ones for motion from rest. Physical meanings may be ascribed to them in the way described earlier. In the particular case when the boundary-layer thickness, δ, is small compared with x_0, that is $\omega x_0^2/\nu \gg 1$, the boundary-layer approximation is applicable and equations similar to (2) and (3) yield an equation similar to (5). Furthermore, if $\omega x_0/U_0$ is large compared with unity a solution may be developed in inverse powers of this parameter. For the validity of this approach it is necessary for the Reynolds number, $U_0 x_0/\nu$, to be large. Moreover, as for motion from rest, there are limitations on the order to which the series can be carried. On the other hand, cases also occur in which δ is of the same order as x_0, so that $\omega x_0^2/\nu$ is of the order unity, and the boundary-layer approximation is not applicable. But if $\omega x_0/U_0$ is sufficiently large, a solution may again be developed in inverse powers of this parameter. In this case the Reynolds number is small, and to the first order the slow-motion equations are applicable. Such cases are discussed in Section IV. 2 as well as in this chapter.

In the case of a periodic boundary layer with an imposed mean flow, the velocity at the edge of the layer fluctuates about a non-zero mean. For small fluctuations, the mean flow in the boundary layer is unaffected by the Reynolds stress of the oscillation and is given by the steady boundary-layer equation, while linearization about this mean yields an oscillation boundary-layer equation. If U_0 is a reference mean-velocity, and x_0 a reference length, then the two parameters which enter into the theory are the Reynolds number, $U_0 x_0/\nu$, and the frequency parameter, $\lambda = \omega \delta_{10}^2/\nu$, where δ_{10} is the mean displacement thickness at some particular station, say $x = x_0$. For most boundary layers δ_{10} is of the order $\sqrt{(\nu x_0/U_0)}$, so that λ is proportional to $\omega x_0/U_0$. The physical meaning of this parameter may be represented in terms of convection and diffusion in the way discussed earlier. Alternatively, we may say that λ represents the ratio of the square of the mean displacement thickness to the square of the representative thickness, $[\sqrt{(\nu/\omega)}]$, within which the oscillation is affected by viscous forces. If λ is large this thickness is small compared with the mean displacement thickness, and the oscillatory part of the flow is virtually independent of the mean flow. In fact the oscillatory flow is almost exactly like a periodic boundary layer in the absence of an impressed mean flow, and may conveniently be referred to as a secondary boundary layer. For moderate values of λ, however, the oscillation is subject to interaction with the mean flow, and the 'secondary' boundary layer has a thickness of the same order of magnitude as that of the mean boundary layer.

It can be seen from equations (5) and (11) that for cases in which a boundary-layer theory is applicable, the relevant equations for two-dimensional unsteady flow are equations (V.3) and (V.16) with appropriate boundary conditions, namely

$$\frac{\partial u}{\partial t}+u\frac{\partial u}{\partial x}+w\frac{\partial u}{\partial z} = \frac{\partial U}{\partial t}+U\frac{\partial U}{\partial x}+\nu\frac{\partial^2 u}{\partial z^2},$$

$$\frac{\partial u}{\partial x}+\frac{\partial w}{\partial z} = 0,$$

$$u = w = 0 \quad \text{at } z = 0, \qquad u \to U \quad \text{as } z \to \infty, \qquad (13)$$

where the form of the solution depends on the parameters discussed in this section.

2. Classes of solutions of the unsteady Navier–Stokes equations

Many of the flows described in this chapter are particular members of a general class of exact solutions whose existence, as a class, was shown by Lin (1958a). They are all flows which are bounded by an infinite plane, which we can take to be the x_1, x_2 plane. If x_3 is the distance normal to the surface, then a solution of the Navier–Stokes equations in Cartesian coordinates (equations (III.12) with $X = Y = Z = 0$; $x, y, z \equiv x_1, x_2, x_3$; $u, v, w \equiv u_1, u_2, u_3$) exists in the form

$$u_i = x_1 f_{i1}(x_3, t)+x_2 f_{i2}(x_3, t)+f_{i3}(x_3, t) \quad (i = 1, 2),$$

$$u_3 = \qquad\qquad f_{33}(x_3, t),$$

$$-p/\rho = \tfrac{1}{2}a_{11}x_1^2+a_{12}x_1 x_2+\tfrac{1}{2}a_{22}x_2^2+a_{13}x_1+a_{23}x_2+P(x_3, t), \quad (14)$$

where the functions $a_{11}(t)$, etc., are given. The seven velocity functions and P are determined by the following eight partial differential equations in x_3 and t with suitable boundary conditions (the summation convention is not applicable):

$$\frac{\partial f_{ij}}{\partial t}+f_{ij}f_{ii}+f_{kj}f_{ik}+f_{33}\frac{\partial f_{ij}}{\partial x_3} = a_{ij}+\nu\frac{\partial^2 f_{ij}}{\partial x_3^2},$$

where $a_{21} = a_{12} \quad (i = 1, 2; j = 1, 2, 3; i+k = 3),$

$$\frac{\partial f_{33}}{\partial t}+f_{33}\frac{\partial f_{33}}{\partial x_3} = \frac{\partial P}{\partial x_3}+\nu\frac{\partial^2 f_{33}}{\partial x_3^2},$$

$$f_{11}+f_{22}+\frac{\partial f_{33}}{\partial x_3} = 0. \qquad (15)$$

For the sub-class of flow with rotational symmetry, it can be deduced that the following simplifications are valid, namely,

$$f_{11} = f_{22}; \qquad f_{12} = -f_{21}; \qquad f_{13} = f_{23} = 0;$$

$$a_{11} = a_{22}; \qquad a_{12} = a_{13} = a_{23} = 0. \tag{16}$$

It then follows that the components of velocity in cylindrical polar coordinates (Section III. 12 with $z \equiv x_3$, $v_z \equiv u_3$) are

$$v_r = rf_{11}(x_3, t), \qquad v_\theta = rf_{21}(x_3, t); \qquad v_z = f_{33}(x_3, t),$$

where f_{11}, f_{21}, and f_{33} are determined by three appropriate equations which result from equations (15) with the substitutions (16). The pressure is given by

$$\frac{-p}{\rho} = \tfrac{1}{2}r^2 a_{11}(t) + P(x_3, t),$$

where P is determined by the relevant equation (15).

Cases of steady motion which fall within this general class are discussed in Sections III. 15 (a), III. 19 (a), III. 19 (b), III. 20, VIII. 5, VIII. 21, and VIII. 22. They include the asymptotic-suction flow, stagnation-point flows, rotating-disk and rotating-fluid flows, and the flow in a two-dimensional channel.

Within the present chapter, all the flows described in Sections 3 (a), 9, 14, and 16 fall within Lin's class of solutions, as well as the unsteady stagnation-point flows discussed in Section 8 (equation 75). These are all cases in which the set of partial differential equations (15) can be reduced to a set of ordinary differential equations. The unsteady rotating-disk and rotating-fluid flows mentioned at the end of Section 8 and the oscillatory stagnation-point flow discussed in Sections 13 and 15 also fall within the class; however, the equations in these cases cannot be reduced to a finite set of ordinary differential equations, and the exact solutions have not yet been calculated.

A different class of exact solutions of the Navier–Stokes equations has been found by Birkhoff (1950, pp. 137–9), who showed that a solution of the equations in Cartesian coordinates (equation III.12) exists in the form

$$\{u; v; w\} = g(t)\{f_1(\chi_1, \chi_2, \chi_3); f_2(\chi_1, \chi_2, \chi_3); f_3(\chi_1, \chi_2, \chi_3)\},$$

$$\frac{-p}{\rho} = a(t)P(\chi_1, \chi_2, \chi_3),$$

where $\chi_1 = h(t)x, \qquad \chi_2 = h(t)y, \qquad \chi_3 = h(t)z,$

provided $g = h = t^{-\frac{1}{2}}, \qquad a = t^{-1},$

The four equations determining the functions f_1, f_2, f_3, and P are

$$-\frac{1}{2}\Big(f_i + \sum_{k=1}^{3} \chi_k \frac{\partial f_i}{\partial \chi_k}\Big) + \sum_{k=1}^{3} f_k \frac{\partial f_i}{\partial \chi_k} = \frac{\partial P}{\partial \chi_i} + \nu \sum_{k=1}^{3} \frac{\partial^2 f_i}{\partial \chi_k^2} \quad (i = 1, 2, 3),$$

$$\sum_{k=1}^{3} \frac{\partial f_k}{\partial \chi_k} = 0, \tag{17}$$

subject to suitable boundary conditions.

There are two degenerate sub-classes of Birkhoff's class of solutions, valid for cases in which the non-linear convection terms vanish identically. They are

$$\text{(i)} \quad g = t^\alpha, \qquad h = t^{-\frac{1}{2}}, \qquad a = t^{\alpha - \frac{1}{2}},$$

where α is a constant, and

$$\text{(ii)} \quad g = e^{ct}, \qquad h = 1, \qquad a = e^{ct},$$

where c is a constant.

The equations for these two sub-classes can be derived for the special cases of flow in which the non-linear convection terms do vanish, but they will not be given here.

The flows described in Sections 3 and 5 of the present chapter fall within Birkhoff's class of solutions; however, except for the example in Section 3 of a flow with its u component of velocity proportional to x/t, they are degenerate solutions and are members of sub-class (i) or sub-class (ii).

PART I

BOUNDARY-LAYER MOTION FROM REST

3. Some exact solutions of the unsteady Navier–Stokes equations and of the unsteady boundary-layer equations

(a) *Navier–Stokes equations*

The simplest solution, which has been treated in Section III. 14, is that for Rayleigh's problem of an infinite flat plate started impulsively into motion in its own plane with velocity U. The velocity u of the fluid at time t at distance z from the plane is

$$u = U \operatorname{erfc}\{z/2\surd(\nu t)\} = \frac{2U}{\surd\pi} \int_{z/2\surd(\nu t)}^{\infty} e^{-x^2}\, dx. \tag{18}$$

When t tends to infinity the integral tends to $\frac{1}{2}\surd\pi$, and we have the well-known result that the velocity tends to U for a fixed value of z.

The reader is referred to Mallick (1957) for a similar impulsive-flow solution for a rotating cylinder.

Consider now an infinite plane starting from rest and moving with velocity $U(t)$. It has been shown that, if $U(t)$ is zero for $t < 0$ and is a constant for $t \geqslant 0$, the velocity induced in a semi-infinite mass of fluid is of the form $Uf(zt^{-\frac{1}{2}})$. It is now proposed to determine which functions $U(t)$ yield a velocity of the form $U(t)f[zk(t)]$, where $k(t)$ depends on the form of $U(t)$. We shall refer to such solutions of the diffusion equation (Section III. 14) as 'similar solutions', and the appropriate forms of $U(t)$ can be determined. By writing $u = U(t)f(\eta)$, $\eta = zk(t)$, in the diffusion equation, Watson (1955) has shown that

(i) $U(t) = At^{\alpha}$; $k(t) = \beta t^{-\frac{1}{2}}$ (β real, positive, and α real)

and   (ii) $U(t) = Ae^{ct}$, $k = $ constant

lead to similar solutions. Thus in case (i), with $\beta = \frac{1}{2}/\sqrt{\nu}$, the diffusion equation becomes

$$f'' + 2\eta f' - 4\alpha f = 0. \tag{19}$$

The solution of this equation, which satisfies the conditions $f = 1$ at $\eta = 0$ and $f \to 0$ as $\eta \to \infty$, is

$$f = 2^{\alpha+\frac{1}{2}}\pi^{-\frac{1}{2}}\Gamma(\alpha+1)e^{-\eta^2/2}D_{-2\alpha-1}(\eta\sqrt{2}),$$

where $D_{-2\alpha-1}$ is a parabolic-cylinder function (Whittaker and Watson 1946, section 16.5). For $\alpha \geqslant 0$ this solution is the only one which tends to zero as η tends to infinity. But if $\alpha < 0$ and is not a negative integer, there is also a second basic solution which tends to zero much less rapidly (as $\eta^{2\alpha}$, as against $e^{-\eta^2}\eta^{-2\alpha-1}$ for the solution given), and can therefore be disregarded.

In case (ii), with $k = \sqrt{(c/\nu)}$, the diffusion equation becomes

$$f'' = f, \tag{20}$$

and the solution which satisfies $f = 1$ at $\eta = 0$ and $f \to 0$ as $\eta \to \infty$ is $f = e^{-\eta}$. It can be seen that c must be positive for the solution to satisfy the boundary conditions, so that $U(-\infty) = 0$. For further details, the reader is referred to Watson (1955).

All the solutions discussed above are members of Lin's class of solutions, and all are members of one or the other of Birkhoff's degenerate sub-classes of solutions. A flow which falls within Lin's class and Birkhoff's general formulation is the flow defined by

$$u = \frac{mx}{t}F'(\eta), \qquad w = -m\sqrt{\left/\left(\frac{2\nu}{t}\right)\right.}F(\eta), \qquad \eta = \frac{z}{\sqrt{(2\nu t)}},$$

$$\frac{-(p-p_0)}{\rho} = \frac{m(m-1)x^2}{2t^2} + \frac{m\nu}{t}(F' + mF^2 + \eta F + P_0), \tag{21}$$

where m, p_0, and P_0 are constants and F is given by

$$F''' + \eta F'' + 2m(FF'' - F'^2) + 2F' - 2 + 2m = 0$$

subject to

$$F = F' = 0 \quad \text{at } \eta = 0; \qquad F' \to 1 \quad \text{as } \eta \to \infty. \tag{22}$$

Schuh (1955) was the first to discuss equations (22), though his derivation of them was based on the boundary-layer equations. Yang (1958a) has since solved the problem of equations (22) for several values of m, and has found, amongst other results, that the solution has zero skin friction for $m = 0.315$ and positive skin friction for $m > 0.315$. Yang (1958b) has also considered the related problems with variable fluid properties, and with axial symmetry.

(b) Boundary-layer equations

In the paper mentioned immediately above, Schuh (1955) analysed the unsteady boundary-layer equations (13) for possible 'similar' solutions. Steady similar solutions are defined and described in Section V. 21, and for the unsteady generalization we substitute the following in equations (13), namely

$$u = U(x,t)F'(\eta), \qquad \eta = z/N(x,t). \tag{23}$$

Schuh found an ordinary differential equation of the third order for F, which shows the possibility of the following similar solutions:

  (i) the steady solutions of Section V. 21,
  (ii) the solution for $U(t) = At^\alpha$, $N = 2\sqrt{(\nu t)}$,
  (iii) the solution for $U(t) = Ae^{ct}$, $N = \sqrt{(\nu/c)}$,
  (iv) the solution for $U(x,t) = mx/t$, $N = \sqrt{(2\nu t)}$,
  (v) the solution for $U(x,t) = U_0$, $N = \sqrt{(k_1 \nu t + k_2 \nu x/U_0)}$ (where U_0, k_1, and k_2 are constants).

As pointed out earlier, cases (ii), (iii), and (iv) are also exact solutions of the Navier–Stokes equations. Schuh found an approximate solution for case (iv) using the method described at the beginning of Section 7. Schuh's work has been extended somewhat by Geis (1956). The reader is referred also to a paper by Rozin (1957a) for a treatment of some 'similar' solutions of the unsteady boundary-layer equations.

4. Impulsive motion of a semi-infinite flat plate normal to its edge

The flow generated by a semi-infinite flat plate which starts suddenly from rest with a velocity U can be analysed in a general way by means of the dimensional analysis described in Section 1. It is clear from the discussion there given that, if t is the time and x is the distance measured from the leading edge parallel to the flow, $Ut/x = \tau$ is likely to be a very important variable in the mathematical description of the flow. If τ is very large, the flow approximates closely to Blasius flow past a semi-infinite flat plate and is independent of time; this occurs for a certain distance downstream from the leading edge. On the other hand, if τ is small, the flow approximates closely to impulsive Rayleigh flow past an infinite plate, and is unaffected by the leading edge; this occurs in a region extending to infinity from a point at a certain distance downstream from the leading edge. Since the position of the transition region between Blasius and Rayleigh flows depends on τ, the Blasius-flow region extends farther and farther along the plate as time progresses. Thus at an infinite time from the commencement of motion the Blasius régime of flow is dominant everywhere, and has replaced the Rayleigh flow which was dominant almost everywhere when t was small. These results can be deduced from the equations of motion without actually solving them.

Stewartson (1951) considered the boundary-layer equations in the light of the above points and obtained some approximate solutions of them. The first method of approximation utilizes Rayleigh's analogy, in which it is assumed that all convection takes place at the free-stream speed relative to the plate. Thus the convection terms $u\,\partial u/\partial x + w\,\partial u/\partial z$ are replaced by $U\,\partial u/\partial x$. Consider axes fixed in the body so that we set up an impulsive flow of the fluid. In this case the boundary-layer equation becomes

$$\frac{\partial u}{\partial t} + U\frac{\partial u}{\partial x} = \nu\frac{\partial^2 u}{\partial z^2}, \tag{24}$$

which, with $\zeta = z/\sqrt{(\nu t)}$ and $\tau = Ut/x$, can be shown to have the solution

$$u = U\operatorname{erf}(\zeta/2) = U\operatorname{erf}\{z/2\sqrt{(\nu t)}\} \quad \text{when } \tau < 1, \tag{25}$$

and $\qquad u = U\operatorname{erf}(\zeta\tau^{\frac{1}{2}}/2) = U\operatorname{erf}\{\tfrac{1}{2}z\sqrt{(U/\nu x)}\} \quad \text{when } \tau > 1, \tag{26}$

where $\operatorname{erf}x$ is defined in equation (III. 58). Consequently for $\tau < 1$, the flow is independent of x, and for $\tau > 1$ it is independent of t. These solutions illustrate qualitatively how the transition from Blasius- to Rayleigh-type flow moves along the plate as time increases. Strictly the approximation is valid only near the edge of the boundary layer, where u is nearly equal to U.

A second method of approximation is to use the boundary-layer momentum-integral equation (V. 42) from which Stewartson obtained the approximate result

(i) $\qquad \left(\mu\dfrac{\partial u}{\partial z}\right)_w = 0\cdot534\rho U\sqrt{(\nu/t)}$ when $\tau \leqslant 2\cdot65,$ $\qquad\qquad$ (27)

(ii) $\qquad \left(\mu\dfrac{\partial u}{\partial z}\right)_w = 0\cdot328\rho U\sqrt{(U\nu/x)}$ when $\tau \geqslant 2\cdot65,$ $\qquad\qquad$ (28)

for the skin friction on the wall. Formula (27) is in very good agreement with the Rayleigh formula for skin friction on an infinite flat plate (coefficient 0·565) and the formula (28) is in good agreement with the skin friction in Blasius flow (coefficient 0·332). Similar results were obtained by Schuh (1953a) and Oudart (1953).

Both methods described above show an abrupt change from one type of flow to another at a definite value of τ, a feature which is physically unrealistic. But the methods do suggest that for $\tau < \tau_1$, say, the flow is approximately a Rayleigh flow, and that for $\tau > \tau_2$, say, the flow is approximately a Blasius flow. The two approximate methods suggest that $\tau_1 = 1$ and $\tau_2 = 2\cdot65$ may be reasonable estimates. A more exact treatment of the full equations has not, so far, yielded conclusive results. Cheng (1957) and Cheng and Elliott (1957) have also considered the problem.

The case in which a semi-infinite flat plate moves from rest with uniform acceleration has been treated by Moore (1951) and by Schuh (1953a). Moore has also considered the case in which the dependence of the velocity of the plate on time is arbitrary, and has suggested that a series of parameters, $xU'(t)/U^2$, $x^2U''(t)/U^3,..., x^nU^{(n)}(t)/U^{n+1}$ may be necessary to specify the flow. In many cases which have been considered, the parameters reduce to a single one (Tsuji 1953). However, if the velocity of the plate fluctuates about a mean value, Moore's calculations in terms of the above parameters are relevant to the topic of Section 13, where a comparison is made with other work.

5. Impulsive motion of fluid along corners and edges of infinite length

In this section and the following one we shall consider the flow generated by a body of infinite length which at time $t = 0$ is started impulsively from rest with a constant velocity parallel to its length. Attention in the present section will be focused on the case of a body consisting of two semi-infinite planes intersecting at a given angle to form a wedge, which moves parallel to the line of intersection. The fluid is therefore set into motion in a wedge-shaped region of angle β, say, where β may lie between 0 and 2π. The flow discussed in Section 2, namely that due to an infinite plane, is clearly the case of $\beta = \pi$. Howarth (1950) discussed and solved the problem for $\beta = 2\pi$, which is the case of flow due to a semi-infinite flat plate which moves parallel to its edge, and Sowerby (1951) the problem for $\beta = \pi/n$, n being a non-zero positive integer. The general case has been solved by Hasimoto (1951) and Sowerby and Cooke (1953).

Since the wedge is of infinite length, we expect the flow to be parallel to the wedge and, from the equation of continuity, independent of distance along it. Thus the flow is uni-directional, but it is three-dimensional in the sense that the velocity depends upon both coordinates in the plane normal to the motion. Vorticity generated at the boundary is diffused outwards by viscous action and, since the physical situation is similar in all planes normal to the direction of flow, we can refer to the flow as being diffusive and non-convective. The flow is, in fact, governed by the diffusion equation discussed in Section III. 14. Thus there is an analogy with the problem of heat conduction in a wedge-shaped solid, initially at a given temperature, when the temperature of the boundary is suddenly raised by a finite amount. In this analogy, the temperature corresponds to the velocity and the thermometric conductivity to the kinematic viscosity. For solutions of such problems the reader is referred to Carslaw and Jaeger (1947). Here we shall refer mainly to the papers of Hasimoto (1951, 1952) and Sowerby and Cooke (1953).

The importance of the study of flows of the type described above lies in the use of the Rayleigh analogy to find the *steady* flow past a semi-infinite body of the same section, and for this aspect of the theory the reader is referred to Sections III. 14 and VIII. 25.

Consider a wedge composed of two semi-infinite planes defined by $\theta = 0$ and $\theta = \beta$, where $0 \leqslant \beta \leqslant 2\pi$, and take cylindrical polar coordinates r, θ, z, with z parallel to the line of intersection. Let the wedge be set impulsively into motion at time $t = 0$ with velocity W. Since there are no pressure gradients, the velocity, w, of the fluid is governed by the Navier–Stokes equation

$$\frac{\partial w}{\partial t} = \nu \left(\frac{\partial^2 w}{\partial r^2} + \frac{1}{r} \frac{\partial w}{\partial r} + \frac{1}{r^2} \frac{\partial^2 w}{\partial \theta^2} \right), \tag{29}$$

with the boundary conditions

$$
\begin{aligned}
w &= 0 \quad \text{when} \quad t = 0, \quad 0 < \theta < \beta, \\
w &= W \quad \text{when} \quad \theta = 0 \quad \text{and} \quad \theta = \beta \\
w &\to 0 \quad \text{when} \quad r \to \infty, \quad 0 < \theta < \beta
\end{aligned}
\left. \right\} \; t > 0. \tag{30}
$$

The mathematical details of the solution of the problem defined by (29) and (30), which are given in the papers by Hasimoto and by Sowerby and Cooke, present no features of particular interest for the fluid dynamics, so we shall now proceed to a description of the main results obtained.

Two simple particular solutions are worthy of note, namely the Rayleigh flat-plate case ($\beta = \pi$), for which

$$w = W[1 - \operatorname{erf}(\eta \sin \theta)], \tag{31}$$

and the case of flow inside a right-angled corner ($\beta = \frac{1}{2}\pi$), for which

$$w = W[1 - \operatorname{erf}(\eta \cos \theta)\operatorname{erf}(\eta \sin \theta)], \tag{32}$$

where

$$\eta = r/2\sqrt{(\nu t)} \tag{33}$$

and $\operatorname{erf} x$ is defined in equation (III. 58). In the general case the skin friction, τ_w, is, by symmetry, the same on each of the planes, $\theta = 0$ and $\theta = \beta$, and is given by

$$\tau_w = \frac{-\mu}{r}\left(\frac{\partial w}{\partial \theta}\right)_{\theta=0} = \frac{-\mu}{2\eta\sqrt{(\nu t)}}\left(\frac{\partial w}{\partial \theta}\right)_{\theta=0} \tag{34}$$

Sowerby and Cooke (1953) and Hasimoto (1951) give details of the calculations from this formula. Once the skin friction is known it is possible to calculate the excess (or deficiency) of frictional force due to the presence of a corner by comparing the skin friction with the value for an infinite flat plate. The frictional force on a strip of plate of unit length in the direction of motion, and width b (extending from the corner), is

$$F = \int_0^b \tau_w \, dr, \tag{35}$$

while the force on a similar strip in the case of a flat plate is

$$F_1 = \frac{\mu W b}{\sqrt{(\pi \nu t)}}, \tag{36}$$

as can be seen from equation (18). It follows that as b tends to infinity, $F - F_1 (= T)$ will represent the excess of frictional force on the strip of plate due to the presence of the corner. Sowerby and Cooke (1953) and Hasimoto (1951) give tables of $K = T/\mu W$ for various values of β, and these results were later plotted graphically by Batchelor (1954a) as in Fig. VII. 1. If β is greater than π the frictional force is greater, and if β is less than π it is less, than in the case of a flat plate.

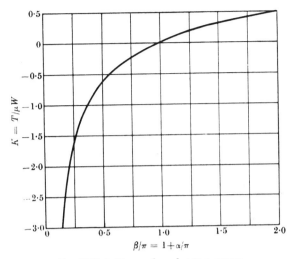

FIG. VII. 1. Excess drag due to a corner.

6. Impulsive motion of an infinite cylinder parallel to its axis

In the present section we shall deal with flows which are similar to those discussed in Section 5, except that the motion is generated by an infinite cylinder starting impulsively from rest. The theory is mainly due to Batchelor (1954a) and to Hasimoto (1954, 1955, 1956). The equation governing the velocity, w, parallel to the cylinder is again the diffusion equation and may be written

$$\frac{1}{\nu}\frac{\partial w}{\partial t} = \frac{\partial^2 w}{\partial x^2} + \frac{\partial^2 w}{\partial y^2}, \tag{37}$$

where x and y are coordinates in a plane normal to the (z) direction of motion, subject to the conditions

$$w = 0 \quad \text{when } t = 0$$

$$\left.\begin{array}{ll} w = W & \text{at the cylinder boundary} \\ w \to 0 & \text{at large distances from the cylinder} \end{array}\right\} \; t > 0. \tag{38}$$

There are two exact solutions which are illustrative of the general characteristics of flow past an arbitrary cylinder (Batchelor 1954a). The first is that for an infinite flat plate, for which (from equation 18) the skin friction is $\mu W/\sqrt{(\pi\nu t)}$. The second solution is that for a circular cylinder, and it satisfies equation (29) with axial symmetry, subject to the boundary conditions (38). Using the analogy with heat conduction and a solution due to Carslaw and Jaeger (1947), Batchelor obtained the velocity and skin friction as integrals involving Bessel functions.

For sufficiently small values of $\nu t/a^2$, where a is the radius of the cylinder, the skin friction takes the form

$$\tau_w = \frac{\mu W}{a}\left\{\left(\frac{a^2}{\pi \nu t}\right)^{\frac{1}{2}} + \frac{1}{2} - \frac{1}{4}\left(\frac{\nu t}{\pi a^2}\right)^{\frac{1}{2}} + \frac{1}{8}\left(\frac{\nu t}{a^2}\right) + \ldots\right\}. \tag{39}$$

The first term gives the skin friction on an infinite flat plate because, for small values of $\nu t/a^2$, the boundary-layer thickness, which is of order $\sqrt{(\nu t)}$, is very much smaller than the radius. For a cylinder of arbitrary cross-section, but without corners, the first two terms of a series analogous to (39) are

$$\tau_w = \mu W\{(\pi \nu t)^{-\frac{1}{2}} + (2R_0)^{-1}\}, \tag{40}$$

where R_0 is the local radius of curvature (Batchelor 1954). The force per unit length on the cylinder is, to the same degree of approximation,

$$F = 2\mu\pi W\{l/(\pi \nu t)^{\frac{1}{2}} + \tfrac{1}{2}\}, \tag{41}$$

where $2\pi l$ is the perimeter of the arbitrary cylinder. This is the same as the force on a circular cylinder of radius l. Hasimoto (1955) obtained higher approximations to the skin friction on an arbitrary cylinder, and derived a formula to the same approximation as (39).

For a cylinder with corners separated by curved arcs, it is necessary to add a contribution due to the presence of the corners. Batchelor (1954a) has done this by using the theory of flow parallel to a wedge, as discussed in Section 5. To the same approximation as equation (41), the total friction per unit length on a cylinder with n corners of angle $\pi + \alpha_r$ $(r = 1, 2, \ldots, n)$ is found to be

$$F = \mu W\left\{\frac{2\pi l}{(\pi \nu t)^{\frac{1}{2}}} + \tfrac{1}{2}\left(2\pi - \sum_{r=1}^{n}\alpha_r\right) + 2\sum_{r=1}^{n}K(\alpha_r)\right\}. \tag{42}$$

This formula was first obtained by Batchelor (1954a), but he overlooked the fact that the function $K(\alpha)$ gives the excess friction on only *one* of the planes forming a wedge and consequently omitted a factor of 2. The corrected formula was given by Hasimoto (1955). Since $[2K(\alpha) - \tfrac{1}{2}\alpha]$ can be shown to be negative when α is positive, it follows that the skin friction on a convex cylinder with corners is *less* than the friction on a convex cylinder without corners but with the same perimeter.

For the particular case of a flat plate of breadth πl, equation (42) gives

$$F = 2\pi\mu W\left\{l/(\pi \nu t)^{\frac{1}{2}} + \frac{1}{\pi}\right\}. \tag{43}$$

The exact solution for a flat plate has been given by Levine (1957).

Some results to the approximation of equations (41) and (42) are illustrated in Fig. VII. 2 ($vt/l^2 < 1$), which, essentially, is due to Batchelor (1954). The curve for a circular cylinder is very near to the exact curve, while that for a flat plate of the same perimeter always lies below it. Results for elliptic cylinders may be found in a paper by Hasimoto (1955).

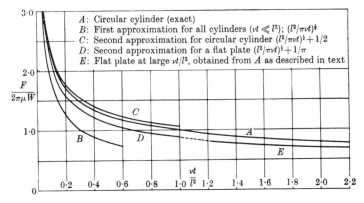

A: Circular cylinder (exact)
B: First approximation for all cylinders ($vt \ll l^2$); $(l^2/\pi vt)^{\frac{1}{2}}$
C: Second approximation for circular cylinder $(l^2/\pi vt)^{\frac{1}{2}} + 1/2$
D: Second approximation for a flat plate $(l^2/\pi vt)^{\frac{1}{2}} + 1/\pi$
E: Flat plate at large vt/l^2, obtained from A as described in text

FIG. VII. 2. Force on a cylinder moving impulsively from rest parallel to its axis.

For large values of vt/l^2 a large volume of fluid surrounding the body has a velocity near to W, within which changes with time are small and w approximately satisfies Laplace's equation, $\nabla^2 w = 0$. In Fig. VII. 2 the exact curve of $F/2\pi\mu W$ against vt/l^2 is given for the case of a circular cylinder; Batchelor has shown that to obtain the curve for any arbitrary shape of cylinder (of perimeter $2\pi l$) for large vt/l^2, it is merely necessary to multiply each abscissa by b^2/l^2 for a given ordinate $(F/2\pi\mu W)$, where b is the radius of an 'equivalent' circular cylinder. The determination of b/l had been discussed by Morris (1937), who obtained the following results: for a regular polygon of n sides b/l ranges from $\frac{1}{4}\pi$ ($n = 2$) through 0·885 ($n = 3$), 0·925 ($n = 4$), to 1·0 ($n = \infty$, circle); for an ellipse, b/l ranges from $\frac{1}{4}\pi$ for a flat plate to 1·0 for a circle. The curve for a flat plate of perimeter $2\pi l$, as obtained by the method described above, is given in Fig. VII. 2 as curve E ($vt/l^2 > 1\cdot2$). A more complete investigation of the form of the skin friction at large values of vt/l^2, with application to the elliptic cylinder, has been made by Hasimoto (1954).

A related flow which has been studied by Nielsen (1956) is that generated by a circular cylinder which is moved from rest by the sudden application of a force which thereafter remains constant. An exact solution to the problem has been obtained by analogy with the solution of a problem in supersonic wing-body interference.

7. Unsteady motion of an infinite cylinder normal to its axis

It is clear that the occurrence of separation produces considerable complication in an exact treatment of the growth of the boundary layer. Even without this complication, the equations of unsteady boundary-layer flow present difficulties, and it is often necessary to have recourse to approximate methods. Schuh (1953a) has evolved a method based on the momentum-integral equation (V. 42) (with $w_s = 0$) in which it is convenient to have the coordinates fixed in the body. This method is described below. For further work on approximate methods, with inclusion of heat transfer, the reader is referred to Yang (1959). Later in the section, an expansion of the solution of the boundary-layer equation, valid for small values of the time, will be described. For a discussion of our neglect of compressibility see Section I. 2.6.

In equation (V. 42) we may use, for example, Pohlhausen (Section VI. 13) or 'similar' profiles (Section V. 16). The single parameter which represents the assumed profile is

$$\lambda = -\frac{\delta_2^2}{U}\left(\frac{\partial^2 u}{\partial z^2}\right)_w = \frac{\delta_2^2}{\nu}\left(\frac{\partial U}{\partial x} + \frac{1}{U}\frac{\partial U}{\partial t}\right), \tag{44}$$

and the two important boundary-layer characteristics,

$$T = (\delta_2/U)(\partial u/\partial z)_w \quad \text{and} \quad H = \delta_1/\delta_2,$$

are functions of λ only. These functions are given in Table VI. 2 for Pohlhausen profiles; for the functions based on the similar profiles, the reader is referred to the paper by Schuh (1953a).

With a few transformations, equation (V. 42) becomes

$$f\frac{\partial Z}{\partial \xi} + \left(H + 2\lambda\frac{dH}{d\lambda}\right)\frac{\partial Z}{\partial \tau} = 2\epsilon - 2\lambda(H+2) - 2Z\left(\frac{dH}{d\lambda}\frac{\lambda}{g}\frac{\partial g}{\partial \tau} - \frac{2}{f}\frac{\partial f}{\partial \tau}\right), \tag{45}$$

where

$$Z = \frac{\delta_2^2 U_0}{\nu x_0}, \qquad \xi = x/x_0, \qquad \tau = tU_0/x_0,$$

$$f = U/U_0, \qquad g(\xi,\tau) = \lambda/Z = \frac{\partial f}{\partial \xi} + \frac{1}{f}\frac{\partial f}{\partial \tau}, \tag{46}$$

x_0 being a typical length and U_0 a typical velocity, say the free-stream velocity. Since λ is a function of Z, ξ, and τ, and since ϵ and H are

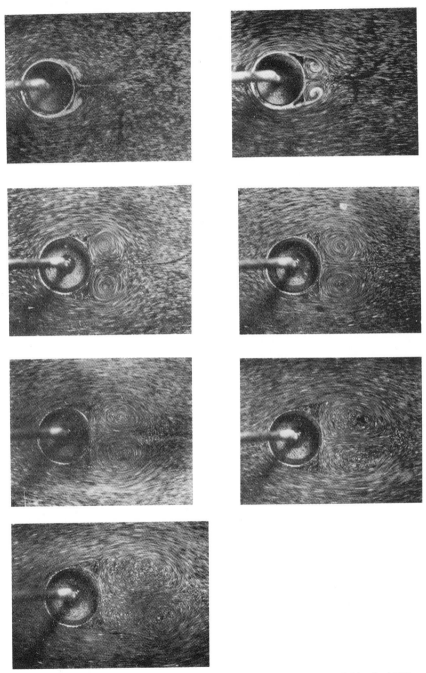

Fig. VII. 3. Flow due to impulsive motion of a circular cylinder. (Goldstein 1938)

functions of λ, equation (45) is of the form

$$A(Z,\xi,\tau)\frac{\partial Z}{\partial \xi} + B(Z,\xi,\tau)\frac{\partial Z}{\partial \tau} = C(Z,\xi,\tau) \qquad (47)$$

and can be solved when two solutions of the related equations

$$\frac{d\xi}{A(Z,\xi,\tau)} = \frac{d\tau}{B(Z,\xi,\tau)} = \frac{dZ}{C(Z,\xi,\tau)} \qquad (48)$$

are known. In general, a numerical procedure is required.

The case of a circular cylinder starting impulsively from rest provides an interesting example. It is found theoretically that, after a certain lapse of time, separation starts at the rear stagnation point; the point of separation then moves around the cylinder until at large values of the time it coincides with the point of laminar separation for steady flow. Experimental evidence, in the form of photographs due to Rubach, is given in Fig. VII. 3 (Plate). Before, and for a very short period of time after, separation starts the pressure distribution may be assumed to be that appropriate to potential flow with the original boundary, but this assumption soon loses validity. However, Schuh (1953a) has made a calculation in which the pressure distribution of the potential flow *is* assumed to be valid for all values of the time. The results have only qualitative value, but in the absence of more realistic calculations they are of interest and are now described.

For impulsive motion both g and f are obviously independent of τ. Thus equations (45) and (46) may be simplified. Furthermore, it is known (see Section VI. 18) that with Pohlhausen profiles $[2\epsilon - 2\lambda(H+2)]$ is approximately given by $a - b\lambda$, where a is taken to be 0.470 and b is taken to be 6 in Schuh's work. The boundary condition is that $Z = 0$ when $\tau = 0$. Two independent integrals of equations (48) are

$$Z = \frac{a}{f(\xi)^b} \int_{\xi_0}^{\xi} \{f(\xi)\}^{b-1}\, d\xi, \qquad \tau = \int_{\xi_0}^{\xi} \frac{H + 2\lambda(dH/d\lambda)}{f(\xi)}\, d\xi, \qquad (49)$$

where, in the second integral, $\lambda = Z\, df/d\xi$, the function $Z(\xi)$ being given by the first integral. It is known from the theory of first-order partial differential equations that the particular solution which satisfies the boundary condition and equation (45) can be formed by elimination of ξ_0 from the two independent integrals. For the case of a circular cylinder, $f(\xi) = 2\sin 2\xi$ and the characteristic length, x_0, is the diameter d. The results of Schuh's calculation are illustrated in Fig. VII. 4 and Fig. VII. 5, which show respectively the development of displacement thickness and the shift of separation. Initially the displacement thickness is almost constant but, as τ increases, δ_1 becomes much larger and separation commences at the rear stagnation point. A shift to the ultimate steady separation point of $107.2°$ from the forward stagnation

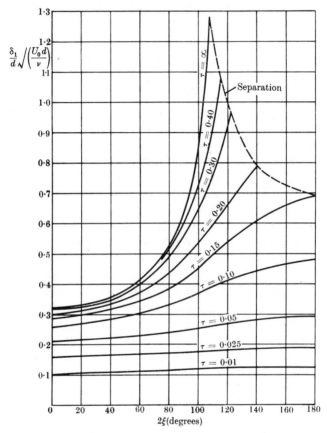

FIG. VII. 4. Development of displacement thickness of boundary layer on a circular cylinder. Impulsive start from rest. Potential flow pressure distribution.

point then takes place, the boundary layer being very thick in the separation region. This predicted limiting position of separation is much farther back than the value calculated for steady flow ($81°$) with an experimental pressure distribution (Section VI. 10), because of the neglect of the upstream influence of separation. A comparison in Fig. VII. 5 with the graph derived from a series solution in ascending powers of τ, which will now be described, suggests that the latter method is not valid for values of τ greater than about 0.3.

We shall now describe the method of solution in series as developed for impulsive motion of a stream past a cylinder, since the same general principles also hold for uniformly, and non-uniformly, accelerated flows. Blasius (1908) first considered the problem, and his work was later extended and developed by Goldstein and Rosenhead (1936), Görtler (1944, 1948b), and Watson (1955).

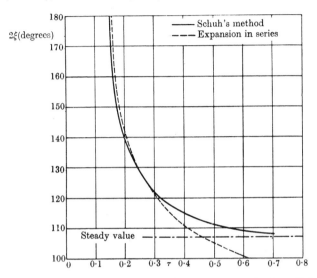

Fig. VII. 5. Movement of the point of separation on a circular cylinder with impulsive start from rest.

Let us refer the coordinates and velocity components to standard values and define a stream function ψ to satisfy the equation of continuity, by the transformations

$$\eta = z/2\sqrt{(\nu t)}, \qquad u = U_0 \frac{\partial \psi}{\partial \eta}, \qquad w = \frac{-2U_0\sqrt{(\nu t)}}{x_0} \frac{\partial \psi}{\partial \xi}, \qquad (50)$$

with ξ, τ, and f as defined in (46). For impulsive flow, f is a function of ξ only. The boundary-layer equation (13) then becomes

$$\tau \frac{\partial^2 \psi}{\partial \eta \partial \tau} - \tfrac{1}{2}\eta \frac{\partial^2 \psi}{\partial \eta^2} - \frac{1}{4}\frac{\partial^3 \psi}{\partial \eta^3} = \tau\left(f\frac{df}{d\xi} - \frac{\partial \psi}{\partial \eta}\frac{\partial^2 \psi}{\partial \eta \partial \xi} + \frac{\partial \psi}{\partial \xi}\frac{\partial^2 \psi}{\partial \eta^2}\right), \qquad (51)$$

subject to the boundary conditions

$$\left.\begin{array}{l} \psi = \partial\psi/\partial\eta = 0 \quad \text{at } \eta = 0 \\[4pt] \partial\psi/\partial\eta \to f(\xi) \quad \text{as } \eta \to \infty \end{array}\right\} \quad \tau \geqslant 0. \qquad (52)$$

Now let us put

$$\psi = \psi_0(\eta,\xi) + \tau\psi_1(\eta,\xi) + \tau^2\psi_2(\eta,\xi) + \dots. \qquad (53)$$

Substituting (53) into (51) and equating successive powers of τ to zero, we obtain the series of equations

$$\frac{\partial^3 \psi_0}{\partial \eta^3} + 2\eta \frac{\partial^2 \psi_0}{\partial \eta^2} = 0, \tag{54}$$

$$\frac{\partial^3 \psi_1}{\partial \eta^3} + 2\eta \frac{\partial^2 \psi_1}{\partial \eta^2} - 4\frac{\partial \psi_1}{\partial \eta} = 4\left\{ -f\frac{df}{d\xi} + \frac{\partial \psi_0}{\partial \eta}\frac{\partial^2 \psi_0}{\partial \eta \partial \xi} - \frac{\partial \psi_0}{\partial \xi}\frac{\partial^2 \psi_0}{\partial \eta^2} \right\}, \tag{55}$$

$$\frac{\partial^3 \psi_2}{\partial \eta^3} + 2\eta \frac{\partial^2 \psi_2}{\partial \eta^2} - 8\frac{\partial \psi_2}{\partial \eta} = 4\left\{ \frac{\partial \psi_0}{\partial \eta}\frac{\partial^2 \psi_1}{\partial \eta \partial \xi} + \frac{\partial \psi_1}{\partial \eta}\frac{\partial^2 \psi_0}{\partial \eta \partial \xi} - \frac{\partial \psi_0}{\partial \xi}\frac{\partial^2 \psi_1}{\partial \eta^2} - \frac{\partial \psi_1}{\partial \xi}\frac{\partial^2 \psi_0}{\partial \eta^2} \right\}, \tag{56}$$

with the boundary conditions ($n \geqslant 0$)

$$\psi_n = \partial\psi_n/\partial\eta = 0 \quad \text{at } \eta = 0,$$
$$\partial\psi_0/\partial\eta \to f(\xi), \quad \partial\psi_{n+1}/\partial\eta \to 0 \quad \text{as } \eta \to \infty. \tag{57}$$

The solution ψ_0 of (54) was given by Blasius (1908) and is

$$\psi_0 = f(\xi) \int_0^\eta \operatorname{erf} u \, du, \tag{58}$$

while the corresponding velocity components are

$$u_0 = U_0 \, \partial\psi_0/\partial\eta = U \operatorname{erf} \eta,$$

$$w_0 = -2U_0 f'(\xi)\frac{\sqrt{(\nu t)}}{x_0} \int_0^\eta \operatorname{erf}\eta \, d\eta = -2\sqrt{(\nu t)}\frac{dU}{dx}\left\{ \eta \operatorname{erf}\eta - \frac{1}{\sqrt{\pi}}(1 - e^{-\eta^2}) \right\}, \tag{59}$$

in accord with the solution for impulsive motion of an infinite flat plate. As η tends to infinity the velocity component w_0 approaches

$$[-zU'(x) + 2U'(x)\sqrt{(\nu t/\pi)}],$$

the first term representing continuity of flow and the second the diffusion of vorticity from the boundary (or, in other terms, the displacement effect of the boundary layer on the external flow). But for moderate values of η, w_0 is smaller than u_0 by a factor of order $\sqrt{(\nu t)}/x_0$, in accord with the general formulation of Section 1.

The function ψ_1 (Blasius 1908) is given by

$$\psi_1 = f(\xi)f'(\xi) \int_0^\eta g(u) \, du, \tag{60}$$

where

$$g(u) = \tfrac{1}{2}(2u^2 - 1)\operatorname{erf}^2 u + \frac{3}{\sqrt{\pi}}u e^{-u^2}\operatorname{erf} u + 1 - \frac{4}{3\pi}e^{-u^2} + \frac{2}{\pi}e^{-2u^2} -$$
$$- \left(1 + \frac{2}{3\pi}\right)(2u^2 + 1) + \frac{1}{\sqrt{\pi}}\left(1 + \frac{4}{3\pi}\right)\{\tfrac{1}{2}\sqrt{\pi}(2u^2 + 1)\operatorname{erf} u + u e^{-u^2}\}. \tag{61}$$

This function has been tabulated by Goldstein and Rosenhead (1936), and in much greater detail by Wundt (1955). Goldstein and Rosenhead (1936) have calculated the function ψ_2. Here we content ourselves with noting the fact that ψ_2 is of the form

$$\psi_2 = f^2(\xi)f''(\xi) \int_0^\eta g_1(u)\,du + f(\xi)f'^2(\xi) \int_0^\eta g_2(u)\,du, \qquad (62)$$

where $g_1(u)$ and $g_2(u)$ are complicated functions which have been calculated by Goldstein and Rosenhead (1936) and by Wundt (1955). Wundt (1955) has pointed out that Goldstein and Rosenhead's tabulations of the functions $g_1(u)$ and $g_2(u)$ are incorrect; he also gives very extensive corrected tables. Fortunately, the quantities $g_1'(0)$ and $g_2'(0)$, which determine the skin friction, are not in error and agree with Wundt (1955).

The position of separation at a given time can be calculated once the external velocity distribution is specified, and occurs when

$$1 + \left(1 + \frac{4}{3\pi}\right)\tau f'(\xi) = 0 \qquad (63)$$

with just the ψ_0 and ψ_1 functions. Thus the time interval before separation begins is given by

$$\tau_s = \left\{\left(1 + \frac{4}{3\pi}\right)(-f'_{\max}(\xi))\right\}^{-1} = 0\cdot70205/(-f')_{\max}. \qquad (64)$$

In the circular-cylinder case, $f(\xi) = 2\sin 2\xi$ and $x_0 = d$, the cylinder diameter, so $\tau_s = 0\cdot1755$. A more complicated calculation by Goldstein and Rosenhead (1936) shows that, to the next approximation (ψ_2), the time at which separation occurs at any particular place is given by

$$\tau_s^{-1} = -0\cdot7122f'(\xi) + \sqrt{\{0\cdot7271f'(\xi)^2 + 0\cdot05975f(\xi)f''(\xi)\}}. \qquad (65)$$

For a circular cylinder, the minimum time required for separation is $\tau_s = 0\cdot16$ to this approximation. This compares with the value $\tau_s = 0\cdot15$ given by Schuh's (1953a) calculation (see Fig. VII. 4). In this case, separation begins at the rear stagnation point, because $(-f'(\xi))$ has its greatest value there. To the first approximation, (ψ_1), separation always begins where $(-f'(\xi))$ has its greatest value, which may be at the rear stagnation point; but when the second approximation, (ψ_2), is included τ has its least value when $(-f'(\xi))$ is greatest only if $f(\xi)$ is zero there. For bodies much bluffer than a circular cylinder, $(-f'(\xi))$ may not have its greatest value at the rear stagnation point and separation may start elsewhere. For example, Tollmien (1931) has shown that for an elliptic cylinder moving impulsively from rest parallel to its minor axis, separation takes place initially at the rear stagnation point only if the ratio of the squares of the axes does not exceed 4/3. As the ratio is increased the two positions of separation move round the cylinder towards the ends of the major axis. Görtler (1948b) has studied the problem for an elliptic cylinder in more detail. A case of an elliptic cylinder with axes in the ratio 1:6 and with its major axis at an angle of 7° to the stream has been considered by Howarth (1935a) and by Goldstein and Rosenhead (1936) as an example of a cylinder of asymmetrical section. Tollmien (1931) has considered the flow past a rotating cylinder, the whole system being started impulsively from rest.

A more comprehensive theory, analogous to the 'similar' solutions discussed in Section 3 but generalized to take account of cylindrical shapes, has been given by Görtler (1944) for a cylinder velocity $V(t) = At^n$ (where n is a positive integer), and by Watson (1955) for a velocity $V(t) = At^\alpha$ (α real and positive) or $V(t) = Ae^{ct}$ (c real and positive). The velocity outside the boundary layer is $U(x,t) = V(t)f(\xi)$. For the case $V(t) = At^\alpha$ the stream function, ψ, which is defined by $u = V(t)\partial\psi/\partial\eta$, $w = -2V(t)\sqrt{(\nu t/x_0^2)}\ \partial\psi/\partial\xi$, may be expanded in the form

$$\psi = \psi_0(\xi,\eta) + \tau^{\alpha+1}\psi_1(\xi,\eta) + \tau^{2\alpha+2}\psi_2(\xi,\eta) + \ldots, \tag{66}$$

where $\tau = tU_0/x_0$ and $U_0 = A^{1/(\alpha+1)}x_0^{\alpha/(\alpha+1)}$. In this general case it is more convenient to consider the distance, s_s, which the cylinder moves before separation commences, rather than the time, τ_s. Watson (1955) has shown that, using the ψ_0 and ψ_1 functions, the value of s_s at the commencement of separation is given by $(s_s/x_0)\{-f'(\xi)\}_{max} = \sigma(\alpha)$, where $\sigma(0) = 0.702$ and σ tends to 1.707 as α tends to infinity. For a circular cylinder, for which x_0 is the diameter, s_s/x_0 equals 0.176 when $\alpha = 0$ and tends to 0.427 as α tends to infinity. Görtler (1948b) has calculated the dependence of s_s on b/a for an elliptic cylinder, both for $n = \alpha = 0$ (impulsive motion) and $n = \alpha = 1$ (uniformly accelerated motion). The case $V(t) = Ae^{ct}$ discussed by Watson (1955) is the limiting case as α tends to infinity, so that, in this case, $\sigma = 1.707$.

An experimental investigation of the changes in pressure distribution which occur about a circular cylinder after an impulsive start from rest has been made by Schwabe (1935). His method was to photograph the flow at many different stages, and from the photographs he determined the velocity and pressure successively. When the régime is one in which two symmetrical vortices are formed behind the cylinder, the flow closes up again behind the vortices, so there is a stagnation point behind them. This rear stagnation point, which is on the cylinder for the potential flow, moves downstream as the pattern changes and becomes a free stagnation point. Schwabe's (1935) results are shown in Fig. VII. 6 as curves of $(p-p_0)/(\frac{1}{2}\rho U_0^2)$ plotted against the angular distance θ from the forward stagnation point for various values of D/d, where D is the distance of the rear stagnation point from the centre of the cylinder

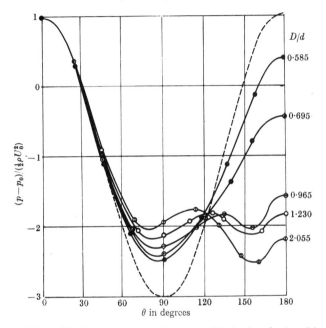

FIG. VII. 6. Schwabe's experimental pressure distributions for impulsive motion of a circular cylinder.

and d is the diameter. The dotted line represents the result for potential flow. The Reynolds number, $U_0 d/\nu$, appropriate to the figure is 560. It is noteworthy that even at $D/d = 0.585$, the magnitude of the pressure minimum is considerably less than the value for potential flow. The pressure distributions are similar to those for steady flow, but there are differences in detail.

The form drag was calculated from the pressure distribution, and is shown in Fig. VII. 7, in the form of a form-drag coefficient C_D (form drag per unit length divided by $\frac{1}{2}\rho U_0^2 d$) plotted against $\tau = U_0 t/d$, for $U_0 d/\nu = 580$. (If the skin-friction drag were added, the drag coefficient would, of course, be infinite at $\tau = 0$, as can be seen from formula (59).) The vortices were attached to the cylinder for values of τ in

Fig. VII. 7. The form-drag coefficient rises to 2·07 at $\tau = 4·5$, whereas its value under steady conditions is about 1. It appears, therefore, that the consumption of energy in the development of the eddies is large enough to cause the drag coefficient to rise to about double its 'steady' value. When asymmetry has made its appearance the alternating eddy formation causes an alternating lift on the cylinder. At a

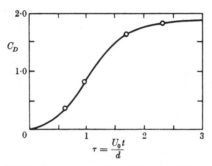

FIG. VII. 7. Form-drag coefficient for impulsive motion of a circular cylinder.

certain stage of the oscillation, with $U_0 d/\nu = 735$, Schwabe found a lift coefficient of 0·45 from the instantaneous pressure distribution. The drag coefficient was then 1·09 and the lift, therefore, was about 40 per cent. of the form drag. For a calculation of the flow due to a circular cylinder started impulsively from rest, the reader is referred to Payne (1958).

8. Three-dimensional unsteady motion

The method of solution in series described in Section 7 has been extended by L. C. Squire (1954) to three-dimensional flows, based on the three-dimensional boundary-layer equations (VIII. 17), (VIII. 18), (VIII. 19). At time $t = 0$, a flow $v_1 = U(x_1, x_2)$, $v_2 = V(x_1, x_2)$ is started impulsively relative to axes x_1, x_2, x_3 fixed in the body, x_3 being normal to the surface. As in Section 7, it is required to determine how the boundary layer develops with time. The precise details of the analysis are even more complex than for two-dimensional flow, and here only the first two terms in a solution in ascending powers of the time will be given. The initial approximation to the boundary-layer flow generated by the impulsive motion is given by the solutions of the diffusion equations

$$\frac{\partial v_1}{\partial t} = \nu \frac{\partial^2 v_1}{\partial x_3^2}; \qquad \frac{\partial v_2}{\partial t} = \nu \frac{\partial^2 v_2}{\partial x_3^2}, \qquad (67)$$

namely $v_{10} = U(x_1, x_2)\operatorname{erf} \eta; \qquad v_{20} = V(x_1, x_2)\operatorname{erf} \eta, \qquad (68)$

where $\eta = x_3/2\sqrt{(\nu t)}$. The component of velocity normal to the surface is

$$v_{30} = 2\sqrt{(\nu t)} . N\{\eta \, \mathrm{erf} \, \eta - \pi^{-\frac{1}{2}}(1 - e^{-\eta^2})\}, \tag{69}$$

where N denotes $-(1/h_1 h_2)\partial(Uh_2)/\partial x_1 - (1/h_1 h_2)\partial(Uh_1)/\partial x_2$.

In accord with the theory of Section 7, let us now make the generalized transformations

$$U(x_1, x_2) = U_0 f(\xi, \zeta); \qquad V(x_1, x_2) = U_0 g(\xi, \zeta);$$

$$x_1 = x_0 \xi, \qquad x_2 = x_0 \zeta, \qquad x_3 = 2\eta \sqrt{(\nu t)}, \qquad t = \tau x_0/U_0;$$

$$\kappa_1 = -\frac{1}{h_1 h_2} \frac{\partial h_2}{\partial \xi}; \qquad \kappa_2 = -\frac{1}{h_1 h_2} \frac{\partial h_1}{\partial \zeta}, \tag{70}$$

where x_0 is a characteristic length and U_0 a speed. Then the velocity components are given by

$$v_1 = v_{10} + \tau v_{11} + \tau^2 v_{12} + ...,$$

$$v_2 = v_{20} + \tau v_{21} + \tau^2 v_{22} + ...,$$

$$v_3 = \left(\frac{\nu t}{x_0^2}\right)^{\frac{1}{2}} \{v_{30} + \tau v_{31} + ...\}, \tag{71}$$

where v_{10} and v_{20} are given by (68), v_{30} by (69), and

$$v_{11} = U_0 \left\{ -f\left(\kappa_1 f + \kappa_2 g - \frac{1}{h_1}\frac{\partial f}{\partial \xi} - \frac{1}{h_2}\frac{\partial g}{\partial \zeta}\right)\alpha_{11}(\eta) + \right.$$

$$\left. + \left(\frac{g}{h_1}\frac{\partial g}{\partial \xi} + f[\kappa_1 f + \kappa_2 g] - \frac{f}{h_2}\frac{\partial g}{\partial \zeta}\right)\alpha_{12}(\eta) \right\}, \tag{72}$$

$$v_{21} = U_0 \left\{ -g\left(\kappa_1 f + \kappa_2 g - \frac{1}{h_1}\frac{\partial f}{\partial \xi} - \frac{1}{h_2}\frac{\partial g}{\partial \zeta}\right)\alpha_{11}(\eta) + \right.$$

$$\left. + \left(\frac{f}{h_2}\frac{\partial f}{\partial \zeta} + g[\kappa_1 f + \kappa_2 g] - \frac{g}{h_2}\frac{\partial f}{\partial \zeta}\right)\alpha_{12}(\eta) \right\}, \tag{73}$$

while the function v_{31} is obtainable by integration from the equation of continuity. The functions $\alpha_{11}(\eta)$ and $\alpha_{12}(\eta)$ are illustrated graphically in Fig. VII. 8, taken from Squire (1954).

The next approximation (τ^2) has also been considered by Squire (1954), though it should be noted that he makes use of the τ^2 approximation given by Goldstein and Rosenhead (1936) which, as mentioned in Section 7, is incorrect. Consequently, the velocity distribution terms in τ^2 in Squire's paper require correction, though the skin friction is correct.

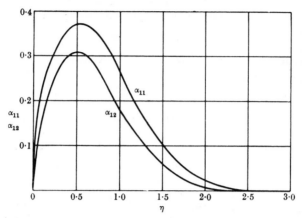

Fig. VII. 8. Functions for three-dimensional impulsive motion.

Up to terms in τ, the skin friction is given by

$$2\left(\frac{\nu x_0}{U_0^3}\right)^{\frac{1}{2}}\left(\frac{\partial v_1}{\partial x_3}\right)_w = \tau^{-\frac{1}{2}}\left[1\cdot1284f+\tau\left\{-1\cdot6073f\left(\kappa_1f+\kappa_2g-\frac{1}{h_1}\frac{\partial f}{\partial\xi}-\frac{1}{h_2}\frac{\partial g}{\partial\zeta}\right)+\right.\right.$$
$$\left.\left.+1\cdot4370\left(\frac{g}{h_1}\frac{\partial g}{\partial\xi}+f(\kappa_1f+\kappa_2g)-\frac{f}{h_2}\frac{\partial g}{\partial\zeta}\right)\right\}\right],$$

$$2\left(\frac{\nu x_0}{U_0^3}\right)^{\frac{1}{2}}\left(\frac{\partial v_2}{\partial x_3}\right)_w = \tau^{-\frac{1}{2}}\left[1\cdot1284g+\tau\left\{-1\cdot6073g\left(\kappa_1f+\kappa_2g-\frac{1}{h_1}\frac{\partial f}{\partial\xi}-\frac{1}{h_2}\frac{\partial g}{\partial\zeta}\right)+\right.\right.$$
$$\left.\left.+1\cdot4370\left(\frac{f}{h_2}\frac{\partial f}{\partial\zeta}+g(\kappa_1f+\kappa_2g)-\frac{g}{h_2}\frac{\partial f}{\partial\zeta}\right)\right\}\right]. \quad (74)$$

If g, κ_1, and κ_2 are all put equal to zero the first-approximation result appropriate to two dimensions is obtained. Squire (1954) gives the results for skin friction up to the term τ^2, and uses these skin friction formulae to discuss the nature of separation in three-dimensional flow, a matter which receives attention in Section VIII. 26.

The theory of axisymmetrical boundary layers had earlier been treated by Boltze (1908), who showed for a sphere that separation started at the rear stagnation point after a time given by

$$\tau = U_0t/d = 0\cdot1955,$$

U_0 being the speed and d the diameter. Illingworth (1954) has extended Boltze's work to the case of flow past a body of revolution spinning about its axis, which is parallel to the stream, the whole flow being started impulsively from rest. One effect of rotation is to advance the onset of separation with increase of $\omega d/U_0$, where ω is the angular speed. A similar effect occurs in accelerated flow (Wadhwa 1958).

The case of unsteady flow past a yawed infinite cylinder, a flow in which the boundary-layer velocity is independent of distance parallel to the axis and in which the chordwise velocity component is independent of the axial component (see Section VIII. 22), has been treated by Wundt (1955) for a main-stream velocity of the form At^n, where n is an integer. This is a generalization of Görtler's (1944) investigation for unyawed cylinders. In addition, the case $n = 0$ is a special case of Squire's investigation.

Wuest (1952) has considered a class of unsteady flows in which it is possible to separate the unsteady part of the motion from the steady part because the unsteadiness in'the velocity occurs in one coordinate only. This situation arises physically when an infinite cylinder, which is moving unsteadily parallel to its axis, is also embedded in a steady uniform stream flowing normal to its axis. The theory has been developed by Wuest for the case of a cylinder velocity $v_w e^{\alpha t}$, where v_w and α are constants. The differential equations of the flow are equations (VIII. 191), (VIII. 192), and (VIII. 193), but with $\partial v/\partial t$ added to the left-hand side of (VIII. 192). Derivatives with respect to y do not appear because the flow is independent of distance (y) in the spanwise direction. Distance normal to the surface is denoted by z, and that along the plane, from the stagnation point, by x. It can be seen that the equations (VIII. 191), (VIII. 193) define the u and w components of velocity subject to the boundary conditions (VIII. 194). The other equation, (VIII. 192) with $\partial v/\partial t$ added, which is analogous to that of an unsteady temperature boundary layer, defines the v component of velocity with the boundary conditions $v = v_w e^{\alpha t}$ at $z = 0$, $v \to 0$ as $z \to \infty$, which are analogous to the appropriate ones of (VIII. 194).

Let us now restrict considerations to the region near the forward stagnation point. With the transformations $U = ax$, $\eta = z\sqrt{(a/\nu)}$, $u = axf'(\eta)$, $w = -\sqrt{(a\nu)}.f(\eta)$, the first two of our differential equations and boundary conditions reduce to equations (III. 103), (III. 104), which are discussed in Section III. 19. With the transformation $v = v_w e^{\alpha t}\zeta(\eta)$, equation (VIII. 192) and its boundary conditions become

$$\zeta'' + f\zeta' - \gamma\zeta = 0,$$
$$\zeta = 1 \quad \text{at } \eta = 0, \qquad \zeta \to 0 \quad \text{as } \eta \to \infty, \tag{75}$$

where $\gamma = \alpha/a$. The solutions for $\gamma = 1$ (accelerating flow), $\gamma = -1$ (decelerating flow), and $\gamma = 0$ (steady flow) are illustrated in Fig. VII. 9, due to Wuest (1952). For an accelerating cylinder, the v component of velocity is everywhere less than $v_w e^{\alpha t}$, but for a decelerating cylinder the time lag of the fluid motion behind that of the cylinder means that fluid near the boundary is actually moving faster than the cylinder. This flow is an exact solution of the Navier–Stokes equations.

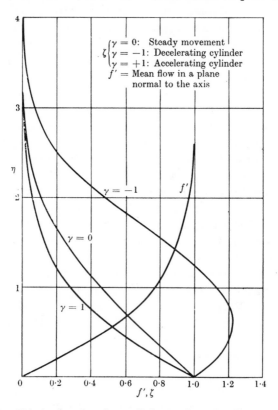

FIG. VII. 9. Velocity functions for a cylinder moving unsteadily parallel to its axis in a steady stream normal to its axis.

Further examples of unsteady three-dimensional boundary layers are afforded by (i) the case of a stationary disk of infinite radius which at $t = 0$ is suddenly given a uniform angular velocity Ω; and by (ii) the case of an infinite disk and an infinite body of fluid which are together roating with angular velocity Ω until at $t = 0$ the disk is brought suddenly to rest. In the first case the flow, as $t \to \infty$, approaches the Kármán–Cochran steady flow due to a rotating disk, while in the second case the flow approaches the Bödewadt solution for a fluid which rotates with uniform angular velocity at large distances from an infinite plane. For descriptions of these steady solutions the reader is referred to

Section III. 20. The initial flow can be obtained by expansion in powers of $\tau = \Omega t$; this has been done independently by Thiriot (1940, 1950) and Nigam (1951) for the first problem, and by Thiriot (1940, 1950) for the second. It should be noted that Thiriot's first paper contains two errors, which are corrected in the second paper. A solution of the energy equation for case (i) above, that of the rotating disk starting impulsively from rest, has been given by Probstein (1953) for zero heat transfer between the wall and the fluid, including only terms linear in t.

The flow due to a rotating sphere which starts impulsively from rest has been considered by Nigam and Rangasami (1953), who have shown that, when the solution is linearized in t, the equations resemble those for the analogous rotating-disk problem.

PART II

PERIODIC BOUNDARY LAYERS

9. The flow due to an oscillating infinite plane

The flow generated in a semi-infinite mass of fluid by viscous action at an infinite plate oscillating in its own plane is given by a simple exact solution of the Navier–Stokes equations; the solution, which is due to Stokes (1851), was one of the first exact solutions to be obtained.

Let x, y be the coordinates in the plane, and z the distance normal to it. The flow generated by the oscillation is everywhere parallel to the plane and in the x-direction. Thus the Navier–Stokes and continuity equations give, since there are no pressure gradients,

$$\frac{\partial u}{\partial t} = \nu \frac{\partial^2 u}{\partial z^2}. \tag{76}$$

If the wall has a velocity given by the real part of $u_w e^{i\omega t}$, we define $u = \zeta(\eta) u_w e^{i\omega t}$, where $\eta = z\sqrt{(\omega/2\nu)}$ and $\zeta(\eta)$ is given by

$$2i\zeta = d^2\zeta/d\eta^2. \tag{77}$$

The appropriate solution for ζ, which must satisfy the boundary conditions $\zeta = 1$ at $\eta = 0$ and $\zeta \to 0$ as $\eta \to \infty$, is $\zeta = e^{-\eta(1+i)}$. Thus the velocity is given by

$$u = u_w e^{-\eta} \cos(\omega t - \eta), \tag{78}$$

which represents shear waves travelling outwards from the surface with velocity $\sqrt{(2\nu\omega)}$ and decaying exponentially with distance from the surface. The boundary layer, which has thickness of order $\sqrt{(\nu/\omega)}$, exists because vorticity, which is produced at the surface, changes sign as it diffuses outwards. (On the other hand, in the cases of unsteady motion discussed in Part I of this chapter, the boundary layer exists because the vorticity is convected as it diffuses.)

The aerodynamic heating of an oscillating surface has been considered by Ostrach (1954). Because viscous dissipation of energy is proportional to the square of the velocity, a temperature field is built up which has a mean part and a part which fluctuates with twice the frequency of the surface.

Another type of flow which involves shear waves propagated outwards from a surface is that due to an infinite circular cylinder performing rotatory oscillations about its axis. The exact theory of Stokes (1886) and Coster (1919) was amply confirmed by experiments of Winny (1932).

10. The theory of periodic boundary layers in the absence of a mean flow

Consider an infinite plane wall and let the velocity outside the boundary layer of, and parallel to, the wall be $U = U_0(x)\cos \omega t$, or $U_0(x)e^{i\omega t}$ in complex notation. On grounds of continuity, the component of velocity normal to the wall outside the boundary layer is $-(z+c)U_0'(x)e^{i\omega t}$, where c is a complex constant. The boundary-layer thickness is clearly of order $(\nu/\omega)^{\frac{1}{2}}$ in accord with the general discussion of Section 1. In practice, the oscillatory flow, $U_0(x)e^{i\omega t}$, could be generated by a circular cylinder, for example, oscillating along a diameter. In this particular case $U_0(x) = 2U_\infty \sin 2x/d$, where $U_\infty \cos \omega t$ is the cylinder velocity and x is the distance along the wall. A typical length, x_0, parallel to the wall, is the cylinder diameter, d. Thus the frequency parameter $\omega x_0/U_0$ of Section 1 is $\omega d/U_\infty$; the frequency parameter $\omega x_0^2/\nu$ is $\omega d^2/\nu$. Suppose that $\nu/\omega d^2$ is small enough for (13) to be applicable; following Schlichting (1932a) the first of these equations may then be written

$$\frac{\partial u}{\partial t} - \nu \frac{\partial^2 u}{\partial z^2} - \frac{\partial U}{\partial t} = U\frac{\partial U}{\partial x} - u\frac{\partial u}{\partial x} - w\frac{\partial u}{\partial z}, \tag{79}$$

where the terms on the right-hand side are small (of order $U_\infty/\omega d$) compared with those on the left. It can be shown that, provided our main object is to calculate the first-order oscillatory motion together with the dominant part of the resulting second-order steady motion, equations (13) are accurate enough if both $\nu/\omega d^2$ and $U_\infty/\omega d$ are sufficiently small. If it is desired to go to higher order, however, the boundary-layer approximation *may* be invalid and it may be necessary to include effects of surface curvature, if present; these matters depend on the relative magnitudes of the two parameters quoted above. The neglect of compressibility implies that $\omega d/c \ll 1$, where c is the sound speed.

If $\eta = z\sqrt{(\omega/2\nu)}$, a first approximation (ψ_1) to the stream function (ψ) is given by

$$\psi_1 = (2\nu/\omega)^{\frac{1}{2}} U_0(x) \zeta_1(\eta) e^{i\omega t}, \tag{80}$$

where ζ_1 satisfies $\zeta_1''' + 2i(1 - \zeta_1') = 0,$

and the conditions $\zeta_1 = \zeta_1' = 0$ at $\eta = 0$, $\zeta_1' \to 1$ as $\eta \to \infty$. Thus

$$\zeta_1 = -\frac{(1-i)}{2}(1 - e^{-(1+i)\eta}) + \eta. \tag{81}$$

This refers to that part of the boundary layer which has a harmonic response of the same frequency as the external flow. The skin friction is $\mu(\omega/2\nu)^{\frac{1}{2}} U_0(x) \cos(\omega t + \frac{1}{4}\pi)$, written in real instead of complex terms, and thus has a phase lead of $\frac{1}{4}\pi$ over the velocity fluctuations.

The component of velocity parallel to the surface is

$$u_1 = U_0(x)\{\cos \omega t - e^{-\eta} \cos(\omega t - \eta)\}, \tag{82}$$

which is analogous to the solution for the flow due to an oscillating wall discussed in the previous section. The component of velocity normal to the wall is

$$w_1 = -\left(\frac{2\nu}{\omega}\right)^{\frac{1}{2}} U_0'(x)\left\{\eta \cos \omega t + \frac{1}{\sqrt{2}} \cos\left(\omega t + \frac{3\pi}{4}\right) + \frac{e^{-\eta}}{\sqrt{2}} \cos(\omega t - \eta - \tfrac{1}{4}\pi)\right\}. \tag{83}$$

Outside the boundary layer the third term tends to zero, while the first represents continuity of the main flow and the second the displacement effect of the boundary layer on the external flow, or, in other words, the diffusion of periodic vorticity.

In order to take into account higher-order terms we put $\psi = \psi_1 + \psi_2$ where ψ_2 is of order $U_\infty/\omega d$ times ψ_1. Since ψ_2 is proportional to the square of ψ_1, it involves terms both of zero frequency and of a frequency (2ω) *twice* that of the basic flow. Therefore we put

$$\psi_2 = \left(\frac{2\nu}{\omega}\right)^{\frac{1}{2}} \frac{U_0 U_0'}{\omega}\{\zeta_{20} + \zeta_{22} e^{2i\omega t}\}, \tag{84}$$

and after substituting in the differential equation (79), utilizing the known form of ψ_1, and satisfying the boundary conditions

$$\zeta_{20} = \zeta'_{20} = \zeta_{22} = \zeta'_{22} = 0 \quad \text{at } \eta = 0,$$

$$\zeta'_{22} \to 0 \text{ and } \zeta'_{20} \text{ remains finite as } \eta \to \infty, \tag{85}$$

we obtain the expressions

$$\zeta_{22} = \frac{(1+i)}{4\sqrt{2}} e^{-(1+i)\eta\sqrt{2}} + \frac{i\eta}{2} e^{-(1+i)\eta} - \frac{1+i}{4\sqrt{2}}, \tag{86}$$

$$\zeta_{20} = \tfrac{13}{8} - \tfrac{3}{4}\eta - \tfrac{1}{8}e^{-2\eta} - \tfrac{3}{2}e^{-\eta}\cos\eta - e^{-\eta}\sin\eta - \tfrac{1}{2}\eta e^{-\eta}\sin\eta. \tag{87}$$

The important result which this solution shows is that a small steady motion is generated which persists outside the boundary layer. At large values of η, corresponding to the edge of the boundary layer, $\zeta'_{20} = -\tfrac{3}{4}$, and the steady flow has a component $-3U_0\,U'_0/4\omega$ parallel to the wall. In addition there is a steady component of velocity normal to the wall outside the boundary layer, namely

$$\frac{1}{\omega}\frac{d}{dx}(U_0\,U'_0)\left\{\tfrac{3}{4}z - \frac{13}{8}\left(\frac{2\nu}{\omega}\right)^{\frac{1}{2}}\right\}.$$

It is clear that this steady motion is generated by the Reynolds stress (see Appendix to Chapter IX) associated with the oscillatory part of the flow within the boundary layer and that it persists outside the oscillatory boundary layer because of the action of viscosity, though the intensity of the steady motion diminishes with distance from the surface. The steady velocity at the edge of the boundary layer has been shown above to have a magnitude of order $U_\infty^2/\omega d$; this characteristic velocity, together with the length d, may be used to define a Reynolds number, namely $R_s = U_\infty^2/\omega\nu$. The nature of the steady flow outside the boundary layer naturally depends on the magnitude of this Reynolds number. It has been pointed out (Stuart 1960b) that the work of Rayleigh (1883) and Schlichting (1932a) on the calculation of the steady flow outside the boundary layer is applicable when the Reynolds number, R_s, is small enough for linearization to be a valid approximation to the Navier–Stokes equations; the type of flow which arises in this case will be described in the next paragraph. When the Reynolds number, R_s, is large, there exists a second, outer boundary layer at the edge of which the steady velocity component, u_{20}, tends to zero. Within this outer layer it is not valid to neglect the non-linear inertia terms, and the usual concepts of boundary-layer theory show that its thickness is of order $d(\nu\omega)^{\frac{1}{2}}/U_\infty$; this is large compared with the 'inner' boundary-layer thickness (of order $(\nu/\omega)^{\frac{1}{2}}$) by virtue of the assumption that $\omega d/U$

is large. For a discussion of the mechanics of the outer layer, for large values of R_s, the reader is referred to Stuart (1960b) and to a paper by Rosenblat (1959), where a similar theory is developed for a disk performing torsional oscillations.

We now confine our attention to the case when R_s is small. In the calculation of the flow outside the boundary layer it should be noted that derivatives with respect to distance parallel to the surface cannot be neglected compared with derivatives normal to the surface, because viscosity is effective for the slow steady streaming over a much greater distance than is compatible with a boundary-layer theory. Consequently there is a pressure variation normal to the surface. Furthermore, since the frequency parameter $\omega d/U_\infty$ is large, the steady velocity is small and linearization is permissible to a first approximation. (Note that the Reynolds stresses of the oscillatory potential flow are countered by pressure gradients.) Thus outside the boundary layer, derivatives with respect to x and z are retained, and a solution of the steady slow-motion equations is obtained. The solution must be linked to the boundary-layer solution. A calculation of this sort (Rayleigh 1883) shows that the steady flow outside the boundary layer, for the case when

$$U_0(x) = U_\infty \cos kx,$$

is given approximately by the stream function

$$\psi_{20} = \frac{3kU_\infty^2}{8\omega}\left\{z - \frac{13}{6}\left(\frac{2\nu}{\omega}\right)^{\frac{1}{2}}\right\}e^{-2kz}\sin 2kx. \tag{88}$$

For this particular velocity distribution $U_0(x)$, the standard length parallel to the surface may be taken to be k^{-1}. Furthermore, just outside the boundary layer z is of order $(\nu/\omega)^{\frac{1}{2}}$, so that $k(\nu/\omega)^{\frac{1}{2}}$ is required to be small (in accord with the general principles of Section 1) for boundary-layer theory to hold. Consequently e^{-2kz} is approximately unity just outside the boundary layer, and the function ψ_{20} yields

$$u_{20} = \frac{3kU_\infty^2}{8\omega}\sin 2kx,$$

$$w_{20} = -\frac{k^2U_\infty^2}{\omega}\left\{\tfrac{3}{4}z - \frac{13}{8}\left(\frac{2\nu}{\omega}\right)^{\frac{1}{2}}\right\}\cos 2kx, \tag{89}$$

which are equal to the components given by boundary-layer theory, when the first-order velocity at the edge of the layer is $U_0(x) = U_\infty \cos kx$. A unified theory for this velocity distribution, valid both inside and outside the boundary layer and not using the ideas underlying the

boundary-layer theory, was given by Lord Rayleigh (1883) both with
and without effects of compressibility in connexion with certain acoustic
phenomena of Kundt's dust tube. In Rayleigh's analysis the boundary
layer is represented by terms of the form $e^{-z\sqrt{\omega/2\nu}}$, as in Schlichting's
analysis, and outside the boundary layer such terms are negligible com-
pared with terms like e^{-2kz} when $k(\nu/\omega)^{\frac{1}{2}}$ is small. The velocity components of the flow outside the boundary layer in the incompressible
case, namely

$$u_{20} = \frac{3kU_\infty^2}{8\omega}(1-2kz)e^{-2kz}\sin 2kx,$$

$$w_{20} = -\frac{k^2U_\infty^2}{\omega}\left\{\frac{3z}{4} - \frac{13}{8}\left(\frac{2\nu}{\omega}\right)^{\frac{1}{2}}\right\}e^{-2kz}\cos 2kx, \tag{90}$$

show that fluid rises over the nodes of the basic flow, $kx = \frac{1}{2}\pi$, $\frac{3}{2}\pi$,
etc., and falls over the loops, $kx = 0$, π, 2π, etc. The motion parallel
to the wall outside the boundary layer changes sign when $z = (2k)^{-1}$.
It can be seen that there is a set of vortices periodic in x with half the
wavelength of the basic flow. Within the boundary layer the solution
given by Rayleigh coincides with that of Schlichting, when $k(\nu/\omega)^{\frac{1}{2}}$ is
small. A further change of sign of the x-component of velocity takes
place at $\eta = 1\cdot016$ approximately, so that altogether there are two
reversals of the x-component of the flow velocity, one inside and one
outside the boundary layer.

Schlichting (1932a) applied his theory to the periodic flow generated
by a circular cylinder oscillating along a diameter. In this case the
function $U_0(x) = 2U_\infty \sin 2x/d$, as discussed earlier in this section.
A streaming is developed by the mechanism discussed above, in which
fluid flows away from the cylinder in the direction of oscillation, and
towards it in the transverse direction. Schlichting linked solution (87)
to a solution valid outside the boundary layer, for cases both with and
without external constraint. This case has also been studied by Holtsmark et al. (1954), both theoretically and experimentally. Photographic
evidence of the streaming may be found in these papers and in that of
Andrade (1931). The condition $\omega d/c \ll 1$ (c is the sound speed) was
satisfied, both in water (Schlichting) and in air (Andrade, Holtsmark). However, it should be noted that in Schlichting's experiments
R_s ($= U_\infty^2/\omega\nu$) was of order 300, while in the other experiments it was
of order $0\cdot05$ to $1\cdot0$. Thus only the latter experiments are quantitatively
comparable with the theory developed above for small values of R_s
(Schlichting observed in his paper that his experiments were performed
at a value of R_s that was not in accord with the assumptions of the

theory). The experimental evidence is in qualitative agreement with
theory, since, whether R_s is large or small, theory predicts a streaming
away from the cylinder in the direction of oscillation (Stuart 1960b), as
observed. Streamlines illustrating the pattern of the steady flow for
$\omega d^2/\nu \gg 1$, $U_\infty/\omega d \ll 1$, are shown in Fig. VII. 10, due to Andres and
Ingard (1953a).

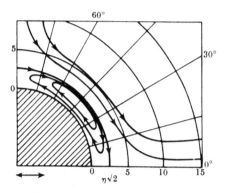

Fig. VII. 10. First-order part of steady streaming
for $\omega d^2/\nu = 400$.

For other ranges of the two frequency parameters the direction of
steady streaming near a circular cylinder may be reversed. References
to experimental work illustrating this, together with discussions, may
be found in papers by Westervelt (1953a) and Andres and Ingard
(1953a, b). Segel (1961) has made a theoretical study, based on the
Navier–Stokes equations, of the flow field between two circular cylinders,
when the motion is produced by a vibration of the outer cylinder. He
has shown that the steady streaming in the direction of vibration is
directed *towards* the inner cylinder when $\omega d^2/\nu$ is small, thus indicating
one possible mechanism. A similar theoretical result was obtained by
Andres and Ingard (1953b), using Oseen's approximation for a cylinder
vibrating in an unbounded fluid. For further discussions of steady
streaming between moving bounding cylinders, and for a discussion on
the usefulness of the concept of steady streaming, see Segel's paper
(1961).

In discussions of oscillatory fluid motion it is necessary to bear in
mind that the associated particle velocity may have a non-zero mean
value, even though the velocity at a point has zero mean (with respect
to time). The mean particle velocity is usually known as the mass-

transport velocity. It is zero in an inviscid standing wave, but is usually non-zero in an inviscid progressive wave (Longuet-Higgins 1953). In the viscous case the mass-transport velocity outside the boundary layer is compounded of the mean velocity at a point (such as equation (90)) and the 'inviscid' mass-transport velocity; the 'inviscid' part is zero in the Rayleigh and Schlichting theories discussed earlier, because the flows they considered were standing waves. For a thorough discussion of this topic the reader is referred to Longuet-Higgins (1953).

The theory of acoustic streaming produced by sound waves incident on an obstacle has been considered in much detail by Andres and Ingard (1953a, b), by Nyborg (1953a, b), by Holtsmark et al. (1954), and by Westervelt (1953b). Furthermore, Maslen and Moore (1956) have studied acoustic streaming as produced by transverse waves in the (cylindrical) combustion chamber of a rocket or jet engine. Another streaming phenomenon occurs when a wave moving along a free surface of water is influenced by the bottom of the channel. For a treatment of this phenomenon and for references, the reader is referred to Longuet-Higgins (1953). For a discussion of streaming produced by torsional oscillations of a sphere, see Carrier and Di Prima (1956), while for a discussion of the flow due to a circular cylinder oscillating inside a bounding cylinder the reader is referred to Segel (1961).

11. Flow in a pipe due to a periodic pressure gradient

The flow in a long straight pipe due to a periodic pressure gradient has been examined experimentally and theoretically by Richardson and Tyler (1929), and theoretically by Sexl (1930), who obtained the solution given below. For a sufficiently long pipe, variations with x are negligible and the only component of flow is that along the pipe. The Navier–Stokes equations yield

$$\frac{\partial u}{\partial t} = C \cos \omega t + \nu\left(\frac{\partial^2 u}{\partial r^2} + \frac{1}{r}\frac{\partial u}{\partial r}\right), \tag{91}$$

where $-\rho C \cos \omega t$ is the pressure gradient and r the radial distance from the pipe centre. The solution which is finite at $r = 0$ and which satisfies the conditions $u = 0$ at $r = a$ is

$$u = -\frac{iC}{\omega}\left\{1 - \frac{J_0\{\sqrt{(-i\lambda)}r/a\}}{J_0\{\sqrt{(-i\lambda)}\}}\right\}e^{i\omega t}, \tag{92}$$

where $J_0(x)$ denotes the Bessel function of zero order (Watson 1944), and $\lambda = \omega a^2/\nu$.

For small values of the parameter, λ, the velocity distribution is parabolic (as for Poiseuille flow) and in phase with the pressure gradient:

$$u = \frac{C}{4\nu}(a^2 - r^2)\cos \omega t. \tag{93}$$

For large values of λ and of $\lambda(r/a)^2$ the velocity takes the form

$$u = \frac{C}{\omega}\sin \omega t - \frac{C}{\omega}\left(\frac{a}{r}\right)^{\frac{1}{2}}\exp\left\{-\left(\frac{\lambda}{2}\right)^{\frac{1}{2}}\left[1 - \frac{r}{a}\right]\right\}\sin\left\{\omega t - \left(\frac{\lambda}{2}\right)^{\frac{1}{2}}\left[1 - \frac{r}{a}\right]\right\}. \tag{94}$$

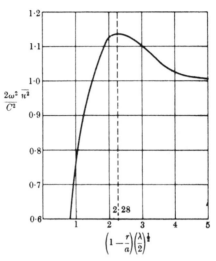

FIG. VII. 11. Profile of the mean-square velocity in a pipe under the action of a periodic pressure gradient. Valid for large values of λ and for $1 - r/a \ll 1$.

Consider now the mean-square velocity $(\overline{u^2})$, which has the form shown in Fig. VII. 11 and equation (95), which is valid for large values of λ:

$$\overline{u^2} = \frac{C^2}{2\omega^2}\left\{1 - 2\left(\frac{a}{r}\right)^{\frac{1}{2}}\exp\left[-\left(\frac{\lambda}{2}\right)^{\frac{1}{2}}\left(1 - \frac{r}{a}\right)\right]\cos\left[\left(\frac{\lambda}{2}\right)^{\frac{1}{2}}\left(1 - \frac{r}{a}\right)\right] + \frac{a}{r}\exp\left[-(2\lambda)^{\frac{1}{2}}\left(1 - \frac{r}{a}\right)\right]\right\}. \tag{95}$$

The maximum occurs very close to the wall, at $r = a(1 - 3 \cdot 22\lambda^{-\frac{1}{2}})$, and is in good agreement with the experiments of Richardson and Tyler (1929).

By a Laplace-transform technique Ito (1953) has generalized the solution described above to an arbitrary unsteady pressure gradient. As particular cases he considers (i) a pressure gradient which changes

linearly with time, (ii) a pressure gradient which suddenly changes, and
(iii) a damped oscillatory pressure gradient. For treatments of other
aspects of unsteady pipe flows the reader is referred to Lance (1956),
Sanyal (1956), and Uchida (1956). For applications to the flow of blood
in arteries see, for example, a paper by Womersley (1955).

12. The forces on vibrating bodies

In Section 10 the main interest in oscillating flow was directed to the
actual field of flow produced, including the phenomenon of steady (or
acoustic) streaming. In the present section a different aspect will be
discussed, namely the forces acting on a body performing oscillations
about a mean position. For simplicity, let us focus attention on a
circular cylinder oscillating rectilinearly along a diameter, since the
ideas involved are basic and can be used in other cases. Let the velocity
of the cylinder be $U_0 \cos \omega t$. If $\omega d/U_0$ is large, that is, if the spatial
amplitude of oscillations is small compared with the diameter d, then
the discussion of Section 1 shows that linearization is permissible.
However, the boundary-layer approximation will not be made, even
for large values of $\omega d^2/\nu$, because it is required to determine the forces,
and therefore pressure, accurately. The equations to be solved are
therefore the linearized forms of equations (III. 49) in two dimensions,
with the boundary conditions that the velocity equals the cylinder
velocity at the cylinder, and that the velocity tends to zero at infinity.
The theory, which was the considerable achievement of Stokes (1851),
is given below. If the pressure is eliminated from (III. 49) and a stream
function in polar coordinates is defined by $v_r = r^{-1} \partial\psi/\partial\theta$, $v_\theta = -\partial\psi/\partial r$,
the equation defining the stream function is

$$\left(\nabla^2 - \frac{1}{\nu}\frac{\partial}{\partial t}\right)\nabla^2\psi = 0, \tag{96}$$

where ∇^2 is defined in Section III. 12. Equation (96) is satisfied by
$\psi = \psi_1 + \psi_2$, where

$$\nabla^2\psi_1 = 0; \qquad \left(\nabla^2 - \frac{1}{\nu}\frac{\partial}{\partial t}\right)\psi_2 = 0. \tag{97}$$

The velocity of the fluid at the cylinder must be $U_0 e^{i\omega t}$ parallel to the
direction of oscillation, so that the conditions to be satisfied by v_r and
v_θ at the cylinder are

$$v_r = U_0 e^{i\omega t}\cos\theta, \qquad v_\theta = -U_0 e^{i\omega t}\sin\theta. \tag{98}$$

It is possible to show that, to the same approximation as that of
linearization, it is permissible to apply the boundary condition at the

mean spatial position of the cylinder. A solution of the equations is then obtainable in the form

$$\psi_1 = F_1(r)e^{i\omega t}\sin\theta, \qquad \psi_2 = F_2(r)e^{i\omega t}\sin\theta, \qquad (99)$$

where
$$F_1 = A/r, \qquad F_2 = BK_1\{r\sqrt{(i\omega/\nu)}\} \qquad (100)$$

are the required solutions. The Bessel function K_1 is defined in Watson (1944), and the constants A and B may be obtained from the boundary conditions at the cylinder. (It should be noted that Stokes (1851) derived from first principles the properties of K_1.)

The resultant force on a length l of the cylinder (radius a) is

$$F = al \int_0^{2\pi} (p_{rr}\cos\theta - p_{r\theta}\sin\theta)\,d\theta, \qquad (101)$$

evaluated at $r = a$, where p_{rr} and $p_{r\theta}$ are defined by equations (III. 45), (III. 48). The following expression for F is then obtained:

$$F = -M'U_0 i\omega \left\{1 - \frac{4K_1\{\sqrt{(i\beta)}\}}{K_1\{\sqrt{(i\beta)}\} + \sqrt{(i\beta)}K_1'\{\sqrt{(i\beta)}\}}\right\}e^{i\omega t}$$

$$= -M'U_0\omega i\{k - ik'\}e^{i\omega t}, \qquad (102)$$

where $M' = \pi\rho a^2 l$ is the mass of fluid displaced by a length l of the cylinder and $\beta = \omega a^2/\nu$.

The real part of the expression (102) gives

$$F = M'U_0\omega(k\sin\omega t - k'\cos\omega t). \qquad (103)$$

Let M denote the mass of a length l of the cylinder. The meaning of the two terms in the expression (103) for F can be seen from the following reasoning. The force required to move the cylinder with velocity $U_0\cos\omega t$ in the absence of air forces is $-MU_0\omega\sin\omega t$. Equation (103) shows that, in addition, a further force $-M'U_0\omega k\sin\omega t$, in phase with the acceleration, is required. This arises because, in moving the cylinder, air is moved as well. The quantity kM' is called the virtual mass of the body, and depends upon the frequency parameter β. The dependence of k on viscosity arises because the fluid is dragged by viscous forces as well as being moved by the pressure forces. In inviscid flow, of course, only forces of the latter type are present. For a circular cylinder in an inviscid fluid, $k = 1$, and the virtual mass equals the mass of fluid displaced. The second term in expression (103), namely $-k'M'U_0\omega\cos\omega t$, always opposes the movement of the body, and is thus a damping force out of phase with the acceleration. This is the force which produces decay of the oscillation of the body.

The functions k and k' are illustrated graphically in Figs. VII. 12. Both decrease as β increases, and tend to infinity as β tends to zero. For large values of β, we have

$$k = 1+2\sqrt{(2/\beta)}, \qquad k' = 2\sqrt{(2/\beta)}+2/\beta, \qquad (104)$$

which can be obtained by use of the asymptotic expansion of the Bessel function. A detailed comparison between theory and experiment was

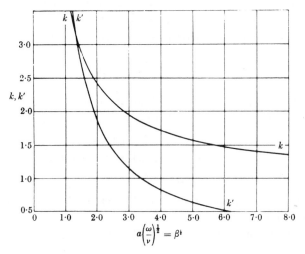

Fig. VII. 12. Virtual inertia (k) and damping (k') coefficients for a vibrating circular cylinder.

made by Stokes (1851). Here we note that the value of k' for large β has more recently been verified experimentally by Martin (1925) and by Stuart and Woodgate (1955). The latter investigators' measurements on an oscillating cylinder at $\beta = 190$ yielded $k' = 0.211$, whereas (104) gives $k' = 0.215$. On the other hand, assuming $k' = C/\sqrt{\beta}$, Stuart and Woodgate found $C = 2.94$ and Martin $C = 2.87$, both in good agreement with the theoretical value of $2\sqrt{2}$. Good agreement between theory and experiment was found for amplitudes of vibration of up to about one-tenth of the diameter. For larger amplitudes Stuart and Woodgate (1955) found an approximately linear variation of k' with amplitude, and gave an empirical theory in support of this result.

For small values of a parameter analogous to β, Ray (1936) has given a theory for the forces on an elliptic cylinder oscillating along an axis. Kanwal (1955) has considered oscillating elliptic cylinders and flat plates at large values of β.

Stokes (1851) also solved the problem for a sphere oscillating rectilinearly along a diameter, which is of considerable physical interest in
connexion with the damping force on a ball pendulum. He obtained
the result (103) with the (exact) coefficients

$$k = \frac{1}{2} + \frac{9}{4}\sqrt{\left(\frac{2}{\beta}\right)}, \qquad k' = \frac{9}{4}\left\{\sqrt{\left(\frac{2}{\beta}\right)} + \frac{2}{\beta}\right\}, \tag{105}$$

where $\beta = \omega a^2/\nu$, a being the radius of the sphere. The mass of fluid
displaced by the sphere is $M' = \frac{4}{3}\pi\rho a^3$, and the virtual mass is kM'.

Before concluding this section, it is worth while to return to a discussion of the reasons why boundary-layer theory is not directly
applicable, even at large values of the frequency parameter β, when it
is desired to calculate the *forces* acting on an oscillating body. If the
boundary-layer theory of Section 10 is used to calculate the flow field
near to an oscillating circular cylinder, the same surface skin friction
is obtained as was calculated by Stokes; but the pressure distribution
is assumed to be, and remains, that of inviscid theory. On the other
hand, Stokes's work shows a small pressure variation due to the
boundary layer; the consequent modification of the surface pressure can
be shown to give a contribution to the damping force of the same order
of magnitude as the contribution from the skin friction. It is important
to note, therefore, that for a bluff body which is oscillating at a high
frequency with a small amplitude, the damping force, though small,
is strongly dependent on the change of pressure due to viscosity. On
the other hand, the virtual mass is mainly given by inviscid considerations, and is not affected very much by the viscosity. (In the case of
steady boundary-layer flow past a bluff body the profile drag is not
strongly affected by pressure changes due to the attached part of the
boundary layer; rather it is affected by the large-scale pressure changes
induced by separation. In the case of steady flow past a sufficiently
slender body, without separation, the drag arising from a small pressure
change due to the boundary layer can be small compared with the
frictional drag.) For a further discussion of this point, and a method
of calculating the forces acting on a convex cylinder oscillating with
high frequency, the reader is referred to Segel (1960).

13. The theory of the response of skin friction to fluctuations in the stream velocity

Fluctuations in a stream incident on a body are known to occur, and
it is important to understand how the boundary layer reacts to the

oscillations of the stream. For example, in the occurrence of flutter on aircraft the boundary-layer effects may be considerable; and by taking axes fixed in the body, the boundary-layer problem again becomes one of response to a fluctuating incident stream. The most general case is that in which the stream fluctuates both in magnitude and in direction, and this has been studied by Gibson (1957). A simpler case, and one which has been treated by Lighthill (1954), is that in which the stream fluctuates in magnitude but not in direction. This particular case avoids the difficulties associated with the oscillating stagnation point, which is the starting-point of the boundary layer. The fluctuations in the main-stream velocity are assumed to be transmitted instantaneously to the (inviscid) flow at the edge of the boundary layer, which will therefore fluctuate in phase with the incident stream. The frequency parameter which arises in the analysis is $\omega\delta^2/\nu$, where ω is the frequency and δ the unperturbed boundary-layer thickness; this parameter is proportional to $\omega U_x/l$, where U_x is the stream velocity and l a standard length parallel to the body. A more precise parameter is $\omega\delta_{10}^2/\nu = \lambda$, where δ_{10} is the displacement thickness of the unperturbed boundary layer.

Let us consider a stream of velocity $U_x(1+\epsilon e^{i\omega t})$, which produces a velocity at the edge of the boundary layer like $U(x,t) = U_0(x)(1+\epsilon e^{i\omega t})$, neglecting fluctuations in the boundary-layer displacement. Then in the boundary-layer equations we put

$$u = u_0(x,z)+\epsilon u_1 e^{i\omega t}, \qquad w = w_0(x,z)+\epsilon w_1(x,z)e^{i\omega t}, \qquad (106)$$

and assume that ϵ is so small that we can linearize. The mean velocity distribution can be calculated by known methods, and the fluctuating part of the velocity is given by

$$i\omega u_1 + u_0\frac{\partial u_1}{\partial x} + u_1\frac{\partial u_0}{\partial x} + w_0\frac{\partial u_1}{\partial z} + w_1\frac{\partial u_0}{\partial z} = i\omega U_0 + \frac{d}{dx}(U_0^2) + \nu\frac{\partial^2 u_1}{\partial z^2};$$

$$\frac{\partial u_1}{\partial x} + \frac{\partial w_1}{\partial z} = 0. \qquad (107)$$

Since u_0 is known to be a function of x/l and $z\sqrt{(U_x/\nu l)}$, where l is a standard length, it follows that the quasi-steady solution as $\omega \to 0$ (i.e. as the velocity of the free stream tends to the steady value $(1+\epsilon)U_\infty$) is

$$u_s = u_0 + \tfrac{1}{2}z\frac{\partial u_0}{\partial z}, \qquad w_s = \tfrac{1}{2}\left(w_0 + z\frac{\partial w_0}{\partial z}\right). \qquad (108)$$

Now putting $(u_1, w_1) = (u_s, w_s) + (u_\omega, w_\omega)$, where (u_ω, w_ω) are of order ω, and using the fact that (u_s, w_s) is a solution for $u_\omega \to 0$, we obtain

$$i\omega u_\omega + u_0 \frac{\partial u_\omega}{\partial x} + u_\omega \frac{\partial u_0}{\partial x} + w_0 \frac{\partial u_\omega}{\partial z} + w_\omega \frac{\partial u_0}{\partial z} - \nu \frac{\partial^2 u_\omega}{\partial z^2} = i\omega(U_0 - u_s);$$

$$\frac{\partial u_\omega}{\partial x} + \frac{\partial w_\omega}{\partial z} = 0, \tag{109}$$

subject to the boundary conditions

$$u_\omega = w_\omega = 0 \quad \text{at } z = 0, \qquad u_\omega \to 0 \quad \text{as } z \to \infty. \tag{110}$$

Lighthill (1954) used a Kármán–Pohlhausen method to solve the equations for u_ω, w_ω ($\equiv i\omega(u_2, v_2)$ in his notation) for sufficiently small values of the frequency parameter $\omega l / U_\infty$. Thus, using the equation of continuity and (108), we have

$$\nu\left(\frac{\partial u_\omega}{\partial z}\right)_{z=0} = \tfrac{1}{2}i\omega \int_0^\infty (U_0 - u_0)\, dz + \left(U_0 \frac{d}{dx} - i\omega\right) \int_0^\infty u_\omega\, dz - 2\frac{d}{dx} \int_0^\infty u_\omega u_0\, dz. \tag{111}$$

As described in Section VI. 13, the velocity profile of the steady flow may be assumed to be given by equation (VI. 168), where $\eta = z/\delta(x)$ and $\Lambda = (\delta^2/\nu)\, dU_0/dx$. Lighthill has shown that u_ω may be assumed to be

$$\frac{u_\omega}{U_0} = \frac{i\omega\delta^2}{\nu}(1-\eta)^2\{A\eta + (2A - \tfrac{1}{2})\eta^2\}. \tag{112}$$

In general A is a function of Λ and of $\omega\delta^2/\nu$, but in practice Lighthill found that to a good approximation A is independent of $\omega\delta^2/\nu$ and is given by $A = (36 - \Lambda)/240$ over the greater part of the boundary layer except close to the point of separation. This is equivalent to neglecting the last two terms in the momentum-integral equation for u_ω (111), so that it may be written

$$\nu\left(\frac{\partial u_\omega}{\partial z}\right)_{z=0} = \tfrac{1}{2}i\omega \int_0^\infty (U_0 - u_0)\, dz = \tfrac{1}{2}i\omega U_0 \delta_{10}. \tag{113}$$

For large values of $\omega\delta^2/\nu$ another method may be used, and this will now be described. According to the theory of differential equations which contain a large parameter, a first approximation to the solution may be obtained by retaining only the terms of the highest order and in the highest derivative. In the present case the large parameter in equation (107) is $\omega\delta^2/\nu$, and the equation therefore becomes

$$i\omega u_1 = i\omega U_0 + \nu \frac{\partial^2 u_1}{\partial z^2}, \tag{114}$$

subject to the conditions, $u_1' = 0$ at $z = 0$ and $u_1 \to U_0(x)$ as $z \to \infty$. Consequently, the relevant solution is

$$u_1 = U_0(x)(1 - e^{-z\sqrt{(i\omega/\nu)}}). \tag{115}$$

This is the solution for the shear-wave boundary layer which has been described in Section 9, and is independent of the presence of a mean flow. Viscosity is only effective for the oscillation within a layer whose thickness is of order $\sqrt{(\nu/\omega)}$, which is very small compared with the main boundary-layer thickness δ (in accord with $\omega\delta^2/\nu \gg 1$). In other words, at high frequencies the fluctuating part of the velocity responds instantly, except within the very thin shear-wave boundary layer close to the wall. This solution was obtained independently by Lin (1956a) and by Lighthill (1954). It was also pointed out by Lin that the high-frequency solution is a valid approximation to the boundary-layer equation at all amplitudes provided the frequency parameter λ is high enough. Furthermore, Lin calculated the distortion of the mean flow by the Reynolds stress of the fluctuation, an aspect of the theory which Gibson (1957) has studied in more detail, both for high and low frequencies (see also Moore and Ostrach 1957).

One of the important results concerns the response of the skin friction to the stream fluctuations. The skin friction is $\mu(\partial u/\partial z)_{z=0}$ and on the low-frequency approximation (obtained by the Pohlhausen approach) it is

$$\tau_w + \epsilon e^{i\omega t}[3\tau_w/2 + \tfrac{1}{2}i\omega U_0\rho\delta_{10}], \tag{116}$$

where τ_w is the unperturbed skin friction. According to the high-frequency approximation, on the other hand, the skin friction is given by

$$\tau_w + \epsilon e^{i\omega t}\mu U_0\sqrt{(i\omega/\nu)}. \tag{117}$$

It can be seen from both formulae that the skin friction has a phase lead over the velocity fluctuation of the stream. This can be interpreted as a consequence of the greater relative effect of the pressure gradient on the slowly moving fluid near the wall, than on the faster-moving fluid near the edge of the boundary layer; this effect overcomes the potential lag in the velocity profile due to inertia (Lighthill 1954). In (116) both the amplitude and phase lead increase with frequency, while in (117) the phase lead has the constant value $\tfrac{1}{4}\pi$ and the amplitude increases with the square root of the frequency. When the frequency parameter, λ, has the value at which the phase lead, according to (116), is $\tfrac{1}{4}\pi$, the amplitude of the skin-friction oscillation is in quite good agreement with that predicted by the high-frequency approximation for the

Blasius and stagnation-point boundary layers (Lighthill 1954). It is suggested by Lighthill (1954) that for values of λ greater than

$$\lambda_0 = 3\delta_{10}(\partial u_0/\partial z)_{z=0}/U_0(x),$$

the high-frequency approximation is applicable, and that for lower values of λ the low-frequency approximation is applicable. Naturally this gives only a rough division between the two régimes of unsteady flow, and there may be some error in the region of the frequency parameter λ_0.

Moore (1951), Gibellato (1955), and Cheng and Elliott (1957) have solved the boundary-layer equations for the low-frequency case of unsteady Blasius flow. The equations for compressible flow have been solved by Illingworth (1958), both for high and low frequencies. Let x be the distance from the stagnation point. Gibellato expanded the solution for fluctuating flow directly in powers of $\omega x/U_0$, which is proportional to λ, whereas Moore expanded in terms of the parameters described in Section 4. However, Moore's calculations can be particularized to the fluctuating*case. The velocity distribution was calculated by both authors, and for the skin friction Moore gives

$$\mu\left(\frac{\partial u}{\partial z}\right)_{z=0} = \tau_w + \epsilon e^{i\omega t}[3\tau_w/2 + 0.493i\omega\rho U_0\delta_{10} + 0.272\rho\omega^2 x\delta_{10}] + \dots$$

(118)

where $\delta_{10} = 1.7208\sqrt{(\nu x/U_0)}$ and $\tau_w = 0.33206\mu U_0\sqrt{(U_0/\nu x)}$ according to the proper solution of the boundary-layer equations (Section V. 12). The coefficient 0.493 in (118) is confirmed by an independent calculation due to Illingworth (1958). Gibellato's paper gives numerical values of the last two coefficients in (118) which are slightly different. The component of skin friction in (116) which is proportional to ω is seen to be in error by only about 2 per cent. The importance of the ω^2 term near to the frequency parameter λ_0 is discussed in Section 15.

For a treatment of fluctuating viscous flow according to a modified Oseen approximation the reader is referred to papers by Carrier (1955) and by Carrier and Di Prima (1957). For later work on fluctuating viscous flow, the reader is referred to papers by Moore (1957a, b, c), by Moore and Ostrach (1957) and, for the Blasius case, by Ghosh (1961).

14. Fluctuating flow past an infinite porous flat plate

An exact solution of the Navier–Stokes equation is known (Stuart 1955) which illustrates some of the properties of fluctuating boundary layers described above. This solution satisfies the following conditions:

(i) the flow is incompressible, two-dimensional, and is bounded by an infinite, plane, porous wall; (ii) the flow is independent of distance parallel to the wall; (iii) the component of velocity parallel to the wall at a large distance from it fluctuates in time about a constant mean; and (iv) the component of velocity normal to the wall is a constant, v_w. The flow is thus a generalization of the asymptotic-suction solution of steady flow (Section III. 15), and is governed by the differential equation

$$\frac{\partial u}{\partial t} + v_w \frac{\partial u}{\partial z} = \frac{\partial U}{\partial t} + v \frac{\partial^2 u}{\partial z^2}. \tag{119}$$

A solution is obtainable in the form

$$U(t) = U_0(1 + \epsilon e^{i\omega t}), \tag{120}$$

$$u = U_0\{\zeta_0(z) + \epsilon \zeta_1(z) e^{i\omega t}\}. \tag{121}$$

Substituting (120) and (121) into (119) with the new variable $\eta = z|v_w|/\nu$, separating into mean and harmonic parts, and solving subject to the boundary conditions $\zeta_0 = \zeta_1 = 0$ at $\eta = 0$ and $\zeta_0, \zeta_1 \to 1$ as $\eta \to \infty$, we obtain

$$\zeta_0 = 1 - e^{-\eta}, \qquad \zeta_1 = 1 - e^{-h\eta}, \tag{122}$$

where

$$h(\lambda) = h_r + ih_i = \tfrac{1}{2}\{1 + \sqrt{(1 + 4i\lambda)}\}, \qquad \lambda = \frac{\omega \nu}{v_w^2} = \frac{\omega \delta_{10}^2}{\nu}. \tag{123}$$

The unperturbed (or mean) displacement thickness is $\delta_{10} = \nu/|v_w|$. The skin friction is given by

$$\frac{\tau_w}{\rho U_0 |v_w|} = 1 + \epsilon |h| e^{i(\omega t + \alpha)}, \tag{124}$$

in which $\alpha = \tan^{-1}(h_i/h_r)$.

A comparison with Lighthill's high- and low-frequency approximations can now be made. For small values of λ, the solution ζ_1 takes the form

$$\zeta_1 = 1 - e^{-\eta} + i\lambda\eta e^{-\eta} + \lambda^2(\eta + \tfrac{1}{2}\eta^2)e^{-\eta} + O(\lambda^3). \tag{125}$$

If λ is so small that λ^2 may be neglected, it can be seen that the velocity fluctuation is the sum of parts proportional to the instantaneous velocity and acceleration of the main stream (cf. Section 13). As λ increases (equivalent to an increase of frequency) the solution is seen to tend to the 'high-frequency' solution as $h(\lambda)$ tends to $\sqrt{(i\lambda)}$, for then

$$\zeta_1 \sim 1 - e^{-z\sqrt{(i\omega/\nu)}},$$

which is equivalent to the solution (115) of the general problem.

The skin friction for these two cases takes the form

$$\frac{\tau_w}{\rho U_0 |v_w|} = 1 + \epsilon(1 + 3\lambda^2)^{\frac{1}{2}} \exp[i(\omega t + \tan^{-1}\lambda)] \tag{126}$$

for the low-frequency approximation, and

$$\frac{\tau_w}{\rho U_0 |v_w|} = 1 + \epsilon \lambda^{\frac{1}{2}} \exp[i(\omega t + \tfrac{1}{4}\pi)] \tag{127}$$

for the high-frequency approximation. The value of the frequency parameter at which the phase lead for the low-frequency approximation

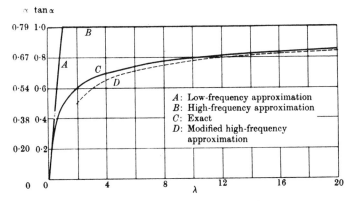

FIG. VII. 13. Skin-friction phase lead plotted against frequency parameter.

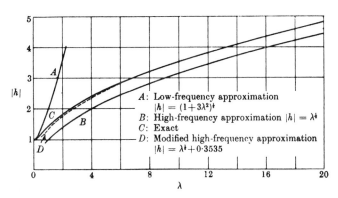

FIG. VII. 14. Skin friction amplitude plotted against frequency parameter.

becomes equal to the phase lead on the high-frequency approximation is $\lambda = \lambda_0 = 1$, and the difference between the combination of high- and low-frequency approximations and the exact solution is illustrated in Figs. VII. 13 and VII. 14 for the phase lead and amplitude of the skin friction. These comparisons show that the approximate solutions may require some modification near the frequency parameter λ_0. The inclusion of extra terms in the high-frequency approximation yields a more exact formula for the skin friction, and the improved agreement with the exact solution is also shown by Figs. VII. 13 and VII. 14, which are taken from Stuart (1955).

A property of fluctuating boundary layers which is of considerable practical importance is the effect of the fluctuation on the nature of separation. In view of the changes in pressure distribution induced by the fluctuations in separation, a quantitative description has not yet

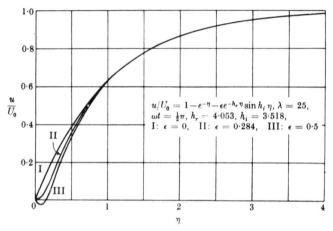

$$u/U_0 = 1 - e^{-\eta} - \epsilon e^{-h_r \eta} \sin h_i \, \eta, \quad \lambda = 25,$$
$$\omega t = \tfrac{1}{2}\pi, \; h_r = 4 \cdot 053, \; h_i = 3 \cdot 518,$$
$$\text{I: } \epsilon = 0, \quad \text{II: } \epsilon = 0 \cdot 284, \quad \text{III: } \epsilon = 0 \cdot 5$$

Fig. VII. 15. Transient velocity profiles.

been obtained. However, some information on this point can be obtained by considering the transient velocity profiles (121). Certain members of the class of transient velocity profiles are found to be of a 'separation' type (with zero skin friction) or 'separated' type (with reverse flow close to the surface). Particular 'separation' (II) and 'separated' (III) profiles are illustrated in Fig. VII. 15 together with the velocity profile for zero fluctuation (I). This illustrates the large influence which a high-frequency oscillation has upon the transient velocity distributions and skin friction. In a separating boundary layer it can be inferred that this would have a large effect on the nature of separation (see Moore 1957b, c).

A generalization of the above solution of equation (119) has been given by Watson (1958) for the case when $U(t)$ is a general function of time, subject to one or two weak conditions (see also Hasimoto 1957). The solution was obtained by using a Laplace-transform technique. Among the types of flow which can be considered by this method are those in which the external stream velocity, $U(t)$, changes with time from one value to another. As a particular case, Watson considers a function, $U(t)$, which has one constant value for $t < 0$ and another constant value for $t > 0$. This is an external flow which changes impulsively from one value to another, and in this sense is more general than the flows described in Section 7, which move impulsively from rest. It is found that the skin friction at first rises sharply when the impulse is applied and then gradually decays to its ultimate limiting value, which is greater than the initial value because of the greater free-stream speed. The initial rise in the skin friction is due to the formation of a secondary boundary layer, whose thickness is of order $\sqrt{(\nu t)}$, superimposed on the main boundary layer. As time progresses the secondary layer, which initially is described by the Rayleigh flow of equation (13), increases in thickness and distorts the flow in such a way that the ultimate skin friction is approached. In a separating boundary layer the large change in skin friction produced by a sharp change in the external stream speed would obviously influence the position of the point of separation.

15. Applications of Lighthill's theory to the stagnation-point and Blasius boundary layers

Hiemenz showed experimentally that over the forward quadrant of a circular cylinder, the velocity at the edge of the boundary layer is given by about $3 \cdot 6 U_\infty x/d$ at a Reynolds number $U_\infty d/\nu = 1 \cdot 85 \times 10^4$, where d is the cylinder diameter and U_∞ the stream velocity, x being the distance from the stagnation point. A boundary-layer calculation for this case by the Pohlhausen method gives $(\partial u_0/\partial z)_w = 1 \cdot 195 a x \sqrt{(a/\nu)}$, $\delta^2 = 7 \cdot 05 \nu/a$, $\delta_{10} = 0 \cdot 655 \sqrt{(\nu/a)}$, where a denotes $3 \cdot 6 U_\infty/d$. Thus

$$\lambda_0 = \omega \delta_{10}^2/\nu$$

has the value $2 \cdot 35$, and the critical frequency ω_0 is about $20 U_\infty/d$. Consequently the low-frequency type of approximation may be applied provided $\omega d/U_\infty$ is less than 20. This type of solution is applicable near to the forward stagnation region of any symmetrical blunt-nosed body which is oscillating parallel to the stream, with the proviso that the quantity a depends on the shape of the body near the forward stagnation region.

The second basically important solution is that for a Blasius boundary layer on a flat plate. For this boundary layer the critical frequency ω_0 decreases with x, where x is the distance from the leading edge. For a velocity U_0 at the edge of the layer, it can be verified that the Pohlhausen method yields $(\partial u_0/\partial z)_w = 0 \cdot 343 U_0 \sqrt{(U_0/\nu x)}$, $\delta^2 = 34 \nu x/U_0$,

$\delta_{10} = 1{\cdot}75\sqrt{(\nu x/U_0)}$. Then it follows that the critical frequency parameter $\lambda_0 = \omega\delta_{10}^2/\nu$ is $1{\cdot}8$, and the critical frequency is about $0{\cdot}6U_0/x$. Thus for x less than $0{\cdot}6U_0/\omega$ the low-frequency solution is applicable, and for x greater than $0{\cdot}6U_0/\omega$ the high-frequency solution is applicable. In the region of $x = 0{\cdot}6U_0/\omega$, neither solution is strictly valid. In fact the calculations of Moore (1951) and Gibellato (1955), described in Section 13, show that when $\omega x/U_0$ equals $0{\cdot}6$ the term proportional to ω^2 is about $0{\cdot}34$ times the terms retained in the low-frequency theory. It is thus of some importance.

The flat-plate Blasius boundary layer may also be used to illustrate the presence of a *virtual* mass due to viscous action, in addition to the real mass of the plate. The drag associated with both sides of a plate of length c, such that $c < 0{\cdot}6U_0/\omega$, is composed of a part equal to the *steady* drag at the instantaneous speed $U(t)$ together with a part equal to $(\rho\Delta_{10}/2)\,dU/dt$. The integrated steady displacement thickness for both sides is termed the displacement area Δ_{10}. Consequently, the force required to accelerate a breadth l of the plate, apart from the force required to overcome the drag associated with the instantaneous speed, is $(M+l\rho\Delta_{10}/2)\,dU/dt$, where M is the mass of the breadth l of the plate. Thus there is a virtual mass $l\rho\Delta_{10}/2$, due to the fact that fluid is being dragged and accelerated by viscous action. For a body, this 'viscous' virtual mass must be added to the ordinary virtual mass, which is due to fluid being accelerated by the unsteady pressure gradient near the body (see Section 11).

16. The flow near an oscillating stagnation point

Let us consider a modification of the classical stagnation-point boundary layer, in which a flow impinges on a wall which is oscillating in its own plane with velocity $\epsilon e^{i\omega t}$. This forms a combination of two classical flows: (i) the plane stagnation-point flow against a plane wall (Section III. 19), and (ii) the infinite wall oscillating in a fluid which would otherwise be at rest (Section VII. 9). (A generalization, not treated here, but discussed by Watson (1959), allows the wall to have a velocity which is any function of t.)

The component of velocity parallel to the wall is $u = u_0+\epsilon u_1 e^{i\omega t}$, while the component normal to the wall is $w = w_0+\epsilon w_1 e^{i\omega t}$, where u_0, u_1, w_0, and w_1 are functions of x and z. As z tends to infinity u_0 tends to ax and w_0 approaches $-az+0{\cdot}6479\sqrt{(a\nu)}$, while within the layer they are given by $u_0 = axf'(\eta)$, $w_0 = -\sqrt{(a\nu)}f(\eta)$, where $\eta = z\sqrt{(a/\nu)}$; the reader is referred to Table V. 2. The problem is to find u_1 and w_1 subject to the conditions that u_1 reduces to a given constant value at the (oscillating) wall, w_1 is zero at the wall, and u_1 tends to zero at large distances from the wall. It is found that an exact solution of the Navier–Stokes equations for all values of ϵ and ω may be obtained in the form $u_1 = \zeta(\eta)$, $w_1 = 0$, where ζ satisfies

$$\zeta'' + f\zeta' - f'\zeta - i\lambda_1 \zeta = 0, \tag{128}$$

and
$$\zeta = 1 \quad \text{at} \quad \eta = 0, \qquad \zeta \to 0 \quad \text{as} \quad \eta \to \infty. \tag{129}$$

The symbol λ_1 denotes ω/a and, since for this flow $\delta_{10} = 0.6479\sqrt{(\nu/a)}$, $\lambda = \omega\delta_{10}^2/\nu$ has the value $0.4198\omega/a = 0.4198\lambda_1$.

The quasi-steady solution as λ_1 tends to zero is $\zeta_0 = f''(\eta)/f''(0)$, where $f''(0) = 1.2326$ (Table V. 2). Thus the velocity for the flow impinging on a wall moving with constant velocity ϵ is given by

$$u = axf'(\eta) + \epsilon f''(\eta)/f''(0), \qquad w = -(a\nu)^{\frac{1}{2}}f(\eta). \tag{130}$$

The solution for small values of λ_1 can be developed as a series in λ_1, as was done by Glauert (1956) and Rott (1956), with ζ_0 as the leading term.

For large values of λ_1, the solution takes the form of a series in descending powers of $\sqrt{\lambda_1}$:

$$\zeta(\eta) \sim e^{-\xi\sqrt{i}} - \frac{\phi''(0)}{\lambda_1^{3/2}}\left(\frac{3\xi}{8i} + \frac{3\xi^2}{8\sqrt{i}} + \frac{\xi^3}{12}\right)e^{-\xi\sqrt{i}} + O(\lambda_1^{-2}), \tag{131}$$

where $\xi = \eta\sqrt{\lambda_1}$. Glauert (1956) obtained this type of solution and gave terms up to λ_1^{-4}. It will be noticed that the first term in the high-frequency solution gives the solution for an oscillating wall *without* a a mean flow, namely the shear-wave boundary layer. This occurs because the thickness of the mean-flow boundary layer, which is of order $\sqrt{(\nu/a)}$, is much greater than that of the shear-wave layer, which is of order $\sqrt{(\nu/\omega)}$, when λ_1 is large, so that there is little interaction between the two parts of the flow.

The important physical quantity is the skin friction, which is given by

$$\tau_w = \mu\left(\frac{\partial u}{\partial z}\right)_{z=0} = \mu\sqrt{\left(\frac{a}{\nu}\right)}[axf''(0) + \epsilon e^{i\omega t}\zeta'(0)]. \tag{132}$$

For small values of λ_1, Glauert gives the series

$$-\zeta'(0) = 0.8113 + 0.4932i\lambda_1 + 0.0947\lambda_1^2 + \dots \tag{133}$$

and for large values of λ_1

$$-\zeta'(0) = (i\lambda_1)^{1/2} + \frac{3f''(0)}{8}(i\lambda_1)^{-1} - \frac{3}{16}(i\lambda_1)^{-3/2} - \frac{33}{128}f''(0)^2(i\lambda_1)^{-5/2} +$$
$$+ \frac{129}{256}f''(0)(i\lambda_1)^{-3} - \frac{139}{512}(i\lambda_1)^{-7/2} + O(i\lambda_1)^{-4}. \tag{134}$$

The skin friction is seen to have a phase lead over the velocity fluctua-

tion. The phase lead ultimately increases to $\frac{1}{4}\pi$ for very large values
of λ_1, as seen from (131). The amplitude of the skin-friction fluctuation
increases with λ_1 and is ultimately proportional to $\lambda_1^{\frac{1}{4}}$. These properties
are illustrated in Fig. VII. 16, which is due to Glauert (1956). Reasonably
good agreement is obtained in the range of overlap.

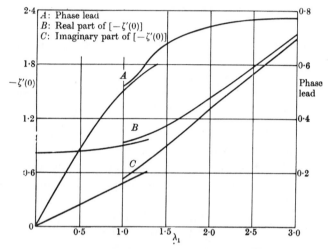

FIG. VII. 16. Comparison of skin-friction amplitude and phase lead near the
oscillating stagnation point for an oscillating plate.

It can be seen from Fig. VII. 16 that we may regard $\lambda_1 = 2$, corresponding to λ about unity, as an approximate lower limit for the
application of the high-frequency series type of solution. For the case
of Schubauer's elliptic cylinder with axes in the ratio 2·96 to 1, for the
air flowing (U_∞) parallel to the major axis, the mean displacement
thickness grows from $0·134\sqrt{(c\nu/U_\infty)}$, where c is the major axis or chord,
at the front stagnation point, to $1·512\sqrt{(c\nu/U_\infty)}$ at separation (Hartree
1939b). For the latter point, it can be seen that $\omega c/U_\infty = 0·435\lambda$. Thus,
supposing that the condition $\lambda > 1$ for a high-frequency type of solution holds generally, the condition is equivalent to $\omega c/U_\infty > 0·435$ for
the flow near separation.

Schlichting and Ulrich (1940) made calculations of the boundary
layer on various elliptic cylinders with the flow parallel to the major
axis, including the case of axis-ratios of 8 to 1. For this case, the
Pohlhausen method gives $\delta_{10} = 2·2\sqrt{(c\nu/U_\infty)}$ at separation, yielding
$\omega c/U_\infty = 0·207\lambda$. Thus a high-frequency series solution may be expected to be valid near separation for $\omega c/U_\infty > 0·207$. In actual flutter

problems $\omega c/U_\infty$ is of order unity, so that the high-frequency theory is valid in the boundary-layer flow immediately ahead of separation, though not in general near the forward stagnation region.

If the wall oscillates not in the x-direction, as in the flow discussed above, but in the y-direction, then the velocity field is $u = axf'(\eta)$,

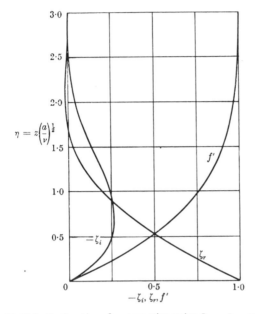

FIG. VII. 17. Velocity functions for stagnation-point flow when the oscillation is parallel to the stagnation line ($\lambda_1 = 0.5$).

$w = -\sqrt{(av)}f(\eta)$, $v = \epsilon\zeta(\eta)e^{i\omega t}$. Wuest (1952) has shown that the function $\zeta(\eta)$ ($= \zeta_r + i\zeta_i$) is given by equation (75), where α is replaced by $i\omega$ and γ is replaced by $i\lambda_1$. The flow is an exact solution of the Navier–Stokes equations. A solution can be obtained by the methods of Rott and Glauert for high and low values of λ_1, and this has been done by Rott (1956). Furthermore, Wuest (1952) obtained a numerical solution for one particular value of λ_1, namely $\lambda_1 = 0.5$. For this case the functions ζ_r and ζ_i are given in Fig. VII. 17, due to Wuest (1952). For high values of λ_1, it is clear that the solution is analogous to those discussed earlier for large λ_1, namely that the amplitude of the skin friction increases like $\lambda_1^{\frac{1}{4}}$ and that the phase lead tends to $\frac{1}{4}\pi$. It is also clear that the phase lead is proportional to λ_1 for small λ_1.

Wuest also analyses the equations for flow past a wedge ($U = ax^m$) and flow past a circular cylinder ($U = a_1 x + a_3 x^3 + a_5 x^5 + ...$) when the wedge or cylinder oscillates along its axis, but does not give any numerical results. In these cases 'similar' solutions do not exist and expansions in powers of x are necessary.

17. Heat transfer and temperature fluctuations in unsteady flow

The theory of the response of heat transfer from a body when the velocity of the main stream fluctuates in magnitude but not in direction has been treated by Lighthill (1954). The temperature of the stream and wall are assumed to be constant, and the heat generated by viscous dissipation is neglected.

The equation governing the temperature in a boundary layer is (Howarth 1953)

$$\frac{\partial T}{\partial t} + u\frac{\partial T}{\partial x} + w\frac{\partial T}{\partial z} = \kappa\frac{\partial^2 T}{\partial z^2}, \tag{135}$$

where κ is the thermal diffusivity and T the temperature, subject to the boundary conditions

$$T = \Theta \quad \text{at } z = 0, \qquad T \to 0 \quad \text{as } z \to \infty. \tag{136}$$

The temperature of the stream may conveniently be taken as the zero.

The mean temperature T_0 is given and, after linearization, we obtain the following equation for the fluctuating part of the temperature T_1 (where $T = T_0 + \epsilon T_1 e^{i\omega t}$):

$$i\omega T_1 + u_0\frac{\partial T_1}{\partial x} + \frac{\partial T_0}{\partial x}u_1 + w_0\frac{\partial T_1}{\partial z} + \frac{\partial T_0}{\partial z}w_1 = \kappa\frac{\partial^2 T_1}{\partial z^2}, \tag{137}$$

where $T_1 = 0$ at $z = 0$ and ∞. As ω tends to zero, the quasi-steady solution is seen to be $T_s = \frac{1}{2}z\,\partial T_0/\partial z$. We then write

$$T_1 = T_s + T_\omega, \tag{138}$$

where T_ω is proportional to $i\omega$. The quantity T_ω satisfies the equation

$$i\omega T_\omega + u_0\frac{\partial T_\omega}{\partial x} + w_0\frac{\partial T_\omega}{\partial z} - \kappa\frac{\partial^2 T_\omega}{\partial z^2} = -i\omega T_s - \frac{\partial T_0}{\partial x}u_\omega - \frac{\partial T_0}{\partial z}w_\omega. \tag{139}$$

The term $-i\omega T_s$ represents the thermal inertia of the fluid which resists the quasi-steady temperature fluctuations, and tends to produce phase lag of the heat transfer. On the other hand, the remaining terms on the right-hand side of (139) represent the additional heat transfer due to the phase advanced velocity fluctuations, and tend to produce phase advance. These facts may be established by detailed numerical considerations. Lighthill (1954) gives a Pohlhausen method for the solution of (139), and from an analysis of this method suggests the use of a temperature which is linear in ω for sufficiently small frequencies. At

high frequencies he gives a solution which is obtained from the theory
of differential equations which contain a large parameter, as in Section
13. Thus for the 'stagnation-point flow' ($U_0 = ax$), with a Prandtl
number of 0·7, the heat transfer on the low-frequency approximation
is approximately

$$-k\left(\frac{\partial T_0}{\partial z}\right)_{z=0}\left\{1+\tfrac{1}{2}\epsilon e^{i\omega t}\left(\frac{1}{1+0·7i\omega/a}\right)\right\},$$

and on the high-frequency approximation it is approximately

$$-k\left(\frac{\partial T_0}{\partial z}\right)_{z=0}\left\{1+\tfrac{1}{2}\epsilon e^{i\omega t}\left(\frac{1·1}{i\omega/a}\right)\right\},$$

where k is the thermal conductivity. The former solution is valid for
$\omega/a < 5·6$ and the latter for $\omega/a > 5·6$ approximately. Reasonable
agreement is obtained for values of ω/a close to 5·6.

Gibellato (1956) has solved the temperature equation for the low-
frequency case of unsteady Blasius flow. An expansion in powers of
$\omega x/U_0$, where x is the distance from the leading edge and U_0 is the free-
stream velocity, gave the unsteady part of the heat transfer from the
body to the stream, for a Prandtl number of 0·7, as

$$-\tfrac{1}{2}k\Theta\epsilon(U_0/\nu x)^{\frac{1}{2}}\{[0·293+0·23(\omega x/U_0)^2]\cos\omega t+[0·039(\omega x/U_0)]\sin\omega t\},$$

$$(140)$$

where Θ is the excess of the body temperature over the free-stream
temperature. Lighthill's Pohlhausen calculation gave 0·305 and 0·021
respectively for the coefficients of the terms independent of, and linear
in, $\omega x/U_0$; the first of these coefficients is in good agreement with the
exact value (0·293), but the second is too low. However, the exact
result (140) confirms the smallness of the coefficient of $\omega x/U_0$, and
emphasizes the importance of the term in $(\omega x/U_0)^2$.

Stuart (1955) has considered the temperature fluctuations of an
infinite flat plate with uniform suction, when there is zero heat transfer
at the surface, using the flow described in Section 14. In this case it
is necessary to take into account dissipation of kinetic energy into heat.
Because this dissipation is proportional to the square of the (fluctuating)
velocity, the temperature has a second-harmonic component as well as
the first-harmonic one, both these components being superimposed on
a mean temperature. At high frequencies the mean heating of the wall
by the fluctuating part of the velocity field is the main effect of the
unsteadiness. The amplitude of the temperature variation of the wall
is not so large as the mean temperature increase and, furthermore, is

primarily in the second harmonic, so that the frequency of the wall temperature is twice that of the external stream. For further details the reader is referred to the original paper.

For later work on unsteady heat transfer the reader is referred to papers by Moore and Ostrach (1957), Sparrow and Gregg (1957, 1958), Sparrow (1958), and Merk (1958). For a study of 'similar' temperature boundary layers, following Schuh's work, see Stojanovic (1959).

VIII

THREE-DIMENSIONAL BOUNDARY LAYERS

PART I

FUNDAMENTAL EQUATIONS

1. Introduction

THE study of three-dimensional boundary layers will be separated into two main Parts. The first of these (Part II) will be concerned with boundary layers which possess a common geometrical property, namely that of rotational symmetry, an example of which is the flow along a surface of revolution when the main stream is parallel to the axis of symmetry. It may be convenient at this stage to remind the reader of the terms to be used to discuss these cases. If (r, θ, z) are conventional cylindrical polar coordinates with $r = 0$ as the axis of symmetry, a flow will be described as rotationally symmetrical if the velocity components (v_r, v_θ, v_z) and the pressure p are independent of θ. Axial symmetry is a particular case of rotational symmetry, the additional condition being $v_\theta = 0$, so that there is no swirl. Thus the example cited above is one of axial symmetry.

Part III will deal with boundary layers on surfaces of a general type. It is necessary to distinguish here between the case where there is singular geometric behaviour of the surfaces (corners and edges, for example) and that where the surface is smoothly curved. The region of flow associated with the former case has been called a 'boundary region', and that associated with the latter a 'boundary sheet' (see Sears 1954b). The general equations of motion which will be derived for use in this chapter will relate only to boundary-sheet problems. Boundary-region problems are also of considerable importance, and certain of them will also be discussed in this chapter.

In the case of flow past a body of general shape, it is again assumed that the effects of viscosity are confined to a thin layer next to the surface of the body. The actual main-stream flow in a three-dimensional case will depend on all three space coordinates, one of which will be a coordinate measured normal to the surface. It will be shown that, within the boundary-layer approximations, the variation in the pressure along any normal can be ignored. The main flow just outside the boundary layer is assumed to be the corresponding inviscid flow on the given surface, and is dependent therefore only on two space coordinates measured along the surface. These assumptions are not necessarily justified in all practical cases, such as occur with comparatively thick boundary layers on swept wings, or at the trailing edge of any wing. Inside the boundary layer, of course, the velocity of the fluid depends on all three space coordinates.

The extension to three-dimensional flow introduces two special effects which were absent in the two-dimensional cases treated in previous chapters. The first of these is due to the convergence or divergence of the streamlines of the main flow parallel to the surface, and the second effect is introduced by the curvature of these streamlines. Convergence or divergence may, of course, occur in two-dimensional flow, the pressure changing in accordance with Bernoulli's theorem. Three-dimensional effects arise only if the pressure changes in such a way that continuity requires convergence in a lateral direction as well as normal to the surface. The influence of the three-dimensional effects is to produce a change in boundary-layer thickness, over and above the two-dimensional boundary-layer growth.

The second effect, which is associated with lateral curvature of the main-stream flow, gives rise to a new pattern of flow. A 'secondary flow' is produced in the boundary layer, in which the motion of the fluid departs from the direction of the streamlines in the main stream in consequence of the lateral pressure gradient. This secondary flow may be defined here as the component of velocity parallel to the surface on which the layer is formed and perpendicular to the streamline above the layer. The earliest discussion of this phenomenon is due to Prandtl (1946). That such an effect must be expected is clear from elementary considerations. The particles of fluid inside the layer are moving with reduced velocity; assuming the pressure field to remain constant through the layer, this causes an increased curvature of the streamlines inside the layer, and hence a transport of fluid in a direction inclined to the direction of the streamlines of the main stream as indicated in Fig. VIII. 1. This argument suggests that such motion must be towards the concave side of these streamlines, but it should be noted that not all the effects of the viscous stresses are considered. In fact, the direction of the secondary flow may change through the layer as, for example, in the case of rotating flow over a fixed plane.

It remains now to establish boundary-layer equations in a suitable system of coordinates. As far as these equations are concerned there is no point, at this stage, in distinguishing between the rotationally symmetrical and the general three-dimensional case, and the system of coordinates will be sufficiently general to include convenient forms of the equations for all cases of boundary sheet flow.

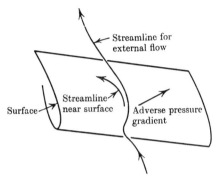

FIG. VIII. 1. Cross flow in a boundary layer for a curved external flow.

2. The boundary-layer equations

The object here is to find equations of motion for boundary-layer flow over a general three-dimensional body, subject only to the restriction that geometrical singularities on the surface of the body are to be excluded. Such equations have been derived by various methods by several authors including Levi-Civita (1929), Lin (see Michal 1947), Timman (1955), Howarth (1951a), and Hayes (1951). There is no doubt that a treatment by the methods of tensor analysis is the most satisfactory from a mathematical viewpoint, but it is not well suited to the requirements of this book. The following discussion is adapted from that of E. J. Watson (unpublished), and is based on the use of operators in vector analysis.

If $\mathbf{v}$ is the velocity vector in the fluid, and ∇ denotes the gradient operator of three-dimensional space, the equations of motion of a viscous incompressible fluid can be expressed in the form

$$\frac{\partial \mathbf{v}}{\partial t} + (\mathbf{v} . \nabla)\mathbf{v} = -\frac{1}{\rho}\nabla p + \nu \nabla^2 \mathbf{v}, \tag{1}$$

where p is the pressure. The equation of continuity is

$$\nabla . \mathbf{v} = 0. \tag{2}$$

Let the surface of the given body be denoted by S; then the position of a point P in space is described by means of its distance x_3 measured along the unit normal $\mathbf{n}$ to S, and the position vector $\mathbf{r}$ on S of the foot P' of the normal. Curvilinear coordinates x_1, x_2 may be taken on S, which is defined by the equation

$$\mathbf{r} = \mathbf{r}(x_1, x_2). \tag{3}$$

Thus, if $\mathbf{R}$ is the position vector of P,

$$\mathbf{R} = \mathbf{r}(x_1, x_2) + x_3 \mathbf{n}(x_1, x_2), \tag{4}$$

so that x_1, x_2, x_3 may be taken as curvilinear coordinates of P. For the purpose of this chapter there is no loss of generality in taking the parametric curves $x_1 = $ const and $x_2 = $ const on S to form an orthogonal net. The system of coordinates is triply orthogonal on S, but not necessarily elsewhere. It is now this system of coordinates that will be used to form boundary-layer equations from equations (1) and (2).

Since the parametric curves on S are orthogonal, the gradient operator ∇_S for the surface S as defined by Weatherburn (1927) is

$$\nabla_S = \frac{\mathbf{a}_1}{h_1} \frac{\partial}{\partial x_1} + \frac{\mathbf{a}_2}{h_2} \frac{\partial}{\partial x_2}, \tag{5}$$

where

$$h_1 = \left| \frac{\partial \mathbf{r}}{\partial x_1} \right|, \quad h_2 = \left| \frac{\partial \mathbf{r}}{\partial x_2} \right|, \quad \mathbf{a}_1 h_1 = \frac{\partial \mathbf{r}}{\partial x_1}, \quad \mathbf{a}_2 h_2 = \frac{\partial \mathbf{r}}{\partial x_2}, \tag{6}$$

and $\mathbf{a}_1$, $\mathbf{a}_2$ are unit vectors tangential respectively to the two parametric curves on S through P'; $\mathbf{a}_1$, $\mathbf{a}_2$, and $\mathbf{n}$ therefore form an orthogonal triad of unit vectors. Since S is supposed to be smoothly curved, it follows that h_1, h_2, their derivatives with respect to x_1 and x_2, and the derivatives of $\mathbf{a}_1$, $\mathbf{a}_2$, and $\mathbf{n}$ are all $O(1)$. All these quantities are, of course, functions of x_1 and x_2 only.

The surfaces $x_3 = $ const are a system of surfaces parallel to S. Let σ denote a typical member of this system. The corresponding gradient operator ∇_σ for σ is slightly more complicated than ∇_S, since the parametric curves $x_1 = $ const and $x_2 = $ const on σ are not necessarily orthogonal. However, it is easy to verify that

$$\nabla_\sigma = \nabla_S + \mathbf{O}(x_3), \tag{7}$$

where the terms $\mathbf{O}(x_3)$ imply operators with coefficients of order x_3. It is not necessary to state these explicitly, since ultimately the terms arising from them will be rejected in the boundary-layer approximation. The gradient operator ∇ for the space is

$$\nabla = \nabla_\sigma + \mathbf{n} \frac{\partial}{\partial x_3}. \tag{8}$$

It is convenient to express the velocity vector $\mathbf{v}$ in the form

$$\mathbf{v} = \mathbf{u} + v_3 \mathbf{n}, \tag{9}$$

where $\mathbf{u}$ is parallel to the tangent plane at the foot P' of the normal from P to S, and v_3 is the component of velocity along the normal; the components of $\mathbf{u}$ in the directions of the unit vectors $\mathbf{a}_1$ and $\mathbf{a}_2$ are v_1 and v_2 respectively.

Thus
$$\mathbf{v} . \nabla = (\mathbf{u} + v_3 \mathbf{n}) . \left(\nabla_\sigma + \mathbf{n} \frac{\partial}{\partial x_3} \right) = \mathbf{u} . \nabla_\sigma + v_3 \frac{\partial}{\partial x_3}, \tag{10}$$

while
$$\nabla^2 = \nabla_\sigma^2 - J_\sigma \frac{\partial}{\partial x_3} + \frac{\partial^2}{\partial x_3^2}, \tag{11}$$

in which J_σ is the first curvature of the surface σ, since $\nabla_\sigma . \mathbf{n} = -J_\sigma$ (see Weatherburn 1927).

If there is a boundary layer on S, then x_3 and v_3 are small, and derivatives with respect to x_3 are large compared with those with respect to x_1 and x_2. In the first place, therefore, ∇_σ can be replaced by ∇_S, etc., and equation (1) takes the form

$$\frac{\partial \mathbf{u}}{\partial t} + \mathbf{n} \frac{\partial v_3}{\partial t} + \left(\mathbf{u} . \nabla_S + v_3 \frac{\partial}{\partial x_3} \right) (\mathbf{u} + v_3 \mathbf{n})$$
$$= -\frac{1}{\rho} \left(\nabla_S p + \mathbf{n} \frac{\partial p}{\partial x_3} \right) + \nu \left(\nabla_S^2 - J_S \frac{\partial}{\partial x_3} + \frac{\partial^2}{\partial x_3^2} \right) (\mathbf{u} + v_3 \mathbf{n}). \tag{12}$$

The terms on the left-hand side of this equation are

$$\frac{\partial \mathbf{u}}{\partial t} + \mathbf{n} \frac{\partial v_3}{\partial t} + \left(\frac{v_1}{h_1} \frac{\partial}{\partial x_1} + \frac{v_2}{h_2} \frac{\partial}{\partial x_2} + v_3 \frac{\partial}{\partial x_3} \right) (v_1 \mathbf{a}_1 + v_2 \mathbf{a}_2 + v_3 \mathbf{n})$$
$$= \mathbf{a}_1 \frac{Dv_1}{Dt} + \mathbf{a}_2 \frac{Dv_2}{Dt} + \mathbf{n} \frac{Dv_3}{Dt} + v_1 \left(\frac{v_1}{h_1} \frac{\partial \mathbf{a}_1}{\partial x_1} + \frac{v_2}{h_2} \frac{\partial \mathbf{a}_1}{\partial x_2} \right) +$$
$$+ v_2 \left(\frac{v_1}{h_1} \frac{\partial \mathbf{a}_2}{\partial x_1} + \frac{v_2}{h_2} \frac{\partial \mathbf{a}_2}{\partial x_2} \right) + \frac{v_1 v_3}{h_1} \frac{\partial \mathbf{n}}{\partial x_1} + \frac{v_2 v_3}{h_2} \frac{\partial \mathbf{n}}{\partial x_2}, \tag{13}$$

since $\mathbf{a}_1$, $\mathbf{a}_2$, and $\mathbf{n}$ are independent of x_3. In the above expression the scalar operator D/Dt is defined by

$$\frac{D}{Dt} = \frac{\partial}{\partial t} + \frac{v_1}{h_1} \frac{\partial}{\partial x_1} + \frac{v_2}{h_2} \frac{\partial}{\partial x_2} + v_3 \frac{\partial}{\partial x_3}. \tag{14}$$

The last two terms in the expression (13) are small in comparison with the remaining terms, and may be neglected. The values of $\partial \mathbf{a}_1 / \partial x_1$, etc., as given by Weatherburn are

$$\frac{\partial \mathbf{a}_1}{\partial x_1} = \frac{L}{h_1} \mathbf{n} - \frac{1}{h_2} \frac{\partial h_1}{\partial x_2} \mathbf{a}_2, \qquad \frac{\partial \mathbf{a}_1}{\partial x_2} = \frac{M}{h_1} \mathbf{n} + \frac{1}{h_1} \frac{\partial h_2}{\partial x_1} \mathbf{a}_2,$$
$$\frac{\partial \mathbf{a}_2}{\partial x_1} = \frac{M}{h_2} \mathbf{n} + \frac{1}{h_2} \frac{\partial h_1}{\partial x_2} \mathbf{a}_1, \qquad \frac{\partial \mathbf{a}_2}{\partial x_2} = \frac{N}{h_2} \mathbf{n} - \frac{1}{h_1} \frac{\partial h_2}{\partial x_1} \mathbf{a}_1, \tag{15}$$

where L, M, N are the 'fundamental magnitudes of the second order' on S.

On the right-hand side of equation (12), the terms involving the viscosity are all small, with the exception of $\nu(\partial^2 \mathbf{u}/\partial x_3^2)$. As in the two-dimensional case, this term is assumed to be of the same order as the inertia terms in the equation.

If the $\mathbf{n}$ components on each side of equation (12) are considered, the principal terms give

$$\frac{L}{h_1^2} v_1^2 + \frac{2M}{h_1 h_2} v_1 v_2 + \frac{N}{h_2^2} v_2^2 = -\frac{1}{\rho} \frac{\partial p}{\partial x_3}. \tag{16}$$

Hence $\partial p/\partial x_3$ is bounded, and the variation of p through the thickness of the boundary layer is small. The pressure in the boundary layer may be supposed, therefore, to be independent of x_3, and to be determined by the inviscid flow above the layer.

The approximate form of the equation of continuity remains to be considered. Since

$$\nabla.\mathbf{v} = \nabla_\sigma.\mathbf{u} - J_\sigma v_3 + \frac{\partial v_3}{\partial x_3},$$

the principal terms in $\nabla.\mathbf{v}$ are clearly

$$\nabla_S.\mathbf{u} + \frac{\partial v_3}{\partial x_3} = \frac{1}{h_1 h_2}\left\{\frac{\partial}{\partial x_1}(h_2 v_1) + \frac{\partial}{\partial x_2}(h_1 v_2)\right\} + \frac{\partial v_3}{\partial x_3}.$$

The appropriate boundary-layer equations can now be stated. The $\mathbf{a}_1$ and $\mathbf{a}_2$ components of each side of equation (12) yield

$$\frac{\partial v_1}{\partial t} + \frac{v_1}{h_1}\frac{\partial v_1}{\partial x_1} + \frac{v_2}{h_2}\frac{\partial v_1}{\partial x_2} + v_3\frac{\partial v_1}{\partial x_3} + \frac{v_1 v_2}{h_1 h_2}\frac{\partial h_1}{\partial x_2} - \frac{v_2^2}{h_1 h_2}\frac{\partial h_2}{\partial x_1} = -\frac{1}{\rho h_1}\frac{\partial p}{\partial x_1} + \nu\frac{\partial^2 v_1}{\partial x_3^2}, \tag{17}$$

$$\frac{\partial v_2}{\partial t} + \frac{v_1}{h_1}\frac{\partial v_2}{\partial x_1} + \frac{v_2}{h_2}\frac{\partial v_2}{\partial x_2} + v_3\frac{\partial v_2}{\partial x_3} - \frac{v_1^2}{h_1 h_2}\frac{\partial h_1}{\partial x_2} + \frac{v_1 v_2}{h_1 h_2}\frac{\partial h_2}{\partial x_1} = -\frac{1}{\rho h_2}\frac{\partial p}{\partial x_2} + \nu\frac{\partial^2 v_2}{\partial x_3^2}, \tag{18}$$

and the equation of continuity is

$$\frac{1}{h_1 h_2}\left\{\frac{\partial}{\partial x_1}(h_2 v_1) + \frac{\partial}{\partial x_2}(h_1 v_2)\right\} + \frac{\partial v_3}{\partial x_3} = 0. \tag{19}$$

These three equations serve to determine v_1, v_2, and v_3, since the pressure is determined by the inviscid flow above the boundary layer. Thus, if $\mathbf{V}(x_1, x_2, t)$ is the main-stream velocity just outside the layer, with components V_1 and V_2 parallel to $\mathbf{a}_1$ and $\mathbf{a}_2$ on S, respectively,

$$\frac{\partial V_1}{\partial t} + \frac{V_1}{h_1}\frac{\partial V_1}{\partial x_1} + \frac{V_2}{h_2}\frac{\partial V_1}{\partial x_2} + \frac{V_1 V_2}{h_1 h_2}\frac{\partial h_1}{\partial x_2} - \frac{V_2^2}{h_1 h_2}\frac{\partial h_2}{\partial x_1} = -\frac{1}{\rho h_1}\frac{\partial p}{\partial x_1}, \tag{20}$$

$$\frac{\partial V_2}{\partial t} + \frac{V_1}{h_1}\frac{\partial V_2}{\partial x_1} + \frac{V_2}{h_2}\frac{\partial V_2}{\partial x_2} - \frac{V_1^2}{h_1 h_2}\frac{\partial h_1}{\partial x_2} + \frac{V_1 V_2}{h_1 h_2}\frac{\partial h_2}{\partial x_1} = -\frac{1}{\rho h_2}\frac{\partial p}{\partial x_2}. \tag{21}$$

Finally, there are boundary conditions which must be satisfied. In the first place,

$$v_1 \to V_1, \quad v_2 \to V_2 \quad \text{as } x_3 \to \infty. \tag{22}$$

Further, if the surface S is porous, and there is a prescribed normal velocity $w_0(x_1, x_2, t)$,

$$v_3 = w_0 \quad \text{when} \quad x_3 = 0 \quad \text{(for suction } w_0 < 0).$$

The remaining boundary conditions when $x_3 = 0$ require further explanation. It has been assumed that the coordinate system is at rest, and this will be understood throughout this chapter unless the contrary is stated. In the case of rotationally symmetrical flow the surface S, which is a surface of revolution, might be rotating about its axis (that is, relative to the coordinate system), and particles of fluid adjacent to S will be in motion with S. In all other cases $v_1 = v_2 = 0$ when $x_3 = 0$.

On the basis of the boundary-layer approximations, the shearing stress across the surface S, or skin friction τ, has components

$$\tau_1 = \mu\left(\frac{\partial v_1}{\partial x_3}\right)_0, \qquad \tau_2 = \mu\left(\frac{\partial v_2}{\partial x_3}\right)_0, \tag{23}$$

in the directions x_1 increasing, x_2 increasing, respectively. These last results are exact when the surface S is impermeable.

The boundary-layer equations (17) to (19) are complicated, and it is not possible to infer from them the features which can be attributed to the curvature of S itself, for these are concealed by the choice of coordinate system. The equations apply, for example, to flow over a plane surface in which no surface curvature effects can arise. On the other hand, it is clear that a considerable simplification is possible for flow over a developable surface, for in this case h_1 and h_2 can be chosen to be unity. The usual Cartesian form of the equations of motion is then obtained, an example of which is the case of flow over cylinders.

These boundary-layer equations have the same form as those given by Timman (1955) and Howarth (1951a). Timman used an argument based on first principles to derive his equations, while Howarth used a system of coordinates which are triply orthogonal everywhere and hence convenient for the direct application of standard results in vector analysis. This approach, however, requires the selection of the lines of curvature on S as the appropriate parametric curves, and this is an undesirable restriction. The treatment of the boundary-layer equations given by Hayes (1951) includes the effects of compressibility and variable viscosity.

3. The momentum equations

The general form of the momentum equations may be derived directly from equations (17) to (21). Since V_1 is independent of x_3, the term $v_3(\partial v_1/\partial x_3)$ in equation (17) may be replaced by $-v_3(\partial/\partial x_3)(V_1-v_1)$. If the equation of continuity (19) is now multiplied by V_1-v_1 and subtracted from equation (17), and the result (20) for $\partial p/\partial x_1$ is used, after some rearrangement the following equation is obtained:

$$\frac{\partial}{\partial t}(V_1-v_1)+\frac{1}{h_1}\frac{\partial}{\partial x_1}\{v_1(V_1-v_1)\}+\frac{1}{h_1}\frac{\partial V_1}{\partial x_1}(V_1-v_1)+\frac{1}{h_2}\frac{\partial}{\partial x_2}\{v_2(V_1-v_1)\}+$$

$$+\frac{1}{h_2}\frac{\partial V_1}{\partial x_2}(V_2-v_2)+\frac{1}{h_1 h_2}\frac{\partial h_1}{\partial x_2}\{v_2(V_1-v_1)+v_1(V_2-v_2)+V_2(V_1-v_1)\}+$$

$$+\frac{1}{h_1 h_2}\frac{\partial h_2}{\partial x_1}\{v_1(V_1-v_1)-v_2(V_2-v_2)-V_2(V_2-v_2)\}+$$

$$+\frac{\partial}{\partial x_3}\{v_3(V_1-v_1)\}+\nu\frac{\partial^2 v_1}{\partial x_3^2}=0. \tag{24}$$

A similar process, applied to equations (18), (19), and (21), yields a second equation, which may be written down from equation (24) by interchange of the suffixes 1 and 2. The momentum equations are obtained by integrating these equations with respect to x_3 between the limits 0 and ∞. It is assumed that $v_3(V_1-v_1)$ and $v_3(V_2-v_2)$ tend to zero as x_3 tends to infinity, and that the infinite integrals in the following equations converge. Further, $\partial v_1/\partial x_3$, $\partial v_2/\partial x_3 \to 0$ as $x_3 \to \infty$. The equations are therefore

$$\frac{\partial}{\partial t}\int_0^\infty (V_1-v_1)\,dx_3+\frac{1}{h_1}\frac{\partial}{\partial x_1}\int_0^\infty v_1(V_1-v_1)\,dx_3+\frac{1}{h_1}\frac{\partial V_1}{\partial x_1}\int_0^\infty (V_1-v_1)\,dx_3+$$

$$+\frac{1}{h_2}\frac{\partial}{\partial x_2}\int_0^\infty v_2(V_1-v_1)\,dx_3+\frac{1}{h_2}\frac{\partial V_1}{\partial x_2}\int_0^\infty (V_2-v_2)\,dx_3+$$

$$+\frac{1}{h_1 h_2}\frac{\partial h_1}{\partial x_2}\int_0^\infty \{v_2(V_1-v_1)+v_1(V_2-v_2)+V_2(V_1-v_1)\}\,dx_3+$$

$$+\frac{1}{h_1 h_2}\frac{\partial h_2}{\partial x_1}\int_0^\infty \{v_1(V_1-v_1)-v_2(V_2-v_2)-V_2(V_2-v_2)\}\,dx_3-$$

$$-w_0(V_1-v_1)_0=\nu\left(\frac{\partial v_1}{\partial x_3}\right)_0=\frac{\tau_1}{\rho}, \tag{25}$$

and a similar equation with the suffixes 1 and 2 interchanged. In equation (25), $(V_1 - v_1)_0$ denotes the value of $V_1 - v_1$ at $x_3 = 0$.

It should be mentioned here that Timman (1952) derived a set of momentum equations suitable for use when the main-stream flow is potential. He used a set of streamline coordinates on the surface, formed by the equipotential lines and streamlines. The equations so derived were used by Zaat, Spiegel, and Timman (1955), and in simplified form later by Zaat (1956), to calculate the laminar boundary layer in a case of flow over an ellipsoid.

The equations given above will be applied later in this chapter to certain cases of rotationally symmetrical flow, and to flow over yawed cylinders; the introduction of displacement and momentum thicknesses will appear in the appropriate sections.

PART II

THE ROTATIONALLY SYMMETRICAL CASE

Boundary-layer flows with rotational symmetry are of considerable practical importance, and provide simplified examples of three-dimensional flow in that they are independent of one of the space coordinates. The extension of two-dimensional boundary-layer theory to this type of flow was first considered by Boltze (1908) and later, independently, by Millikan (1932). Most of the early work appears to be concerned with axisymmetrical motion, but since there are several important cases of motion with swirl, it is necessary to derive a set of equations which will include these cases.

4. The coordinate system and the boundary-layer equations for flow past a body of revolution

The general equations of motion which were derived in Section 2 may be applied to the case of rotationally symmetrical flow past a blunt-nosed body of revolution. The curvilinear coordinates of a point P in space will be taken as (x, θ, z). Here θ is the angle between a fixed meridian plane and the meridian plane containing P; x is the distance OP' measured along a meridian curve Γ from the nose O of the body; and z is the distance $P'P$ measured along the normal from the surface (see Fig. VIII. 2). Let u, v, w be the components of velocity of the fluid at P, in the orthogonal directions of increasing x, θ, z respectively. If r_0 is the distance of P' from the axis of revolution, so that r_0 is a function of x alone, then in the notation of Section 2, $h_1 = 1$ and $h_2 = r_0$. Since the motion is independent of θ, equations (17), (18), and (19) give, as the boundary-layer equations of momentum and continuity,

$$\frac{\partial u}{\partial t}+u\frac{\partial u}{\partial x}+w\frac{\partial u}{\partial z}-\frac{v^2}{r_0}\frac{dr_0}{dx} = -\frac{1}{\rho}\frac{\partial p}{\partial x}+\nu\frac{\partial^2 u}{\partial z^2}, \tag{26}$$

$$\frac{\partial v}{\partial t}+u\frac{\partial v}{\partial x}+w\frac{\partial v}{\partial z}+\frac{uv}{r_0}\frac{dr_0}{dx} = \nu\frac{\partial^2 v}{\partial z^2}, \tag{27}$$

$$\frac{\partial}{\partial x}(r_0 u)+\frac{\partial}{\partial z}(r_0 w) = 0. \tag{28}$$

These equations were derived by Mangler (1945) and are valid in regions where the principal radii of curvature of the body are large in com-

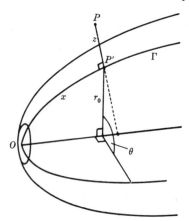

Fig. VIII. 2. The coordinate system for flow past a body of revolution.

parison with the thickness of the layer. Where this condition does not apply (as, for example, in the case of flow along long thin cylinders) it is necessary to include on the right-hand side of equations (26) and (27) certain terms which were previously neglected. A discussion of some of these cases will be found later in this chapter.

If U, V are the appropriate components of velocity of the main-stream flow just outside the boundary layer, the relations between U, V, and p, from equations (20) and (21), are

$$\frac{\partial U}{\partial t}+U\frac{\partial U}{\partial x}-\frac{V^2}{r_0}\frac{dr_0}{dx} = -\frac{1}{\rho}\frac{\partial p}{\partial x}, \tag{29}$$

$$\frac{\partial V}{\partial t}+U\frac{\partial V}{\partial x}+\frac{UV}{r_0}\frac{dr_0}{dx} = 0. \tag{30}$$

In the general case the surface of revolution is rotating about its axis with angular velocity $\Omega(t)$; if it is also porous, the boundary conditions on u, v, and w are

$$u = 0, \quad v = r_0\Omega, \quad w = w_0(x,t) \quad \text{when } z = 0,$$

$$u \to U, \quad v \to V \quad \text{as } z \to \infty. \tag{31}$$

The equation of continuity (28) establishes the existence of a stream function $\psi(x,z,t)$, where

$$r_0 u = \frac{\partial \psi}{\partial z}, \qquad r_0 w = -\frac{\partial \psi}{\partial x}, \tag{32}$$

and these expressions for u and w, or their equivalents, may be used to replace equation (28).

5. Steady flow in the boundary layer along a surface of revolution near the forward stagnation point

In the vicinity of the forward stagnation point in steady axisymmetrical flow past a body of revolution at rest, the components of velocity in the main stream are U, 0, where

$$U = U_1 x/l,$$

the parameter U_1/l being a constant depending on the flow and the shape of the body. For a blunt-nosed body r_0 is very nearly equal to x in this region, and hence

$$u = \frac{1}{x}\frac{\partial \psi}{\partial z}, \qquad w = -\frac{1}{x}\frac{\partial \psi}{\partial x}.$$

Since the body is at rest, equation (27) and the boundary conditions on v are satisfied by taking $v = 0$. Equation (26), with use of the value of $\partial p/\partial x$ given by equation (29), becomes

$$u\frac{\partial u}{\partial x} + w\frac{\partial u}{\partial z} = \left(\frac{U_1}{l}\right)^2 x + \nu\frac{\partial^2 u}{\partial z^2}. \tag{33}$$

Homann (1936 b) reduced this equation to an ordinary differential equation by writing

$$\eta = (U_1/l\nu)^{\frac{1}{2}} z, \qquad \psi = (U_1\nu/l)^{\frac{1}{2}} x^2 f(\eta), \tag{34}$$

so that $\quad u = (U_1 x/l) f'(\eta), \qquad w = -2(U_1\nu/l)^{\frac{1}{2}} f(\eta). \tag{35}$

The equation for $f(\eta)$ is therefore

$$f'^2 - 2ff'' = 1 + f'''. \tag{36}$$

The boundary conditions are $u = w = 0$ when $z = 0$, $u \to U_1 x/l$ as $z \to \infty$, so that the boundary conditions on f are $f(0) = f'(0) = 0$, $f'(\eta) \to 1$ as $\eta \to \infty$.

Homann's numerical solution of equation (36) was corrected by Hannah (1947), but Mangler (see Section 8) showed that the above equation could be reduced to a special case of equation (V. 122). With the change of variables

$$\xi = \sqrt{2}\,\eta, \qquad g(\xi) = \sqrt{2}f(\eta),$$

equation (36) becomes

$$g''' + gg'' = \tfrac{1}{2}(g'^2 - 1), \tag{37}$$

and the boundary conditions on g are $g(0) = g'(0) = 0$, $g'(\xi) \to 1$ as $\xi \to \infty$. This is the special case $\beta = \tfrac{1}{2}$ of equation (V. 122); the solution is given in Table V. 3.

As in the case of two-dimensional flow near a stagnation point, the solution obtained above as a solution of the boundary-layer equations is also a solution of the exact equations of motion if the surface is a plane surface at right angles to the direction of the incident stream; this is discussed in Section III. 19.

6. Steady flow without swirl; expansion in series

The method of expansion in series, as used in Section VI. 2, can be applied also to the boundary-layer flow over a body of revolution. The discussion given below is restricted to flows which are axially symmetrical, and in this case it is possible to obtain expressions for the velocity distribution in a general form; the application to any special case of axial flow can be made with little further calculation.

For steady axisymmetrical flow past a blunt-nosed body of revolution, the equations of motion and of continuity are

$$u\frac{\partial u}{\partial x} + w\frac{\partial u}{\partial z} = -\frac{1}{\rho}\frac{\partial p}{\partial x} + \nu\frac{\partial^2 u}{\partial z^2}, \tag{38}$$

$$\frac{\partial}{\partial x}(r_0 u) + \frac{\partial}{\partial z}(r_0 w) = 0, \tag{39}$$

and the expression for the pressure is

$$-\frac{1}{\rho}\frac{\partial p}{\partial x} = U\frac{dU}{dx}, \tag{40}$$

where $U(x)$ is the component of velocity of the inviscid flow on the surface in the direction of a meridian curve.

The equation of continuity is satisfied by introducing a stream function $\psi(x,z)$, where

$$u = \frac{\partial \psi}{\partial z}, \qquad w = -\frac{1}{r_0}\frac{\partial}{\partial x}(r_0 \psi) \tag{41}$$

(these expressions, rather than those of (32), are introduced to achieve some simplification in the final equations).

The equations above now give for ψ the equation

$$\frac{\partial\psi}{\partial z}\frac{\partial^2\psi}{\partial x\partial z}-\left(\frac{\partial\psi}{\partial x}+\frac{\psi}{r_0}\frac{dr_0}{dx}\right)\frac{\partial^2\psi}{\partial z^2} = U\frac{dU}{dx}+\nu\frac{\partial^3\psi}{\partial z^3}, \tag{42}$$

and the boundary conditions on ψ are

$$\psi = 0, \qquad \frac{\partial\psi}{\partial z} = 0 \quad \text{when } z = 0,$$

$$\frac{\partial\psi}{\partial z} \to U \quad \text{as } z \to \infty. \tag{43}$$

To solve equation (42) expansions are assumed for ψ, U, and r_0 in series of powers of x. For U and r_0 the coefficients in the series are determined by the contour of the body and the given main-stream flow, and for ψ the coefficients are functions of z which remain to be determined. In all cases the expansions for U and r_0 involve only odd powers of x. At this stage it is convenient to introduce non-dimensional coordinates ξ, η, and write

$$r_0 = \alpha_1 l\{\xi+\alpha_3\xi^3+\alpha_5\xi^5+...\}, \tag{44}$$

$$U = U_1\{\xi+\beta_3\xi^3+\beta_5\xi^5+...\}, \tag{45}$$

where

$$\xi = x/l, \qquad \eta = (2U_1/l\nu)^{\frac{1}{2}}z, \tag{46}$$

and l is a length which may be chosen arbitrarily. The parameters α_n depend on the contour of the body, and U_1, β_n depend on the prescribed main-stream velocity distribution; for a blunt-nosed body $\alpha_1 = 1$.

For ψ the assumed expansion is

$$\psi = (\tfrac{1}{2}l\nu U_1)^{\frac{1}{2}}\{\xi f_1(\eta)+2\beta_3\xi^3 f_3(\eta)+3\beta_5\xi^5 f_5(\eta)+4\beta_7\xi^7 f_7(\eta)+...\}, \tag{47}$$

and therefore

$$u = U_1\{\xi f_1'(\eta)+2\beta_3\xi^3 f_3'(\eta)+3\beta_5\xi^5 f_5'(\eta)+4\beta_7\xi^7 f_7'(\eta)+...\}. \tag{48}$$

The substitution of the expression for ψ in equation (42) yields, on equating the coefficients of ξ^2, ξ^4, etc., to zero, a set of ordinary differential equations for the functions f_n, the first two of which are

$$f_1'''+f_1 f_1''+\tfrac{1}{2}(1-f_1'^2) = 0, \tag{49}$$

$$f_3'''+f_1 f_3''-2f_1' f_3'+2f_1'' f_3+(\alpha_3/2\beta_3)f_1 f_1''+1 = 0. \tag{50}$$

The boundary conditions (43) are now

$$f_n(0) = f_n'(0) = 0,$$

$$f_1' \to 1, \quad f_3' \to \tfrac{1}{2}, \quad f_5' \to \tfrac{1}{3}, \quad ..., \quad \text{as } \eta \to \infty. \tag{51}$$

As expected, equation (49) is the same as equation (37) for the flow near a stagnation point. Equation (50) for f_3, and the remaining equations for f_5, f_7, etc., are third-order linear differential equations for these functions. The equations contain α_n and β_n as parameters, but they may be replaced, as in the two-dimensional case, by a set of equations which are independent of these parameters. The full details are to be found in papers by Frössling (1940), who derived the above results, and by Scholkemeier (1949). For f_3 we write

$$f_3 = g_3 + (\alpha_3/\beta_3)h_3, \tag{52}$$

so that equation (50) is replaced by the two equations

$$g_3''' + f_1 g_3'' - 2f_1' g_3' + 2f_1'' g_3 + 1 = 0, \tag{53}$$

$$h_3''' + f_1 h_3'' - 2f_1' h_3' + 2f_1'' h_3 + \tfrac{1}{2}f_1 f_1'' = 0. \tag{54}$$

In the case of f_5 it is necessary to take a sum of five functions, namely

$$f_5 = g_5 + \frac{\alpha_5}{\beta_5}h_5 + \frac{\beta_3^2}{\beta_5}k_5 + \frac{\alpha_3\beta_3}{\beta_5}j_5 + \frac{\alpha_3^2}{\beta_5}q_5, \tag{55}$$

while f_7 can be written as the sum of ten functions,

$$f_7 = g_7 + \frac{\alpha_7}{\beta_7}h_7 + \frac{\alpha_3^2\beta_3}{\beta_7}j_7 + \frac{\beta_3^3}{\beta_7}k_7 + \frac{\alpha_5\beta_3}{\beta_7}l_7 +$$
$$+ \frac{\beta_3\beta_5}{\beta_7}p_7 + \frac{\alpha_3^3}{\beta_7}q_7 + \frac{\alpha_3\alpha_5}{\beta_7}v_7 + \frac{\alpha_3\beta_3^2}{\beta_7}t_7 + \frac{\alpha_3\beta_5}{\beta_7}z_7. \tag{56}$$

The equation for f_5 is replaced, therefore, by five equations for $g_5, h_5, k_5,$ $j_5,$ and q_5 respectively, and that for f_7 by ten equations. The boundary conditions are:

(i) all functions and their first derivatives are zero when $\eta = 0$;

(ii) $f_1' \to 1$, $g_3' \to \tfrac{1}{2}$, $g_5' \to \tfrac{1}{3}$, $g_7' \to \tfrac{1}{4}$, etc., and all other first derivatives tend to zero as $\eta \to \infty$.

The number of new equations is large, and the labour involved in proceeding beyond f_7 appears to be prohibitive. The important feature is that these equations are independent of the parameters α_n, β_n, and so are the boundary conditions associated with them. The solutions, therefore, provide general results available for direct application to any special case, the parameters α_n, β_n being specified by the body contour and the main-stream flow. Solutions of the eight equations associated with f_1, f_3, f_5 were obtained by Frössling, and of the ten equations associated with f_7 by Scholkemeier. Table VIII. 1 shows the values of the derivatives of these functions, and also the limiting values of the functions for large values of η.

7. The flow past a sphere

The flow of a uniform stream past a sphere provides a convenient example for the application of the general results derived in Section 6. The representative length l may be taken to be a, the radius of the sphere, and ξ is then the angle between the radius drawn from the centre to the forward stagnation point, and the radius drawn to a general point on the sphere. Hence $r_0 = a \sin \xi$.

Schlichting calculated the position of the separation ring on the sphere on the assumption of potential flow in the main stream, that is, $U = U_1 \sin \xi$, and using the first four terms of the series (48); the details may be found in Schlichting (1955). Experimental results, however, show a marked difference between the actual pressure distribution round the sphere and the theoretical (potential) distribution, particularly near and after separation. This may be seen from Fage's experiments with a 6-in. diameter sphere (Fage 1936) which include one case in which the flow in the boundary layer was everywhere laminar. The wind-tunnel speed in this case was 50 ft/sec.

Tomotika and Imai (1938) used Fage's results to determine the velocity distribution outside the boundary layer, and calculated the boundary-layer flow using Pohlhausen's approximate method. For the case mentioned above the main-stream velocity was found to be represented, approximately, by

$$U = U_1(\xi - 0{\cdot}2914\xi^3 + 0{\cdot}0987\xi^5 - 0{\cdot}0282\xi^7)$$

within the range $0 \leqslant \xi \leqslant 1{\cdot}48$. In this result the value of U_1 is 75 ft/sec. The values of the coefficients in relations (44), (45) are therefore

$$\alpha_n = (-1)^{\frac{1}{2}(n-1)}(1/n!) \quad (n = 1, 3, 5, ...),$$

$$\beta_3 = -0{\cdot}2914, \quad \beta_5 = 0{\cdot}0987, \quad \beta_7 = -0{\cdot}0282,$$

and the velocity distribution in the boundary layer is given by substitution in result (48). In particular, separation of the flow occurs where the skin friction is zero, that is, where

$$(\partial u / \partial \eta)_{\eta = 0} = 0.$$

This yields an equation to determine the value ξ_s of ξ at which separation occurs. Since Table VIII. 1 provides information only for the first four f_n, the expression for u must be terminated at the term in ξ^7. The equation for ξ_s then gives $\xi = 0$, corresponding to the forward stagnation point, or

$$1 - 0{\cdot}6741\xi^2 + 0{\cdot}3414\xi^4 - 0{\cdot}1356\xi^6 = 0.$$

VIII. 1

Functions for the axially symmetrical boundary layer

(See Section 6)

η	f_1'	g_3'	h_3'	g_5'	h_5'	k_5'	j_5'	q_5'	g_7'	h_7'	j_7'
0	0	0	0	0	0	0	0	0	0	0	0
0·2	0·1755	0·1896	0·0090	0·1612	0·0101	0·0255	0·0058	−0·0049	0·144	0·010	−0·004
0·4	0·3311	0·3400	0·0176	0·2838	0·0198	0·0324	0·0107	−0·0096	0·250	0·019	−0·008
0·6	0·4669	0·4535	0·0254	0·3709	0·0285	0·0241	0·0137	−0·0140	0·322	0·028	−0·010
0·8	0·5833	0·5334	0·0316	0·4270	0·0354	0·0051	0·0134	−0·0176	0·365	0·034	−0·009
1·0	0·6811	0·5842	0·0358	0·4576	0·0399	−0·0195	0·0096	−0·0204	0·385	0·039	−0·006
1·2	0·7614	0·6110	0·0377	0·4683	0·0417	−0·0447	0·0025	−0·0222	0·388	0·040	−0·001
1·4	0·8258	0·6193	0·0372	0·4645	0·0409	−0·0665	−0·0064	−0·0229	0·379	0·039	+0·005
1·6	0·8761	0·6144	0·0346	0·4515	0·0379	−0·0819	−0·0156	−0·0226	0·363	0·036	0·011
1·8	0·9142	0·6015	0·0306	0·4335	0·0334	−0·0897	−0·0234	−0·0212	0·343	0·032	0·016
2·0	0·9422	0·5845	0·0258	0·4139	0·0279	−0·0899	−0·0287	−0·0192	0·324	0·027	0·020
2·2	0·9622	0·5666	0·0207	0·3952	0·0223	−0·0838	−0·0310	−0·0167	0·306	0·021	0·023
2·4	0·9760	0·5500	0·0158	0·3787	0·0170	−0·0733	−0·0304	−0·0139	0·291	0·016	0·023
2·6	0·9853	0·5358	0·0116	0·3652	0·0124	−0·0605	−0·0275	−0·0111	0·278	0·012	0·022
2·8	0·9912	0·5245	0·0081	0·3549	0·0086	−0·0474	−0·0232	−0·0085	0·269	0·008	0·020
3·0	0·9949	0·5161	0·0054	0·3473	0·0058	−0·0352	−0·0184	−0·0062	0·262	0·005	0·016
3·2	0·9972	0·5102	0·0035	0·3420	0·0037	−0·0249	−0·0137	−0·0044	0·258	0·004	0·013
3·4	0·9985	0·5061	0·0022	0·3385	0·0023	−0·0168	−0·0097	−0·0029	0·255	0·002	0·010
3·6	0·9992	0·5036	0·0013	0·3363	0·0013	−0·0109	−0·0065	−0·0019	0·253	0·001	0·007
3·8	0·9996	0·5020	0·0007	0·3350	0·0008	−0·0067	−0·0042	−0·0012	0·252	0·001	0·005
4·0	0·9998	0·5011	0·0004	0·3342	0·0004	−0·0040	−0·0025	−0·0007	0·251	0·000	0·003
4·2	0·9999	0·5006	0·0002	0·3338	0·0002	−0·0022	−0·0015	−0·0004	0·251	0·000	0·002
4·4	0·9999	0·5003	0·0002	0·3336	0·0001	−0·0012	−0·0008	−0·0002	0·250		0·001
4·6	1·0000	0·5001	0·0000	0·3334	0·0000	−0·0006	−0·0004	−0·0001	0·250		0·001
4·8		0·5000		0·3334		−0·0003	−0·0002	+0·0000			0·000
5·0				0·3334		−0·0001	−0·0001	−0·0000			
5·2				0·3334		−0·0000	−0·0000				
5·4				0·3333							

$\eta \to \infty$	
$\eta - f_7$	$\to 0.8046$
$g_3 - \frac{1}{3}\eta$	$\to 0.0231$
h_3	$\to 0.0712$
$g_5 - \frac{3}{8}\eta$	$\to 0.1285$
h_5	$\to 0.0783$
k_5	$\to -0.1340$
j_5	$\to -0.0376$
q_5	$\to 0.0486$
$g_7 - \frac{1}{3}\eta$	$\to 0.165$
h_7	$\to 0.074$
j_7	$\to 0.030$
k_7	$\to 0.179$
l_7	$\to -0.041$
p_7	$\to -0.344$
q_7	$\to 0.037$
t_7	$\to 0.057$
v_7	$\to -0.096$
z_7	$\to -0.058$

$$f_7''(0) = 0.9277$$
$$g_3''(0) = 1.0475$$
$$h_3''(0) = 0.0448$$
$$g_5''(0) = 0.9054$$
$$h_5''(0) = 0.0506$$
$$k_5''(0) = 0.1768$$
$$j_5''(0) = 0.0291$$
$$q_5''(0) = -0.0244$$
$$g_7''(0) = 0.821$$
$$h_7''(0) = 0.050$$
$$j_7''(0) = -0.020$$
$$k_7''(0) = 0.004$$
$$l_7''(0) = 0.041$$
$$p_7''(0) = 0.274$$
$$q_7''(0) = 0.015$$
$$t_7''(0) = 0.010$$
$$v_7''(0) = -0.047$$
$$z_7''(0) = 0.013$$

η	k_7''	l_7''	p_7''	q_7	i_7'	v_7'	z_7'
0	0	0	0	0	0	0	0
0·2	0·001	0·008	0·035	0·003	0·002	−0·009	0·003
0·4	0·002	0·015	0·034	0·006	0·003	−0·018	0·005
0·6	0·006	0·019	0·005	0·009	0·003	−0·026	0·005
0·8	0·012	0·019	−0·041	0·011	0·001	−0·034	0·002
1·0	0·021	0·014	−0·092	0·013	−0·002	−0·039	−0·003
1·2	0·033	0·005	−0·140	0·014	−0·004	−0·043	−0·010
1·4	0·048	−0·006	−0·178	0·015	−0·004	−0·044	−0·019
1·6	0·063	−0·018	−0·200	0·016	0·000	−0·044	−0·026
1·8	0·076	−0·028	−0·207	0·016	+0·006	−0·042	−0·032
2·0	0·086	−0·034	−0·199	0·015	0·015	−0·038	−0·035
2·2	0·090	−0·037	−0·179	0·014	0·023	−0·034	−0·035
2·4	0·089	−0·036	−0·152	0·012	0·031	−0·029	−0·033
2·6	0·083	−0·033	−0·123	0·010	0·035	−0·023	−0·028
2·8	0·073	−0·028	−0·095	0·009	0·036	−0·018	−0·024
3·0	0·061	−0·022	−0·069	0·007	0·034	−0·013	−0·018
3·2	0·048	−0·016	−0·048	0·005	0·030	−0·009	−0·014
3·4	0·036	−0·012	−0·032	0·004	0·024	−0·006	−0·010
3·6	0·025	−0·008	−0·021	0·003	0·019	−0·004	−0·006
3·8	0·017	−0·005	−0·013	0·002	0·014	−0·002	−0·004
4·0	0·011	−0·003	−0·008	0·001	0·009	−0·002	−0·002
4·2	0·007	−0·002	−0·004	0·001	0·006	−0·001	−0·001
4·4	0·004	−0·001	−0·002	0·000	0·004	0·000	−0·001
4·6	0·002	0·000	−0·001	0·000	0·002	0·000	0·000
4·8	0·001	0·000	0·000		0·001		0·000
5·0	0·000		0·000		0·001		
5·2	0·000				0·000		
5·4	0·000				0·000		

This equation is a cubic in ξ^2, and the real positive root gives $\xi_s = 1\cdot388$; the measure in degrees is $79\cdot5°$.

Fage's experimental result for this case showed separation at $83°$, and Tomotika and Imai using the approximate method calculated the position at $84°$. The above result is close to these values, but can be accepted only as a first approximation; even if the assumed expression for U is acceptable as a reasonable approximation, it is clear that further terms in the expansion for u, namely terms of order higher than ξ^7, would be required to confirm and refine this approximation.

8. The transformation to the two-dimensional case

The calculation of axially symmetrical boundary layers on bodies of revolution can be reduced to the calculation of a two-dimensional flow past a cylinder. The establishment of this relation between axially symmetrical and two-dimensional boundary layers is due to Mangler (1948c), who previously (1945) gave the transformation for the case of incompressible flow, which is considered here, and later extended it to include compressible boundary layers.

Since $v = 0$, the boundary-layer equations are

$$u\frac{\partial u}{\partial x}+w\frac{\partial u}{\partial z} = U\frac{dU}{dx}+\nu\frac{\partial^2 u}{\partial z^2}, \tag{57}$$

$$\frac{\partial}{\partial x}(r_0 u)+\frac{\partial}{\partial z}(r_0 w) = 0. \tag{58}$$

These equations are transformed by the introduction of new dependent and independent variables, u', x', etc., defined as follows:

$$x' = \frac{1}{l^2}\int_0^x r_0^2\, dx, \qquad z' = \frac{r_0 z}{l},$$

$$u' = u, \qquad w' = \frac{l}{r_0}\left(w+\frac{zu}{r_0}\frac{dr_0}{dx}\right), \qquad U'(x') = U(x) \tag{59}$$

(l is a constant length, and may be chosen arbitrarily). With these new variables, equations (57) and (58) become

$$u'\frac{\partial u'}{\partial x'}+w'\frac{\partial u'}{\partial z'} = U'\frac{dU'}{dx'}+\nu\frac{\partial^2 u'}{\partial z'^2}, \tag{60}$$

$$\frac{\partial u'}{\partial x'}+\frac{\partial w'}{\partial z'} = 0, \tag{61}$$

which are the equations appropriate to a two-dimensional boundary layer.

The boundary conditions on u and w, for an impermeable surface, are

$$u = w = 0 \quad \text{when } z = 0, \qquad u \to U \quad \text{as } z \to \infty,$$

so that the conditions on u' and w', from the relations (59), are

$$u' = w' = 0 \quad \text{when } z' = 0, \qquad u' \to U' \quad \text{as } z' \to \infty.$$

Hence there is a formal correspondence between axially symmetrical and two-dimensional boundary layers. The relation $U'(x') = U(x)$ gives the main-stream flow over the corresponding two-dimensional surface, and indirectly this enables the surface to be identified; there may be no close resemblance between the contour of this surface and the body of revolution.

It might appear that the above transformation renders unnecessary the calculations of Section 6, but this is not the case. For flow past a blunt-nosed body of revolution, the expansion of U' as a function of x' clearly involves fractional powers of x', and hence the results derived in Section VI. 2 for two-dimensional flow cannot be applied. This may be illustrated by considering the application of the transformation to the flow near a stagnation point. In this case

$$r_0(x) = x, \qquad U(x) = U_1 x/l,$$

and therefore $\qquad x' = x^3/3l^2, \quad \text{or} \quad x = (3l^2 x')^{1/3}.$

Hence $\qquad U'(x') = U_1 x/l = U_1(3x'/l)^{1/3} = Cx'^{1/3}.$

The two-dimensional flow is therefore a special case of the flow $U' = Cx'^m$, which corresponds to flow past a wedge of angle $2m\pi/(m+1)$; see Section V. 16. In this case $m = \tfrac{1}{3}$, and the angle of the wedge is $\tfrac{1}{2}\pi$. The appropriate boundary-layer flow, therefore, is derived from the solution of the equation of similar profiles for the case $\beta = \tfrac{1}{2}$, as alre.dy shown in Section 5.

The steady flow past a cone can also be related to flow past a wedge by use of Mangler's transformation, the above example being a particular case. This type of flow will be treated in Section 10.

9. Efflux through a small hole

As in the case of two-dimensional flow, it is found that the equations of motion for steady rotationally symmetrical flow past a body of revolution possess similar solutions which are valid for certain special types of body contour and main-stream flow. That is, the form of the solution in these cases is such that the partial differential equations of motion are transformed to ordinary differential equations. One example of this is the stagnation-point flow discussed in Section 5, and further examples may be found in Section III. 20. Mangler (1945) and Geis (1955) discussed a general class of solutions of this type, and the flow to be discussed here, and that in Section 10, are simply particular examples of such solutions.

For steady axisymmetrical flow past a body of revolution $v = 0$ everywhere, and the basic equations of motion are equations (57) and (58). In order to treat the boundary-layer flow due to the presence of a hole on a surface, the hole is regarded as a three-dimensional point sink. This point sink may be situated on a plane at rest, or, more generally, at the vertex of a cone at rest. The main-stream flow is then given by

$$U = -m/x^2 \quad (m > 0), \qquad (62)$$

where x is distance measured along the cone from the vertex, and m is the strength of the sink. The relation between r_0 and x for a cone is $r_0 = kx$ ($k = 1$ for a plane). Equation (58) is satisfied identically by writing

$$\left. \begin{array}{l} u = Uf'(\eta) \\[2mm] w = \left(\dfrac{m\nu}{2x^3}\right)^{\frac{1}{2}} \{f - 3\eta f'\} \\[2mm] \end{array} \right\}, \qquad (63)$$

where
$$\eta = z(m/2\nu x^3)^{\frac{1}{2}}$$

and equation (57) is also satisfied provided

$$f''' - ff'' + 4(1 - f'^2) = 0. \qquad (64)$$

From (63) the boundary conditions on f are

$$f = f' = 0 \quad \text{when } \eta = 0,$$
$$f' \to 1 \quad \text{as } \eta \to \infty.$$

Values of f' are given in Table V. 4.

The boundary-layer approximation described above is not valid in the immediate neighbourhood of the hole where, in any case, the assumed main-stream flow cannot represent an actual flow through a hole of small (but finite) diameter.

10. Flow past a cone

The solution of Laplace's equation in a system of spherical polar coordinates leads at once to the result

$$U = U_1(x/l)^n \qquad (65)$$

for flow along the generators of a cone in axially symmetrical flow towards the vertex. The index n is positive and depends on θ_0, where θ_0 is the angle between the axis and any generator of the cone. The variation of n with θ_0 is shown in Fig. VIII. 3, which is reproduced from Mangler (1948a), fig. 26. The result was given by Leuteritz and Mangler (1945), and again by Whitehead and Canetti (1950); in this second paper n and θ_0 have meanings different from those used here. The equations which determine the associated axisymmetrical boundary layer on a cone at rest are equations (57) and (58) as before. In

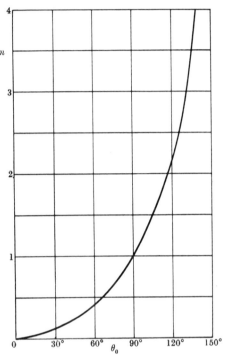

FIG. VIII. 3. The variation of n with θ_0 for axisymmetric potential flow towards a cone.

this case $r_0 = x\sin\theta_0$, and the appropriate similarity solution of the equations is given by

$$
\left.
\begin{aligned}
u &= Uf'(\eta) \\
w &= -\tfrac{1}{2}U\left\{\frac{2l^n\nu}{(3+n)U_1 x^{n+1}}\right\}^{\frac{1}{2}}\{(3+n)f+(n-1)\eta f'\}
\end{aligned}
\right\}, \qquad (66)
$$

where $\quad \eta = \left\{\dfrac{(3+n)U_1 x^{n-1}}{2l^n\nu}\right\}^{\frac{1}{2}}z$

and where f satisfies the equation

$$
f'''+ff''+\left(\frac{2n}{3+n}\right)(1-f'^2) = 0. \qquad (67)
$$

The boundary conditions on f, for flow without suction, are

$$f = f' = 0 \quad \text{when } \eta = 0,$$
$$f' \to 1 \quad \text{as } \eta \to \infty.$$

Thus, as shown by Mangler (1948a) and Whitehead and Canetti (1950), the boundary-layer flow on a cone is related to the two-dimensional flow past a wedge (Falkner and Skan 1930). As in the case of efflux through a small hole, the theory above does not apply to the vicinity of the vertex of the cone, since the original boundary-layer equations are not valid in this region; the extent of the excluded region increases as the angle of the cone decreases.

11. The momentum equations

The momentum equations appropriate to flow past a blunt-nosed body of revolution may be derived from the general results of Section 3. With the notation of Section 4, equation (25) and its companion now become

$$\frac{\partial}{\partial t} \int_0^\infty (U-u)\,dz + \frac{1}{r_0}\frac{\partial}{\partial x}\left\{r_0 \int_0^\infty u(U-u)\,dz\right\} + \frac{\partial U}{\partial x} \int_0^\infty (U-u)\,dz -$$

$$- \frac{r_0'}{r_0}\left\{\int_0^\infty v(V-v)\,dz + V \int_0^\infty (V-v)\,dz\right\} = \frac{\tau_1}{\rho} + w_0\,U, \quad (68)$$

$$\frac{\partial}{\partial t} \int_0^\infty (V-v)\,dz + \left\{\frac{\partial V}{\partial x} + V\frac{r_0'}{r_0}\right\} \int_0^\infty (U-u)\,dz +$$

$$+ \frac{1}{r_0^2}\frac{\partial}{\partial x}\left\{r_0^2 \int_0^\infty u(V-v)\,dz\right\} = \frac{\tau_2}{\rho} + w_0(V-r_0\Omega), \quad (69)$$

since the motion is independent of the coordinate θ.

The application of these equations involves the assumption of suitable expressions for u and v. These expressions will depend on form parameters which, in the general case, will be functions of x and t; equations (68) and (69) are then partial differential equations for these parameters. The expressions for u and v are chosen to satisfy as many of the boundary conditions as may be convenient. In addition to the conditions (31), further boundary conditions at $z = 0$ can be derived from equations (26) to (28) by repeated differentiation of the equations with respect to z, after which z is put equal to 0; for large values of z the various derivatives of u, v with respect to z all tend to zero.

12. Steady axisymmetric flow ; approximate solution with no suction

In this case $v = 0$ everywhere, and if the displacement and momentum thicknesses δ_1, δ_2 are introduced, where

$$U\delta_1 = \int_0^\infty (U-u)\,dz, \tag{70}$$

$$U^2\delta_2 = \int_0^\infty u(U-u)\,dz, \tag{71}$$

then equation (68) takes the form

$$\frac{1}{r_0}\frac{d}{dx}(r_0\,U^2\delta_2) + UU'\delta_1 = \frac{\tau}{\rho}, \tag{72}$$

where $U' = dU/dx$ and $\tau = \mu(\partial u/\partial z)_0$. If a shape parameter λ is introduced, where

$$\lambda = \frac{U'\delta_2^2}{\nu}, \tag{73}$$

equation (72) may be written in the equivalent form

$$\frac{U}{r_0^2}\frac{d}{dx}\left(\frac{r_0^2\lambda}{U'}\right) = \frac{2\tau\delta_2}{U\mu} - 2\lambda(2+H), \tag{74}$$

in which

$$H = \delta_1/\delta_2.$$

A profile for u, depending on the single shape parameter λ, is now assumed, namely

$$u = Uf(\lambda, \eta), \quad \text{with } \eta = z/\delta_2. \tag{75}$$

The function f must be chosen to satisfy certain boundary conditions. For example, it is clear from equations (26) and (29) that $f''(0) = -\lambda$, where the prime on f denotes differentiation with respect to η; other boundary conditions may be imposed as indicated in Section 11. The ratio H, and $(\tau\delta_2/\mu U) = f'(0)$, are simply functions of λ, so that equation (74) is a differential equation for the shape parameter, that is

$$\frac{U}{r_0^2}\frac{d}{dx}\left(\frac{r_0^2\lambda}{U'}\right) = F(\lambda), \tag{76}$$

where

$$F(\lambda) = 2f'(0) - 2\lambda(2+H).$$

This equation can be reduced to the momentum equation for a two-dimensional flow in the form (VI. 166) given by Holstein and Bohlen, by use of the transformation given in Section 8. Furthermore, if the same profiles are used in both the two-dimensional and three-dimensional cases, the shape parameters λ and the functions $F(\lambda)$ are the same in each, so that the equation for a two-dimensional flow can be used un-altered in the discussion of this case of a rotationally symmetrical boundary layer. In the integration of the equation, however, the initial value of λ differs from that in the two-dimensional case. For, near the stagnation point,

$$U = U_1\left(\frac{x}{l}\right) + \ldots,$$

$$r_0 = x + \ldots,$$

and since $d\lambda/dx$ is finite at $x = 0$, the initial value of λ must satisfy the equation

$$F(\lambda) - 2\lambda = 0.$$

Walz (1943), Rott and Crabtree (1952), and Drake (1953) have con-sidered simplified forms of the momentum equation, based on the assumption that $F(\lambda)$ is approximately a linear function of λ. Rott and Crabtree, using Thwaites's discussion (1949 b) for the two-dimensional case, assumed a universal form

$$F(\lambda) = a - b\lambda$$

with $a = 0.45$, $b = 6$ (see Section VI. 18). Equation (76) can then be solved, since it may be written

$$\frac{d}{dx}\left(\frac{U^b}{U'}\lambda r_0^2\right) = ar_0^2\, U^{b-1},$$

and hence

$$\frac{U^b}{U'}\lambda r_0^2 = a \int_0^x r_0^2\, U^{b-1}\, dx.$$

The lower limit in the integral is deduced from the condition that the momentum thickness δ_2 remains finite near the stagnation point $x = 0$. Hence

$$\lambda = ar_0^{-2}U'U^{-b} \int_0^x r_0^2\, U^{b-1}\, dx. \tag{77}$$

13. Steady flow with swirl

An interesting example of a rotationally symmetrical boundary layer is provided by the motion of fluid inside the chamber of a swirl atomizer, a device used in agricultural spraying machinery and in oil-fired fur-naces. The swirling motion is produced by introducing the liquid tan-gentially at the edge of a converging chamber, the liquid emerging finally through a central orifice of small diameter. Taylor (1950) and Cooke (1952) considered the boundary-layer flow in a conical chamber when the main stream has only swirling motion. Binnie and Harris (1950) discussed, on the basis of Taylor's method, the more general case in which the main stream possesses both streaming and swirling motion. From his investigation, Taylor deduced that under certain conditions practically the whole of the outflow from the orifice is provided by the boundary-layer flow in the chamber; his discussion of the problem now follows.

Swirling liquid enters tangentially a chamber in the shape of a frustum of a circular cone of angle 2α. The radius at entry is a, and the liquid emerges through the orifice, of radius b, after passing down the converging cone. In practice the ratio b/a is very small, and the entry conditions are such that the longitudinal component of velocity in the main stream is small compared with the swirl component and may be neglected. The swirling velocity is of magnitude A/r, where A is a swirl constant and r is distance measured from the axis of the cone. Taylor derived his equations of motion using spherical polar coordinates, but his discussion can be simplified a little by proceeding directly from equations (68) and (69). Since $U = 0$, $V = A/r_0$, and $w_0 = 0$, these equations are

$$\frac{1}{r_0}\frac{d}{dx}\left\{r_0\int_0^\infty u^2\,dz\right\} + \frac{r_0'}{r_0}\left\{\int_0^\infty v(V-v)\,dz + V\int_0^\infty (V-v)\,dz\right\} = -\frac{\tau_1}{\rho}, \quad (78)$$

$$\frac{1}{r_0^2}\frac{d}{dx}\left\{r_0^2\int_0^\infty u(V-v)\,dz\right\} = \frac{\tau_2}{\rho}, \quad (79)$$

where x is distance measured along a generator from the vertex of the cone, and z is distance measured along the inward normal. A method of Pohlhausen's type may be applied to the above equations. A finite thickness δ is assumed for the boundary layer, and the profiles chosen for the velocity components in the layer are

$$u = EAf(\eta)/r_0, \qquad v = A\phi(\eta)/r_0, \qquad (80)$$

where
$$\eta = z/\delta,$$

and
$$f(\eta) = \eta - 2\eta^2 + \eta^3, \qquad \phi(\eta) = 2\eta - \eta^2.$$

Thus η varies from 0 to 1 through the layer; outside the layer f is zero and $\phi = 1$. These profiles satisfy the boundary conditions

$$u = v = 0 \quad \text{when } z = 0,$$

$$u = 0, \quad \frac{\partial u}{\partial z} = 0, \quad v = \frac{A}{r_0}, \quad \frac{\partial v}{\partial z} = 0 \quad \text{when } z = \delta.$$

The momentum equations (78) and (79), with use of the assumed expressions for u and v, become ordinary differential equations for E

and δ. The integrands in the infinite integrals vanish when $z > \delta$, so that the upper limit of integration may be replaced by δ. The surface of revolution is a cone with $r_0 = x \sin \alpha$, and if ξ and F are now defined by the relations

$$\xi = \frac{x}{c}, \qquad F = \frac{EA\delta^2}{c^2\nu \sin \alpha}, \qquad c = a \operatorname{cosec} \alpha, \qquad (81)$$

so that c is the length of a generator measured from the vertex to the base of the cone, equations (78) and (79) become

$$\frac{1}{2}\left(3FE\frac{dE}{d\xi} + E^2\frac{dF}{d\xi} - 2\frac{FE^2}{\xi}\right)\int_0^1 f^2\,d\eta + \frac{F}{\xi}\left(1 - \int_0^1 \phi^2\,d\eta\right) = -E^2\xi,$$

$$\frac{1}{2}\left(FE\frac{dE}{d\xi} + E^2\frac{dF}{d\xi}\right)\int_0^1 f(1-\phi)\,d\eta = 2E^2\xi,$$

since $f'(0) = 1$, $\phi'(0) = 2$.

With the values of the integrals substituted in these equations, they may be rearranged to give

$$\frac{dE^2}{d\xi} = E^2\left(\frac{2}{\xi} - \frac{330}{F}\xi\right) - \frac{98}{\xi}, \qquad (82)$$

$$\frac{dF}{d\xi} = F\left(\frac{49}{E^2\xi} - \frac{1}{\xi}\right) + 285\xi. \qquad (83)$$

The boundary layer begins at the base of the cone, so that $E = F = 0$ at $\xi = 1$. Equations (82) and (83) were integrated numerically with these initial conditions, and Table VIII. 2 is the table of results given by Taylor. The angle χ is the inclination of the direction of the skin friction on the surface, measured from the generators, and is deduced from the relation

$$\cot \chi = \left(\frac{\partial u}{\partial \eta} \Big/ \frac{\partial v}{\partial \eta}\right)_0 = \tfrac{1}{2}E,$$

while the boundary-layer thickness may be obtained from the relations (81), namely

$$\delta = a\left(\frac{\nu F}{AE \sin \alpha}\right)^{\frac{1}{2}}. \qquad (84)$$

The pressure in the main stream is

$$p = -\tfrac{1}{2}\rho(A/r)^2 + \text{const},$$

so that if the pressure head over the length of the boundary layer is P,

$$P = \tfrac{1}{2}\rho A^2(b^{-2} - a^{-2}), \quad \text{and therefore } (A/b) < (2P/\rho)^{\frac{1}{2}}.$$

TABLE VIII. 2

Boundary-layer quantities for swirling motion in a conical chamber,
derived from the solution of equations (82) and (83)

ξ	E	$\dfrac{\delta}{c}\left(\dfrac{A}{\nu\sin\alpha}\right)^{\frac{1}{2}}$	χ (degrees)	ξ	E	$\dfrac{\delta}{c}\left(\dfrac{A}{\nu\sin\alpha}\right)^{\frac{1}{2}}$	χ (degrees)
0·05	6·81	1·91	16·4	0·82	1·98	2·518	45·3
0·10	6·45	2·00	17·2	0·84	1·852	2·473	47·2
0·15	6·06	2·10	18·2	0·86	1·720	2·415	49·3
0·20	5·70	2·19	19·3	0·88	1·580	2·355	51·6
0·25	5·35	2·28	20·5	0·90	1·432	2·274	54·4
0·30	5·02	2·35	21·7	0·92	1·273	2·174	57·5
0·35	4·69	2·43	23·1	0·93	1·185	2·115	59·4
0·40	4·38	2·49	24·5	0·94	1·093	2·046	61·3
0·45	4·08	2·56	26·1	0·95	0·990	1·97	63·7
0·50	3·80	2·60	27·7	0·96	0·884	1·870	66·2
0·55	3·515	2·635	29·7	0·97	0·764	1·750	69·1
0·60	3·24	2·658	31·7	0·98	0·625	1·580	72·6
0·65	2·960	2·665	33·9	0·985	0·533	1·449	75·1
0·70	2·684	2·652	36·7	0·990	0·442	1·335	78·5
0·74	2·460	2·627	39·1	0·995	0·309	1·136	81·5
0·77	2·283	2·595	41·2	1·000	0·000	0·000	90·0
0·80	2·117	2·55	43·5				

The contribution of the boundary-layer flow to the efflux from the orifice may be illustrated by the following example, in which the liquid is water:

$$\alpha = 45°,\ b = 1\ \text{mm};\quad a/b = 10,\ P = 10\ \text{atm (so that}$$

$$A/b < 45\ \text{m/sec);}\quad \nu = 0·01\ \text{cm}^2/\text{sec.}$$

Thus, at the orifice, where $\xi = 0·1$, the boundary-layer thickness is greater than 0·11 mm; the boundary layer therefore extends inwards at least a distance of one-ninth the radius of the orifice. In the case of a practical swirl atomizer the swirling component of velocity is large in comparison with the component parallel to the generators (except near the orifice). Further, there is also a large hollow core through the orifice, so that it is clear that much of the outflow reaches the orifice by way of the boundary layer.

Cooke (1952) has shown that an error may be introduced in assuming that the two components u, v, of velocity in the boundary layer attain their main-stream values at the same distance from the boundary. He reconsidered the swirl problem solved by Taylor, and introduced boundary-layer thicknesses δ and Δ corresponding to u and v respectively. The expression for ϕ was replaced by a polynomial in z/Δ of degree 3, and this, with the introduction of the extra unknown quantity Δ, allowed two more boundary conditions to be satisfied; the details of the calculation may be found in the original paper. Fig. VIII. 4, taken from this paper, shows a graph of the function

$$\frac{\delta}{c}\left(\frac{A}{\nu \sin \alpha}\right)^{\frac{1}{2}}$$

compared with that derived from Taylor's results. The difference is most marked for low values of ξ, that is, Cooke's results show a much more rapid decrease in the boundary-layer thickness δ near the apex of the cone than that shown by Taylor.

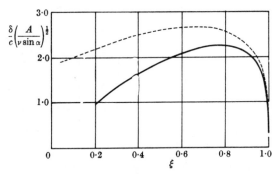

Fig. VIII. 4. Boundary-layer thickness δ for swirling motion in a conical chamber.

Taylor · · · · · ·; Cooke ———

14. The boundary layer on a rotating sphere

Howarth (1951b) has drawn attention to a special feature of the boundary-layer flow set up by a sphere rotating about a diameter in a fluid otherwise at rest. The boundary layers on the two hemispheres originate at the poles, where the flow approximates to that due to a rotating disk, and develop towards the equator, where they interact. Boundary-layer equations are sufficient to account for the flow except in the vicinity of the equator, but consideration of the full equations of motion is required to treat the flow in the region of interaction; this aspect of the problem has been discussed by Stewartson (1957b).

Howarth used Kármán's method to obtain an approximate solution for the boundary-layer flow. The momentum equations (68) and (69) are

$$\frac{1}{r_0}\frac{d}{dx}\left\{r_0 \int_0^\infty u^2 \, dz\right\} - \frac{r_0'}{r_0}\int_0^\infty v^2 \, dz = -\nu\left(\frac{\partial u}{\partial z}\right)_0, \tag{85}$$

$$\frac{1}{r_0^2}\frac{d}{dx}\left\{r_0^2 \int_0^\infty uv \, dz\right\} = -\nu\left(\frac{\partial v}{\partial z}\right)_0, \tag{86}$$

since the fluid outside the layer is at rest. Following Kármán's solution (1921) of the problem of the rotating disk the expressions assumed for u and v are

$$u = (\Omega^2\delta^2 a/\nu)\sin\theta\cos\theta\{\chi(\eta - 3\eta^3 + 2\eta^4) - \tfrac{1}{2}\eta^2 + \eta^3 - \tfrac{1}{2}\eta^4\}, \qquad (87)$$

$$v = \Omega a\sin\theta\{1 - \tfrac{3}{2}\eta + \tfrac{1}{2}\eta^3\}, \qquad (88)$$

where a is the radius of the sphere, Ω the angular velocity, and θ the angle between the axis of rotation and the radius to a point on the surface of the sphere; thus

$$x = a\theta, \quad \text{and} \quad r_0 = a\sin\theta.$$

The variable η is z/δ, where δ is the boundary-layer thickness. For values of $\eta \geqslant 1$, u and v are zero, so that the upper limit in the integrals in the above equations may be replaced by δ. The boundary conditions satisfied by the expressions for u and v are

$$u = 0, \quad \frac{\partial^2 u}{\partial\eta^2} = -\frac{\Omega^2\delta^2 a}{\nu}\sin\theta\cos\theta,$$

$$v = \Omega a\sin\theta, \quad \frac{\partial^2 v}{\partial\eta^2} = 0 \quad \text{when } \eta = 0,$$

$$u = v = \frac{\partial u}{\partial\eta} = \frac{\partial v}{\partial\eta} = 0 \quad \text{when } \eta = 1,$$

the conditions on the second derivatives being obtained directly from the boundary-layer equations (26) to (29).

χ and δ are determined from the momentum equations (85) and (86). The equations may be simplified by noting that, in the problem of the rotating disk,

$$\int_0^\delta v^2\,dz \gg \int_0^\delta u^2\,dz;$$

in this problem it is assumed that the same relationship holds between the terms on the left-hand side of equation (85), and a tentative approach to the solution may be made by neglecting the first term in that equation. χ is then determined immediately, and the value is

$$\chi = 0{\cdot}2357. \qquad (89)$$

In place of δ, a parameter λ is introduced, where

$$\delta = (\nu/\Omega)^{\frac{1}{2}}\lambda, \qquad (90)$$

so that equation (86), with the above value for χ, leads at once to the following differential equation for λ:

$$\tfrac{3}{4}\sin\theta\cos\theta\frac{d\lambda^4}{d\theta} + (4\cos^2\theta - \sin^2\theta)\lambda^4 = 173{\cdot}6. \qquad (91)$$

This first-order differential equation may be integrated at once. Since λ and $d\lambda/d\theta$ are both finite at $\theta = 0$, the appropriate solution is

$$\lambda^4 = \frac{231 \cdot 5}{\sin^{16/3}\theta \cos^{4/3}\theta} \int\limits_0^\theta \sin^{13/3}\theta \cos^{1/3}\theta \, d\theta. \tag{92}$$

The flow near the poles of the sphere must approximate to the flow on a rotating disk, so that it is possible to provide a check on the solution at this stage. For small values of θ,

$$\lambda = 2 \cdot 57, \qquad \left(\frac{\partial u}{\partial z}\right)_0 = \frac{0 \cdot 61\Omega^{3/2}a\theta}{\nu^{1/2}}, \qquad \left(\frac{\partial v}{\partial z}\right)_0 = -\frac{0 \cdot 58\Omega^{3/2}a\theta}{\nu^{1/2}}.$$

Cochran (1934) used the same type of approximate solution for the rotating disk, and retained all the terms in his basic equations. The corresponding numerical coefficients in his solution are $2 \cdot 79$, $0 \cdot 54$, and $-0 \cdot 54$ respectively.

The above results provide an estimate of the rate of inflow of fluid into the boundary layer. If w_δ is the component of velocity normal to the sphere at the edge of the boundary layer, it follows from the equation of continuity (30) that

$$w_\delta = -\frac{1}{\sin\theta}\frac{d}{d\theta}\int\limits_0^\delta u\sin\theta \, dz,$$

since $u = 0$ at the edge of the layer. In terms of λ, with use of equation (91), this result may be written

$$w_\delta = -0 \cdot 0187(\Omega\nu)^{\frac{1}{2}}\lambda^{-1}\{173 \cdot 6 - 2\cos^2\theta\,\lambda^4\}. \tag{93}$$

The table of values of w_δ given by Howarth shows that there is an inflow throughout the whole range of values of θ. From considerations of continuity this, of course, cannot take place. Further examination of the solution shows that λ (and hence δ) behaves like $(\cos\theta)^{-1/3}$ in the vicinity of the equator ($\theta = \frac{1}{2}\pi$), and the neglect of the first term in (85) cannot be justified in this region; indeed, as mentioned already, the basic equations (85) and (86) are not adequate to describe the flow at this stage. The results also show that the limiting values of $(\partial u/\partial z)_0$ and $(\partial v/\partial z)_0$ are zero at the equator, so that an effect akin to separation of the flow occurs here. Howarth suggested that inflow would occur over a large part of the surface of the sphere, the outflow necessary to maintain continuity being confined to the vicinity of the equator.

This problem has been considered also by Nigam (1954), who solved the boundary-layer equations by the method of expansions in series of powers of $\sin \theta$; the resulting ordinary differential equations for the first three coefficients in each series were solved approximately by Pohlhausen's method (Howarth also established expansions of a slightly different type, but did not provide a solution of the differential equations). Fadnis (1954) extended Nigam's work to obtain results for the flow about rotating spheroids, with use of elliptic coordinates to obtain appropriate expansions in series.

Contrary to the view expressed by Howarth, Nigam inferred that the boundary-layer equations were sufficient to describe the motion over the whole surface of the sphere. Stewartson (1957b), in a paper which contains a discussion of several interesting examples of rotating boundary layers, proved that Nigam's conclusion must be incorrect. He showed that a solution of the boundary-layer equations must lead to a situation in which the two boundary layers originating at the poles collide at the equator. The boundary-layer fluid, after collision, moves outward along the equatorial plane and ultimately forms a radial jet (H. B. Squire 1955). The thicknesses of the shear layers both before and after collision are $O(\nu^{\frac{1}{2}})$, and it is reasonable to expect that the region in which the boundary-layer assumptions are no longer valid is within a distance $O(\nu^{\frac{1}{2}})$ of the equator. With a suitable choice of dependent and independent variables to describe the flow in this region, Stewartson considered the limiting form, as $\nu \to 0$, of the full equations of motion. The resulting governing equation is such that two boundary conditions must be abandoned, and it was inferred that the equation is sufficient to describe the flow outside a thin inner shear layer of thickness $O(\nu^{3/4})$.

Kobashi (1957) carried out experiments on the boundary layer of a rotating sphere, using hot-wire measurements to determine the velocity field, and compared his results with Nigam's theoretical solution. He found that there is inflow into the boundary layer at the poles, and outflow at the equator, and that the change occurred at $\theta = 54.5°$. Quantitative agreement with Nigam's solution was rather poor, especially near the equator; Stewartson's criticism provides the explanation.

15. Entry flow in a circular pipe

It will be assumed here that intake conditions are such that fluid, moving in the direction of the axis of the pipe, enters the pipe with a velocity which is practically constant over the whole cross-section. A boundary layer, initially of zero thickness, is formed inside the pipe, and this layer increases in thickness downstream until it becomes equal to the radius of the pipe. Until this happens, there is a core of fluid which is practically uninfluenced by viscosity. Since the flux of fluid across any section is constant, and the boundary-layer thickness is increasing, this core is accelerated, and there is a corresponding fall of pressure. Far downstream from the entrance to the pipe the flow assumes the Poiseuille parabolic distribution, and theoretically this is attained asymptotically. However, there will be a finite distance (the inlet length of the pipe) at which the difference between the actual distribution and the parabolic one is less than the error in experiment. The final state is not necessarily attained when the boundary-layer thickness is equal to the radius of the pipe; the indications are that the whole of the fluid across a section becomes influenced by viscosity before the parabolic distribution is reached.

The discussion of the boundary-layer flow inside the pipe involves a slight change in the basic boundary-layer equations which were developed for general use in this chapter, for they are subject to the restriction that the radius of curvature of the boundary is large in comparison with the thickness of the boundary layer; this condition must now be relaxed. For axisymmetric flow the full equations of motion in cylindrical polar coordinates are

$$u\frac{\partial u}{\partial x}+w\frac{\partial u}{\partial r} = -\frac{1}{\rho}\frac{\partial p}{\partial x}+\nu\left(\frac{\partial^2 u}{\partial r^2}+\frac{1}{r}\frac{\partial u}{\partial r}+\frac{\partial^2 u}{\partial x^2}\right),\tag{94}$$

$$u\frac{\partial w}{\partial x}+w\frac{\partial w}{\partial r} = -\frac{1}{\rho}\frac{\partial p}{\partial r}+\nu\left(\frac{\partial^2 w}{\partial r^2}+\frac{1}{r}\frac{\partial w}{\partial r}-\frac{w}{r^2}+\frac{\partial^2 w}{\partial x^2}\right),\tag{95}$$

where x is distance measured along the axis downstream from the leading (circular) edge of the pipe, and r is distance measured from the axis. The equation of continuity is

$$\frac{\partial}{\partial x}(ru)+\frac{\partial}{\partial r}(rw) = 0.\tag{96}$$

For flow at large Reynolds numbers the usual boundary-layer approximations are valid. Thus the pressure is a function of x alone, and

$$-\frac{1}{\rho}\frac{\partial p}{\partial x} = U\frac{dU}{dx},$$

where $U(x)$ is the main-stream velocity. Further, in equation (94) the term $\nu\,\partial^2 u/\partial x^2$ may be neglected; the term $\nu\,\partial u/r\,\partial r$ must be retained, however, for the boundary-layer thickness is eventually of the same order of magnitude as the radius of the pipe, so that the first two viscosity terms in the equation may be comparable in magnitude.

Previously in this chapter the first term only was retained: The appropriate boundary-layer equations are therefore

$$u\frac{\partial u}{\partial x}+w\frac{\partial u}{\partial r} = U\frac{dU}{dx}+\nu\left(\frac{\partial^2 u}{\partial r^2}+\frac{1}{r}\frac{\partial u}{\partial r}\right) \tag{97}$$

and equation (96).

The boundary-layer flow near the entrance of the pipe was discussed by Atkinson and Goldstein (see Goldstein 1938). For uniform flow towards the pipe, the boundary conditions on u and w are

$$u \to U_0, \quad w \to 0 \quad \text{when } x \to 0,$$
$$u = w = 0 \quad \text{at } r = a, \tag{98}$$

where a is the radius of the pipe. A stream function ψ is defined by the equation of continuity (96), so that

$$u = \frac{1}{r}\frac{\partial \psi}{\partial r}, \qquad w = -\frac{1}{r}\frac{\partial \psi}{\partial x}, \tag{99}$$

and in the region in which there is a core of fluid uninfluenced by viscosity a solution of the boundary-layer equations may be obtained by use of the transformation of variables

$$\xi = \left(\frac{x\nu}{a^2 U_0}\right)^{\frac{1}{2}}, \qquad \eta = \left(\frac{U_0}{x\nu}\right)^{\frac{1}{2}}\left(\frac{a^2-r^2}{4a}\right). \tag{100}$$

A series expansion for ψ is assumed, namely

$$\psi = -a^2 U_0 \sum_{n=1}^{\infty} \xi^n f_n(\eta), \tag{101}$$

and hence

$$u = \tfrac{1}{2}U_0 \sum_{n=1}^{\infty} \xi^{n-1} f_n'(\eta) \tag{102}$$

(this is a generalization of the corresponding expressions in Blasius's solution of the problem of the two-dimensional flat plate).

The velocity in the frictionless core needs special consideration. As explained above, the fluid here is accelerated, and accordingly the assumption $U = U_0\{1+K_1\xi+K_2\xi^2+...\}$ (103)

is made, where the K_n $(n = 1, 2, ...)$ are constants to be determined from the condition of constant flux.

Substitution in equation (97), expressed in the new variables, yields a set of ordinary differential equations for the functions f_n when the coefficients of the various powers of ξ are equated to zero. The first three of these equations are

$$f_1'''+f_1 f_1'' = 0, \tag{104}$$
$$f_2'''+f_1 f_2''-f_1'f_2'+2f_1''f_2 = -4K_1+4\eta f_1'''+4f_1'', \tag{105}$$
$$f_3'''+f_1 f_3''-2f_1'f_3'+3f_1''f_3 = -8K_2-4K_1^2+f_2'^2-2f_2 f_2''+4\eta f_2'''+4f_2''. \tag{106}$$

The boundary conditions on the functions f_n, provided a core exists, are

$$f_n(0) = f'_n(0) = 0,$$

$$f'_1(\eta) \to 2, \qquad f'_n(\eta) \to 2K_{n-1} \quad (n \geqslant 2) \quad \text{as } \eta \to \infty. \tag{107}$$

Equation (104) is Blasius's equation, and its solution, subject to the above boundary conditions, gives the boundary-layer flow over a flat plate for a uniform main stream. The appearance of this equation in this context is not accidental; very near the leading edge of the pipe the flow must be similar to the flow over a flat plate since the radius of the pipe is there large in comparison with the boundary-layer thickness, and the curvature of the boundary may be neglected.

The evaluation of the constants K_n is carried out as follows. For large values of η,

$$f_1 \sim 2\eta + A_1, \quad f_2 \sim 2K_1\eta + A_2, \quad f_3 \sim 2\dot{K}_2\eta + A_3, \quad \text{etc.,}$$

where the values of A_n are determined by the numerical integration of the equations (104), etc. Now since the flux of fluid is constant, the difference in the values of $2\pi\psi$ at $r = a$ (i.e. $\eta = 0$) and at $r = 0$ (i.e. $\eta = 1/(4\xi)$) must equal $\pi a^2 U_0$, the value of the flux at the leading edge. The stream function ψ vanishes at $\eta = 0$, and provided there is a core uninfluenced by viscosity, ξ must be sufficiently small for the above approximations to hold in finding the value of ψ at $\eta = 1/(4\xi)$. The condition of constant flux is therefore

$$\xi\left(\frac{1}{2\xi} + A_1\right) + \xi^2\left(\frac{K_1}{2\xi} + A_2\right) + \xi^3\left(\frac{K_2}{2\xi} + A_3\right) + \dots = \tfrac{1}{2}. \tag{108}$$

Hence $K_1 = -2A_1$, $K_2 = -2A_2$, $K_3 = -2A_3$, etc.

Numerical integration of equation (104), subject to the given boundary conditions, determines the value of A_1. This determines K_1, and the integration of equation (105) can then be performed, so that A_2 is determined, and so on. Thus a solution is obtained for small values of ξ. It is found that the K_n increase rapidly ($K_1 = 3 \cdot 4415$, $K_2 = -9 \cdot 0938$, $K_3 = 141 \cdot 98$, $K_4 = -2,788$), and for values of $\xi \geqslant 0 \cdot 05$ (approximately) the series (102) does not give sufficiently accurate results. For values of $\xi < 0 \cdot 05$ comparison with an approximate calculation due to Schiller (1922) shows that the values of u/U_0 calculated by Schiller's method are accurate to within 1 per cent. for $r/a \leqslant 0 \cdot 8$ and to within 5 per cent. for $r/a = 0 \cdot 9$. Nikuradse (see Prandtl and Tietjens 1934b) carried out measurements of velocity in the inlet length of the pipe, and the results for $r/a = 0$, $0 \cdot 2$, $0 \cdot 4$, $0 \cdot 6$, $0 \cdot 7$, $0 \cdot 8$, and $0 \cdot 9$ are reproduced in Fig. VIII. 5, which also contains results calculated by Schiller's approximate method. It follows that the experimental results do not agree with the accurate solution for very small values of ξ, though some discrepancy very near the entry might be expected in view of the singularity in the solution at $\xi = 0$.

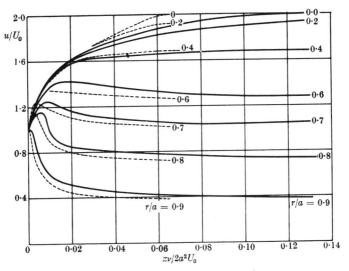

Fig. VIII. 5. Entry flow in a circular cylinder; theoretical results - - - - -, experimental results ———— (Diagram reproduced from Goldstein (1938), p. 304, fig. 80.)

Atkinson and Goldstein also used a method due to Boussinesq (1891 a, b) to extend their solution. In the region where the flow has attained the Poiseuille distribution, the pressure is again a function of x alone, and u is independent of x. Accordingly, to extend the series solution above to this region the term $\nu \, \partial^2 u / \partial x^2$ is again neglected in equation (94), and p is treated as a function of x only; apart from this no expression is assumed for p.

With these approximations, and the change to non-dimensional variables

$$X = 2x/aR, \qquad Y = r^2/a^2,$$

where R is the Reynolds number $2U_0 a/\nu$, equation (96) gives

$$rw = \frac{a}{R} \int_Y^1 \frac{\partial u}{\partial X} \, dY,$$

since $w = 0$ when $Y = 1$.

Equation (94) then becomes

$$u\frac{\partial u}{\partial X}+\frac{\partial u}{\partial Y}\int_Y^1 \frac{\partial u}{\partial X}\,dY = -\frac{1}{\rho}\frac{\partial p}{\partial X}+4U_0\frac{\partial}{\partial Y}\left(Y\frac{\partial u}{\partial Y}\right). \tag{109}$$

Since the flux of fluid is constant, there is the condition

$$\int_0^1 u\,dY = \text{const} = U_0. \tag{110}$$

In the permanent (parabolic) régime,

$$u = 2U_0(1-Y),$$

and an approximation to the flow upstream is obtained by writing

$$u = U_0\{2(1-Y)+u'\} \tag{111}$$

in equation (109), and neglecting squares of u'. Since the pressure is a function of X alone, it may be eliminated from the equation by differentiation with respect to Y; the resulting equation is

$$\left(\frac{1-Y}{Y}\right)\frac{\partial}{\partial X}\left(Y\frac{\partial u'}{\partial Y}\right) = 2\frac{\partial^2}{\partial Y^2}\left(Y\frac{\partial u'}{\partial Y}\right). \tag{112}$$

This is an equation for $Y\,\partial u'/\partial Y$, and a solution may be obtained by writing

$$Y\frac{\partial u'}{\partial Y} = ce^{-2\lambda X}\phi(Y),$$

where ϕ satisfies the differential equation

$$\frac{d^2\phi}{dY^2}+\lambda\left(\frac{1-Y}{Y}\right)\phi = 0. \tag{113}$$

One of the boundary conditions on ϕ is clearly $\phi(0) = 0$. For the other condition, relations (110) and (111) give

$$\int_0^1 u'\,dY = 0,$$

and hence $$\int_0^1 Y\frac{\partial u'}{\partial Y}\,dY = [Yu']_0^1 - \int_0^1 u'\,dY = 0$$

(since $u' = 0$ when $Y = 1$). The boundary conditions on ϕ are thus $\phi(0) = 0$ and $\int_0^1 \phi\,dY = 0$; equation (113) with these boundary conditions shows that the value of λ is one of an infinite set of eigenvalues. If $\lambda_1,...,\lambda_n,...$ are these values, the complete solution of equation (112) is

$$Y\frac{\partial u'}{\partial Y} = \sum_{n=1}^{\infty} c_n e^{-2\lambda_n X}\phi_n(Y),$$

and hence
$$-u' = \sum_{n=1}^{\infty} c_n e^{-2\lambda_n X} F_n(Y), \qquad (114)$$

where
$$F_n(Y) = \int_Y^1 \phi_n(Y) \frac{dY}{Y}.$$

The above solution must be fitted to the series solution (102) at some value of X, and this determines the constants c_n. If the origin of X is transferred so that $X = 0$ is the section from which the solution is started, and u_0' is the value of u' at $X = 0$ as calculated from the series (102) with use of relation (111), the c_n are determined by making the integral

$$\int_0^1 \{u_0' - u'(0, Y)\}^2 \, dY$$

a minimum. That is,

$$\int_0^1 \{u_0' + c_1 F_1 + \dots + c_n F_n + \dots\}^2 \, dY$$

is made a minimum.

Finally, the pressure may be deduced from equation (109). This gives

$$-\frac{1}{\rho} \frac{\partial p}{\partial X} = \left[u \frac{\partial u}{\partial X} - 4U_0 \frac{\partial}{\partial Y} \left(Y \frac{\partial u}{\partial Y} \right) \right]_{Y=0}, \qquad (115)$$

because $\partial p / \partial X$ is independent of Y, and also

$$\int_0^1 \frac{\partial u}{\partial X} \, dY = \frac{\partial}{\partial X} \int_0^1 u \, dY = 0.$$

Atkinson and Goldstein used the first two terms in (114), and also refined the approximation by substituting the result into the neglected terms in (109) and solving again. The solutions (102) and (114) were joined at $\xi = 0.05$. A junction at a higher value of ξ would have been desirable, but the series (102), with the limited number of terms available, is not accurate beyond $\xi = 0.05$.

The change in pressure along the pipe may be calculated from the boundary-layer solution in the first section of the pipe, where

$$-\partial p / \partial x = \rho U \, dU / dx,$$

and then from result (115). For values of x / aR beyond the inlet length the calculations finally lead to the result

$$\frac{p_0 - p}{\frac{1}{2}\rho U_0^2} = \frac{32x}{aR} + 1.41,$$

where p_0 is the pressure at entry $(x = 0)$. For flow from a large cistern where the pressure is P and in which the velocity is negligible, the corresponding result is

$$\frac{P-p}{\frac{1}{2}\rho U_0^2} = \frac{32x}{aR} + 2\cdot41.$$

The effect of the undeveloped flow at the entry to the pipe thus leads to an increase in the change of pressure along the pipe, measured from entry, as compared with the change in a section where the parabolic distribution exists throughout. The difference is $\frac{1}{2}\rho U_0^2 m$, known as the kinetic energy end-correction, and in the result above m has the value $2\cdot41$. This value appears to be rather high; four experimental values given by Schiller are $m = 2\cdot115$, $2\cdot35$, $2\cdot36$, and $2\cdot45$, with an average value $m = 2\cdot32$. There are other experimental results by Reiman (1928) within the range $2\cdot220$ to $2\cdot268$. A theoretical value given by Langhaar (1942) is $2\cdot28$; in his analysis he used the boundary-layer approxima-tions as in equation (97), but in addition made the equation linear by replacing the non-linear terms by the single term $\nu\beta^2 u$, where β is a function of x alone. The theoretical value given by Boussinesq is $m = 2\cdot24$. Boussinesq, however, applied his method right from the entry, and the method should certainly be more accurate when used to continue a series solution as described above.

The discussion above is concerned with axially symmetrical flow; the problem of the decay of swirl along a pipe was considered by Talbot (1954) and Collatz and Görtler (1954). In both cases the equations of motion were made linear by considering a perturbation of the main Poiseuille flow, with rotationally symmetrical swirl superimposed.

16. Flow along the outside of a long thin circular cylinder

The axisymmetric boundary-layer flow along the outside of a cylinder can be treated also by the method described for entry flow; the dis-cussion here is simpler in that there is no condition of constant flux to be satisfied. The method of expansion in series thus provides a solution that is valid near the leading edge. For the region remote from the leading edge, where the boundary layer is thick in comparison with the radius of the cylinder, a solution may be obtained by use of an asymp-totic series. There is an extensive region in which neither of the series representations is valid, but a Pohlhausen approximate method can be used here. Glauert and Lighthill (1955) used a combination of these methods to derive results which are considered to be reliable over the whole of the boundary layer.

The boundary-layer equations are (96) and (97); the main-stream flow is uniform, with velocity U_0 in the direction of the axis of the cylinder, so that the boundary conditions are

$$u = w = 0 \quad \text{when } r = a,$$

$$u \to U_0 \quad \text{as } x \to 0 \text{ or } r \to \infty. \tag{116}$$

Seban and Bond (1951) obtained a solution in series, valid near the leading edge. Their method is the same as that of Atkinson and Goldstein, with η now replaced by $(U_0/\nu x)^{\frac{1}{2}}\{(r^2 - a^2)/4a\}$. The differential equations that they derived for the coefficients in the series are equivalent to equations (104), etc., with the K_n all equal to zero. Kelly (1954) gave some important numerical corrections to their work, and where these results are required for comparison with those of the approximate method the corrected values will be stated without further reference.

The approximate method used by Glauert and Lighthill seems to depend for its success on a careful choice of velocity profile, and has the advantage of being fairly simple mathematically. If z denotes, as usual, distance measured from the surface along the normal, so that $r = a + z$, equations (97) and (96) become

$$u\frac{\partial u}{\partial x} + w\frac{\partial u}{\partial z} = \nu\left\{\frac{\partial^2 u}{\partial z^2} + \frac{1}{a+z}\frac{\partial u}{\partial z}\right\}, \tag{117}$$

$$\frac{\partial u}{\partial x} + \frac{\partial w}{\partial z} + \frac{w}{a+z} = 0. \tag{118}$$

The first of these equations gives, with use of the boundary conditions,

$$\frac{\partial^2 u}{\partial z^2} + \frac{1}{a}\frac{\partial u}{\partial z} = 0 \quad \text{when } z = 0;$$

also, by differentiating the same equation with respect to z, and using the equation of continuity, we obtain

$$\frac{\partial^3 u}{\partial z^3} + \frac{1}{a}\frac{\partial^2 u}{\partial z^2} - \frac{1}{a^2}\frac{\partial u}{\partial z} = 0 \quad \text{when } z = 0.$$

Hence, as $z \to 0$,

$$u = A\left\{\frac{z}{a} - \frac{z^2}{2a^2} + \frac{z^3}{3a^3} + O\left(\frac{z}{a}\right)^4\right\} = A\left\{\log\left(1 + \frac{z}{a}\right) + O\left(\frac{z}{a}\right)^4\right\},$$

where A depends on x.

The profile chosen for u is proportional to $\log(1 + z/a)$. The approximation is good in the important section of the boundary layer near the surface of the cylinder, where the error, as shown, is $O(z/a)^4$. Further, as x increases, the contribution of the acceleration terms in equation

(117) (i.e. those on the left-hand side) decreases, so that the whole profile must tend to $A \log(1+z/a)$, the profile for which the acceleration
vanishes. The approximation for u is therefore

$$u = \frac{U_0}{\alpha} \log\left(1+\frac{z}{a}\right) \quad (z \leqslant \delta = a(e^\alpha-1))$$

$$= U_0 \qquad (z \geqslant \delta), \tag{119}$$

where δ is the boundary-layer thickness, to be treated primarily as a
convenient parameter. α is determined from the momentum equation,
which in this case is found to be

$$\frac{d}{dx}\left\{ \int_0^\delta \rho u(U_0-u)(a+z)\,dz \right\} = a\tau_0, \tag{120}$$

with
$$\tau_0 = \mu\left(\frac{\partial u}{\partial z}\right)_0 = \frac{\mu U_0}{a\alpha}.$$

The substitution of the expression for u, and a change of variable
$z = a(e^t-1)$ in the integral gives, on solving equation (120),

$$\frac{4\nu x}{U_0 a^2} = e^{2\alpha}+3-\frac{2}{\alpha}(e^{2\alpha}-1)+\int_0^{2\alpha}\frac{e^t-1}{t}\,dt, \tag{121}$$

since $\alpha \to 0$, as $x \to 0$ (the boundary layer is of zero thickness at the
leading edge of the cylinder).

Tables of the integral in result (121) exist, so that the variation of
$4\nu x/U_0 a^2$ with α, and hence with τ_0, can be determined numerically.
For comparison with the exact solution, however, the right-hand side
of (121) may be expanded to give, after inversion,

$$\alpha = \left(\frac{12\nu x}{U_0 a^2}\right)^{1/2} - \frac{2}{3}\left(\frac{12\nu x}{U_0 a^2}\right) + \frac{119}{180}\left(\frac{12\nu x}{U_0 a^2}\right)^{3/2} - ..., \tag{122}$$

and hence

$$\frac{a\tau_0}{\mu U_0} = \frac{1}{\alpha} = \left(\frac{12\nu x}{U_0 a^2}\right)^{-1/2} + \frac{2}{3} - \frac{13}{60}\left(\frac{12\nu x}{U_0 a^2}\right)^{1/2} + ...$$

$$= 0{\cdot}289\left(\frac{\nu x}{U_0 a^2}\right)^{-1/2} + 0{\cdot}667 - 0{\cdot}751\left(\frac{\nu x}{U_0 a^2}\right)^{1/2} + ... \tag{123}$$

The corresponding coefficients in the exact expression, from the results
of Kelly, Seban, and Bond, are $0{\cdot}332$, $0{\cdot}696$, and $-0{\cdot}797$ respectively.
Young (1939) used an approximate method based on the Blasius
velocity profile, and obtained the values $0{\cdot}332$ and $1{\cdot}328$ for the first
two coefficients; the second coefficient is almost twice as large as the
exact value.

In place of the displacement thickness δ_1, a displacement area Δ may be defined, where

$$\Delta = 2\pi \int_0^\infty \left(1 - \frac{u}{U_0}\right)(a+z)\,dz, \tag{124}$$

so that

$$\frac{\Delta}{\pi a^2} = \frac{1}{2\alpha}(e^{2\alpha}-1-2\alpha). \tag{125}$$

Hence, from result (122), for small values of α

$$\frac{\Delta}{\pi a^2} = 3\cdot46\left(\frac{\nu x}{U_0 a^2}\right)^{1/2} + 4\cdot39\left(\frac{\nu x}{U_0 a^2}\right)^{3/2} + \dots \tag{126}$$

$\Big($the exact result is

$$\frac{\Delta}{\pi a^2} = 3\cdot44\left(\frac{\nu x}{U_0 a^2}\right)^{1/2} - 0\cdot15\left(\frac{\nu x}{U_0 a^2}\right) + 3\cdot20\left(\frac{\nu x}{U_0 a^2}\right)^{3/2} + \dots\Big).$$

The frictional drag on a section of the cylinder can be derived from equation (120); thus, if D is the drag on a length x of the cylinder, measured from the leading edge,

$$D = 2\pi \int_0^\delta \rho u(U_0-u)(a+z)\,dz = \frac{\pi a^2 \rho U_0^2}{2\alpha^2}\{(\alpha-1)e^{2\alpha}+\alpha+1\}. \tag{127}$$

From the approximate solution above asymptotic expansions for τ_0, Δ, and D may be developed in inverse powers of $\log(4\nu x/U_0 a^2)$. An asymptotic solution of the basic equations (96) and (97) was also given by Glauert and Lighthill; they derived the results

$$\frac{a\tau_0}{\mu U_0} \sim \frac{2}{\beta} + \frac{2\gamma}{\beta^2} + \frac{2\gamma^2 - \frac{1}{2}\pi^2 - 4\log 2}{\beta^3} + \dots, \tag{128}$$

$$\frac{\Delta}{\pi a^2} \sim \frac{4\nu x}{U_0 a^2}\left\{\frac{1}{\beta} + \frac{1+\gamma+2\log 2}{\beta^2} + \dots\right\}, \tag{129}$$

$$\frac{D}{\pi a^2 \rho U_0^2} \sim \frac{4\nu x}{U_0 a^2}\left\{\frac{1}{\beta} + \frac{1+\gamma}{\beta^2} + \frac{2+2\gamma+\gamma^2-\frac{1}{4}\pi^2-2\log 2}{\beta^3} + \dots\right\}, \tag{130}$$

where $\beta = \log(4\nu x/U_0 a^2)$ and Euler's constant γ is $0\cdot5772$. An asymptotic expansion, in agreement with the above, was obtained independently by Stewartson (1955). In a later paper on the subject of asymptotic expansions in boundary-layer theory Stewartson (1957a) discussed the order of the error which is inherent in expansions such as those above; he attributed this to the fact that in an asymptotic solution no account is taken of one of the boundary conditions, namely the condition at $x = 0$. With this restriction, the above results will be described as 'exact'. They were used to test the corresponding expansions derived from the approximate method. In each case the first coefficients are in agreement. Further, in the case of Δ, the approximate method gives the value of the second coefficient as 3, the 'exact' value being 2·96. A partial explanation of this close agreement may rest in the fact that the form of the velocity profile near the surface of the cylinder has a greater influence on Δ than on the other quantities; the same effect is evident in the application of a Pohlhausen method to the boundary layer on a flat plate.

TABLE VIII. 3

Skin-friction τ_0, drag D, and displacement area Δ for flow along the outside of a circular cylinder

$\log_{10}(\nu x/U_0\, a^2)$	$\log_{10}(2\pi a\tau_0/\mu U_0)$	$\log_{10}(D/\rho U_0^2\, \pi a^2)$	$\log_{10}(\Delta/\pi a^2)$
$-3\cdot0$	1·85	$\bar{2}$·64	$\bar{1}$·04
$-2\cdot5$	1·61	$\bar{2}$·89	$\bar{1}$·29
$-2\cdot0$	1·39	$\bar{1}$·16	$\bar{1}$·54
$-1\cdot5$	1·19	$\bar{1}$·44	$\bar{1}$·80
$-1\cdot0$	1·00	$\bar{1}$·73	0·06
$-0\cdot5$	0·84	0·04	0·33
0·0	0·70	0·37	0·62
0·5	0·59	0·73	0·94
1·0	0·49	1·11	1·28
1·5	0·40	1·50	1·64
2·0	0·32	1·91	2·02
2·5	0·25	2·33	2·42
3·0	0·19	2·76	2·84

The satisfactory agreement of the approximate solution with the solutions valid for small and large values of x indicates its usefulness as a basis for interpolation in the region in which neither of the series solutions is valid. Since only a limited number of terms in each series is available, the extent of this region will depend on the quantity considered; for τ_0, for example, it is estimated to be $0\cdot05 < \nu x/U_0 a^2 < 100$. In this way, Glauert and Lighthill produced recommended curves for τ_0, Δ, and D (or their equivalents), and these are shown in Fig. VIII. 6, together with the curves obtained from the approximate and the series solutions. The approximate solution for Δ was considered to be sufficiently accurate to justify its acceptance, without modification, for the recommended curve. The results are shown in Table VIII. 3; the method of tabulation was chosen to make linear interpolation permissible. The tabulated values should not be in error by more than about 1 in the last place, which corresponds to a 2 per cent. error in the natural values.

The case of uniform flow parallel to the generators of a cylinder of arbitrary cross-section was considered by Cooke (1957). This is an example of a general three-dimensional boundary layer, since rotational symmetry no longer exists, but since the analysis is a direct extension of that of Seban and Bond and of Glauert and Lighthill, it is convenient to include the main results here. With the restriction that the radius

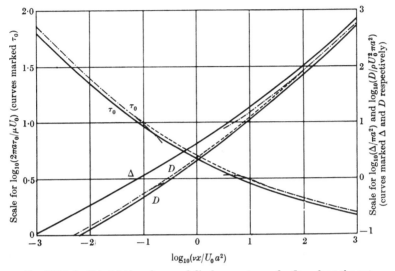

$$\log_{10}(\nu x / U_0 a^2)$$

Fig. VIII. 6. Skin-friction, drag, and displacement area for flow along the outside of a circular cylinder; solutions in series −·−·−·−, approximate solution ———, recommended interpolation between solutions in series − − − − −.

of curvature of the cross-section curve is nowhere of higher order of smallness than the boundary-layer thickness Cooke derived a set of boundary-layer equations. From these he deduced that the fluid moves in planes passing through the generators and normal to the cylinder. If θ is the angle between such a plane and a fixed plane, x the distance measured from the leading edge of the cylinder, and κ the appropriate curvature of the cross-section curve (so that κ is a function of θ only), the expression for τ, derived from a series solution, is

$$\frac{\tau}{\kappa\mu U} = 1{\cdot}328\xi^{-1} + 0{\cdot}696 - 0{\cdot}199\xi + ...,$$

where $\xi = 4\kappa(\nu x / U)^{\frac{1}{2}}$ and U is the main-stream speed. An application of the Pohlhausen method yields the result

$$\frac{\tau}{\kappa\mu U} = 1{\cdot}155\xi^{-1} + 0{\cdot}667 - 0{\cdot}188\xi - 0{\cdot}251\xi^2 + ...$$

It should be mentioned that in the above series the coefficients of the higher powers of ξ are, in general, functions of θ. Cooke's results are in agreement with previous corresponding results in this section when the surface is a circular cylinder of radius a, so that the curvature κ is constant and equal to $1/a$.

17. The rotationally symmetrical jet; decay of swirl

The approximations of boundary-layer theory are also valid in certain regions of a fluid where the special nature of the flow introduces large rates of shearing stress. This is the case in a region containing a jet of fluid, or in the wake behind an obstacle.

The flow in a jet may be considered to arise, for example, from fluid issuing under pressure from a small circular hole in a wall into a region of the same fluid which, apart from the influence of the jet, is at rest. For the purposes of this discussion, however, a detailed knowledge of the conditions prevailing near the source is not required. The motion is taken to be rotationally symmetrical, so that in the general case there is swirling as well as forward motion in the jet. Schlichting (1933a) discussed the case of a jet without swirl, and his results were extended by Loitsianskii (1953), and by Görtler (1954), to include the effect of swirl. In the former case the variation of pressure across the jet may be neglected, but this variation may not be neglected in a swirling jet.

The appropriate boundary-layer equations are derived, by use of the usual boundary-layer approximations, from the full equations of motion and continuity in cylindrical coordinates as given in Chapter III. They are:

$$u\frac{\partial u}{\partial x}+w\frac{\partial u}{\partial r} = -\frac{1}{\rho}\frac{\partial p}{\partial x}+\nu\left(\frac{\partial^2 u}{\partial r^2}+\frac{1}{r}\frac{\partial u}{\partial r}\right), \tag{131}$$

$$\frac{v^2}{r} = \frac{1}{\rho}\frac{\partial p}{\partial r}, \tag{132}$$

$$u\frac{\partial v}{\partial x}+w\frac{\partial v}{\partial r}+\frac{vw}{r} = \nu\left(\frac{\partial^2 v}{\partial r^2}+\frac{1}{r}\frac{\partial v}{\partial r}-\frac{v}{r^2}\right), \tag{133}$$

$$\frac{\partial}{\partial x}(ru)+\frac{\partial}{\partial r}(rw) = 0, \tag{134}$$

where x denotes distance measured along the axis from some point, and r denotes distance from the axis. Since the motion decays at large distances from the axis of the jet, the boundary conditions are u, $v \to 0$ as $r \to \infty$; also $w = v = 0$ when $r = 0$, and u must remain finite when $r = 0$ $(x \neq 0)$.

There are two constants, M and L, associated with the motion, where

$$M = 2\pi \int_0^\infty r(p+\rho u^2)\,dr, \qquad (135)$$

$$L = 2\pi\rho \int_0^\infty r^2 uv\,dr. \qquad (136)$$

The first of these results is derived by multiplying both sides of equation (131) by r, followed by integration with respect to r between the limits 0 and ∞, and use of the equation of continuity and the boundary conditions; it is assumed that $r\,\partial u/\partial r \to 0$ and $ruw \to 0$ as $r \to \infty$. In this result p refers to the variable part only of the pressure. Similarly, multiplication of equation (133) by r^2, followed by the same process, leads to the result (136). L depends on the degree of swirl in the motion, and is zero when there is no swirl.

The solution of the boundary-layer equations which is to be derived is an asymptotic solution. Thus, if a stream function ψ is introduced, with

$$u = \frac{1}{r}\frac{\partial\psi}{\partial r}, \qquad w = -\frac{1}{r}\frac{\partial\psi}{\partial x}, \qquad (137)$$

and non-dimensional variables ξ, η are chosen, where

$$\xi = x/l, \qquad \eta = \alpha r/x, \qquad (138)$$

the expressions assumed for ψ, v, and the pressure p, are

$$\psi = vl\xi\left\{g_0 + \frac{g_1}{\xi} + \frac{g_2}{\xi^2} + \frac{g_3}{\xi^3} + \ldots\right\}, \qquad (139)$$

$$v = \alpha^2\left(\frac{v}{l}\right)\left\{\frac{f_1}{\xi} + \frac{f_2}{\xi^2} + \frac{f_3}{\xi^3} + \ldots\right\}, \qquad (140)$$

$$\frac{p}{\rho} = \left(\frac{\alpha^2 v}{l}\right)^2\left\{\frac{h_1}{\xi} + \frac{h_2}{\xi^2} + \frac{h_3}{\xi^3} + \ldots\right\}, \qquad (141)$$

where the coefficients g_n, f_n, h_n in these series are functions of η only. The quantities l and α are not specified at this stage, but the relations (135) and (136) serve to determine them as functions of the constants L and M. With the above change of variables substitution in equations (131), (132), and (133) yields, on equating the coefficients of the various powers of ξ to zero, a set of ordinary differential equations for the functions g_n, f_n, h_n. In the same way a set of relations may be derived from relations (135) and (136); none of these results will be stated here.

Reference to the boundary conditions on u, v, and w shows that the conditions to be satisfied by the functions are

$$g_0 = g_0' = g_1' = g_2 = g_2' = \dots = 0 \left.\right\} \text{ when } \eta = 0,$$
$$f_n = 0$$
$$f_n \to 0 \quad \text{as } \eta \to \infty,$$

and also, since the pressure must be constant at infinity,

$$h_n \to 0 \quad \text{as } \eta \to \infty.$$

Using the leading term only in each of the expansions, the results for the flow in the jet are found to be:

$$u = \frac{3M}{8\pi\mu x(1+\frac{1}{4}\eta^2)^2}, \tag{142}$$

$$v = \frac{3L(3M\rho)^{1/2}}{64\pi^{3/2}\mu^2} \cdot \frac{\eta}{x^2(1+\frac{1}{4}\eta^2)^2}, \tag{143}$$

$$w = \left(\frac{3M}{\pi\rho}\right)^{1/2} \cdot \frac{\eta(1-\frac{1}{4}\eta^2)}{4x(1+\frac{1}{4}\eta^2)^2}, \tag{144}$$

$$\frac{p}{\rho} = -\frac{9L^2M}{2^{11}(\pi\mu)^3\nu} \cdot \frac{1}{x^4(1+\frac{1}{4}\eta^2)^3}, \tag{145}$$

where
$$\eta = \frac{r}{4\nu x}\left(\frac{3M}{\pi\rho}\right)^{1/2}.$$

The boundary-layer assumptions are thus seen to be valid provided $M/\rho\nu^2$ is large. The origin of x in the above results is not specified, and it depends on the initial conditions in the jet.

The whole motion in the jet decays as x increases, but the swirling motion decays more rapidly than the forward motion. Thus even though in practice some swirl may well be present near the source the main part of the jet may be practically free from swirl.

Schlichting's results for a jet without swirl are obtained by putting $L = 0$. In this case M is the constant rate at which momentum flows across a section of the jet, and the flux of mass Q across any section is given by

$$Q = 2\pi\rho \int_0^\infty ur\,dr = 8\pi\mu x. \tag{146}$$

Thus Q is independent of the flow of momentum in the jet, that is, of the pressure producing the motion at the source. If this pressure is large, the jet remains relatively narrow; if smaller, the jet broadens out more, setting more undisturbed fluid in motion.

Squire (1951, 1952) obtained a solution of the full equations of motion for the axially symmetrical jet (see Section III. 18), and showed that in the central part of the jet the flow is very similar to that deduced by Schlichting. Andrade and Tsien (1937) provided experimental confirmation of these results. They used a water-into-water jet, issuing from a cylindrical tube with a tapering approach to a circular orifice of diameter 0·91 mm. Particles of aluminium powder were introduced into the liquid, and the distribution of velocity was measured by photographing the traces made by the particles, using a measured short exposure. Measurements of velocity were thus obtained in planes at right angles to the axis of the jet, and at distances 0·8, 1·8, and 3·3 cm respectively from the orifice, for various mean velocities of flow at the orifice. The results showed excellent agreement with the theoretical values obtained from Schlichting's results. In the immediate neighbourhood of the orifice, of course, the results cannot agree since the theoretical solution is not valid in this region.

18. The axially symmetrical wake

As in the two-dimensional case, the application of boundary-layer approximations in the discussion of flow in a round wake yields a comparatively simple result. For steady uniform motion outside the wake, far downstream from the obstacle, the pressure is approximately constant everywhere. The equation of motion for flow in the wake therefore takes the form

$$u\frac{\partial u}{\partial x} + w\frac{\partial u}{\partial r} = \frac{\nu}{r}\frac{\partial}{\partial r}\left(r\frac{\partial u}{\partial r}\right), \tag{147}$$

where x is now distance measured along the axis from an origin, initially unspecified, in the vicinity of the obstacle.

If U_0 is the constant axial velocity of the undisturbed stream, then far downstream in the wake u is very nearly equal to U_0, and w is small. Hence, with the substitution

$$u = U_0 - u_1, \tag{148}$$

a first approximation to u_1 satisfies the equation

$$U_0\frac{\partial u_1}{\partial x} = \frac{\nu}{r}\frac{\partial}{\partial r}\left(r\frac{\partial u_1}{\partial r}\right). \tag{149}$$

Since the drag D on the obstacle is given by the relation

$$D = 2\pi\rho U_0 \int_0^\infty u_1 r\, dr, \tag{150}$$

which must be independent of x, a solution of equation (149) may be sought in the form

$$u_1 = Af(\eta)/x$$

with
$$\eta = (U_0/4\nu x)^{\frac{1}{2}}r \bigg\}. \tag{151}$$

The equation for f is accordingly

$$(\eta f')' + 2\eta^2 f' + 4\eta f = 0, \tag{152}$$

with boundary conditions $f \to 0$ as $\eta \to \infty$, and f' finite at $\eta = 0$. The equation can be integrated, and the solution which satisfies these conditions is $f = \exp(-\eta^2)$. Hence

$$u_1 = \frac{A}{x}\exp\left\{-\frac{U_0 r^2}{4\nu x}\right\}. \tag{153}$$

The constant A is determined in terms of the drag D by the relation (150), so that $D = 4\pi\mu A$. The above result may be compared with that given by Goldstein (1929a) who applied the Oseen approximation to the flow in a wake.

PART III

THE GENERAL THREE-DIMENSIONAL CASE

The effects associated with boundary-layer flow over a general curved surface were described in Section 1; in particular reference was made to the existence of secondary flow in the layer under certain conditions of flow in the main stream, and this can now be established as an immediate consequence of the general equations of motion of Section 2.

19. Secondary flow in a boundary layer

This effect may be illustrated by the example of a three-dimensional boundary layer arising from steady flow over a flat plate, when conditions in the main stream are such that its streamlines are curved in planes parallel to the plate. In the notation of Section 2, these streamlines may be selected as the family $x_2 = $ const of parametric curves on the plate, and their orthogonal trajectories as the second family $x_1 = $ const. The term 'streamline' in this context will be taken to refer to the main-stream flow. Thus v_1 is the component of velocity in the boundary layer in the direction of a streamline, and the secondary flow is determined by the component v_2.

If there is no secondary flow in the layer, then $v_2 = 0$ everywhere.
It follows therefore from equation (18) that

$$\frac{v_1^2}{h_1}\frac{\partial h_1}{\partial x_2} = \frac{1}{\rho}\frac{\partial p}{\partial x_2},$$

and if κ is the curvature of a streamline at any point,

$$\kappa = (h_1 h_2)^{-1}(\partial h_1/\partial x_2),$$

so that the above relation becomes

$$\kappa v_1^2 h_2 = \frac{1}{\rho}\frac{\partial p}{\partial x_2}. \tag{154}$$

Now the right-hand side of this relation is independent of x_3, as is also κ, whereas v_1 is a non-constant function of x_3 by virtue of the boundary conditions. It follows therefore that relation (154) cannot be true unless $\kappa = 0$ everywhere, in which case the streamlines are straight. Hence curvature of the streamlines in planes parallel to the plate implies the existence of secondary flow in the boundary layer.

In the case of steady flow over a curved surface, a special feature is associated with geodesic curves on the surface. L. C. Squire (1955) has shown that for streamlines which are geodesics on the surface the boundary-layer flow parallel to the surface is in the direction of the main stream. Let $x_2 = $ const be such a streamline, so that $\partial h_1/\partial x_2 = 0$ since it is a geodesic. Equations (18) and (21) then give

$$\frac{v_1}{h_1}\frac{\partial v_2}{\partial x_1}+\frac{v_2}{h_2}\frac{\partial v_2}{\partial x_2}+v_3\frac{\partial v_2}{\partial x_3}+\frac{v_1 v_2}{h_1 h_2}\frac{\partial h_2}{\partial x_1} = \nu\frac{\partial^2 v_2}{\partial x_3^2}, \tag{155}$$

since $V_2 = 0$. The boundary conditions on v_2 are $v_2 = 0$ when $x_3 = 0$ and $v_2 \to 0$ as $x_3 \to \infty$, and hence the required solution of equation (155) is $v_2 = 0$. Conversely, if v_2 and V_2 are zero on any curve, that curve must be a geodesic, for in this case equations (18) and (21) give

$$(h_1 h_2)^{-1}(V_1^2-v_1^2)(\partial h_1/\partial x_2) = 0,$$

which is true for all values of x_3. Thus, since $V_1 \neq v_1$ for all values of x_3, it follows that $\partial h_1/\partial x_2 = 0$; that is, the curve is a geodesic.

20. Parabolic flow over a flat plate

An example of secondary flow in a boundary layer, arising from curvature of streamlines in the main-stream flow, was discussed by Sowerby (1954) and by Loos (1955). The case is that of the boundary layer on a flat plate at zero incidence; the flow in the main stream is steady, and the streamlines lie in planes parallel to the plate and form a system of parabolic translates. The common axis of the system is taken parallel to the leading edge of the plate.

A system of rectangular Cartesian coordinates $Oxyz$ may be chosen, with the plate forming the half-plane $z = 0$, $x \geqslant 0$. Thus, with the

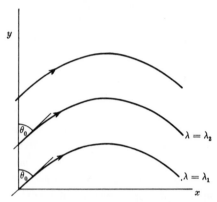

FIG. VIII. 7. Family of parabolic translates as streamlines of a curved external flow over a flat plate.

introduction of parameters as indicated in Fig. VIII. 7, the family of parabolic translates is represented by the equation

$$y = \lambda + x(\beta - \tfrac{1}{2}cx), \tag{156}$$

where
$$\beta = \cot\theta_0, \tag{157}$$

and β and c are constant for a given system of translates. Variation of the parameter λ gives different members of the family, while variation of c changes the scale of the parabolas; c may be regarded therefore as a parameter which determines the curvature of the streamlines, and in particular the streamlines are straight when $c = 0$.

The Cartesian components of the main-stream flow are

$$U = \text{constant}, \qquad V = U(\beta - cx), \tag{158}$$

so that the main-stream flow is rotational, and there is a spanwise pressure gradient. The flow everywhere is independent of y, and if u, v, w are the components of velocity in the boundary layer the equations of motion are

$$u\frac{\partial u}{\partial x} + w\frac{\partial u}{\partial z} = \nu\frac{\partial^2 u}{\partial z^2}, \tag{159}$$

$$u\frac{\partial v}{\partial x} + w\frac{\partial v}{\partial z} = -cU^2 + \nu\frac{\partial^2 v}{\partial z^2}, \tag{160}$$

$$\frac{\partial u}{\partial x} + \frac{\partial w}{\partial z} = 0, \tag{161}$$

with boundary conditions

$$u = v = w = 0 \quad \text{when } z = 0 \quad (x > 0),$$

$$u \to U, \quad v \to U(\beta - cx) \quad \text{when } z \to \infty \text{ or } x \to 0. \tag{162}$$

It is clear that the required solution of the above equations provides an extension of the Blasius solution for two-dimensional uniform flow over a flat plate (Section V. 12), since the latter is the case $\beta = 0$, $c = 0$; also the case of uniform flow across a sheared plate is obtained by taking $c = 0$. In the general case the additional term in the equations of motion is the term cU^2 in equation (160), which clearly arises from the curvature of the streamlines.

The solution is obtained by introducing Prandtl's transformation

$$\eta = \tfrac{1}{2}(U/\nu x)^{\frac{1}{2}}z, \tag{163}$$

and writing

$$u = \tfrac{1}{2}Uf'(\eta), \qquad v = U\{\beta g(\eta) - cxh(\eta)\}, \tag{164}$$

where f, g, h are functions of η only. Then all the equations of motion and boundary conditions are satisfied provided

$$w = \tfrac{1}{2}(U\nu/x)^{\frac{1}{2}}(\eta f' - f), \tag{165}$$

and f, g, h satisfy the equations

$$f''' + ff'' = 0, \tag{166}$$

$$g'' + fg' = 0, \tag{167}$$

$$h'' + fh' - 2f'h + 4 = 0, \tag{168}$$

with boundary conditions

$$f = f' = g = h = 0 \quad \text{when } \eta = 0,$$

$$f' \to 2, \quad g \to 1, \quad h \to 1 \quad \text{when } \eta \to \infty. \tag{169}$$

The required solution of equation (166) was obtained by Blasius, and the appropriate solution of equation (167) is

$$g = \tfrac{1}{2}f'. \tag{170}$$

The remaining equation (168) is linear, and was solved numerically by Sowerby with the use of Howarth's values (1938) for the coefficients f and f'. Loos has shown, however, that the solution is related to a solution of another equation given previously by Mager and Hansen (1952). The asymptotic form of (168) is of some interest, since the equation can be transformed, for large values of η, to a special case of Weber's equation. Numerical values of h and $h - \tfrac{1}{2}f'$ are given in Table VIII. 4.

The expressions for the components of velocity in the boundary layer are easily obtained. If the component along a streamline is denoted by

TABLE VIII. 4

Functions for the components of velocity in parabolic flow over a flat plate, calculated from equations (166) to (168)

η	h	$h-\tfrac{1}{2}f'$	η	h	$h-\tfrac{1}{2}f'$
0	0·0	0·0	2·1	1·0284	0·0615
0·1	0·2637	0·1973	2·2	1·0210	0·0452
0·2	0·4879	0·3552	2·3	1·0153	0·0326
0·3	0·6743	0·4754	2·4	1·0109	0·0231
0·4	0·8252	0·5604	2·5	1·0076	0·0161
0·5	0·9433	0·6135	2·6	1·0053	0·0110
0·6	1·0322	0·6384	2·7	1·0035	0·0074
0·7	1·0956	0·6393	2·8	1·0023	0·0048
0·8	1·1373	0·6205	2·9	1·0015	0·0032
0·9	1·1611	0·5864	3·0	1·0010	0·0020
1·0	1·1708	0·5410	3·1	1·0006	0·0013
1·1	1·1697	0·4884	3·2	1·0004	0·0008
1·2	1·1608	0·4318	3·3	1·0003	0·0005
1·3	1·1469	0·3744	3·4	1·0002	0·0003
1·4	1·1300	0·3185	3·5	1·0001	0·0002
1·5	1·1120	0·2659	3·6	1·0001	0·0002
1·6	1·0941	0·2180	3·7	1·0001	0·0001
1·7	1·0772	0·1755	3·8	1·0001	0·0001
1·8	1·0621	0·1387	3·9	1·0000	0·0001
1·9	1·0488	0·1077	4·0	1·0000	0·0000
2·0	1·0377	0·0821			

v_1 and the component normal to it by v_n, so that v_n is the secondary flow and is measured positive towards the centre of curvature, the results are

$$v_1 = U\{1+(\beta-cx)^2\}^{-\frac{1}{2}}\{\tfrac{1}{2}f' + (\beta-cx)(\tfrac{1}{2}\beta f' - cxh)\},\qquad (171)$$

$$v_n = Ucx\{1+(\beta-cx)^2\}^{-\frac{1}{2}}\{h - \tfrac{1}{2}f'\}.\qquad (172)$$

The third component w, normal to the plate, is given by result (165).

It is clear that the secondary flow here is always directed towards the centre of curvature of the streamlines. As an illustration of its magnitude, consider the case where $\beta = 1$ and $c > 0$. Then when $cx = 2$,

$$v_1 = V_1 h \quad \text{and} \quad v_n = V_1(h - \tfrac{1}{2}f'),$$

where V_1 is the main-stream speed for this value of cx. These two profiles are shown in Fig. VIII. 8, and it will be seen that v_1 also departs from a normal profile. It appears that v_1 attains a maximum value (when $\eta = 1\cdot0$) at about $1\cdot17V_1$, and the secondary flow v_n a maximum value (when $\eta = 0\cdot7$) at about $0\cdot64V_1$. For the same value of cx the change in direction of flow through the boundary layer is shown in Fig. VIII. 9; the changes are seen to be considerable. Further illustrations may be found in the paper by Loos.

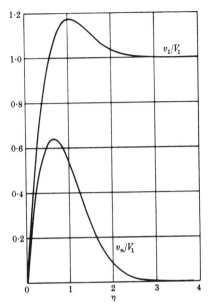

FIG. VIII. 8. Velocity components in the boundary layer on a flat plate with a parabolic main stream, for the values $\beta = 1$, $cx = 2$. The component v_n is the secondary flow in the layer.

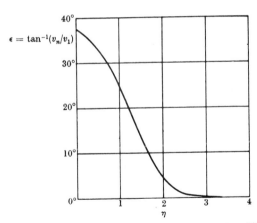

FIG. VIII. 9. Parabolic flow over a flat plate. ϵ is the deviation of the direction of flow in the boundary layer from an external streamline, for the values $\beta = 1$, $cx = 2$.

21. Flow near a stagnation point on a general curved surface

The discussion of the flow in the neighbourhood of a stagnation point on a general surface was given by Howarth (1951c). If A is a stagnation point on the surface S, it may be selected as the origin of the coordinate system, so that $x_1 = x_2 = x_3 = 0$ at the stagnation point. As usual, it is supposed that S is regular at A, and without loss of generality it may be assumed that x_1 and x_2 are so defined that $h_1 = h_2 = 1$ at A. Thus, in the vicinity of the stagnation point,

$$h_1 = 1 + \left(\frac{\partial h_1}{\partial x_1}\right)_0 x_1 + \left(\frac{\partial h_1}{\partial x_2}\right)_0 x_2, \qquad h_2 = 1 + \left(\frac{\partial h_2}{\partial x_1}\right)_0 x_1 + \left(\frac{\partial h_2}{\partial x_2}\right)_0 x_2,$$
(173)

approximately. The main-stream flow is taken to be irrotational, and hence

$$\frac{\partial}{\partial x_2}(h_1 V_1) - \frac{\partial}{\partial x_1}(h_2 V_2) = 0. \tag{174}$$

Further, both V_1 and V_2 are zero at the stagnation point; therefore, since condition (174) must be satisfied,

$$V_1 = ax_1 + bx_2, \qquad V_2 = bx_1 + cx_2, \tag{175}$$

for small values of x_1 and x_2, where a, b, c are constants of the main-stream flow.

The flow in the boundary layer will be dominated by the main-stream flow, so that the desired solution of the boundary-layer equations is an approximate solution of the first order in x_1 and x_2. For this approximation the terms in v_1^2, $v_1 v_2$, and v_2^2 in equations (17) and (18) may be neglected, while h_1 and h_2 may be replaced by unity. It is then seen that the equations of motion and the condition that the main-stream flow is irrotational are, within the approximations made, exactly the same as if the surface were plane. This implies that the coordinate system can be so chosen that $b = 0$, that is that the velocity components of the main-stream flow may be taken to be

$$V_1 = Ux_1/l, \qquad V_2 = Vx_2/l, \tag{176}$$

where U and V are constant velocities, and l is a representative length. With the above approximations, and this choice of coordinates understood, equations (17) to (21) now give for the boundary-layer equations and the equation of continuity

$$v_1 \frac{\partial v_1}{\partial x_1} + v_2 \frac{\partial v_1}{\partial x_2} + v_3 \frac{\partial v_1}{\partial x_3} = \left(\frac{U}{l}\right)^2 x_1 + \nu \frac{\partial^2 v_1}{\partial x_3^2}, \tag{177}$$

$$v_1 \frac{\partial v_2}{\partial x_1} + v_2 \frac{\partial v_2}{\partial x_2} + v_3 \frac{\partial v_2}{\partial x_3} = \left(\frac{V}{l}\right)^2 x_2 + \nu \frac{\partial^2 v_2}{\partial x_3^2}, \tag{178}$$

$$\frac{\partial v_1}{\partial x_1} + \frac{\partial v_2}{\partial x_2} + \frac{\partial v_3}{\partial x_3} = 0 \tag{179}$$

with boundary conditions

$$v_1 = v_2 = v_3 = 0 \quad \text{when} \quad x_3 = 0,$$

$$v_1 \to U(x_1/l), \quad v_2 \to V(x_2/l) \quad \text{as} \quad x_3 \to \infty. \tag{180}$$

It should be mentioned that the quantities V_1, V_2 do not in themselves satisfy the equation of continuity, but do so after due account is taken of the outflow from the boundary layer, just as in the corresponding two-dimensional problem. The solution now proceeds as an immediate extension of this standard solution; the equation of continuity is satisfied by writing

$$v_1 = (Ux_1/l)f'(\eta), \tag{181}$$

$$v_2 = (Vx_2/l)g'(\eta), \tag{182}$$

$$v_3 = -(\nu/lU)^{\frac{1}{2}}\{Uf(\eta)+Vg(\eta)\}, \tag{183}$$

where

$$\eta = (U/\nu l)^{\frac{1}{2}}x_3, \tag{184}$$

since U may be taken to be positive without loss of generality. The boundary-layer equations then become the ordinary differential equations

$$f'^2-(f+\alpha g)f'' = 1+f''', \tag{185}$$

$$g'^2-\left(g+\frac{1}{\alpha}f\right)g'' = 1+\frac{1}{\alpha}g''', \tag{186}$$

in which

$$\alpha = V/U, \tag{187}$$

with boundary conditions

$$f = g = f' = g' = 0 \quad \text{when} \quad \eta = 0,$$

$$f' \to 1, \quad g' \to 1 \quad \text{as} \quad \eta \to \infty. \tag{188}$$

At this stage reference may be made to the special cases which have previously been discussed:

(i) $\alpha = 0$, which corresponds to the two-dimensional case, equation (V.112);

(ii) $\alpha = 1$, which corresponds to the flow round a body of revolution placed symmetrically in a stream. Here $g = f$, so that

$$f'^2-2ff'' = 1+f''',$$

which is Homann's equation (equation 36).

Howarth obtained numerical solutions of equations (185) and (186) for certain positive values of α, corresponding to nodal points of attachment of the flow at the stagnation point (see Sections II. 2.6 and II. 2.7). Recently Davey (1961) gave a detailed account of solutions corresponding to saddle points of attachment, for which $\alpha < 0$. Howarth's results are given in Table VIII. 5, which includes also the results for

TABLE VIII. 5

Functions for the flow near a stagnation point in three-dimensional flow, calculated from equations (185) and (186)

	α = 0		α = ¼		α = ½		α = ¾		α = 1
η	f'	g'	f'	g'	f'	g'	f'	g'	$f'=g'$
0·0	0·000	0·000	0·000	0·000	0·000	0·000	0·000	0·000	0·000
0·1	0·118	0·057	0·120	0·079	0·122	0·097	0·124	0·113	0·126
0·2	0·227	0·114	0·230	0·156	0·233	0·190	0·238	0·218	0·242
0·3	0·325	0·171	0·330	0·230	0·335	0·277	0·342	0·315	0·349
0·4	0·415	0·228	0·420	0·301	0·428	0·359	0·436	0·405	0·445
0·5	0·495	0·284	0·502	0·369	0·511	0·435	0·521	0·488	0·532
0·6	0·566	0·339	0·574	0·434	0·585	0·506	0·596	0·562	0·609
0·7	0·630	0·393	0·639	0·496	0·650	0·572	0·663	0·630	0·677
0·8	0·686	0·446	0·696	0·554	0·708	0·631	0·722	0·690	0·736
0·9	0·735	0·498	0·746	0·608	0·758	0·686	0·772	0·742	0·787
1·0	0·778	0·547	0·789	0·658	0·802	0·734	0·816	0·789	0·830
1·1	0·815	0·594	0·826	0·704	0·839	0·777	0·852	0·828	0·865
1·2	0·847	0·639	0·858	0·746	0·870	0·815	0·883	0·862	0·896
1·3	0·874	0·681	0·884	0·784	0·896	0·848	0·909	0·891	0·920
1·4	0·897	0·720	0·907	0·817	0·918	0·877	0·929	0·914	0·940
1·5	0·916	0·756	0·926	0·847	0·936	0·901	0·946	0·934	0·955
1·6	0·932	0·789	0·941	0·873	0·951	0·921	0·959	0·949	0·967
1·7	0·946	0·819	0·954	0·896	0·962	0·938	0·970	0·962	0·975
1·8	0·957	0·846	0·964	0·915	0·971	0·952	0·978	0·971	0·983
1·9	0·966	0·870	0·972	0·932	0·979	0·963	0·984	0·979	0·988
2·0	0·973	0·891	0·979	0·946	0·984	0·972	0·988	0·984	0·992
2·1	0·979	0·910	0·984	0·957	0·988	0·979	0·992	0·989	0·995
2·2	0·984	0·926	0·988	0·966	0·992	0·984	0·994	0·992	0·997
2·3	0·988	0·939	0·991	0·974	0·994	0·988	0·996	0·994	0·998
2·4	0·991	0·951	0·993	0·980	0·996	0·991	0·997	0·996	0·999
2·5	0·993	0·961	0·995	0·985	0·997	0·994	0·998	0·997	0·999
2·6	0·995	0·969	0·996	0·988	0·998	0·996	0·998	0·998	
2·7	0·996	0·975	0·997	0·991	0·998	0·997	0·999	0·998	
2·8	0·997	0·981	0·998	0·993	0·999	0·998	0·999	0·999	
2·9	0·998	0·985	0·998	0·995	0·999	0·998	0·999	0·999	
3·0	0·998	0·988	0·999	0·997	0·999	0·999	1·000	0·999	
3·1	0·999	0·991							
3·2	0·999	0·993							
3·3	0·999	0·995							
3·4	1·000	0·996							
3·5		0·997							
3·6		0·998							
3·7		0·999							
3·8		0·999							
3·9		0·999							
4·0		1·000							
$\int_0^\infty (1-f')\,d\eta$	0·648		0·628		0·608		0·588		0·568
$\int_0^\infty (1-g')\,d\eta$	1·026		0·829		0·711		0·630		0·568

the cases $\alpha = 0$ and $\alpha = 1$. The skin-friction components τ_1 and τ_2 are given by

$$\tau_1 = \rho\nu^{1/2}(U/l)^{3/2}x_1 f''(0),$$

$$\tau_2 = \alpha\rho\nu^{1/2}(U/l)^{3/2}x_2 g''(0), \qquad (189)$$

and numerical values of $f''(0)$ and $g''(0)$ are given in Table VIII. 6. Since conditions appeared to change most rapidly when α was small, Howarth also gave expansions of f and g in series of powers of α, and numerical values may be found in the original paper.

TABLE VIII. 6

The skin friction in three-dimensional flow near a stagnation point

(*See results (189)*)

$$\tau_1 = kx_1 f''(o), \qquad \tau_2 = k\alpha x_2 g''(o)$$

α	o	$\tfrac{1}{4}$	$\tfrac{1}{2}$	$\tfrac{3}{4}$	1
$f''(o)$	1·233	1·247	1·267	1·288	1·312
$g''(o)$	0·570	0·805	0·998	1·164	1·312

For the purposes of notation, the axes Ax_1 and Ax_2 may be called, respectively, the major and minor principal axes of the main stream. The changes with α are seen to be relatively small for the velocity component in the major direction, but marked in the minor direction as shown in Fig. VIII. 10. In addition to this there are appreciable changes in the direction of the velocity vector in passing through the layer at a particular station, as a consequence of secondary flow in the boundary layer. There is a limiting direction of the flow at the surface S, which is also the direction of the resultant skin friction, and this direction is inclined to the main stream at an angle ϵ, where

$$\epsilon = \tan^{-1}\left\{\frac{g''(0)}{f''(0)}\frac{\alpha x_2}{x_1}\right\} - \tan^{-1}\left(\frac{\alpha x_2}{x_1}\right). \qquad (190)$$

The maximum values of the changes in direction are 21°, 14°, 6°, 3°, and 0° for $\alpha = 0$, $\tfrac{1}{4}$, $\tfrac{1}{2}$, $\tfrac{3}{4}$, and 1 respectively; the first four occur when $\alpha x_2/x_1$ takes the values 1·47, 1·25, 1·13, and 1·05 respectively. The values given for $\alpha = 0$ are the largest, but these are really limiting values as $\alpha \to 0$. The above results indicate, however, how quickly the immediate neighbourhood of the stagnation point is affected as soon as the main stream flow departs from the two-dimensional pattern. Another tendency which is most marked at $\alpha = 0$ is that g' approaches the main-stream value less rapidly than f'. Only in the case of flow on a body of revolution ($\alpha = 1$) are the values of

$$\int_0^\infty (1-f')\,d\eta \quad \text{and} \quad \int_0^\infty (1-g')\,d\eta$$

the same, when they are equal to 0·568; other values are shown in Table VIII. 5. These show, in the first place, the effect of divergence of the main-stream flow in thinning the boundary layer, as mentioned

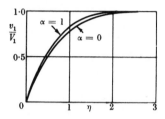

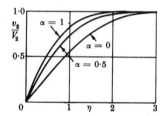

FIG. VIII. 10. Velocity components for flow near a stagnation point on a general curved surface.

previously; secondly, it is possible to introduce the artificial concept of two boundary-layer thicknesses, one associated with each principal direction. This characteristic is found in other three-dimensional boundary-layer flows, and Cooke (1951) pointed out that failure to take into account this difference in the two boundary-layer thicknesses, though it may be small, can lead to considerable differences in the results obtained by use of approximate methods.

The solution described above is, in fact, also an exact solution of the full equations of viscous motion in Cartesian coordinates, when x_1, x_2, and x_3 are replaced by the conventional Cartesian variables x, y, and z.

The above solution for flow near a stagnation point represents the first step in a solution in series of powers of the surface coordinates x_1, x_2. The labour involved in obtaining higher-order terms is considerable, since the series involved are necessarily double series, and, moreover, the process is not entirely straightforward. L. C. Squire (1955) considered this problem, and extended Howarth's solution to include the terms quadratic in x_1, x_2. The appropriate coefficients are tabulated in detail in Squire's report.

22. Flow over sheared wings and yawed cylinders

The effects due to sweepback of wings in modern aircraft have provided a practical need for study of the boundary-layer flow over yawed cylinders. For example, it is known from experience that there is a strong outflow from the boundary layer near the trailing edge on the suction side of a sweptback wing at incidence, and this outflow produces a detrimental effect on the aerodynamic properties of the wing. The physical explanation of this phenomenon is the presence of secondary flow in the boundary layer, as described in Section 1.

The inviscid flow over a yawed infinite cylinder may be determined by the superposition of two flows, one lying in planes normal to the axis, and the other parallel to the generators of the cylinder. And since the cylinder is a developable surface, the boundary-layer equations may be taken in simple 'Cartesian' form. The coordinate system used is shown in Fig. VIII. 11, in which x is distance measured along the surface in a direction perpendicular to the generators, y is distance measured parallel to the generators, and z is distance measured from the surface along a normal. All the physical quantities involved are taken to be independent of y, so that if u, v, w are the components of velocity in the boundary layer, and U, V the components in the main stream, the equations of motion and of continuity (17) to (20) reduce to

$$u\frac{\partial u}{\partial x}+w\frac{\partial u}{\partial z} = U\frac{dU}{dx}+\nu\frac{\partial^2 u}{\partial z^2}, \tag{191}$$

$$u\frac{\partial v}{\partial x}+w\frac{\partial v}{\partial z} = \nu\frac{\partial^2 v}{\partial z^2}, \tag{192}$$

$$\frac{\partial u}{\partial x}+\frac{\partial w}{\partial z} = 0, \tag{193}$$

with boundary conditions

$$u = v = w = 0 \quad \text{when } z = 0,$$
$$u \to U, \quad v \to V \quad \text{as } z \to \infty. \tag{194}$$

These equations were given implicitly by Prandtl (1946) in a paper on three-dimensional boundary layers, and were employed by him as the basis of a general method using momentum equations for the calculation of such flows. An independent treatment of the corresponding case of compressible flow was given by Struminsky (1946).

An examination of the equations shows that u and w can be calculated from equations (191) and (193) independently of the spanwise component v, and that subsequent substitution in equation (192) yields an equation for v alone. This useful feature has been called the 'independence

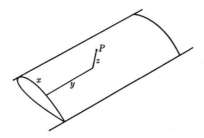

FIG. VIII. 11. The coordinates of a point P for flow over a yawed infinite cylinder.

principle' by Jones (1947). The solution for u and w is, in fact, the same as in the corresponding two-dimensional case. Further, the equation for $v(x,z)$ is identical with that for the temperature $T(x,z)$ in steady two-dimensional boundary-layer flow provided that the Prandtl number is unity and that viscous heating is neglected.

The simplest example is that of uniform flow over a yawed flat plate, so that U and V are both constant. It then follows from the equations that the solutions for u and v are related linearly, namely

$$v/u = V/U, \qquad (195)$$

so that at each point in the boundary layer the component of velocity parallel to the plate is in the direction of the main-stream flow. The boundary-layer flow, therefore, is not affected by the yaw of the leading edge of the plate. This case is the special one $c = 0$ of the flow discussed in Section 20, and was treated by Jones (1947) and, independently, by Sears (1948).

Prandtl gave the solution for flow in the vicinity of the 'stagnation line' of a yawed infinite cylinder, in which the main-stream flow is given by

$$U = U_1 x/l, \qquad V = \text{constant}, \qquad (196)$$

where U_1 is constant, and l is a representative length for the flow. It must be pointed out that this is not a special case of the flow discussed in Section 21, unless $V = 0$, in which case there is a true stagnation

line and the flow is two-dimensional. Prandtl's results may be extended
to the general case of flow over a yawed infinite cylinder; in this case
the series expansion for the main stream is

$$U = U_1(x/l) + U_3(x/l)^3 + ...,$$
$$V = \text{constant.} \tag{197}$$

The calculations were given by Schubart (1945, unpublished) and Sears
(1948), and extended by Görtler (1952b). The procedure is similar to
that used in the two-dimensional case as described in Section VI. 2.
With the introduction of the Blasius non-dimensional variable

$$\eta = (U_1/\nu l)^{\frac{1}{2}} z, \tag{198}$$

and the relations $\quad u = \dfrac{\partial \psi}{\partial z}, \quad w = -\dfrac{\partial \psi}{\partial x}, \tag{199}$

to replace equation (193), the functions ψ and v are expressed in the
form

$$\psi = \left(\frac{\nu l}{U_1}\right)^{\frac{1}{2}}\left\{U_1\left(\frac{x}{l}\right)f_1(\eta) + 4U_3\left(\frac{x}{l}\right)^3 f_3(\eta) + ...\right\}, \tag{200}$$

$$v = V\left\{g_0(\eta) + \frac{U_3}{U_1}\left(\frac{x}{l}\right)^2 g_2(\eta) + ...\right\}. \tag{201}$$

These expressions are substituted in the equations of motion and coefficients of the various powers of x are equated to zero. For the coefficients
f_n the resulting set of ordinary differential equations, and their solutions,
are those obtained in the two-dimensional case. The first two of the
equations for the coefficients g_n are

$$g_0'' + f_1 g_0' = 0, \tag{202}$$

$$g_2'' + f_1 g_2' - 2f_1' g_2 = -12 f_3 g_0', \tag{203}$$

and the boundary conditions are

$$g_0 = g_2 = ... = 0 \quad \text{when} \quad \eta = 0,$$
$$g_0 \to 1, \quad g_2, g_4, ... \to 0 \quad \text{as} \quad \eta \to \infty. \tag{204}$$

The appropriate solution of equation (202) is

$$g_0 = A \int_0^\eta \exp\left(-\int_0^\xi f_1(\zeta)\,d\zeta\right) d\xi, \tag{205}$$

where the constant A is obtained from the boundary condition at
infinity, and is found to be 0·570.

The function $g_0(\eta)$, which is the ratio v/V for the 'stagnation line'
flow of a yawed infinite cylinder, is identical with the function $g_0'(\eta)$
tabulated by Howarth (1951c), and reappears in Table VIII. 7 below

as a special case of another set of exact solutions of equations (191) to (193) given by Cooke (1950). It is plotted in Fig. VIII. 10 as v_2/V_2 for $\alpha = 0$.

Cooke considered the boundary layer for flow over an infinite yawed wedge at zero angle of attack, and thus extended the two-dimensional solution by calculating the spanwise component of velocity in the layer. In this case the main-stream flow is given by

$$U = U_m(x/l)^m, \qquad V = \text{constant.} \tag{206}$$

The solution for u is the same as in the corresponding two-dimensional case ($V = 0$), and has been given in Section V. 16. Thus the required solution of the boundary-layer equations is obtained by selecting as independent variable

$$\eta = \{(m+1)U/2\nu x\}^{\frac{1}{2}}z \tag{207}$$

and for ψ, v the expressions

$$\psi = \left(\frac{2U\nu x}{m+1}\right)^{\frac{1}{2}}f(\eta), \tag{208}$$

$$v = Vg(\eta), \tag{209}$$

so that the equations reduce to the ordinary differential equations

$$f''' + ff'' + \beta(1 - f'^2) = 0. \tag{210}$$

$$g'' + fg' = 0, \tag{211}$$

where $\qquad\qquad \beta = 2m/(m+1), \tag{212}$

with boundary conditions

$$f = f' = g = 0 \quad \text{when } \eta = 0,$$

$$f' \to 1, \quad g \to 1 \quad \text{as } \eta \to \infty. \tag{213}$$

The solution of equation (211) is obtained by quadratures as before, once f has been determined. The results are tabulated for various values of β in Table VIII. 7 and in particular the solution $g(\eta)$ for $m = 1$ (i.e. $\beta = 1$) is that given by Sears and Schubart for their $g_0(\eta)$, and by Howarth for his $g_0'(\eta)$.

The solutions described above are of considerable value in providing standards for any approximate method of solution that may be required to treat more complicated cases. An extension of the Pohlhausen method for calculating two-dimensional flows by use of the momentum equation was proposed by Wild (1949), who assumed for the profile of v a quartic expression in terms of the variable z/δ_y, where δ_y is the boundary-layer thickness associated with v (since the assumption of a finite thickness

TABLE VIII. 7

Solution of equation (211)

η	$\beta = -0.19884$	$\beta = -0.1$	$\beta = 0$	$\beta = 0.2$	$\beta = 0.6$	$\beta = 1.0$	$\beta = 1.6$	$\beta = 2.0$
	g	g	g	g	g	g	g	g
0.0	0.0000	0.0000	0.0000	0.0000	0.0000	0.0000	0.0000	0.0000
0.1	0.0326	0.0437	0.0470	0.0507	0.0547	0.0570	0.0594	0.0605
0.2	0.0652	0.0873	0.0939	0.1013	0.1093	0.1140	0.1187	0.1210
0.3	0.0977	0.1310	0.1408	0.1519	0.1638	0.1709	0.1779	0.1812
0.4	0.1303	0.1746	0.1876	0.2024	0.2182	0.2275	0.2367	0.2411
0.5	0.1629	0.2180	0.2342	0.2525	0.2721	0.2836	0.2948	0.3003
0.6	0.1954	0.2613	0.2806	0.3023	0.3254	0.3389	0.3521	0.3584
0.7	0.2280	0.3043	0.3265	0.3515	0.3778	0.3932	0.4081	0.4152
0.8	0.2605	0.3470	0.3720	0.3999	0.4292	0.4462	0.4625	0.4703
0.9	0.2929	0.3891	0.4167	0.4474	0.4792	0.4975	0.5151	0.5233
1.0	0.3253	0.4307	0.4606	0.4936	0.5276	0.5469	0.5653	0.5739
1.2	0.3896	0.5116	0.5453	0.5817	0.6184	0.6388	0.6579	0.6667
1.4	0.4533	0.5884	0.6244	0.6625	0.6998	0.7200	0.7385	0.7469
1.6	0.5157	0.6600	0.6967	0.7345	0.7704	0.7892	0.8061	0.8137
1.8	0.5765	0.7253	0.7611	0.7968	0.8295	0.8462	0.8608	0.8672
2.0	0.6350	0.7833	0.8167	0.8490	0.8773	0.8913	0.9032	0.9084
2.2	0.6906	0.8334	0.8633	0.8911	0.9145	0.9257	0.9350	0.9389
2.4	0.7424	0.8755	0.9011	0.9239	0.9424	0.9509	0.9578	0.9607
2.6	0.7899	0.9096	0.9306	0.9486	0.9625	0.9686	0.9735	0.9755
2.8	0.8324	0.9364	0.9529	0.9664	0.9764	0.9807	0.9840	0.9853
3.0	0.8695	0.9566	0.9691	0.9788	0.9857	0.9885	0.9907	0.9915
3.2	0.9011	0.9714	0.9804	0.9871	0.9916	0.9934	0.9947	0.9953
3.4	0.9270	0.9818	0.9880	0.9924	0.9953	0.9964	0.9972	0.9975
3.6	0.9478	0.9888	0.9929	0.9957	0.9974	0.9981	0.9985	0.9987
3.8	0.9638	0.9933	0.9960	0.9976	0.9986	0.9990	0.9993	0.9993
4.0	0.9756	0.9962	0.9978	0.9987	0.9993	0.9995	0.9996	0.9997
4.2	0.9842	0.9979	0.9988	0.9994	0.9997	0.9998	0.9998	0.9999
4.4	0.9901	0.9989	0.9994	0.9997	0.9998	0.9999	0.9999	0.9999
4.6	0.9940	0.9994	0.9997	0.9998	0.9999	1.0000	1.0000	1.0000
4.8	0.9965	0.9997	0.9999	0.9999	1.0000			
5.0	0.9980	0.9999	0.9999	1.0000				
5.2	0.9989	0.9999	1.0000					
5.4	0.9994	1.0000						
5.6	0.9997							
5.8	0.9999							
6.0	0.9999							
6.2	1.0000							
$g'(0)$	0.3258	0.4368	0.4696	0.5068	0.5468	0.5705	0.5939	0.6052
$\int_0^\infty (1-g)\,d\eta$	1.6694	1.2969	1.2168	1.1376	1.0646	1.0262	0.9916	0.9760
$\int_0^\infty g(1-g)\,d\eta$	0.6176	0.4968	0.4696	0.4425	0.4174	0.4042	0.3924	0.3872

for the layer does not imply that u and v attain their main-stream values for the same value of z). The boundary conditions on v determine the coefficients in the quartic, which then becomes

$$\frac{v}{V} = 2\left(\frac{z}{\delta_y}\right) - 2\left(\frac{z}{\delta_y}\right)^3 + \left(\frac{z}{\delta_y}\right)^4, \quad (0 \leqslant z \leqslant \delta_y). \tag{214}$$

The momentum equation associated with v is obtained directly from the companion equation of (25). Since V is again taken to be constant, the equation reduces to the simple form

$$\frac{d}{dx} \int_0^\infty u(V-v)\, dz = \nu\left(\frac{\partial v}{\partial z}\right)_0, \tag{215}$$

where in fact the integral is finite since $v = V$ when $z \geqslant \delta_y$. On substitution of the assumed expressions for u and v this equation becomes in effect an ordinary differential equation for the ratio δ_x/δ_y, since the solution for δ_x is already known. The equation takes one of two forms, depending on the relative magnitudes of δ_x and δ_y, but the necessity of distinguishing between the two cases does not introduce undue complication in the calculations for the solution, for which Wild used the method of isoclines.

Cooke (1951) has given a detailed discussion of the Pohlhausen method as applied to three-dimensional boundary layers, and compared results obtained by this method for flow over an infinite yawed wedge with the exact calculations which he himself had made (1950). The agreement was good for accelerated flow in the x-direction (normal to the leading edge), but Cooke found that the assumed velocity profile based on a quartic expression is not sufficiently accurate in the region of retarded flow in the main stream. This is still the case if the method is modified by using the known exact solution for u, and the Pohlhausen quartic only for v. In more general cases it is doubtful if the accuracy of the method is worth the labour involved.

In view of the limited accuracy of standard approximate methods, it is desirable to have available a simpler and more rapid approximate method of calculating the laminar boundary layer on a yawed cylinder. Rott and Crabtree (1952) proposed a method based on the use of universal profiles for u and v, and as a preliminary to their discussion it is convenient to introduce here certain momentum thicknesses and also the parameter λ previously defined in Section VI. 13. They are

$$\delta_{2x} = \int_0^\infty \frac{u}{U}\left(1 - \frac{u}{U}\right) dz, \qquad \delta_{2y} = \int_0^\infty \frac{v}{V}\left(1 - \frac{v}{V}\right) dz,$$

$$\delta_{2xy} = \int_0^\infty \frac{u}{U}\left(1 - \frac{v}{V}\right) dz, \qquad \lambda = \frac{dU}{dx}\frac{\delta_{2x}^2}{\nu}, \tag{216}$$

so that the momentum equation (215) becomes

$$\frac{d}{dx}(U\delta_{2xy}) = \frac{\nu}{V}\left(\frac{\partial v}{\partial z}\right)_0. \tag{217}$$

One of the boundary conditions to be satisfied by v is

$$(\partial^2 v/\partial z^2)_0 = 0. \tag{218}$$

Rott and Crabtree suggested the assumption of a universal spanwise profile v/V which will represent adequately any profile for v when reduced to the proper scale. The boundary condition (218) is the same as the condition on u for the two-dimensional boundary layer in uniform flow over a flat plate, when $\lambda = 0$ (the reader should henceforward refer also to Section VI. 18). On the basis of this result, and the fact that $\partial^3 v/\partial z^3$ is also zero at $z = 0$, it was decided that the universal profile should be taken to be the special case $\lambda = 0$ of the two-dimensional family of profiles $u = Uf(z/\delta_{2x}, \lambda)$, namely the Blasius profile. The assumption is thus

$$v = Vf(z/\delta_{2y}, 0). \tag{219}$$

Reference to the theory and results of Section VI. 18 gives

$$\frac{1}{V}\left(\frac{\partial v}{\partial z}\right)_0 = \frac{a}{2\delta_{2y}}, \quad \text{where } a = 0\cdot45, \tag{220}$$

so that equation (217) is now

$$\delta_{2y}\frac{d}{dx}(U\delta_{2xy}) = \tfrac{1}{2}av, \tag{221}$$

or

$$q\delta_{2x}\frac{d}{dx}(U\delta_{2x}s) = \tfrac{1}{2}av, \tag{222}$$

where

$$s = \delta_{2xy}/\delta_{2x} \quad \text{and} \quad q = \delta_{2y}/\delta_{2x}. \tag{223}$$

Since

$$s = \int_0^\infty f(z,\lambda)\{1 - f(z/q, 0)\}\,dz, \tag{224}$$

s is a universal function of λ and q; the relationship may be evaluated once the family of profiles f is specified. The quantities U, δ_{2x}, and λ are given functions of x, since the last two quantities are known from the 'chordwise' flow (normal to the leading edge), which is calculated independently of the spanwise flow. As q is a prescribed function of s and λ, equation (222) is a differential equation for s or q, that is, for δ_{2y}, or the 'scale' to which the universal profile for v must be reduced. This is the only remaining unknown after making the basic simplifying assumption of a universal profile for v.

The function $s(q, \lambda)$ was evaluated by Rott and Crabtree with use of the Pohlhausen quartic for f, and curves were drawn for a series of values of λ ranging from $+0.10$ to -0.15. These curves may be used to reduce the amount of numerical calculation involved in the determination of the spanwise flow, and were used as the basis of a general discussion in the original paper; a step-by-step procedure was described for purposes of practical calculation. However, in regions of favourable pressure gradient, for which $\lambda > 0$, the curves $s(q)$ for different values of λ lie close together, and the use of a much simpler method is possible. The approximation

$$s = q^2 \tag{225}$$

was found to represent closely the actual dependence of s on q in the domain near the stagnation point, and is in good agreement with results obtained from Cooke's exact solutions. The introduction of this approximation into the momentum equation yields, on integration,

$$s = \frac{\delta_{2xy}}{\delta_{2x}} = (U\delta_{2x})^{-1}\left\{\frac{3a\nu}{4}\int_0^x \left(\frac{U}{\delta_{2x}}\right)^{1/2} dx\right\}^{2/3} \tag{226}$$

Rott and Crabtree made use of this last result in a simple iterative method to compensate for the introduction of the additional assumption (225). The method was applied to the case of a yawed circular cylinder, and the calculated surface streamline showed good agreement with experimental surface streamline patterns obtained by use of the paraffin-lampblack technique in a wind-tunnel.

The comparative simplicity of the mathematical treatment of laminar flow over yawed cylinders arises from the 'independence principle', which is a direct consequence of the equations of motion. Both in theoretical and experimental work there is still some doubt whether the flow after the laminar separation point, and the mechanism producing transition to turbulence, are also independent of the spanwise flow, even in the absence of dynamical instability arising from secondary flow in the layer. Bursnall and Loftin (1951) made measurements of the pressure distribution about a yawed circular cylinder in the critical Reynolds number range, and confirmed as a 'rule of thumb' that the critical Reynolds number based on the velocity component perpendicular to the axis of the cylinder is independent of yaw up to an angle of 45°. A marked difference is shown in their results at 60° yaw, however, and a reduction in the critical Reynolds number was observed.

23. Swept wings

There are no theoretical methods available for the treatment of flow over swept wings of finite span, and experimental observations are rather meagre, though reference may be made to the work of Kuethe *et al.* (1949), Brebner (1951), and Emslie *et al.* (1953). However, the results obtained for laminar boundary layers on infinite sheared wings may be taken to have qualitative value when applied here. We first consider briefly the effect of the introduction of a kink at the centre section of the wing, and the effect of finite span on the potential flow pressure distribution. At zero lift the pressure distribution at any spanwise station may be represented approximately by two terms, the first of which is the pressure distribution on a sheared wing of infinite span, while the second is a distortion term which is greatest at the centre and at the tip, and is of opposite sign at these two stations. The magnitude of this distortion term decreases with distance along the span from both centre and tip, measured in terms of the wing chord, so that there will be at least one station, and possibly a finite region of the wing between centre section and tip, where conditions associated with the infinite sheared wing are very nearly realized. At the centre section the suction peak is moved back along the chord so that transition may be delayed, and at the same time the adverse pressure gradient at the rear is increased. The opposite effect is produced at the tip, where the suction peak is moved farther forward; here the possibility of laminar separation near the leading edge is enhanced, but in any case the transition point will move forward. For a wing at lift these effects are exaggerated, and the suction peak is also reduced at the centre section and made sharper at the wing tip. At intermediate sections, which are far from both centre and tip, the pressure distribution still resembles that on an infinite sheared wing.

With the introduction of effects due to viscosity, one of the most important characteristics of a three-dimensional boundary layer is the secondary flow which appears as an outflow towards the tips on a sweptback wing. Such outflows also occur in a turbulent boundary layer, and produce important changes in the characteristics of the flow, including large regions of separation on sweptback wings of high aspect ratio. The basic phenomena are present, and may be studied, in flow over an infinite sheared wing. It appears that the direction of the velocity vector changes gradually on moving into the boundary layer, and turns towards the centre of curvature of the potential flow streamlines. The angle of deflexion is a maximum at the surface where the direction of the limiting streamline, as given by the approximate method of Rott and Crabtree (1952), is

$$\frac{dy}{dx} = \frac{\tau_y}{\tau_x} = \frac{0 \cdot 225 V \delta_{2x}}{f'(0,\lambda) U \delta_{2y}} \tag{227}$$

in the notation of Section 22. The slope of the potential flow streamline is V/U, so that the maximum deflexion ϵ from the potential flow streamline is

$$\epsilon = \tan^{-1}\left(\frac{0 \cdot 225 V \delta_{2x}}{f'(0,\lambda) U \delta_{2y}}\right) - \tan^{-1}\left(\frac{V}{U}\right). \tag{228}$$

The existence of secondary flow is associated with lateral curvature of the streamlines in the main stream, and hence with a pressure gradient

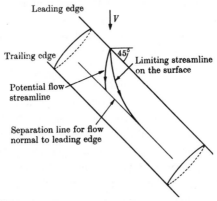

FIG. VIII. 12. Plan view of potential streamline and limiting streamline at the surface of a 6:1 elliptic cylinder at 45° angle of yaw, with lift coefficient $C_L = 0 \cdot 47$.

perpendicular to the direction of flow. In the case of uniform flow over a flat plate the streamlines are straight and there is no secondary flow. This result also follows from (228), for in this case $\lambda = 0$, and the value of $f'(0,\lambda)$ is $0 \cdot 225$. Further, $\delta_{2y} = \delta_{2x}$, and therefore $\epsilon = 0$. In other cases it appears that ϵ increases as x increases, and this increasing deflexion reaches a limit, which may not always be attained when the flow near the surface becomes purely spanwise; in this case τ_x is zero, which means that the component of flow normal to the leading edge has separated.

The outflow phenomenon is well illustrated by the calculations of Wild (1949) for an elliptic cylinder at an angle of incidence corresponding to the maximum lift coefficient of $0 \cdot 47$, and for which the two-dimensional characteristics had been calculated previously by Howarth (1935b). Fig. VIII. 12 shows the limiting streamline at the surface as calculated by Wild, and the corresponding potential streamline at the edge of the boundary layer on a projected plan view of the cylinder at 45° of yaw. A strong outflow in the boundary layer is indicated.

On a sweptback wing of finite aspect ratio two main effects modify the pattern of outflow in the boundary layer. At the centre section there can be no outflow for reasons of symmetry, but strong outflows appear at very short spanwise distances from the centre, particularly near the trailing edge. This is illustrated in Fig. VIII. 13 which was obtained from measurements of the directions indicated by tufts attached to a wing surface. These measurements do not strictly represent the direc-

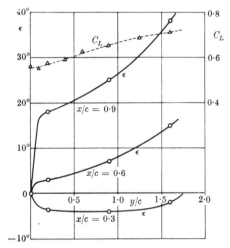

FIG. VIII. 13. The angle ϵ of deflexion of flow from the direction of the main stream, as measured near the surface of an untapered 45° sweptback wing spanning a wind-tunnel (tuft observations); C_L is the local lift coefficient. The thickness/chord ratio is 0·12, and the Reynolds number, based on the chord c, is $1·6 \times 10^6$. (For details of wing and surface pressures see Küchemann *et al.* (1951).)

tion of the limiting streamline at the surface, but some direction intermediate between that and the direction of the potential streamline at the edge of the boundary layer. Although much of the boundary layer in these experiments was turbulent, these general conclusions are equally valid for a boundary layer which is completely laminar.

The second effect arises because the spanwise loading is not normally uniform, so that even if the chordwise pressure distribution is like that on an infinite sheared wing there may be strong spanwise pressure gradients. In a case like that represented in Fig. VIII. 13, where the lift increases away from the centre section, the angle of deflexion of flow increases also, whereas on an infinite sheared wing this angle would necessarily be constant along the span. After separation the flow is practically in a spanwise direction near to the surface, but the subsequent development of the boundary layer still requires investigation. The spanwise outflow leads to considerable increase in the displacement thickness of the boundary layer (the distance by which the external potential flow is displaced from the surface), and therefore to a reduction in circulation. As a measure of this reduction, it is instructive to consider the ratio of the slope of the measured curve of lift coefficient of a section against inclination α, to the theoretical value for an inviscid flow. For a two-dimensional wing of chord c this theoretical value is

$$\frac{dC_L}{d\alpha} = 2\pi,$$

according to the theory of thin aerofoils, where the lift coefficient C_L is given by the relation

$$\tfrac{1}{2}\rho V^2 c C_L = \text{lift per unit span,}$$

and V is the speed of the incident stream. The same theory gives, for an infinite wing sheared by an angle ϕ,

$$dC_L/d\alpha = 2\pi \cos \phi$$

(see Thwaites 1959, chapter vi). In the example of the wing in Fig. VIII. 13, where the sweepback is 45°, this ratio of actual section lift slope to the theoretical slope has a limiting value of 0·92 at zero lift ($C_L = 0$) at all spanwise stations. The value decreases as C_L increases; at $C_L = 0·6$ the value is 0·87 at the centre section, 0·81 at a spanwise distance of 0·2 chords, and 0·75 at a spanwise distance of 1·6 chords. On a two-dimensional wing with a similar chordwise pressure distribution at the same Reynolds number, the ratio would have fallen from 0·92 to 0·88 over the same range of values of C_L (see Küchemann 1955).

The calculation of the defect in circulation due to the boundary layer, by extending the methods of Preston and Spence for two-dimensional flow, requires a knowledge of the displacement effect of a three-dimensional boundary layer. This has been considered by Moore (1953) and Lighthill (1958), and is discussed in Section II. 2.8. In particular it is found that the height of the displacement surface above the body surface for flow about a yawed infinite cylinder is equal to the displacement thickness of the velocity profile of the flow normal to the leading edge.

In practice it is important to have an estimate of the drag on a sweptback wing. For a boundary layer which is completely laminar the skin-friction drag may be obtained by integration of the resultant shear stress at the surface, which may be derived, for example, by the method of Rott and Crabtree. Such calculations, however, do not allow for the effects of finite span, and in any case are not valid as soon as separation occurs or the transition point is reached. Young and Booth (1951) have given a method of obtaining the profile drag of a section of a yawed infinite wing by calculation of the momentum thickness of the boundary layer at the trailing edge of the wing. This is an extension of the method of Squire and Young for two-dimensional wings, and it assumes the independence principle to hold for both laminar and turbulent boundary layers. The principles are not trivially identical in the two cases, as was shown by Rott and Crabtree in a simple calculation for a yawed flat plate. Later experimental work (Ashkenas and Riddell 1955) has shown that the turbulent boundary layer grows slightly more rapidly on a yawed flat plate than on an unyawed plate, whereas the independence principle would predict a significantly slower growth on the yawed plate, at the same Reynolds number. These investigations emphasize the importance of controlling three-dimensional effects (such as spanwise pressure gradients) in any experimental work, as pointed out by Clauser (1954).

For practical purposes it is desirable to have a rapid means of estimating the overall profile drag of sweptback wings, in which case some rather crude approximations can be made. This was done by Weber and Brebner (1952), who again assumed the independence principle for both laminar and turbulent boundary layers. For a flat plate, subject to this assumption, the result showed a reduction of drag due to sweep. If U_0 is the uniform velocity of the main stream, c the chord measured in the direction of the main stream, ϕ the angle of sweep, and the drag coefficient $C_D(R, \phi)$, where $R = U_0 c/\nu$, then there is a relationship

$$C_D(R, \phi) = C_D(R \cos^2\phi, 0)\cos\phi. \qquad (229)$$

For thick wings the component of the drag normal to the leading edge can be determined easily by the above methods. This component includes form drag as well as skin friction, whereas the component of drag parallel to the leading edge involves only skin friction. Two different approximations are available for obtaining an estimate of the latter; a lower limit will be given by the corresponding value for a flat plate at the same Reynolds number, and an upper limit may be obtained by use of the skin-friction coefficient for an unswept thick aerofoil. A comparison of the results in some typical cases shows that the values obtained from the relation (229) lie between the two approximations for the thick wing, which therefore suggests that this relation may also be used for wings of moderate thickness. This result is very convenient for rapid estimates, because known values of the drag coefficient of the unswept wing (Squire and Young 1937) can be used, and the actual thickness of the wing need not be taken specifically into account. Results arising from the use of this method show good agreement with experiment, which indicates that centre and tip effects, and possibly other errors arising from the approximations involved, cancel out. The reduction in drag due to sweep is appreciable, and in many cases compensates for the increase in drag due to earlier transition.

Another case in which it is important to know the development of the laminar boundary layer on a sweptback wing is that where separation is involved. This occurs at moderate to high lift coefficients, particularly near the tips of the wing, and leads to the formation of bubbles or large dead-air regions and the shedding of additional vortex sheets from the wing surface (Küchemann 1953; Maskell 1955). For a given inviscid flow pressure distribution, if we assume that the sectional properties of aerofoils of infinite span may be used for particular spanwise stations on a sweptback wing of finite span, then the method of Rott and Crabtree may be used to calculate the development of the laminar boundary layer up to the position of separation.

In practical cases taper of a wing, either in plan form or in thickness, produces another three-dimensional effect in the boundary layer, which again leads to secondary flow. If the taper is small, approximations can be made by use of known two-dimensional results. Mager (1954) has considered this problem and discussed some examples.

24. Rotating blades

Important practical applications of boundary-layer theory are to be found in cases of rotation about an axis perpendicular to the body, as in the cases of propeller and helicopter blades and turbo-machinery. In all these cases considerable difficulties are encountered even in calculating the potential flow, especially when the blades are working as lifting surfaces with complicated patterns of trailing vorticity. Progress in the calculation of boundary layers became possible when Sears (1950) found the solution for the potential flow over a rotating infinite cylindrical blade. The simplification introduced by this concept is similar to that in the case of the infinite sheared wing in that thickness effects are included, but there is no trailing vorticity. However, as in the case of ordinary lifting surfaces there is the possibility of applying solutions for the infinite aerofoil to sections of a surface of finite span, assuming that the main effect of trailing vorticity is to change the effective incidence at a particular section. The restriction to blades of infinite span is therefore not so serious; for example, any results should be applicable to helicopter blades, where the aspect ratio is large, for stations not too close to the centre of rotation or the tip.

The blade is assumed to be rotating with constant angular velocity Ω in fluid otherwise at rest. If a set of rectangular Cartesian axes $OXYZ$ is chosen, rotating rigidly with the blade, with OZ as the axis of rotation, OY an axis along a generator, and OX perpendicular to both, the result obtained by Sears for the potential flow is

$$U' = \Omega Y \frac{\partial \phi_1}{\partial X}, \quad V' = \Omega(\phi_1 - 2X), \quad W' = \Omega Y \frac{\partial \phi_1}{\partial Z}, \qquad (230)$$

where U', V', W' are the components referred to these axes of the velocity of the fluid *relative* to the blade, and $\phi_1(X, Z)$ is the potential for plane steady flow past the blade, when at rest in a parallel stream of unit speed. This potential is known from two-dimensional theory.

For the boundary-layer approximation the system of curvilinear coordinates used for the yawed infinite cylinder is suitable (Fig. VIII. 11), so that the motion is now referred to a system which is rotating rigidly with the blade; the coordinate y is distance measured spanwise from the axis of rotation, so that $y = Y$. The equations derived by Fogarty (1951) are appropriate only to regions far out on the blade, that is, where c/y is small, if c is the chord of the blade. On the assumption also that the surface curvature of the blade is small, and that the normal is everywhere inclined at a small angle to the axis of rotation, the boundary-layer equations are

$$u' \frac{\partial u'}{\partial x} + w' \frac{\partial u'}{\partial z} = U' \frac{\partial U'}{\partial x} + \nu \frac{\partial^2 u'}{\partial z^2}, \qquad (231)$$

$$u' \frac{\partial v'}{\partial x} + w' \frac{\partial v'}{\partial z} + 2u'\Omega = U' \frac{\partial U'}{\partial y} + \nu \frac{\partial^2 v'}{\partial z^2}, \qquad (232)$$

where u', v', w' are the components of velocity *relative* to the blade. The third equation of motion shows that the pressure is constant through the boundary layer, as usual, while the equation of continuity becomes

$$\frac{\partial u'}{\partial x} + \frac{\partial w'}{\partial z} = 0. \qquad (233)$$

In these equations the values of U', $\partial U'/\partial x$, and $\partial U'/\partial y$ are taken on the surface of the blade. If, in addition, ϕ_1 is the value of the potential on the surface of the blade, the boundary conditions are

$$u' = v' = w' = 0 \quad \text{when } z = 0,$$

$$u' \to \Omega y(\partial \phi_1/\partial x), \quad v' \to \Omega(\phi_1 - 2x), \quad \text{as } z \to \infty. \qquad (234)$$

The equations (231) and (233) exhibit the 'principle of independence as in the case of the yawed infinite cylinder in Section 22. Further, since equations (231) and (233) are the same as those for the steady two-dimensional laminar boundary layer they can be solved by any of the methods available for that case. With u' and w' thus determined, (232) becomes a linear equation for v', and may be solved separately.

Fogarty calculated the spanwise flow in the cases of a rotating flat plate and a rotating symmetrical cylinder. In the latter case a particular contour was chosen, for which

$$U' = \beta y \Omega \{(x/c) - (x/c)^3\}, \tag{235}$$

where β is a parameter related to the thickness of the blade. In both these cases the two-dimensional boundary-layer solutions are known, and equation (232) was used to determine v'. In view of the importance of secondary flow in a boundary layer, the results for the flat plate are shown in Fig. VIII. 14, where for convenience the velocity relative to the plate is given in terms of the radial component v'_r and the tangential component v'_θ (for components parallel to the plate) in a system of cylindrical polar coordinates. Thus v'_r is the secondary flow in the boundary layer, and since the theory applies only to stations remote from the axis of rotation the approximations

$$v'_r = v' + (x/y)u', \qquad v'_\theta = u' \tag{236}$$

can be made. These approximations depend also on the result that the ratio v'/u' is $O(x/y)$. The direction of the skin-friction at any point on the plate is given by

$$\tan \alpha = \left(\frac{\partial v'}{\partial z} \Big/ \frac{\partial u'}{\partial z}\right)_0,$$

where α is the angle between this direction and the x-axis; this yields the approximation

$$\alpha = 2x/y, \tag{237}$$

so that α is small by virtue of the basic assumption that c/y is small.

There are no extensive experimental investigations available by which these results might be checked, but the work of Himmelskamp (1950) provides some means of comparison. The experimental velocity profiles exhibit the same characteristics as those in Fig. VIII. 14 and, unless separation of the flow occurs, the outflow angles are small. It would appear in general that the secondary flow in the boundary layer presents a more serious problem on swept wings than it does on rotating blades.

The solutions given by Fogarty are of the first order in x/y, and Tan (1953) has shown how solutions of higher order may be obtained. The boundary-layer equations (231) to (233) have also been used in a thesis discussion by Smith (1952) of a number of examples in which he considered a series of velocity profiles of the type treated by Falkner and

Skan. For an arbitrary cylinder an application of the Kármán–Pohlhausen method can be made, following Wild's calculations for the yawed wing (Section 22), but the resulting differential equation contains a large number of terms and the calculation becomes very laborious.

However, Graham (1954) has given a method for the solution of such cases by the use of Smith's results and the application of the simplified procedure used previously by Rott and Crabtree in the case of yawed cylinders, so that a practical method is available for the routine calculation of boundary layers on rotating blades.

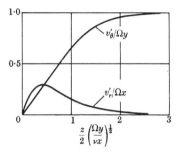

Fig. VIII. 14. Radial and tangential components of velocity
in the boundary layer on a rotating flat plate.

There are two other papers which must be mentioned briefly in conclusion. Burgers (1941) derived boundary-layer equations appropriate to flow in rotating pumps, and discussed certain features of the flow. Mager (1951) obtained boundary-layer equations for an orthogonal curvilinear coordinate system which rotates with uniform angular velocity about an arbitrary axis, and derived from them the momentum-integral equations. Subsequent development in Mager's work is restricted to turbulent boundary layers.

25. Flow along corners and edges

This part of the chapter is intended to give a brief account of certain important types of three-dimensional boundary-layer flow which, for reasons of mathematical difficulty, have received, as yet, comparatively little successful treatment. The flow over surfaces which possess geometrical singularities, such as corners and edges, cannot be treated on the basis of the boundary-layer equations derived in Section 2, though suitable equations can be obtained to describe the flow in such regions.

The first attempt to investigate a boundary-region flow is due to Carrier (1946), who considered the extension of the well-known method of Blasius (Section V. 12) to the case of uniform flow along a right-angled corner formed by the intersection of two flat plates. Thus, in a suitable system of rectangular Cartesian coordinates $Oxyz$ the two plates form the portions of the planes $y = 0$, $x \geqslant 0$, and $z = 0$, $x \geqslant 0$, respectively, so that the corner is the axis $y = z = 0$. The main stream is uniform, with velocity U parallel to this axis. On either plate, at distances sufficiently remote from the corner, it may be expected that the boundary-layer flow will not differ appreciably from the two-dimensional flow over a flat plate. Accordingly, it is natural to seek a solution of the type required by starting from the full equations of motion and using Prandtl's transformation of coordinates. Thus, if u, v, w are the components of velocity in the boundary layer, and new variables

$$X = \left(\frac{\nu}{Ux}\right)^{\frac{1}{2}}, \qquad \xi = y\left(\frac{U}{\nu x}\right)^{\frac{1}{2}}, \qquad \eta = z\left(\frac{U}{\nu x}\right)^{\frac{1}{2}} \tag{238}$$

are selected, the following expansions for the velocity distribution and the pressure are assumed:

$$u = U(f_0 + Xf_1 + X^2f_2 + ...), \tag{239}$$

$$v = U(Xg_1 + X^2g_2 + ...), \tag{240}$$

$$w = U(Xh_1 + X^2h_2 + ...), \tag{241}$$

$$p = \rho U^2(p_0 + Xp_1 + X^2p_2 + ...), \tag{242}$$

where f_n, g_n, h_n, and p_n are functions of ξ and η only. Substitution of these expressions in equations (1) and (2), and the equating of coefficients of X^n to zero in the various equations leads to the following equations for the leading terms in the series:

$$-\tfrac{1}{2}f_0\left(\xi\frac{\partial f_0}{\partial \xi} + \eta\frac{\partial f_0}{\partial \eta}\right) + g_1\frac{\partial f_0}{\partial \xi} + h_1\frac{\partial f_0}{\partial \eta} = \frac{\partial^2 f_0}{\partial \xi^2} + \frac{\partial^2 f_0}{\partial \eta^2}, \tag{243}$$

$$-\tfrac{1}{2}f_0\left(g_1 + \xi\frac{\partial g_1}{\partial \xi} + \eta\frac{\partial g_1}{\partial \eta}\right) + g_1\frac{\partial g_1}{\partial \xi} + h_1\frac{\partial g_1}{\partial \eta} = -\frac{\partial p_2}{\partial \xi} + \frac{\partial^2 g_1}{\partial \xi^2} + \frac{\partial^2 g_1}{\partial \eta^2}, \tag{244}$$

$$-\tfrac{1}{2}f_0\left(h_1 + \xi\frac{\partial h_1}{\partial \xi} + \eta\frac{\partial h_1}{\partial \eta}\right) + g_1\frac{\partial h_1}{\partial \xi} + h_1\frac{\partial h_1}{\partial \eta} = -\frac{\partial p_2}{\partial \eta} + \frac{\partial^2 h_1}{\partial \xi^2} + \frac{\partial^2 h_1}{\partial \eta^2}, \tag{245}$$

$$-\tfrac{1}{2}\left(\xi\frac{\partial f_0}{\partial \xi} + \eta\frac{\partial f_0}{\partial \eta}\right) + \frac{\partial g_1}{\partial \xi} + \frac{\partial h_1}{\partial \eta} = 0, \tag{246}$$

$$\frac{\partial p_0}{\partial \xi} = \frac{\partial p_0}{\partial \eta} = \frac{\partial p_1}{\partial \xi} = \frac{\partial p_1}{\partial \eta} = 0. \tag{247}$$

Equations (243) to (246) are the required boundary-layer equations for the type of flow under discussion. Reference to the expressions for u, v, and w shows that the solution of these equations yields a first-order approximation to the flow provided that ν/Ux is small—that is, as in the two-dimensional case, the solution is valid at sufficiently 'large' distances from the leading edges of the plates, though in practice the excluded region may indeed be quite small. The essential boundary conditions on the functions are

$$f_0 = g_1 = h_1 = 0 \quad \text{when} \quad \xi = 0 \quad \text{or} \quad \eta = 0,$$

$$\lim_{\xi, \eta \to \infty} f_0 = 1. \tag{248}$$

The complicated nature of these equations is at once apparent. They are elliptic type partial differential equations, whereas the equations associated with all cases of boundary-sheet flow are of parabolic type; moreover, no less than four basic equations are required to describe the flow. For the purposes of solution it is true that these equations can be reduced in number to two, since with the introduction of new dependent variables $q(\xi, \eta)$ and $\psi(\xi, \eta)$ the equation of continuity (246) may be replaced by the general expressions

$$f_0 = \frac{\partial^2 q}{\partial \xi \partial \eta}, \qquad g_1 = \tfrac{1}{2}\left(\xi \frac{\partial^2 q}{\partial \xi \partial \eta} - \frac{\partial q}{\partial \eta}\right) + \frac{\partial \psi}{\partial \eta}, \qquad h_1 = \tfrac{1}{2}\left(\eta \frac{\partial^2 q}{\partial \xi \partial \eta} - \frac{\partial q}{\partial \xi}\right) - \frac{\partial \psi}{\partial \xi}.$$

$$\tag{249}$$

With these substitutions the two required equations are now equation (243) and the equation obtained by eliminating p_2 between equations (244) and (245). The complexity of the resulting equations may be compared with the simplicity of equation (V. 85) which determines the corresponding boundary-layer flow over a flat plate.

Carrier attempted to obtain a solution by the method of relaxation, but his results were in error in that he omitted the terms in ψ from his solution of equation (246) and took no account of equations (244) and (245). Sears (1954 b) and Moore (1956) have reported that the necessary corrections were later made by Carrier and Dowdall (to be published), and that the errors in the original solution were found, in fact, to be quite small.

This example of steady flow along a corner has been given in some detail to illustrate the complexity of the boundary-layer equations associated with boundary-region flows. The use of relaxation methods in the solution may be suitable in certain cases, but in others difficulties may arise owing to the presence of singularities; in the case of flow along a sharp edge, for example, such evidence as there is suggests that there is a singularity in the skin friction on the edge itself (though the drag on any *finite* portion of the plate remains finite). For these reasons, it is worth while to seek also for qualitative information where possible, and a fruitful source of such information is obtained by the use of

Rayleigh's hypothesis (see Section III. 14) applied to certain of the problems of impulsive flow of Chapter VII.

Consider, for example, the motion set up in a region of fluid which is bounded by two semi-infinite flat plates intersecting at an angle β, when both plates are set in motion suddenly from rest with uniform velocity U parallel to their line of intersection. This was discussed in Section VII. 5; it was shown that a solution of the hydrodynamical equations exists in which the velocity u' of the fluid is everywhere parallel to the line of intersection of the planes, and that u' satisfies the two-dimensional form of the equation of heat conduction (VII. 29) subject to certain boundary conditions (VII. 30). The motion of the fluid, of course, depends on the space coordinates and on the time t. There is a related steady-flow problem, in which a uniform stream U impinges at zero incidence on the straight leading edges of two flat plates intersecting at an angle β, the line of intersection being perpendicular to each of the leading edges. Rayleigh's hypothesis suggests that qualitative information about this case of steady flow can be obtained by replacing the time t by the variable x/U, and u' by $U-u$ in the results for the impulsive motion problem, where x is distance measured downstream from a leading edge, and u is the component of velocity parallel to the axis. The usefulness of this hypothesis was demonstrated by Howarth (1950), who applied it in his discussion of flow along a semi-infinite plate (the case $\beta = 2\pi$).

The case of flow along a right-angled corner will serve as a convenient example. For the impulsive motion problem there is the comparatively simple result (VII. 32),

$$\frac{u'}{U} = 1 - \mathrm{erf}\left(\frac{y}{2(\nu t)^{\frac{1}{2}}}\right)\mathrm{erf}\left(\frac{z}{2(\nu t)^{\frac{1}{2}}}\right), \tag{250}$$

where
$$\mathrm{erf}\,\xi = (2/\sqrt{\pi}) \int_0^\xi \exp(-s^2)\,ds.$$

Hence, by use of the hypothesis, the result for the related steady-flow problem is
$$u = U\,\mathrm{erf}\,Y\,\mathrm{erf}\,Z, \tag{251}$$
with
$$Y = \tfrac{1}{2}y(U/\nu x)^{\frac{1}{2}}, \qquad Z = \tfrac{1}{2}z(U/\nu x)^{\frac{1}{2}}.$$

The function $\mathrm{erf}\,\xi$ increases steadily from zero, when $\xi = 0$, and tends to the value 1 as ξ tends to infinity; the value is 0·995 when $\xi = 2$. Thus the indications are that for practical purposes the effect of the corner is confined to the region $0 \leqslant Y \leqslant 2$, $0 \leqslant Z \leqslant 2$, and that outside this region the boundary-layer flow on either plate will differ but little from the flow over a flat plate. The skin friction τ on the plate $z = 0$ is given by

$$\tau = \mu\left(\frac{\partial u}{\partial z}\right)_0 = \mu U\left(\frac{U}{\pi\nu x}\right)^{\frac{1}{2}} \operatorname{erf} Y. \qquad (252)$$

Hence, in the corner itself ($y = z = 0$) the skin-friction is zero, and as $Y \to \infty$, $\tau \to \mu(U^3/\pi\nu x)^{\frac{1}{2}}$, which is the result for the skin-friction on a flat plate as derived from Rayleigh's hypothesis. Comparison with the true value (V. 88) shows that the *form* of this result is correct, but that the Rayleigh value is too large. Cooke (Sowerby and Cooke 1953), in an attempt to provide a better approximation, has suggested a modified form of the hypothesis, based on a comparison between the steady flow along a circular cylinder (Section 16) and the flow set up by the impulsive motion of an infinite circular cylinder in the direction of its axis.

In the case where the plates intersect at a general angle β it is convenient to use cylindrical polar coordinates (r, θ, x), where r is distance measured from the line of intersection. The expected behaviour of the skin friction τ may be deduced from the results of Sowerby and Cooke (1953), so that, for small values of $r(U/\nu x)^{\frac{1}{2}}$,

$$\tau \simeq \frac{2\mu U}{\beta}\left(\frac{U}{\nu x}\right)^{\frac{1}{2}} \frac{\Gamma((\pi/2\beta)+1)}{\Gamma((\pi/\beta)+1)}\left(\frac{r^2 U}{4\nu x}\right)^{\frac{1}{2}(\pi/\beta)-\frac{1}{2}}. \qquad (253)$$

Thus if $\beta < \pi$, $\tau \to 0$ as $r \to 0$, but if $\beta > \pi$, τ is not bounded near $r = 0$. It is not difficult to show also that τ tends in all cases to the (Rayleigh) flat-plate value away from the line of intersection of the plates. The value of $r(U/\nu x)^{\frac{1}{2}}$ at which a 1 per cent. difference, say, is attained varies with β, and decreases as β increases. In this connexion it is interesting to consider the effect on the frictional drag when a flat plate is bent. For flow on both sides of the plate, it is clear from the above results that the bending will produce a decrease in drag on one side ($\beta < \pi$), but an increase on the other side ($\beta > \pi$). The total effect may be estimated (see, for example, Fig. VII. 1). The case of a right-angled bend again provides a convenient example; the calculations show that for a section of plate containing a right-angled bend, of unit length, and of width sufficient to ensure that the skin friction settles down to its flat-plate value on either side of the bend, the frictional drag is in defect of the corresponding drag on a flat plate by a quantity $0.6712\mu U$.

It must be emphasized that these results are not exact, since they are based on Rayleigh's hypothesis, but they serve to provide information of qualitative value in the absence of exact results. For further results concerning flow along corners and edges reference may be made to papers by Howarth (1950), Sowerby (1951), Hasimoto (1951, 1954), Sowerby and Cooke (1953), and Batchelor (1954a). The application also of the Pohlhausen approximate method has been considered by Loitsianskii and Bolshakov (1951).

26. Flow separation in three dimensions

While the phenomenon of separation in two-dimensional flow is fairly well understood, the situation in three dimensions is much more complicated and far from clear. The position has also been obscured by the habit of thinking in terms of the two-dimensional concept of separation, which is no longer useful. Since the usual boundary-layer theory breaks down as soon as separation occurs, the main purpose of this section is to indicate this limitation of the boundary-layer theory by describing the types of flow near three-dimensional separation lines, but without discussing the details of the flow beyond separation, where very little is as yet known.

Chapter II (Sections 2.6 and 2.7) considers the mechanism of attachment and separation in three dimensions. Here we discuss in some more detail two basic forms of structure of the viscous region when flow separation has occurred, each characterized by a particular form of surface flow pattern. These basic components are free shear (or vortex) layers and bubbles. The discussion is based on the work of Maskell (1955) who studied the significance of separation in the flow as a whole without using boundary-layer concepts.

These two typical cases of separation from a general curved surface are illustrated in Fig. VIII. 15, where the possible extent of the viscous region is also indicated, external to which the flow may be considered as predominantly inviscid. Fig. VIII. 15 (a) represents the case where a 'bubble' is formed whereas Fig. VIII. 15 (b) represents the formation of a free shear layer. In the first case the surface of separation encloses fluid which is not part of the main stream but is carried along with the body; in the second case the space outside the body on either side of the surface of separation is filled wholly by main-stream fluid. The limiting streamlines in the surface are indicated, and also how they join the separation line and form the surface of separation. The bubble formation requires the existence of one singular point S (a saddle point in the terminology of Chapter II), where the behaviour of the flow is the same as near a separation point in two-dimensional flow. All other points along the lines of separation in Fig. VIII. 15 are ordinary separation points as defined by Maskell. This explains why concepts based on two-dimensional flow, where separation lines must be normal to the main stream and composed of singular points, are of little use in the discussion of flow separation in three dimensions.

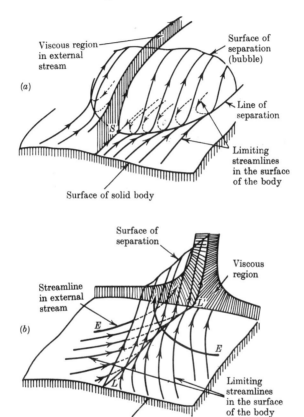

FIG. VIII. 15. Separation effects in three dimensions. (a) Separation with an isolated singular point S. (b) Separation from a line LL′ of ordinary points.

The examples in Fig. VIII. 15 also serve to show that while the concepts of boundary-layer theory may be applicable upstream of and away from the separation line on the body, they are clearly not adequate in the neighbourhood of the separation line. The viscous region around the surface of separation does not necessarily possess the properties of a boundary layer either. The shear layer in Fig. VIII. 15 (b) may be thought of as a vortex sheet in its effects on the main stream; but in the case of Fig. VIII. 15 (a) viscous eddies must arise inside the closed bubble and form an essential part of the flow.

In cases similar to that in Fig. VIII. 15 (b), the flow direction may be reversed and the attachment of a flow to a solid surface thus obtained. The extent of the viscous region then differs from that in Fig. VIII. 15 (b) and this, again, has not yet been treated except in the special cases of one singular attachment point or an attachment line normal to the main stream and composed of singular attachment points.

In practice, a combination of the two types of flow with a bubble and with a free shear layer is the most likely result of flow separation in general. Maskell showed how each type of flow is characterized by a particular form of surface flow pattern and demonstrated how this approach can simplify greatly the construction of three-dimensional skeletons of complex flow patterns. A number of examples were considered in the original paper and also in Chapter II.

It is not possible in general to predict even the qualitative nature of the flow about any given body. The present approach can provide only an unlimited sequence of possible patterns and only in a very few restricted and simplified cases is it possible to calculate the flow pattern including the effects of separation. Even then empirical relations are needed, as in the calculation of two-dimensional bubble flows on thin aerofoils (see Crabtree 1957).

A few cases may be mentioned where two-dimensional concepts can be partly retained, but then only up to the separation line. Sears (1948, 1955) and Jones (1947) both discussed the 'component separation' on a yawed infinite wing, for instance, and pointed out that this is defined by vanishing surface shear in the direction of the chordwise flow, that is normal to the leading edge. This is a simple extension of the definition of separation in plane flow, namely the vanishing of the wall shear stress; in a general three-dimensional case, however, it is difficult to know what component of the shear stress is to be considered. This was pointed out by Hayes (1951) who suggested assessing the validity of the boundary-layer assumptions as a criterion of separation. Moore (1956) showed that this is not altogether satisfactory in the case of a yawed cone in supersonic flow. He suggested instead that in general separation may be identified by the existence of a bubble of fluid in the boundary layer which does not exchange fluid with its surroundings. This can only be a part of the story though, as we have already seen.

Squire (1954) studied the development of separation on an ellipsoid during acceleration from rest. He compared the results of applying two definitions of separation, one the vanishing of the skin-friction in the external streamline direction, and the other Hayes's suggestion that regions of separated and unseparated flow must be separated by a limiting surface streamline or skin-friction line. The comparison was not completely conclusive, however.

Eichelbrenner and Oudart (1954, 1955) considered the case of a slender body of revolution at a small angle of attack. The boundary-layer development was calculated by a modified Pohlhausen method, and a comparison with flow visualization tests in a water-tunnel showed that the location of the separation line could be fairly accurately predicted.

Note added in 1966 *reprint*

Attention is drawn to a recent review of the subject by J. C. Cooke and M. G. Hall, 'Boundary layers in three dimensions', *Prog. in Aeron. Sci.* **2**, 221–82, 1962 (Pergamon Press).

IX

HYDRODYNAMIC STABILITY

1. Introduction

THE earlier chapters of this book have been concerned with the many possible types of laminar flow which, to varying degrees of approximation, are solutions of the Navier–Stokes equations. In view of the observed fact that a turbulent form of motion is often more likely to occur than the appropriate laminar form, the question of the relative stability of the two types of flow naturally arises. It has been observed experimentally that laminar flow occurs at low Reynolds numbers and that in this range viscosity damps out any deviations from laminar flow. Clearly, at such Reynolds numbers, this type of flow is more stable than the turbulent form. On the other hand, at high Reynolds numbers turbulent motion occurs, apparently naturally, and laminar flow can be realized, if at all, only by excluding *all* possible disturbances, however small. At such Reynolds numbers, therefore, turbulent flow appears to be the more stable form.

From the above remarks it seems that laminar flow poses a problem of stability and that, in a statistical sense possibly, turbulent flow does also. Up to the present time, attention has largely been focused on the former problem, and it is with this that we shall be concerned in the present chapter. Because of the mathematical simplifications associated with linearization, and because linearized theory is able to give the critical conditions for the occurrence of instability for infinitesimal disturbances, the stability theory has largely been developed with this restriction. However, the role of non-linearity in flow instability has received some study and will be discussed in the last section of the chapter. A final point of general significance is that although the laminar-stability theory has been developed almost exclusively for *steady* flow, its application to unsteady flow, under suitable conditions of unsteadiness, is not precluded.

The mathematical problem of hydrodynamic stability can be formulated by taking the given steady-state solution of the equations of motion and superimposing a disturbance of a suitable kind; this results in a set of (non-linear) 'disturbance' equations, which govern the behaviour of the disturbance. If the disturbance *ultimately* decays to zero, the flow is said to be stable, but if a disturbance results which is permanently different from zero, the flow is said to be unstable. It does not follow that instability leads to turbulent motion, because another, probably more complex, form of laminar motion may be the result. Indeed, this is often found to be the case.

When the 'disturbance differential equations' are linearized for small disturbances, they become homogeneous and it is possible to consider disturbances which contain an exponential time factor of the form $e^{\sigma t}$, t being the time. The boundary conditions on the disturbance equations require the *vanishing* at the boundaries of quantities like the disturbance velocity components. Consequently the boundary conditions also are homogeneous, and we have an eigenvalue problem for the determination of the quantity σ. If it is possible for σ to have a positive real part, the flow is said to be unstable according to linearized theory; otherwise the flow is stable. The possible eigenvalues of σ depend, of course, on quantities such as flow speed, kinematic viscosity, thermal diffusivity, and disturbance wavelength.

There are three basic types of instability which will be considered in succeeding sections of this chapter. They are:

(i) The instability of curved flows due to centrifugal forces, exemplified by the flow between concentric rotating cylinders.

(ii) Thermal instability, such as that due to gravity acting on a horizontal layer of fluid which is heated from below.

(iii) The instability of two-dimensional parallel flows, as illustrated by Poiseuille flow between parallel planes, in which viscosity itself may play a destabilizing role.

In each of these cases instability occurs when a certain parameter, representing the ratio of destabilizing to stabilizing forces, reaches a critical value. In case (iii), for example, the parameter is the Reynolds number. The three basic types of instability will be treated in Sections 2, 3, and 4, and the meanings and importance of the parameters governing the instabilities will be established there. In Sections 5, 6, and 7 the theory of case (iii) will be extended to other problems, including two-dimensional and three-dimensional boundary-layer flows and flows such as those in jets and wakes. Comparisons with experiment will be made whenever possible. 'Finite-amplitude' effects will be discussed in Section 8.

In discussions of the mechanics of instability the concept of the Reynolds stress is almost indispensable; a treatment of Reynolds stresses has therefore been given in some detail and can be found in the Appendix to this chapter.

Since the present book is limited to a treatment of viscous incompressible flow, considerations of the instability of compressible boundary layers are not included in this chapter except as isolated references. For a discussion of the effects of compressibility the reader is referred to the book by Lin (1955) and, in particular, to papers by Lees and Lin (1946), Lees (1947), Gazley (1953), and Dunn and Lin (1955).

2. Centrifugal instability

The phenomenon of instability in rotating fluids was first considered by Lord Rayleigh (1916b) who, by neglecting viscosity, derived a simple condition for the occurrence of instability with respect to rotationally symmetric disturbances. (In this chapter, as in other chapters, the terms 'rotational symmetry' and 'axial symmetry' are defined, after Synge (1938b) and in the notation of Section III. 12, as follows: A motion will be said to possess *rotational* symmetry if the body forces possess a potential independent of θ, and if v_r, v_θ, v_z, and p are independent of θ; *axial* symmetry is a particular case of rotational symmetry, with the additional condition $v_\theta = 0$.) Rayleigh's criterion is that, if the square of the circulation increases outwards, the flow is stable, whereas if the square of the circulation decreases outwards, the flow is unstable. This result was obtained by Rayleigh from energy considerations. An explanation of the result, in terms of centrifugal force and pressure gradient, was given by Kármán (1934). Let r denote the distance from the axis, p the pressure, and ρ the density, and let us suppose that the rotational velocity in the fluid is v, which is a known function of r. (As a particular case, we may consider a fluid confined between two concentric rotating cylinders of infinite length.) Since the fluid elements are moving in circular paths, a centripetal force, of magnitude $\rho v^2/r$ per unit volume, is required for steady motion, and this is supplied by the pressure gradient $(-dp/dr)$. Consider now a fluid element of velocity v_1 at radius r_1, and suppose that the element is displaced to a radius r_2 which is greater than r_1. Since the angular momentum of the fluid element will remain unchanged, its new velocity will be $r_1 v_1/r_2$. If the element were to be in equilibrium at its new radius, it would require a centripetal force $\rho r_1^2 v_1^2/r_2^3$. However, the pressure gradient at radius r_2 supplies an inward force of magnitude $\rho v_2^2/r_2$, where v_2 is the velocity at radius r_2, and this force is not, in general, equal to the centripetal force required for the newly arrived fluid element. Consequently, if $\rho v_2^2/r_2 > \rho r_1^2 v_1^2/r_2^3$ the fluid element will be forced back to its original position, whereas if $\rho v_2^2/r_2 < \rho r_1^2 v_1^2/r_2^3$ it will tend to move even farther away. Therefore the flow is stable if $(r_2 v_2)^2 > (r_1 v_1)^2$, and unstable if $(r_2 v_2)^2 < (r_1 v_1)^2$. Since, apart from a constant multiplier, rv is the circulation, this is Rayleigh's criterion. For a mathematical derivation of this result from the inviscid equations of motion, the reader is referred to a paper by Synge (1933) or to the book by Lin (1955).

Rayleigh's criterion can be applied to the case of viscous flow between concentric rotating cylinders, provided we suppose that viscosity serves to maintain the steady flow but does not affect the occurrence of instability. Let Ω_1 and Ω_2 denote the respective angular velocities of the inner and outer cylinders, and r_1 and r_2 the respective radii. Then, if the cylinders rotate in the same direction, the flow is unstable if $\Omega_1 r_1^2 > \Omega_2 r_2^2$. In particular, the flow is unstable if the inner cylinder rotates and the outer is at rest, and stable if the outer cylinder rotates and the inner is at rest. If the cylinders rotate in opposite directions, however, the circulation decreases outwards in at least part of the field of flow, and the flow is unstable. In a real fluid, viscosity affects the disturbance and stabilizes the flow up to a definite rotational speed. The theory of instability of flow between rotating cylinders, including effects of viscosity, is given in Section 2.1.

Centrifugal instability may occur also in the boundary layer on a concave surface, in the flow near the forward stagnation point of a body, and in the flow in a two-dimensional curved channel. Details of the instability theories, and some results for these cases, will be given in Sections 2.2 and 2.3. For a discussion of the effect of a magnetic field on centrifugal instability the reader is referred to papers by Chandrasekhar (1953b), Michael (1954), and Niblett (1958).

2.1. *The instability of flow between rotating cylinders*

(a) *General considerations*

Let us consider the viscous flow between two concentric, rotating cylinders of infinite length. Let r, θ, z be cylindrical polar coordinates and v_r, v_θ, v_z the corresponding components of velocity. Then, with the remainder of the notation as in Section III. 12, the Navier–Stokes and continuity equations are given by equations (III. 46) and (III. 49). If the inner cylinder has angular velocity Ω_1 and radius r_1, and the outer cylinder has angular velocity Ω_2 and radius r_2, the steady motion is given by

$$v_\theta = \bar{v} = Ar + \frac{B}{r}; \qquad v_r = v_z = 0; \qquad \frac{dp}{dr} = \frac{d\bar{p}}{dr} = \rho\frac{\bar{v}^2}{r};$$

where

$$A = \Omega_1(1 - mr_2^2/r_1^2)/(1 - r_2^2/r_1^2),$$

$$B = r_1^2\Omega_1(1 - m)/(1 - r_1^2/r_2^2),$$

and

$$m = \Omega_2/\Omega_1. \tag{1}$$

It was shown experimentally by G. I. Taylor (1923b), as part of his brilliant theoretical and experimental investigation, that, when instability occurs, the disturbance takes the form of a set of cellular, toroidal vortices spaced regularly along the axis of the cylinders (Fig. IX. 1, Plate). There are also theoretical reasons which suggest that the disturbed flow should be assumed to be periodic in the axial direction. The reasons are that such an assumption (i) is equivalent to a Fourier analysis in the z-direction, and (ii) yields a solution which is bounded at infinity. We therefore assume, following Taylor (1923b),

$$v_r = u(r)e^{kt}\cos\alpha z,$$

$$v_\theta = \bar{v}(r) + v(r)e^{kt}\cos\alpha z,$$

$$v_z = w(r)e^{kt}\sin\alpha z,$$

$$p = \bar{p}(r) + p'(r)e^{kt}\cos\alpha z. \tag{2}$$

We now insert these expressions into the Navier–Stokes and continuity equations, and assume that the disturbance is so small that squares and products of the perturbation velocities can be neglected. Then, if the pressure is eliminated, we obtain the following disturbance equations, namely

$$\mathscr{D}^*u + \alpha w = 0,$$

$$2Au = \nu(\mathscr{D}\mathscr{D}^* - \alpha^2 - k/\nu)v,$$

$$2\alpha^2(\bar{v}v/r) = \nu(\mathscr{D}\mathscr{D}^* - \alpha^2)(\mathscr{D}\mathscr{D}^* - \alpha^2 - k/\nu)u, \tag{3}$$

where

$$\mathscr{D} \equiv \frac{d}{dr} \quad \text{and} \quad \mathscr{D}^* \equiv \frac{d}{dr} + \frac{1}{r}. \tag{4}$$

If u is eliminated between the second and third of equations (3), we obtain

$$(\mathscr{D}\mathscr{D}^* - \alpha^2)(\mathscr{D}\mathscr{D}^* - \alpha^2 - k/\nu)^2 v = (4A\Omega/\nu^2)\alpha^2 v, \tag{5}$$

where $\Omega(r)$, which is equal to $\bar{v}/r$, denotes the angular velocity of the mean motion. The boundary conditions for this sixth-order differential equation are that u, v, and w shall be zero at each of the bounding cylinders. Using equations (3) we find that these conditions are equivalent to

$$v = \mathscr{D}\mathscr{D}^*v = \mathscr{D}^*(\mathscr{D}\mathscr{D}^* - \alpha^2 - k/\nu)v = 0 \quad \text{at } r = r_1, r_2. \tag{6}$$

Fɪɢ. IX. 1. Vortices between rotating cylinders

From equation (5) and the boundary conditions (6), it was shown conclusively by Synge (1938a) that a sufficient condition for stability is

$$\Omega_2 r_2^2 > \Omega_1 r_1^2 > 0.$$

The case which has received most attention, because the analysis simplifies considerably, is that in which the distance between the cylinders is very small compared with the radii, and an approximation of this type will now be considered. Let

$$r = r_0 + \zeta d, \qquad 2r_0 = r_1 + r_2, \qquad d = r_2 - r_1,$$
$$\lambda = \alpha d, \qquad \sigma = kd^2/\nu, \qquad D \equiv d/d\zeta, \qquad (7)$$

where λ and σ are the non-dimensional wave number and amplification number respectively. If terms of order d/r_0 are neglected, $\mathscr{D}^*$ is equivalent to $\mathscr{D}$ and, with the substitutions (7), equation (5) becomes

$$(D^2 - \lambda^2)(D^2 - \lambda^2 - \sigma)^2 v = \frac{4A\Omega\, d^4}{\nu^2}\lambda^2 v. \qquad (8)$$

The boundary conditions (6) become

$$v = D^2 v = D(D^2 - \lambda^2 - \sigma)v = 0 \quad \text{at} \ \zeta = \pm\tfrac{1}{2}. \qquad (9)$$

The angular velocity, Ω, is a function of ζ and may be expanded in powers of (d/r_0); if terms of order (d/r_0) are neglected we obtain from (1) and (7)

$$\Omega(\zeta) = \frac{\Omega_1}{2}(1+m) + \zeta[-\Omega_1(1-m)]. \qquad (10)$$

The quantity A may also be expanded and yields, to a first approximation, $A = -r_0\Omega_1(1-m)/2d$.

(b) Cylinders rotating in the same direction

If Ω_2 and Ω_1 are nearly equal, so that m is close to unity, it is clear that the ζ term in equation (10) is small compared with the constant term. Consequently, as $m \to 1$, we can approximate and replace Ω by its value, Ω_0, at $\zeta = 0$. It can be seen that, when terms of order d/r_0 are neglected, $\Omega_0 = \tfrac{1}{2}(\Omega_1 + \Omega_2)$ is the average angular velocity. Then the differential equation (8) becomes

$$(D^2 - \lambda^2)(D^2 - \lambda^2 - \sigma)^2 v + \lambda^2 T v = 0, \qquad (11)$$

where
$$T = -4A\Omega_0 d^4/\nu^2 \qquad (12)$$

is now usually called the Taylor number. If A is replaced by its approximate value for small d/r_0, the Taylor number takes the form

$$T = \frac{r_0\Omega_1^2 d^3}{\nu^2}(1-m^2) = \frac{r_0 d^3}{\nu^2}(\Omega_1^2 - \Omega_2^2). \qquad (13)$$

It can be shown, as follows, that the Taylor number in the form (13) represents the ratio of the (destabilizing) centrifugal force to the (stabilizing) viscous force. Consider a perturbation, of scale $r_0\Omega_1$, in the velocity component v. It can be seen from the momentum equation in the θ-direction, which is the second of equations (3), that, in order for the inertia force to be of the same order of magnitude as the viscous force, the velocity component u must be of scale $r_0\Omega_1\nu/Ad^2 \sim \nu/d(1-m)$; the velocity component w, because of continuity of flow, must also have this scale. Associated with the perturbation is a destabilizing centrifugal force of scale $\rho v\bar{v}/r \sim \rho r_0\Omega_0\Omega_1$ per unit volume, since $\bar{v}/r$ is of order Ω_0; this is opposed by a radial viscous force, which is of scale $\mu\nu/d^3(1-m)$ per unit volume. The ratio of these two scales of force is the Taylor number

$$r_0 d^3(\Omega_1^2-\Omega_2^2)/\nu^2.$$

The problem of the solution of equation (11) subject to the boundary conditions (9) is an eigenvalue problem leading to a relation between λ, σ, and T, namely $F(\lambda, \sigma, T) = 0$. It can be foreseen that instability will be possible if T is greater than some critical value, for then the effect of the (destabilizing) centrifugal force will outweigh the effect of the (stabilizing) viscous force. The precise value of the critical value of T is of considerable importance. In this connexion, it should be noted that Pellew and Southwell (1940) and Meksyn (1946b) have shown, from equation (11), that the situation in neutral (marginal) stability is given by $\sigma = 0$, and not merely by the vanishing of the real part of σ. This result is sometimes known as 'the principle of exchange of stabilities'. [The reason for the use of this phrase is not clear, since it does not have exactly the same meaning as in the general theory of stability of mechanical systems (Lyttleton 1953). We mention it here only because its use has become conventional (Jeffreys 1926; Chandrasekhar 1952a) in the theory of hydrodynamic stability.] As a consequence the critical Taylor number is given by the solution of $F(\lambda, 0, T) = 0$. The minimum critical Taylor number (T_c) is the minimum value of T, as a function of λ, given by this expression. For $T > T_c$ it can be inferred that a disturbance within the band of unstable wavelengths is an amplifying, non-oscillatory flow. The validity of the 'principle of exchange of stabilities' has not been proved in the more general cases of equations (5) and (8), but is generally assumed to be true. Experimental evidence supports the assumption (Taylor 1923b, p. 303).

When $\sigma = 0$, equation (11) becomes

$$(D^2-\lambda^2)^3v+\lambda^2Tv = 0 \tag{14}$$

and is subject to the conditions

$$v = D^2v = D(D^2 - \lambda^2)v = 0 \quad \text{at } \zeta = \pm\tfrac{1}{2}. \tag{15}$$

It can be proved that the following variational condition is an equivalent statement of the problem posed by equation (11) subject to conditions (9), namely

$$\lambda^2 T = \frac{\displaystyle\int_{-\frac{1}{2}}^{\frac{1}{2}} [(D^2 - \lambda^2)P][(D^2 - \lambda^2 - \sigma)P] \, d\zeta}{\displaystyle\int_{-\frac{1}{2}}^{\frac{1}{2}} [(Dv)^2 + (\lambda^2 + \sigma)v^2] \, d\zeta},$$

$$\delta(\lambda^2 T) = 0,$$

where

$$P \equiv (D^2 - \lambda^2 - \sigma)v. \tag{16}$$

The corresponding relation with $\sigma = 0$ was given and proved by Chandrasekhar (1953b). If, for given values of λ and σ, $\lambda^2 T$ is maximized or minimized with respect to variations of v, the resulting values of T are eigenvalues. In practice a function v is assumed which contains one arbitrary constant ($\mathscr{A}$) and satisfies the boundary conditions; for given λ and σ, the extremals of T, with respect to variations of $\mathscr{A}$, are eigenvalues.

Calculations have mostly been made for $\sigma = 0$. Pellew and Southwell (1940) solved the problem of equation (14) both exactly and by use of a variational condition which, however, is different from (16). Chandrasekhar (1953b) solved the problem using (16) with $\sigma = 0$. The accepted value for the minimum critical Taylor number is $T_c = 1{,}707{\cdot}8$ at $\lambda = 3{\cdot}13$ (Pellew and Southwell 1940). Furthermore, Pellew and Southwell showed that, for a given value of λ, there is a succession of critical Taylor numbers ($\sigma = 0$), each corresponding to a different mode of instability. However, in practice, the lowest mode is the important one for the onset of instability. The fact that the minimum critical Taylor number occurs at $\lambda = 3{\cdot}13$, which is approximately π, means that the predicted instability vortices have a wavelength ($2\pi/\alpha$) which is approximately $2d$. Since one wavelength corresponds to two toroidal vortices, this result means that the vortices are approximately square in section. Experiments carried out by Taylor (1923b) showed this to be correct, as can be seen from Fig. IX. 1.

Taylor (1923b) solved equation (5) with $k = 0$ by using series of Bessel functions, and obtained results to a higher degree of approximation in d/r_0 and in $(1 - m)$ than the results obtained from equation (14).

Taylor's result can be expressed in the form

$$T_c = (-4A\Omega_0\, d^4/\nu^2)_c = \frac{\pi^4}{P}\left(\frac{1+m}{1-m}\right),$$

where

$$P = 0\cdot0571\left(\frac{1+m}{1-m}-0\cdot652\frac{d}{r_1}\right)+0\cdot00056\left(\frac{1+m}{1-m}-0\cdot652\frac{d}{r_1}\right)^{-1}. \tag{17}$$

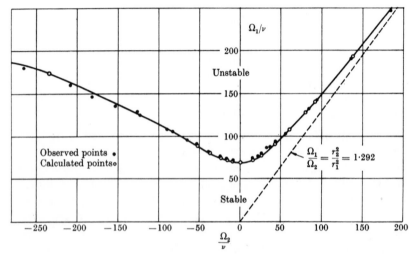

FIG. IX. 2. Comparison between theory and experiment for flow between rotating cylinders.

If terms in P which involve d/r_1 are neglected, and if the term

$$0\cdot00056\{(1+m)/(1-m)\}^{-1}$$

is also neglected, we obtain $T_c = 1,706$, which is very close to Pellew and Southwell's value of $1,707\cdot8$. If terms which involve d/r_1 are still neglected, but the other two terms in P are retained, it can be seen that the error involved in replacing $\Omega(\zeta)$ by Ω_0 is only about 1 per cent. of the Taylor number, even for $m = 0$. Thus, provided d/r_1 is small enough, the result

$$T_c = (-4A\Omega_0\, d^4/\nu^2)_{\text{crit}} = 1,707\cdot8$$

may be regarded as accurate, within about 1 per cent, for $0 \leqslant m \leqslant 1$. For negative values of m the formula ceases to be valid for reasons which will shortly be discussed. Some of Taylor's experimental and theoretical results, as given by (17), are illustrated in Fig. IX. 2. For more recent work on equation (5) the reader is referred to Chandrasekhar (1958) and Kirchgässner (1961).

Calculations based on equation (8) have been made by Meksyn (1946b), who used asymptotic series, Chandrasekhar (1954d), who included the term of (10) which is linear in ζ, and Steinman (1956), who included also the terms of order (d/r_0) of equation (10). The methods of Meksyn and Chandrasekhar are both much simpler than that of Taylor and their results, with those of Steinman, are very close to Taylor's.

A final point worth noting is that the variational condition (16), with $\sigma = 0$, can be shown to be equivalent to an energy-balance relationship, in which the rate of energy transfer from the mean flow to the disturbance precisely balances the rate of dissipation of kinetic energy.

(c) Cylinders rotating in opposite directions

It is clear that, when the cylinders rotate in opposite directions ($m < 0$), the velocity changes sign between the cylinders, so that $\Omega(\zeta)$ is zero for a particular value of ζ within the range $-\frac{1}{2} < \zeta < \frac{1}{2}$. Consequently, it is no longer a good approximation to replace $\Omega(\zeta)$ by Ω_0. It is necessary to make a better approximation to $\Omega(\zeta)$, and therefore to retain at least the term linear in ζ. This is a valid approximation provided d/r_0 is small. Methods of solution of equation (8), with Ω a linear function of ζ, have been given by Meksyn (1946b), Chandrasekhar (1954d), and DiPrima (1955); Steinman (1956) used Chandrasekhar's method but included additional terms of order d/r_0 in $\Omega(\zeta)$. The results are generally in agreement with Taylor's experimental results (Fig. IX. 2), as is a calculation, based on equation (5), made by Taylor (1923b) for a particular negative value of m. For further details the reader is referred to the papers mentioned above and to the book by Lin (1955).

Additional experimental information on the instability of flow between rotating cylinders may be found in papers by Lewis (1928), Cornish (1933), Fage (1938), Hagerty (1950), Schultz-Grunow and Hein (1956), Donnelly (1958), Gazley (1958), and Kaye and Elgar (1958). The last two papers are concerned with the effects of axial flow and heat transfer, while those of Cornish and Fage are concerned, in part, with effects of axial flow. More recently Brewster and Nissan (1958), Brewster, Grosberg, and Nissan (1959), and DiPrima (1959) have done experimental and theoretical work on two other aspects of instability of flow between rotating cylinders: (i) when the liquid is pumped around the annulus as well as rotated by the inner cylinder; (ii) when the cylinders are horizontal, the liquid has a free surface, and the inner cylinder rotates.

2.2. *The instability of the boundary layer on a concave surface*

In the two-dimensional boundary-layer flow on a concave surface, the velocity and circulation increase as the distance from the centre of curvature of the surface decreases. Consequently, the flow may be expected to be centrifugally unstable for sufficiently high speeds of the external stream. The problem was studied theoretically by Görtler (1940b), who showed that the instability generates vortices whose axes are parallel to the main stream, as shown in Fig. IX. 3, which is due

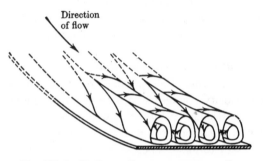

Fig. IX. 3. Görtler vortices on a concave wall.

to Görtler (1940b). Experimental confirmation of the occurrence of this form of instability on the concave flap of a Griffith suction-aerofoil was found by Gregory and Walker (1950), using the 'china-clay technique' (Section X. 15).

Let x denote the coordinate in the flow direction, z the coordinate in a direction normal to the surface, and y the third coordinate. Görtler assumed that the growth of the boundary layer could be neglected, and he therefore ignored both the x-dependence of the flow and the small z-component of flow. If δ gives a measure of the boundary-layer thickness, and r is the radius of curvature of the surface, then the following differential equations can be obtained when a number of small terms of order δ/r are neglected:

$$(D^2-\lambda^2-\sigma)u = w.DU,$$

$$(D^2-\lambda^2)(D^2-\lambda^2-\sigma)w = -\lambda^2 TuU. \tag{18}$$

Distances are referred to the boundary-layer thickness, δ, and velocities to the external flow velocity, U_0. The main flow is $U(\eta)$, where $\eta = z/\delta$, and the perturbation velocities in the x, y, z directions are

$$(U_0\delta/\nu)u(\eta)e^{kt}\cos\alpha y, \quad v(\eta)e^{kt}\sin\alpha y, \quad \text{and} \quad w(\eta)e^{kt}\cos\alpha y.$$

Furthermore,

$$D \equiv \frac{d}{d\eta}, \qquad \lambda = \alpha\delta, \qquad \sigma = k\delta^2/\nu, \qquad T = 2\left(\frac{U_0\delta}{\nu}\right)^2\frac{\delta}{r}. \qquad (19)$$

The boundary conditions are

$$u = w = Dw = 0 \quad \text{at} \quad \eta = 0 \quad \text{and} \quad \eta = \infty. \qquad (20)$$

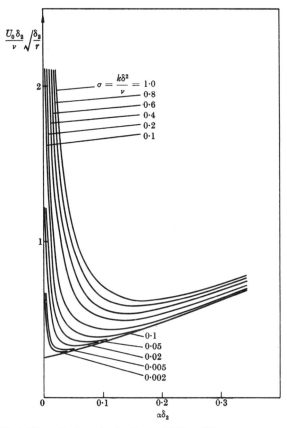

FIG. IX. 4. Theoretical results for the instability of flow on a concave wall.

Equations (18), subject to these boundary conditions, define an eigenvalue problem for T, λ, and σ. The parameter T is the Taylor number (cf. equation 13) for the problem. Neutral stability is defined by $\sigma = 0$. For several velocity profiles, U, Görtler obtained the value of T for neutral stability as a function of λ. Hämmerlin (1955a) later solved equations (18) more rigorously and showed that the minimum critical value T_c of the parameter T occurs for $\lambda = 0$ (see Fig. IX. 4).

This result does not agree with physical experience, since $\lambda = 0$ corresponds to a disturbance of infinite wavelength. Hämmerlin pointed out, however, that the approximations made in deriving equations (18) are not valid for small values of λ. By taking into account certain terms of order δ/r, which were ignored by Görtler, Hämmerlin (1956) obtained more exact differential equations, which have the property that the minimum critical value of T occurs at a finite value of λ. However, it is possible that the growth of the boundary layer is also important for small values of λ. A calculation by Smith (1955) included terms representing boundary-layer growth as well as those of order δ/r included by Hämmerlin (1956), and yielded a result similar to that of Hämmerlin (1956). It is not clear yet which of the two small effects mentioned above, namely those of curvature (δ/r) and boundary-layer growth, is the more important.

A result which has been well established, by Görtler (1940b) and by Hämmerlin (1955a), is that the curve of neutral stability is not particularly sensitive to the shape of the velocity profile when the momentum thickness, δ_2, is used as a characteristic length instead of δ. The curve of neutral stability for a particular velocity profile, namely that consisting of a linear portion within the boundary layer with a constant velocity outside, is shown in Fig. IX. 4, which is due to Hämmerlin (1955a). He obtained similar curves for other velocity profiles and also calculated curves of constant amplification (σ) for the particular straight-line profile mentioned above (Fig. IX. 4). The essential result of these calculations and those of Hämmerlin (1956) is that the minimum critical value of $(U_0 \delta_2/\nu)\sqrt{(\delta_2/r)}$ is about 0·3. Moreover, DiPrima and Dunn (1956) have shown that heating and cooling have a negligible effect on the instability, provided that gravity may be ignored; if gravity is included Görtler (1959) has shown that there is a strong effect of heating (from below) on the centrifugal instability (cf. Section 3).

For a given value of λ or $\alpha\delta_2$ there are many modes, with successively higher critical values of T. Higher modes were calculated by Meksyn (1950c); his method, however, was such that the lowest mode possible was not given by the calculations, and the lowest mode given by his work is probably the second. Lin (1955) refers to unpublished calculations of D'Arcy, who calculated higher modes by ignoring the viscous terms of equations (18). For the second mode he obtained streamlines showing two cells spaced one above the other in the z-direction, whereas for the basic mode he obtained streamlines of the form shown in Fig. IX. 3.

For a discussion of the shear stresses due to the vortices, the reader is referred to Gregory, Stuart, and Walker (1955), and for experimental evidence of the importance of the parameter $(U_0 \delta_2/\nu)\sqrt{(\delta_2/r)}$ for the occurrence of transition to turbulence, to Liepmann (1943, 1945).

2.3. Other examples of instability due to centrifugal forces

(a) Flow in a curved channel

Consider a two-dimensional curved channel along which fluid is flowing under the action of a pressure gradient. Owing to the combination of velocity gradient in the radial direction together with the effects of curvature, the flow is centrifugally unstable. Dean (1928) examined the instability of the flow with respect to disturbances in the form of vortices with their axes parallel to the flow direction (similar, that is, to the vortices which occur between rotating cylinders and in the boundary layer on a concave surface). If $2h$ denotes the distance between the walls, r the radius of the inner wall, and U_m the mean velocity, Dean found that instability occurs at a certain critical value of the parameter $(U_m h/\nu)\sqrt{(h/r)}$, namely 12·7 (see also Reid 1958; Hämmerlin 1958). The square of this dimensionless parameter is analogous to the Taylor number for flow between rotating cylinders. In Section 4 it is shown that instability of plane Poiseuille flow in a straight two-dimensional channel occurs at a critical Reynolds number $(\frac{3}{2}U_m h/\nu)$ of 5,780. Thus even for quite small curvatures, instability of Dean's kind would occur at a lower Reynolds number than would the two-dimensional wave disturbances considered in Section 4.

(b) Flow near a stagnation point

Following experimental evidence and ideas advanced by Piercy and Richardson (1928, 1930), Görtler (1955b) has examined the possibility of centrifugal instability occurring in the stagnation-point boundary-layer flow, which is described in Section III. 19 (a). In such a flow, there are certainly regions where the 'circulation' (product of local velocity and local radius of curvature) increases as the local centre of curvature is approached normal to the curved streamlines; consequently Rayleigh's criterion suggests instability. The disturbance differential equations derived by Görtler naturally relate to instability with respect to disturbances periodic in a direction normal to the plane of flow, and Hämmerlin's (1955b) study of the equations suggests that instability can occur. A notable feature is that there is no Reynolds number for the problem because the basic flow has only two disposable parameters,

ν and k of Section III. 19 (a), and these do not have the same dimensions. Therefore the flow is unstable at all speeds.

In applying the theory to the flow near the stagnation point of a two-dimensional body, however, the reader will note that a viscous flow of the type described in Section III. 19 (a) only exists if the Reynolds number, $U_0 r/\nu$, is large enough, where U_0 denotes the stream velocity and r the radius of curvature at the stagnation point. Furthermore, the convex curvature of the wall will exert some stabilizing influence. Consequently there is a limit to the validity of the above theory when applied to real flows, and a critical Reynolds number, $U_0 r/\nu$, may exist.

The existence of velocity fluctuations near the stagnation point of a body was shown experimentally by Piercy and Richardson (1928, 1930), who suggested that they could be a result of centrifugal instability. An experimental investigation by Schuh (1953b) of the heat transfer near the stagnation point gave values in excess of the calculations for laminar flow, and this also was attributed to the phenomenon discussed above. Some experiments of Kuethe (1958) at the nose of a body of revolution showed the existence of oscillations, though their origin is not yet known (see also Section 6.3).

3. Thermal instability

Instability phenomena of fluids which are heated or cooled are of considerable interest in meteorology (Brunt 1934), and will receive attention partly in this section and partly in Section 5.3. Here we are concerned with cases in which a layer of fluid is unstably stratified, namely, in which it is heated from below or cooled from above. Numerous experimental investigations have been carried out on layers of fluid which are either confined between two horizontal planes or have a free surface, and it appears that the fluid, which is initially at rest, convects into vertical cells of polygonal section, usually known as Bénard cells. Most of the experiments have been carried out by heating a layer of fluid from below, but Bénard (1901) used a volatile liquid with a free surface, thus inducing cooling from above. (It should be noted that Pearson (1958) has pointed out that Bénard's cells may have been induced by an instability due to surface-tension effects.) When there is an initial two-dimensional shear motion of the fluid, the convection cells are rectangular and of infinite length in the direction of shear (Jeffreys 1928), and we can refer to the flow as a system of longitudinal vortices. On the other hand, it seems that a uniform stream with no shear would merely convect the cells with its own speed. The theory of thermal instability will be developed for zero initial flow.

Let the fluid be bounded below by a rigid plane at $z = -\frac{1}{2}h$, and above either by a rigid plane or by a free surface at $z = \frac{1}{2}h$; and let the coordinates in the horizontal plane be x, y. If c_p denotes the specific heat at constant pressure, κ the thermal diffusivity $(k/\rho c_p)$, g the gravitational acceleration, T the absolute temperature, and other symbols have the usual meaning, the equations of continuity, motion, and energy are given by equations (III. 4), (III. 12) (with $X = Y = 0$ and $Z = -g$), and (III. 29). The equation of state of the (almost incompressible) fluid is

$$\rho = \rho_0[1 - \alpha\{T - \overline{T}(0)\}], \tag{21}$$

where α is the coefficient of thermal expansion, and ρ_0 is the density at the reference temperature $\overline{T}(0)$ °K, which may be taken to be the mean of the temperatures at $z = \pm\frac{1}{2}h$. Viscous dissipation is ignored and the quantities μ, ν, k, κ, c_p, and α are assumed to be constant. Furthermore, density variations are ignored except in association with gravity (Rayleigh 1916a). This is a good approximation provided $\alpha\Delta\overline{T} \ll 1$, where $\Delta\overline{T}$ is the temperature variation from top to bottom.

Let us now consider the state of equilibrium before instability arises. The pressure gradient which balances the gravitational force is given by the third of equations (III. 12) with $u = v = w = 0$:

$$\frac{\partial\bar{p}}{\partial z} = -g\rho_0[1 - \alpha\{\overline{T} - \overline{T}(0)\}]. \tag{22}$$

The initial temperature, $\overline{T}$, can be deduced from equation (III. 29), and is

$$\overline{T} = \overline{T}(0) + \beta z, \tag{23}$$

where β must clearly be negative for instability to occur.

We now write

$$z = h\zeta, \quad t = h^2\tau/\nu, \quad T = \overline{T} + T', \quad p = \bar{p} + p' \tag{24}$$

and substitute them into equations (III. 4), (III. 12), and (III. 29), which are then linearized on the assumption that T' and the velocity components are small. (The horizontal boundaries are now at $\zeta = \pm\frac{1}{2}$.) Thus we obtain a set of perturbation equations. In order to reduce these equations to a manageable form it is necessary to specify in some degree the geometry of the convection cells. In the early theory, as developed by Rayleigh (1916a) and Jeffreys (1926, 1928), these were assumed, for simplicity, to be rectangular. Later, Pellew and Southwell (1940) showed how to take into account other shapes of cell wall, including the case of a hexagonal cell.

They put
$$w' = w(z)e^{\sigma\tau}f(x,y),$$
$$T' = \Theta(z)e^{\sigma\tau}f(x,y), \tag{25}$$

with related transformations for u' and v'. By separation of variables in the perturbation equations, it can be shown that f must satisfy

$$\frac{\partial^2 f}{\partial x^2} + \frac{\partial^2 f}{\partial y^2} + \frac{\lambda^2 f}{h^2} = 0. \tag{26}$$

The functional form of f is determined by the shape of the cell, and has been evaluated in analytic form for a rectangular cell by Rayleigh (1916a), for a hexagonal cell by Christopherson (1940), and for a rotationally-symmetric annular cell by Zierep (1958). The quantity λ is a representative dimensionless wave number for the system. It should be noted that it is not possible on linearized theory to determine the *shape* of the cell; for a given wave number, λ, all that can be done is to determine the *size* of a cell of a given shape. (Malkus and Veronis (1958) discuss non-linearity and its importance in the prediction of cell shape.)

The equation for $\Theta(z)$ is found from the perturbation equations to be

$$(D^2 - \lambda^2)(D^2 - \lambda^2 - \sigma)(D^2 - \lambda^2 - \sigma\mathscr{P})\Theta + \lambda^2\mathscr{R}\Theta = 0, \tag{27}$$

where w is related to Θ by

$$w = \frac{\kappa}{h^2\beta}(D^2 - \lambda^2 - \sigma\mathscr{P})\Theta \tag{28}$$

and D denotes $d/d\zeta$. The symbol $\mathscr{R}$ denotes the Rayleigh number, namely,
$$\mathscr{R} = -\alpha\beta gh^4/\nu\kappa, \tag{29}$$

and $\mathscr{P}$ is the Prandtl number, ν/κ.

The Rayleigh number may be interpreted as the ratio of the destabilizing gravitational force to the stabilizing viscous force. Consider a perturbation in the temperature, of scale $(-\beta h)$. Associated with this perturbation is a destabilizing gravitational force per unit volume of scale $-\rho_0\,\alpha\beta gh$, as can be seen from (21). When convection takes place, convection and diffussion of heat have the same order of magnitude (equation 28), and this implies that the vertical velocity component has a scale κ/h. The viscous force opposing the convective motion is thus of scale $\mu\kappa/h^3$ per unit volume; this is the stabilizing force. The ratio of the destabilizing to the stabilizing force is $-\alpha\beta gh^4/\kappa\nu$, which is the Rayleigh number.

It can be shown that, at a rigid plane which is maintained at a fixed temperature, the boundary conditions are

$$\Theta = D^2\Theta = D(D^2 - \lambda^2 - \sigma\mathscr{P})\Theta = 0. \tag{30}$$

On the other hand, if there is a free surface maintained at a fixed temperature the boundary conditions there are

$$\Theta = D^2\Theta = D^4\Theta = 0. \tag{31}$$

Equation (27) together with boundary conditions (30) or (31) at each plane determines an eigenvalue problem for the parameters $\mathscr{R}$, λ, and σ.

It can be seen from (27) and (28) that an equation similar to (27), but with w replacing Θ, can be derived. In this formulation the boundary conditions are

$$w = Dw = (D^2 - \lambda^2)(D^2 - \lambda^2 - \sigma)w = 0 \tag{32}$$

at a rigid surface and

$$w = D^2w = D^4w = 0 \tag{33}$$

at a free surface. It is clear, of course, that equation (27) with either w or Θ boundary conditions must yield the same eigenvalues, $\mathscr{R}$, as functions of λ and σ. [Equation (27) is self-adjoint; furthermore, the differential system defined by (27) subject to (32) is the adjoint of the system defined by (27) and (30). On the other hand, the differential system defined by (27), subject to (31) at each boundary, is self-adjoint. In the case of the rotating-cylinder problem (11), subject to (9), it should be noted that the adjoint system is the same physical problem formulated in terms of the radial velocity, u, instead of the azimuthal velocity, v. For a treatment of adjoint differential systems, see Coddington and Levinson (1955), for example.]

Two types of disturbance are physically conceivable: (i) a steady convection in cells; (ii) an amplifying wave motion. However, Pellew and Southwell (1940) have shown that when the temperature decreases upwards the only type of disturbance which can appear is that with σ real, so that an amplifying wave motion is not possible. Thus the situation in neutral (marginal) stability is governed by $\sigma = 0$.

Putting $\sigma = 0$, we have from (27)

$$(D^2 - \lambda^2)^3\Theta + \lambda^2\mathscr{R}\Theta = 0 \tag{34}$$

with the boundary conditions (30), with $\sigma = 0$, at a rigid surface and (31) at a free surface. Equation (34) with its boundary conditions yields a relation between λ and $\mathscr{R}$ for marginal stability. A particular value of λ yields the minimum critical Rayleigh number $(\mathscr{R}_c)$.

If both boundaries are rigid and the Θ formulation of the problem is used for $\sigma = 0$, it can be seen that (34) with boundary conditions (30) at both surfaces is mathematically equivalent to the marginal stability problem for viscous flow between two concentric cylinders rotating in the same sense (equation 14), provided the angular velocity (10) is replaced by an averaged value. This was pointed out by G. I. Taylor and by Low, and the fact was demonstrated by Jeffreys (1928) and Low (1929). On the other hand, it should be noted that the same equivalence is true for amplified disturbances (equation 27) only if $\nu = \kappa$, that is, if the Prandtl number is unity.

A variational condition for the solution of (27) with its boundary conditions (30) alone, (30) and (31), or (31) alone, can be derived, namely

$$\lambda^2 \mathscr{R} = \frac{\int_{-\frac{1}{2}}^{\frac{1}{2}} [(D^2 - \lambda^2)P][(D^2 - \lambda^2 - \sigma)P] \, d\zeta}{\int_{-\frac{1}{2}}^{\frac{1}{2}} [(D\Theta)^2 + (\lambda^2 + \sigma\mathscr{P})\Theta^2] \, d\zeta},$$

$$\delta(\lambda^2 \mathscr{R}) = 0,$$

where

$$P = (D^2 - \lambda^2 - \sigma\mathscr{P})\Theta. \tag{35}$$

For $\sigma = 0$ and any value of $\mathscr{P}$, and for $\sigma \neq 0$ and $\mathscr{P} = 1$, this variational condition is equivalent to (16). A different variational condition, based on equation (34) with the boundary conditions (32) alone, (32) and (33), or (33) alone, for $\sigma = 0$, was given by Pellew and Southwell (1940). With $\sigma = 0$, equation (35) can be shown to be equivalent to an energy-balance relation, in which the rate of supply of kinetic energy to the velocity field precisely balances the rate of dissipation of kinetic energy (see Jeffreys 1956).

3.1. *Mathematical results for thermal instability*

A very simple, but physically unrealistic, case which was solved by Rayleigh (1916a) is that in which both upper and lower surfaces are free. The solution of (34) or (27) which satisfies (31) at both surfaces is

$$\Theta = \sin n\pi(\zeta + \tfrac{1}{2}), \tag{36}$$

where the relation between the eigenvalues λ and $\mathscr{R}$ for marginal stability is

$$(n^2\pi^2 + \lambda^2)^3 = \lambda^2 \mathscr{R} \tag{37}$$

and n is an integer. The minimum value of $\mathscr{R}$ for instability is given by $n = 1$; $\lambda = \tfrac{1}{2}\pi\sqrt{2}$, $\mathscr{R} = 27\pi^4/4 = 657{\cdot}51$. If, for a fixed value of λ, the value of n is increased, the critical Rayleigh number increases. For a given value of n there is a definite relationship between λ and $\mathscr{R}$ for marginal stability, and successive values of n give successively higher modes of instability. This illustrates a general result of thermal instability, namely that many modes are possible. Naturally, however, the lowest mode, once established, tends to dominate.

When both surfaces are rigid planes, the solution is more complicated and has been evaluated for the basic mode of instability by Pellew and Southwell both by an exact solution in exponential functions, and by using a variational principle. The minimum value of $\mathscr{R}$ for the basic mode of instability is $\mathscr{R}_c = 1{,}707{\cdot}8$ at $\lambda = 3{\cdot}13$ (or, approximately, π). Similar results were obtained by Taylor (1923b), Jeffreys (1928), Meksyn (1946b), Chandrasekhar (1952a, 1953b, c), and Reid and Harris (1958).

For the case when the lower plane is rigid and the upper surface is free, Pellew and Southwell give a critical Rayleigh number of $1{,}100{\cdot}65$. Furthermore, they give results for higher modes of instability and show also how the wave number, λ, can be related to the dimensions of a given shape of cell.

Work on the instability of a fluid sphere heated from within has been done by Wasiutinski (1946), Jeffreys (1952, 1956), Jeffreys and Bland (1951), Chandrasekhar (1952b, 1953a, 1957), and Backus (1955). The effects of Coriolis forces and magnetic fields on thermal instability have been discussed by Thompson (1951) and by Chandrasekhar (1952a, 1953c, 1954a, b, c, 1956). For discussions of instability of fluids in vertical channels and tubes, when heated from below, the reader is referred to Hales (1937), Ostrach (1955a, b), Slavnov (1956), Yih (1959), and to a related paper by Taylor (1954).

3.2. *Experimental work on thermal instability*

Experiments on the instability of a fluid confined between two rigid planes or with a free surface have been carried out by Bénard (1901), Phillips and Walker (1932), Graham (1933), Schmidt and Milverton (1935), Schmidt and Saunders (1938), Chandra (1938), Bénard and Avsec (1938), Volkovisky (1939), de Graaf and van der Held (1953), Malkus (1954a), Tippelskirch (1956), Silveston (1958), and Soberman (1958, 1959). A typical example of the cells formed during convection is shown in Fig. IX. 5 (Plate), due to Chandra (1938). The experiments by Malkus (1954a) gave a critical Rayleigh number of $1{,}700 \pm 80$ for water confined between two rigid, horizontal, brass plates at a distance apart of order 1 cm. The temperature difference was of order 1° K, with a mean temperature of order 300° K. The condition $\alpha \Delta \overline{T} \ll 1$

certainly held, since α is of order 10^{-4} per $°K$ at the mean temperature of the experiment.

For critical discussions of the topic of thermal instability, with reference to the theoretical and experimental aspects, the reader is referred to papers by Batchelor (1954b) and Ostroumov (1952).

4. The instability of two-dimensional parallel flows

In deriving the equations governing the instability of flows which are parallel, or almost parallel, we shall first confine our attention to the case of two-dimensional flow between parallel planes. It can be shown that the same disturbance equations are approximately valid for boundary-layer and other flows which, although not parallel, can be regarded as such for the purposes of the instability theory.

Let x_1 denote the distance parallel to the flow, x_2 the distance at right angles to the flow but coplanar with the bounding planes, and x_3 the distance normal to the planes. Let u_1, u_2, and u_3 be the corresponding components of velocity and let P denote pressure, t the time, v the kinematic viscosity, and ρ the density. Let us also introduce a reference length h and a reference velocity U_0, and define

$$x_1 = hx, \qquad x_2 = hy, \qquad x_3 = hz,$$
$$u_1 = U_0 u, \qquad u_2 = U_0 v, \qquad u_3 = U_0 w,$$
$$P = p\rho U_0^2, \qquad t = h\tau/U_0. \tag{38}$$

Then the Navier–Stokes equations (III. 12) and equation of continuity (III. 4) for an incompressible fluid may be written

$$\frac{\partial u}{\partial \tau} + u\frac{\partial u}{\partial x} + v\frac{\partial u}{\partial y} + w\frac{\partial u}{\partial z} = -\frac{\partial p}{\partial x} + \frac{1}{R}\nabla^2 u,$$

$$\frac{\partial v}{\partial \tau} + u\frac{\partial v}{\partial x} + v\frac{\partial v}{\partial y} + w\frac{\partial v}{\partial z} = -\frac{\partial p}{\partial y} + \frac{1}{R}\nabla^2 v,$$

$$\frac{\partial w}{\partial \tau} + u\frac{\partial w}{\partial x} + v\frac{\partial w}{\partial y} + w\frac{\partial w}{\partial z} = -\frac{\partial p}{\partial z} + \frac{1}{R}\nabla^2 w,$$

$$\frac{\partial u}{\partial x} + \frac{\partial v}{\partial y} + \frac{\partial w}{\partial z} = 0,$$

$$\nabla^2 \equiv \frac{\partial^2}{\partial x^2} + \frac{\partial^2}{\partial y^2} + \frac{\partial^2}{\partial z^2}, \tag{39}$$

where $R = U_0 h/v$ denotes the Reynolds number for the problem.

There are two simple, fundamental, two-dimensional, steady solutions of equations (39), namely

(i) $\qquad \bar{u} = \tfrac{1}{2}z, \quad \bar{v} = \bar{w} = 0, \quad p = \text{const}, \tag{40}$

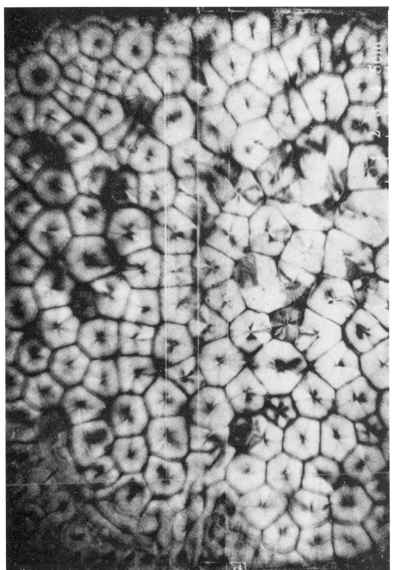

Fig. IX. 5. Bénard cells due to thermal instability

in which one plane, that at $z = +1$, moves with velocity $\frac{1}{2}U_0$, and the other plane, that at $z = -1$, moves with velocity $-\frac{1}{2}U_0$;

(ii) $\qquad \bar{u} = 1-z^2, \quad \bar{v} = \bar{w} = 0, \quad \bar{p} = -2x/R+\text{const}, \qquad$ (41)

in which the planes are fixed at $z = \pm 1$. The maximum velocity of the flow is U_0.

In each case h denotes the half-distance between the planes. More generally, the steady flow may consist of a combination of these two types of flow. For the moment we shall leave $\bar{u}$ unspecified and derive equations for the perturbation as a function of $\bar{u}$ and certain parameters, such as the Reynolds number.

Let us write

$$u = \bar{u}+u', \quad v = v', \quad w = w', \quad p = \bar{p}+p', \qquad (42)$$

for the case in which the mean flow, $\bar{u}$, is parallel to the x-axis. On substituting in (39) and linearizing, we obtain the following equations for the disturbance:

$$\frac{\partial u'}{\partial \tau}+\bar{u}\frac{\partial u'}{\partial x}+w'\frac{d\bar{u}}{dz} = -\frac{\partial p'}{\partial x}+\frac{1}{R}\nabla^2 u',$$

$$\frac{\partial v'}{\partial \tau}+\bar{u}\frac{\partial v'}{\partial x} = -\frac{\partial p'}{\partial y}+\frac{1}{R}\nabla^2 v',$$

$$\frac{\partial w'}{\partial \tau}+\bar{u}\frac{\partial w'}{\partial x} = -\frac{\partial p'}{\partial z}+\frac{1}{R}\nabla^2 w',$$

$$\frac{\partial u'}{\partial x}+\frac{\partial v'}{\partial y}+\frac{\partial w'}{\partial z} = 0. \qquad (43)$$

It is now assumed that the disturbance functions u', v', w', and p' are all proportional to $\exp[i(\alpha x+\beta y-\alpha c\tau)]$, so that we consider a single component of a Fourier series in x and y to represent the flow; the assumption also ensures that the velocity is bounded at infinity. The quantities α and β are real and are the wave numbers appropriate to the directions x and y. On the other hand, c is complex; the real part of c, namely c_r, is the wave velocity, and the imaginary part of c, namely c_i, represents the amplification or damping of the oscillation with the passage of time. If c_i is positive the disturbance amplifies and is unstable, while if it is negative the disturbance decays and is stable. The situation in neutral stability is governed by $c_i = 0$. We write

$$\{u',v',w',p'\} \equiv \{u_1(z),v_1(z),w_1(z),p_1(z)\}\exp[i(\alpha x+\beta y-\alpha c\tau)], \quad (44)$$

where the real parts of the expressions are the physical quantities.

When equations (44) are substituted in (43) and the boundary conditions

$$u_1 = v_1 = w_1 = 0 \quad \text{at } z = \pm 1 \tag{45}$$

are applied, we obtain an eigenrelation between α, β, c, and R, which involves i and the mean-velocity function $\bar{u}$. Since it involves i, it is equivalent to two real relations.

After a few transformations and the elimination of p, it can be shown that the equations which result when equations (44) are substituted in (43) are the following:

$$(\bar{u}-c)(D^2-\gamma^2)w_1 - w_1 D^2\bar{u} = \frac{-i}{\alpha R}(D^2-\gamma^2)^2 w_1,$$

$$(\bar{u}-c)(\beta u_1-\alpha v_1)-(i\beta/\alpha)w_1 D\bar{u} = \frac{-i}{\alpha R}(D^2-\gamma^2)(\beta u_1-\alpha v_1),$$

$$i\alpha u_1 + i\beta v_1 + Dw_1 = 0, \tag{46}$$

where $D \equiv d/dz$ and $\gamma^2 = \alpha^2 + \beta^2$. Actually the eigenvalues are determined by the first of the equations (46) with the boundary conditions

$$w_1 = Dw_1 = 0 \quad \text{at } z = \pm 1. \tag{47}$$

The second of these two conditions follows from (45) and the last equation of (46). Thus, on linearized theory, w_1 is determined except for a scale factor. The quantities u_1 and v_1 follow from the second two equations of (46) with the appropriate boundary conditions of (45).

A result, sometimes known as Squire's theorem, can be deduced from the first equation (46) as follows. If we replace αR by $\gamma \bar{R}$ we have an equation of the same form as that appropriate to two dimensions ($\beta = 0$), except that γ and $\bar{R}$ appear instead of α and R. Furthermore, since $\bar{R} = \alpha R/\gamma$, $\bar{R}$ is less than R. Consequently the problem of three-dimensional instability at a Reynolds number, R, is equivalent to a two-dimensional problem at a lower Reynolds number $\bar{R}$. In the case of neutral disturbances we can immediately deduce that the minimum critical Reynolds number (R_{cm}) occurs for a two-dimensional disturbance so that, in a calculation of R_{cm}, it is only necessary to consider two-dimensional disturbances. This result is Squire's theorem, and for another proof of it the reader is referred to Section 6.

In a generalization of Squire's work Watson (1960a), following Jungclaus (1957), has proved some important results concerning amplifying three-dimensional disturbances; these results are:

(i) In an unstable parallel flow, the disturbance with the greatest rate of amplification (greatest value of αc_i) at a given Reynolds number, R, is two-dimensional provided that R is less than the value, R_m, at which c_i has its maximum positive value for two-dimensional disturbances. For $R > R_m$ no statement has been rigorously deduced.

(ii) If the x-wise wave number, α, is fixed as well as R, the disturbance with the greatest value of αc_i is three-dimensional provided α lies in a certain range, which is defined by Watson (1960a).

Although both these results are conveniently stated here, the reader is advised to study them in conjunction with Fig. IX. 7, which is discussed in Section 4.4. (For more recent work, see Michael 1961.)

In the two-dimensional theory ($\beta = 0$), with which the rest of this section is concerned, it is convenient to define

$$u_1 = \frac{\partial \phi}{\partial z}, \qquad w_1 = -i\alpha\phi, \tag{48}$$

where the stream function is

$$\psi = \phi(z)e^{i\alpha(x-ct)}. \tag{49}$$

Thus the first equation of (46) becomes

$$(\bar{u}-c)(\phi''-\alpha^2\phi)-\bar{u}''\phi = \frac{-i}{\alpha R}(\phi^{iv}-2\alpha^2\phi''+\alpha^4\phi), \tag{50}$$

where the primes denote differentiation with respect to z; this is known as the Orr–Sommerfeld equation. The boundary conditions are

$$\phi = \phi' = 0 \quad \text{at } z = \pm 1. \tag{51}$$

Equation (50) has been derived for strictly parallel, incompressible, two-dimensional flow between parallel planes. An important result, which is due to Pretsch (1941b), is that many flows which are nearly parallel may, to a good approximation, be treated as though they are parallel, in the sense that terms neglected in (50) have little effect on the solution. The flow at a given section is considered to be a parallel flow with the velocity profile appropriate to that section. Consequently, we may regard $\bar{u}$ as a general function of z, and not only as one of the functions (40) and (41). For considerations of instability it should be noted that boundary-layer, wake, and jet flows often fall into this category of nearly parallel flows. In such cases boundary conditions different from (51) will be operative. For example, for a boundary-layer flow we have $\phi = \phi' = 0 \quad \text{at } z = 0 \text{ and } \infty,$ (52)

where $z = 0$ represents the wall. It should also be noted that the work of Squire (1933) and Watson (1960a), described above, applies to the nearly parallel flows discussed in this paragraph.

4.1. *Energy considerations in two-dimensional parallel flows*

It is clear that, when a disturbance is present in a fluid, the energy contained within the disturbance must arise from the mean motion itself, and a study of the mechanism of this transfer of energy between the mean motion and the disturbance motion is obviously important. Discussions of hydrodynamic stability based on energy principles were given by Orr (1907), Lorentz (1896b), and others, before the linearized instability theory based on equation (50) was properly developed.

The derivation and form of the energy equation will now be given for the important case of a two-dimensional disturbance which is periodic in x and is superimposed on a parallel flow. Averages are conveniently taken with respect to x, and the function $\bar{u}$ is the mean velocity. The quantities u' and w' have zero means. The velocity field is $u = \bar{u}+u'$, $w = w'$, and the pressure is $p = \bar{p}+p'$. From equations (39) with $v = 0$ and omission of derivatives with respect to y, we obtain for the perturbation parts of the equations

$$\frac{\partial u'}{\partial \tau}+\bar{u}\frac{\partial u'}{\partial x}+w'\frac{\partial \bar{u}}{\partial z}+\chi_1 = -\frac{\partial p'}{\partial x}+\frac{1}{R}\nabla^2 u',$$

$$\frac{\partial w'}{\partial \tau}+\bar{u}\frac{\partial w'}{\partial x}+\chi_2 = -\frac{\partial p'}{\partial z}+\frac{1}{R}\nabla^2 w',$$

$$\partial u'/\partial x+\partial w'/\partial z = 0, \tag{53}$$

where

$$\chi_1 = u'\frac{\partial u'}{\partial x}+w'\frac{\partial u'}{\partial z}-\overline{u'\frac{\partial u'}{\partial x}}-\overline{w'\frac{\partial u'}{\partial z}}$$

and

$$\chi_2 = u'\frac{\partial w'}{\partial x}+w'\frac{\partial w'}{\partial z}-\overline{u'\frac{\partial w'}{\partial x}}-\overline{w'\frac{\partial w'}{\partial z}}. \tag{54}$$

It should be noted that the non-linear terms, χ_1 and χ_2, are retained. A bar above a quantity denotes the mean value. We now multiply the first and second equations of (53) by u' and w', add, and integrate over a domain bounded by one wavelength $(2\pi/\alpha)$ of the two-dimensional disturbance, and by the planes $z = \pm 1$. (In the case of nearly parallel flows, such as boundary-layer, wake, and jet flows, the domain is bounded by the wall and the edge of the boundary layer or by the edges of the wake or jet.) We then obtain

$$\frac{\partial}{\partial \tau}\iint \tfrac{1}{2}(u'^2+w'^2)\,dx\,dz = \iint \overline{(-u'w')}\frac{\partial \bar{u}}{\partial z}\,dx\,dz-\frac{1}{R}\iint \left(\frac{\partial w'}{\partial x}-\frac{\partial u'}{\partial z}\right)^2 dx\,dz,$$

or

$$\frac{\partial I_1}{\partial \tau} = I_2-\frac{1}{R}I_3. \tag{55}$$

The non-linear terms disappear in the process of integration and do not affect the final result. All the terms in (55) are non-dimensional, but if we multiply by the appropriate scale factor, $\rho U_0^3 hb$, where b is a reference distance in the y-direction, we can relate the terms to physical quantities in the following way. The term $\partial I_1/\partial \tau$ represents the rate of increase with time of the disturbance energy. On the right-hand side the integral I_2 is the integral of the product of the Reynolds stress (see Appendix to this chapter), $-\rho U_0^2 \overline{u'w'}$, and the mean-velocity gradient, $(U_0/h)\partial \bar{u}/\partial z$, and therefore represents the energy transfer between the mean flow and the disturbance through the action of the Reynolds shear stress (Prandtl 1935, pp. 178–90). If it is positive, energy is being transferred from the mean flow to the disturbance, while if it is negative, energy is being transferred from the disturbance to the mean flow. This integral will be referred to as the 'energy-supply' or 'energy-transfer' integral. Turning now to I_3/R we note that it is always positive and is μ times the integral of the square of the vorticity,

$$(U_0^2/h^2)[\partial w'/\partial x - \partial u'/\partial z]^2.$$

It follows, therefore, that this integral, which will be called the 'dissipation' integral, represents the rate of dissipation of kinetic energy into heat.

It is clear that, if the disturbance is to grow in amplitude, I_2 must be *positive* and greater than I_3/R; consequently there must be a dominant region of the flow in which the Reynolds stress has the same sign as the mean-velocity gradient. If there is no such region the energy-supply integral (I_2) will be negative and the disturbance energy will necessarily decrease, in which case the flow is stable. Furthermore, it can be seen from (55) that the Reynolds number, R, plays an important role in the mechanism of instability: for if the Reynolds number is small enough, I_3/R will be greater than I_2 and the flow therefore stable. On the other hand, if the Reynolds number is high enough I_2 may be greater than I_3/R and the flow may be unstable. On physical grounds, therefore, we expect the existence of a critical Reynolds number, above which the flow is unstable. It is not possible from the energy equation (55) to show just how the Reynolds stress develops the sign appropriate to a condition of instability, but this can be done by a proper examination of the Orr–Sommerfeld equation (50). However, we can reason at this stage that viscosity cannot act only as a damping agent, for if it did a Reynolds stress of the required kind would never be built up at all in cases of stability in the absence of viscosity. In fact, Prandtl (1935, pp. 178–90) has shown that viscous forces produce a phase shift of the two components of velocity, thus enabling the development of an appropriate Reynolds stress for instability.

Several authors, including Orr (1907) and Lorentz (1896b), have used the energy relation to estimate the critical Reynolds number; simple forms of disturbance velocities, u' and w', were chosen to satisfy the boundary conditions, but they were not solutions of the equations of motion and satisfactory values of the critical Reynolds number were not, therefore, obtained. In fact, the values obtained were much lower than those observed experimentally. For a rather more detailed discussion of this work, and for further references, the reader is referred to Lin (1955).

4.2. *The instability of two-dimensional parallel flows at infinite Reynolds number*

If, in equation (50), we let R tend to infinity in such a way that αR also tends to infinity, even if α tends to zero, we obtain the equation

$$(\bar{u}-c)(\phi''-\alpha^2\phi)-\bar{u}''\phi = 0. \tag{56}$$

The effects of viscosity on the disturbance are ignored and, as can be seen from (56), one mathematical effect of this is to lower the order of the Orr–Sommerfeld equation from four to two. This means that we must drop the viscous boundary condition of no slip at the walls. For flow between parallel planes, the boundary conditions to be applied are, therefore,

$$\phi = 0 \quad \text{at } z = \pm 1. \tag{57}$$

For boundary-layer flows the following boundary conditions are applicable, namely

$$\phi = 0 \quad \text{at } z = 0 \text{ and } \infty, \tag{58}$$

where $z = 0$ represents the wall. In general, we may refer to the boundary conditions (57) or (58) as being applicable at $z = z_1$ and $z = z_2$.

The theory of instability in perfect fluids was examined and developed by Lord Rayleigh in a series of papers, beginning with those of 1880 and 1887. In this section we confine our attention to symmetrical profiles in a channel and to profiles of the boundary-layer type (the velocity profiles of which vary monotonically across the half-channel or across the boundary layer). A very important result obtained by Rayleigh (1880) was that a necessary condition for instability in an inviscid fluid is that the profile $\bar{u}$ should contain a point of inflexion. The proof is as follows: let

$$L(\phi) \equiv \phi''-\alpha^2\phi-\bar{u}''\phi/(\bar{u}-c), \tag{59}$$

from which it can be shown that

$$\tilde{\phi} L(\phi) - \phi \tilde{L}(\tilde{\phi}) = \tilde{\phi}\phi'' - \phi\tilde{\phi}'' - 2ic_i\,\bar{u}''\phi\tilde{\phi}/|\bar{u}-c|^2, \qquad (60)$$

where the symbol $\sim$ denotes a conjugate complex quantity. Integrating between z_1 and z_2 and using the boundary conditions, we obtain

$$\int_{z_1}^{z_2} [\tilde{\phi} L(\phi) - \phi \tilde{L}(\tilde{\phi})]\, dz \equiv -2ic_i \int_{z_1}^{z_2} \frac{\bar{u}''\phi\tilde{\phi}\, dz}{|\bar{u}-c|^2}. \qquad (61)$$

Since, from (56), $L(\phi)$ and $\tilde{L}(\tilde{\phi})$ are identically zero, the integral on the left-hand side of (61) is identically zero. It can be seen from (49) that an amplified disturbance requires $c_i > 0$, so that, according to (61), $\bar{u}''$ must vanish somewhere within the range of integration. It might be supposed at first sight that we have proved that damped disturbances ($c_i < 0$) also require $\bar{u}$ to contain a point of inflexion. This is not the case, however, as was pointed out by Lin (1945, 1955), and the above result applies only to amplified disturbances: this difference between amplified and damped disturbances arises because the case of an inviscid fluid must be regarded as a limiting one as the viscosity tends to zero. In physical terms the presence of viscosity, even though it is vanishingly small, is sufficient to ensure damped disturbances. It follows that a necessary condition for oscillations to be amplified is that the velocity profile, $\bar{u}$, shall contain a point of inflexion. (Actually there are two inflexion points in the case of symmetrical profiles in a channel, symmetrically disposed about the channel centre.) For discussions of physical aspects of the instability the reader is referred to Taylor (1915), Lin (1945, 1954b, 1955) and Foote and Lin (1950), and to Section II. 3.1.

A second important result for the solution of (56) is due to Fjørtoft (1950) and Høiland (1953a). This shows that a further condition necessary for instability (for a velocity profile which varies monotonically across a half-channel or a boundary layer) is that the numerical value of the vorticity, $|\bar{u}'|$, at the point of inflexion must be a maximum. The proof follows from the fact, which is easily deduced, that

$$\int_{z_1}^{z_2} [\tilde{\phi} L(\phi) + \phi \tilde{L}(\tilde{\phi})]\, dz$$

$$\equiv -2\alpha^2 \int_{z_1}^{z_2} \phi\tilde{\phi}\, dz - 2 \int_{z_1}^{z_2} \tilde{\phi}'\phi'\, dz - 2 \int_{z_1}^{z_2} \frac{\bar{u}''(\bar{u}-c_r)\phi\tilde{\phi}\, dz}{|\bar{u}-c|^2}, \qquad (62)$$

The left-hand side is necessarily equal to zero. We add to the right-hand side of (62) the quantity

$$+2 \int_{z_1}^{z_2} \frac{\bar{u}''(\bar{u}_I - c_r)\phi\bar{\phi}\, dz}{|\bar{u}-c|^2}$$

(which from (61) is known to be zero), where $\bar{u}_I$ denotes the velocity of the fluid at the point(s) of inflexion, z_I. It can then be seen from (62) that

$$\int_{z_1}^{z_2} \frac{\bar{u}''(\bar{u}-\bar{u}_I)\phi\bar{\phi}\, dz}{|\bar{u}-c|^2} < 0. \tag{63}$$

Consequently, a necessary condition for the existence of amplified oscillations is

$$\bar{u}''(\bar{u}-\bar{u}_I) < 0 \tag{64}$$

over an appreciable region of the flow. For the cases we are considering of profiles which vary monotonically across a half-channel or a boundary layer, condition (64) is either true or untrue over the whole field $z_1 < z < z_2$ except at $z = z_I$. If it is true, it can be seen that the modulus of the vorticity, $|\bar{u}'|$, has a maximum at the point(s) of inflexion.

Tollmien (1935) has shown that, for symmetrical velocity profiles in a channel, and for the boundary-layer velocity profiles, the condition $\bar{u}''(z) = 0$ is a sufficient condition for instability. It can be verified that the Fjørtoft–Høiland condition holds for these profiles. For further details of proofs of sufficiency the reader is referred to the work of Tollmien (1935) and Lin (1945, 1955).

If the given velocity profile, $\bar{u}$, has a point of inflexion, then for symmetrical profiles in a channel and boundary-layer profiles there is a band of wavelengths, $\alpha\, (<\alpha_s)$, for which $c_i > 0$. The band is bounded by the neutral state

$$\phi = \phi_s(z), \quad \alpha = \alpha_s, \quad c = \bar{u}_I, \quad c_i = 0. \tag{65}$$

Tollmien's proof of sufficiency consists of showing the existence of this neutral oscillation and of the neighbouring amplified solution. For the neutral case, equation (46) is not singular, and the value of α_s can be determined from a variational condition, namely

$$\alpha_s^2 = \int_{z_1}^{z_2} [K(z)\phi^2 - \phi'^2]\, dz \bigg/ \int_{z_1}^{z_2} \phi^2\, dz, \tag{66}$$

$$\delta(\alpha_s^2) \equiv 0,$$

where
$$K(z) = -\bar{u}''/(\bar{u}-c). \tag{67}$$

In formula (66), ϕ, which is unknown, is chosen to satisfy the boundary conditions and to contain one or more arbitrary constants. The quantity α_s^2, as a function of these constants, is then maximized or minimized. The resulting positive extremal value of α_s^2 gives the eigenvalue; for further details and for a proof of the variational principle the reader is referred to Friedrichs (1942) and to Gregory *et al.* (1955).

Particular calculations of α_s^2 have been made for retarded boundary-layer flows by many authors (see Section 5) employing various methods, and the case of flow in a diverging channel has been solved by Rosenbrook (1937). Applications of the theory to jet and wake flows, and to three-dimensional boundary layers, will be described in Sections 6 and 7.

4.3. *The theory of the instability of two-dimensional parallel flows at finite Reynolds number*

Let us consider the solution of the Orr–Sommerfeld equation (50) with the boundary conditions (51) or (52) for a general function $\bar{u}$, which represents the flow in a channel or in a boundary layer. An essential feature of such flows is that at least one rigid boundary is present.

A point to note about many of the flows considered in this section is that they have no point of inflexion and are therefore stable at infinite Reynolds number. At finite Reynolds numbers the flow is destabilized by viscosity, which assists in developing a suitable Reynolds stress, but it becomes stable as the Reynolds number tends to infinity. The same theory holds at finite Reynolds numbers for profiles, $\bar{u}$, with a point of inflexion, but with the difference that as the Reynolds number tends to infinity the flow still remains unstable. As well as giving the basic theory, we shall here discuss applications to the cases of plane Poiseuille flow in a two-dimensional channel, and the Blasius boundary layer on a flat plate. The theory was first developed by Heisenberg (1924) and Tollmien (1929, 1947), and their work was followed by that of many others, including Tietjens (1925), Schlichting (1933b, 1935a), Lin (1945), Meksyn (1946a, 1947, 1948c), Holstein (1950), Tatsumi (1952b), Thomas (1953), Shen (1954), and Zaat (1958). For further details of the theory outlined below, the reader is referred to these papers and to Lin (1954a, 1955). Another theory, avoiding some of the approximations used below, has been given by Lin (1956b, 1958b) and by Rabenstein (1958).

The Orr–Sommerfeld equation (50) is of the fourth order; the solution therefore contains four arbitrary constants, consists of a linear combination of four basic solutions, and may be written

$$\phi = c_1\phi_1 + c_2\phi_2 + c_3\phi_3 + c_4\phi_4. \tag{68}$$

The functions ϕ_1 and ϕ_2 are known as 'inviscid' solutions, since over large regions of the flow they are virtually unaffected by viscosity and are approximately identical with the two solutions of the inviscid Orr–Sommerfeld equation (56). However, it can be seen that this equation has a singularity at $\bar{u} = c$, whereas the full Orr–Sommerfeld equation has not, so that (56) is not a valid approximation to (50) near such singularities. It can be inferred, therefore, that in the vicinity of points where $\bar{u} = c$ there will be viscous layers or, as they are sometimes called, 'critical' layers. The other two basic solutions of (50), namely ϕ_3 and ϕ_4, are usually known as 'viscous' solutions, and correspond physically to secondary viscous layers on the walls. When considering a particular rigid boundary of the flow, one of the viscous solutions (ϕ_3) decreases exponentially with distance from the wall and is the one which is physically realistic, while the other (ϕ_4) increases exponentially with distance from the wall. It should be noted that the critical layer and the secondary viscous layer on the wall often overlap (see pp. 524–8).

We can now use these general properties of the solutions of the Orr–Sommerfeld equation to discuss simplified forms of the boundary conditions (51) and (52). For Poiseuille flow $\bar{u}$ is an even function, so that the general solution, ϕ, of the Orr–Sommerfeld equation may be split into odd and even solutions. Here we shall consider only the even solution, corresponding to an anti-symmetric disturbance; attention may therefore be focused on the half-channel $z = -1$ to $z = 0$. If we ignore the solution which increases exponentially with distance from the wall, the following three boundary conditions are required for Poiseuille flow, namely

$$\phi = \phi' = 0 \text{ at } z = -1 \quad \text{and} \quad \phi' = 0 \text{ at } z = 0. \qquad (69)$$

The reader is referred to Lin (1955) for further details about the derivation of (69). Since viscous effects are negligible at the channel centre, ϕ is there given by (56). Consequently, the condition $\phi''' = 0$ at $z = 0$ automatically follows from (69).

In Blasius flow (and, indeed, in boundary flows generally) we assume that the effects of viscosity are negligible for the disturbance at the edge of, and outside, the boundary layer. If this is the case, the flow in this region is given by (56) with $\bar{u}$ equal to a constant and the two solutions are proportional to $e^{\pm\alpha z}$, of which only $e^{-\alpha z}$ is physically realistic. Eliminating z from this asymptotic form of ϕ, we find that the boundary condition to be applied on ϕ at $z = z_\delta$, the edge of the boundary layer, is $\phi' + \alpha\phi = 0$. Thus the three boundary conditions appropriate for boundary-layer flows are

$$\phi = \phi' = 0 \text{ at } z = 0 \quad \text{and} \quad \phi' + \alpha\phi = 0 \text{ at } z = z_\delta. \quad (69\,a)$$

In this case a convenient reference velocity is the local free-stream velocity, U_0, and a convenient reference length is the local displacement thickness, δ_1.

The eigenrelation resulting from (69) for Poiseuille flow is found to be

$$\frac{\phi_{3w}}{\phi'_{3w}} = \frac{\phi_{1w}\phi'_{20} - \phi_{2w}\phi'_{10}}{\phi'_{1w}\phi'_{20} - \phi'_{2w}\phi'_{10}}, \quad (70)$$

where the second suffix, w or 0, denotes the wall or the centre of the channel, respectively.

For Blasius flow, the eigenrelation is found to be

$$\frac{\phi_{3w}}{\phi'_{3w}} = \frac{\phi_{1w}\Phi_{2\infty} - \phi_{2w}\Phi_{1\infty}}{\phi'_{1w}\Phi_{2\infty} - \phi'_{2w}\Phi_{1\infty}}, \quad (71)$$

where $\Phi_{n\infty} = \phi'_{n\infty} + \alpha\phi_{n\infty}$ and the second suffix, w or ∞, denotes the wall or the edge of the boundary layer.

Solutions of the Orr–Sommerfeld equation

The inviscid solutions of equation (50) may be derived from the series expansion

$$\phi = \phi^{(0)}(z) + \frac{1}{\alpha R}\phi^{(1)}(z) + \ldots, \quad (72)$$

from which it can be seen that, for large Reynolds numbers, ϕ is given approximately by the inviscid equation (56). Generally it is sufficiently accurate to ignore in (72) the terms of order $(\alpha R)^{-1}$. Two methods have been devised for the solution of (56). One, which was used by Tollmien (1929), is the Frobenius method. The second, which is due to Heisenberg (1924), gives the solutions as convergent series in powers of α^2, namely

$$\phi_1(z) = (\bar{u} - c)[1 + \alpha^2 h_2(z) + \alpha^4 h_4(z) + \ldots],$$

$$\phi_2(z) = (\bar{u} - c)[k_1(z) + \alpha^2 k_3(z) + \alpha^4 k_5(z) + \ldots],$$

where

$$h_{2n+2}(z) = \int^z (\bar{u} - c)^{-2}\, dz \int^z (\bar{u} - c)^2 h_{2n}(z)\, dz$$

and

$$k_1(z) = \int^z (\bar{u} - c)^{-2}\, dz,$$

$$k_{2n+3}(z) = \int^z (\bar{u} - c)^{-2}\, dz \int^z (\bar{u} - c)^2 k_{2n+1}(z)\, dz. \quad (73)$$

The lower limit of integration is arbitrary and can be chosen to suit the

particular conditions of the problem under consideration. For a discussion of the convergence and analytical properties of solutions of
this type, the reader is referred to Lin (1945).

It is known that the value of c, if real, is such that $(\bar{u}-c)$ has a zero
in the range $z_1 < z < z_2$ (see, for example, Lin 1955). If c is complex,
the zero is at a complex value of z. In either case the solutions (73)
contain a singularity, the form of which can be seen more clearly when
the basic solutions of (56) are obtained by the Frobenius method.
Consider, for example, c to be real; then

$$\phi_A = (z-z_c)+a_2(z-z_c)^2+a_3(z-z_c)^3+...,$$
$$\phi_B = 1+b_1(z-z_c)+b_2(z-z_c)^2+...+(\bar{u}_c''/\bar{u}_c')\phi_A\ln(z-z_c) \qquad (74)$$

for z greater than z_c, the point where $\bar{u} = c$. The solutions ϕ_A and ϕ_B
are each linear combinations of ϕ_1 and ϕ_2 of (73). For z less than z_c it
is necessary to determine which of the continuations $[\ln(z_c-z)+n\pi i]$ is
appropriate.

The solution of this problem for *the case of c real* will now be discussed,
and simultaneously the two viscous solutions will be obtained. We
recognize that viscous effects cannot be ignored in layers of rapid change
as, for example, near the singularities of the inviscid equation. Therefore we distort the coordinate z in a way suggested by equation (50)
and put
$$z-z_c = \epsilon\eta, \quad \text{where } \epsilon = (\alpha R\bar{u}_c')^{-1/3}. \qquad (75)$$

Expanding $(\bar{u}-c)$ in powers of $(z-z_c)$ and putting
$$\phi = \chi_0+\epsilon\chi_1+\epsilon^2\chi_2+..., \qquad (76)$$
we obtain the equations
$$i\frac{d^4\chi_0}{d\eta^4}+\eta\frac{d^2\chi_0}{d\eta^2} = 0, \qquad (77)$$

and
$$i\frac{d^4\chi_1}{d\eta^4}+\eta\frac{d^2\chi_1}{d\eta^2} = \frac{\bar{u}_c''}{\bar{u}_c'}\chi_0-\frac{1}{2}\frac{\bar{u}_c''}{\bar{u}_c'}\eta^2\frac{d^2\chi_0}{d\eta^2}, \qquad (78)$$

together with higher-order equations. The four basic solutions of
(77) are
$$\chi_0^{(1)} = 1,$$
$$\chi_0^{(2)} = \eta,$$
$$\chi_0^{(3)} = \int_\infty^\eta d\eta \int_\infty^\eta \eta^{1/2}H_{1/3}^{(1)}[\tfrac{2}{3}(i\eta)^{3/2}]\,d\eta,$$
$$\chi_0^{(4)} = \int_{-\infty}^\eta d\eta \int_{-\infty}^\eta \eta^{1/2}H_{1/3}^{(2)}[\tfrac{2}{3}(i\eta)^{3/2}]\,d\eta, \qquad (79)$$

where $H_{1/3}^{(1)}$, $H_{1/3}^{(2)}$ denote Hankel functions of order $\frac{1}{3}$. These four solutions are the first terms in expansions in powers of ϵ of the four solutions of the Orr–Sommerfeld equation. The solutions $\chi_0^{(1)}$ and $\chi_0^{(2)}$ correspond to the first terms of ϕ_B and ϕ_A of (74) when these forms of solution are expanded in such series. On the other hand, the integrals $\chi_0^{(3)}$ and $\chi_0^{(4)}$ are viscous solutions. It can be shown by using the asymptotic properties of the Hankel functions for large values of η that $\chi_0^{(3)}$ tends to zero for large positive η and $\chi_0^{(4)}$ tends to zero for large negative η. Since in general $\bar{u}_c'$ is positive, ϵ is positive; η is therefore negative at the wall and positive on the other side of the singularity. Consequently, the integral $\chi_0^{(3)}$ is the physically realistic one representing the secondary boundary layer on the wall. In most calculations $\chi_0^{(3)}$ has been used as an approximation to ϕ_3, but Lock (1954, 1955) has shown how the higher-order term $\chi_1^{(3)}$, which is given by (78), can be used in calculations of instability. The function $\chi_0^{(3)}$ and its first two derivatives are tabulated in Table IX. 1, due to Holstein (1950).

In order to see how the logarithmic term of (74) is transformed through the singularity we follow Heisenberg (1924), Tollmien (1929), and Lin (1945) and proceed as follows. The second solution of (74), namely the singular one ϕ_B, has $\chi_0^{(1)}$ as its first term in an expansion in powers of ϵ. Thus the term proportional to ϵ, namely $\chi_1^{(1)}$, is given by

$$i\frac{d^4\chi_1^{(1)}}{d\eta^4} + \eta\frac{d^2\chi_1^{(1)}}{d\eta^2} = \frac{\bar{u}_c''}{\bar{u}_c'}. \tag{80}$$

Now from (76) and (77), when ϵ is positive ϕ_B can be written

$$\phi_B = 1 + \epsilon\left[b_1\eta + \frac{\bar{u}_c''}{\bar{u}_c'}\eta(\ln\eta + \ln\epsilon)\right] + \dots \tag{81}$$

Thus it is necessary to find a solution of (80) which tends to $(\bar{u}_c''/\bar{u}_c')\eta\ln\eta$ for large positive η; in addition, the transformation of $\eta\ln\eta$ for large negative η must be obtained. Effects of viscosity on the regular terms of (81) can be expected to be small.

In the region of the singularity it has been shown that $\eta\ln\eta$ must be replaced by a function $N(\eta)$ which behaves like $\eta\ln\eta$ for large positive η and like $\eta\ln|\eta| - \pi i\eta$ for large negative η, where the solution of (80) is $\chi_1^{(1)} = (\bar{u}_c''/\bar{u}_c')N(\eta)$. Thus it follows that $\ln(z-z_c)$ tends to $[\ln|z-z_c| - \pi i]$ for $z < z_c$. For a more detailed discussion of the derivation of the transformation through the singularity, see Holstein's paper (1950). The function $N(\eta)$ and its first two derivatives are tabulated in Table IX. 2, which is due to Holstein (1950). For determining

TABLE IX. 1

The viscous integral, $\chi_0^{(3)}$, and its first two derivatives, as defined by equation (79). Suffixes r and i denote real and imaginary parts

η	$\chi_{0r}^{(3)\prime\prime}$	$\chi_{0i}^{(3)\prime\prime}$	$\chi_{0r}^{(3)\prime}$	$\chi_{0i}^{(3)\prime}$	$\chi_{0r}^{(3)}$	$\chi_{0i}^{(3)}$
-8	$-24{,}504$	$+5{,}003$	$-4{,}781$	$-7{,}678$	$-933\cdot0$	$+3{,}187$
$-7\cdot5$	$+3{,}567$	$+8{,}807$	$+1{,}488$	$-3{,}232$	$-1{,}317\cdot8$	$+393\cdot7$
-7	$-2{,}007$	$+3{,}148$	$+1{,}428$	$-264\cdot6$	$-475\cdot2$	$-359\cdot7$
$-6\cdot5$	$-1{,}514$	$+127\cdot7$	$+457\cdot1$	$+415\cdot0$	$-15\cdot1$	$-259\cdot4$
-6	$-446\cdot1$	$-459\cdot6$	$-12\cdot7$	$+270\cdot9$	$+73\cdot5$	$-75\cdot8$
$-5\cdot5$	$+21\cdot9$	$-279\cdot7$	$-95\cdot2$	$+76\cdot6$	$+36\cdot8$	$+7\cdot4$
-5	$+99\cdot3430$	$-80\cdot6134$	$-55\cdot5342$	$-8\cdot9098$	$-2\cdot9339$	$+20\cdot2894$
$-4\cdot5$	$+60\cdot6109$	$+5\cdot4856$	$-14\cdot1558$	$-23\cdot5597$	$-19\cdot5132$	$+10\cdot3989$
-4	$+20\cdot6566$	$+22\cdot1652$	$+5\cdot3696$	$-14\cdot9220$	$-20\cdot8723$	$+0\cdot4475$
$-3\cdot5$	$+1\cdot0234$	$+15\cdot7821$	$+10\cdot0130$	$-5\cdot0795$	$-16\cdot6208$	$-4\cdot4131$
-3	$-4\cdot7230$	$+7\cdot2490$	$+8\cdot7035$	$+0\cdot5859$	$-11\cdot8249$	$-5\cdot3573$
$-2\cdot5$	$-4\cdot6734$	$+1\cdot8631$	$+6\cdot2323$	$+2\cdot7209$	$-8\cdot0934$	$-4\cdot4186$
-2	$-3\cdot2284$	$-0\cdot6462$	$+4\cdot2472$	$+2\cdot9316$	$-5\cdot5041$	$-2\cdot9537$
$-1\cdot5$	$-2\cdot0057$	$-1\cdot5002$	$+2\cdot9601$	$+2\cdot3479$	$-3\cdot7278$	$-1\cdot6163$
-1	$-1\cdot3134$	$-1\cdot5649$	$+2\cdot1509$	$+1\cdot5605$	$-2\cdot4644$	$-0\cdot6380$
$-0\cdot5$	$-1\cdot0082$	$-1\cdot2832$	$+1\cdot5819$	$+0\cdot8395$	$-1\cdot5375$	$-0\cdot0439$
0	$-0\cdot8696$	$-0\cdot8696$	$+1\cdot1154$	$+0\cdot2989$	$-0\cdot8660$	$+0\cdot2320$
$+0\cdot5$	$-0\cdot7399$	$-0\cdot4535$	$+0\cdot7114$	$-0\cdot0299$	$-0\cdot4120$	$+0\cdot2906$
$+1$	$-0\cdot5605$	$-0\cdot1260$	$+0\cdot3842$	$-0\cdot1697$	$-0\cdot1419$	$+0\cdot2339$
$+1\cdot5$	$-0\cdot3521$	$+0\cdot0660$	$+0\cdot1559$	$-0\cdot1788$	$-0\cdot0112$	$+0\cdot1428$
$+2$	$-0\cdot1670$	$+0\cdot1295$	$+0\cdot0281$	$-0\cdot1253$	$+0\cdot0309$	$+0\cdot0655$
$+2\cdot5$	$-0\cdot0436$	$+0\cdot1101$	$-0\cdot0216$	$-0\cdot0631$	$+0\cdot0299$	$+0\cdot0188$
$+3$	$+0\cdot0133$	$+0\cdot0618$	$-0\cdot0267$	$+0\cdot0199$	$+0\cdot0167$	$-0\cdot00093$
$+3\cdot5$	$+0\cdot0243$	$+0\cdot0212$	$-0\cdot0160$	$+0\cdot00016$	$+0\cdot00575$	$-0\cdot00499$
$+4$	$+0\cdot0158$	$+0\cdot00052$	$-0\cdot00564$	$+0\cdot00479$	$+0\cdot00052$	$-0\cdot00333$
$+4\cdot5$	$+0\cdot0057$	$+0\cdot00478$	$-0\cdot00043$	$+0\cdot00326$	$-0\cdot00078$	$-0\cdot00121$
$+5$	$+0\cdot00034$	$-0\cdot00332$	$+0\cdot00086$	$+0\cdot00114$	$-0\cdot00057$	$-0\cdot00013$
$+5\cdot5$	$-0\cdot0094$	$-0\cdot00110$	$+0\cdot00059$	$+0\cdot00007$	$-0\cdot00019$	$-0\cdot00014$
$+6$	$-0\cdot0061$	$-0\cdot00009$	$+0\cdot00018$	$-0\cdot00016$	$-0\cdot000009$	$+0\cdot000092$
$+6\cdot5$	$-0\cdot0016$	$+0\cdot000189$	$-0\cdot000005$	$-0\cdot000094$	$+0\cdot000025$	$+0\cdot000024$
$+7$	$+0\cdot000021$	$+0\cdot000021$	$-0\cdot000030$	$-0\cdot000020$	$+0\cdot000013$	$+0\cdot000002$
$+7\cdot5$	$+0\cdot000034$	$+0\cdot000034$	$-0\cdot000012$	$+0\cdot000005$	$+0\cdot000002$	$-0\cdot000004$
$+8$	$+0\cdot000011$	$+0\cdot000007$	$-0\cdot000001$	$+0\cdot000005$	$-0\cdot000001$	$-0\cdot000001$

TABLE IX. 2

The function $N(\eta)$ and its first two derivatives, as defined by equation (80). Suffix i denotes imaginary part

η	$N''(\eta)$ Real	$N''(\eta)$ Imag.	$N'(\eta)$ Real	$N'(\eta)$ Imag.	$N(\eta)$ Real	$N(\eta)$ Imag.
0	0	1·2879	0·2494	−1·5708	0	0·9389
0·5	0·4434	1·1677	0·3634	−0·9472	0·1437	0·3120
1·0	0·7475	0·8594	0·6691	−0·4349	0·3953	−0·0271
1·5	0·8454	0·4878	1·0760	−0·0983	0·8293	−0·1526
2·0	0·7657	0·1777	1·4845	0·0631	1·4709	−0·1548
2·5	0·5969	−0·0061	1·8268	0·1008	2·3021	−0·1099
3·0	0·4281	−0·0704	2·0817	0·0776	3·2826	−0·0640
3·5	0·3082	−0·0635	2·2633	0·0423	4·3711	−0·0342
4·0	0·2419	−0·0348	2·3990	0·0176	5·5379	−0·0198
4·5	0·2105	−0·0122	2·5110	0·0063	6·7659	−0·0144
5·0	0·1936	−0·0021	2·6107	0·0031	8·0467	−0·0122
5·5	0·1801	0·0000	2·7052	0·0029	9·3760	−0·0107
6·0	0·1668	−0·0005	2·7919	0·0028	10·7504	−0·0092
6·5	0·1538	−0·0011	2·8719	0·0024	12·16	−0·0079
7·0	0·1428	−0·0008	2·9460	0·0019	13·62	−0·0068
7·5	0·1333	−0·0006	3·0149	0·0016	15·11	−0·0059
8·0	0·1250	−0·0005	3·0795	0·0013	16·64	−0·0052
	Odd function of η	*Even function of η*	*Even function of η*	$\frac{1}{2}\pi + N_i'(\eta)$ *is an odd function of η*	*Odd function of η*	$\frac{1}{2}\pi\eta + N_i(\eta)$ *is an even function of η*

the continuation of the table for negative η, the following facts should be used:

(i) the real parts of $N''(\eta)$ and $N(\eta)$ are odd functions of η, and the real part of $N'(\eta)$ is an even function;

(ii) the imaginary part of $N''(\eta)$ is even, $\frac{1}{2}\pi$ plus the imaginary part of $N'(\eta)$ is odd, and $\frac{1}{2}\pi\eta$ plus the imaginary part of $N(\eta)$ is even.

An important result established by Lin (1945, 1955) and Wasow (1948) for amplified ($c_i > 0$) and damped ($c_i < 0$) disturbances is that a similar transformation of $\eta \ln \eta$ still holds in these cases.

For the eigenvalue problem it is generally sufficient to use the asymptotic forms $\ln(z-z_c)$ and $[\ln|z-z_c| - \pi i]$, since at the boundaries η is so large that the asymptotic forms of $N(\eta)$ are valid. Thus for $z < z_c$, ϕ_B becomes

$$\phi_B = 1 + b_1(z-z_c) + \ldots + (\bar{u}_c''/\bar{u}_c')\phi_A[\ln|z-z_c| - \pi i], \tag{82}$$

and similar transformations are made in the (more practical) inviscid integrals (73). However, for calculations of ϕ at various values of z (as is required, for example, in calculating the Reynolds stress) the function

$N(\eta)$ must be used instead of $\eta \ln \eta$. Thus in the inviscid integrals, wherever the expression $(z-z_c)^n \ln(z-z_c)$ appears (n integral), we write

$$(z-z_c)^n \ln(z-z_c) = (z-z_c)^{n-1}[\epsilon\{N(\eta)+\eta \ln \epsilon\}]. \tag{83}$$

Thus, to recapitulate, ϕ_1 and ϕ_2 are given approximately by (73), subject to the modification (83), ϕ_3 is given approximately by $\chi_0^{(3)}$ of (79) and ϕ is then given by (68). It is emphasized that the above analysis assumes that the wall viscous layer is embedded within the critical layer; this feature is present in most calculations.

Solution of the eigenvalue problem

The right-hand sides of (70) and (71) can be calculated from (73), with the transformation discussed. The left-hand sides can be calculated from $\phi_3 = \chi_0^{(3)}$. If z_1 denotes the value of z at the wall (-1 for plane Poiseuille flow and 0 for boundary-layer flow), we can define

$$Z = -[\eta]_{\text{wall}} = (\alpha R \bar{u}_c')^{1/3}(z_c-z_1),$$

$$F(Z) = \frac{-\int\limits_\infty^{-Z} d\eta \int\limits_\infty^\eta \eta^{1/2} H_{1/3}^{(1)}[\tfrac{2}{3}(i\eta)^{3/2}]\, d\eta}{Z \int\limits_\infty^{-Z} \eta^{1/2} H_{1/3}^{(1)}[\tfrac{2}{3}(i\eta)^{3/2}]\, d\eta}, \tag{84}$$

and the eigenrelation is then

$$F(Z) = \frac{1}{(z_1-z_c)}\left[\frac{\phi_{1w}\phi_{20}'-\phi_{2w}\phi_{10}'}{\phi_{1w}'\phi_{20}'-\phi_{2w}'\phi_{10}'}\right] \tag{85}$$

for Poiseuille flow, and

$$F(Z) = \frac{1}{(z_1-z_c)}\left[\frac{\phi_{1w}\Phi_{2\infty}-\phi_{2w}\Phi_{1\infty}}{\phi_{1w}'\Phi_{2\infty}-\phi_{2w}'\Phi_{1\infty}}\right] \tag{86}$$

for Blasius flow. The function $F(Z)$ was first tabulated by Tietjens (1925). More accurate calculations have been made by Lin (1945), Holstein (1950), and Lock (1954).

Consider, as before, the case of c real ($c_i = 0$; neutral disturbance). It can be seen that the right-hand sides of (85) and (86) are functions of c (or z_c) and α only, while the left-hand side is a function of Z only. Two methods of solving the problem have been devised, one graphical, due to Tollmien (1929), and the other iterative-numerical, due to Lin (1945). Lin's method is based on rewriting (85) and (86) in the form

$$F(Z) = E/(z_1-z_c), \tag{87}$$

which is equivalent to

$$[1-(1+\lambda)F(Z)]^{-1} = (1+\bar{u}'_w E/c)^{-1} = u+iv, \qquad (88)$$

where λ is defined by $c = \bar{u}'_w(z_c-z_1)/(1+\lambda)$ and $\bar{u}'_w$ denotes the value of $\bar{u}'$ at the wall. For small values of c, λ is small. Lin therefore puts

$$\mathscr{F}(Z) = [1-F(Z)]^{-1}, \qquad (89)$$

and (88) becomes $\mathscr{F}(Z) = \dfrac{(1+\lambda)(u+iv)}{1+\lambda(u+iv)}.$ \qquad (90)

The function $\mathscr{F}(Z)$ is tabulated in Table IX. 3, due to Lin (1945). For further details of the calculation of the inviscid integral (73) and for details of the iterative method of solving the boundary-value problem, the reader is referred to Lin (1945, 1955).

TABLE IX. 3

The function $\mathscr{F}(Z)$, as defined by equation (89)

Z	$\mathscr{F}_r(Z)$	$\mathscr{F}_i(Z)$
1·0	0·80630	−2·60557
1·2	1·77012	−2·29854
1·4	2·26836	−1·71669
1·6	2·44985	−1·18600
1·8	2·48104	−0·75892
2·0	2·43927	−0·41253
2·2	2·35196	−0·12348
2·4	2·22724	0·11916
2·6	2·06929	0·31558
2·8	1·88566	0·46043
3·0	1·68938	0·54872
3·2	1·49726	0·58082
3·4	1·32516	0·56401
3·6	1·18429	0·51074
3·8	1·07982	0·43560
4·0	1·01118	0·35220
4·2	0·97361	0·27133
4·4	0·96056	0·20038
4·6	0·95989	0·13601
4·8	0·97659	0·09503
5·0	0·99582	0·07266

The eigenrelation, (85) or (86), depends on α, c_r, and R; since it is a complex relation, it may be separated into two real relations. If c_r, for example, is then eliminated we have a relation between α and R. The result of plotting α against R is called the 'neutral' curve, or the curve of neutral stability. Two possible types, one applicable to flows which are stable at infinite Reynolds number (A) and the other to flows which are unstable at infinite Reynolds number (B), are illustrated in Fig. IX. 6. The lowest Reynolds number on each curve is the critical Reynolds number. The inside of each curve is a region of instability.

Curves of constant c_i or αc_i can be calculated from the neutral curve by a perturbation procedure (Schlichting 1933b; Shen 1954).

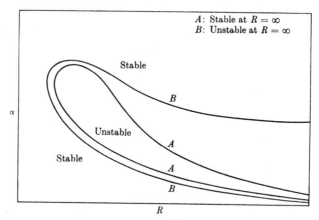

FIG. IX. 6. Typical curves of neutral stability for boundary-layer flow.

4.4. Results for the instability of plane Poiseuille flow

The problem of the instability of plane Poiseuille flow was first considered by Heisenberg (1924) and, although he did not calculate the critical Reynolds number, he did show that the flow is unstable at large but finite Reynolds numbers. Later calculations have been made by Lin (1945), who obtained a critical Reynolds number ($R = U_0 h/\nu$) of 5,300; by Thomas (1953), who obtained 5,780; by Lock (1955), who obtained 6,000; and by several others. In the last-named calculation the more accurate form of the viscous solution, including the term of order ϵ, was used. Thomas (1953) solved the Orr–Sommerfeld equation (50) by numerical integration on a high-speed digital computer. Thomas's results, which were obtained for both damped and amplified disturbances, may therefore be regarded as 'exact' ones, with which other results may be compared. It is noteworthy that the result obtained by Lock, using a more refined technique of approximation, is the nearest to the critical Reynolds number calculated by Thomas. Most of the results obtained by Thomas (1953) were for non-neutral disturbances ($c_i \neq 0$) and it is not possible to compare his results with the neutral curve obtained by analytical methods. However, Shen (1954) has calculated curves of constant c_i by perturbing the neutral curve obtained by Lin (1945). His results are compared with those of Thomas in Fig. IX. 7. It can be seen that the results obtained by Shen agree well with those of Thomas, though there is some discrepancy.

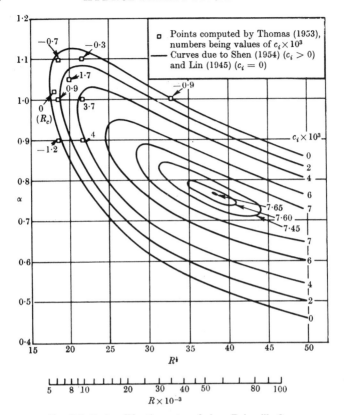

FIG. IX. 7. Amplification rates of plane Poiseuille flow.

As the Reynolds number tends to infinity, both branches of the neutral curve approach the axis and the flow becomes stable. Tollmien (1929) and Lin (1945) have calculated the behaviour of the neutral curve at large Reynolds number. The results of Lin are that on the upper branch

$$R^{1/3} = 8 \cdot 44(\alpha^2)^{-11/6}; \qquad c = 4\alpha^2/15, \tag{91}$$

while on the lower branch

$$R^{1/3} = 5 \cdot 96(\alpha^2)^{-7/6}; \qquad c = 0 \cdot 611\alpha^2. \tag{92}$$

Lin has also given a rapid approximate method to estimate the critical Reynolds number for velocity profiles of the type found in a channel, for example Poiseuille flow. As before, we consider the half-channel $z = -1$ to $z = 0$. In this case c is given by the solution of

$$-\pi \bar{u}'_w (\bar{u} \bar{u}'' / \bar{u}'^3)_c = 0 \cdot 58, \tag{93}$$

where $\bar{u}'_w$ denotes the gradient of $\bar{u}$ at $z = -1$, and the suffix c denotes the point where $\bar{u} = c$. Equation (93) can be solved numerically by plotting the left-hand side against z and then finding the value of $\bar{u}$ where the left-hand side takes the value 0·58. This value of $\bar{u}$ is, of course, the value of c, and the values of α and R are given by

$$\alpha^2 = \bar{u}'_w c / H_{10}, \qquad R_c = \frac{30\bar{u}'_w}{c^3} \sqrt{\left(\frac{H_{10}\,\bar{u}'_w}{c}\right)},$$

where

$$H_{10} = \int_{-1}^{0} \bar{u}^2\, dz. \qquad (94)$$

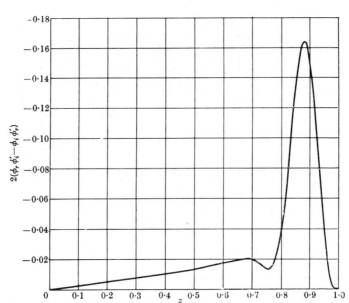

FIG. IX. 8. Reynolds stress for plane Poiseuille flow.

For Poiseuille flow, the formula yields a critical Reynolds number of about 5,500 (Lin 1955).

When the eigenvalues of the flow are known, it is possible to obtain the distribution of ϕ for different values of z. This has been done by Thomas on a high-speed computing machine for the case, $R = 10^4$, $\alpha = 1$, $c = 0.2375 + 0.0037i$. From Thomas's calculations it is possible to calculate the Reynolds stress function $2(\phi_r \phi'_i - \phi_i \phi'_r)$. This is illustrated in Fig. IX. 8 for the range $0 \leqslant z \leqslant 1$ (ϕ is even and the Reynolds stress is odd). The Reynolds stress is of such a sign that energy is transferred from the basic flow to the disturbance at all z (Section 4.1).

Furthermore, it should be noted that the Reynolds stress has a strong maximum near the point where $\bar{u} = c_r$.

4.5. *Numerical results and comparison with experiment for Blasius flow*

The theoretical problem of the instability of boundary-layer flows was first studied by Tietjens (1925) for the case of velocity profiles consisting of combinations of broken straight lines. He took into account the secondary viscous layer on the wall, but because of the fact that $\bar{u}''$

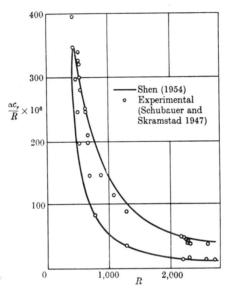

FIG. IX. 9. Comparison of neutral curve with experiment for Blasius flow.

equalled zero at every part of the velocity profile there was no singularity at $\bar{u} = c$ and no critical layer. No critical Reynolds number was calculated. This defect was remedied by Tollmien (1929), who developed the theory for curved velocity profiles, including both the critical layer and the secondary viscous layer on the wall. Tollmien calculated the neutral curve and obtained a critical Reynolds number ($R = U_0 \delta_1/\nu$) of 420, where U_0 is the free-stream velocity and δ_1 is the local displacement thickness. A more recent calculation by Lin (1945) has given a neutral curve and critical Reynolds number substantially the same as Tollmien's. Lin's neutral curve of $\beta_r \nu/U_0^2 (= \alpha c_r/R)$, where β_r is the frequency of the disturbance, plotted against R, is shown together with the experimental results of Schubauer and Skramstad (1947) in Fig. IX. 9, taken from Shen (1954).

Schlichting (1933b) has calculated the eigenvalues for amplified oscillations, giving curves of constant amplification factor, αc_i; more recently
Shen (1954) has made a similar calculation based on a perturbation of
Lin's more accurate neutral curve, but giving the results in the form
of curves of constant c_i. At a given Reynolds number the dimensionless
amplification factor, $\beta_i \delta_1/U_0$ ($= \alpha c_i$), varies with α and is zero at those

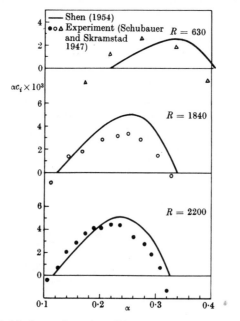

FIG. IX. 10. Comparison of amplification rates for Blasius flow.

values of α corresponding to the neutral curve. Values of αc_i calculated
by Shen for three values of R are shown together with experimental
results due to Schubauer and Skramstad in Fig. IX. 10. The agreement
of the theoretical values with experiment is quite good, especially at
the higher Reynolds numbers.

Schlichting (1935a) has also calculated the distribution of amplitude
across the boundary layer for two particular neutral oscillations.
Schubauer and Skramstad carried out experimental traverses through
the boundary layer at substantially the same Reynolds numbers and
frequencies with the result, for the component of perturbation velocity
parallel to the wall, shown in Fig. IX. 11. The agreement with theory
is remarkable, especially with regard to the shift of phase of the
perturbation velocity at about seven-tenths of the boundary-layer

thickness from the surface. The reader is referred also to a paper by Zaat (1958).

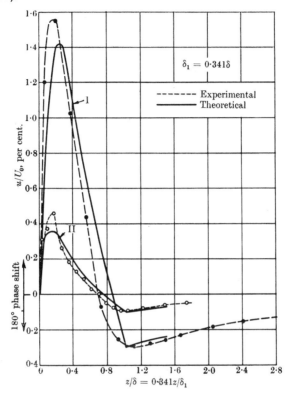

FIG. IX. 11. Distribution of amplitude of oscillations across the boundary layer. Experimental data: I, $R = 900$, $\alpha c_r/R = 61\cdot4 \times 10^{-6}$; II, $R = 2080$, $\alpha c_r/R = 40\cdot6 \times 10^{-6}$.

A rapid approximate method for calculating the minimum critical Reynolds number, similar to the one already described in Section 4.4 for channel flows, has also been given by Lin. As before, formula (93) is used to determine the value of c. Then α and R are given by

$$\alpha = \bar{u}_w' c, \qquad R_c = 25\bar{u}_w'/c^4. \tag{95}$$

These formulae may be expected to give an approximate critical Reynolds number for any boundary-layer flow. For the particular case of Blasius flow it gives $R_c = 500$, which is in reasonably good agreement with the rigorously derived neutral curve and with the experimental results.

An account of hydrodynamic instability in the case of Blasius flow in a boundary layer would be incomplete without a description of the historically important and scientifically interesting experiments of Schubauer and Skramstad (1947). Before this work was done the instability theory was very much at a discount, and it was generally believed that the selective amplification of infinitesimal disturbance had little to do with the phenomenon of transition. In contrast with this belief, one of the most important experiments of Schubauer and

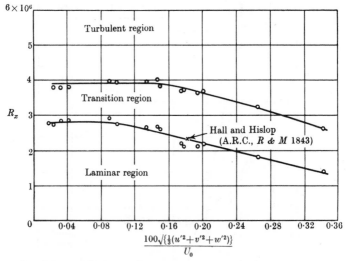

Fig. IX. 12. Effects of turbulence on Reynolds number of transition.
($R_x = U_0 x/\nu$, x = distance from leading edge.)

Skramstad showed that, if the turbulence in the free stream was reduced to a level of very low intensity, transition was preceded by instability waves of the kind predicted by Tollmien and Schlichting. For higher levels of turbulence intensity, transition to turbulence in the boundary layer was found to be related to the actual level of turbulence. These features are illustrated in Figs. IX. 12 and 13, due to Schubauer and Skramstad (1947). The turbulence in the free stream was reduced by increase in the number of, and decrease of the coarseness of, the damping screens. As the turbulence was reduced, the Reynolds number of the transition region rose; however, decrease of the turbulence level below about 0·08 per cent. of the free-stream speed had little further effect on the position of transition (Fig. IX. 12), and experiments showed that transition was preceded by oscillations, as shown in Fig. IX. 13 for a turbulence level of 0·03 per cent. (It should be noticed, however, that Bennett (1953) showed that similar oscillations play a

role in the boundary layer even when the free-stream turbulence is
as high as 0·42 per cent.) The oscillograms were obtained by hot-wire
anemometry (Section X. 13) and show the nature of the oscillation at
different distances from the leading edge. It can be seen from Fig. IX.
13 that, in the region close to the leading edge, a regular sinusoidal
oscillation was present, which later became distorted until, just before

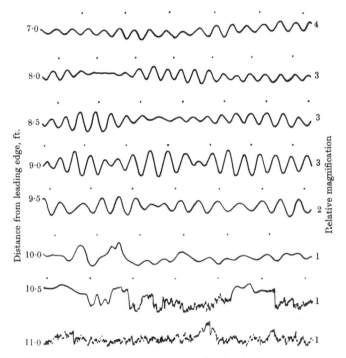

FIG. IX. 13. Oscillograms of u-fluctuations showing laminar boundary-layer
oscillations in boundary layer of flat plate. Distance from surface, 0·023 in.;
$U_0 = 53$ ft/sec; time interval between dots, 1/30 sec.

transition, bursts of irregular fluctuations appeared. (The reader is
referred to Section 8.3 for a discussion of the latter phenomenon.)

The observations mentioned above led Schubauer and Skramstad to
compare the frequencies of natural sinusoidal oscillations with the
frequencies of the waves predicted by the instability theory of Tollmien
and Schlichting for Blasius flow. They found that when the frequency
was plotted against Reynolds number, the points lay on the 'upper'
branch of a curve similar to that shown in Fig. IX. 9. They inferred
from this feature that a disturbance of a given frequency was amplified

as it passed downstream into regions of higher Reynolds number and attained its maximum amplitude at a point on the upper branch of the neutral curve, unless it had by then caused transition. Thus, at a given Reynolds number, the strongest disturbance of those present would be that corresponding to a point on the upper branch of the neutral curve.

Once it was established that instability waves of the kind predicted by theory really did occur, it was clearly desirable to perform controlled experiments with artificially produced disturbances of suitable frequency. Schubauer and Skramstad tried several methods of producing disturbances, including sound from a loudspeaker and sound introduced into the boundary layer through a hole in the flat plate. By far the most satisfactory method, however, proved to be the use of a 'vibrating ribbon'. This consisted of a thin, flat strip of phosphor bronze placed edgewise to the flow and oscillated by means of electromagnets (which were outside the region of flow). In this way a disturbance which was reasonably two-dimensional was obtained.

A hot-wire anemometer was used to measure the amplitude, wavelength, and frequency of the disturbance at different distances downstream. From the measurements of amplitude at different distances it was possible to determine the rate of amplification or damping of the disturbance. Some of Schubauer and Skramstad's results are shown in Figs. IX. 9, IX. 10, and IX. 11, which have been described earlier in this section.

Bennett (1953) also has studied boundary-layer oscillations by means of a hot-wire anemometer, while Wortmann (1953, 1955) and Bergh and Van den Berg (1958) have studied them by means of electro-chemical methods of flow visualization (see also Bergh 1958). For some photographic evidence by interferometry of instability in the free-convection boundary layer on a vertical flat plate, the reader is referred to Eckert and Soehngen (1951) and to Eckert, Soehngen, and Schneider (1955).

4.6. *Some important stability problems*

One of the classical problems of hydrodynamic stability which still remains unsolved is that of the instability of plane Couette motion, generated when two parallel planes are in relative motion. Many authors, including Hopf (1914), Southwell and Chitty (1930), Morawetz (1952), Wasow (1953), and Grohne (1954), have considered the problem, and their results combine to show that there is every likelihood that the flow is completely stable for infinitesimal disturbances, though this has never been proved rigorously for all hydrodynamically possible modes of disturbance. There is little doubt, however, that if the Reynolds number is high enough the flow can be unstable and become turbulent (see Taylor 1936, p. 562), and it is very important to know just how this occurs. It is quite possible that plane Couette flow is unstable for finite disturbances, even though it is stable for infinitesimal ones. However, a solution of the problem of the instability of plane Couette flow for finite disturbances still has to be found. A related possibility, suggested by Schlichting (1932b), is that instability in Couette flow may occur during the initial period when the flow is developing from rest by the impulsive motion of one of the planes. (However, for the disturbance to persist, steady Couette flow must be unstable for finite disturbances.) By examining the instability of the velocity profiles during this initial period (see Section VII. 3), Schlichting found a minimum critical Reynolds number, based on the distance between the planes, of about 19,000.

A flow related to plane Couette flow is that between concentric cylinders when the outer one rotates and the inner one is at rest, for then the centrifugal forces act in a stabilizing sense and the type of instability described in Section 2 does not occur. However, there remains the possibility of instability for two-dimensional disturbances. In this connexion, Schlichting (1932c) examined theoretically the stability of the flow which is generated when the outer cylinder is started impulsively from rest, and found a critical Reynolds number of 66,000 based on the radius and velocity of the outer cylinder. It seems likely that the steady flow is stable for infinitesimal disturbances, but probably unstable for finite disturbances.

The instability of Poiseuille flow in a straight pipe of circular section has been considered by Sexl (1927a, b), Pretsch (1941c), Belyakova (1950), Sexl and Spielberg (1958), and Corcos and Sellars (1959), and it seems that the flow is probably stable for axi-symmetric infinitesimal disturbances. Experimentally, both Ekman (1910) and Taylor (unpublished) obtained laminar flow up to Reynolds numbers of order 5×10^4, based on mean flow and radius, when great care was taken to exclude all possible disturbances. On the other hand, Tatsumi (1952a) has shown theoretically that the flow in the entry region of the pipe is unstable at a Reynolds number of order 10^4. The reader is referred to some experimental work by Leite (1959) on the stability of the flow for finite disturbances (see also Kuethe 1956).

In connexion with the results for the instability of plane Poiseuille flow (Section 4.4) it is of interest to note that Hahnemann, Freeman, and Finston (1948) have shown that the flow in the entry region of the channel is more stable for infinitesimal disturbances than fully developed Poiseuille flow.

For discussions of the effects of a magnetic field on the stability of parallel flow of a conducting fluid, the reader is referred to papers by Michael (1953), Stuart (1954b), Lock (1955), and Rossow (1958), and to the book by Cowling (1957). For work on instability in the presence of a free surface see Benjamin (1957) and Binnie (1959).

5. Applications of the instability theory to two-dimensional boundary layers

In this section we shall be concerned with the effects of such factors as pressure gradient, suction, and density stratification on the instability of boundary-layer flows. As before, the boundary layer is replaced by a parallel flow. Unless otherwise stated the reference length and reference velocity are, respectively, δ_1, the local displacement thickness, and U_0, the *local* external flow velocity. The external velocity is $U(x)$, where x is the distance from the stagnation point.

Surface curvature will be neglected. However, a result due to Görtler (1940a) is of some interest, namely that a necessary condition for instability with respect to two-dimensional disturbances at infinite Reynolds number is that $(\bar{u}'' + \bar{u}'/\rho)$ shall change sign. The quantity ρ denotes the ratio of the curvature to the displacement thickness, and is positive for a convex and negative for a concave wall. Normally, of course, ρ is large and the influence of wall curvature is small, as far as two-dimensional disturbances are concerned. But if the wall is concave, instability of the kind discussed in Section 2.2 may be expected.

5.1. *Effects of pressure gradient*

Many calculations have been made of the effects of pressure gradient on hydrodynamic stability; Schlichting (1940), for example, considered velocity profiles for flow along a semi-infinite plane with the external velocity distribution $U(x) = \beta_0 - \beta_1 x$, where x is the distance from the leading edge. If ξ $(= \beta_1 x/\beta_0)$ is positive the flow is retarded, whereas if ξ is negative it is accelerated. It was found that as ξ increases through positive values, corresponding to an increase in the adverse pressure gradient, the critical local Reynolds number $(U_0 \delta_1/\nu)$ drops; on the other hand, as ξ increases in magnitude through negative values, corresponding to an increase in the favourable pressure gradient, the critical

Reynolds number rises. A noteworthy feature is that for retarded flow the velocity profiles have a point of inflexion and thus are unstable even at infinite Reynolds number (Fig. IX. 6, curve B); on the other hand, for accelerated flow the curves of neutral stability are similar to that for Blasius flow (Fig. IX. 6, curve A).

Other velocity profiles which have been examined for instability include:

(i) The Falkner–Skan profiles (Section V. 16) (Pretsch 1941b, 1942; Hahnemann et al. 1948; Tetervin 1953).

(ii) Profiles replaced by sixth-order polynomial approximations (Schlichting and Ulrich 1940; Hahnemann et al. 1948), or by combinations of sinusoidal and exponential functions (Tetervin and Levine 1952).

Schlichting (1940), Pretsch (1941b), and Schlichting and Ulrich (1940) used the original method as developed by Tollmien (1929) and Schlichting (1933b, 1935a) for Blasius flow. On the other hand, Hahnemann et al. (1948), Tetervin and Levine (1952), and Tetervin (1953) calculated the critical Reynolds number from (93) and (95). To judge from a comparison with the well-known result for Blasius flow, the calculations made by Lin's method, (93) and (95), appear to be the more reliable.

All the velocity profiles mentioned above are either members of one-parameter families or are assumed to be, and the results for the critical Reynolds number ($R_{2c} = U_0 \delta_2/\nu$) based on momentum thickness (δ_2) are shown plotted against the parameter λ_2 (= $(\delta_2^2/\nu)dU/dx$) in Fig. IX. 14. The curve is drawn to pass through the accepted value for Blasius flow ($R_c = 420$, $R_{2c} = 160$), and more weight has been attached to calculations made by use of equations (93) and (95). Alternatively, the parameter $H = \delta_1/\delta_2$ may be used instead of λ_2, and a curve showing the relationship between R_c (based on displacement thickness) and H is shown in Fig. IX. 15. On the same diagram is shown a similar curve obtained from calculations for velocity profiles with suction. Except for a slight divergence for values of H close to 2, the two curves are almost coincident. To a reasonable approximation, therefore, the critical Reynolds number for any velocity profile is a function of H only. This is not, in general, *strictly* true; to remedy the deficiency Head (1957a) has approximated the boundary layer by a two-parameter family of velocity profiles, the parameters being $T = (\delta_2/U_0)(\partial u/\partial z)_w$ and $m = (\delta_2^2/U_0)(\partial^2 u/\partial z^2)_w$. (The latter parameter is equal to $(-\lambda_2)$ in the case of zero suction.) Results of Head's stability calculations, which were made with Lin's formulae, (93) and (95), are shown in Fig. IX. 16. (The author states his belief that, in the region to the right of the dotted line, the results are as accurate as Lin's formulae.)

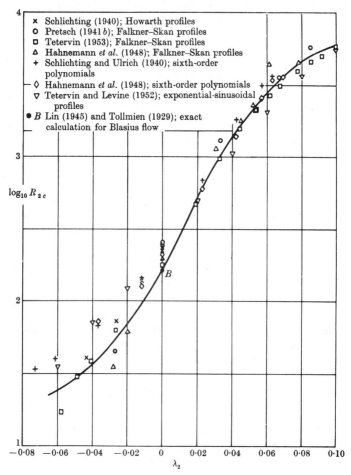

Fig. IX. 14. Critical Reynolds number as a function of the pressure-gradient parameter.

It can be seen that a favourable pressure gradient greatly enhances the stability of a flow, in the sense that the critical Reynolds number is higher than for Blasius flow. On the other hand an unfavourable pressure gradient destabilizes the flow through the formation of boundary-layer profiles containing a point of inflexion, with an associated high degree of instability.

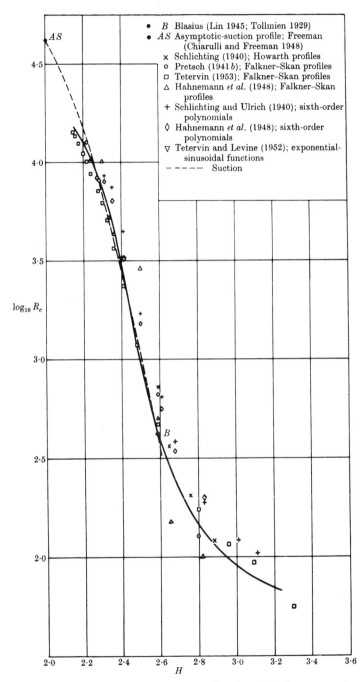

FIG. IX. 15. Critical Reynolds number as a function of the shape parameter.

If it is desired to calculate the point on a body where instability first arises, the boundary-layer calculation for different values of x is used to plot R_{2c} against x. The calculated distribution of δ_2 as a function of x is then used to plot the actual local Reynolds number, R_2, against x on the same diagram. The intersection of the two curves gives the point on the body where instability first occurs. For an account of

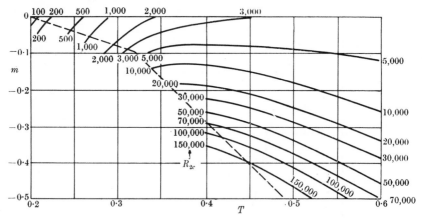

Fig. IX. 16. R_{2c} as a function of T and m for a two-parameter family of boundary-layer profiles (curves of constant R_{2c}).

calculations of this sort the reader is referred to the book by Schlichting (1955), where reference is made to the work of Schlichting and Ulrich (1940) and to that of Bussmann and Ulrich (1943); additional work on the topic has been done by Tetervin and Levine (1952).

Experimentally, Schubauer and Skramstad (1943) and Liepmann (1945) showed qualitatively that a pressure gradient was stabilizing or destabilizing according to whether the gradient was favourable or adverse.

5.2. Effects of suction

It has long been known that the laminar boundary layer is stabilized by suction applied through the bounding surface, and the practical importance of this is obvious. The stabilization occurs through two effects:

(i) the boundary layer is thinned, so that a higher velocity is required to attain the same local Reynolds number; and

(ii) the boundary-layer profile is altered in shape to a form consistent with greater stability, in the sense that the local critical Reynolds number is higher than it would be without suction.

The first effect can be evaluated quantitatively from an ordinary boundary-layer calculation, whereas the second effect requires an examination of instability. Here we shall concern ourselves with the second effect. For a discussion of the calculation of the steady laminar boundary layer with suction the reader is referred to Chapters V and VI.

Calculations of the instability of the asymptotic suction profile (Section III. 15) have been made by several authors, and the most reliable result appears to be that of Freeman (see Chiarulli and Freeman 1948). His calculation is novel in that he solved the inviscid Orr–Sommerfeld equation exactly and gave the inviscid solutions in terms of hypergeometric functions. He obtained a critical Reynolds number, based on displacement thickness, of $4 \cdot 2 \times 10^4$, whereas a calculation by formulae (93) and (95) gave $3 \cdot 9 \times 10^4$. For a discussion of the effect of higher approximations to the viscous solutions, the reader is referred to a paper by Lock (1955).

Ulrich (1944) and Freeman (see Hahnemann et al. 1948 and Chiarulli and Freeman 1948) have considered the instability of the velocity profiles corresponding to the following cases of boundary-layer flow with suction:

(i) semi-infinite flat plate with suction velocity proportional to $x^{-\frac{1}{2}}$, where x is the distance from the leading edge;

(ii) semi-infinite flat plate with constant suction;

(iii) stagnation-point flow with constant suction.

Their results are illustrated in Fig. IX. 17, where the critical Reynolds number (R_c) based on displacement thickness is plotted against $H = \delta_1/\delta_2$; several of the points are for 'blowing profiles'. A mean curve has been drawn with greater weight attached to Freeman's values, which were obtained from equations (93) and (95). The curve has been drawn to pass through the accepted values for Blasius flow ($R_c = 420$) and for the asymptotic-suction profile ($R_c = 4 \cdot 2 \times 10^4$). There are, as in Section 5.1, cases in which the boundary layer may not be represented by a single parameter. For the general boundary layer, when it is approximated by a two-parameter family of velocity profiles, Head's stability diagram (Fig. IX. 16) is both appropriate and valuable.

For the case of flow along a semi-infinite plane with constant suction both Ulrich and Freeman have calculated the minimum amount of suction required to maintain laminar flow. In this case the boundary layer near the leading edge is approximately a Blasius flow, and it

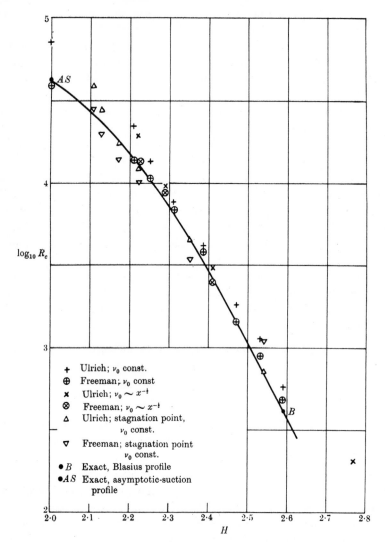

FIG. IX. 17. Critical Reynolds number as a function of the shape parameter
for flows with suction.

tends to the asymptotic-suction profile at large distances from the
leading edge. In Fig. IX. 18 the local Reynolds number (R) is plotted
against $\sqrt{\xi} = C_Q \sqrt{(U_0 x/\nu)}$, where C_Q denotes the ratio of the suction
velocity to the free-stream velocity, for a series of values of C_Q. On
the same diagram is plotted a curve of R_c against $\sqrt{\xi}$, obtained from
the stability calculations. It can be seen that the Reynolds number is

everywhere below the critical value provided $C_Q > 1 \cdot 428 \times 10^{-4}$. This value is due to Freeman; Ulrich obtained a value of the same order of magnitude but slightly smaller. Head has carried out flight experiments on a wing which was designed to have uniform pressure over a large part of the chord, with uniform suction applied through the surface

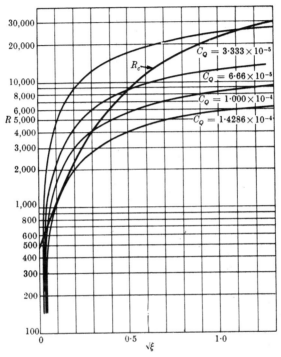

FIG. IX. 18. Curves for the determination of the minimum suction required to maintain laminar flow on a flat plate.

except close to the leading edge. The boundary-layer flow thus approximated to that past a semi-infinite plane with uniform suction. It was found that a suction quantity of about $C_Q = 1 \cdot 5 \times 10^{-4}$ was required to maintain laminar flow, in good agreement with Freeman's result. (See Jones and Head 1951, and Pankhurst 1955.)

Wuest (1953) has examined the form and stability of the velocity profiles of the boundary layer downstream of a suction slot. It appears that the stabilization effect is much less than that produced by uniform suction, because with increasing distance from the slot the velocity profile tends to the Blasius shape.

5.3. *Effects of density stratification*

The stability of the flow of a fluid which is stably stratified, that is, one whose density decreases upwards, has been discussed by many authors. The phenomena are very different from those occurring in an unstably stratified fluid, such as a layer of fluid heated from below, where the instability occurs in the form of convection cells (Section 3). Instability can only occur in a stably stratified layer if the fluid is moving, and then it takes the form of a progressive wave motion. Richardson (1920) and Prandtl (1929) both showed the importance of the parameter

$$\Theta = \left(\frac{-g}{\rho}\frac{d\rho}{dz}\right)\Big/\left(\frac{dU}{dz}\right)^2,$$

where z is the vertical height, ρ the density, and U the fluid velocity. The number Θ is now known as the Richardson number, and represents the ratio of buoyancy forces, caused by the density variation, to the inertia forces. It is clear that if the Richardson number is high enough the stabilizing effect of the buoyancy forces will outweigh the destabilizing action of the inertia forces, resulting in a complete stability of the flow. Such a result was indeed obtained by Richardson (1920), who found the critical value of Θ to be 1, while a calculation of Prandtl (1929), as refined by Taylor (1931a), gave the same value. In order to obtain this approximate result, which was derived for a constant velocity gradient, the work done by the Reynolds stresses to produce turbulence against the action of gravity was calculated. The result suggests that turbulence will be suppressed if Θ is (roughly) greater than unity.

Taylor (1931b) and Goldstein (1931b) considered the instability of various combinations of fluid layers, each layer having either constant velocity or constant vorticity; density gradients and density variations were, of course, present but viscosity was entirely neglected. Further studies of this type have been made by Høiland (1953b), and Eliassen, Høiland, and Riis (1953). Drazin (1958) has studied the inviscid instability of an unbounded shear layer of the form $\bar{u} = V\tanh{(z/d)}$, with a density distribution $\rho \sim \exp(-\beta z)$. The Richardson number in this case may be defined as $g\beta d^2/V^2$; for this parameter Drazin obtained a critical value of $\frac{1}{4}$, above which the flow was stable. (The reader is referred to Section 7 for a discussion of the instability of a shear layer in the absence of a density gradient.) The papers of Lock (1954) and Feldman (1957) should also be studied for work on stability in the presence of density variations.

Schlichting (1935b) calculated the instability (including viscous effects) of the Blasius flow above a horizontal boundary, with a density which decreased exponentially from the boundary; the velocity and density were constant outside the boundary layer. The critical Richardson number given by the analysis was $\Theta_c = \frac{1}{24} = 0\cdot0417$, where the value of (dU/dz) is taken at the boundary. A curve of critical Reynolds number (R) against Richardson number is shown in Fig. IX. 19, and

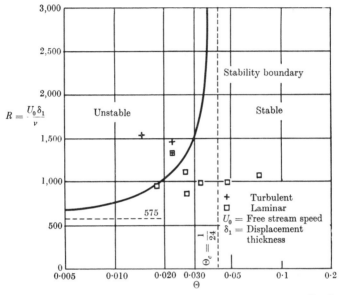

FIG. IX. 19. Critical Reynolds numbers for flows with density stratification.

it can be seen that the curve of neutral stability tends to infinity with R as Θ tends to $\frac{1}{24}$. On the same diagram are some experimental results due to Reichardt (see Prandtl and Reichardt 1934); the measurements show laminar flow in the stable region of Schlichting's curve, and turbulent flow in the unstable regions. The experiments were made in a wind-tunnel whose upper surface was heated by steam and whose lower surface was cooled by water.

6. The instability of three-dimensional boundary layers

In this section we shall extend the theory of the instability of two-dimensional boundary layers to three-dimensional boundary layers of the type described in Chapter VIII. However, a note on experimental matters is appropriate by way of introduction. It was noticed by Gray (1952) that on a swept wing the boundary layer in flight tests became

turbulent much closer to the leading edge than on a corresponding
unswept wing. Just upstream of transition an 'evaporation' method
of boundary-layer visualization (see Section X. 15) suggested the
existence in the boundary layer of a set of vortices with their axes lying
roughly in the direction of the local external stream. Wind-tunnel tests
by Anscombe and Illingworth and by Gregory and Walker (see Gregory,
Stuart, and Walker 1955) confirmed the existence of the phenomenon.
(A photograph, due to N. Gregory, is shown in Fig. IX. 20.) This led
Gregory and Walker to their elegant demonstration, by means of the
china-clay technique, of the instability of the boundary-layer flow induced by a rotating disk (Frontispiece), where the instability takes the
form of spiral vortices with axes lying in a plane parallel to the surface
of the disk. These phenomena can be explained, as H. B. Squire and
P. R. Owen first suggested, by the theory described below.

Consider a surface upon which there is a three-dimensional boundary
layer and, furthermore, consider a localized region of the flow with
orthogonal curvilinear coordinates such that two of the coordinates are
in the surface and one is normal to the surface. The experimental
observations suggest that disturbances periodic in some direction or
other can appear; the coordinates in the surface can be selected so that
one of the coordinate directions is coincident with the wave fronts.
As a reference speed, U_0, we can take the resultant speed at the edge
of the boundary layer at some point, and as a reference length a displacement thickness, δ_1, at the same point. Let x denote the dimensionless coordinate in the direction of periodicity, y the other coordinate in
the surface, and z the coordinate normal to the surface. The appropriate
dimensionless steady components of velocity are $\bar{u}, \bar{v}, \bar{w}$, and the components of the perturbation are u', v', w'. It is then assumed, as described
above, that

$$(u', v', w') \equiv (u_1, v_1, w_1)\exp[i(\alpha x - \alpha c\tau)], \qquad (96)$$

where τ denotes the dimensionless time $U_0 t/\delta_1$. If we substitute this
perturbed velocity field in the Navier–Stokes equations of motion in
orthogonal curvilinear coordinates (Section III. 11) and linearize, we
obtain a set of three equations which govern the disturbance components u_1, v_1, and w_1. We now exclude from further discussion flows
(such as those on a concave surface) for which centrifugal instability
can occur. In other cases it is found that, provided the displacement
thickness is very small compared with the typical radii of curvature
of the surface and of the flow, and provided the growth of the boundary
layer along the surface is negligible (which implies $\bar{w} = \partial/\partial x = \partial/\partial y = 0$

Fig. IX. 20. Vortices in the boundary layer of a swept wing

approximately), the disturbance equations referred to above reduce to

$$(\bar{u}-c)\left(\frac{\partial^2 w_1}{\partial z^2}-\alpha^2 w_1\right)-\frac{\partial^2 \bar{u}}{\partial z^2}w_1+\frac{i}{\alpha R}\left(\frac{\partial^4 w_1}{\partial z^4}-2\alpha^2\frac{\partial^2 w_1}{\partial z^2}+\alpha^4 w_1\right)=0,$$

$$(\bar{u}-c)v_1+\frac{i}{\alpha R}\left(\frac{\partial^2 v_1}{\partial z^2}-\alpha^2 v_1\right)-\frac{i}{\alpha}w_1\frac{\partial \bar{v}}{\partial z}=0,$$

$$i\alpha u_1+\frac{\partial w_1}{\partial z}=0, \quad (97)$$

where R represents the Reynolds number $U_0\delta_1/\nu$. These equations were derived by H. B. Squire, by Owen and Randall (unpublished), by Dunn and Lin (1955), and by Gregory *et al.* 1955.

The boundary conditions are

$$u_1 = v_1 = w_1 = 0 \quad \text{for } z = 0 \text{ and } \infty \quad (98)$$

which, as the last of equations (97) shows, can be replaced by

$$u_1 = w_1 = \partial w_1/\partial z = 0 \quad \text{for } z = 0 \text{ and } \infty. \quad (99)$$

The boundary conditions involving w_1, together with the first and last of equations (97), determine an eigenvalue problem for α, c, and R.

The first equation (97) is the Orr–Sommerfeld equation (50). Thus, in a localized region of a three-dimensional boundary layer, the velocity component in the direction of propagation of the disturbance may be regarded, for stability purposes, as a two-dimensional flow and the usual two-dimensional stability theory may be applied. (Squire's theorem (Section 4) may readily be derived from this result.) Disturbances propagated in different directions will give different critical Reynolds numbers, but there will be a unique lowest critical Reynolds number, corresponding to a particular form of disturbance.

(a) The form of the boundary-layer velocity distribution

In Sections 3 and 4 attention has been focused on velocity profiles, $\bar{u}$, which are of the conventional Blasius or Poiseuille type. Here, however, we are concerned primarily with more complicated functions which may change sign. To be specific, let us consider the velocity distribution in the boundary layer of a yawed infinite cylinder (see Section VIII. 22). At any particular point we can resolve the velocity into components along, and at right angles to, the potential streamline outside the boundary layer. The component parallel to the potential streamline is of the ordinary boundary-layer form, whereas the transverse component ('secondary flow') is zero at the wall and tends to zero at the edge of the layer. This secondary flow arises because the retarded fluid in the boundary layer has insufficient 'centrifugal force' to balance the centripetal force supplied by the pressure field, which does not change through the boundary layer and is just sufficient to balance the 'centrifugal force' of the external flow. For any other direction, the velocity profile is a combination of these two extreme (that is, tangential and normal) cases. The situation is illustrated qualitatively in Fig. IX. 21, where a class of velocity profiles, each

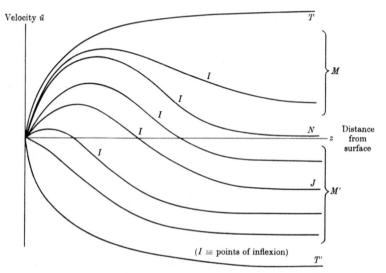

FIG. IX. 21. Components of velocity in a three-dimensional boundary layer.

corresponding to a particular direction, is shown. In some cases, the class of profiles may show differences in detail from those shown in Fig. IX. 21.

(b) Some general results

Firstly, we note that the first and third equations of (97) can be written in the form (50), namely

$$(\bar{u}-c)(\phi''-\alpha^2\phi)-\bar{u}''\phi = \frac{-i}{\alpha R}(\phi^{\mathrm{iv}}-2\alpha^2\phi''+\alpha^4\phi),$$

where
$$u_1 = \frac{\partial \phi}{\partial z}, \qquad w_1 = -i\alpha\phi.$$

On grounds similar to those mentioned in Section 4, the boundary conditions can be reduced to the form (69 a). If we consider the velocity profiles illustrated in Fig. IX. 21, we note that there may be *two* points where $\bar{u} = c$, and hence that there may be two internal viscous layers as well as the perturbation viscous layer on the wall. This complicates the problem considerably, and attention is here mainly directed to the inviscid problem, $R \to \infty$ (equation (56) with boundary conditions (58)). For work on the viscous problem see Pfenninger (1958) and Brown (1961).

There is, however, one important result which can be deduced from (50), which includes the effects of viscosity. Consider a yawed flat plate at zero incidence in a stream of speed U_0, for which the flow is everywhere in the direction of the external stream (Section VIII. 22). Since the velocity profiles of Fig. IX. 21 in all directions are similar in shape, the most unstable profile is that with the largest maximum value, because $R_c = (U_0 \, \delta_1 / \nu)_c$ is inversely proportional to the maximum of $\bar{u}$. Consequently the instability waves, when they appear, are propagated in the flow direction (Dunn and Lin 1955). The particular case of zero yaw gives Squire's theorem (Section 4).

For the class of velocity profiles of Fig. IX. 21 at infinite R, the existence of disturbances has been discussed by Gregory et al. (1955). The work follows closely the treatment of two-dimensional flow given in Section 4.2; the existence of a point of inflexion is again a necessary condition for instability. One of the most important results is that the velocity profile (J) for which the point of inflexion lies at the point of zero velocity generates a neutral disturbance of zero wave velocity $(c = 0)$. The variational condition (66) can be applied to this profile and the accuracy of the method has been checked by comparison with an exact solution. The velocity profile (J) for a rotating disk with suction (Stuart 1954a; Gregory et al. 1955) yields a function

$$K(z) = 4(e^z - 1)^{-1},$$

and the exact solution of (56) is $\phi = (e^{-3z/2} - e^{-5z/2})$ with $\alpha = \frac{3}{2}$. With an approximate form of ϕ containing one arbitrary constant, $\alpha = 1.495$ is obtained by the variational method, involving an error of about $\frac{1}{3}$ per cent. (The standard length upon which α is based is the displacement thickness evaluated from the flow in the direction of rotation of the disk.)

6.1. *The flow on swept wings*

The vortices which have been observed in the laminar boundary layer of a swept wing are clearly related to the mode of instability generated by the particular velocity profile which has a zero at its point of inflexion, since the vortex streaks shown in experiment are fixed relative to the surface. (For a discussion of cases where such disturbances may not be possible, the reader is referred to Moore 1956.) If the velocity distribution within the boundary layer is known, the calculation of the profile J yields, as a by-product, the angle which the vortex axes make with the direction of the external stream. Comparison with the experiments of Anscombe and Illingworth (1952) show good agreement for this angle. However, the wavelength predicted by the inviscid instability theory is only about half that observed, a discrepancy which may be due to viscosity.

A development of the theory, due to Owen and Randall, will now be described. As before we have as reference quantities the local speed U_0 and displacement thickness δ_1. The maximum speed, $U_0 \bar{u}_{N\mathrm{max}}$, of the secondary flow profile (N) may be taken as representative of the three-dimensionality of the flow, in the sense that it shows by how much the flow differs from a two-dimensional one. Owen and Randall (unpublished) have suggested basing a Reynolds number, χ, on this maximum secondary velocity and on a suitable representative thickness of the boundary layer. Thus

$$\chi = \frac{U_0 \bar{u}_{N\mathrm{max}} \delta_1 \delta_N}{\nu} = \left(\frac{U_0 \delta_1}{\nu}\right) \bar{u}_{N\mathrm{max}} \delta_N, \qquad (100)$$

where $\bar{u}_{N\mathrm{max}}$ and δ_N are dimensionless quantities, referred to U_0 and δ_1. The quantity δ_N can either be based on the main component (T) of boundary-layer flow or, preferably, on the secondary (N) flow. For example, we can define

$$\delta_N = \int_0^\infty (\bar{u}_N / \bar{u}_{N\mathrm{max}})\, dz, \qquad (101)$$

where z is the dimensionless distance normal to the surface, referred to δ_1. This definition then yields

$$\chi = R \int_0^\infty \bar{u}_N\, dz, \qquad (102)$$

where $R = U_0 \delta_1 / \nu$. Owen and Randall defined a Reynolds number, which we shall call χ_δ, based on a suitable 'width' (δ) of the secondary (N) profile; the value of δ seems to be about $2\frac{1}{2}$ times the value of $\delta_1 \delta_N$ as defined by (101).

Owen and Randall made a comparison with experiment of the values of χ_δ at which vortex streaks occurred; this was done by calculating the boundary layer, and therefore χ_δ, appropriate to regions of the wing where Anscombe and Illingworth observed the onset of vortex instability. They suggested a value of χ_δ for the onset of instability $(\chi_{\delta c})$ of about 125. Transition occurred at $\chi_\delta = 175$ approximately. These numbers should not be taken as being of universal applicability, since the value of $\chi_{\delta c}$ may vary from profile to profile according to the shape. In fact Kármán and Lin (1955) quote an estimate of the critical value of χ for instability, based on δ_N, of about 230 (Section 6.3), whereas in Owen and Randall's case the value is about 50. Moreover, it should be remembered that in the swept-wing case the velocity profile J, of Fig. IX. 21, is more relevant than the profile N, upon which the above calculations depend. For other work on the topic of instability on swept wings, see Pfenninger (1958), Eichelbrenner and Michel (1958) and Brown (1961).

Owen and Randall (unpublished) and Sinha (1956) also examined the effects of suction on the instability, and found that suction has a strong stabilizing influence through the reduction of both the magnitude of the secondary flow and of the boundary-layer thickness. Their results were confirmed to some extent by experiments of Anscombe and Butler (1954).

The existence of a strong boundary-layer instability on swept wings at supersonic speeds has been demonstrated experimentally by Scott-Wilson and Capps (1954) and Dunning and Ulmann (1955). The observations by Scott-Wilson and Capps at a Mach number of 1·61 suggest that compressibility has a destabilizing influence compared with incompressible flow.

6.2. The flow due to a rotating disk

Three-dimensional boundary-layer instability occurs on a rotating disk because a secondary velocity profile (N) is produced in the radial direction due to centrifugal action. The steady flow is described in Section III. 20, and an experimental investigation by Gregory and Walker (see Gregory et al. 1955) adequately confirmed the theoretical velocity profiles. The phenomenon of instability was demonstrated by using the china-clay technique (see Section X. 15), with the result shown in the Frontispiece (see also Fales 1955). The dark region in the centre denotes laminar flow, while the white annular region at the edge of the disk denotes turbulent flow. In between is a series of spiral streaks, whose existence denotes regions of high shear and, it can be inferred, of vortices. The vortex axes appear to lie roughly along equiangular spirals. In addition to this form of disturbance, fixed relative to the surface, the simultaneous existence of other modes of disturbance, moving relative to the surface, is not precluded. In fact, an analysis of the flow using a moving-coil microphone fitted with a probe tube showed the presence of other disturbances; the reader is referred also to Theodorsen and Regier (1947) and Smith (1947). In Gregory and Walker's experiments the disturbance fixed relative to the surface was the strongest.

The Reynolds number for a rotating disk is proportional to the radius, since a local Reynolds number is $R = \Omega r \delta_1 / \nu$, where $\delta_1 = 1\cdot271\sqrt{(\nu/\Omega)}$, Ω is the angular speed, and r is the radius (also $U_0 = \Omega r$). Another Reynolds number is $R_r = \Omega r^2 / \nu$. A secondary-flow Reynolds number, χ, can also be defined; the maximum value of $U_0 \bar{u}_N$ (the radial flow) is $0\cdot181r\Omega$ and we find that $\chi = 0\cdot445 R_r^{\frac{1}{2}}$. The critical value of R_r for instability was found to be about $1\cdot85 \times 10^5$, with transition at $R_r = 2\cdot85 \times 10^5$. These values are equivalent to $\chi = 190$ for instability and $\chi = 250$ for transition. The china-clay record showed the presence in the boundary layer of between 28 and 31 spiral vortices (Frontispiece), and this was confirmed by an harmonic analysis of the flow with a moving-coil microphone (Gregory et al. 1955). A measurement of the angle of the spiral gave a value of about $14°$ from the direction of rotation.

Application of the theory for $R \to \infty$ shows that the axes of the disturbance lie in equiangular spirals, as follows. The flow on a rotating disk is known to be 'similar' at all stations, in the sense that the velocity profiles are everywhere of the same shape with a magnitude proportional to the radius. Thus the fixed-vortex mode of neutral disturbance generated by the velocity profile (J) will be the same at all points on the disk within the instability region. In particular the angle at which the J-profile is inclined to the direction of flow is the same at all points. Consequently, the disturbances lie in the form of equiangular spirals. The angle given by theory is found to be about $13\frac{1}{4}°$ to the direction of rotation, which is in good agreement with the experimental value. The amplitude of the disturbance, which is not given by linearized theory, will vary with the radius.

A calculation of the wave number, α, referred to the displacement thickness, has been made using the variational condition (66), with the result $\alpha = 1\cdot45$. This yields between 113 and 140 for the number of vortices on the disk. Thus the wave number calculated on the basis of inviscid theory is about 4 times too high; the discrepancy may be due to the neglect of the effects of viscosity on the disturbance. On the other hand, the mode of instability, namely the angle of the vortex spirals, is given correctly by inviscid theory. Thus it appears that the inertial forces producing the instability determine the *directional* mode, this being little affected by viscous damping, while the wave number *is* affected by viscous damping. (But see Brown 1961.)

The effects of uniform suction on the rotating-disk flow have been calculated by Stuart (1954a) and suggest that suction will stabilize the flow in the way described in Section 6.1.

6.3. *Other work on, or related to, the instability of three-dimensional flows*

A type of flow which does not fall strictly within the category of this section, but which may conveniently be discussed here because it has the profile N of the class of Fig. IX. 21, is that produced in the following way. Consider an infinite plate which has been moving for some time, so that a boundary layer of some (growing) thickness has been formed. Now let the plate suddenly be brought to rest; the fluid will continue to move except at the plate, where it will be reduced to rest. In fact, a secondary boundary layer will be formed at the plate which spreads outwards and tends to reduce the whole flow to rest; the resultant effect of the secondary boundary layer and the original boundary layer, at any instant, is a flow with a velocity profile like that of the profile N of Fig. IX. 21. Such a flow (if assumed to be steady) is unstable and generates vortices transverse to the direction of motion of, and moving relative to, the plate. The phenomenon described above was discovered by Fales (1955) and several photographs of the vortex flow are given in his paper. The explanation of the phenomenon given above was put forward by Kármán and Lin (1955). They mention a calculation by J. E. Plapp for the instability of a typical profile, namely

$$\bar{u} = A\eta(1-\eta)^2, \qquad \eta = z/\delta, \qquad (103)$$

where z is the distance normal to the plate, which yields a critical Reynolds number $(U\delta/\nu)$ of about 400, where $U = 4A/27$ is the maximum value of $\bar{u}$. The wavelength and wave velocity were also calculated and reasonable agreement with Fales's experimental observations was obtained. The critical value of χ, as defined by (100), is 230. For further discussions of this kind of instability, the reader is referred to Hama (1957) and Hegarty (1958) and (for unsteadiness) to Shen (1961).

Work on the instability of axisymmetric boundary layers has been done by Pretsch (1941a), who calculated the curve of neutral stability for flow at the stagnation point of a body of revolution. (The reader is referred also to a paper by Tetervin (1958).) Pretsch found that the axisymmetric stagnation-point flow (with an axisymmetric disturbance) is more unstable than plane stagnation flow (with a two-dimensional disturbance). The critical Reynolds number based on displacement thickness and local external stream velocity was found to be 4,200 in the former case and 12,600 in the latter case. Pretsch also showed that the problem of instability of a general axisymmetric boundary-layer flow can be reduced to the solution of the inviscid equation (56) and viscous equation (77) for plane flow, provided that the local displacement thickness is small compared with the radius of curvature of the body. For some experimental observations of instability at the nose of a bluff body of revolution, the reader is referred to Kuethe (1958) and to Section 2.3.

7. The instability of wakes, jets, and laminar mixing regions

In Section 4 it has been shown that secondary viscous layers may be present both on walls and in the interior of the fluid remote from boundaries. In the case of flows with no fixed boundaries, such as wakes, jets, and laminar mixing regions, only the internal viscous ('critical') layers appear, and effects associated with secondary viscous layers on walls are not present. The mathematical corollary of this is that the two viscous solutions of (79) must be ignored, because each becomes large at a sufficiently large distance from the axis of the flow, either in one direction or in the other. The two inviscid solutions (73), suitably modified by viscosity, may be regarded as forming the mathematical basis of the theory of instability in unlimited fields of flow. It is assumed, as in Sections 4 and 5, that the flow may be regarded as parallel for the purposes of the stability theory, so that the stability is governed by equation (50). However, this assumption may lose its validity at low Reynolds numbers (see Fox and Lessen 1955) because of the strong divergence of the streamlines of the basic flow. For example, Tatsumi and Kakutani (1958) have pointed out that, for a jet at its critical Reynolds number, as calculated on the assumption of parallel flow, the crosswise component of velocity is of the same order of magnitude as the streamwise component; consequently, such a calculation of the critical Reynolds number can yield only a qualitative estimate with regard to the actual viscous flow. However, it is of some interest to obtain solutions of the Orr–Sommerfeld equation with the assumption of parallel flow, and work of this kind will now be described.

A typical calculation based on the ideas discussed above is that due to Lessen (1949) for the velocity profile of the laminar mixing region formed when a stream of fluid flows over a layer of fluid at rest, as described in Section V. 22; for a related instability calculation, see

Esch (1957). Lessen obtained the solution of the Orr–Sommerfeld equation, (50), by expanding in powers of $(\alpha R)^{-1}$, and using a high-speed computing machine. His calculation, however, did not yield a minimum critical Reynolds number. (For a treatment at lower Reynolds numbers, see Tatsumi and Gotoh (1960).) The results are shown in Fig. IX. 22, where the characteristic length is $\delta = \sqrt{(\nu x/U_1)}$ and the

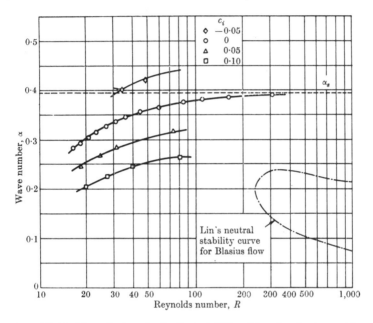

Fig. IX. 22. Theoretical results for the instability of flow in a laminar mixing region.

characteristic velocity is U_1 in the notation of Section V. 22. It is noteworthy that the wave number of the neutral curve is everywhere less than the value for $R \to \infty$, in contrast with the cases of boundary-layer profiles with an inflexion point (see Section 5). In some experiments carried out by Sato (1956) oscillations were found at Reynolds numbers, $U_1\delta/\nu$, above 86; experiments were not performed at lower values, but clearly the value 86 may be regarded as an upper limit to the minimum critical Reynolds number. Furthermore, Sato's measurements of the dimensionless wave velocity (which, according to Lessen's calculation, varies very little with α and R) were very close to the values calculated by Lessen. On the other hand, the experimental wave number (α) was less than half the appropriate value on Lessen's neutral curve. This was probably due mainly to the fact that (as Sato suggests) the disturbances were amplifying ones with lower values of α, but an additional point is that the profile was not everywhere of Lessen's form. The theory of instability of a mixing region in compressible flow, for infinite Reynolds number, has been treated by Lin (1953).

Another instability problem which arises is that of a two-dimensional jet emerging from a hole in a plane wall, and this has been treated by several authors. When the spread of the jet can be ignored (an approximation which is valid sufficiently far downstream) the velocity profile of the equivalent parallel flow is $\bar{u} = \text{sech}^2 z$. (In the notation of Section V. 23 the characteristic length is $\delta = \{0 \cdot 2752(M/\rho v^2 x^2)^{1/3}\}^{-1}$ and the characteristic speed is $U_0 = 0 \cdot 4543(M^2/\rho^2 v x)^{1/3}$. The Reynolds number, R, is $U_0 \delta/v$.) Since $\bar{u}$ is even the function ϕ may be considered to be either even or odd. The case of ϕ even (antisymmetrical oscillation) is of greater physical interest, since (see Andrade 1932) it is the case which is found to occur experimentally.

The problem has been studied theoretically by Curle (1957), Tatsumi and Kakutani (1958), Howard (1959), and Clenshaw and Elliott (1960). Curle's work is based on an approximate 'integral' method due to McKoen (1955), which ignores the term ϕ^{iv} in equation (50) except close to the critical layer. However, since the term ϕ^{iv} is of the same order as ϕ'' and ϕ, it *cannot* be ignored and the method can be expected to yield only qualitative results. Even so, the neutral curve obtained is in reasonable agreement with Tatsumi and Kakutani's curve (which was more rigorously derived), as can be seen from Fig. IX. 23. Tatsumi and Kakutani solved the problem of neutral stability (ϕ even) by using two types of expansion; the first, in powers of $(\alpha R)^{-1}$, is valid on the upper branch (see Fig. IX. 23) of the neutral curve; the second, in powers of αR, is valid on the lower branch. Another method has been devised by Howard (1959), who, by converting the Orr–Sommerfeld equation into an integral equation, has obtained a rigorous solution appropriate to the lower branch of the neutral curve (for the case of ϕ even). Tatsumi and Kakutani (1958) and Howard agree that, on the lower branch,

$$\alpha = kR^{-2} + O(R^{-4}),$$

$$\alpha \to 0, \quad R \to \infty, \tag{104}$$

where k is a constant equal to $0 \cdot 954$. (The latter value is due to Howard. Tatsumi and Kakutani's paper gives a different value of k; however, Dr. Tatsumi has informed the writer that there is a small error in their paper, and that their analysis, when corrected, leads to $k = 0 \cdot 954$.)

Thus, as $R \to \infty$ on the lower branch of the neutral curve, αR tends to zero like R^{-1}. Consequently, the degenerate solution of the inviscid equation (56), namely $\phi = \bar{u}$ with $\alpha = 0$ and $c = 0$, is *not* a limit of the viscous solution as $R \to \infty$. On the other hand, Tatsumi and Kakutani's work shows that, as $\alpha R \to \infty$ on the upper branch, the viscous solution does tend to the inviscid solution, which is $\phi = \bar{u}$,

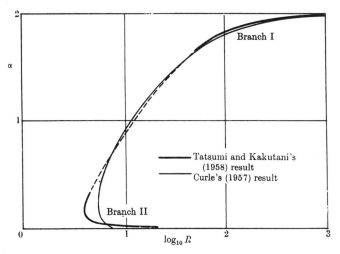

Branch I

Tatsumi and Kakutani's (1958) result
Curle's (1957) result

Branch II

$\log_{10} R$

FIG. IX. 23. Curve of neutral stability for a plane jet.

$\alpha = 2, c = \frac{2}{3}$ (Savic 1941). For some experimental results on jet oscillations at high Reynolds number, in good agreement with inviscid theory, see Sato (1960). For further theoretical work, see Drazin (1961).

For critical Reynolds number, $(U_0 \delta/\nu)_c = R_c$, both Tatsumi and Kakutani, and Howard, obtained a value of about 4. In each case it was given by the solution of the type appropriate to small values of αR, and was near to the limit of convergence of the solution. Consequently, greater accuracy was difficult to obtain. Clenshaw and Elliott (1960) obtained a similar value of R_c. Curle's work gave $R_c = 5 \cdot 5$, in reasonable agreement with the more rigorous calculations. The value observed experimentally by Andrade (1939) was several times greater than the values calculated, and it seems likely that the spread of the jet accounts for some of this difference.

For the profile $\bar{u} = \operatorname{sech}^2 z$ with ϕ odd, Clenshaw (unpublished, see Clenshaw and Elliott, 1960) has shown that, with $\alpha = 0$ and $R = \infty$, equation (50) has an eigenvalue $\alpha R = 18 \cdot 96$ for a neutral disturbance. An inviscid odd solution is also known, namely $\phi = \operatorname{sech} z \tanh z$,

$\alpha = 1$, $c = \frac{2}{3}$ (Savic and Murphy 1943). For an approximate calculation of the neutral curve in this case, the reader is referred to a paper by Lew and Fanucci (1954).

For an experimental study of the phenomena of instability and transition in an axisymmetric jet, see Wehrmann and Wille (1958).

The question of stability of the velocity profile of the wake far downstream of a symmetrical body of typical length l has been studied by Arkhipov (1958) and Curle (1958b), who have shown that

$$(U_0 l/\nu)C_D > A \tag{105}$$

for instability, where A is a constant, U_0 is the free-stream speed, and C_D is the drag coefficient (namely, drag per unit length divided by $\frac{1}{2}\rho U_0^2 l$). Arkhipov used Galerkin's method and obtained $A = 48$, approximately, for antisymmetrical oscillations. (Curle obtained a less accurate value $A = 22$, by aproximating the wake profile by a 'jet' profile, $a \operatorname{sech}^2 bz$.) For the particular case of a flat plate of length l at zero incidence formula (105), with $A = 48$ and $C_D = 2 \cdot 656(U_0 l/\nu)^{-\frac{1}{2}}$, yields a critical value of $(U_0 l/\nu)$ of 325. This value is of the same order of magnitude as observational values (of order 600 to 700) due to Hollingdale (1940) and Taneda (1958). In cases when instability occurs close to the body, relation (105) may not be valid. For experimental information about periodic wakes, the reader is referred to Kovásznay (1949), Roshko (1954a, b), Taneda (1956), and Tritton (1959).

8. Non-linear aspects of the mechanics of instability

Earlier in this chapter it has been emphasized that the theory of hydrodynamic instability is primarily linear, whereas turbulence involves non-linear velocity fluctuations of finite size. Consequently, the linear theory cannot predict how turbulence occurs as a consequence of instability. In mathematical terms the deficiency of the linear theory lies in its prediction of a disturbance (above a critical Reynolds number) which increases exponentially with time. It has occasionally been inferred from this property that turbulence would necessarily ensue from the growth of the disturbance, but in fact this does not appear to be the case. On the other hand, it has been argued that the non-linear terms may stabilize completely a flow which is unstable according to linearized theory, but such arguments can generally be refuted (see Stuart 1956a). It seems, therefore, that a treatment of the non-linear aspects of instability is highly desirable, and a limited discussion of this topic will now be given.

Let us consider a flow whose local Reynolds number does not vary with position, such as a flow between parallel planes or concentric cylinders, and let the flow be perturbed. As discussed in the Appendix to this chapter, it is convenient to separate the flow into a mean part and a disturbance part, where the disturbance has zero mean, and averages are taken with respect to a suitable spatial variable. Consider a small disturbance which, initially, is growing exponentially with time according to linear theory. As it amplifies it must eventually reach a size such that the mean transport of momentum by the finite fluctuations is appreciable, and such that the associated mean stress (the *Reynolds stress* described in the Appendix) has an appreciable effect on the mean flow. The resulting distortion of the mean flow clearly alters the rate of transfer of energy from the mean flow to the disturbance and, since this energy transfer is the cause of the growth of the disturbance, the rate of growth of the latter is altered. The disturbance is also modified by the generation of harmonics of the fundamental component. Thus there is a mutual interaction between the mean and disturbance parts of the flow, and a self-distortion of the disturbance part.

It is natural to ask if there can be an equilibrium state in which the disturbance has a definite finite amplitude and the mean flow exhibits a definite deviation from the original, laminar flow. Clearly, such a state of equilibrium requires that the rate of transfer of energy from the mean flow to the disturbance shall exactly balance the rate of viscous dissipation of kinetic energy by the disturbance. If this happens, $I_2 = I_3/R$ in the notation of Section 4.1. Experimental confirmation that an equilibrium state is possible, at least in certain cases, is provided by G. I. Taylor's observations on the vortex instability in flow between rotating cylinders. Taylor (1923, p. 342) observed that 'A moderate increase in the speed of the apparatus merely increased the vigour of the circulation in the vortices without altering appreciably their spacing or position', and suggested that 'The experiments . . . indicate that the effect of the second order terms is to prevent the vortices from increasing indefinitely in activity.' This example suggests that, in some cases, the effect of the instability is to replace the original laminar motion by another laminar motion, consisting of a mean motion and a superimposed finite disturbance. We may refer to this as the 'equilibrium flow', at a given Reynolds number, appropriate to the given mode of disturbance. A theory which gives results in agreement with the above experimental evidence is described in Section 8.2.

In the above discussion, attention has been paid to equilibrium flows which can develop when the original laminar flow is unstable according to linearized theory. Some flows, however, such as Couette flow between parallel planes, and Poiseuille flow in a circular pipe, are almost certainly completely stable with respect to infinitesimal disturbances. Even so, turbulence can occur at sufficiently high Reynolds numbers. Furthermore, turbulence occurs in some flows (for example, in Poiseuille flow between parallel planes) at a lower Reynolds number than the critical value according to linearized theory (that is, when the laminar flow is stable with respect to infinitesimal disturbances). A suggestion which may lead to an explanation of such phenomena is that the appropriate laminar flow may be unstable with respect to *finite* disturbances. When a disturbance of suitable magnitude is present, the mean flow and the oscillation may be distorted to such forms that the rate of transfer of energy to the disturbance can overcome the rate of dissipation of energy by viscosity.

It will be convenient to refer to non-linear disturbances as existing under *supercritical* conditions if they arise spontaneously above a critical Reynolds number for linearized instability, and as existing under *subcritical* conditions if they occur at a Reynolds number for which the flow is stable with respect to infinitesimal disturbances.

When an equilibrium flow is established, it does not follow that it is stable at all values of the Reynolds number higher than the critical value at which it first occurs. Moreover, it is intuitively clear that an equilibrium flow must become unstable in some way before producing turbulence. For example, in the case of flow between rotating cylinders mentioned above, Taylor observed that 'a large increase [in the angular speed] caused the symmetrical motion [of the cellular vortices] to break down into some kind of turbulent motion, which it was impossible to follow by eye'. When an equilibrium flow *is* unstable with respect to another mode of disturbance, it is sometimes said to exhibit secondary instability.

The development of a non-linear instability theory for boundary-layer flows, where the flow changes in the stream direction, presents additional difficulties. Whereas in the linear theory of instability it is permissible to regard a boundary-layer flow as nearly parallel, and therefore to neglect boundary-layer growth, it seems that such an approximation is not permissible in a non-linear theory. Because the local Reynolds number increases in the downstream direction, any disturbance convects into regions of higher Reynolds number and the effects of this change of Reynolds number would have to be taken into account. Consequently, the detailed theories which have been developed for flows with constant local Reynolds number (Sections 8.1 and 8.2) cannot be expected to apply to the case of the boundary layer. However, certain of the physical *concepts* involved are possibly applicable. For a discussion of experimental information on the development of turbulence from instability in a boundary layer the reader is referred to Section 8.3.

The basic ideas of the non-linear stability theory discussed above were put forward and studied by Landau (1944b), Malkus and Veronis (1958), and Stuart (1958). Further developments may be found in papers by Meksyn and Stuart (1951), Pillow (1952), Stuart (1956b, 1960a), Watson (1960b), Gorkov (1957), Veronis (1959), Kirchgässner (1960), and Donnelly and Simon (1960), and in a review article (Stuart 1960c).

A suggestion regarding secondary instability in the case of plane boundary-layer flows with Tollmien–Schlichting waves as the first mode of disturbance has been made by Görtler (1955b), namely that the second mode of disturbance may take the form of secondary Taylor–Görtler vortices because of the curvature of the streamlines. For a treatment of this suggestion, the reader is referred to Görtler and Witting (1958) and Witting (1957, 1958). Evidence of the occurrence of a secondary instability of Taylor-vortex flow between rotating cylinders is shown by photographs by Schultz-Grunow and Hein (1956).

8.1. *Finite disturbances under subcritical conditions in Poiseuille flow between parallel planes*

In the linear instability theory of plane Poiseuille flow the disturbance is defined mathematically by equations (48) and (49). However, in the non-linear theory other harmonic components must be taken into account, and the linearized exponential disturbance is just the first term in a Fourier series.

Consider a two-dimensional disturbance of wavelength $2\pi/\alpha$ and wave velocity c_r with a stream function

$$\psi = \phi_0(z,\tau) + \phi_1(z,\tau)e^{i\alpha(x-c_r\tau)} + \tilde{\phi}_1(z,\tau)e^{-i\alpha(x-c_r\tau)} +$$
$$+ \phi_2(z,\tau)e^{2i\alpha(x-c_r\tau)} + \tilde{\phi}_2(z,\tau)e^{-2i\alpha(x-c_r\tau)} + \dots$$
$$= \phi_0(z,\tau) + \phi'(x,z,\tau), \tag{106}$$

where $\sim$ denotes a complex conjugate quantity, and dimensional quantities are defined as in (38). Averages are taken with respect to the distance x, so that ϕ_0 represents the mean flow and ϕ' denotes the disturbance part of the flow. The mean $(\bar{u})$ and disturbance velocity components are

$$\bar{u}(z,\tau) = \frac{\partial \phi_0}{\partial z}, \qquad u' = \frac{\partial \phi'}{\partial z}, \qquad w' = \frac{\partial \phi'}{\partial x}, \tag{107}$$

where a bar above a quantity denotes its mean value, and a prime denotes a perturbation. Attention is restricted to a neutral oscillation, so that $\bar{u}$, ϕ_1, ϕ_2, etc., are independent of τ. If (106) and (107) are substituted in the dimensionless Navier–Stokes equations (39), a set of equations results for the quantities $\bar{u}$, ϕ_1, ϕ_2, and their complex conjugates. The mean-motion equation is

$$\frac{\partial}{\partial z}\overline{(u'w')} = -\frac{\partial \bar{p}}{\partial x} + \frac{1}{R}\frac{d^2\bar{u}}{dz^2}, \tag{108}$$

where the term on the left-hand side represents the effect of the Reynolds stress (see Appendix to this chapter) on the mean flow, and where

$$\overline{u'w'} = i\alpha\{\phi_1'\tilde{\phi}_1 - \tilde{\phi}_1'\phi_1 + 2(\phi_1^2\tilde{\phi}_2 - \tilde{\phi}_2'\phi_2) + \ldots\}. \tag{109}$$

The equation for the first harmonic, ϕ_1, is

$$(\bar{u}-c_r)(\phi_1''-\alpha^2\phi_1) - \bar{u}''\phi_1 + (i/\alpha R)(\phi_1^{\mathrm{iv}} - 2\alpha^2\phi_1'' + \alpha^4\phi_1) = \sum (\phi_1\phi_2), \tag{110}$$

where the right-hand side is the sum of products of ϕ_1, ϕ_2, and their derivatives, a typical term being $\phi_2'\tilde{\phi}_1''$. The equation for the second harmonic, ϕ_2, is

$$(\bar{u}-c_r)(\phi_2''-4\alpha^2\phi_2) - \bar{u}''\phi_2 + (i/2\alpha R)(\phi_2^{\mathrm{iv}} - 8\alpha^2\phi_2'' + 16\alpha^4\phi_2)$$
$$= -\tfrac{1}{2}(\phi_1'\phi_1'' - \phi_1\phi_1'''). \tag{111}$$

There are corresponding equations for the complex-conjugate functions, $\tilde{\phi}_1$ and $\tilde{\phi}_2$, and for higher harmonics. The equations were derived by Heisenberg (1924).

Equation (108) states that the mean motion is given by a balance of Reynolds stress, pressure gradient, and viscous stress. The first-harmonic disturbance equation (110) is the Orr–Sommerfeld equation with a non-zero right-hand side; the terms $\sum (\phi_1\phi_2)$ represent the effect on ϕ_1 of its interaction with the harmonic component ϕ_2.

Meksyn and Stuart (1951) made the assumption that, for small amplitudes, the most important non-linear interaction is that between the mean motion $(\bar{u})$ and the basic disturbance components $(\phi_1$ and $\tilde{\phi}_1)$. The functions ϕ_2, ϕ_3, etc., are then ignored. An approximate method of solving the eigenvalue problem of equations (108), (109), and (110), with $\phi_2 \equiv 0$, has been given by Meksyn and Stuart (1951) and Stuart (1956b). They found that the Reynolds number at which a finite neutral disturbance can exist is related to its amplitude parameter, a, by the curve shown in Fig. IX. 24. As the amplitude rises the Reynolds number drops to a minimum and then rises again. At a given Reynolds number there are two possible amplitudes. A calculation of the mean

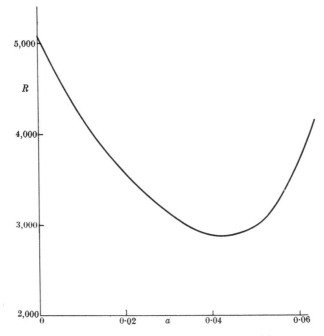

Fig. IX. 24. Amplitude of disturbance as a function of Reynolds number for plane Poiseuille flow.

flow corresponding to the minimum Reynolds number, $R = 2,900$, shows that the flow profile is distorted from its original parabolic shape (equation 41). The velocity gradient at the wall is higher than for laminar flow with the same maximum velocity, and a larger pressure gradient is required to maintain the same maximum velocity because of the work which must be done by the pressure gradient to maintain the disturbance. For further work on finite disturbances between parallel planes, including the effect of ϕ_2, see Stuart (1960a) and Watson (1960b), where a more complete discussion can be found.

For the flow corresponding to the minimum Reynolds number, Meksyn and Stuart found that $(\overline{u'^2})^{\frac{1}{2}}$, the root-mean-square velocity fluctuation in the flow direction, had a maximum value of $0·08U_0$. This is of the same order of magnitude as the value found in turbulence measurements by Reichardt (1938) and Laufer (1950).

The critical Reynolds number for transition to turbulence is about 1,000 (Davies and White 1928), compared with the minimum value of 2,900 given in Fig. IX. 24 for a particular equilibrium flow.

8.2. *Finite disturbances under supercritical conditions, with special reference to flow between rotating cylinders*

An example illustrating disturbances under supercritical conditions is that of viscous flow between rotating cylinders. The type of disturbance which arises has been discussed in Section 2 and takes the form of steady, cellular, toroidal vortices spaced regularly along the axis of the cylinders. Consequently, an appropriate variable with respect to which averages can conveniently be taken is z, the distance along the axis. As before v_r, v_θ, v_z denote components of velocity in cylindrical coordinates r, θ, z, and the time is t. It is assumed that the disturbance is periodic in z with wavelength $2\pi/\alpha$, and that the velocity components have the form

$$v_r = u' = u_1(r,t)e^{i\alpha z} + u_2(r,t)e^{2i\alpha z} + \ldots + \tilde{u}_1(r,t)e^{-i\alpha z} + \tilde{u}_2(r,t)e^{-2i\alpha z} + \ldots,$$

$$v_\theta = \bar{v} + v' = \bar{v}(r,t) + v_1(r;t)e^{i\alpha z} + v_2(r,t)e^{2i\alpha z} + \ldots +$$
$$+ \tilde{v}_1(r,t)e^{-i\alpha z} + \tilde{v}_2(r,t)e^{-2i\alpha z} + \ldots,$$

$$v_z = w' = w_1(r,t)e^{i\alpha z} + w_2(r,t)e^{2i\alpha z} + \ldots +$$
$$+ \tilde{w}_1(r,t)e^{-i\alpha z} + \tilde{w}_2(r,t)e^{-2i\alpha z} + \ldots, \quad (112)$$

where $\bar{v}$ is the mean motion.

If we substitute formulae (112) into the Navier–Stokes equations in cylindrical polar coordinates and separate the Fourier components, we obtain a set of partial differential equations in r and t, including the following equations for the mean motion:

$$\frac{1}{r}\frac{\partial}{\partial r}(r\overline{u'^2}) - \frac{1}{r}(\overline{v'^2} + \bar{v}^2) = -\frac{1}{\rho}\frac{\partial\bar{p}}{\partial r}, \quad (113)$$

$$\frac{\partial\bar{v}}{\partial t} + \frac{1}{r^2}\frac{\partial}{\partial r}(r^2\overline{u'v'}) = \nu\left(\frac{\partial^2}{\partial r^2} + \frac{1}{r}\frac{\partial}{\partial r} - \frac{1}{r^2}\right)\bar{v}, \quad (114)$$

where $\bar{p}$ is the mean pressure. The boundary conditions on $\bar{v}$ are

$$\bar{v} = r_1\Omega_1 \quad \text{at } r = r_1; \qquad \bar{v} = r_2\Omega_2 \quad \text{at } r = r_2, \quad (115)$$

where r_1, r_2 denote the radii of the inner and outer cylinders, with Ω_1, Ω_2 the corresponding angular velocities. Equation (113) gives the radial pressure gradient required to balance the centrifugal force and Reynolds stresses; in the absence of the latter, the equation is the usual one appropriate to rotating flow. On the other hand, equation (114) gives the mean velocity, $\bar{v}$, as a function of the Reynolds stress. If the flow is steady, and is therefore an equilibrium flow, $\partial\bar{v}/\partial t = 0$ and the viscous and Reynolds stresses balance. Equation (114) can then be integrated to give

$$\bar{v} = Ar + \frac{B}{r} + \frac{r}{\nu}\int_{r_1}^{r_2}\frac{\overline{u'v'}}{r}\,dr,\tag{116}$$

where

$$A = \frac{\Omega_1(1-mr_2^2/r_1^2)}{1-r_2^2/r_1^2} + \frac{1}{\nu(r_1^2/r_2^2-1)}\int_{r_1}^{r_2}\frac{\overline{u'v'}\,dr}{r},$$

$$B = \frac{r_1^2\Omega_1(1-m)}{1-r_1^2/r_2^2} + \frac{r_1^2}{\nu(1-r_1^2/r_2^2)}\int_{r_1}^{r_2}\frac{\overline{u'v'}\,dr}{r},$$

and $m = \Omega_2/\Omega_1.$ (117)

In the case of zero Reynolds stress, these relations are equivalent to equations (1) for laminar Couette flow between rotating cylinders.

In addition to the equations for the mean motion, there are equations for the first and higher harmonic components of the disturbance. However, as in Section 8.1, the assumption can be made that the most important nonlinear interaction is between $\bar{v}$ and the fundamental components (u_1, v_1, w_1, and conjugates). Then the equations reduce to a set similar to equations (3), where $2A$ is replaced by $\mathscr{D}^*\bar{v}$, and $\bar{v}$ is given by (116). This assumption is discussed by Stuart (1960c).

A simple procedure of approximation can be devised by considering the equation of the energy balance for the disturbance. For flow between rotating cylinders this takes the form

$$\frac{\partial}{\partial t}\iiint \tfrac{1}{2}\rho(u'^2+v'^2+w'^2)r\,dr d\theta dz$$
$$= \iiint (-\rho\overline{u'v'})\left(\frac{\partial\bar{v}}{\partial r}-\frac{\bar{v}}{r}\right)r\,dr d\theta dz - \mu\iiint(\xi'^2+\eta'^2+\zeta'^2)r\,dr d\theta dz,\tag{118}$$

where ξ', η', ζ' denote the three components of disturbance vorticity, corresponding to the formulae of Section III. 12. The three terms in equation (118) may be interpreted in a way similar to that described in Section 4.1 for the energy balance relation (55) for plane flow. Let us now consider an equilibrium flow, in which case the left-hand side of (118) is zero. Then the mean flow, $\bar{v}$, is given by equation (116), so that equation (118) really involves integrals of various products of disturbance velocities and their derivatives. If the integrations with respect to z and θ are carried out, equation (118) involves the amplitude functions $u_1(r)$, $v_1(r)$, and $w_1(r)$ of equations (112). Higher-order components of the disturbance are neglected in accord with the approximation already mentioned.

A second assumption is now introduced, that the functions $u_1(r)$, $v_1(r)$, and $w_1(r)$ are given in *shape* by linearized theory for marginal disturbances, but with an unknown amplitude, a. Then equation (118) gives a relation between terms involving the second and fourth powers of the amplitude parameter (a). The terms of order a^4 arise from the effect of the Reynolds stress through the distortion of $\bar{v}$. It follows that the solution of this equation gives the quantity a as a function of the Taylor number, T, for a given wavelength of disturbance.

Let us now consider the case when the outer cylinder is at rest and d/r_0 is small, where the notation used is given by equation (7). In this case a good approximation to the marginal disturbance velocity distribution is given by the variational condition (16) with $\sigma = 0$. Then if S denotes an approximation to the velocity v_1 and

$$P = (D^2 - \lambda^2)S,$$

we obtain from equation (118) the relation

$$0 = \gamma_1 a^2 - \gamma_2 R^2 a^4 - \frac{\gamma_3 a^2}{\lambda^2 T}, \tag{119}$$

where

$$\gamma_1 = \int_{-\frac{1}{2}}^{\frac{1}{2}} (-SP)\, d\zeta,$$

$$\gamma_2 = -2\left[\int_{-\frac{1}{2}}^{\frac{1}{2}} (-SP)\, d\zeta \right]^2 + 2 \int_{-\frac{1}{2}}^{\frac{1}{2}} S^2 P^2\, d\zeta,$$

$$\gamma_3 = \int_{-\frac{1}{2}}^{\frac{1}{2}} [(D^2 - \lambda^2)P]^2\, d\zeta, \tag{120}$$

and R denotes the Reynolds number $r_0 \Omega_1 d/\nu$. It should be noted that when the outer cylinder is at rest $(m = 0)$ and d/r_0 is small, the Taylor number is given to a first approximation by $T = R^2 d/r_0$. This is the Taylor number denoted by T in equation (119). If the Reynolds-stress term $(-\gamma_2 R^2 a^4)$ is neglected, the energy equation (119) is equivalent to the variational condition (16) with $\sigma = 0$, due to Chandrasekhar (1953b). The critical Taylor number (T_c) is given by $\lambda^2 T_c = \gamma_3/\gamma_1$ and the amplitude is

$$a^2 = \frac{\gamma_1}{\gamma_2 R^2}\left(1 - \frac{T_c}{T}\right). \tag{121}$$

Thus the square of the amplitude is proportional to the difference between the actual Taylor number and the critical number.

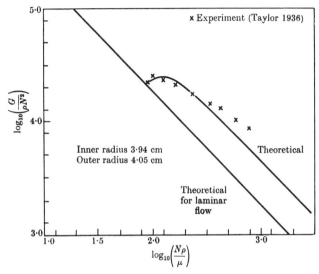

FIG. IX. 25. Comparison of theoretical and experimental torque for flow between rotating cylinders.

For the case of $\lambda = \pi$, which corresponds to a disturbance with a wavelength almost the same as that for the minimum critical Taylor number, a suitable approximation is

$$S = -\frac{1}{8\pi^2} + \frac{1}{\pi^4} + \frac{\zeta^2}{2\pi^2} + \frac{\cos \pi\zeta}{4\pi^3} + \frac{\mathscr{A}}{2\pi^3}[1 + \tfrac{1}{5}\cos 2\pi\zeta] - \frac{1}{\pi^4}\left[1 + \frac{2\pi\mathscr{A}}{5}\right]\frac{\cosh \pi\zeta}{\cosh \tfrac{1}{2}\pi},$$
(122)

with $\mathscr{A} = -0\cdot02686$. Then for a range of Taylor numbers at this particular wave number, $\lambda = \pi$, the amplitude can be evaluated according to (120) and (121). Thus we find

$$a^2 = \frac{5\cdot425 \times 10^4}{R^2}\left(1 - \frac{1,708}{T}\right),$$
(123)

where the critical value of T is 1,708.

In order to check the theory, the torque on the inner cylinder, which can be calculated from the mean flow (116) with (112), (122), and (123), is compared with Taylor's (1936) measurements in Fig. IX. 25. (See also Donnelly and Simon 1960.) The torque is G g cm^2 sec^{-2} and the angular speed of the inner cylinder is N rev sec^{-1}, the outer cylinder being at rest. It can be seen that the agreement is good for Taylor numbers up to about 10 times the critical, which corresponds to a Reynolds number of about $3\frac{1}{2}$ times the critical. It seems likely that the divergence between theory and experiment is due to the 'shape' assumption, the influence of the second harmonic terms (u_2, v_2, w_2), and to the occurrence of other instabilities.

The non-linear theory of thermal convection has been considered by several authors. Gorkov (1957), Malkus and Veronis (1958), and Veronis (1959) have studied expansions in powers of amplitude of the non-linear solution of the instability problem, and Pillow (1952) has examined the flow in a two-dimensional convective cell at large Rayleigh numbers. An essential feature of all this work is that the temperature distribution, which in the theory of Section 3 is linear, is allowed to distort under the action of the finite convection. (This effect is analogous to the distortion of the mean flow by the Reynolds stress in the hydrodynamic-stability theory.) The change in mean temperature causes a change of density, so that the amount of potential energy released from the gravitational field is modified. This alters the energy supply to the convection, and the (non-linear) effects of this are similar to those discussed on p. 563. Furthermore, the method of expansion used by Gorkov and by Malkus and Veronis allows for the generation of harmonics of the basic mode of disturbance. (A theory of this kind would also be valid for the rotating-cylinder case.) For a theory of turbulent thermal convection the reader is referred to Malkus (1954a, b).

8.3. The development of turbulence from instability waves in a boundary layer

As mentioned earlier in Section 8, a theoretical treatment of even the simplest non-linear problem of instability in a boundary layer is made difficult by the growth of the boundary layer in the flow direction. At the present time knowledge of the development of waves into turbulence in a boundary layer is largely dependent on experimental evidence. It is, therefore, with work of the latter kind that the present section is mainly concerned.

The reader will recall that in Section 4.5 it was mentioned that a reduction of the free-stream turbulence below a certain level does not produce any further increase in the Reynolds number of transition to turbulence in the boundary layer of a flat plate. This feature is due to the occurrence of natural instability waves which amplify and give rise to turbulence. In Section 4.5 attention was focused on a comparison of the characteristics of the waves observed experimentally

with the predictions of the linearized instability theory; in the present
section we shall be concerned with the departure of the characteristics
of the observed waves from the predictions of linearized theory, due
to the influence of (non-linear) amplitude effects. As before, the basic-
flow configuration to be discussed is that associated with a flat plate
at zero incidence in a uniform stream (the Blasius case). In their in-

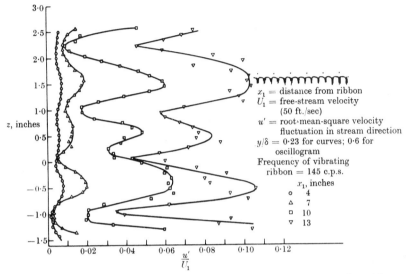

FIG. IX. 26. Wave intensity warping into peaks and valleys. ($\delta = 3\delta_1$; ribbon
35 in. from leading edge; y = distance from surface = 0·046 in., so that $y/\delta \sim 0·23$
to 0·21.) Oscillogram of characteristic breakdown at peaks.

vestigations, Schubauer and Klebanoff (1955) and Klebanoff and
Tidstrom (1959) used a flat plate of the same dimensions as that used
in the earlier instability experiments of Schubauer and Skramstad
(1947) (see Section 4.5), together with similar apparatus; in particular,
a 'vibrating-ribbon' mechanism was used to generate the waves.

One of the most important features of the initially two-dimensional
wave motion generated by the vibrating ribbon was a definite tendency
for it to become three-dimensional (Klebanoff and Tidstrom 1959; see
also Schubauer 1958). This phenomenon manifested itself as a nearly
periodic variation in the intensity of the velocity fluctuation in the
spanwise direction, with the fluctuation energy concentrated along
certain 'streets' parallel to the flow. Schubauer, Klebanoff, and Tidstrom refer to the regions of energy concentration as 'peaks', and to
regions of energy depletion as 'valleys'. Experimental observations of
Klebanoff and Tidstrom (1959) are shown in Fig. IX. 26, where u'

denotes the root-mean-square velocity fluctuation in the flow direction, U_1 denotes the local external velocity, and z denotes the spanwise direction; both x_1 (the distance from the ribbon) and z are measured in inches. It can be seen that, as the wave progresses downstream, the concentration of energy into streets increases. On the same figure is shown an oscillogram of a typical velocity fluctuation at a peak, the

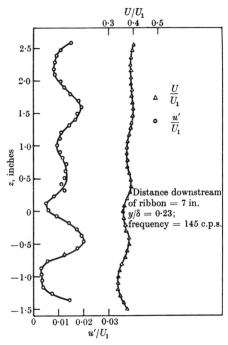

FIG. IX. 27. Comparison of spanwise variations of mean velocity and wave intensity.

downward spikes denoting high-frequency fluctuations towards lower velocities; they occur once in each cycle of the basic wave. This will be discussed later.

Further experiments showed that the warping of the wave into peaks and valleys was always accompanied by associated variations in the local mean velocity of the flow, as illustrated in Fig. IX. 27. It seems that the wave has an inherent tendency to warp after a fashion dictated by small velocity variations in the mean flow in the boundary layer. The spatial variations in the mean flow (namely those which appeared to trigger the three-dimensional, warping instability of the wave) were found to arise from minor irregularities in the oncoming stream, and were found to be affected by change of the turbulence damping screens in the wind-tunnel. However, although the initial warping of the wave arose from spatial variations in the mean flow, the growth of the warp to large amplitudes was clearly a non-linear effect of an instability, once the initial warp of a definite wavelength had appeared. (In Klebanoff and Tidstrom's experiments, the wave was nearly periodic in the spanwise direction, with a wavelength of about 1 inch.)

The rate of amplification of the disturbance is illustrated by Figs. IX. 28 and IX. 29 for conditions at a peak and a valley respectively. The curves are for different values of the reference amplitude (u_0'), which is that at a position 2 in. downstream of the vibrating ribbon. For amplitudes which are sufficiently small the wave grows and then decays; this is in accordance with linearized theory (curve A of Fig. IX. 6), since it represents a small disturbance moving to higher Reynolds numbers, amplifying inside the neutral curve and then decaying as it passes outside it at higher Reynolds numbers. However, for larger initial amplitudes (curves B, C, D of Fig. IX. 28) the amplitude curve for the peak deviates from that of linearized theory and grows much more strongly. On the other hand, the amplitude curve for the valley initially deviates towards lower amplitudes (curves B, C, D of Fig. IX. 29), but later recovers and grows at a much faster rate than that of linearized theory. At both peak and valley, the point of departure from the rate of amplification of linearized theory takes place farther and farther upstream as the initial amplitude rises. However, at a frequency of 145 c.p.s. the point of departure seemed always to be given by $u'/U_1 = 0.01$ approximately, whereas for a frequency of 70 c.p.s. it took place at about $u'/U_1 = 0.02$.

When the velocity fluctuation at the peak of the wave becomes large enough, bursts of turbulence occur, these being represented by points marked 'breaking point' on Fig. IX. 28. This breaking into turbulence was found to occur at a local amplitude of oscillation of about $u'/U_1 = 0.074$, approximately independent of the frequency of oscillation. Beyond the breaking point the disturbance grew to a large amplitude, which appeared not to be quantitatively reproducible, and then settled down to an equilibrium turbulent state at a lower amplitude than the maximum attained. The bursts of turbulence which occur at the breaking amplitude of the peaks appear to be embryo turbulent spots, to which attention will be paid later. The bursts of turbulence do not appear in the valleys, but turbulence spreads from the neighbouring peaks more and more strongly as transition is approached. It is also noteworthy that the turbulent bursts at the peaks depend markedly on the distance from the wall.

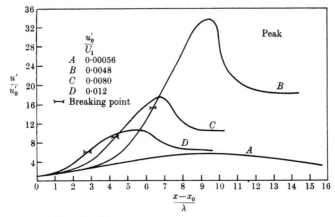

FIG. IX. 28. Wave growth at peaks. ($x - x_0$ = distance from reference position = $x_1 - 2$ in., λ = streamwise wavelength = 1·46 in., frequency = 145 c.p.s., U_1 = 50 ft/sec, R = 1625 at ribbon, y = 0·046 in.)

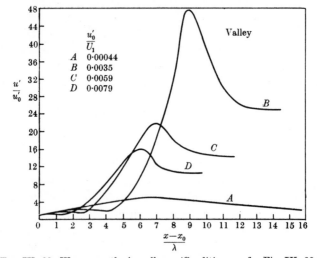

FIG. IX. 29. Wave growths in valleys. (Conditions as for Fig. IX. 28.)

Associated with the development of the three-dimensionality of the instability waves is a transfer of energy spanwise from valleys to peaks, once the departure from an amplification rate of linearized theory has taken place. This is shown by hot-wire measurement (by Klebanoff and Tidstrom, 1959) of the mean quantity $\overline{wu^2}$, where u is the velocity fluctuation in the stream direction and w that in the spanwise direction; $\overline{wu^2}$ represents energy transfer in the spanwise direction, and the measurements do show that energy flows from valleys to peaks. This phenomenon appears to account for the initial drop in amplitude in the valleys when the departure occurs from amplification of linearized theory (Fig. IX. 29). The amount of energy transfer in the spanwise direction is strongly dependent on the distance from the wall.

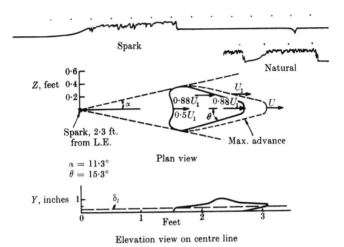

Fig. IX. 30. Turbulent spot initiated by electric spark between needle electrode and surface. Oscillograms with 1/60-sec timing dots shown above, time progression from right to left, upper showing spark discharge on right and spot passage on left, lower showing natural transition.

The turbulent spots which appear at the breaking amplitude of the peaks have been studied for the case of the boundary layer on a flat plate by Schubauer and Klebanoff (1955), Narasimha (1957), and Dhawan and Narasimha (1958). The original idea of turbulent spots was advanced by Emmons (1951) (see also Emmons and Bryson 1951), and involves the concept of each point of a boundary layer having a definite probability of being turbulent. In the purely laminar region the probability is zero, while in the turbulent region the probability is unity. The fraction of time during which a point in the transition region is turbulent is termed the 'intermittency factor' (γ); measurements by Schubauer and Klebanoff (1955) and Dhawan and Narasimha (1958) showed that $\gamma(x)$ is approximately of the form (see also Narasimha 1957)

$$\gamma(x) = 1 - \exp[-k(x-x_t)^2], \tag{124}$$

where k is a constant and x_l is the value of x at which transition begins (or, put in another way, where turbulent-spot production starts).

Fig. IX. 30 shows many of the important features of turbulent spots, as shown by Schubauer and Klebanoff (1955). The spot was generated artificially by a spark, and at the top (labelled 'spark') is a hot-wire record of the response at a point downstream. At the extreme right-hand side the kick-down of the trace represents the time at which the spot was started (time flows from right to left); the passage of the spot is shown by a rise in the trace, followed by a turbulent section and a slow fall to the original constant level. A trace due to natural passage of spots is also shown in the same figure for comparison. Some of the geometrical and kinematical properties of a spot initiated by a spark are also illustrated; in the elevation view, δ_l represents the normal thickness of the laminar layer. As x increases from the beginning of transition to the end, more and more spots are produced and swept downstream until, in the turbulent region, the flow may be thought of as a complete agglomeration of turbulent spots.

Other work on transition to turbulence in boundary layers has been done by Hama, Long, and Hagerty (1957), Weske (1957), and many others, but this work has less direct connexion with the instability theory and is not reported in detail here. For reviews of this and other work, the reader is referred to papers by Dryden (1955, 1956), Kuethe (1956), and Morkovin (1958).

APPENDIX TO CHAPTER IX
Reynolds stresses

When a flow is fluctuating, either in space or in time, it is convenient to analyse the flow into mean and fluctuating parts, where the 'mean part' is an average defined in some suitable way and the 'fluctuating part' has zero mean. For a discussion of methods of averaging, particularly with reference to turbulent flow, the reader is referred to the book by Batchelor (1953). In the (non-linear) theory of hydrodynamic stability, with which we are concerned here, the fluctuations are of a fairly regular kind and it is often convenient to consider an average with respect to one (or two) of the spatial dimensions. For example, in centrifugal instability between cylinders an average is taken with respect to the distance parallel to the axis, in thermal instability between parallel planes it is taken with respect to the two co-planar directions, and in Poiseuille flow between parallel planes it is taken with respect to distance parallel to the flow. An average of this kind avoids, at least for these stability problems, any difficulty associated with the fact that the mean flow may vary with time because of energy interchange between the mean and fluctuating parts of the flow.

Consider now the Navier–Stokes equations in Cartesian coordinates (III. (12) with $X = Y = Z = 0$) and define (in dimensional notation)

$$u = \bar{u} + u', \quad v = \bar{v} + v', \quad w = \bar{w} + w', \quad p = \bar{p} + p', \tag{125}$$

where a bar above a quantity denotes the mean part and a prime denotes the fluctuating part. Substituting (125) into the first of equations (III. 12) and averaging, we obtain

$$\frac{\partial \bar{u}}{\partial t} + \bar{u}\frac{\partial \bar{u}}{\partial x} + \bar{v}\frac{\partial \bar{u}}{\partial y} + \bar{w}\frac{\partial \bar{u}}{\partial z} = \frac{\partial}{\partial x}(\bar{p}_{xx} - \rho \overline{u'^2}) + \frac{\partial}{\partial y}(\bar{p}_{yx} - \rho\overline{u'v'}) + \frac{\partial}{\partial z}(\bar{p}_{zx} - \rho\overline{u'w'}), \tag{126}$$

where $\bar{p}_{xx}$, $\bar{p}_{yx}$, $\bar{p}_{zx}$ are given by the averages of the expressions (III. 8). In the non-linear stability theory, the mean flow is often independent of one (or two) of x, y, z; consequently, differentials of the velocity components and their products with respect to such a variable (or variables) are zero.

It can be seen that (126) is of the same form as the first Navier–Stokes equation except for the additional terms $-\rho\overline{u'^2}$, $-\rho\overline{u'v'}$, $-\rho\overline{u'w'}$. In fact the six stresses of formulae (III. 8) are replaced in the equations of the *mean* motion by

$$\bar{p}_{xx} - \rho\overline{u'^2}, \quad \bar{p}_{yy} - \rho\overline{v'^2}, \quad \bar{p}_{zz} - \rho\overline{w'^2},$$

$$\bar{p}_{yz} - \rho\overline{v'w'}, \quad \bar{p}_{zx} - \rho\overline{w'u'}, \quad \bar{p}_{xy} - \rho\overline{u'v'}. \tag{127}$$

These virtual stresses, which are usually known as Reynolds stresses, arise from the fact that there is a mean transport of momentum due to the velocity fluctuations.

Within the scheme of analysis which we have adopted, namely that in which mean and fluctuating parts of the flow are separated, the Reynolds stresses represent the non-linear effect of the fluctuating flow on the mean flow. Consequently, these two parts of the flow are mutually dependent. Thus a disturbance which amplifies in an unstable mean flow does so because the Reynolds stresses do work to transfer energy from the mean flow to the disturbance. For a further discussion of these topics in connexion with turbulence, the reader is referred to books by Lamb (1932, p. 674) and Townsend (1956).

It should be noted that, if the formulation discussed above is used in the laminar stability theory, the mean flow $(\bar{u}, \bar{v}, \bar{w})$, whose stability is under investigation, distorts under the action of the Reynolds stresses. The 'disturbance' (u', v', w'), a perturbation from the mean flow, is then periodic in space or time with zero mean. An alternative formulation is to retain the notation $\bar{u}$, $\bar{v}$, $\bar{w}$ for the original laminar flow, while the disturbance (u', v', w') now contains a mean part. However, the former approach seems to be the more illuminating both physically and mathematically, and has been used in this chapter.

Note added in proof

For more recent references appropriate to this Chapter see p. 688.

X

EXPERIMENTAL METHODS

1. Introduction

T H E main purpose of this chapter is to provide an account of methods available for experimental investigations of the properties of laminar boundary layers in incompressible flow. The discussion will observe fairly strictly the restriction to fluids of sensibly constant density. The restriction to laminar flow, however, will be interpreted more freely and relaxed where it is expedient to do so, as for instance when discussing methods of determining transition position; in any case, many of the methods are equally applicable whether the boundary layer is laminar or turbulent. Further, an attempt will be made to build into the chapter a sketch of the whole range of experimental methods in incompressible flow, in the hope that this, although necessarily less detailed, will serve to set the purely boundary-layer techniques in proper perspective. Most of the methods to be described have been furthest developed for experiments in air, but some reference will also be made to corresponding techniques used for experiments in water. Other fluids have been used but seldom.

2. Various methods of producing relative motion

A boundary layer forms because there is no slip between a solid surface and the layer of fluid in contact with it, whilst the fluid farther away is in motion relative to the surface. The first task of an experiment on boundary layers, therefore, is to create the relative motion. This is generally accomplished by moving a body through stationary fluid or by testing a body without translational motion in a stream which flows past it; occasionally a combination of both methods is employed.

Methods in which the test vehicle moves through stationary fluid can conveniently be divided into two main classes according as the motion of the body is free or constrained. The former class includes full-scale flight tests, ship trials, and investigations using models which are self-propelled (as in the case of ground-launched rockets or ship models in a steering basin), fired (in air, under water, or from air into water), or dropped (as in freely falling models in air); another example is the ditching tank. Techniques in which the path of the model is constrained are exemplified by high-speed railways or towing tanks (including seaplane tanks), by tethered dynamic models, and by whirling arms or annular water channels.

The methods in which a model is tested in a moving stream likewise fall into two classes, according to whether or not the body is in translational motion relative to the ground. Those in which this translational velocity is zero are instanced by wind-tunnels, water-tunnels, circulating water channels and flumes, and the spinning tunnel (in which the model is allowed to spin freely in a vertical jet whose speed can be adjusted so that the model remains in the same vertical position throughout the test). Those in which the body and the fluid are both in translational motion are exemplified by the technique of discharging a model upstream into a wind-tunnel, by gust-tunnels, and by the crosswind ballistic range.

Each technique has its proper field of application and each has its own advantages and disadvantages. Full-scale tests necessarily form the ultimate check to be applied to all other methods of investigation, whether theoretical or experimental.

In any method in which the test vehicle moves through the atmosphere or the sea, it is often difficult to achieve satisfactorily steady conditions, and occasionally weather conditions may be entirely unsuitable. Full-scale flight tests are also costly and can be dangerous, although the latter objection can be overcome to some extent, for example by the use of unmanned aircraft. Scale models offer advantages in respect of convenience, economy, and ease of manufacture and modification. The results, however, are liable to scale effect, and in the case of free-flying models the need for remote observation and control introduces additional complications. The whirling arm and the annular tank are unique in that they are able to reproduce effects peculiar to steady motion in a circular path.

Probably the most widely used method is that of wind-tunnel experiment. A tunnel large enough to accommodate full-scale aircraft and sufficiently highly powered to provide full-scale flight speeds would offer most of the advantages of flight testing combined with complete safety, independence of weather conditions, closer control over conditions of experiment, greater ease of instrumentation, and increased facilities for observation. Tunnels in which scale-models are tested make it necessary to allow for scale effect when interpreting the results, but otherwise provide the advantages already indicated for a full-scale tunnel, combined with greater economy of capital expenditure and running costs, as well as the advantages arising from small model size. Again, a tunnel makes it possible to test conveniently only part of an aircraft or other vehicle, and is also the obvious choice for investigations of the flow past stationary obstacles such as buildings, piers, bridges, land masses, and windmills.

Water-tunnels are basically similar in design to wind-tunnels, but provision should be made for varying the pressure in the working section. This is necessary because the onset of cavitation depends critically on the working pressure. It may also be necessary to provide special apparatus to vary the air content of the water.

Results from tunnel experiments usually need to be corrected for the effect of the finite transverse extent of the stream, as this imposes a constraint on the flow and so gives rise to tunnel interference. The necessary corrections can usually be calculated with sufficient accuracy, provided the model is not excessively large in relation to the tunnel cross-section.

3. Types of measurement

The measurements which can be made on a system comprising a body and a fluid in relative motion can be broadly classified into those concerned with the changes which the relative motion produces in the fluid and those concerned with the reaction experienced by the body. In the exploration of the flow field, methods are available for such measurements as local velocity and static pressure, for locating trailing vortices and vortex sheets, and for visualizing the flow pattern. The main concern of this chapter is the application of such methods to the study of boundary-layer growth and development, transition, separation, and related phenomena. The important subject of boundary layers in compressible flow, and their interaction with shock waves, is beyond the scope of this chapter, but many of the methods to be described are applicable to compressible flow as well.

As a result of the relative motion, the body experiences an aerodynamic or hydrodynamic reaction which may equally form the object of experimental investigation. Methods are available for measuring the resultant forces and moments on the body, and for determining local forces such as the distribution of surface friction or static pressure. Deductions can also be made from observations of the handling quality of aircraft, from their performance, and from their degree of stability and response to control movements. Aerodynamic reactions may also be deduced from the observed trajectories of missiles. Ship trials provide another example in which measurements are made of the reaction experienced by the test vehicle.

4. Wind-tunnels

The function of a wind-tunnel is to provide an airstream of the required speed, type, and extent, and to do so with an acceptably low expenditure of power; the various components are subservient to this end and the central feature is the working section. In most recent low-speed tunnels, the working sections have been of the 'closed' type (i.e. bounded by solid walls), but open jets have also been used extensively in the past. Slotted or perforated walls have been used for special purposes, such as reducing wind-tunnel interference by balancing the opposite interference effects due to closed and open working sections; an example is the use of such walls for minimizing shock-wave reflection at transonic speeds. Tunnels with closed working sections need rather less power than similar designs with open jets; and their constraint effects, although in some cases larger, can be calculated with greater confidence. Open jets have at times exhibited unexpected flow pulsations, which have necessitated special devices for their suppression, but tunnels of this type do offer the advantage of greater convenience which for some investigations may well be an over-riding consideration.

In the so-called straight-through type of tunnel (Fig. X. 1) the air is usually returned to the entry by way of the room in which the tunnel is erected; in the return-circuit type (Fig. X. 2) the air is made to recirculate through a specially designed return duct. Most modern designs are of the return-circuit type. The straight-through tunnel is usually less economical in power requirements, although these can be very substantially reduced by providing a long and efficient diffuser. Again, a straight-through tunnel needs to be situated in a large room, as the velocity of the air returning to the tunnel intake has to be kept small; for particular investigations, however, this type of tunnel may be more suitable than the return-circuit type. For instance, a smoke tunnel is more conveniently made of this type because unwanted smoke concentrations build up too rapidly in a return circuit; better still, the air passing through the tunnel can be discharged outside the building altogether, a fresh supply being drawn in at the tunnel intake.

The airstream usually approaches the working section through a contraction which speeds up the flow, increases its transverse uniformity, and reduces the intensity of turbulence. The flow uniformity may also be improved, and stream turbulence decreased, by means of a honeycomb straightener or gauze screens. In several tunnels, some improvement in flow uniformity has been obtained by means of a freely rotating windmill in the return circuit. Downstream of the working section the airstream is gradually expanded through a diffuser whose purpose

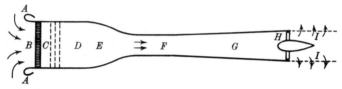

FIG. X. 1. Typical straight-through wind-tunnel. A: flared inlet; B: honeycomb; C: gauze screens; D: settling length; E: contraction; F: working section; G: diffuser; H: fan; I: distributor.

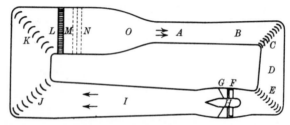

FIG. X. 2. Typical return-circuit wind-tunnel (plan). A: working section; B, D, I: diffusing passages; C, E, J, K: corners with cascades of guide vanes; F: fan; G: straighteners; H: motor nacelle; L: honeycomb; M: gauze screens; N: settling length; O: contraction.

is to reduce the stream velocity as efficiently as possible, the kinetic energy being largely recovered as an increase in static pressure. At any bends, such as the corners of a return-circuit tunnel, it is usual to incorporate guide vanes in order to improve the flow and reduce losses.

Low-speed tunnels are usually driven by an axial fan through a variable-speed electric motor. In some tunnels two-stage fans have been used; in others, contra-rotating fans. Most wind-tunnel fans are of fixed pitch, although variable pitch has been used on some installations. In some cases, too, power has been provided by an internal-combustion engine or a water turbine.

The most important properties of general-purpose low-speed tunnels, apart from spatial uniformity and temporal steadiness of the flow, are the size, the speed range, and the operating pressure of the airstream in the working section, as together these determine the Reynolds numbers attainable. The layout sketched in Fig. X. 2 is typical of a modern general-purpose tunnel. The working section of such a tunnel is frequently rectangular in shape, with corner fillets; two sizes in common use are 9 ft × 7 ft and 13 ft × 9 ft. Top speeds are typically in the region of 300 ft/sec; at higher tunnel speeds the air would no longer behave as an incompressible fluid in regions of high local velocity such as the areas of peak suction on a wing at high incidence. Tunnel speeds higher than 300 ft/sec may be needed, however, if the experiment deliberately seeks to reproduce local compressibility effects which are expected to occur in full-scale conditions.

For special investigations such as studies of free-stream turbulence and boundary-layer behaviour (including stability, transition, and separation) it is essential to use an airstream of very low turbulence and exceptional uniformity and steadiness; these are achieved by means of large contraction ratios (in the region of 16:1 in contrast to 5:1 or 6:1 for a typical general-purpose tunnel), turbulence-reducing gauze screens, and (in the case of a return-circuit tunnel) a well-designed low-loss diffuser.

For some investigations, particularly the study of the incidence stall and boundary-layer separation problems in general, high Reynolds numbers are essential. The power required in order to achieve them can be substantially reduced by running at increased pressure, as in the American variable-density tunnel (V.D.T.) and the British compressed-air tunnel (C.A.T.). The V.D.T. (1923, rebuilt 1928) has a closed working section of 5 ft diameter and a speed of about 60 ft/sec at a pressure of 20·7 atm; the C.A.T. (1931) has a circular open-jet working section of 6 ft diameter and a speed of 90 ft/sec at a pressure of 25 atm. It is now known that such tunnels should be designed to have low turbulence levels as well, as boundary-layer behaviour can vary markedly with stream turbulence. In a tunnel operating at such high pressures it is difficult to make frequent or continuous adjustments to the model, and most measurements have to be made by remote recording. Illumination, visual observation, and photography of the model also present problems, and the tendency today is to use rather lower maximum pressures (say 5 or 10 atm) combined with a larger working section (say 50 sq. ft.) and a higher top speed (say 200 ft/sec at maximum pressure or 350 ft/sec at atmospheric pressure).

Occasionally, special-purpose tunnels have been built to reproduce particular types of flow, such as curved-flow tunnels for investigating aerodynamic camber derivatives, and rolling-flow tunnels; and many otherwise conventional tunnels have incorporated unusual features in order to suit them for special types of investigation.

5. Water-tunnels

Water-tunnels incorporate many of the features of wind-tunnels, such as turbulence-reducing screens, a contraction to the working section, subsequent diffusion, and guide vanes at corners. A typical water-tunnel is sketched in Fig. X. 3. Again, as in a wind-tunnel, the boundaries

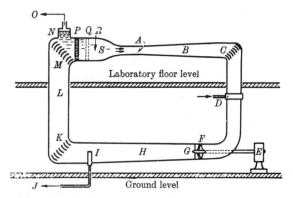

Fig. X. 3. Typical water-tunnel (elevation). A: working section; B, H, L: diffusing passages; C, K, M: corners with cascades of guide vanes; D: inlet from by-pass filter; E: external driving motor; F: impeller; G: straighteners; I: by-pass outlet; J: to filter bed and cooling plant; N: free surface; O: to pressure control (atmospheric, vacuum, or pressure supply); P: honeycomb; Q: gauze screens; R: settling length; S: contraction.

of the working section may be closed, slotted, or open (surrounded by water at rest); 'free' jets (i.e. water jets surrounded by air) have also been used. The tunnel may be driven by an axial-flow impeller or by a centrifugal pump. The tunnel circuit is always arranged to be in the vertical plane, and the impeller or centrifugal pump is placed sufficiently low in the circuit to avoid cavitation. Where possible it is advisable to mount the impeller with its plane of rotation horizontal, so that the pressure is constant over the whole of the disk area.

Practically all water-tunnels are used for studies of cavitation. For this reason it is essential to be able to vary the static pressure in the working section. In order to cover a wide range of cavitation conditions at high Reynolds number, it is necessary to be able to raise the pressure above atmospheric as well as to lower it below atmospheric. In modern tunnels provision is also made for varying the concentration of dissolved air and maintaining it constant at a set value. Varying the air content is accomplished by means of aerating and de-aerating plant, usually in a by-pass circuit; for maintaining it constant when cavitation occurs it is necessary to incorporate in the main circuit some form of 'resorber' whose function is to return the released air into solution.

In both the wind-tunnel and the water-tunnel all the energy delivered to the stream by the driving unit is eventually dissipated as heat, and in both cases it may be necessary to provide refrigerating plant. In some water-tunnels, on the other hand, provision has been made for heating the water in order to increase the Reynolds number (by decreasing the viscosity) and lower the cavitation number attainable (by increasing the vapour pressure), although in fact this facility appears never to have been used. In wind-tunnels it is seldom necessary to make provision for complete elimination of dust except for delicate hot-wire anemometry, but a water-tunnel should be provided with filtration plant for removing solid particles.

The essential characteristics of a given problem are often identical in both aero- and hydro-dynamics. Experimental investigations may then be undertaken in either air or water according to the relative ease of experimentation, and the results from the one medium are equally applicable to the corresponding physical system in the other provided that the Reynolds number is the same, that cavitation does not occur in the liquid, and that the Mach number in the gas is sufficiently low for the effects of compressibility to be negligible. In practice, water behaves as a sensibly incompressible medium because, although the speed of sound is little more than 4 times that in air, the velocities involved are much less and the Mach numbers correspondingly low.

The density (ρ), viscosity (μ), and kinematic viscosity (ν) of water are respectively about 800, 60, and 0·080 times those of air. A given Reynolds number may therefore be obtained in water with a model one-third the linear size (l) and at one-quarter the velocity (V) needed in air. The load on the model, however, is proportional to $\rho l^2 V^2$ and would be nearly 6 times as great in water as in air. Compared with a wind-tunnel whose size of working section bears the same ratio to that of the model, a water-tunnel would require nearly 1·5 times as much power, as this is proportional to $\rho l^2 V^3$.

6. Tunnel balances

The aerodynamic or hydrodynamic reaction on the model is usually determined by means of a tunnel balance, whose function is basically to segregate the required force and moment components and to measure them to the required accuracy. If tests are to cover all full-scale conditions, provision must be made for setting the model in any orientation relative to the stream and a six-component balance is needed in order to obtain all the force and moment components. If only the longitudinal motion is to be investigated, however, only the incidence needs to be adjustable and a three-component balance suffices to measure lift, drag, and pitching moment. Auxiliary balances may be introduced additionally for the separate measurement of such items as hinge moment or propeller torque reaction.

In nearly all low-speed wind-tunnel balances, and in many water-tunnel balances, segregation of moment and force components is effected mechanically by means of linkage systems which allow the model to rotate about appropriate axes or to translate in the direction of required force components. Each force and moment component is commonly measured by means of a mechanical weighbeam, and manual operation is rapidly giving place to automatic balancing and recording, especially for routine tests and industrial use. Other devices, such as the Kelvin-type electric-current balance, have also been employed. Both the mechanical weighbeam and the current balance are null methods.

Reference should also be made to strain-gauge balances, although in the case of wind-tunnels their use has mostly been restricted to high-speed conditions, when the model is often mounted from the rear on a single 'sting' support. Balances of this type measure essentially the strains at chosen locations in the model support or supports, which are otherwise rigid; the force and moment components are then obtained by combining these readings appropriately, usually by electrical means so that the required values are presented as the final output. Strain gauges may alternatively be used to measure forces and moments which have already been resolved into components by means of a mechanical linkage system. When strain gauges are used, allowance has to be made for model deflexion, as this is inherent in any strain-gauge measurement; the corrections needed are determined during a preliminary calibration.

7. Tunnel interference

It has already been pointed out that conditions in a tunnel necessarily differ from those in free air or open water because of the limited transverse extent of the test stream, which introduces constraint effects known as tunnel interference. The boundary condition for a solid wall is that the component of the fluid velocity normal to the surface must be zero; in the case of an open jet, the boundary condition is that the static pressure along the boundary of the jet must be the same as that of its surroundings. The latter condition is difficult to apply in calculating the interference, partly because the geometrical position of the edge of the jet is ill defined and also because it is displaced to an unknown extent by the presence of the model.

The analytical treatment of tunnel constraint is usually based on the method of images, but other methods have also been used, such as conformal transformation and direct numerical solutions of Laplace's equation. A vast variety of cases have been considered including two-dimensional flow, bodies of revolution, and finite wings of various planforms and with various types of spanwise loading (including asymmetrical distributions), in some cases with the model central or off-set from the tunnel axis. Special cases have also been considered, such as propellers and oscillating aerofoils. Most analyses have been concerned with the effect of the tunnel constraint on the overall forces and moments of the model and on the mean velocity of flow past the model, but in a few cases calculations have also been made of the effect produced on the pressure distribution over the model surface.

The common object of all such investigations is to determine the difference between the behaviour of the system in the constrained flow in the tunnel and that in a stream of unlimited extent in corresponding conditions, so that the behaviour in the unconstrained flow can be deduced from that observed in the tunnel by applying appropriate corrections. These fall into two broad categories.

The first category comprises the effects of the constraint on the mean speed past the model. These are known as blockage corrections and arise (in a closed working section) from the speeding up of the general flow past the model which must take place in order to preserve continuity of mass flow; in the tunnel the outermost streamlines must follow the walls, whereas in unconstrained flow the streamlines at the same distance from the body would be displaced slightly outwards. This speeding up of the general flow is partly local, due to the constriction created by the model itself (solid blockage) and partly extended because of the reduced velocities in the wake behind the model (wake blockage). A further speeding up of the general flow occurs because of the steadily increasing thickness of the boundary layers on the tunnel walls, but as this is also present in the empty tunnel it is usually taken into account in the tunnel calibrations. Sometimes compensation is introduced by a slow progressive increase in working-section area. In the case of an open-jet tunnel, application of the boundary condition of constant pressure 'shows that the pressure at any point near the body is greater than it would have been in unconstrained flow, and the velocity therefore less. Hence the solid blockage for an open jet is opposite in sign to that for a closed working section. Wake blockage is usually taken to be zero for an open jet.

The second category is concerned with the effect which the constraint produces on the aerodynamic reaction on the model. The solid blockage effect already described is local in the sense that if it were the only constraint effect present the flow velocity far downstream of the body would return to its original upstream value. Wake blockage, on the other hand, is an extended effect in the sense that the wake continues downstream and the flow velocity outside the wake remains greater (in a tunnel with a closed working section) far downstream. By virtue of Bernoulli's equation this increase in velocity from upstream to downstream of the model is accompanied by a decrease in static pressure, to which is added any variation of static pressure which may be present in the empty tunnel, and the resultant longitudinal pressure gradient gives rise to an extra downwind force which the body would not experience in unconstrained flow. Quite apart from this 'horizontal buoyancy' effect, the fact that the model is effectively being tested in accelerated flow gives rise to a further drag increment due to its virtual mass. This increment would also occur in unconstrained accelerated flow, but it has to be allowed for because the ultimate object of the tunnel tests is almost invariably to determine the forces which would have occurred if the undisturbed stream were uniform as well as unlimited in extent.

When the model is developing lift, a further interference ('lift effect') arises, however small the model, because the finite extent of the working section produces an effective upwash or downwash at the body which would be absent in free air. This is readily visualized by the mathematical artifice of replacing the model by an equivalent vortex and considering the velocity field of its images in the tunnel walls. The upwash or downwash causes an effective change in wing incidence; and as it varies along the chord there is also an effective change of camber. In the case of a finite wing the effective change in wing incidence due to the images of the trailing vorticity also causes an equivalent angular rotation of the lift vector and so gives rise to a downwind component, of the nature of an induced drag, which likewise would not be present in free air. Although the reason is not evident from the simplified model here considered, this drag correction does not arise in two-dimensional flow. This conclusion has been reached in a more rigorous treatment in which the aerofoil is represented not by a line vortex but by a vortex distribution along the camber-line. In an open-jet tunnel the incidence needs to be further corrected because the lift of the model imparts an overall deflexion to the jet (downward when the lift is positive).

Solid blockage and lift effect can be eliminated by shaping the walls of a closed working section so as to coincide with the paths which would be followed by the streamlines at that distance from the body in an unlimited stream. Both these types of constraint would occur in inviscid flow. Wake blockage, on the other hand, would be zero in the absence of drag. The longitudinal gradient of static pressure also would be zero in inviscid flow in so far as it is due to the growth of the tunnel-wall boundary layers over the length of the working section; and in fact this pressure gradient can be eliminated by displacing the tunnel walls outwards by an amount which is everywhere equivalent to the displacement thickness of the wall boundary layer.

Additional types of interference may arise in special cases. For example, in tests of two-dimensional aerofoils the model is mounted so as to span the tunnel completely. Unwanted secondary-flow effects may then occur at the junctions with the tunnel walls, where the relatively thick boundary layer on the wall will interfere with the development of that on the model itself. Again, the velocity gradient through the tunnel-wall boundary layers is itself a departure from the conditions of true two-dimensional flow. Although in many practical cases these effects are not serious, difficulty has been experienced in high-lift tests in which the adverse pressure gradients over the upper surface of the aerofoil have been considerably increased by means of boundary-layer control. Confronted with this abnormally severe adverse gradient and unaided by artificial means, the wall boundary layer has separated and caused substantial departures from the conditions of two-dimensional flow.

Additional corrections may be needed for the flow distortion due to model supports (solid blockage, wake blockage, and interference with the flow over the surface of the model), for extraneous forces and moments on exposed parts of the supports which are measured in the experiment but which would not occur in free flight, and for any inclination of the test stream to the tunnel axis. Scale effect also may have to be estimated when the tests are done at Reynolds numbers different from those of full scale; and in some investigations the probable effect of tunnel stream turbulence needs to be borne in mind when interpreting the results.

8. Measurement of velocity

The method adopted for measuring velocity in any particular case depends entirely on the circumstances, as no one method is applicable generally. Direct measurement of the distance travelled by an element of fluid in a known interval of time, though scarcely a practical routine method, has been used successfully in a number of investigations. In air at atmospheric pressure, for instance, Townend (1931, 1937a) used a spark discharge to create a local hot spot whose passage downstream was followed using optical methods; by generating a series of sparks at regular intervals it was possible to incorporate a ready-made time scale in the photographs. Ionization also has been used as the method of identifying elements of the fluid, whose passage downstream was then timed electronically; suitable instrumentation has been described by Boyd, Dorsch, and Brodie (1952). Another method, which has been used mainly in water, is the 'fluid-motion microscope' (Fage and Townend 1932; Fage 1955), with which the motion of small particles in the flow is followed by rotating the objective about an off-set axis parallel to that of the microscope. A further example is provided by the determination of the distribution of velocity in the boundary layer (Geller 1955; Clutter and Smith 1961); in this case the tracer consisted of a line of bubbles generated electrolytically by passing a current through a wire set up normal to the wall. Other electro-chemical reactions have also been used from time to time.

For most purposes it is necessary to resort to indirect methods, which usually depend either on a pressure difference (as in the pitot-static tube) or on the cooling experienced by a heated body immersed in the flow (as in hot-wire anemometry, Section 13). Methods in the first category involve the determination of the pressure differentials themselves, as in the pitot-static tube, or make use of overall aerodynamic reactions on a solid obstacle, as in cup and vane anemometers. The second category consists mainly of hot-wire instruments (Section 13).

The velocity distribution over the surface of a body, at the outer edge of the boundary layer, can conveniently be inferred from measurements of static pressure obtained from pressure tappings (flush holes) on the surface. It is usually sufficiently accurate to assume that this pressure is sensibly constant across the boundary layer.

The mean velocity in a duct can be determined in some cases by a direct-displacement method. Usually, however, the measurement is based on the pressure difference caused by a change in cross-sectional area, for example in a venturi tube or the orifice plate, though other methods may be more suitable in particular circumstances. Occasionally it may be necessary to determine the distribution of velocity across the duct by traversing a suitable instrument and to obtain the mean flow by integration. Alternatively, the mean flow may be deduced from a spot reading in conjunction with previous calibration or an assumed velocity profile. This type of method is exemplified by the 'three-quarter-radius meter' (Preston 1950c) for the measurement of the flow through a pipe of circular cross-section. In this method a reading is obtained from four pitot tubes symmetrically disposed at $0.75R$ (where R is the radius of the pipe) and flush static holes in the wall.

The account that follows is intended to give a general description of some of the methods and instruments in everyday use.

9. The pitot-static tube in a uniform stream

Essentially the pitot-static tube is an instrument for determining local velocity from a single measurement of the difference between the static pressure (p_0) and the total pressure (H); the velocity (V) is then given, in incompressible flow, by the equation

$$H = p_0 + \tfrac{1}{2}\rho V^2.$$

In order to determine V absolutely it is necessary to know the density of the fluid (ρ). Very often, however, it suffices to know only the product ρV^2, as this alone determines aerodynamic reactions on simple test models, and Reynolds numbers are usually given to sufficient accuracy by assuming a standard value for ρ. When this procedure is not sufficient, however, the density would normally be calculated from the temperature and the static pressure, together with the humidity if necessary.

A pitot tube on its own (named after Henri Pitot, 1695–1771) is essentially an open-ended tube aligned into wind with its mouth facing upstream (Fig. X. 4). Fluid elements directly approaching the mouth are brought to rest and a manometer connected to the tube records the stagnation pressure, which in incompressible flow is indistinguishable from H. The design of a pitot tube presents no difficulty, as almost any suitably located upwind orifice has been found to record the total pressure to a satisfactory degree of accuracy. Further, the reading of a pitot tube is very insensitive to yaw. For a thin-walled pitot tube, for instance, an angular displacement of 20° affects the reading by less than 0·5 per cent. of $\frac{1}{2}\rho V^2$; for a tube with a hemispherical head and an internal diameter about half the external diameter, the corresponding figure is 10°. Extreme insensitivity to yaw can be achieved by mounting the pitot tube within a venturi-type constriction as sketched in Fig. X. 5; by this means the error can be kept less than 1 per cent. of $\frac{1}{2}\rho V^2$ for angles of yaw up to over 60° (Russell *et al.* 1951).

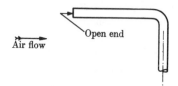

Air flow →   Open end

Fig. X. 4. Pitot tube.

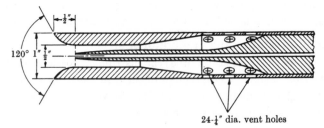

120°   1″ $\frac{1}{2}$″

24-$\frac{1}{4}$″ dia. vent holes

Fig. X. 5. Section of a shielded pitot tube.

The influence of Reynolds number on the reading of a pitot tube is negligible for most practical purposes, except for very small tubes or very low airspeeds. It has been confirmed (MacMillan 1954a) that a blunt-nosed instrument of circular cross-section gives the true total pressure to within 1 per cent. of the dynamic pressure for all Reynolds numbers above about 40 (based on the *internal* radius of the tube). At lower Reynolds numbers the measured pressure coefficient rises rapidly, as shown in Fig. X. 6. It is interesting to note that the results from various investigations can be correlated more closely when the Reynolds numbers are based on internal radius instead of external radius. Hemispherical heads give a somewhat different curve (Sherman 1953), though similar in shape; the rapid rise in measured c_p with decreasing Reynolds number occurs rather earlier (i.e. at a slightly higher Reynolds number as shown in Fig. X. 6) and the results agree closely with those calculated by Homann (1936 b) for the flow past a sphere when the Reynolds numbers are this time based on external dimensions. Reynolds number effects for the special shapes of head shown in Fig. X. 8 (c) and (d) have been measured for $R_a > 20$ and found to be substantially the same as for blunt-nosed instruments. Reynolds number effects on a flattened pitot tube are described in Section 18.

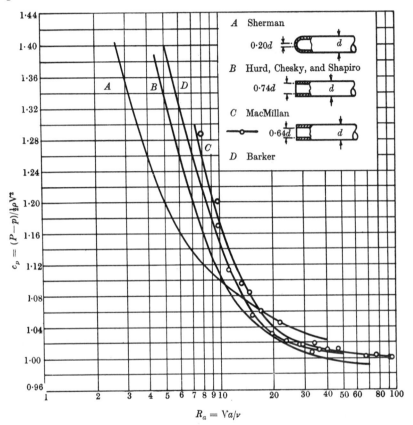

$$R_a = \mathrm{V}a/\nu$$

Fig. X. 6. Pressure coefficient indicated by pitot tube at low Reynolds numbers (based on internal radius of mouth). P = reading of tube, p = static pressure.

It is not so simple to measure static pressure: even a hole drilled in a solid boundary affects the measurement. Shaw (1960) gives results showing how measurements of static pressure on the wall of a pipe vary with diameter and depth of hole when connected to tubing of twice the diameter. He also emphasizes the very large errors caused by minute burrs.

The measurement of static pressure in a uniform stream is also influenced by the flow disturbances inevitably introduced by the measuring instrument. The form of static tube in general use (Fig. X. 7) consists of a right-angled tube, one arm of which is sealed at the end and aligned with the local direction of flow; a hole or holes farther downstream transmit the local external surface pressure to a manometer connected to the stem of the instrument. The acceleration of the flow over the arm (A) causes the pressure at the holes to fall below

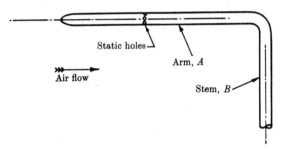

FIG. X. 7. Static tube.

its value in the absence of the instrument, to an extent which depends greatly on the shape of the nose; the presence of the stem (B), on the other hand, causes a deceleration of the flow upstream of itself, and a consequent increase in pressure. The pressure tappings are usually made as close as possible to points where these two opposing effects balance out, although this is not essential if the required correction is first obtained by calibration. A static tube is much more sensitive to yaw than is a pitot tube: in some typical case, for example, an angular deflexion of $10°$ could affect the reading by $2\frac{1}{2}$ per cent. of $\frac{1}{2}\rho V^2$.

Pitot and static tubes are often combined into a single instrument, so that velocity can be determined from a single measurement of the difference ΔP between the pitot pressure and the pressure at the static holes. Three such pitot-static tubes are shown in Fig. X. 8; many variants exist. They are usually designed so that the calibration factor is unity (i.e. so that ΔP is exactly equal to $\frac{1}{2}\rho V^2$) except in so far as scale effect, turbulence, and compressibility influence the reading, but reliability of the factor is more important than equality with unity.

The original N.P.L. standard (Fig. X. 8 (a)) was designed in 1912, and a 'short head' version of the hemispherical nose type (Fig. X. 8 (b)) some time later. Their factors were then believed to be exactly unity, although more recent work has shown them to be slightly different. The original standard is relatively sensitive to yaw and its sharp nose can easily be damaged. The round-nose type is much more robust and

more suitable for use when the direction of the flow is uncertain, and
has therefore been more commonly used.

On both types of head, the boundary layer on the nose separates to
an extent that varies with Reynolds number and stream turbulence and
so affects the calibration factor, which is in fact uncertain for these
tubes at very low Reynolds numbers. The separation can be eliminated

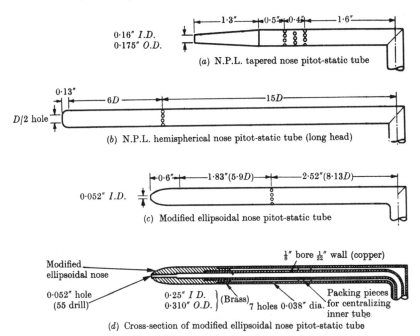

FIG. X. 8. Forms of pitot-static tube.

by reducing the local velocity peak by using special shapes of head
(Kettle 1954; Salter 1953, 1955); that shown in Figs. X. 8 (c) and (d)
is a modified ellipsoid, and this type of instrument is now regarded as
the best available standard. Incidentally, the head shown in Figs. X. 8
(c) and (d) gives a calibration factor within ±1 per cent. of unity for
angles of yaw up to 14° and is therefore preferable to that shown in
Fig. X. 8 (b) if the flow direction is known within these limits.

A pitot-static tube is often used to measure the mean velocity $\overline{V}$
in a uniform stream with superposed turbulent velocity fluctuations
(u, v, w). If it is assumed that the eddies are large enough for the oncoming flow to be treated as quasi-steady, yet weak enough for the
effect of yaw angle to be unimportant, then in such a flow a pitot tube

records the mean total pressure, which exceeds $p + \frac{1}{2}\rho\overline{V}^2$ (where p denotes the mean static pressure) by $\frac{1}{2}\rho(\overline{u^2} + \overline{v^2} + \overline{w^2})$; this is consistent with the interpretation of total pressure as a measure of the energy content per unit volume of the fluid, and is confirmed by detailed analysis (Goldstein 1936).

In the case of a static tube, however, the same assumptions do not affect the reading provided the tube pressure coefficient is zero. But if the greater sensitivity of the static tube to yaw (compared with the pitot tube) is taken into account then the effect of the transverse fluctuations on the reading of a static tube would be expected to be given by $-K\frac{1}{2}\rho(\overline{v^2} + \overline{w^2})$, where K is positive and typically of order unity. This is based on a reduction in indicated pressure proportional to the square of the yaw angle and hence to $(\overline{v^2} + \overline{w^2})/\overline{V}^2$. The stream turbulence in a modern low-speed tunnel $(\sqrt{\overline{u^2}}/U \sim 0\cdot001)$ is small enough for the above corrections to be negligible, but they are appreciable in a turbulent boundary layer and in fully developed pipe flow. It must not be overlooked that, on account of the Reynolds stresses, the true static pressure at a wall is less than the static pressure outside the surrounding turbulent shear layer, or at the centre of a pipe: for a flat wall the difference is $\rho\overline{w^2}$. The above arguments assume that the instrument records a true time-average of the fluctuating pressures presented to it; the effects of lag, damping, resonance, etc., have not been considered. Some information on these aspects is given in Section 12.

The special problems of using pitot tubes in boundary-layer explorations are further discussed in Section 18, where reference is also made to the effects of transverse gradients of total pressure and to the effects of proximity to a wall.

10. Yawmeters

Flow direction can be determined roughly by using a round-nosed pitot tube with a small orifice and aligning it so that its reading is a maximum; its axis then lies along the required direction. This method lacks accuracy, however, because the reading of a pitot tube is not very sensitive to changes of direction in this region. For determining flow direction in two-dimensional conditions, two pitot tubes disposed symmetrically at an angle to one another are frequently employed; such a 'claw-type' instrument is sketched in Fig. X. 9, which shows the setting angles for greatest sensitivity determined by Schulze, Ashby, and Erwin (1952). In use, the probe is rotated about an axis normal to the flow until the two arms record the same pressure. The flow direction should then be along the axis of symmetry of the instrument, subject to any corrections needed to allow for inaccuracies in construction, as revealed by a preliminary calibration. Three-dimensional flow fields can be explored similarly by incorporating two further tubes in a plane at right angles to that of the first pair, whilst the addition of

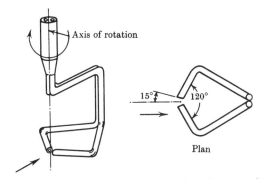

FIG. X. 9. Two-tube claw-type yawmeter of maximum sensitivity.

a central pitot tube in the direction of the axis of symmetry of the probe enables the wind speed to be determined as well as its direction.

Another class of pressure-type yawmeter depends on the variation of pressure round a suitable symmetrical obstacle placed in the flow. For example, the flow direction in two-dimensional conditions may be determined using a circular cylinder mounted perpendicularly to the flow and provided with two pressure holes at different angular positions. These will give equal readings when the holes are symmetrically disposed about the flow direction. The corresponding yawmeter for use in three-dimensional flow has a hemispherical head, as shown in Fig. X. 10 (a); this, however, is difficult to construct accurately in small sizes. Alternative types of probe are shown in Figs. X. 10 (b) to (g). Those shown in Figs. X. 10 (b), (c), and (d) consist of several tubes symmetrically arranged, with the forward faces of the side tubes chamfered; the two-tube version (Fig. X. 10 (b)) has become known as the Conrad yawmeter. In the forms shown in Figs. X. 10 (e), (f), and (g), the tubes fit into an outer sheath; the interstices are filled up and the forward end of the probe ground to a chisel, conical, or pyramidal shape.

Other methods of using yawmeters, and the merits of the various forms, have been discussed in detail by Winternitz (1956) and by Bryer, Walshe, and Garner (1955). As already indicated, in one method the probe is orientated until all the side tubes read the same; the flow then lies along the axis of symmetry of the instrument. Another method relies on a calibration relating the out-of-balance pressure to the angle of yaw of the instrument; in three-dimensional flows, this enables the second rotation (which requires elaborate traverse gear) to be omitted. In the technique due to Templin, using the probe shown in Fig. X.10 (c) and discussed by Bryer *et al.* (1955), the instrument is first rotated

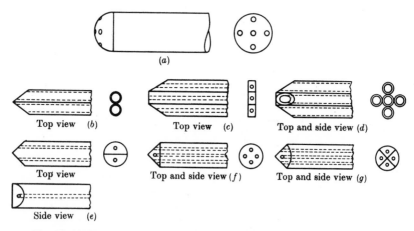

FIG. X. 10. Forms of yawmeter probe. (a) 5-hole hemispherical head; (b), (c), (d) 2-tube, 3-tube, and 5-tube Conrad type probes; (e), (f), (g) chisel probe, conical probe, pyramidal probe.

about its longitudinal axis until the readings of the side tubes are equal. An additional reading is then taken after the tube has been further rotated through 90°; the windspeed and flow direction are determined by reference to previous calibration. In general, Bryer *et al.* (1955) conclude that for boundary-layer work where the flow is parallel to the fixed surface, the Conrad type is to be preferred, and that in all cases a sharp-edged probe is more satisfactory than a rounded one as it is less affected by changes of Reynolds number.

Hot-wire yawmeters are mentioned in Section 13.

11. Manometers

Fluid dynamics is often concerned with pressure differences rather than absolute values; for instance, the pressure at any point in the flow is frequently best related to the static pressure of the undisturbed stream. Except where fluctuating pressures are concerned, such pressure differences are nearly always measured by means of a manometer in which the pressure difference is balanced against that due to a column

of liquid, and non-dimensional values (when required) may be obtained
as the ratio of the appropriate lengths of liquid column without converting each separately to pressure units. While the simple vertical
U-tube is adequate for many purposes, the sensitivity can be increased
by inclining the plane of the limbs. Some manometers incorporate more
than two limbs (multi-tube manometers) or adopt more elegant means

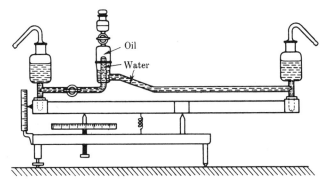

FIG. X. 11. Chattock gauge.

of increasing the sensitivity. In addition, mechanical refinements may
be introduced, such as a device for 'freezing' the liquid levels so that
they may be read at leisure, thus reducing tunnel running time. Another
modification is the provision of a large reservoir so as to minimize the
change in level in each measuring tube due to changes in level in the
others. In low-speed aerodynamics the gauging liquids most commonly
used are water and alcohol. Besides simple vertical and inclined U-tube
and multi-tube instruments, frequent use is also made of the Chattock
gauge, null-reading inclined-tube devices, and the Betz manometer.

The Chattock gauge (Fig. X. 11) is essentially a water U-tube mounted
on a metal frame and used as a null-reading instrument by tilting the
frame by means of a micrometer screw; the null position is indicated by
the meniscus formed by a water-oil interface in the middle arm of the
instrument. In the form now used (Pannell 1913; also Ower 1949, see
pp. 214–16), the outer arms (to which the pressure difference to be
measured is applied) consist of cups of 2 in. diameter, normally 13 in.
or 26 in. apart. If this distance is denoted by L, and l is the distance
between the micrometer screw and the fulcrum, then the required
pressure difference (expressed as a head of the gauging liquid) is RpL/l
to the first order of small quantities, where R is the number of turns
of the micrometer screw needed to restore the meniscus to its null

position and p is the screw pitch. Various modifications of the standard Chattock gauge have been used for further increasing its sensitivity (e.g. Lavender in Simmons and Jones 1927; Falkner 1934) and for eliminating zero drift due to temperature changes during use (Duncan 1927).

A more modern type of null-reading U-tube manometer is sketched in Fig. X. 12. In this instrument the null indicator is the liquid meniscus

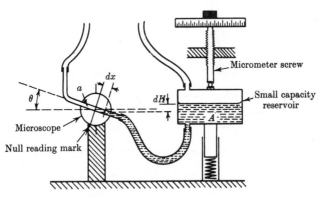

FIG. X. 12. Null-reading U-tube manometer.

in the small-bore inclined tube which forms one arm of the U-tube; the other arm is the reservoir, whose height relative to that of the inclined tube is adjusted by means of a micrometer screw. The sensitivity of the instrument is given (MacMillan 1954b) by the equation

$$\frac{dx}{dH} = \frac{1}{a/A + \sin\theta},$$

where dx (Fig. X. 12) represents the displacement of the meniscus from the fiducial mark due to a pressure change dH (expressed as head of gauging liquid), dx being measured along the inclined tube, whose inclination to the horizontal is θ and cross-sectional area a; A is the cross-sectional area of the reservoir. The sensitivity thus depends on the ratio a/A and the angle θ. For high sensitivity the instrument should be designed so that A/a is large; but A must not be increased excessively if the reservoir has to be connected to capillary tubing, or the resulting instrument lag may become unacceptable. The required sensitivity may still be achieved, however, by making θ negative. Variable sensitivity can be obtained if the inclined tube is mounted in such a way that θ can be altered during use. Zero changes due to temperature variations can be eliminated by suitable design, as the

effect of the change in surface tension is of opposite sign to that due
to thermal expansion of the liquid, reservoir, and inclined tube. Further
details about the design of instruments of this type have been described
by Smith and Murphy (1955a) as well as by MacMillan (1954b). The
accuracy attainable, if all possible precautions are taken, has been
estimated to be about ± 0.0001 in. head of liquid, with small lag.

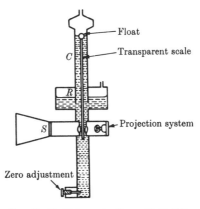

Fig. X. 13. Betz projection manometer.

Another convenient form of sensitive manometer is the projection
type due to Betz and sketched in Fig. X. 13. The pressure difference
to be measured creates a corresponding difference in level between liquid
in the reservoir R and that in the cylinder C; the latter supports a float
which carries a transparent graduated scale. An image of the scale is
projected on the ground-glass screen S, which bears a fiducial mark
and a short scale so that the required reading can be obtained precisely.
This type of instrument combines range with accuracy, but for some
purposes its lag may be excessive, owing to its large air volume.

Certain precautions need to be taken when using high-precision manometers. These include providing a firm support; taking care not to
move any flexible leads containing gauge liquid in such a way as to
cause changes in volume; surrounding the instrument by a constant-
temperature enclosure if temperature differences or temperature variations are otherwise unavoidable; ensuring that no spurious pressure
differential is introduced by temperature effects in the connecting leads;
and arranging that the meniscus or bubble indicator is not heated
appreciably by the light used to illuminate it or to project its image on
to a screen. Temperature changes may also be troublesome during
calibration. For very small pressure differences the instrument is usually

calibrated by connecting it and a standard instrument to a common reservoir, and a further difficulty arises because adjustment of the one affects the reading of the other. Both difficulties can be overcome by using a water-sealed reservoir (Preston 1951).

The choice of gauging liquid for any manometer depends on the pressure range to be covered and on other requirements of the mano-meter. Common choices are water, alcohol (specific gravity 0·8), and mercury (13·6). Liquids of intermediate density (carbon tetrachloride,

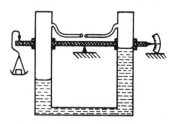

Fig. X. 14. Tunnel-speed gauge.

1·6; ethylene bromide, 2·2; acetylene tetrabromide, 3·0) have been used for special purposes despite various objectionable characteristics such as the property of attacking rubber or metals. Other properties to be considered include any tendency to absorb water (as this could affect its density); coefficient of thermal expansion; surface tension; wetting properties and viscosity (as these affect the response of the manometer to changes in applied pressure difference); and volatility.

A pressure gauge that is well suited to the measurement of tunnel speed is shown in Fig. X. 14. It consists essentially of a U-tube balance; the applied pressure difference displaces liquid from one arm to the other, and equilibrium is restored by weights on the scale-pan. An interesting feature of this balance is that the required restoring load for a given applied pressure difference depends only on the geometry of the instrument; the density of the gauging liquid is not involved except in so far as it affects the vertical dimensions of the gauge.

The above discussion relates mainly to the measurement of steady-state pressures. When fluctuating pressures are required, the mano-meter used must be of low inertia so that its natural frequency is well above those of the fluctuations to be recorded. The type used is generally some form of pressure capsule, in which the pressure difference is applied across an elastic diaphragm whose resultant strain is recorded by a beam of light, photocell, or interferometer, or electrically through a change in capacitance, inductance, or resistance. Varying pressures

have also been converted directly to electrical signals by allowing them
to stress a piezo-electric crystal.

12. Lag in leads

It is often vital to minimize lag in the leads connecting the recording
instrument to the pressures being measured. When conditions are
changed from one steady state to another, for instance, excessive lag
may intolerably increase the time taken before the changed pressure
is transmitted to the recording instrument. Other examples of the need
to minimize lag are provided by aircraft flight tests in a steady dive or
climb, in which the ambient static pressure varies continuously, and
by investigations in which fluctuating pressures themselves are to be
measured.

Troublesome lag in steady-state experiments occurs in such investigations as boundary-layer traverses using a very small pitot tube, or
pressure-plotting measurements in which space restrictions make the
use of small-bore leads unavoidable within the model. An improvement
can be effected by keeping the leads as short as possible. Increasing
their diameter likewise reduces their resistance to the flow through
them; at the same time, however, it increases the volume of air that
has to pass before equilibrium conditions are reached. Indeed, if the
lead from a pressure hole to the recording instrument consists of a series
of tubes of various lengths and successively increasing diameters, some
of which are fixed by space restrictions, then there exists one optimum
diameter for all the other tubing. Sinclair and Robins (1952) have
shown that this optimum diameter is given approximately by the
equation
$$d_{\text{opt}} = \sqrt[6]{[8V/\pi \sum (l_n/d_n^4)]},$$

where V is the volume of the whole system including that of the recording instrument but excluding the tubing whose diameter is to be made
an optimum, and $l_1,..., l_n$ and $d_1,..., d_n$ are the lengths and diameters
of the other tubes.

In instrumentation for flight tests in a dive or climb, the lag is kept
as small as possible by minimizing the lengths of the leads, the number
of bends and joints, and the air volume of the recording instruments,
and by increasing the diameter of the leads. What lag remains, however, has to be allowed for (Smith, K. 1954), the corrections to the instrument readings (functions of the rate of climb or descent) being determined preferably by simulating the steadily changing pressure due to
variation of altitude in a ground rig and applying additional corrections

for the temperature variation that accompanies the pressure variation in flight.

When fluctuations are to be measured, as in investigations of turbulence or oscillating aerofoils, the first requirement is a recording instrument of high natural frequency; indeed, the lowest natural frequency of the whole system should be at least twice that of any of the fluctuations, in order to avoid resonance. Uniformity of response over the frequency range concerned can be secured by arranging that the value of the damping factor is about 0·65. The concomitant phase lag may also need to be taken into account. In many cases, however, lag problems can be greatly reduced or eliminated by converting the fluctuating pressures or velocities to an electrical signal as early as possible, using a pressure capsule or hot-wire anemometer. A nomogram method for estimating the response time for a single length of tubing connected to a pressure transducer of negligible volume has been given by Tiffany (1957).

In many investigations the pressures required are mean values in a fluctuating flow; in others, flow fluctuations represent a failure to produce experimentally the desired steady-state conditions, which are then assumed to be closely represented by a time average. In both cases, resonance must again be avoided but resistance in manometer leads is an advantage as it damps the unwanted fluctuations. If the damping is not already sufficient it can be increased by inserting a length of capillary tubing. This makes it easier to get some sort of average reading where otherwise it might be almost impossible, but with very severe fluctuations an apparently steady reading does not automatically imply that the observed mean is the required value.

13. Hot-wire anemometry ; turbulence measurements

The hot-wire anemometer consists essentially of a short length of very fine wire supported between two metal prongs and heated electrically. It is usually aligned normal to the airstream. In the usual form of the instrument the windspeed is deduced from the cooling produced, either by recording the current needed to maintain the wire temperature (and hence its resistance) at a given value as indicated by a Wheatstone bridge circuit, or by measuring the potential difference across the wire with a constant current passing through it. There is little to choose between the two methods at windspeeds of a few feet per second; at speeds of the order of 100 ft/sec the first method is the more accurate. In the instrument due to Simmons (1949) (see also Cowdrey 1950) the hot wire is enclosed in one bore of a small twin-bore silica tube of 0·04 in. external diameter; the other bore carries a thermo-couple.

The outstanding advantages of hot-wire instruments are that they are small in size and that their response can be extremely rapid, which makes them especially well suited to the measurement of velocity fluctuations. Indeed it is for investigations of free-stream turbulence that the instrument has been most extensively developed. If a bridge incorporating a hot-wire anemometer is balanced for the mean flow velocity, then turbulence will result in fluctuating out-of-balance voltages. These signals are amplified electronically and fed into circuits which compensate for the thermal inertia of the hot wire (Dryden and Kuethe 1929) and operate on the input signals in such a way that the final output represents the required function, usually as the reading of a thermo-milliammeter. The functions used in the specification of free-stream turbulence include the root-mean-square values of the turbulent velocity components, their various correlation coefficients, the energy spectrum of the turbulence, and its micro- and macro-scales. For details of these and other turbulence measurements by means of hot-wire instruments reference should be made to Cooper and Tulin (1955), Willis (1945), and Kovásznay (1955).

Besides being universally used in turbulence investigations, hot wires are also of great value in the detection and measurement of velocity fluctuations generally, and for the determination of windspeeds below the practical lower limit of applicability of the pitot-static tube. Their small size can be exploited in the measurement of boundary-layer velocity profiles. They can also be used qualitatively for revealing whether a boundary layer is laminar or turbulent. Their use for detailed study of the growth of disturbances in a laminar layer played a vital part in the experimental confirmation by Schubauer and Klebanoff (1955) of Emmons's model of the mechanism of transition through the growth of turbulent 'bursts' (Emmons 1951; Emmons and Bryson 1951).

The calibration of a hot-wire instrument can be seriously affected by deposited dust or oil (Collis 1952). This source of error is minimized in the shielded instrument already described (Simmons 1949), which has proved a valuable means of measuring low airspeeds. This instrument cannot, however, be used for turbulence measurements.

Another possible source of error in hot-wire measurements of turbulence is that arising from the finite length of wire; the appropriate corrections have been detailed by Dryden *et al.* (1937), Dryden (1943), and Frenkiel (1954). In measurements of turbulence of low intensity, trouble may also be experienced if the signal due to random electronic 'noise' or to spurious mechanical vibration of high frequency becomes comparable to the out-of-balance signal to be measured. The electronic circuits themselves must always be designed so that the amplifier performance remains satisfactory over the whole frequency range concerned (Kovásznay 1954).

Hot wires can be used for measuring wind direction by using two or more identical wires symmetrically disposed. The simplest yawmeter of this type, suitable for use in two-dimensional flow, consists of two such wires mounted symmetrically at a small angle to each other (say 10°) and connected so that each forms one arm of a Wheatstone bridge. The position of the instrument is adjusted, with the apex pointing into the wind, until the heat loss from each wire is the same; the direction of the mean flow should then bisect the included angle, though calibration is required in practice. For exploring flow fields in three dimensions, three or more (usually four) identical wires are arranged in the form of a regular pyramid; the orientation of the instrument is adjusted until the bridge remains balanced for every pair of wires. Another procedure in two-dimensional flow is to use two parallel wires a short distance apart, with their axes perpendicular to the plane of the flow. One of the wires is rotated about the other until the maximum out-of-balance is obtained; the one wire is then in the heated wake of the other.

Hot films have been used in place of hot wires when high mechanical strength is required (Ling and Hubbard 1956). The film consists of a narrow band of metal, of the order of 10^{-6} cm thick, deposited on the surface of an insulator of suitable shape, for example a spherical-headed or wedge shaped probe.

14. Flow visualization

Flow-visualization methods, as the term implies, consist of techniques in which the flow conditions are determined by visual observation instead of being deduced indirectly from instrument readings. They can be used to establish whether the flow is steady or fluctuating, laminar or turbulent, attached or separated; to indicate the fluid particle paths, filament lines, or streamlines; and to provide information about the velocity field. They are used extensively for observing flow patterns in general, whilst special methods (Section 15) have been developed for obtaining information about the boundary-layer flow over a solid surface.

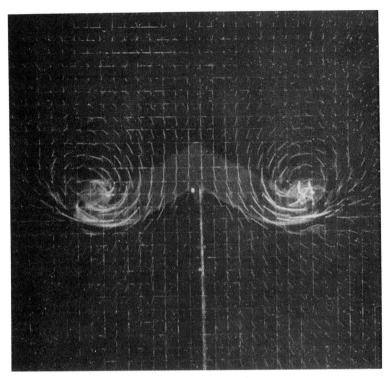

Fig. X. 15. Tuft-grid visualization of flow downstream of a 60° sweptback
wing at 20° incidence

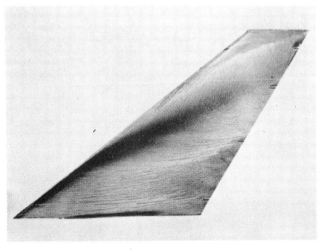

Fig. X. 16. Oil-flow visualization of part-span vortex from leading
edge of sweptback wing

In order to follow the path of a fluid element as it passes downstream one must mark the element in some way. Methods of doing so with a view to determining velocity as well have already been mentioned in Section 8. If only the flow pattern is required, however, other methods are available such as the use of foreign particles dispersed throughout the field. A photograph thus obtained using a short time-exposure displays an aggregate of streaks, each of which is an element of the corresponding particle path in that view. If a tracer is introduced continuously at a given point in the field, then at any instant the trace observed shows the positions then reached by all the fluid particles which have previously passed through that point. In steady motion such filament lines coincide with the particle paths and also with the streamlines.

In practice, visualization of flow patterns has been successfully accomplished in water using aluminium particles, polystyrene beads, or oil drops dispersed throughout the medium; in air, clouds of balsa dust or smoke have occasionally been used in the same way. For the visualization of filament lines, a continuous stream of dye is often employed in water, or a filament of smoke in air.

Ideally the density of the foreign particles should be the same as that of the fluid medium. When their density differs substantially, their paths can differ appreciably from those of adjacent fluid elements because their inertial and gravitational forces are different from those of the fluid elements. For instance, owing to their very low relative density, air bubbles introduced into a water flow tend to move towards regions of low pressure, such as vortex cores, instead of following the streamlines; for the same reason they also tend simply to rise upwards. Conversely, when smoke is used in a curved airflow, the greater relative density of the smoke particles tends to make them move outwards, and smoke in air at low speeds descends appreciably under the action of gravity. These effects are generally not serious, however, as long as due care is exercised. In water, droplets of the same density can be introduced by using a mixture of suitable proportions of carbon tetrachloride and either xylol, nitrobenzene, or benzene.

For wind-tunnel investigations the smoke now generally preferred is that derived from paraffin oil using a generator of the type described by Preston and Sweeting (1943) or that described by Meijer Drees and Hendal (1951), although solid smokes and steam have also been used successfully. In order to obtain satisfactory filaments the flow in the feed tube at the point of emission must be sufficiently free from turbulence, and the tube must not introduce serious disturbances itself. In some cases this can be ensured by locating the tube in the contraction upstream of the working section, as is the usual practice in specially designed smoke tunnels (see, for example, Hazen 1955); in other cases it may be necessary to suppress the wake of the tube by means of boundary-layer control.

The importance of adequate illumination can scarcely be overemphasized, especially when photographs are to be taken. The camera (or the observer) should be shielded from the light source; glare should be avoided by suitable arrangement of the light source and by using a model with a matt black surface. The contrast can be further improved by providing a black background. When a technique is used in which particles are distributed throughout the field, it is often advantageous to confine the illumination to a narrow sheet in order to visualize the flow effectively in a plane.

Instead of marking elements of the fluid, the flow direction may be found by fixing threads or streamers of wool, silk, or nylon to the surface of the model or to an exploring wand. To avoid misleading results at low speeds the tufts must be very flexible, or else fixed in such a way that they have no preferred set, and they need to have a high drag/weight ratio. Light paper cones attached to streamers have occasionally been used. An effective method of visualizing the flow in a cross-wind plane (Bird 1952) employs an array of tufts which are freely attached to the intersections of the wires of a grid, and viewed from downstream. The photograph reproduced as Fig. X. 15 (Plate), which was taken in an N.P.L. 9 ft. × 7 ft. wind-tunnel (Lambourne and Pusey 1958), depicts the flow downstream of a 60° sweptback wing at 20° incidence as visualized by this technique. The photograph was given an exposure of 1/25 sec, which was long enough to show up the unsteadiness in the vortex regions: the presence of disturbed regions of flow may be missed altogether if too short an exposure is used, such as that provided by an electronic flash, though superposition of a number of flash exposures is better than a continuous exposure in very disturbed flow.

Another type of flow visualization, purely optical, is based on the changes in refractive index consequent upon the density changes which accompany velocity changes in a compressible fluid. Techniques of this type are the direct-shadow, interferometer, and schlieren methods. Although mainly employed with high-speed flow, some of them have been used at airspeeds as low as 200 ft/sec at which the flow can usually be regarded as otherwise incompressible. In addition, the schlieren technique is a useful adjunct to other methods, such as the heated-wire method for the observation of filament lines.

An optical method occasionally used for studying fluid flow makes use of the phenomenon of streaming bi-refringence, i.e. the property of double refraction developed in shear flow by certain pure liquids, homogeneous solutions, and colloidal suspensions. This makes it possible for an analysis to be made using polarized light as in the analogous subject of photo-elasticity. Although the existence of streaming bi-refringence has been known since 1873, the method has not been extensively used as a research tool because the phenomenon is still not fully understood. In the case of colloidal suspensions the double refraction is thought to be due partly to the deformation of the particles under the action of the principal stresses and partly to the fact that, being rod-shaped, the particles possess a preferred orientation in shear flow; the latter effect, however, may cause even dilute solutions to exhibit thixotropic characteristics (see Section I. 4.5). In the case of pure liquids and homogeneous solutions, the double refraction is due primarily to the action of the principal stresses. The doubly refracting media used include dilute colloidal suspensions of benzopurin (e.g. Binnie and Fowler 1947) and bentonite clay (e.g. Wayland 1955), an aqueous solution of 'milling yellow' (an organic dye) (Peebles, Garber and Jury 1953), and pure liquid ethyl cinnamate (Wayland 1955). A review of the literature has been made by Rosenberg (1952).

15. Visualization of boundary-layer flow

The use of tufts and smoke can readily be applied to the visualization of boundary-layer flow. Surface tufts or threads may indicate whether the boundary layer is laminar or turbulent by the amount of their movement, and readily show up regions of separated flow both by their violent motion and by indicating characteristic changes in flow direction, such as flow reversal in many two-dimensional cases or converging streamlines in certain three-dimensional conditions (Maskell 1955). Care should, however, be taken to avoid locating them permanently in a region where conditions are critical so that they themselves cause a substantial modification of the flow: for example, when used in a laminar boundary layer they frequently precipitate a wedge of turbulent flow downstream.

When smoke is used for boundary-layer flow visualization, it is either allowed to exude into the boundary layer through a small hole in the surface of the model, or else is introduced into a streamtube just outside the boundary layer. The type of indication obtained varies correspondingly: in the first method, for instance, the smoke filament remains well defined when the boundary layer is laminar but diffuses rapidly when turbulent. In the second method the filament only reaches the surface when brought there by turbulent mixing, and Wijker (1951) suggests that when viewed at grazing incidence, the coalescence of the smoke filament with its reflection in the surface (assumed polished) may be taken to indicate transition. In water flow, filaments of dye can be used in much the same way as smoke in air, and this method is frequently used in tank tests of ship models.

The use of smoke becomes increasingly difficult as the wind speed is increased, owing to more rapid dissipation of the smoke filament. It is then often more convenient to use a chemical method in which the smoke is replaced by a chemically active gas and the part of the model being examined is first coated with a suitable preparation which changes colour when the gas comes in contact with it. By this means the effects are cumulative and a permanent record is obtained. The state of the boundary layer is deduced from the character of the stains produced; both transition and separation may be detected. The best results in wind-tunnel tests have been obtained by emitting hydrogen sulphide from a hole in the surface of the model which is painted with lead carbonate (Preston and Sweeting 1945). Wijker (1951) has pointed out that it is possible to remove the stain and reactivate the paint for further use by applying 30 per cent. hydrogen peroxide. Great care must be taken, however, in the use of these toxic chemicals. In flight Gray (1944) has obtained a record of transition by coating the wing surface with a gas-detector paint and flying the aircraft through a cloud of chlorine.

Various methods are available for revealing the state of the boundary layer over a wide area of surface. An important group of such methods depends on the differential rate of sublimation, evaporation, or (in water) solution of a surface coating of a suitable chemical, according as the boundary layer is laminar or turbulent, attached or separated. At some time after the start of the test, the coating will have been entirely removed in the region of the turbulent boundary layer whilst remaining in the laminar layer except near the leading edge where the layer is thin and the skin friction relatively high. The downstream edge of the remaining coating will therefore indicate transition. Normally, the transition region is short and the surface indicator method gives a well-defined line. But when the transition is spread over a region the indication will first appear where turbulence is fully established and if the experiment is continued, the line of demarcation will slowly move to the start of the transition region. Exceptionally in these circumstances, no clear indication may be obtained at all. The rate of evaporation of the coating in separation regions may again be different from that in the laminar and turbulent boundary layers. Detailed comments on the patterns which may be obtained when closed bubbles or open regions of separated flow are present are given in Wijker (1951), which also compares the various methods.

The calculation of the theoretical rate of transport of a gas to or from the surface of a two-dimensional body in an airstream is discussed in Owen and Ormerod (1951) using the analogies between mass transfer, heat transfer, and skin friction.

Substances which have been used for the sublimation method include camphor, naphthalene, and borneol, dissolved in a highly volatile solvent and sprayed on to the surface from such a distance that they are deposited in the dry state. In water, hydroquinone diacetate has been found to be the most suitable soluble-coating transition indicator. However, owing to the greater difficulty experienced in water tests in preparing the model and observing and photographing the indicated result, coupled with the limited run available when the technique is used in towing tanks, this method has been largely superseded in favour of the dye filament technique. The merits of various chemicals for these techniques have been discussed by Main-Smith (1950).

The evaporation technique (in air) has two main variants. In the one due to Gray (1946) a thin film of the liquid (generally a suitable fraction of paraffin oil) is applied to the surface by means of a chamois leather without any other previous preparation. The technique requires careful lighting as there is not much contrast between the wet region of the laminar boundary layer and the dry turbulent region where the coating has evaporated. In the other variant, the china-clay method of Richards and Burstall (1945), the contrast is greatly increased. The model should preferably be coated with a chemically resistant black lacquer; it is afterwards permanently coated with an absorbent lacquer containing a high proportion of china clay which dries white. The model is then sprayed with a suitable liquid, such as methyl salicylate (oil of wintergreen). This indicating liquid has much the same refractive index as the crystalline china-clay coating, which therefore becomes transparent and reveals the contrasting colour of the model beneath. Paraffin oil may also be used. As this does not soften the china clay like methyl salicylate it may alternatively be wiped on, and then it is not necessary to dry out the model completely between each test. The use of paraffin oil does not yield such a good contrast, however, as it does not render the china-clay coating so nearly transparent. An interesting example of the use of the china-clay technique is provided by the Frontispiece, which shows how the laminar flow in the centre of a rotating disk is separated from turbulent flow towards the periphery by an intervening annulus where spiral vortices are present within the laminar boundary layer.

The evaporation methods are applicable over a wide range of speed. Surface indicator techniques have indeed been used from speeds of a few knots in water to several times the speed of sound in air, in the compressed-air tunnel at high pressure, and in flight at altitudes up to 15,000 ft.

Another surface indicator method frequently used nowadays to assist in the interpretation of the flow over sweptback wings is the oil-flow method in which the surface of the model is coated with a layer of oil containing a powder in suspension. The viscosity of the oil should be chosen to suit the tunnel speed: for low speeds paraffin oil is suitable, at 300 ft/sec a light diesel oil should be used, and still heavier oils would be better at higher speeds. In an early application of this method by Abbott and Sherman (1938) lampblack was used for the solid, but as models are now generally finished black, current practice is to use titanium oxide with a little oleic acid to act as a decoagulant (Haines 1954), though this may not be needed if a detergent oil is used. When the tunnel is started the oil flows over the surface and eventually dries off or is swept away, leaving a flow pattern recorded in the powder which is deposited on the surface. A typical photograph obtained by this technique is shown in Fig. X. 16 (Plate), which shows the location of the part-span vortex emanating from about one-quarter of the semi-span along the leading edge of a sweptback wing at 8° incidence (Hall and Berry 1957). The airflow over the vortex separates at the leading edge and reattaches along the centre of the herring-bone pattern; a secondary separation under the vortex is also indicated. Patterns obtained by this method, however, need cautious interpretation, especially as the manner in which they develop may well be as significant as the final result. The need for caution arises from the fact that the oil particles move in such a way as to maintain equilibrium between their own gravitational, inertial, and viscous forces and the external pressure forces and surface shears: the oil motion may thus differ appreciably

from that of air particles within the adjacent boundary layer. If the
oil is extremely viscous, or in regions of separated flow, the oil will
follow mainly the external pressure gradient, and circulation of accumulated oil in the vicinity of low-pressure regions should not necessarily
be taken to indicate the existence of a concentrated vortex (Küchemann
1953; Haines 1954). Lines of three-dimensional separation or of reattachment are, however, generally quite clearly indicated by a herring-
bone pattern.

A surface-indicator technique for delineating lines of separation has
been described by Smith and Murphy (1955b). The model is smeared
in the vicinity of the anticipated separation line with such a thin coat
of oil that there is no danger of the oil film running. A stream of talc or
other similar powder is slowly discharged from a dispenser, whose nozzle
is held in the separated region. The dust is carried forward in the reversed flow and some of it is deposited on the model: the forward edge
of the dust pattern indicates the line of flow separation.

The surface-indicator methods described all offer the advantage of
indicating how conditions vary over the whole of the surface and not
just locally. They are, however, unsuitable for the study of transient
phenomena as they depend on cumulative effects. Again, several of
the techniques described need considerable experience if their indications are to be interpreted correctly, and it may often be advisable
to use more than one visualization method, or to examine the results
in conjunction with other types of measurement such as pressure-
plotting, determination of boundary-layer velocity profiles, or hot-wire
explorations.

16. Other techniques for detecting the state of the boundary layer

Besides the visualization methods already described, a number of
other techniques are available for detecting the state of the boundary
layer. These depend either on the characteristics of the velocity profile
(i.e. velocity as a function of distance normal to the surface) or on the
detection of turbulent velocity fluctuations.

Measurement of the complete velocity profile, discussed in Section 18, readily distinguishes between laminar and turbulent flow by
virtue of the much greater initial slope in the latter case, as sketched in
Fig. X. 17, which also includes a typical profile for a separated laminar
layer.

Laminar and turbulent flow can be distinguished more simply, when the complete velocity profile is not needed, by means of a small pitot tube attached to the surface (axis at A in Fig. X. 17). The tube reads higher in a turbulent layer than in a laminar layer, owing to the more rapid increase in velocity with distance from the surface. Sometimes it is more convenient to adopt an alternative procedure in which the pitot tube is moved along the surface at a fixed height which is rather

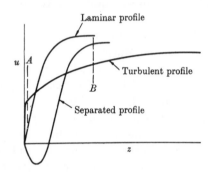

FIG. X. 17. Types of boundary-layer velocity profile.

greater than the thickness of the laminar layer (position B in Fig. X. 17). Where the boundary layer is laminar, therefore, the tube records the total pressure of the undisturbed stream. As the boundary layer thickens rapidly after transition, the total pressure recorded begins to fall when the tube passes downstream through the transition front, although the indication is not as definite as with the tube on the surface.

Methods depending on the detection of turbulent fluctuations employ either a hot-wire probe as described in Section 13 or a pitot probe used as an acoustic detector (Pfenninger 1943). The pitot probe (or a static-pressure hole in the surface of the model) may be connected to the ear by flexible tubing, thus forming a simple stethoscope; alternatively, it can be connected to a microphone and the signals displayed or analysed electrically. Owing to the difficulty of distinguishing between total-pressure fluctuations due to turbulence and static-pressure fluctuations due to noise, however, this method does not give such detailed information about the flow structure as does hot-wire analysis of the turbulent velocity fluctuations.

Qualitative measurements of separated flow in three-dimensional conditions, such as the flow over a swept wing at high incidence, can be made using the yawmeter probes described in Section 10 (other than the two-tube designs). The position of the shear layers formed by the separation of turbulent boundary layers has also been determined by means of the acoustic probe referred to above.

17. Transition fixing

It is often necessary to fix boundary-layer transition artificially at some chosen position; in experiments at reduced Reynolds numbers, for instance, transition would otherwise usually occur relatively farther downstream and the results would not be representative of full-scale conditions. Forward transition is usually precipitated by attaching to the surface some form of obstacle (a spanwise wire, row of excrescences, or distributed roughness) or by allowing air to exude into the (laminar) layer from within the model. In the absence of a theoretical treatment of the problem of the onset of transition due to the finite disturbances thus introduced, the analyses of the effects of size of wire, etc., have necessarily been empirical. Although the minimum size necessary to precipitate transition can thus be calculated roughly, in practice it is always advisable to check that the desired result has been achieved by making use of one of the methods of transition indication already described.

In the case of a spanwise wire in two-dimensional flow, the diameter (d) needed to cause transition at the wire position has been shown by Fage and Preston (1941), over a limited range of conditions, to be given approximately by a value of 400 for $(u_d d/\nu)_{\text{crit}}$, where u_d denotes the velocity in the undisturbed laminar boundary layer (i.e. without wire) at distance d from the surface. If the wire is well immersed in the linear part of the boundary-layer velocity profile, the above condition is equivalent to

$$U_\tau d/\nu \simeq 20,$$

which expresses the necessary wire diameter in terms of the local friction velocity U_τ, or (using the relations for boundary-layer development on a flat plate) to

$$U d/\nu \simeq 35(Ux/\nu)^{1/4},$$

where U is the speed at the edge of the boundary layer and x denotes distance along the surface from the front stagnation point. More recent experiments (e.g. Cowled 1954; Klebanoff, Schubauer and Tidstrom 1955) have shown that the effects of pressure gradient and tunnel turbulence may be appreciable, and values of $(u_d d/\nu)_{\text{crit}}$ ranging from 140 to 1,000 have been reported. The above relations should therefore be taken as indicating only the order of magnitude of the wire size.

If the wire is replaced by a row of isolated excrescences (e.g. spheres, cones, or cylinders) spaced some two or three diameters apart, each behaves independently of its neighbours and gives rise to the characteristic spreading 'wedge' of turbulent flow downstream. Although at first sight the size of excrescence needed to bring the wedge apex up to the roughness itself might be expected to be greater than the corresponding wire diameter in two-dimensional flow, the nature of the turbulence-precipitating disturbance is different in the two cases.

After analysing available experimental results for conical and cylindrical roughness elements, Klanfer and Owen of the R.A.E. have suggested that the above relations can still be used provided the Reynolds number based on boundary-layer displacement thickness (R_{δ_1}) exceeds 1,000 (or $R_x > 3.4 \times 10^5$), whilst it appears from Klebanoff, Schubauer and Tidstrom's results that the diameters of spherical excrescences need to be something like half as large again as for a two-dimensional wire.

The use of air ejection through a spanwise row of holes was suggested by Fage and Sargent (1944), who established that they produced results broadly similar to those obtained with a row of isolated excrescences. In a typical case the amount of air needed is about 0.02 of the flow within the laminar boundary layer. It should be emphasized that the essence of this method is to allow the air to exude into the boundary layer, for high-velocity jets would produce quite different effects, in which turbulent mixing with the external flow would play a vital part and give spurious results by delaying boundary-layer separation.

Distributed roughness is usually produced by fixing a strip of sandpaper or similar material on the surface, or by dusting grains of sand or carborundum powder on a coating of adhesive, or by painting or spraying a suspension of the particles in a suitable lacquer. Available information on the effect of particle size does not appear to be extensive enough to determine with confidence the minimum needed to precipitate transition, and more systematic data are needed concerning the required chordwise extent and position of the roughness strip. Although care must be taken to ensure that the roughness used to precipitate transition is not so great as to cause premature separation, this method of producing transition has several advantages over those previously described, especially in the case of small models (Haines, Holder, and Pearcey 1954). In particular it caters for a range of incidence (range of stagnation position) and is easier to apply than the others when transition is to be precipitated right at the leading edge. It is also more easily applicable than a wire in the case of a tapered wing and is likely to interfere much less with the cross flow.

It should be noted that, in any of these methods of forcing transition, the boundary-layer velocity profile is distorted by the imposed disturbance and a considerable downstream distance is needed before the boundary layer assumes the characteristics of naturally established turbulent flow (Klebanoff and Diehl 1952). Moreover, as a laminar boundary layer is inherently stable against infinitesimal disturbances at low Reynolds numbers (for a flat plate when $R_{\delta_1} < 520$, $R_x < 9 \times 10^4$) the disturbances introduced artificially may differ greatly from true turbulence. The results may therefore not be entirely the same as if turbulence had set in naturally at the position where the disturbance was introduced, but these uncertainties are usually less than the differences in flow which would occur if the boundary layer were allowed to remain laminar.

18. Boundary-layer profiles

The detailed study of boundary-layer growth and behaviour often involves the determination of the complete velocity profile. The methods most commonly used are those in which a pitot probe or a hot-wire probe is traversed across the boundary layer by means of remotely controlled micrometer gear which enables the distance from the surface to be set accurately for each reading of the probe. In the pitot traverse it is usually sufficiently accurate to assume that the static pressure remains constant across the boundary layer. In order to achieve accuracy in exceptional circumstances such as on a highly curved surface, however, it may be necessary to make a static-pressure traverse as well. Visualization methods (see Sections 8 and 14) have also been used (e.g. spark discharge in air (Townend 1937b); electrolysis in water (Geller 1955; Clutter and Smith 1961)), but although they have the advantage of not involving boundary-layer traverses, they have only a limited field of application.

Within the boundary layer the total pressure varies rapidly with distance from the surface. The dimension of the exploring tube in the direction normal to the surface must therefore be small compared with the boundary-layer thickness; for this reason, flattened tubes are often employed. Because of the small size of the pitot tube, coupled with the small velocities near the surface, it may be necessary to apply corrections to the readings to allow for the effects of the low Reynolds numbers. For circular pitot tubes these have been discussed in Section 9; the corresponding corrections for a flattened tube (MacMillan 1954c) are shown in Fig. X. 18.

Allowance has also to be made for the transverse gradient of velocity, for proximity to the wall, and (strictly, although this is often neglected in practice) for the velocity fluctuations in a turbulent layer (see Section 9).

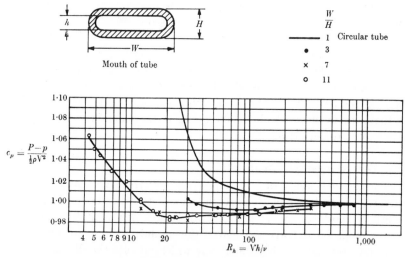

FIG. X. 18. Pressure coefficient indicated by flattened pitot tube at low Reynolds numbers (based on internal 'height' of mouth). P = reading of tube, p = static pressure.

The transverse velocity gradient gives rise to a highly complex flow pattern in the mouth of the tube, where the viscosity of the fluid produces marked effects. As a result, the reading of the tube is not obviously related to the total pressure of any of the approaching stream filaments and the observed total pressure differs from that of the filament occupying the position of the axis of the tube before its introduction into the flow. The effect can alternatively be represented by a displacement of the 'effective centre' of the tube. This approach is the more convenient in practice, especially as the apparent increment in velocity at the tube centre is found experimentally to be roughly proportional to velocity gradient and hence the displacement of the effective centre is roughly constant. According to Young and Maas (1936) the effective displacement (Δz) for a square-cut head in turbulent flow is towards the region of higher velocity and is given by the equation

$$\Delta z/D = 0\cdot13 + 0\cdot08 d/D,$$

where d and D are the internal and external diameters of the tube. When $d/D = 0.6$, therefore, $\Delta z/D = 0.18$. For conical heads with sharp lips, however, Livesey (1956) has shown that the effective displacement is negligible. A further investigation of square-cut heads by MacMillan (1956) suggests that the Young and Maas value (0.18) was a little high

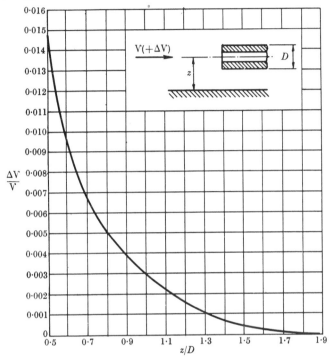

Fig. X. 19. Velocity correction for a circular pitot tube near the wall of a pipe (turbulent flow).

and that the correction probably lies between $0.14D$ and $0.16D$ provided the geometric centre of the tube is at a distance of at least $2D$ from the wall. A subsequent paper by Davies (1958) has confirmed these results in a wake except that (as noted in chapter xii of *Incompressible Aerodynamics*) the displacement is reduced at low rates of shear. Unlike MacMillan, Davies obtained no appreciable displacement for any size of tube in boundary-layer flow.

When the tube is closer to the surface than twice its diameter, the effects of wall proximity act in the opposite direction to the effects of velocity gradient and a further correction is required. For turbulent pipe flow MacMillan (1956) finds that the correction may conveniently be expressed (Fig. X. 19) as an increment ΔV to be added to the measured velocity, and indicates that a correction of the same order is applicable in boundary-layer flow as well. Davies's results, however, suggest that his negligible correction in boundary-layer flow is maintained right to the wall for all sizes of tube. The reason for these discrepancies is somewhat obscure.

As boundary-layer pitot probes need to be so small, the lag in the pressure leads should be reduced to a minimum (see Section 12). The speed of response of the probe itself can similarly be increased by increasing the bore of the tube as close to its mouth as possible: a method of making such tubes in brass has been described by Bradfield and Yale (1951), and a technique for producing tapered tubes of quartz has been reported by Cooke (1955).

When exploring boundary layers in three-dimensional flow it is necessary to use a yawmeter type of probe (see Section 10) and to make provision, in the design of the traverse gear, for orientating the tube about two axes. One suitable scheme is described in Bryer (1956).

All the pitot-tube methods necessarily record time-averaged values at each point; velocity fluctuations can be recorded only if the sensing instrument has satisfactorily low inertia. As already indicated (Section 13) the hot-wire anemometer is especially suited to this purpose and has been developed to an advanced state. For full details reference should be made to the papers cited.

19. Determination of intensity of surface friction

The aerodynamic reaction experienced by a body arises partly from the distribution of normal pressure over its surface and partly from the surface shear stresses. In the main, the methods available for measuring the local intensity of surface friction (shear stress) comprise direct balance measurements, methods based on the shape of the boundary-layer velocity profile close to the surface, and methods based on the rate of heat transfer or evaporation from the surface. The local surface friction can also be deduced from the streamwise changes of momentum in the boundary layer (Fage and Falkner 1930). The effects of turbulent velocity fluctuations have usually been neglected but may become important in regions of adverse gradient, especially near separation; they have been investigated theoretically by Goldschmied (1951) and by Bidwell (1951). In fully developed flow in a straight pipe the surface friction can be obtained directly from the pressure drop along its length.

In the balance method a small portion of the surface is arranged to form a floating element separated from the rest of the surface by a narrow gap. So far this method appears to have been applied only to flat plates, though not only with zero pressure gradient. The element is attached to some form of delicate balance housed within the model, so that the tangential force on the element of surface is obtained by direct measurement. One suitable apparatus (Hakkinen 1955, following

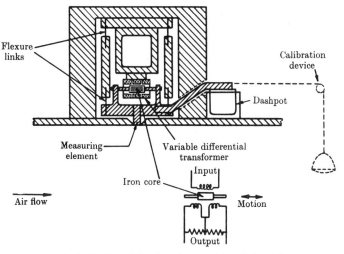

FIG. X. 20. Section of floating-element skin-friction balance.

Dhawan 1953) is shown in Fig. X. 20, in which the small streamwise deflexion of the floating element against the elastic deformation of the flexure links is measured by means of a variable differential transformer acting as a displacement gauge. Null methods have also been used (Coles 1954; Korkegi 1956), which offer the advantage of a smaller gap between the floating element and the rest of the surface. In any case the effect of varying the gap should be investigated. It should be noted, however, that the result obtained by extrapolation to zero gap width may not necessarily be the true surface friction, because (as pointed out by Preston) the very presence of any gap, however small, may cause a discontinuous change in the variation of the shear stress at the surface.

The surface friction at the wall is equal to the value of $\mu \, \partial u/\partial z$ at the surface, where u is the tangential velocity at distance z from the surface, and in principle could therefore be obtained directly from the boundary-layer velocity profile. In practice, however, it is not possible to obtain measurements sufficiently close to the surface. This applies especially in the case of turbulent boundary layers, for which the distance over which the velocity increases linearly (the so-called laminar sub-layer) is extremely small. This difficulty can be surmounted to some extent, however by the use of the 'surface pitot tube' which was originated by Stanton, Marshall and Bryant (1920) and consists essentially of a very small pitot tube, one wall being formed by the surface itself.

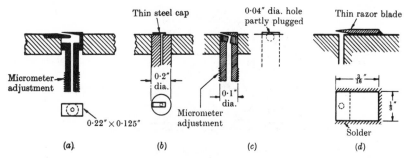

Fig. X. 21. Forms of surface tube. (a) Stanton, Marshall and Bryant (1920); (b) Fage and Falkner (1930); (c) Fage and Sargent (1947); (d) Hool (1956).

Several forms are shown in Fig. X. 21; the upper lip of the tube is typically about 0·003 in. from the surface. As nothing can be assumed in advance about the significance of the reading of such a tube, owing to the low Reynolds number and the severe transverse velocity gradient, it is necessary to calibrate the instrument in known flow conditions and thus obtain the required wall stress indirectly.

A much more convenient method (Preston 1954) employs an ordinary circular flat-ended pitot tube in contact with the surface. By using a similarity argument and assuming a universal form for the velocity profile near the wall in fully developed turbulent flow in a pipe, it can be proved that there is a corresponding universal non-dimensional relation between the wall shear stress (τ_w) and the reading of the pitot tube on the surface (P). Preston's experiments show that this relation could be written in the form

$$\log_{10}\frac{\tau_w d^2}{\rho\nu^2} = A + B\log_{10}\frac{(P-p)d^2}{\rho\nu^2},$$

where d is the diameter of the pitot tube and p the static pressure on the surface, and A and B are constants determined by the experiment.

For boundary layer flow on a flat plate, Relf, Pankhurst, and Walker (1954) found that a different value of A was necessary to fit this relation to their measurements. It is now thought, however, that the semi-logarithmic inner law does apply equally to both boundary layers and fully developed pipe flow, following the careful investigations by Head and Rechenberg (1962). In this experiment, a pitot tube was used on the wall of a short length of large-diameter pipe which could either form part of a very much longer pipe giving fully developed turbulent pipe flow, or could be preceded by a conventional contraction and screens giving a developing turbulent boundary layer. This experiment and the investigation of Bradshaw (1964) also revealed that earlier conflicting results were most likely due to the considerable spanwise or peripheral variations in skin friction which can occur in some circumstances with the use of wind tunnel screens. The most reliable determination of the constants is that carried out recently by Ferriss (1965) who found values, $A = -1.350$ and $B = 0.881$.

Surface friction can also be found from the measured velocity profile outside the laminar sub-layer by assuming a universal velocity distribution for two-dimensional turbulent boundary layers (Clauser 1954).

The heat-transfer method developed by Ludwieg (1949) (see also Ludwieg and Tillmann 1949) used a small copper block fitted flush with the surface, thermally insulated from the rest of the surface and heated electrically; subsequently Liepmann and Skinner (1954) used a hot wire embedded in a groove in an insulating material. The surface shear is related to the equilibrium temperature of the hot element and is obtained by calibration.

A novel method has been used by Murphy and Smith (1956) in which the surface friction is deduced from the rate of evaporation of a thin film of liquid on the surface as measured by means of an interferometer.

20. Estimation of profile drag from wake traverse measurements

The drag of a body can be deduced from the energy losses in the flow downstream. The method makes use of total-pressure and static-pressure explorations of the wake and gives the value of the profile drag (the sum of the surface-friction drag and the normal-pressure ('form') drag). It can conveniently be applied in flight as well as in a tunnel, and is especially suitable for the determination of the drag of a two-dimensional aerofoil.

Consider a body in two-dimensional flow and let $ABCD$ be a contour enclosing the body, as shown in Fig. X. 22. AB and DC are parallel to the undisturbed flow, while CB and DA are perpendicular to it, with CB at any position downstream of the body and DA sufficiently far upstream for the velocity and static pressure to be the same as in the undisturbed stream. By applying the momentum equation and taking due account of the outflow across AB and DC it may be shown (Taylor 1937b) that, provided AB and DC are far enough away from the body for the velocity to be of the same magnitude (though not

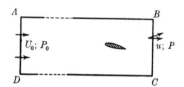

FIG. X. 22. Application of momentum theorem.

necessarily in the same direction) as that of the undisturbed flow, the drag can be expressed in the form

$$D = \int \rho u (U_0 - u)\, dz + \int (P_0 - P)\, dz,$$

where P and u are respectively the static pressure and the velocity component in the drag direction (i.e. parallel to the undisturbed flow) at points along CB; P_0 and U_0 are the static pressure and velocity far upstream, and z denotes distance perpendicular to the undisturbed stream. As the above equation requires a knowledge of the local flow direction in order to obtain the component u from the resultant velocity, it is more convenient to base the drag determination on the form assumed by the equation when the downstream plane is assumed to recede to infinity, namely

$$D = \int \rho u_\infty (U_0 - u_\infty)\, dz.$$

In practice the measurements are made at a station 1 (see Fig. X. 23) fairly close to the body and perpendicular to the local flow direction; the corresponding values at infinity downstream may then be calculated sufficiently accurately by neglecting mixing and applying Bernoulli's equation and the equation of continuity to each streamtube (Jones 1936), so that

$$u_\infty = \sqrt{\left\{\frac{2}{\rho}(H_1 - P_0)\right\}}$$

and

$$\rho u_\infty\, dz = \rho \mathrm{v}_1\, dz_1,$$

where z_1 denotes distance perpendicular to the local flow direction at the measurement station and v_1 is the velocity (not just the u-component) there. Hence

$$D = 2 \int \{\sqrt{(H_0 - P_0)} - \sqrt{(H_1 - P_0)}\}\sqrt{(H_1 - P_1)}\, dz_1.$$

Writing $$g = \frac{H_1 - P_0}{H_0 - P_0} = 1 - \frac{H_0 - H_1}{H_0 - P_0}$$

and $$p = \frac{P_1 - P_0}{H_0 - P_0},$$

the above equation can conveniently be written in the form

$$C_D = 2 \int (1 - \sqrt{g})\sqrt{(g - p)}\, d(z_1/c),$$

where c is the length used for forming the non-dimensional coefficient (e.g. aerofoil chord). This treatment neglects the tangential stresses

FIG. X. 23. Flow downstream of measurement station.

downstream of the measurement plane; the error thus introduced has been examined by Taylor (1937b), and appears usually to be of little practical importance. Another method of deriving the profile drag from the observations was given earlier by Betz (see Betz 1925; Prandtl and Tietjens 1934b, pp. 125–43; and Prandtl 1935, pp. 202–8); in this case the assumptions involved are such that it is difficult to estimate the errors they introduce.

In the Jones method, the value of $u(U_0 - u)\, dz$ at infinite distance downstream is obtained from the measurements at station 1 by applying Bernoulli's equation to each streamtube separately, the drag then being obtained by integration. Alternatively, the drag could be obtained by integrating $v_1(V_1 - v_1)\, dz_1$ across the wake in the measurement plane (where V_1 is the velocity at the edge of the wake) and applying the momentum equation to derive the required integral at infinite distance downstream as suggested by Squire and Young (1937) in their paper on the calculation of profile drag. The results obtained in a particular case by the Jones method, the Betz method, and the Squire–Young method have been shown by Pfenninger (1943) to agree very closely with one another and with balance measurements.

The exact downstream location of the measurement station is not critical. To avoid the difficulties of obtaining readings in markedly curved flow, however, a station should be chosen which is far enough from the body for the curvature of the streamlines to have become acceptably small and sensibly constant across the wake, but not so far downstream that the wake has become so diffused that the total-pressure losses are too small to be easily measured with the required accuracy; in practice a wide margin of position is usually available. As the transverse gradient of static pressure is then correspondingly small, only a limited number of static-pressure readings is needed. Instead of traversing a single pitot tube, the observations are usually made by means of a bank of tubes arranged in the form of a 'comb' or 'rake', in which it is usually sufficient to incorporate only a few static-pressure tubes if the measurement station is chosen as indicated above. In the reduction of the observations a correction should be applied to allow for the displacement of effective centre of a pitot tube due to the transverse gradient of total head (see Section 18).

In three-dimensional flow the profile drag can again be obtained as above, by integrating with respect to area (instead of transverse distance) in the downstream planes. The trailing-vortex drag ('induced' drag) is not included in the above equations, as it is not manifested as a loss in total pressure and so cannot be evaluated from pitot-traverse measurements; neglecting mixing, it is given by

$$\int \tfrac{1}{2}\rho(v_\infty^2 + w_\infty^2)\,dA,$$

where v_∞ and w_∞ are the velocity components, and dA an element of area, far downstream and normal to the undisturbed flow.

REFERENCES AND AUTHOR INDEX

THE list which follows should not be considered as a comprehensive bibliography. It consists of the titles of papers and books, and the names of their authors, to which reference is made in *Laminar Boundary Layers* (but see pp. 579 and 688); it will also serve as an Author Index. The numbers in square brackets refer to the pages on which the references appear.

The full titles and places of origin of all the journals and periodicals quoted are given in Current Paper 444 of the Aeronautical Research Council, London; copies of the paper may be obtained from Her Majesty's Stationery Office, London.

ABBOTT, I. H. *See* Jacobs and Abbott (1932).

ABBOTT, I. H., and SHERMAN, A. (1938). Flow observations with tufts and lampblack of the stalling of four typical airfoil sections in the N.A.C.A. variable density tunnel. *Tech. Notes nat. adv. Comm. Aero., Wash.* No. *672.* [614]

ABRAMOWITZ, M. (1949). On backflow of a viscous fluid in a diverging channel. *J. Math Phys.* **28**, *1–21.* [148]

ACKERET, J. (1931). Kavitation (Hohlraumbildung). *Handbuch der Experimentalphysik*, **4**, Tl. 1, *463–86.* Akademische Verlagsgesellschaft, Leipzig. [27]

ALDEN, H. L. (1948). Second approximation to the laminar boundary layer flow over a flat plate. *J. Math. Phys.* **27**, *91–104.* [227]

ALLEN, D. N. DE G., and SOUTHWELL, R. V. (1955). Relaxation methods applied to determine the motion, in two dimensions, of a viscous fluid past a fixed cylinder. *Quart. J. Mech.* **8**, *129–45.* [163]

ALLEN, H. J., and PERKINS, E. W. (1951). A study of effects of viscosity on flow over slender inclined bodies of revolution. *Rep. nat. adv. Comm. Aero., Wash.* No. *1048.* [112]

ANDRADE, E. N. DA C. (1931). On the circulations caused by the vibrations of air in a tube. *Proc. Roy. Soc.* A **134**, *445–70.* [386, 388]

ANDRADE, E. N. DA C. (1939). The velocity distribution in a liquid-into-liquid jet. The plane jet. *Proc. phys. Soc. Lond.* **51**, *784–93.* [561]

ANDRADE, E. N. DA C., and TSIEN, L. C. (1937). The velocity distribution in a liquid-into-liquid jet. *Proc. phys. Soc. Lond.* **49**, *381–91.* [455]

ANDRES, J. M., and INGARD, U. (1953a). Acoustic streaming at high Reynolds numbers. *J. acoust. Soc. Amer.* **25**, *928–32.* [387, 388]

ANDRES, J. M., and INGARD, U. (1953b). Acoustic streaming at low Reynolds numbers. *J. acoust. Soc. Amer.* **25**, *932–8.* [387, 388]

ANSCOMBE, A., and BUTLER, S. F. J. (1954). The effect of sweepback on the laminar boundary layer. Wind tunnel experiments with leading-edge suction. *Rep. aero. Res. Coun., Lond.* No. *17525.* [555]

ANSCOMBE, A., and ILLINGWORTH, L. N. (1952). Wind tunnel observations of boundary layer transition on a wing at various angles of sweepback. *Rep. Memor. aero. Res. Coun., Lond.* No. *2968.* [550, 554]

AOI, T. *See* Tomotika and Aoi (1950), (1951); Tomotika, Aoi, and Yosinabu (1953).

APELT, C. J. (1958). The steady flow of a viscous fluid past a circular cylinder at Reynolds numbers 40 and 44. *Rep. aero. Res. Coun., Lond.* No. *20502.* [164]

ARKHIPOV, V. N. (1958). *Dokl. Ak. Nauk S.S.S.R.* **123**, *620–2* (in Russian). (Translated as 'Formation of oscillations in the wake of a body', *Sov. Phys.—Dokl.* **3**, *1117–20*.) [562]

ASHBY, G. C. *See* Schulze, Ashby, and Erwin (1952).

ASHKENAS, H. I., and RIDDELL, R. F. (1955). Investigation of the turbulent boundary layer on a yawed flat plate. *Tech. Notes nat. adv. Comm. Aero., Wash.* No. 3383. [479]

AVSEC, D. *See* Bénard and Avsec (1938).

BACKUS, G. E. (1955). On the application of eigenfunction expansions to the problem of the thermal instability of a fluid sphere heated within. *Phil. Mag.* (7), **46**, 1310–27. [511]

BAILEY, G. W. *See* Wright and Bailey (1939).

BAIRSTOW, L., CAVE, B. M., and LANG, E. D. (1923). The resistance of a cylinder moving in a viscous fluid. *Phil. Trans.* A **223**, 383–432. [183]

BALLISTICS RESEARCH LABORATORIES, Aberdeen Proving Ground (1958). Unpublished photograph. [Plate]

BARKER, M. (1922). On the use of small pitot-tubes for measuring wind velocities. *Proc. Roy. Soc.* A **101**, 435–45. [595]

BASSET, A. B. (1888). *Hydrodynamics.* Cambridge University Press. [4]

BATCHELOR, G. K. (1951). Note on a class of solutions of the Navier–Stokes equations representing steady rotationally-symmetric flow. *Quart. J. Mech.* **4**, 29–41. [162]

BATCHELOR, G. K. (1953). *The theory of homogeneous turbulence.* Cambridge University Press. [99, 578]

BATCHELOR, G. K. (1954a). The skin friction on infinite cylinders moving parallel to their length. *Quart. J. Mech.* **7**, 179–92. [138, 364, 365, 366, 367, 488]

BATCHELOR, G. K. (1954b). Heat convection and buoyancy effects in fluids. *Quart. J. R. met. Soc.* **80**, 339–58. [512]

BATCHELOR, G. K. (1956). A proposal concerning laminar wakes behind bluff bodies at large Reynolds number. *J. Fluid Mech.* **1**, 388–98. [104]

BATCHELOR, G. K., and DAVIES, R. M. *See* Lane and Green (1956); Lighthill (1956a).

BATEMAN, H. *See* Dryden, Murnaghan, and Bateman (1932).

BELYAKOVA, V. K. (1950). Concerning the stability of the motion of a viscous fluid in a straight circular tube. *Prikl. Mat. Mekh.* **14**, 105–10 (in Russian). [539]

BÉNARD, H. (1901). Les tourbillons cellulaires dans une nappe liquide transportant de la chaleur par convection en régime permanent. *Ann. Chim. (Phys.)*, **23**, 62–144. [506, 511]

BÉNARD, H., and AVSEC, D. (1938). Travaux récents sur les tourbillons cellulaires et les tourbillons en bandes. Applications à l'astrophysique et à la météorologie. *J. Phys. Radium*, Series 7, **9**, 486–500. [511]

BENJAMIN, T. B. (1957). Wave formation in laminar flow down an inclined plane. *J. Fluid Mech.* **2**, 554–74. Numerical corrections in *J. Fluid Mech.* **3**, 657 (1958). [540]

BENNETT, H. W. (1953). An experimental study of boundary-layer transition. *Kimberley-Clark Corporation Report*, Neenah, Wisconsin. [536, 538]

BERG, B. VAN DEN. *See* Bergh and Berg (1958).

BERGH, H. (1958). A method for visualizing periodic boundary layer phenomena. *Proc. Symp. boundary layer Res., Int. Union theoret. appl. Mech.* Freiburg i. Br. (1957), 173–9. [538]

BERGH, H., and BERG, B. VAN DEN (1958). On the visualization of laminar boundary-layer oscillations and the transition to turbulent flow. *Z. angew. Math. Phys.* **9b**, 97–104 (Festschrift Jacob Ackeret). [538]

BERRY, A., and SWAIN, L. M. (1923). On the steady motion of a cylinder through infinite viscous fluid. *Proc. Roy. Soc.* A **102**, 766–78. [172]

BERRY, C. J. *See* Hall and Berry (1957).

BETZ, A. (1925). Ein Verfahren zur direkten Ermittlung des Profilwiderstandes. *Z. Flugtech.* **16**, 42–44. [627]

BETZ, A. (1950). Reihendarstellung der Geschwindigkeitsverteilung in laminaren Grenzschichten. *Arch. Math., Karlsruhe*, **2**, 220–2. [288]

BETZ, A. (1955). Zur Berechnung des Überganges laminarer Grenzschichten in die Aussenströmung. *50 Jahre Grenzschichtforschung* (Editors: Görtler, H., and Tollmien, W.), Vieweg, Braunschweig, 63–70. [216]

BETZ, A. See Prandtl (1904); Prandtl, Wieselsberger, and Betz (1923).

BICKLEY, W. G. (1937). The plane jet. *Phil. Mag.* (7), **23**, 727–31. [254]

BIDWELL, J. M. (1951). Application of the von Kármán momentum theorem to turbulent boundary layers. *Tech. Notes nat. adv. Comm. Aero., Wash.* No. 2571. [622]

BINNIE, A. M. (1959). Instability in a slightly inclined water channel. *J. Fluid Mech.* **5**, 561–70. [540]

BINNIE, A. M., and FOWLER, J. S. (1947). A study by a double refraction method of the development of turbulence in a long circular tube. *Proc. Roy. Soc.* A **192**, 32–44. [611]

BINNIE, A. M., and HARRIS, D. P. (1950). The application of boundary layer theory to swirling liquid flow through a nozzle. *Quart. J. Mech.* **3**, 89–106. [432]

BIRD, J. D. (1952). Visualization of flow fields by use of a tuft grid technique. *J. aero. Sci.* **19**, 481–5. [610]

BIRD, R. B. See Hirschfelder, Curtiss, and Bird (1954).

BIRKHOFF, G. (1950). Hydrodynamics: a study in logic, fact and similitude. Princeton University Press (also Dover Publications). [143, 357, 358, 359]

BIRKHOFF, G., and ZARANTONELLO, E. H. (1957). Jets, wakes and cavities. Academic Press, New York. [25, 27]

BLAND, M. E. M. See Jeffreys and Bland (1951).

BLASIUS, H. (1908). Grenzschichten in Flüssigkeiten mit kleiner Reibung. *Z. Math. Phys.* **56**, 1–37. (Translated as 'The boundary layers in fluids with little friction', *Tech. Memor. nat. adv. Comm. Aero., Wash.* No. 1256.) [200, 222, 223, 231, 260, 371, 372]

BLASIUS, H. (1910). Laminare Strömung in Kanälen wechselnder Breite. *Z. Math. Phys.* **58**, 225–33. [148]

BÖDEWADT, U. T. (1940). Die Drehströmung über festem Grunde. *Z. angew. Math. Mech.* **20**, 241–53. [161, 380]

BOHLEN, T. See Holstein and Bohlen (1940).

BOLSHAKOV, V. P. See Loitsianskii and Bolshakov (1951).

BOLTZE, E. (1908). Grenzschichten an Rotationskörpern in Flüssigkeiten mit kleiner Reibung. *Göttingen dissertation.* [378, 417]

BOND, R. See Seban and Bond (1951).

BOOTH, T. B. See Young and Booth (1951).

BOUSSINESQ, J. (1891a). Sur la manière dont les vitesses, dans un tube cylindrique de section circulaire, évasé à son entrée, se distribuent depuis cette entrée jusqu'aux endroits où se trouve établi un régime uniforme. *C.R. Acad. Sci., Paris,* **113**, 9–15 [443, 446]

BOUSSINESQ, J. (1891b). Calcul de la moindre longueur que doit avoir un tube circulaire, évasé à son entrée, pour qu'un régime sensiblement uniforme s'y établisse, et de la dépense de charge qu'y entraîne l'établissement de ce régime. *C.R. Acad. Sci., Paris,* **113**, 49–51. [443, 446]

BOYD, B., DORSCH, R. G., and BRODIE, G. H. (1952). True airspeed measurement by ionization-tracer technique. *Res. Memor. nat. adv. Comm. Aero., Wash.* E52C31. [592]

BRADFIELD, W. S., and YALE, G. E. (1951). Small pitot tubes with fast pressure response time. *J. aero. Sci.* **18**, 697–8. [622]

BRADSHAW, P. (1964). Wind tunnel screens. Flow instability and its effect on aerofoil boundary layers. *J.R. aero. Soc.* **68**, 198. [625]

BREBNER, G. G. (1951). Boundary layer measurements on wings of 45° sweep at low speed. Unpublished report, Min. Aviation, London. [475]

BREBNER, G. G. See Weber and Brebner (1952)

BREWSTER, D. B., GROSBERG, P., and NISSAN, A. H. (1959). The stability of viscous flow between horizontal concentric cylinders. *Proc. Roy Soc.* A **251**, 76–91. [501]

BREWSTER, D. B., and NISSAN, A. H. (1958). The hydrodynamics of flow between horizontal concentric cylinders—I. *Chemical Engineering Science,* **7**, 215–21 Pergamon Press. [501]

BRODIE, G. H. See Boyd, Dorsch, and Brodie (1952).

BROWN, W. B. (1961). A stability criterion for three-dimensional boundary layers. Contribution to *Boundary layer and flow control* (Editor: Lachmann, G. V.). Pergamon Press, **2**, *903–13*. [553, 555, 557]

BROWN, W. B., and DONOUGHE, P. L. (1951). Tables of exact laminar-boundary-layer solutions when the wall is porous and fluid properties are variable. *Tech. Notes nat. adv. Comm. Aero., Wash.* No. *2479*. [248, 251]

BRUNAUER, S. (1944). *Physical adsorption of gases and vapours.* Oxford University Press, London. [17]

BRUNT, D. (1934). *Physical and dynamical meteorology.* Cambridge University Press. [506]

BRYANT, C. N. *See* Stanton, Marshall, and Bryant (1920).

BRYER, D. W. (1956). A remotely-controlled traversing yawmeter for boundary-layer exploration. *J. sci. Instrum.* **33**, *173–5*. [622]

BRYER, D. W., WALSHE, D. E., and GARNER, H. C. (1955). Pressure probes selected for mean flow measurements. Exploration of turbulent boundary layers. *Rep. Memor. aero. Res. Coun., Lond.* No. *3037*. [599, 600]

BRYER, D. W. *See* Garner and Bryer (1959).

BRYSON, A. E. *See* Emmons and Bryson (1951).

BURGERS, J. M. (1941). Some considerations on the development of boundary layers in the case of flows having a rotational component. *Proc. Acad. Sci., Amsterdam*, **44**, *13–25*. [483]

BURSNALL, W. J., and LOFTIN, L. K. (1951). Experimental investigation of the pressure distribution about a yawed circular cylinder in the critical Reynolds number range. *Tech. Notes nat. adv. Comm. Aero., Wash.* No. *2463*. [474]

BURSTALL, F. H. *See* Richards and Burstall (1945).

BUSSMANN, K., and ULRICH, A. (1943). Systematische Untersuchungen über den Einfluss der Profilform auf die Lage des Umschlagspunktes. *Jb. dtsch. Luftfahrtf.* **1**, *1–19*. See also *Technische Berichte* **10**, Heft 9. (Translated as 'Systematic investigations of the influence of the shape of the profile upon the position of the transition point', *Tech. Memor. nat. adv. Comm. Aero., Wash.* No. *1185*.) [544]

BUSSMANN, K., and ULRICH, A. (1944). Die laminare Reibungsschicht am Kreiszylinder mit Absaugung und Ausblasen. *Untersuch. Mitt. dtsch. Luftfahrtf.* No. *2073*. [334, 336, 347]

BUSSMANN, K. *See* Schlichting and Bussmann (1943).

BUTLER, S. F. J. *See* Anscombe and Butler (1954).

CAMBRIDGE UNIVERSITY AERONAUTICS LABORATORY. *See* Jones, B. M., and Cambridge University Aeronautics Laboratory (1936).

CANETTI, G. S. *See* Whitehead and Canetti (1950).

CAPPS, D. S. *See* Scott-Wilson and Capps (1954).

CARRIER, G. F. (1946). The boundary layer in a corner. *Quart. appl. Math.* **4**, *367–70*. [483]

CARRIER, G. F. (1955). The mechanics of the Rijke tube. *Quart. appl. Math.* **12**, *383–95*. [397]

CARRIER, G. F., and DOWDALL, R. B. Note on the solution of boundary layer in a corner. (Unpublished.) [485]

CARRIER, G. F., and LIN, C. C. (1948). On the nature of the boundary layer near the leading edge of a flat plate. *Quart. appl. Math.* **6**, *63–68*. [181, 230]

CARRIER, G. F., and DI PRIMA, R. C. (1956). On the torsional oscillations of a solid sphere in a viscous fluid. *J. appl. Mech.* **23**, *601–5*. [388]

CARRIER, G. F., and DI PRIMA, R. C. (1957). On the unsteady motion of a viscous fluid past a semi-infinite flat plate. *J. Math. Phys.* **35**, *359–83*. [397]

CARRIER, G. F. *See* Lewis and Carrier (1949).

CARSLAW, H. S., and JAEGER, J. C. (1947). *Conduction of heat in solids.* Clarendon Press, Oxford. [23, 136, 363, 365]

CAVE, B. M. *See* Bairstow, Cave, and Lang (1923).

CHANDRA, K. (1938). Instability of fluids heated from below. *Proc. Roy. Soc.* A **164**, *231–42*. [511]

COLLIS, D. C. (1952). The dust problem in hot-wire anemometry. *Aeronaut. Quart.* **4,** 93–102. [607]

COOKE, J. C. (1950). The boundary layer of a class of infinite yawed cylinders. *Proc. Camb. phil. Soc.* **46,** 645–8. [470]

COOKE, J. C. (1951). Pohlhausen's method for three-dimensional laminar boundary layers. *Aeronaut. Quart.* **3,** 51–60. [466, 472]

COOKE, J. C. (1952). On Pohlhausen's method with application to a swirl problem of Taylor. *J. aero. Sci.* **19,** 486–90. [432, 435]

COOKE, J. C. (1957). The flow of fluid along cylinders. *Quart. J. Mech.* **10,** 312–21. [451]

COOKE, J. C. *See* Sowerby and Cooke (1953).

COOKE, J. R. (1955). The use of quartz in the manufacture of small diameter pitot tubes. *Curr. Pap. aero. Res. Coun., Lond.* No. *193.* [622]

COOPER, R. D., and TULIN, M. P. (1955). Turbulence measurements with the hot-wire anemometer. *AGARDograph* No. *12.* [607]

COPPEL, W. A. (1960). On a differential equation of boundary-layer theory. *Phil. Trans.* A **253,** 101–36. [248]

CORCOS, G. M., and SELLARS, J. R. (1959). On the stability of fully-developed flow in a pipe. *J. Fluid Mech.* **5,** 97–112. [539]

CORNISH, R. J. (1933). Flow of water through fine clearances with relative motion of the boundaries. *Proc. Roy. Soc.* A **140,** 227–40. [501]

COSTER, D. (1919). The rotational oscillations of a cylinder in a viscous liquid. *Phil. Mag.* (6), **37,** 587–94. [382]

COULOMB, C. A. (1800). Expériences destinées a déterminer la cohérence des fluides et les lois de leur résistance dans les mouvements très lents. *Mém. Inst. nat. Sci. Art., Paris,* **3,** 246–305. [3]

COWDREY, C. F. (1950). A note on the calibration and use of a shielded hot-wire anemometer for very low speeds. *J. Sci. Instrum.* **27,** 327–9. [606]

COWLED, E. H. (1954). The effects of surface irregularities on transition in the laminar boundary layer. *Rep. aero. Res. Lab., Melbourne,* No. *A.86.* [617]

COWLING, T. G. (1957). *Magneto-hydrodynamics.* Interscience, New York. [540]

COWLING, T. G. *See* Chapman and Cowling (1952).

CRABTREE, L. F. (1957). Effects of leading-edge separation on thin wings in two-dimensional incompressible flow. *J. aero. Sci.* **24,** 597–604. [490]

CRABTREE, L. F. *See* Rott and Crabtree (1952).

CROCCO, L. (1939). A characteristic transformation of the equations of the boundary layer in gases. *Rep. aero. Res. Coun., Lond.* No. *4582* (translated from *Atti di Guidonia,* **17,** No. *7, 118*). [213, 283]

CURLE, N. (1957). On hydrodynamic stability in unlimited fields of viscous flow. *Proc. Roy. Soc.* A **238,** 489–501. [560]

CURLE, N. (1958a). Accurate solutions of the laminar-boundary-layer equations, for flows having a stagnation point and separation. *Rep. Memor. aero. Res. Coun., Lond.* No. *3164.* [330, 331]

CURLE, N. (1958b). Hydrodynamic stability of laminar wakes. *Phys. Fluids* **1,** 159–60. [562]

CURLE, N. (1960). The estimation of laminar skin friction, including effects of distributed suction. *Aeronaut. Quart.* **11,** 1–21. [328, 331, 341]

CURLE, N., and SKAN, S. W. (1957). Approximate methods for predicting separation properties of laminar boundary layers. *Aeronaut. Quart.* **8,** 257–68. [307, 328, 331]

CURRY, W. H. *See* Kuethe, McKee, and Curry (1949).

CURTISS, C. F. *See* Hirschfelder, Curtiss, and Bird (1954).

DAVEY, A. (1961). Boundary-layer flow at a saddle point of attachment. *J. Fluid Mech.* **10,** 593–610. [463]

DAVIES, P. O. A. L. (1958). The behaviour of a pitot tube in transverse shear. *J. Fluid Mech.* **3,** 441–56. [621]

DAVIES, S. J., and WHITE, C. M. (1928). An experimental study of the flow of water in pipes of rectangular section. *Proc. Roy. Soc.* A **119,** 92–107. [568]

DEAN, W. R. (1928). Fluid motion in a curved channel. *Proc. Roy. Soc.* A *121, 402–20.* [505]

DEAN, W. R. (1934). Note on the divergent flow of fluid. *Phil. Mag.* (7), *18, 749–77.* [144]

DEAN, W. R. (1950). Note on the motion of liquid near a position of separation. *Proc. Camb. phil. Soc.* **46**, *293–306.* [210]

DHAWAN, S. (1953). Direct measurements of skin friction. *Rep. nat. adv. Comm. Aero., Wash.* No. *1121.* [623]

DHAWAN, S., and NARASIMHA, R. (1958). Some properties of boundary layer flow during the transition from laminar to turbulent motion. *J. Fluid Mech.* **3**, *418–36.* [95, 98, 102, 577]

DIEHL, Z. W. See Klebanoff and Diehl (1952).

DI PRIMA, R. C. (1955). Application of Galerkin's method to the calculation of the stability of curved flows. *Quart. appl. Math.* **13**, *55–62.* [501]

DI PRIMA, R. C. (1959). The stability of viscous flow between rotating concentric cylinders with a pressure gradient acting round the cylinders. *J. Fluid Mech.* **6**, *462–8.* [501]

DI PRIMA, R. C., and DUNN, D. W. (1956). The effect of heating and cooling on the stability of the boundary-layer flow of a liquid over a curved surface. *J. aero Sci.* **23**, *913–16.* [504]

DI PRIMA, R. C. See Carrier and Di Prima (1956), (1957).

DOENHOFF, A. E. VON (1938). A method of rapidly estimating the position of the laminar separation point. *Tech. Notes nat. adv. Comm. Aero., Wash.* No. *671.* [322, 327, 331]

DONNELLY, R. J. (1958). Experiments on the stability of viscous flow between rotating cylinders. I. Torque measurements. *Proc. Roy. Soc.* A *246, 312–25.* [501]

DONNELLY, R. J., and SIMON, N. J. (1960). An empirical torque relation for supercritical flow between rotating cylinders. *J. Fluid. Mech.* **7**, *401–18.* [565, 571]

DONOUGHE, P. L. See Brown and Donoughe (1951).

DORSCH, R. G. See Boyd, Dorsch, and Brodie (1952).

DOWDALL, R. B. See Carrier and Dowdall.

DRAKE, R. M. (1953). Calculation method for three-dimensional symmetrical laminar boundary layers with arbitrary free stream velocity and arbitrary wall temperature variation. *J. aero. Sci.* **20**, *309–16.* [432]

DRAZIN, P. G. (1958). The stability of a shear layer in an unbounded heterogeneous fluid. *J. Fluid Mech.* **4**, *214–24.* [548]

DRAZIN, P. G. (1961). Discontinuous velocity profiles for the Orr-Sommerfeld equation. *J. Fluid Mech.* **10**, *571–83.* [561]

DRYDEN, H. L. (1943). A review of the statistical theory of turbulence. *Quart. appl. Math.* **1**, *7–42.* [607]

DRYDEN, H. L. (1955). Transition from laminar to turbulent flow at subsonic and supersonic speeds. *Proc. Conf. high-speed Aeronaut. Poly. Inst., Brooklyn, 41–74.* [578]

DRYDEN, H. L. (1956). Recent investigations of the problem of transition. *Z. Flugwiss.* **4**, *89–95.* [578]

DRYDEN, H. L., and KUETHE, A. M. (1929). The measurements of fluctuations of airspeed in turbulent flow. *Rep. nat. adv. Comm. Aero., Wash.* No. *320.* [607]

DRYDEN, H. L., MURNAGHAN, F. D., and BATEMAN, H. (1932). Hydrodynamics. *Bulletin of National Research Council, Washington,* No. *84, 295–332.* (Reprinted 1956. Dover Publications, New York.) [166]

DRYDEN, H. L., SCHUBAUER, G. B., MOCK, W. C., and SKRAMSTAD, H. K. (1937). Measurements of intensity and scale of wind-tunnel turbulence and their relation to the critical Reynolds number of spheres. *Rep. nat. adv. Comm. Aero., Wash.* No. *581.* [607]

DUNCAN, W. J. (1927). On a modification of the Chattock tilting pressure gauge designed to eliminate the changes of zero with temperature. *J. sci. Instrum.* **4**, *376–9.* [602]

DUNN, D. W., and LIN, C. C. (1955). On the stability of the boundary-layer in a compressible fluid. *J. aero. Sci.* **20**, *455–77.* [494, 551, 553]

DUNN, D. W. See Di Prima and Dunn (1956).

DUNNING, R. W., and ULMANN, E. F. (1955). Effects of sweep and angle of attack on boundary layer transition on wings at Mach number 4·04. *Tech. Nøtes nat. adv. Comm. Aero., Wash.* No. *3473.* [555]

DURAND, W. F. *See* Prandtl (1935).

ECKERT, E. R. G., and SOEHNGEN, E. (1951). Interferometric studies on the stability and transition to turbulence of a free-convection boundary layer. *Proc. gen. Dis. Heat Transf., Lond. 321–3.* [538]

ECKERT, E. R. G., SOEHNGEN, E., and SCHNEIDER, P. J. (1955). Studien zum Umschlag laminar-turbulent der freien Konvektions-Strömung an einer senkrechten Platte. *50 Jahre Grenzschichtforschung* (Editors: Görtler, H., and Tollmien, W.), Vieweg, Braunschweig. *407–18.* [538]

EICHELBRENNER, E. A., and MICHEL, R. (1958). Vergleich von theoretischen Ansatzen zur Bestimmung des Umschlags laminar-turbulent in drei Dimensionen mit Versuchen im Windkanal der O.N.E.R.A. zu Cannes. *Proc. Symp. boundary layer Res., Int. Union theoret. appl. Mech. Freiburg i. Br.* (1957), *161–72. See also* 'Observations sur la transition laminar-turbulent en trois dimensions', *Rech. aéro.* No. *65, 3–10* (1958). [555]

EICHELBRENNER, E. A., and OUDART, A. (1954). Observations sur un critère de décollement laminaire dans la couche-limite tridimensionelle. *Rech. aéro.* No. *40.* [491]

EICHELBRENNER, E. A., and OUDART, A. (1955). Le décollement laminaire en trois dimensions. *Rech. aéro.* No. *47. See also* Méthode de calcul de la couche limite tridimensionelle. Application à un corps fuselé incliné sur le vent. *Publ. Off. nat. Étud. aéro.* No. *76.* [491]

EINSTEIN, A. (1906). Eine neue Bestimmung der Moleküldimensionen. *Ann. Phys., Lpz.* (4), *19, 289–306.* [166]

EINSTEIN, A. (1911). Berichtigung zu meiner Arbeit: Eine neue Bestimmung der Moleküldimensionen. *Ann. Phys., Lpz.* (4), *34, 591–2.* [166]

EKMAN, V. W. (1910). On the change from laminar to turbulent motion of liquids. *Ark. Mat. Astr. Fys.* **6**, No. *12.* [539]

ELGAR, E. *See* Kaye and Elgar (1958).

ELIASSEN, A., HØILAND, E., and RIIS, E. (1953). Two-dimensional perturbation of a flow with constant shear of a stratified fluid. *Publ. Inst. Weath. Clim. Res., Oslo* No. *1.* [548]

ELLIOTT, D. *See* Cheng and Elliott (1957); Clenshaw and Elliott (1960).

ELMSLIE, J., HOSKING, L., and MARCHALL, W. S. D. (1953). Some experiments on the flow in the boundary layer of a 45° sweptback untapered wing of aspect ratio 4. *Rep. Coll. Aero., Cranfield.* No. *69.* [475].

EMMONS, H. W. (1951). The laminar-turbulent transition in a boundary layer, Part I. *J. aero. Sci.* **18**, *490–8.* [95, 577, 607]

EMMONS, H. W. (Editor) (1958). *Fundamentals of gas dynamics. High speed aerodynamics and jet propulsion,* III. Oxford University Press, London. [8, 25].

EMMONS, H. W., and BRYSON, A. E. (1951). The laminar-turbulent transition in a boundary layer, Part II. *Proc. 1st U.S. nat. Congr. appl. Mech. 859–68.* [577, 607]

EMMONS, H. W., and LEIGH, D. C. (1953). Tabulation of the Blasius function with blowing and suction. *Curr. Pap. aero. Res. Coun., Lond.* No. *157.* [242]

ERWIN, J. R. *See* Schulze, Ashby, and Erwin (1952).

ESCH, R. E. (1957). The instability of a shear layer between two parallel streams. *J. Fluid Mech.* **3**, *289–303.* [559]

EVANS, H. L. *See* Spalding and Evans (1961).

EYRING, H. *See* Glasstone, Laidler, and Eyring (1941).

FADNIS, B. S. (1954). Boundary layer on rotating spheroids. *Z. angew. Math. Phys.* **5**, *156–63.* [439]

FAGE, A. (1936). Experiments on a sphere at critical Reynolds numbers. *Rep. Memor. aero. Res. Coun., Lond.* No. *1766* (1937 Vol.). [108, 423]

FAGE, A. (1938). The influence of wall oscillations, wall rotation and entry eddies on the breakdown of laminar flow in an annular pipe. *Proc. Roy. Soc.* A **165**, *513–17.* [501]

FAGE, A. (1955). Studies of boundary-layer flow with a fluid-motion microscope. *50 Jahre Grenzschichtforschung* (Editors: Görtler, H., and Tollmien, W.), Vieweg, Braunschweig. *132–46.* [592]

FAGE, A., and FALKNER, V. M. (1930). An experimental determination of the intensity of friction on the surface of an aerofoil. *Proc. Roy. Soc.* A **129**, *378–410*. See also *Rep. Memor. aero. Res. Coun., Lond.* No. *1315* (1930–1 Vol.). [622, 624]

FAGE, A., and FALKNER, V. M. (1931). Further experiments on the flow round a circular cylinder. *Rep. Memor. aero. Res. Coun., Lond.* No. *1369* (1930–1 Vol.). [329]

FAGE, A., FALKNER, V. M., and WALKER, W. S. (1929). Experiments on a series of symmetrical Joukowski sections. *Rep. Memor. aero. Res., Coun., Lond.* No. *1241* (1929–30 Vol.). [109]

FAGE, A., and PRESTON, J. H. (1941). On transition from laminar to turbulent flow in the boundary layer. *Proc. Roy. Soc.* A **178**, *201–27*. See also Fage (1955). [617]

FAGE, A., and SARGENT, R. F. (1944). An air-injection method of fixing transition from laminar to turbulent flow in a boundary layer. *Rep. Memor. aero. Res. Coun., Lond.* No. *2106.* [618]

FAGE, A., and SARGENT, R. F. (1947). Shock-wave and boundary-layer phenomena near a flat surface. *Proc. Roy. Soc.* A **190**, *1–20*. [624]

FAGE, A., and TOWNEND, H. C. H. (1932). An examination of turbulent flow with an ultramicroscope. *Proc. Roy. Soc.* A **135**, *656–77*. [592]

FALES, E. N. (1955). A new laboratory technique for the investigation of fluid turbulence. *J. Franklin Inst.* **259**, *491–515*. [555, 557]

FALKNER, V. M. (1934). A modified Chattock gauge of high sensitivity. *Rep. Memor. aero. Res. Coun., Lond.* No. *1589* (1933–4 Vol.). [602]

FALKNER, V. M. (1937). A further investigation of solutions of the boundary layer equations. *Rep. Memor. aero. Res. Coun., Lond.* No. *1884* (1939 Vol.). [266, 267]

FALKNER, V. M. (1941). Simplified calculation of the laminar boundary layer. *Rep. Memor. aero. Res. Coun., Lond.* No. *1895.* [269]

FALKNER, V. M., and SKAN, S. W. (1930). Some approximate solutions of the boundary-layer equations. *Rep. Memor. aero. Res. Coun., Lond.* No. *1314* (1929–30 Vol.). See also Solutions of the boundary-layer equations. *Phil. Mag.* (7), **12**, *865–96* (1931). [235, 266, 430]

FALKNER, V. M. *See* Fage and Falkner (1930), (1931); Fage, Falkner, and Walker (1929).

FANUCCI, J. B. *See* Lew and Fanucci (1954).

FARREN, W. S. (1935). The reaction on a wing whose angle of incidence is changing rapidly. *Rep. Memor. aero. Res. Coun., Lond.* No. *1648* (1934–5 Vol.). [112]

FARREN, W. S. (1938). *Modern developments in fluid dynamics* (Editor: Goldstein, S.), Plate 19b. Clarendon Press, Oxford. [Plate]

FAXÉN, H. *See* Olsson and Faxén (1927).

FEINSILBER, A. M. (1946). Reduction of boundary-layer equations for gases to the type of thermal conductivity equation. *Dokl. Ak. Nauk S.S.S.R.* **51**, *501–4*. [275]

FELDMAN, S. (1957). On the hydrodynamic stability of two viscous incompressible fluids in parallel uniform shearing motion. *J. Fluid Mech.* **2**, *343–70*. [548]

FERRISS, D. H. (1965). Preston tube measurements in turbulent boundary layers and fully developed pipe flow. *Rep. aero. Res. Coun., Lond.* No. *26,678.* [625]

FETTIS, H. E. (1956). On the integration of a class of differential equations occurring in boundary layer and other hydrodynamic problems. *Proc. 4th midwest Conf. Fluid Mech., Purdue University, September, 1955, 93–114.* [161]

FILON, L. N. G. (1926). The forces on a cylinder in a stream of viscous fluid. *Proc. Roy. Soc.* A **113**, *7–27*. [194]

FILON, L. N. G. (1928). On the second approximation for the Oseen solution for the motion of a viscous fluid. *Phil. Trans.* A **227**, *93–135*. [196]

FINSTON, M. *See* Hahnemann, Freeman, and Finston (1948).

FJØRTOFT, R. (1950). Application of integral theorems in deriving criteria of stability for laminar flows and for the baroclinic circular vortex. *Geofys. Publ., Oslo*, **17**, No. 6. [519]

FOGARTY, L. E. (1951). The laminar boundary layer on a rotating blade. *J. aero. Sci.* **18**, *247–52*. [481]

FOOTE, J. R., and LIN, C. C. (1950). Some recent investigations in the theory of hydrodynamic stability. *Quart. appl. Math.* **8**, *265–80*. [519]

FOURNIER, P. G. *See* Russell, Gracey, Letko, and Fournier (1951).

FOWLER, J. S. *See* Binnie and Fowler (1947).

FOWLER, R. H., and GUGGENHEIM, E. A. (1939). *Statistical thermodynamics*. Cambridge University Press. [6]

FOX, J. A., and LESSEN, M. (1955). The stability of boundary layer type flows with infinite boundary conditions. *50 Jahre Grenzschichtforschung* (Editors : Görtler, H., and Tollmien, W.), Vieweg, Braunschweig. *122–6*. [558]

FREEMAN, J. C. *See* Chiarulli and Freeman (1948) ; Hahnemann, Freeman, and Finston (1948).

FRENKIEL, F. N. (1954). Effects of wire length in turbulence investigations with a hot-wire anemometer. *Aeronaut. Quart.* **5**, *1–24*. [608]

FRIEDRICHS, K. O. (1942). *Fluid dynamics*, Chap. IV, *200–10*, Brown University, Rhode Island. [521]

FRÖSSLING, N. (1940). Verdunstung, Wärmeübergang und Geschwindigkeitsverteilung bei zweidimensionaler und rotations symmetrischer laminarer Grenzschichtströmung. *Lunds Univ. Årsskr. N.F. Avd. 2,* **36**, No. *4*. (Translated as 'Evaporation, heat transfer and velocity distribution in two-dimensional and rotationally symmetrical laminar boundary-layer flow', *Tech. Memor. nat. adv. Comm. Aero., Wash.* No. *1432*.) [261, 422]

GADD, G. E. (1952). The numerical integration of the laminar compressible boundary-layer equations, with special reference to the position of separation when the wall is cooled. *Curr. Pap. aero. Res. Coun., Lond.* No. *312*. [283]

GADD, G. E. (1957). A theoretical investigation of laminar separation in supersonic flow. *J. aero. Sci.* **24**, *759–71*. [329]

GARBER, H. J. *See* Peebles, Garber, and Jury (1953).

GARNER, H. C., and BRYER, D. W. (1959). Experimental study of surface flow and part-span vortex layers on a cropped arrowhead wing. *Rep. Memor. aero. Res. Coun., Lond.* No. *3107*. [75]

GARNER, H. C. *See* Bryer, Walshe, and Garner (1955). .

GARSTANG, T. E. (1937). The forces on a solid body in a stream of viscous fluid. *Phil. Trans.* A **236**, *25–75*. [197]

GAZLEY, C. (1953). Boundary layer stability and transition in subsonic and supersonic flow. *J. aero. Sci.* **20**, *19–28*. [494]

GAZLEY, C. (1958). Heat-transfer characteristics of the rotational and axial flow between rotating cylinders. *Trans. Amer. Soc. mech. Engrs* **80**, *79–90*. [501]

GEIS, T. (1955). Ähnliche Grenzschichten an Rotationskörpern. *50 Jahre Grenzschichtforschung* (Editors : Görtler, H., and Tollmien, W.), Vieweg, Braunschweig. *294–303*. [428]

GEIS, T. (1956). Bemerkung zu den 'ähnlichen' instationären laminaren Grenzschichtströmungen. *Z. angew. Math. Mech.* **36**, *396–8*. [360]

GELLER, E. W. (1955). An electrochemical method of visualizing the boundary layer. *J. aero. Sci.* **22**, *869–70*. [592, 619]

GHOSH, A. (1961). Contribution à l'étude de la couche limite laminaire instationnaire. *Publ. sci. Minist. Air* No. *381*. [397]

GIBELLATO, S. (1955). Strato limite attorno ad una lestra piana investita da un fluido incompressibile dotato di una velocità che è somma di una parte constante e di una parte alternata. *Atti Accad. Torino,* **89**, *180–92* (1954–5), and **90**, *1–12* (1955–6). [397, 402]

GIBELLATO, S. (1956). Strato limite termico attorno a una lestra piana investita da una corrente lievemente pulsante di fluido incompressible. *Atti Accad. Torino,* **91**, *152–70* (1956–7). [407]

GIBSON, W. E. (1957). Unsteady laminar boundary-layer flow. *Ph.D. Mathematics Thesis Mass. Inst. Tech.* [394, 396]

GILBARG, D. (1957). Free-streamline theory and steady-state cavitation. *Proc. 1st Symp. nav. Hydr., Wash., 281–95.* [27]

GILLES, A., HOPF, L., and KÁRMÁN, TH. v. *See* Levi-Civita (1929); Prandtl (1929).

GLASSTONE, S., LAIDLER, K. J., and EYRING, H. (1941). *The theory of rate processes.* McGraw Hill, New York. [30]

GLAUERT, H. (1926). *Aerofoil and airscrew theory.* Cambridge University Press. [36]

GLAUERT, M. B. (1956). The laminar boundary layer on oscillating plates and cylinders. *J. Fluid Mech.* **1**, *97–110.* [403, 404, 405]

GLAUERT, M. B. (1957). A boundary layer theorem, with applications to rotating cylinders. *J. Fluid Mech.* **2**, *89–99.* [212]

GLAUERT, M. B., and LIGHTHILL, M. J. (1955). The axisymmetric boundary layer on a long thin cylinder. *Proc. Roy. Soc.* A **230**, *188–203.* [446–51]

GOLDSCHMIED, F. R. (1951). Skin friction of incompressible turbulent boundary layers under adverse pressure gradients. *Tech. Notes nat. adv. Comm. Aero., Wash.* No. *2431.* [622]

GOLDSTEIN, S. (1929a). The forces on a solid body moving through a viscous fluid. *Proc. Roy. Soc.* A **123**, *216–25.* [197, 456]

GOLDSTEIN, S. (1929b). The steady flow of a viscous fluid past a fixed spherical obstacle at small Reynolds numbers. *Proc. Roy. Soc.* A **123**, *225–35.* [176]

GOLDSTEIN, S. (1930). Concerning some solutions of the boundary-layer equations in hydrodynamics. *Proc. Camb. phil. Soc.* **26**, *1–30.* [217, 223, 233, 278, 328, 343]

GOLDSTEIN, S. (1931a). The forces on a solid body moving through viscous fluid. *Proc. Roy. Soc.* A **131**, *198–208.* [197]

GOLDSTEIN, S. (1931b). On the stability of superposed streams of fluid of different densities. *Proc. Roy. Soc.* A **132**, *524–48.* [548]

GOLDSTEIN, S. (1933). On the two-dimensional steady flow of a viscous fluid behind a solid body. Part I. *Proc. Roy. Soc.* A **142**, *545–62.* [280, 281]

GOLDSTEIN, S. (1936). A note on the measurement of total head and static pressure in a turbulent stream. *Proc. Roy. Soc.* A **155**, *570–5.* [598]

GOLDSTEIN, S. (Editor) (1938). *Modern developments in fluid dynamics.* Clarendon Press, Oxford. *See also* Farren (1938). [36, 102, 340, 441]

GOLDSTEIN, S. (1939). A note on the boundary-layer equations. *Proc. Camb. phil. Soc.* **35**, *338–40.* [244, 251]

GOLDSTEIN, S. (1948a). Low-drag and suction aerofoils: the eleventh Wright Brothers Lecture. *J. aero. Sci.* **15**, *189–214.* [111]

GOLDSTEIN, S. (1948b). On laminar boundary-layer flow near a position of separation. *Quart. J. Mech.* **1**, *43–69.* [219]

GOLDSTEIN, S. (1960). *Lectures on fluid mechanics.* Interscience, London and New York. [228]

GOLDSTEIN, S., and ROSENHEAD, L. (1936). Boundary-layer growth. *Proc. Camb. phil. Soc.* **32**, *392–401.* [371, 373, 374, 377]

GORKOV, L. P. *Zh. Eksp. Teor. Fiz.* **33**, *402–7* (in Russian). (Translated as 'Steady convection in a plane liquid layer near the critical heat-transfer point' in *Sov. Phys.— JETP,* **6**, *311–15*.) [565, 572]

GÖRTLER, H. (1939). Weiterentwicklung eines Grenzschichtprofils bei gegebenem Druckverlauf. *Z. angew. Math. Mech.* **19**, *129–40.* [264, 282, 285, 286]

GÖRTLER, H. (1940a). Über den Einfluss der Wandkrümmung auf die Entstehung der Turbulenz. *Z. angew. Math. Mech.* **20**, *138–47.* [90, 540]

GÖRTLER, H. (1940b). Über eine dreidimensionale Instabilität laminarer Grenzschichten an konkaven Wänden. *Nachr. Ges. Wiss. Göttingen, Math.-phys. Kl.* **1**, *1–26.* (Translated as 'On the three-dimensional instability of laminar boundary layers on concave walls', *Tech. Memor. nat. adv. Comm. Aero., Wash.* No. *1375.*) [502, 504]

GÖRTLER, H. (1942). Berechnung von Aufgaben der freien Turbulenz auf Grund eines neuen Näherungsansatzes. *Z. angew. Math. Mech.* **22**, *244–54.* [252]

GÖRTLER, H. (1944). Verdrängungswirkung der laminaren Grenzschichten und Druckwiderstand. *Ingen.-Arch.* **14**, *286–305.* (Translated as 'Displacement effect of the laminar boundary layer and the pressure drag', *Tech. Memor. nat. adv. Comm. Aero., Wash.* No. *1315.*) [371, 374, 379]

GÖRTLER, H. (1946). A method of differences for the calculation of laminar boundary layers. Unpublished translation Min. Aviation, London. (From 'Ein Differenzenverfahren zur Berechnung laminarer Grenzschichten', *Untersuch. Mitt. dtsch. Luftfahrtf. No. 6615* (1944).) [272, 283, 285]

GÖRTLER, H. (1948a). Ein Differenzenverfahren zur Berechnung laminarer Grenzschichten. *Ingen.-Arch.* **16**, *173–87*. [272, 283, 285]

GÖRTLER, H. (1948b). Grenzschichtentstehung an Zylindern bei Anfahrt aus der Ruhe. *Arch. Math., Karlsruhe*, **1**, *138–47*. [371, 374]

GÖRTLER, H. (1949). Zur Approximation stationärer laminarer Grenzschichtströmungen mit Hilfe der abgebrochenen Blasiusschen Reihe. *Arch. Math., Karlsruhe*, **1**, *235–40*. [264]

GÖRTLER, H. (1952a). Eine neue Reihenentwicklung für laminare Grenzschichten. *Z. angew. Math. Mech.* **32**, *270–1*. [270]

GÖRTLER, H. (1952b). Zur laminaren Grenzschicht am schiebenden Zylinder. *Arch. Math., Karlsruhe*, **3**, *216–31*. [469]

GÖRTLER, H. (1954). Theoretical investigation of the laminar boundary layer. Problem II—decay of swirl in an axially symmetrical jet, far from the orifice. *Report for United States Air Force (Office of Scientific Research) Contract No. AF 61(514)-627-C.* [452]

GÖRTLER, H. (1955a). A new series for the calculation of steady laminar boundary layer flows. Unpublished report of the Mathematisches Institut Universität Freiburg i. Br. See also *J. Math. Mech.* **6**, *1–66* (1957). [270–2, 307]

GÖRTLER, H. (1955b). Dreidimensionale Instabilität der ebenen Staupunktströmung gegenüber wirbelartigen Störungen. *50 Jahre Grenzschichtforschung* (Editors : Görtler, H., and Tollmien, W.), Vieweg, Braunschweig. *304–14.* [505, 565]

GÖRTLER, H. (1957a). On the calculation of steady laminar boundary layer flows with continuous suction. *J. Math. Mech.* **6**, *323–40*. [335]

GÖRTLER, H. (1957b). Zahlentafeln universeller Funktionen zur neuen Reihe für die Berechnung laminarer Grenzschichten. *Ber. dtsch. VersAnst. Luftfahrt, Mülheim, No. 34.* [272]

GÖRTLER, H. (1959). Über eine Analogie zwischen den Instabilitäten laminarer Grenzschichtströmungen an konkaven Wänden und an erwärmten Wänden. *Ingen.-Arch.* **28**, *71–78* (Festschrift Richard Grammel). [504]

GÖRTLER, H., and WITTING, H. (1958). Theorie der secundären Instabilität der laminaren Grenzschichten. *Proc. Symp. boundary layer Res., Int. Union theoret. appl. Mech. Freiburg i. Br.* (1957), *110–26.* [565]

GÖRTLER, H. *See* Collatz and Görtler (1954).

GÖRTLER, H., and TOLLMIEN, W. *See* Betz (1955) ; Coles (1955) ; Eckert, Soehngen and Schneider (1955) ; Fage (1955) ; Fox and Lessen (1955) ; Geis (1955) ; Görtler (1955b) ; Hämmerlin (1955b) ; Iglisch and Kemnitz (1955) ; Ostrach (1955a) ; Rheinboldt (1955) ; Schuh (1955) ; Squire (1955) ; Thwaites (1955) ; Wortman (1955).

GOTOH, K. *See* Tatsumi and Gotoh (1960).

GRAAF, J. G. A. DE, and HELD, E. F. M. VAN DER (1953). The relation between heat transfer and the convection phenomena in enclosed plane air layers. *Appl. sci. Res., A. Hague*, **3**, *393–409*. [511]

GRACEY, W. *See* Russell, Gracey, Letko, and Fournier (1951).

GRAHAM, A. (1933). Shear patterns in an unstable layer of air. *Phil. Trans.* A **232**, *285–96*. [511]

GRAHAM, M. E. (1954). Calculation of the laminar boundary layer on rotating blades. *Thesis, Cornell Univ.* [483]

GRAY, A. -E. (1944). A chemical method of indicating transition in the boundary layer. *Rep. aero. Res. Coun., Lond. No. 8034.* [612]

GRAY, W. E. (1946). A simple visual method of recording boundary-layer transition (liquid film). *Rep. aero. Res. Coun., Lond. No. 10028.* [613]

GRAY, W. E. (1952). The nature of the boundary layer at the nose of a swept back wing. Unpublished work Min. Aviation, London. [549]

GREEN, H. L. *See* Lane and Green (1956).

GREEN, J. J. (1930). The viscous layer associated with a circular cylinder. *Rep. Memor. aero. Res. Coun., Lond. No. 1313* (1929–30 Vol.). See also *Phil. Mag.* (7), **12**, *1–41* (1931). [286]

HÄMMERLIN, G. (1958). Die Stabilität der Strömung in einem gekrümmten Kanal. *Arch. rat. Mech. Anal., Heidelberg,* **1**, *212–24.* [505]

HANCOCK, G. J. (1953). The self-propulsion of microscopic organisms through liquids. *Proc. Roy. Soc.* A **217**, *96–121.* [170, 173]

HANNAH, D. M. (1947). Forced flow against a rotating disc. *Rep. Memor. aero. Res. Coun., Lond.* No. *2772.* [160, 420]

HANSEN, A. G. See Mager and Hansen (1952).

HARDY, G. H. (1939). A note on a differential equation. *Proc. Camb. phil. Soc.* **35**, *652–3.* [251]

HARRINGTON, R. P. See Libby, Kaufman, and Harrington (1952).

HARRIS, D. L. See Reid and Harris (1958).

HARRIS, D. P. See Binnie and Harris (1950).

HARRISON, W. J. (1919). The pressure in a viscous liquid moving through a channel with diverging boundaries. *Proc. Camb. phil. Soc.* **19**, *307–12.* [144]

HARTREE, D. R. (1937a). On an equation occurring in Falkner and Skan's approximate treatment of the equations of the boundary layer. *Proc. Camb. phil. Soc.* **33**, *223–39.* [235, 247, 248, 267]

HARTREE, D. R. (1937b). Note on a set of solutions of the equation $y'' + (2/x)y' - y^2 = 0$. *Mem. Manchr lit. phil. Soc.* **81**, *19–28.* [251]

HARTREE, D. R. (1939a). A solution of the laminar boundary-layer equation for retarded flow. *Rep. Memor. aero. Res. Coun., Lond.* No. *2426* (Spec. Vol. I). [218, 219, 265, 282, 283]

HARTREE, D. R. (1939b). The solution of the equations of the laminar boundary layer for Schubauer's observed pressure distribution for an elliptic cylinder. *Rep. Memor. aero. Res. Coun., Lond.* No. *2427* (Spec. Vol. II). [283, 329–31, 404]

HASIMOTO, H. (1951). Note on Rayleigh's problem for a bent flat plate. *J. phys. Soc. Japan,* **6**, *400–1.* [138, 363, 364, 488]

HASIMOTO, H. (1952). Rayleigh's problem for a plate of finite breadth. *Proc. 1st Japan nat. Congr. appl. Mech. 447–52.* [363]

HASIMOTO, H. (1954). Rayleigh's problem for a cylinder of arbitrary shape. *J. phys. Soc. Japan,* **9**, *611–19.* [365, 367, 488]

HASIMOTO, H. (1955). Rayleigh's problem for a cylinder of arbitrary shape, II. *J. phys. Soc. Japan,* **10**, *397–406.* [365, 366, 367]

HASIMOTO, H. (1956). The unsteady axial motion of an infinitely-long cylinder in a viscous fluid. *Proc. 9th int. Congr. appl. Mech., Brussels,* **3**, *135–44.* [365]

HASIMOTO, H. (1957). Boundary-layer growth on a flat plate with suction or injection. *J. phys. Soc. Japan,* **12**, *68–72.* [400]

HATSCHEK, E. (1928). *The viscosity of liquids.* Bell, London. [28, 30]

HAYES, W. D. (1951). The three-dimensional boundary layer. *Rep. U.S. nav. Ordnance Lab.* No. *1313.* [411, 415, 490]

HAZEN, D. C. (1955). Some results of the Princeton University smoke flow visualization programme. *Proc. 5th anglo-amer. aero. Conf. R. aero. Soc. 316–52.* [610]

HEAD, M. R. (1951). The boundary layer with distributed suction. *Rep. Memor. aero. Res. Coun., Lond.* No. *2783.* [344, 345]

HEAD, M. R. (1957a). An approximate method of calculating the laminar boundary layer in two-dimensional incompressible flow. *Rep. Memor. aero. Res. Coun., Lond.* No. *3123.* [312, 338, 541, 545]

HEAD, M. R. (1957b). Approximate calculations of the laminar boundary layer with suction, with particular reference to the suction requirements for boundary layer stability on aerofoils of different thickness/chord ratio. *Rep. Memor. aero. Res. Coun., Lond.* No. *3124.* [339]

HEAD, M. R., and RECHENBERG, I. (1962). The Preston tube as a means of measuring skin friction. *J. Fluid Mech.* **14**, *1–17.* [625]

HEAD, M. R. See Jones and Head (1951).

HEGARTY, J. C. (1958). Investigation of transition caused by the stopping of a flat plate. *Tech. Notes Inst. Fluid Dyn. appl. Math., Univ. Maryland BN-141.* [557]

HEGARTY, J. C. See Hama, Long, and Hegarty (1957).

HEGGE ZIJNEN, B. VAN DER. See Hinze and Hegge Zijnen (1949).

HEIN, H. *See* Schultz-Grunow and Hein (1956).

HEISENBERG, W. (1924). Über Stabilität und Turbulenz von Flüssigkeitsströmen. *Ann. Phys.*, *Lpz.* (4), **74**, *577–627*. (Translated as 'On stability and turbulence of fluid flows', *Tech. Memor. nat. adv. Comm. Aero.*, *Wash.* No. *1291*. [521, 523, 524, 530, 566]

HELD, E. F. M. VAN DER. *See* Graaf and Held (1953).

HELMHOLTZ, H. VON (1868). Über diskontinuierliche Flüssigkeitsbewegungen. *Mber. K. Akad. Wiss. Berlin* **23**, *215–28*. See also *Phil. Mag.* **36**, *337–46*. [2]

HENDAL, W. P. *See* Meijer Drees and Hendal (1951).

HERMANS, J. J. (Editor) (1953). *Flow properties of disperse systems.* North Holland Publ. Co., Amsterdam. [28]

HIEMENZ, K. (1911). Die Grenzschicht an einem in den gleichförmigen Flüssigkeitsstrom eingetauchten geraden Kreiszylinder. *Dinglers J.* **326**, *321–4, 344–8, 357–62, 372–6, 391–3, 407–10*. [156, 231, 260, 264, 285, 329, 401]

HILL, T. L. (1956). *Statistical mechanics.* McGraw-Hill, New York. [24]

HIMMELSKAMP, H. (1950). Profiluntersuchungen an einem umlaufenden Propeller. *Mitt. Max-Planck-Inst.* No. *2.* [482]

HINZE, J., and HEGGE ZIJNEN, B. VAN DER (1949). Transfer of heat and matter in the turbulent mixing zone of an axially symmetrical jet. *Appl. sci. Res., A.* Hague, **1**, *435–61.* [155]

HIRSCHFELDER, J. O., CURTISS, C. F., and BIRD, R. B. (1954). *Molecular theory of gases and liquids.* Wiley, New York. [14]

HOCKING, L. M. (1959). The Oseen flow past a circular disk. *Quart. J. Mech.* **12**, *464–75.* [183]

HØILAND, E. (1953a). On two-dimensional perturbation of linear flow. *Geofys. Publ.*, Oslo, **18**, No. *9* [519]

HØILAND, E. (1953b). On the dynamic effect of variation of density on two-dimensional perturbations of flow with constant shear. *Geofys. Publ., Oslo*, **18**, No. *10.* [548]

HØILAND, E. *See* Eliassen, Høiland, and Riis (1953).

HOLDER, D. W. *See* Pankhurst and Holder (1952); Haines, Holder, and Pearcey (1954).

HOLLINGDALE, S. H. (1940). Stability and configuration of the wakes produced by solid bodies moving through fluids. *Phil. Mag.* (7), **29**, *209–57.* [562]

HOLSTEIN, H. (1943). Aehnliche laminare Reibungsschichten an durchlässigen Wänden. *Untersuch. Mitt. dtsch. Luftfahrt.* No. *3050.* [251, 252]

HOLSTEIN, H. (1950). Über die äussere und innere Reibungsschichten bei Störungen laminarer Strömungen. *Z. angew. Math. Mech.* **30**, *25–49.* [521, 525, 528]

HOLSTEIN, H., and BOHLEN, T. (1940). Ein einfaches Verfahren zur Berechnung laminarer Reibungsschichten, die dem Näherungsansatz von K. Pohlhausen genügen. *Ber. Lilienthal-Ges. Luftfahrt. S10, 5–16. See also* Mangler (1948b). [294]

HOLTSMARK, J., JOHNSEN, I., SIKKELAND, T., and SKAVLEM, S. (1954). Boundary layer flow near a cylindrical obstacle in an oscillating incompressible fluid. *J. acoust. Soc. Amer.* **26**, *102.* [388]

HOMANN, F. (1936a). Einfluss grosser Zähigkeit bei Strömung um Zylinder. *ForschArb. IngWes.* **7**, *1–10.* [10, Plate]

HOMANN, F. (1936b). Der Einfluss grosser Zähigkeit bei der Strömung um den Zylinder und um die Kugel. *Z. angew. Math. Mech.* **16**, *153–64.* (Translated as 'The effect of high viscosity on the flow around a cylinder and around a sphere', *Tech. Memor. nat. adv. Comm. Aero., Wash.* No. *1334.*) [156, 233, 419, 594]

HOOL, J. N. (1956). Measurement of skin friction using surface tubes. *Aircr. Engng*, **28**, *52–54.* [624]

HOPF, L. (1914). Der Verlauf kleiner Schwingungen auf einer Strömung reibender Flüssigkeit. *Ann. Phys., Lpz.* (4), **44**, *1–60.* [538]

HOPF, L. *See* Levi-Civita (1929); Prandtl (1929).

HOSKING, L. *See* Elmslie, Hosking, and Marchall (1953).

HOWARD, L. N. (1959). Hydrodynamic stability of a jet. *J. Math. Phys.* **37**, *283–98.* See also *Proc. Symp. boundary layer Res., Int. Union theoret. appl. Mech.* Freiburg i. Br. (1957), *157–60.* [560]

HOWARTH, L. (1934). On calculation of the steady flow in the boundary layer near the surface of a cylinder in a stream. *Rep. Memor. aero. Res. Coun., Lond.* No. *1632* (1934–5 Vol.). [156, 231, 260, 261, 286]

HOWARTH, L. (1935a). Note on the development of circulation round a thin elliptic cylinder. *Proc. Camb. phil. Soc.* **31**, *582–4*. [374]

HOWARTH, L. (1935b). The theoretical determination of the lift coefficient for a thin elliptic cylinder. *Proc. Roy. Soc.* A **149**, *558–86*. [476]

HOWARTH, L. (1938). On the solution of the laminar boundary layer equations. *Proc. Roy. Soc.* A **164**, *547–79*. [219, 223, 265, 266, 309, 330, 331, 459]

HOWARTH, L. (1950). Rayleigh's problem for a semi-infinite plate. *Proc. Camb. phil. Soc.* **46**, *127–40*. [138, 363, 486, 488]

HOWARTH, L. (1951a). The boundary layer in three-dimensional flow. Part I: Derivation of the equations for flow along a general curved surface. *Phil. Mag.* (7), **42**, *239–43*. [411, 415]

HOWARTH, L. (1951b). Note on the boundary layer on a rotating sphere. *Phil. Mag.* (7), **42**, *1308–15*. [436]

HOWARTH, L. (1951c). The boundary layer in three-dimensional flow. Part II: The flow near a stagnation point. *Phil. Mag.* (7), **42**, *1433–40*. [78, 461, 469]

HOWARTH, L. (Editor) (1953). *Modern developments in fluid dynamics: High speed flow.* Clarendon Press, Oxford. [8, 19, 23, 42, 43, 125, 126, 406]

HUBBARD, P. G. *See* Ling and Hubbard (1956).

HUDIMOTO, B. (1941). An approximate method for calculating the laminar boundary layer. *J. Soc. aero. Sci., Japan*, **8**, *279–82*. In Japanese. Quoted by Tani (1954). [304]

HURD, C. W., CHESKY, K. P., and SHAPIRO, A. H. (1953). Influence of viscous effects on impact tubes. *J. appl. Mech.* **20**, *253–6*. [595]

IGLISCH, R. (1944). Exakte Berechnung der laminaren Grenzschicht an der längsangeströmten ebenen Platte mit homogener Absaugung. *Schr. dtsch. Akad. Luftfahrtf.* **8B**, *1–51*. (Translated as 'Exact calculation of laminar boundary layer in longitudinal flow over a flat plate with homogeneous suction', *Tech. Memor. nat. adv. Comm. Aero., Wash.* No. *1205*.) [288, 305, 337, 342, 345]

IGLISCH, R. (1953). Elementarer Existenzbeweis für die Strömung in der laminaren Grenzschicht zur Potentialströmung $U = u_1 x^m$ mit $m > 0$ bei Absaugen und Ausblasen. *Z. angew. Math. Mech.* **33**, *143–7*. [248, 251]

IGLISCH, R. (1954). Elementarer Beweis für die Eindeutigkeit der Strömung in der laminaren Grenzschicht zur Potentialströmung $U = u_1 x^m$ mit $m \geqslant 0$ bei Absaugen und Ausblasen. *Z. angew. Math. Mech.* **34**, *441–3*. [248, 251]

IGLISCH, R., and GROHNE, D. (1945). Die laminare Grenzschicht an der längsangeströmten ebenen Platte mit schrägem Absaugen und Ausblasen. *Ber. Inst. Math. tech. Hochsch., Braunschweig 1/45.* Quoted by Mangler (1948a) and Iglisch (1953). [242]

IGLISCH, R., and KEMNITZ, F. (1955). Über die in der Grenzschichttheorie auftretende Differentialgleichung $f''' + ff'' + \beta(1 - f'^2) = 0$ für $\beta < 0$ bei gewissen Absauge- und Ausblasegesetzen. *50 Jahre Grenzschichtforschung.* (Editors: Görtler, H., and Tollmien, W.), Vieweg, Braunschweig. *34–46*. [248]

ILLINGWORTH, C. R. (1954). Boundary-layer growth on a spinning body. *Phil. Mag.* (7), **45**, *1–8*. [378]

ILLINGWORTH, C. R. (1958). The effects of a sound wave on the compressible boundary-layer on a flat plate. *J. Fluid Mech.* **3**, *471–93*. [397]

ILLINGWORTH, L. N. *See* Anscombe and Illingworth (1952).

IMAI, I. (1951). On the asymptotic behaviour of viscous fluid flow at a great distance from a cylindrical body, with special reference to Filon's paradox. *Proc. Roy. Soc.* A **208**, *487–516*. [185, 196, 229]

IMAI, I. (1954). A new method of solving Oseen's equations and its application to the flow past an inclined elliptic cylinder. *Proc. Roy. Soc.* A **224**, *141–60*. [184]

IMAI, I. (1957a). *Theory of bluff bodies.* University of Maryland, College Park, Maryland. [104, 105]

IMAI, I. (1957b). Second approximation to the laminar boundary layer flow over a flat plate. *J. aero. Sci.* **24**, *155–6*. [229]

IMAI, I. *See* Tomotika and Imai (1938).

INGARD, U. *See* Andres and Ingard (1953a), (1953b).

ITO, H. (1953). Theory of laminar flow through a pipe with non-steady pressure gradients. *Rep. Inst. high-speed Mech., Tôhoku Univ.* No. 3, 163–80. [389]

JACOBS, E. N., and ABBOTT, I. A. (1932). The N.A.C.A. variable-density wind tunnel. *Rep. nat. adv. Comm. Aero., Wash.* No. 416. [107]

JAEGER, J. C. *See* Carslaw and Jaeger (1947).

JEFFERY, G. B. (1915). The two-dimensional steady motion of a viscous fluid. *Phil. Mag.* (6), 29, 455–65. [144]

JEFFREYS, B. S. *See* Jeffreys and Jeffreys (1950).

JEFFREYS, H. (1926). The instability of a layer of fluid heated below. *Phil. Mag.* (7), 2, 833–44. [498, 507, 511]

JEFFREYS, H. (1928). Some cases of instability in fluid motion. *Proc. Roy. Soc.* A 118, 195–208. [507, 510, 511]

JEFFREYS, H. (1931). *Cartesian tensors.* Cambridge University Press. [119]

JEFFREYS, H. (1952). Problems of thermal instability in a sphere. *Mon. Not. R. astr. Soc. geophys. Suppl.* 6, 272–7. [511]

JEFFREYS, H. (1956). The thermodynamics of thermal instability in liquids. *Quart. J. Mech.* 9, 1–5. [510]

JEFFREYS, H., and BLAND, M. E. M. (1951). The instability of a fluid sphere heated within. *Mon. Not. R. astr. Soc. geophys. Suppl.* 6, 148–58. [511]

JEFFREYS, H., and JEFFREYS, B. S. (1950). *Methods of mathematical physics* (second edition). Cambridge University Press. [148]

JEFFREYS, H. *See* Hales (1937).

JENSON, V. G. (1959). Viscous flow round a sphere at low Reynolds numbers (< 40). *Proc. Roy. Soc.* A 249, 346–66. [105, 163]

JOHNSEN, I. *See* Holtsmark, Johnsen, Sikkeland, and Skavlem (1954).

JONES, B. M., and Cambridge University Aeronautics Laboratory (1936). The measurement of profile drag by the pitot-traverse method. *Rep. Memor. aero. Res. Coun., Lond.* No. 1688 (1935–6 Vol.). [626, 627]

JONES, B. M., and HEAD, M. R. (1951). The reduction of drag by distributed suction. *Proc. 3rd anglo-amer. aero. Conf. R. aero. Soc., Brighton, 199–230.* See also *Rep. Memor. aero. Res. Coun., Lond.* No. 2783. [547]

JONES, C. W. (1948). On a solution of the laminar boundary-layer equation near a position of separation. *Quart. J. Mech.* 1, 385–407. [219, 221, 321]

JONES, R. *See* Simmons and Jones (1927).

JONES, R. T. (1947). Effects of sweepback on boundary-layer and separation. *Rep. nat. adv. Comm. Aero., Wash.* No. 884. [468, 490]

JUNGCLAUS, G. (1957). On the stability of laminar flow with three-dimensional disturbances. *Tech. Notes Inst. Fluid Dyn. appl. Math., Univ. Maryland BN–110.* [514]

JURY, S. H. *See* Peebles, Garber, and Jury (1953).

KAKUTANI, T. *See* Tatsumi and Kakutani (1958).

KANWAL, R. P. (1955). Vibrations of an elliptic cylinder and of a flat plate in a viscous fluid. *Z. angew. Math. Mech.* 35, 17–22. [392]

KAPLAN, W. (1958). Ordinary differential equations. *Addison-Wesley, Reading, Massachusetts.* [74, 76]

KAPLUN, S. (1954). The rôle of co-ordinate systems in boundary-layer theory. *Z. angew. Math. Phys.* 5, 111–35. [181, 238]

KAPLUN, S. (1957). Low Reynolds number flow past a circular cylinder. *J. Math. Mech.* 6, 595–603. [164, 187, 188, 192]

KAPLUN, S., and LAGERSTROM, P. A. (1957). Asymptotic expansions of Navier–Stokes solutions for small Reynolds numbers. *J. Math. Mech.* 6, 585–93. [164, 187, 188]

KÁRMÁN, TH. v. (1921). Über laminare und turbulente Reibung. *Z. angew. Math. Mech.* 1, 233–52. [157, 201, 206, 292, 380, 437]

KÁRMÁN, TH. V. (1924). Über die Oberflächenreibung von Flüssigkeiten. *Vorträge aus dem Gebiete der Hydro- und Aerodynamik* (Editors: Kármán, Th. v., and Levi-Civita, T.). Springer, Berlin. *150–1.* [144]

KÁRMÁN, TH. V. (1934). Some aspects of the turbulence problem. *Proc. 4th int. Congr. appl. Mech., Cambridge, 54–59.* [494]

KÁRMÁN, TH. V., and LIN, C. C. (1955). Theoretical comments on the paper of Mr. E. N. Fales. *J. Franklin Inst.* **259**, *517–18.* [555, 557]

KÁRMÁN, TH. V., and MILLIKAN, C. B. (1934). On the theory of laminar boundary layers involving separation. *Rep. nat. adv. Comm. Aero., Wash.* No. *504.* [214, 219, 318, 331]

KÁRMÁN, TH. V. *See* Levi-Civita (1929); Prandtl (1929).

KÁRMÁN, TH. V., and LEVI-CIVITA, T. *See* Kármán, Th. v. (1924).

KAUFMAN, L. *See* Libby, Kaufman, and Harrington (1952).

KAWAGUTI, M. (1953). Numerical solution of the Navier–Stokes equations for the flow around a circular cylinder at Reynolds number 40. *J. phys. Soc. Japan,* **8**, *747–57.* [164]

KAWAGUTI, M. (1956). The flow of a viscous fluid past a bluff body. *Proc. 9th int. Congr. appl. Mech., Brussels,* **3**, *232–40.* [163]

KAWAGUTI, M. (1959). Note on Allen and Southwell's paper 'Relaxation methods applied to determine the motion, in two dimensions, of a viscous fluid past a fixed cylinder'. *Quart. J. Mech.* **12**, *261–3.* [164]

KAY, J. M. (1948). Boundary-layer flow along a flat plate with uniform suction. *Rep. Memor. aero. Res. Coun., Lond.* No. *2628.* [345]

KAYE, J., and ELGAR, E. (1958). Modes of adiabatic and diabatic fluid flow in an annulus with an inner rotating cylinder. *Trans. Amer. Soc. mech. Engrs,* **80**, *753–65.* [501]

KELLOGG, O. D. (1929). *Foundations of potential theory.* Springer, Berlin. [55]

KELLY, H. R. (1954). A note on the laminar boundary layer on a circular cylinder in axial incompressible flow. *J. aero. Sci,* **21**, *634.* [447, 448]

KEMNITZ, F. *See* Iglisch and Kemnitz (1955).

KETTLE, D. J. (1954). The design of static and pitot-static tubes for subsonic speeds. *J.R. aero. Soc.* **58**, *835–7.* [597]

KEULEGAN, G. H. (1944). Laminar flow at the interface of two liquids. *J. Res. nat. Bur. Stand.* **32**, *303–27.* [252]

KIRCHHOFF, G. (1869). Zur Theorie freier Flüssigkeitsstrahlen. *J. reine angew. Math.* **70**, *289.* [2]

KLANFER, L. *See* Owen and Klanfer (1955).

KLEBANOFF, P. S., and DIEHL, Z. W. (1952). Some features of artificially thickened fully developed turbulent boundary layers with zero pressure gradient. *Rep. nat. adv. Comm. Aero., Wash.* No. *1110.* [619]

KLEBANOFF, P. S., SCHUBAUER, G. B., and TIDSTROM, K. D. (1955). Measurements of the effects of two-dimensional and three-dimensional roughness elements on boundary-layer transition. *J. aero. Sci.* **22**, *803–4.* [617, 618]

KLEBANOFF, P. S., and TIDSTROM, K. D. (1959). The evolution of amplified waves leading to transition in a boundary layer with zero pressure gradient. *Tech. Notes. nat. Aero. Space Admin., Wash. D–195.* [573, 576]

KLEBANOFF, P. S. *See* Schubauer and Klebanoff (1955).

KLEIN, A. L. *See* Millikan and Klein (1933).

KOBASHI, Y. (1957). Measurements of boundary layer of a rotating sphere. *J. Sci. Hiroshima Univ. Ser. A* **20**, *149–56.* [439]

KORGKEGI, R. H. (1956). Transition studies and skin-friction measurements on an insulated flat plate at a Mach number of 5·8. *J. aero. Sci.* **23**, *97–107.* [623]

KOVÁSZNAY, L. S. G. (1948). Laminar flow behind a two-dimensional grid. *Proc. Camb. phil. Soc.* **44**, *58–62.* [139]

KOVÁSZNAY, L. S. G. (1949). Hot wire investigation of the wake behind cylinders at low Reynolds numbers. *Proc. Roy. Soc. A* **198**, *174–90.* [562]

KOVÁSZNAY, L. S. G. (1954). Development of turbulence-measuring equipment. *Rep. nat. adv. Comm. Aero., Wash.* No. *1209.* [608]

LEES, L., and LIN, C. C. (1946). Investigation of the stability of the laminar boundary layer in a compressible fluid. *Tech. Notes nat. adv. Comm. Aero., Wash.* No. *1115.* [494]

LEGENDRE, R. (1956). Séparation de l'écoulement laminaire tridimensionnel. *Rech. aéro.* No. *54, 3–8.* [73]

LEIBENSON, L. S. (1935). The energy form of the integral condition in the theory of the boundary layer. *Dokl. Ak. Nauk S.S.S.R.* **2**, *22–24.* [206, 308]

LEIGH, D. C. *See* Emmons and Leigh (1953).

LEIGH, D. C. (1955). The laminar boundary-layer equation: a method of solution by means of an automatic computer. *Proc. Camb. phil. Soc.* **51**, *320–32.* [219, 265, 283]

LEITE, R. J. (1959). An experimental investigation of the stability of Poiseuille flow. *J. Fluid Mech.* **5**, *81–96.* [539]

LESSEN, M. (1949). On the stability of the free laminar boundary layer between parallel streams. *Rep. nat. adv. Comm. Aero., Wash.* No. *979.* [252, 558, 559]

LESSEN, M. *See* Fox and Lessen (1955).

LETKO, W. *See* Russell, Gracey, Letko, and Fournier (1951).

LEUTERITZ, R., and MANGLER, W. (1945). Die symmetrische Potentialströmung gegen einen Kreiskegel. *Untersuch. Mitt. dtsch. Luftfahrtf.* No. *3226.* [429]

LEVI-CIVITA, T. (1929). Allgemeine Folgerungen aus der Prandtlschen Grenzschicht-theorie. *Vorträge aus dem Gebiete der Aerodynamik und verwandter Gebiete, Aachen* (Editors: Gilles, A., Hopf, L., and Kármán, Th. v.), Springer, Berlin. *30–50.* [411]

LEVI-CIVITA, T. *See* Kármán (1924).

LEVINE, D. A. *See* Tetervin and Levine (1952).

LEVINE, H. (1957). Skin friction on a strip of finite width moving parallel to its length. *J. Fluid Mech.* **3**, *145–58.* [366]

LEVINSON, N. *See* Coddington and Levinson (1955).

LEW, H. G., and FANUCCI, J. B. (1954). The stability of two-dimensional jets by the variational and Galerkin methods, Part V, Hydrodynamic stability. *Rep. Dept. aero. Engng, Penn. State Univ.* No. 2. [562]

LEWIS, B. *See* Kovásznay (1955).

LEWIS, J. A., and CARRIER, G. F. (1949). Some remarks on the flat plate boundary layer. *Quart. appl. Math.* **7**, *228–34.* [181, 241]

LEWIS, J. W. (1928). An experimental study of the motion of a viscous liquid contained between two coaxial cylinders. *Proc. Roy. Soc.* A **117**, *388–407.* [501]

LIBBY, P. A., KAUFMAN, L., and HARRINGTON, R. P. (1952). An experimental investigation of the isothermal laminar boundary layer on a porous flat plate. *J. aero. Sci.* **19**, *127–34.* [345]

LIEPMANN, H. W. (1943). Investigations on laminar boundary-layer stability and transition on curved boundaries. *Wartime Rep. nat. adv. Comm. Aero., Wash.* W107 (*ACR3H30*). [505]

LIEPMANN, H. W. (1945). Investigation of boundary layer transition on concave walls. *Wartime Rep. nat. adv. Comm. Aero., Wash.* W87 (*ACR4J28*). [505, 544]

LIEPMANN, H. W., and SKINNÉR, G. T. (1954). Shearing-stress measurements by use of a heated element. *Tech. Notes. nat. adv. Comm. Aero., Wash.* No. *3268.* [625]

LIFSHITZ, E. M. *See* Landau and Lifshitz (1959).

LIGHTHILL, M. J. (1952). On the squirming motion of nearly spherical deformable bodies through liquids at very small Reynolds numbers. *Commun. pure appl. Math.* **5**, *109–18.* [174]

LIGHTHILL, M. J. (1954). The response of laminar skin friction and heat transfer to fluctuations in the stream velocity. *Proc. Roy. Soc.* A **224**, *1–23.* [394, 395, 396, 397, 401, 406]

LIGHTHILL, M. J. (1956a). Viscosity effects in sound waves of finite amplitude. *Surveys in Mechanics* (Editors: Batchelor, G. K., and Davies, R. M.), *250–351.* Cambridge University Press. [15, 18, 19]

LIGHTHILL, M. J. (1956b). The image system of a vortex element in a rigid sphere. *Proc. Camb. phil. Soc.* **52**, *317–21.* [56]

LIGHTHILL, M. J. (1958). On displacement thickness. *J. Fluid Mech.* **4**, *383–92.* [61, 85, 478]

LIGHTHILL, M. J. *See* Glauert and Lighthill (1955).

LIN, C. C. (1945). On the stability of two-dimensional parallel flows. *Quart. appl. Math.* **3**, *117–42, 218–34, 277–301*. [90, 93, 339, 519, 520, 521, 524, 525, 527, 528, 529, 530, 531, 533, 542, 543]

LIN, C. C. (1953). On the stability of the laminar mixing region between two parallel streams in a gas. *Tech. Notes nat. adv. Comm. Aero., Wash.* No. *2887*. [560]

LIN, C. C. (1954a). Hydrodynamic stability. *Proc. 5th Symp. appl. Math. 1–18.* [521]

LIN, C. C. (1954b). Some physical aspects of the stability of parallel flows. *Proc. nat. Acad. Sci., Wash.* **40**, *741–7*. [93, 519]

LIN, C. C. (1955). The theory of hydrodynamic stability. Cambridge University Press. [91, 94, 494, 495, 501, 504, 518, 519, 520, 521, 522, 524, 525, 527, 529, 532]

LIN, C. C. (1956a). Motion in the boundary-layer with a rapidly oscillating external flow. *Proc. 9th int. Congr. appl. Mech., Brussels,* **4**, *155–67*. [396]

LIN, C. C. (1956b). On uniformly valid asymptotic solutions of the Orr-Sommerfeld equation. *Proc. 9th int. Congr. appl. Mech., Brussels,* **1**, *136–48.* [521]

LIN, C. C. (1958a). Note on a class of exact solutions in magneto-hydrodynamics. *Arch. rat. Mech. Anal.* **1**, *391–5.* [356, 357, 359]

LIN, C. C. (1958b). On the instability of laminar flow and its transition to turbulence. *Proc. Symp. boundary layer Res., Int. Union theoret. appl. Mech. Freiburg i. Br.* (1957), *144–60.* [521]

LIN, C. C. *See* Carrier and Lin (1948); Dunn and Lin (1955); Foote and Lin (1950); Kármán and Lin (1955); Lees and Lin (1946).

LING, S. C., and HUBBARD, P. G. (1956). The hot-film anemometer: a new device for fluid mechanics research. *J. aero. Sci.* **23**, *890–1.* [608]

LIVESEY, J. L. (1956). The behaviour of transverse cylindrical and forward facing total-pressure probes in transverse total-pressure gradients. *J. aero. Sci.* **23**, *949–55.* [621]

LOCK, R. C. (1951). The velocity distribution in the laminar boundary layer between parallel streams. *Quart. J. Mech.* **4**, *42–63.* [252]

LOCK, R. C. (1954). Hydrodynamic stability of the flow in the boundary layer between parallel streams. *Proc. Camb. phil. Soc.* **50**, *105–24.* [525, 528, 548]

LOCK, R. C. (1955). The stability of the flow of an electrically-conducting fluid between parallel planes under a transverse magnetic field. *Proc. Roy. Soc.* A **233**, *105–25.* [525, 530, 540, 545]

LOFTIN, L. K. *See* Bursnall and Loftin (1951).

LOITSIANSKII, L. G. (1949). *Prikl. Mat. Mekh.* **13**, *513–24* (in Russian). (Translated as 'Approximate method of integration of laminar boundary layer in incompressible fluid', *Tech. Memor. nat. adv. Comm. Aero., Wash.* No. *1293*.) [317, 331]

LOITSIANSKII, L. G. (1953). Propagation of a whirling jet in an infinite space filled with the same fluid. *Prikl. Mat. Mekh.* **17**, *3–16* (in Russian). [452]

LOITSIANSKII, L. G., and BOLSHAKOV, V. P. (1951). On motion of fluid in boundary layer near line of intersection of two planes. *Tech. Memor. nat. adv. Comm. Aero., Wash.* No. *1308.* [488]

LONG, J. D. *See* Hama, Long, and Hegarty (1957).

LONGHORN, A. L. (1952). The unsteady, subsonic motion of a sphere in a compressible inviscid fluid. *Quart. J. Mech.* **5**, *64–81.* [13]

LONGUET-HIGGINS, M. S. (1953). Mass transport in water waves. *Phil. Trans.* A **245**, *535–81.* [388]

LOOS, H. G. (1955). A simple laminar boundary layer with secondary flow. *J. aero. Sci.* **22**, *35–40.* [457]

LORENTZ, H. A. (1896a). A general theorem concerning the motion of a viscous fluid and a few consequences derived from it. *Collected Papers,* **4**, *7–14.* Martinus Nijhoff, The Hague (1937). Revised German version in *Abhandlungen über theoretische Physik,* **1**, *23–42.* Teubner, Leipzig and Berlin. (1907.) [182]

LORENTZ, H. A. (1896b). On the resistance experienced by a flow of liquid in a cylindrical tube. *Collected Papers,* **4**, *15–35.* Martinus Nijhoff, The Hague (1937). Revised German version in *Abhandlungen über theoretische Physik,* **1**, *43–71.* Teubner, Leipzig and Berlin (1907). [516, 518]

Love, A. E. H. (1927). *Treatise on the mathematical theory of elasticity.* Cambridge University Press. [129, 131, 135]

Low, A. R. (1929). On the criterion for stability for a layer of fluid heated from below. *Proc. Roy. Soc.* A **125**, *180–95.* [510]

Luckert, H.-J. (1934). Über die Integration der Differentialgleichung einer Gleitschicht in zäher Flüssigkeit. *Schr. Inst. angew. Math. Univ., Berl.* **1**, *245–74.* [281]

Ludwieg, H. (1949). Ein Gerät zur Messung der Wandschubspannung turbulenter Reibungsschichten. *Ingen.-Arch.* **17**, *207–18.* (Translated as 'Instrument for measuring the wall shearing stress of turbulent boundary layers'. *Tech. Memor. nat. adv. Comm. Aero., Wash.* No. *1284.*) [625]

Ludwieg, H., and Tillmann, W. (1949). Untersuchungen über die Wandschubspannung in turbulenten Reibungsschichten. *Ingen.-Arch.* **17**, *288–99.* (Translated as 'Investigations of the wall-shearing stress in turbulent boundary layers'. *Tech. Memor. nat. adv. Comm. Aero., Wash.* No. *1285.*) [625]

Lyttleton, R. A. (1953). *The stability of rotating liquid masses.* Cambridge University Press. [498]

Maas, J. N. *See* Young and Maas (1936).

McAdams, W. H. (1951). *Heat transmission*, 2nd edition. McGraw-Hill, London. [194]

McKee, P. B. *See* Kuethe, McKee, and Curry (1949).

McKoen, C. H. (1955). Stability of laminar wakes. *Curr. Pap. aero. Res. Coun., Lond.* No. *303.* [560]

MacMillan, F. A. (1954a). Viscous effects on pitot tubes at low speeds. *J. R. aero. Soc.* **58**, *570–2.* [594, 595]

MacMillan, F. A. (1954b). Liquid manometers with high sensitivity and small time-lag. *J. sci. Instrum.* **31**, *17–20.* [602, 603]

MacMillan, F. A. (1954c). Viscous effects on flattened pitot tubes at low speeds. *J. R. aero. Soc.* **58**, *837–9.* [620]

MacMillan, F. A. (1956). Experiments on pitot tubes in shear flow. *Rep. Memor. aero. Res. Coun., Lond.* No. *3028.* [621]

Mager, A. (1951). Generalisation of boundary layer momentum integral equations to three-dimensional flow including those of rotating system. *Tech. Notes nat. adv. Comm. Aero., Wash.* No. *2310.* [483]

Mager, A. (1954). Three-dimensional laminar boundary layer with small cross flow. *J. aero. Sci.* **21**, *835–45.* [480]

Mager, A., and Hansen, A. G. (1952). Laminar boundary layer over flat plate in a flow having circular streamlines. *Tech. Notes nat. adv. Comm. Aero., Wash.* No. *2658.* [459]

Main-Smith, J. D. (1950). Chemical solids as diffusible coating films for visual indications of boundary-layer transition in air and water. *Rep. Memor. aero. Res. Coun., Lond.* No. *2755.* [613]

Malkus, W. V. R. (1954a). Discrete transitions in turbulent convection. *Proc. Roy. Soc.* A **225**, *185–95.* [511, 572]

Malkus, W. V. R. (1954b). The heat transport and spectrum of thermal turbulence. *Proc. Roy. Soc.* A **225**, *196–212.* [572]

Malkus, W. V. R., and Veronis, G. (1958). Finite-amplitude cellular convection. *J. Fluid Mech.* **4**, *225–60.* [508, 565]

Mallick, D. D. (1957). Non-uniform rotation of an infinite circular cylinder in an infinite viscous liquid. *Z. angew. Math. Mech.* **37**, *385–92.* [359]

Mangler, K. W., and Smith, J. H. B. (1959). A theory of the flow past a slender delta wing with leading edge separation. *Proc. Roy. Soc.* A **251**, *200–17.* [81]

Mangler, W. (1941). Die allgemeine Lösung der Prandtlschen Grenzschichtgleichungen. *Ber. Lilienthal-Ges. Luftfahrtf.* No. *141*, *3–7.* (Translated as 'General solution of Prandtl's boundary-layer equation'. *Tech. Memor. nat. adv. Comm. Aero., Wash.* No. *1278.*) [274]

Mangler, W. (1943). Die 'ähnlichen' Lösungen der Prandtlschen Grenzschichtgleichungen. *Z. angew. Math. Mech.* **23**, *241–51.* [244]

MANGLER, W. (1944a). Laminare Grenzschicht mit Absaugen und Ausblasen. *Untersuch. Mitt. dtsch. Luftfahrtf. 3087.* [244, 249]

MANGLER, W. (1944b). Das Impulsverfahren zur näherungsweisen Berechnung der laminaren Reibungsschicht. *Z. angew. Math. Mech.* **24**, *251–6.* [297]

MANGLER, W. (1945). Boundary layers on bodies of revolution in symmetrical flow. *Ber. aerodyn. VersAnst. Göttingen 45/A/17.* [418, 426, 428]

MANGLER, W. (1948a). Special exact solutions, Section 1.2 of Boundary Layers (Editor: Tollmien, W.). *Monogr. aerodyn. VersAnst. Göttingen B.* See also unpublished translation, Min. Aviation, London. [251, 429, 430]

MANGLER, W. (1948b). Approximate methods, Section 1.3 of Boundary Layers (Editor: Tollmien, W.). *Monogr. aerodyn. VersAnst. Göttingen B.* See also unpublished translation, Min. Aviation, London. [337]

MANGLER, W. (1948c). Zusammenhang zwischen ebenen und rotations-symmetrischen Grenzschichten in kompressiblen Flüssigkeiten. *Z. angew. Math. Mech.* **28**, *97–103.* [426]

MANGLER, W. See Leuteritz and Mangler (1945).

MARCHALL, W. S. D. See Elmslie, Hosking, and Marchall (1953).

MARSHALL, D. See Stanton, Marshall, and Bryant (1920).

MARTIN, H. (1925). Über Tonhöhe und Dämpfung der Schwingungen von Saiten in verschiedenen Flüssigkeiten. *Ann. Phys., Lpz.* (4), **77**, *627–57.* [392]

MASKELL, E. C. (1955). Flow separation in three dimensions. *Rep. aero. Res. Coun., Lond.* No. *18063.* [79, 480, 488, 611]

MASLEN, S. H., and MOORE, F. K. (1956). On strong transverse waves without shocks in a circular cylinder. *J. aero. Sci.* **23**, *583–93.* [388]

MAYER, J. E., and MAYER, M. G. (1940). *Statistical mechanics.* Wiley, New York. [6, 24]

MAYER, M. G. See Mayer and Mayer (1940).

MEIJER DREES, J., and HENDAL, W. P. (1951). The field of flow through a helicopter rotor, obtained from wind tunnel smoke tests. *Rep. nat. LuchtvLab., Amsterdam* No. *1205.* See also *Aircr. Engng*, **23**, *107–11.* [609]

MEKSYN, D. (1946a). Fluid motion between parallel planes. Dynamical stability. *Proc. Roy. Soc.* A **186**, *391–409.* [521]

MEKSYN, D. (1946b). Stability of viscous flow between rotating cylinders. *Proc. Roy. Soc* A **187**, *115–28, 480–91, 492–504.* [498, 501, 511]

MEKSYN, D. (1947). Asymptotic integrals of a fourth order differential equation containing a large parameter. *Proc. Lond. math. Soc.* (2), **49**, *436–57.* [521]

MEKSYN, D. (1948a). The laminar boundary-layer equations. I. Motion of an elliptic and circular cylinders. *Proc. Roy. Soc.* A **192**, *545–67.* [288]

MEKSYN, D. (1948b). Note on stability of laminar viscous flow between parallel planes. *Proc. Roy. Soc.* A **195**, *174–9.* [521]

MEKSYN, D. (1950a). Integration of the laminar boundary layer equation. I. Motion of an elliptic cylinder. Separation. *Proc. Roy. Soc.* A **201**, *268–78.* [289]

MEKSYN, D. (1950b). Integration of the laminar boundary layer equation. II. Retarded flow along a semi-infinite plane. *Proc. Roy. Soc.* A **201**, *279–83.* [289]

MEKSYN, D. (1950c). Stability of viscous flow over concave cylindrical surfaces. *Proc. Roy. Soc.* A **203**, *253–65.* [504]

MEKSYN, D. (1951). Motion in the wake of a thin plate at zero incidence. *Proc. Roy. Soc.* A **207**, *370–80.* [289]

MEKSYN, D. (1956). Integration of the boundary layer equations. *Proc. Roy. Soc.* A **237**, *543–59.* [290, 291]

MEKSYN, D. (1958). The boundary layer equations of compressible flow. Separation. *Z. angew. Math. Mech.* **38**, *372–9.* [292]

MEKSYN, D. (1961). *New methods in laminar boundary-layer theory.* Pergamon Press, Oxford. [288]

MEKSYN, D., and STUART, J. T. (1951). Stability of viscous motion between parallel planes for finite disturbances. *Proc. Roy. Soc.* A **208**, *517–26.* [565, 566, 567]

MEREDITH, F. W. See Griffith and Meredith (1936).

MERK, H. J. (1958). Analysis of heat-driven oscillations of gas flows. I. On the mechanism of the Rijke-tube phenomenon. *Appl. sci. Res., A. Hague* A **6**, *402–20.* [408]

MEYER, O. E. (1899). *The kinetic theory of gases.* Longmans, Green & Co., London. [7, 14, 15]

MICHAEL, D. H. (1953). Stability of plane parallel flows of electrically-conducting fluids. *Proc. Camb. phil. Soc.* **49**, *166–8.* [540]

MICHAEL, D. H. (1954). The stability of an incompressible electrically-conducting fluid rotating about an axis when the current flows parallel to the axis. *Mathematika,* **1**, *45–50.* [495]

MICHAEL, D. H. (1961). Note on the stability of plane parallel flows. *J. Fluid Mech.* **10**, *525–8.* [515]

MICHAL, A. D. (1947). *Matrix and tensor calculus.* Wiley, New York. [411]

MICHEL, R. *See* Eichelbrenner and Michel (1958).

MILES, J. W. (1951). On virtual mass and transient motion in subsonic compressible flow. *Quart. J. Mech.* **4**, *388–400.* [13]

MILLER, J. C. P. (Editor) (1955). *Tables of Weber parabolic cylinder functions.* Her Majesty's Stationery Office, London. [256]

MILLIKAN, C. B. (1932). The boundary layer and skin friction for a figure of revolution. *Trans. Amer. Soc. mech. Engrs (Appl. Mech. Sect.),* **54**, *29–43.* [109, 417]

MILLIKAN, C. B., and KLEIN, A. L. (1933). The effect of turbulence. *Aircr. Engng* **5**, *167–74.* [107]

MILLIKAN, C. B. *See* Kármán and Millikan (1934).

MILLIKAN, R. A. (1947). *Electrons (+ and –), protons, photons, neutrons, mesotrons, and cosmic rays.* Revised edition. University of Chicago Press, Chicago. [166]

MILLSAPS, K., and POHLHAUSEN, K. (1953). Thermal distributions in Jeffery-Hamel flows between non-parallel plane walls. *J. aero. Sci.* **20**, *187–96.* [144, 146, 150]

MILVERTON, S. W. *See* Schmidt and Milverton (1935).

MISES, R. v. (1927). Bemerkungen zur Hydrodynamik. *Z. angew. Math. Mech.* **7**, *425–31.* [212]

MITCHELL, A. R., and THOMSON, J. Y. (1958). Finite difference methods of solution of the von Mises boundary layer equation with special reference to conditions near a singularity. *Z. angew. Math. Phys.* **9**, *26–37.* [213, 285]

MOCK, W. C. *See* Dryden, Schubauer, Mock, and Skramstad (1937).

MÖLLER, W. (1938). Experimentelle Untersuchungen zur Hydrodynamik der Kugel. *Phys. Z.* **39**, *57–80.* [105]

MOORE, F. K. (1951). Unsteady laminar boundary-layer flow. *Tech. Notes nat. adv. Comm. Aero., Wash.* No. 2471. [362, 397, 402]

MOORE, F. K. (1953). Displacement effect of a three-dimensional boundary layer. *Rep. nat. adv. Comm. Aero., Wash.* No. 1124. [478]

MOORE, F. K. (1955). Lift hysteresis at stall as an unsteady boundary-layer pheno-menon. *Rep. nat. adv. Comm. Aero., Wash.* No. 1291. [388]

MOORE, F. K. (1956). Three-dimensional boundary-layer theory. *Advanc. appl. Mech.* **4**, *159–228.* Academic Press, New York. [485, 490, 553]

MOORE, F. K. (1957a). The unsteady laminar boundary-layer of a wedge, and a related three-dimensional problem. *Heat Transf. Fluid Mech. Inst.* (1957). [397]

MOORE, F. K. (1957b). On the separation of the unsteady laminar boundary layer. *Proc. Symp. boundary layer Res., Int. Union theoret. appl. Mech. Freiburg i. Br.* (1957), *296–311.* [397, 400]

MOORE, F. K. (1957c). Aerodynamic effects of boundary-layer unsteadiness. *Proc. 6th anglo-amer. aero. Conf. R. aero. Soc., Folkestone, 439–71.* [397, 400]

MOORE, F. K., and OSTRACH, S. (1957). Average properties of compressible boundary layer on flat plate with unsteady flight velocity. *Rep. nat. adv. Comm. Aero., Wash.* No. 1325. [396, 397, 408]

MOORE, F. K. *See* Lagerstrom (to be published); Maslen and Moore (1956).

MORAWETZ, C. S. (1952). The eigenvalues of some stability problems involving viscosity. *J. rat. Mech. Anal., Indiana Univ.* **1**, *579–603.* [538]

MORGAN, A. J. A. (1952). The reduction by one of the number of independent variables in some systems of partial differential equations. *Quart. J. Math.* (2), **3**, *250–9.* [143]

MORGAN, A. J. A. (1956). On a class of laminar viscous flows within one or two bounding cones. *Aeronaut. Quart.* **7**, *225.* [152]

MORKOVIN, M. V. (1958). Transition from laminar to turbulent flow—a review of some advances in its understanding. *Trans. Amer. Soc. mech. Engrs*, **80**, *1121-8*. [578]

MORRIS, R. M. (1937). Two-dimensional potential problems. *Proc. Camb. phil. Soc.* **33**, *474-84*. [367]

MORTON, B. R. (1957). On the equilibrium of a stratified layer of fluid. *Quart. J. Mech.* **10**, *433-47*. [506-11]

MURNAGHAN, F. D. *See* Dryden, Murnaghan, and Bateman (1932).

MURPHY, J. S., and SMITH, A. M. O. (1956). Measurement of shearing stress by means of an evaporating liquid film. *J. appl. Phys.* **27**, *1097-1103*. [625]

MURPHY, J. S. *See* Smith and Murphy (1955a), (1955b).

MURPHY, J. W. *See* Savic and Murphy (1943).

NARASIMHA, R. (1957). On the distribution of intermittency in the transition region of a boundary layer. *J. Aero. Sci.* **24**, *711-12*. [577]

NARASIMHA, R. *See* Dhawan and Narasimha (1958).

NAVIER, C. L. M. H. (1823). Mémoire sur les lois du mouvement des fluides. *Mém. Acad. R. Sci., Paris*, **6**, *389-416*. [121]

NIBLETT, E. R. (1958). The stability of Couette flow in an axial magnetic field. *Canad. J. Phys.* **36**, *1509-25*. [495]

NIELSEN, J. N. (1956). Tables of characteristic functions for solving boundary-value problems of the wave equation with application to supersonic interference. *Tech. Notes nat. adv. Comm. Aero., Wash. No. 3873*. [367]

NIGAM, S. D. (1951). Rotation of an infinite plane: laminar boundary-layer growth: motion started impulsively from rest. *Quart. appl. Math.* **9**, *89-91*. [381]

NIGAM, S. D. (1954). Note on the boundary layer on a rotating sphere. *Z. angew. Math. Phys.* **5**, *151-5*. [438]

NIGAM, S. D., and RANGASAMI, K. S. I. (1953). Growth of boundary layer on a rotating sphere. *Z. angew. Math. Phys.* **4**, *221-3*. [381]

NISSAN, A. H. *See* Brewster, Grosberg, and Nissan (1959); Brewster and Nissan (1958).

NOETHER, F. (1931). *Handbuch der physikalischen und technischen Mechanik*, **5**, *733-6*. J. A. Barch, Leipzig. [144]

NYBORG, W. L. (1953a). Acoustic streaming due to attenuated plane waves. *J. acoust. Soc. Amer.* **25**, *68-75*. [388]

NYBORG, W. L. (1953b). Acoustic streaming equations: laws of rotational motion for fluid elements. *J. acoust. Soc. Amer.* **25**, *938-44*. [388]

OBERBECK, A. (1876). Über stationäre Flüssigkeitsbewegungen mit Berücksichtigung der inneren Reibung. *J. reine angew. Math.* **81**, *62-80*. [171]

OLSSON, O., and FAXÉN, H. (1927). Laminare Bewegung zäher Flüssigkeit in logarithmischen Spiralen. *Z. angew. Math. Mech.* **7**, *496-8*. [150]

ORMEROD, A. O. *See* Owen and Ormerod (1951).

ORR, W. M. F. (1907). The stability or instability of the steady motions of a liquid. *Proc. R. Irish Acad. A* **27**, *9-27, 69-138*. [516, 518]

OSEEN, C. W. (1910). Über die Stokessche Formel und über eine verwandte Aufgabe in der Hydrodynamik. *Ark. Mat. Astr. Fys.* **6**, No. *29*. [175]

OSEEN, C. W. (1927a). *Hydrodynamik*. Akad. Verlag, Leipzig. [4, 166, 181, 182]

OSEEN, C. W. (1927b). Exakte Lösungen der hydrodynamischen Differentialgleichungen. I. *Ark. Mat. Astr. Fys.* **20A**, No. *14*. [150]

OSTERLE, J. F. *See* Rouleau and Osterle (1955).

OSTRACH, S. (1954). Note on the aerodynamic heating of an oscillating surface. *Tech. Notes nat. adv. Comm. Aero., Wash. No. 3146*. [382]

OSTRACH, S. (1955a). On the flow, heat transfer and stability of viscous fluids subject to body forces and heated from below in vertical channels. *50 Jahre Grenzschicht-forschung* (Editors: Görtler, H., and Tollmien, W.), Vieweg, Braunschweig. *226-35*. [511]

OSTRACH, S. (1955b). Unstable convection in vertical channels with heating from below, including effects of heat sources and frictional heating. *Tech. Notes nat. adv. Comm. Aero., Wash. No. 3458*. [511]

OSTRACH, S. *See* Moore and Ostrach (1957).

OSTROUMOV, G. A. (1952). *Moscow and Leningrad: State Publ. House, Tech.-Theor. Lit.* (in Russian). (Translated as 'Free convection under the conditions of the internal problem'. *Tech. Memor. nat. adv. Comm. Aero., Wash.* No. *1407.*) [512]

OUDART, A. (1953). Mise en régime de la couche limite de la plaque plane dans l'impulsion brusque à partir du repos. *Rech. aéro.* No. *31, 7–12.* See also *Proc. 8th int. Congr. appl. Mech., Istanbul* (1952), *285–6.* [362]

OUDART, A. *See* Eichelbrenner and Oudart (1954), (1955).

OWEN, P. R., and KLANFER, L. (1955). On the laminar boundary layer separation from the leading edge of a thin aerofoil. *Curr. Pap. aero. Res. Coun., Lond.* No. *220.* [112]

OWEN, P. R., and ORMEROD, A. O. (1951). Evaporation from the surface of a body in an airstream (with particular reference to the chemical method of indicating boundary-layer transition). *Rep. Memor. aero. Res. Coun., Lond.* No. *2875.* [20, 613]

OWEN, P. R., and RANDALL, D. G. Unpublished Min. Aviation work. [551, 554, 555]

OWER, E. (1949). *The measurement of air flow.* 3rd edition. Chapman and Hall, London. [601]

PANKHURST, R. C. (1955). Some recent British work on boundary-layer control. *Proc. Symp. boundary layer effects Aerodyn., nat. phys. Lab.* [547]

PANKHURST, R. C., and HOLDER, D. W. (1952). *Wind-tunnel technique.* Pitman, London. [38, 111]

PANKHURST, R. C. *See* Relf, Pankhurst, and Walker (1954).

PANNELL, J. R. (1913). Experiments with a tilting manometer for measurement of small pressure differences. *Engineering, Lond.* **96**, *343–4.* [601]

PAYNE, R. B. (1956). A numerical method for calculating the starting and perturbation of a two-dimensional jet at low Reynolds number. *Rep. Memor. aero. Res. Coun., Lond.* No. *3047.* [57, 59]

PAYNE, R. B. (1958). Calculations of unsteady viscous flow past a circular cylinder. *J. Fluid Mech.* **4**, *81–86.* [57, 59, 376]

PEARCEY, H. H. *See* Haines, Holder, and Pearcey (1954).

PEARSON, J. R. A. (1958). On convection cells induced by surface tension. *J. Fluid Mech.* **4**, *489–500.* [506]

PEARSON, J. R. A. *See* Proudman and Pearson (1957).

PEASE, R. N. *See* Kovásznay (1955).

PEEBLES, F. N., GARBER, H. J., and JURY, S. H. (1953). Preliminary studies of flow phenomena utilizing a doubly refractive liquid. *Proc. 3rd midwest Conf. Fluid Mech. University of Minnesota, 441–50.* [611]

PELLEW, A., and SOUTHWELL, R. V. (1940). On maintained convective motion in a fluid heated from below. *Proc. Roy. Soc.* A **176**, *312–43.* [498, 499, 507, 509, 510, 511]

PERKINS, E. W. *See* Allen and Perkins (1951).

PFENNINGER, W. (1943). Vergleich der Impulsemethode mit der Wägung bei Profilwiderstandsmessungen. *Mitt. Inst. Aerodyn., Zürich* No. *8.* [616, 627]

PFENNINGER, W. (1958). Contribution to discussion on 'Stability of Laminar Flow'. *Proc. Symp. boundary layer Res., Int. Union theoret. appl. Mech. Freiburg i. Br.* (1957), *179–80.* [553, 555]

PHILLIPS, A. C., and WALKER, G. T. (1932). The forms of stratified clouds. *Quart. J. R. met. Soc.* **58**, *23–30.* [511]

PHILLIPS, O. M. (1956). The intensity of Aeolian tones. *J. Fluid Mech.* **1**, *607–24.* [105]

PIERCY, N. A. V., and PRESTON, J. H. (1936). A simple solution of the flat plate problem of skin friction and heat transfer. *Phil. Mag.* (7), **21**, *995–1005.* [272]

PIERCY, N. A. V., PRESTON, J. H., and WHITEHEAD, L. G. (1938). The approximate prediction of skin-friction and lift. *Phil. Mag.* (7), **26**, *791–815.* [273]

PIERCY, N. A. V., and RICHARDSON, E. G. (1928). The variation of velocity amplitude close to the surface of a cylinder moving through a viscous fluid. *Phil. Mag.* (7), **6**, *970–7.* [506]

PIERCY, N. A. V., and RICHARDSON, E. G. (1930). The turbulence in front of a body moving through a viscous fluid. *Phil. Mag.* (7), **9**, *1038–41.* [506]

PIERCY, N. A. V., and WHITEHEAD, L. G. (1949). Boundary layer calculations. *Aircr. Engng*, **21**, *17–19*. [276, 277]

PIERCY, N. A. V., WHITEHEAD, L. G., and TYLER, R. A. (1948). The laminar boundary layer. *Aircr. Engng*, **20**, *354–9*. [276]

PIERCY, N. A. V., and WINNY, H. F. (1933). The skin friction of flat plates to Oseen's approximation. *Proc. Roy. Soc.* A **140**, *543–61*. [183]

PILLOW, A. F. (1952). The free convection cell in two dimensions. *Rep. aero. Res. Lab.*, *Melbourne A79*. [565, 572]

PLESSET, M. S. (1957). Physical effects in cavitation and boiling. *Proc. 1st Symp. nav. Hydr.*, *Wash. 297–318*. [25, 27]

POHLHAUSEN, K. (1921). Zur näherungsweisen Integration der Differentialgleichung der laminaren Grenzschicht. *Z. angew. Math. Mech.* **1**, *252–68*. [206, 236, 251, 292, 294, 331]

POHLHAUSEN, K. See Millsaps and Pohlhausen (1953).

POISEUILLE, J. L. M. (1840). Recherches expérimentales sur le mouvement des liquides dans les tubes de tres petits diamètres. *C.R. Acad. Sci.*, *Paris*, **11**, *961–7*; **11**, *1041–8*; **12**, *112–15*. [3]

POISSON, S. D. (1831). Mémoire sur les équations générales de l'équilibre et du mouvement du corps solides élastiques et des fluides. *J. Éc. polyt.*, *Paris*, **13**, *139–66*. [121]

PRANDTL, L. (1904). Über Flüssigkeitsbewegung bei sehr kleiner Reibung. *Verh. III. int. Math. Kongr.*, *Heidelberg*, *1904*. Teubner, Leipzig. (Also available in German in *Vier Abhandlungen zur Hydrodynamik und Aerodynamik*, Prandtl, L., and Betz, A. (1927), Göttingen, and in English as 'Motion of fluids with very little viscosity'. *Tech. Memor. nat. adv. Comm. Aero.*, *Wash.* No. *452*.) [14, 46, 200]

PRANDTL, L. (1914). Der Widerstand von Kugeln. *Nachr. Ges. Wiss. Göttingen*, *Math.-phys. Kl. 177–90*. [47, 89]

PRANDTL, L. (1927). The generation of vortices in fluids of small viscosity. *J. R. aero. Soc.* **31**, *720–40*. [47]

PRANDTL, L. (1929). Einfluss stabilisierender Kräfte auf die Turbulenz. *Vorträge aus dem Gebiete der Aerodynamik und verwandter Gebiete*, *Aachen* (Editors: Gilles, A., Hopf, L., and Kármán, Th. v.), *1–17*. Springer, Berlin. [548]

PRANDTL, L. (1935). The mechanics of viscous fluids. Division Of, *Aerodynamic Theory* (Editor: Durand, W. F.), **3**, *34–208*. Springer, Berlin. [1, 339, 517, 627]

PRANDTL, L. (1938). Zur Berechnung der Grenzschichten. *Z. angew. Math. Mech.* **18**, *77–82*. (Translated as 'Note on the calculation of boundary layers', *Tech. Memor. nat. adv. Comm. Aero.*, *Wash.* No. *959*.) [211, 282]

PRANDTL, L. (1946). On boundary layers in three-dimensional flow. *Rep. aero. Res. Coun.*, *Lond.* No. *9828*. See also *Betz Festschr.*, *Göttingen* (1945). [410, 467]

PRANDTL, L. (1952). *Essentials of fluid dynamics*. (Translated by W. M. Deans.) Blackie, London. [1, 26, 44, 225]

PRANDTL, L., and BETZ, A. See Prandtl (1904).

PRANDTL, L., and REICHARDT, H. (1934). Einfluss von Wärmeschichtung auf die Eigenschaften einer turbulenten Strömung. *Dtsch. Forsch.* **21**, *110–21*. [549]

PRANDTL, L., and TIETJENS, O. G. (1934a). *Fundamentals of Hydro- and Aeromechanics*. McGraw-Hill, New York. [44]

PRANDTL, L., and TIETJENS, O. G. (1934b). *Applied Hydro- and Aeromechanics*. McGraw-Hill, New York. [442, 627]

PRANDTL, L., WIESELSBERGER, C., and BETZ, A. (1923). Der Widerstand von Zylindern. *Ergebn. aerodyn. VersAnst. Göttingen*, **2**, *23–28*. [106]

PRESTON, J. H. (1946). The boundary-layer flow over a permeable surface through which suction is applied. *Rep. Memor. aero. Res. Coun.*, *Lond.* No. *2244*. [242, 339, 344]

PRESTON, J. H. (1950a). The steady circulatory flow about a circular cylinder with uniformly distributed suction at the surface. *Aeronaut. Quart.* **1**, *319–38*. [142]

PRESTON, J. H. (1950b). Non-steady flows under asymptotic suction conditions. *Quart. J. Mech.* **3**, *435–45*. [See pp. 397–401]

PRESTON, J. H. (1950c). The 'three-quarter radius pitot tube' type of flow meter. *Engineer*, *Lond.* **190**, *400–2*. [593]

PRESTON, J. H. (1951). Simple method of comparing manometers. *Engineering, Lond.* **172, 645 6.** [604]

PRESTON, J. H. (1954). The determination of turbulent skin friction by means of pitot tubes. *J. R. aero. Soc.* **58, 109-21.** [624]

PRESTON, J. H., and SWEETING, N. E. (1943). An improved smoke generator for use in the visualization of airflow, particularly boundary-layer flow at high Reynolds numbers. *Rep. Memor. aero. Res. Coun., Lond.* No. *2023.* [609]

PRESTON, J. H., and SWEETING, N. E. (1945). Experiments on the measurement of transition position by chemical methods. *Rep. Memor. aero. Res. Coun., Lond.* No. *2014.* [612]

PRESTON, J. H. *See* Piercy and Preston (1936); Piercy, Preston, and Whitehead (1938); Fage and Preston (1941).

PRETSCH, J. (1941a). Über die Stabilität einer Laminarströmung um eine Kugel. *Luftfahrtforsch.* **18, 341-4.** (Translated as 'The stability of laminar flow past a sphere', *Tech. Memor. nat. adv. Comm. Aero., Wash.* No. *1017.*) [557]

PRETSCH, J. (1941b). Die Stabilität einer ebenen Laminarströmung bei Druckgefälle und Druckansteig. *Jb. dtsch. Luftfahrtf.* **1, 158-75.** [91, 515, 541, 542, 543]

PRETSCH, J. (1941c). Über die Stabilität einer Laminarströmung in einem geraden Rohr mit kreisförmigem Querschnitt. *Z. angew. Math. Mech.* **21, 204-17.** [539]

PRETSCH, J. (1942). Die Anfachung instabiler Störungen in einer laminaren Reibungsschicht. *Jb. dtsch. Luftfahrtf.* *154-71.* (Translated as 'The excitation of unstable perturbations in a laminar friction layer', *Tech. Memor. nat. adv. Comm. Aero., Wash.* No. *1343.*) [541]

PRETSCH, J. (1944a). Die laminare Grenzschichte bei starkem Absaugen und Ausblasen. *Untersuch. Mitt. dtsch. Luftfahrtf.* No. *3091.* [241, 252, 345, 347]

PRETSCH, J. (1944b). Grenzen der Grenzschichtbeeinflussung. *Z. angew. Math. Mech.* **24, 264-7.** [241, 345, 347]

PROBSTEIN, R. F. (1953). On a solution of the energy equation for a rotating plate started from rest. *Quart. appl. Math.* **11, 240-4.** [381]

PROUDMAN, I., and PEARSON, J. R. A. (1957). Expansions at small Reynolds numbers for the flow past a sphere and a circular cylinder. *J. Fluid Mech.* **2, 237-62.** [187, 188]

PUSEY, P. S. *See* Lambourne and Pusey (1958).

RABENSTEIN, A. L. (1958). Asymptotic solutions of $u^{iv} + \lambda^2(zu'' + \alpha u' + \beta u) = 0$ for large $|\lambda|$. *Arch. rat. Mech. Anal., Heidelberg,* **1, 418-37.** [521]

RANDALL, D. G. *See* Owen and Randall.

RANGASAMI, K. S. I. *See* Nigam and Rangasami (1953).

RAY, M. (1936). The vibration of an infinite elliptic cylinder in a viscous fluid. *Z. angew. Math. Mech.* **16, 99-108.** [392]

RAYLEIGH, Lord. (1880). On the stability, or instability, of certain fluid motions. I. *Scientific Papers,* **1, 474-87.** [518]

RAYLEIGH, Lord (1883). On the circulation of air observed in Kundt's tubes, and on some allied acoustical problems. *Phil. Trans.* A **175,** 1-21. See also *Scientific Papers,* **2,** *239-57.* [384, 385, 386]

RAYLEIGH, Lord (1887). On the stability, or instability, of certain fluid motions. II. *Scientific Papers,* **3,** 2-23. [518]

RAYLEIGH, Lord (1894). *Theory of sound,* 2nd edition. Macmillan, London. [12]

RAYLEIGH, Lord (1911). On the motion of solid bodies through viscous liquids. *Phil. Mag.* (6), **21, 697-711.** [137, 358]

RAYLEIGH, Lord (1916a). On convection currents in a horizontal layer of fluid when the higher temperature is on the under side. *Scientific Papers,* **6,** *432-46.* [507, 508, 510]

RAYLEIGH, Lord (1916b). On the dynamics of revolving fluids. *Scientific Papers,* **6,** *447-53.* [494]

RECHENBERG, I. *See* Head and Rechenberg (1962).

REGIER, A. *See* Theodorsen and Regier (1947).

REICHARDT, H. (1938). Messungen turbulenter Schwankungen. *Naturwissenschaften.* **26, 406-8.** [568]

REICHARDT, H. *See* Prandtl and Reichardt (1934).

REID, W. H. (1958). On the stability of viscous flow in a curved channel. *Proc. Roy. Soc.* A **244**, *186–98*. [505]

REID, W. H., and HARRIS, D. L. (1958). Some further results on the Bénard problem. *Phys. Fluids*, **1**, *102–10*. [511]

RELF, E. F. (1914). Discussion of the results of measurements of the resistance of wires, with some additional tests on the resistance of wires of small diameter. *Rep. Memor. aero. Res. Coun., Lond.* No. *102* (1913–14 Vol.). [106]

RELF, E. F., PANKHURST, R. C., and WALKER, W. S. (1954). The use of pitot tubes to measure skin friction on a flat plate. *Rep. aero. Res. Coun., Lond.* No. *17025*. Incorporated in *Rep. Memor. aero. Res. Coun., Lond.* No. *3185*. [624]

REYNOLDS, O. (1883). An experimental investigation of the circumstances which determine whether the motion of water shall be direct or sinuous, and of the law of resistance in parallel channels. *Phil. Trans.* **174**, *935–82*. [35]

RHEINBOLDT, W. (1955). Über die äussere Randbedingung bei den Grenzschichtgleichungen. *50 Jahre Grenzschichtforschung* (Editors: Görtler, H., and Tollmien, W.), Vieweg, Braunschweig, *328–33*. [203]

RHEINBOLDT, W. (1956). Zur Berechnung stationärer Grenzschichten bei kontinuierlicher Absaugung mit unstetig veränderlicher Absaugegeschwindigkeit. *J. rat. Mech. Anal., Indiana Univ.* **5**, *539–604*. [343]

RICHARDS, E. J., and BURSTALL, F. H. (1945). The china clay method of indicating transition position. *Rep. Memor. aero. Res. Coun., Lond.* No. *2126*. [613]

RICHARDS, G. J. (1933). An experimental investigation of the wake behind an elliptic cylinder. *Rep. Memor. aero. Res. Coun., Lond.* No. *1590* (1934–5 Vol.). [Plate]

RICHARDSON, E. G., and TYLER, E. (1929). The transverse velocity gradients near the mouths of pipes in which an alternating or continuous flow of air is established. *Proc. phys. Soc. Lond.* **42**, *1–15*. [388, 389]

RICHARDSON, E. G. *See* Piercy and Richardson (1928), (1930).

RICHARDSON, L. F. (1920). The supply of energy to and from atmospheric eddies. *Proc. Roy. Soc.* A **97**, *354–73*. [548]

RIDDELL, F. R. *See* Ashkenas and Riddell (1955).

RIEMAN III, W. (1928). The value of the Hagenbach factor in the determination of viscosity by the efflux method. *J. Amer. chem. Soc.* **50**, *46–55*. [446]

RIIS, E. *See* Eliassen, Høiland, and Riis (1953).

RINGLEB, F. O. (1952). Computation of the laminar boundary layer with suction. *J. aero. Sci.* **19**, *48–54*. [287, 344]

ROBINS, A. W. *See* Sinclair and Robins (1952).

ROBINSON, A., and LAURMANN, J. A. (1956). *Wing theory*. Cambridge University Press. [36, 41]

ROSENBERG, B. (1952). The use of doubly refracting solutions in the investigation of fluid flow phenomena. *Rep. Taylor Model Basin, Wash.* No. *617*. [611]

ROSENBLAT, S. (1959). Torsional oscillations of a plane in a viscous fluid. *J. Fluid Mech.* **6**, *206–20*. [385]

ROSENBLATT, A. (1933). Solutions exactes des équations du mouvement des liquides visqueux. *Mémor. Sci. math.* No. *72*. [150]

ROSENBROOK, G. (1937). Instabilität der Gleitschicht im schwach divergenten Kanal. *Z. angew. Math. Mech.* **17**, *8–24*. [521]

ROSENHEAD, L. (1940). The steady two-dimensional radial flow of viscous fluid between two inclined plane walls. *Proc. Roy. Soc.* A **175**, *436–67*. [144, 146]

ROSENHEAD, L., and SIMPSON, J. H. (1936). Note on the velocity distribution in the wake behind a flat plate placed along the stream. *Proc. Camb. phil. Soc.* **32**, *385–91*. [281]

ROSENHEAD, L. *See* Goldstein and Rosenhead (1936).

ROSHKO, A. (1954a). On the development of turbulent wakes from vortex streets. *Rep. nat. adv. Comm. Aero., Wash.* No. *1191*. [562]

ROSHKO, A. (1954b). On the drag and shedding frequency of two-dimensional bluff bodies. *Tech. Notes nat. adv. Comm. Aero., Wash.* No. *3169*. [562]

ROSSOW, V. J. (1958). Boundary-layer stability diagrams for electrically-conducting fluids in the presence of a magnetic field. *Tech. Notes nat. adv. Comm. Aero., Wash.* No. 4282. See also *NASA Report R-37.* [540]

ROTT, N. (1956). Unsteady viscous flow in the vicinity of a stagnation point. *Quart. appl. Math.* **13**, 444-51. [403, 405]

ROTT, N., and CRABTREE, L. F. (1952). Simplified laminar boundary layer calculations for bodies of revolution and for yawed wings. *J. aero. Sci.* **19**, 553-65. [432, 472]

ROTT, N., and SMITH, W. E. (1956). Some examples of laminar boundary layer flow on rotating blades. *J. aero. Sci.* **23**, 991-6. See also Smith (1952). [482]

ROULEAU, W. T., and OSTERLE, J. F. (1955). The application of finite difference methods to boundary-layer type flows. *J. aero. Sci.* **22**, 249-54. [285, 343]

ROUSE, H. (1950). *Engineering hydraulics.* Wiley, New York. [27]

ROZIN, L. A. (1957a). Some cases of similar solutions of incompressible, unsteady, laminar boundary-layer flow. *Prikl. Mat. Mekh.* **21**, 361-7 (in Russian). [360]

ROZIN, L. A. (1957b). Approximate integration of the equations of unsteady laminar boundary-layer flow in an incompressible fluid. *Prikl. Mat. Mekh.* **21**, 615-23 (in Russian). Translated as *NASA Tech. Trans. F-22.* [See pp. 368-70]

ROZIN, L. A. (1958). *Prikl. Mat. Mekh.* **22**, 407-12 (in Russian). (Translated as 'The growth of a laminar boundary layer on a flat plate set impulsively into motion', *Appl. Math. Mech.—P.M.M.* **22**, 568-75.) [See pp. 360-2]

RUSSELL, W. R., GRACEY, W., LETKO, W., and FOURNIER, P. G. (1951). Wind-tunnel investigation of six shielded total-pressure tubes at high angles of attack. *Tech. Notes nat. adv. Comm. Aero., Wash.* No. 2530. [594]

SAINT-VENANT, B. (1843). Mémoire sur la dynamique des fluides. *C.R. Acad. Sci., Paris,* **17**, 1240-2. [121]

SALTER, C. (1953). Preliminary note on a proposed new design of N.P.L. standard pitot-static tube. *Rep. aero. Res. Coun., Lond.* No. 16374. [597]

SALTER, C. (1955). Further notes on the proposed new design of N.P.L. standard pitot-static tube. *Rep. aero. Res. Coun., Lond.* No. 17863. [597]

SANYAL, L. (1956). The flow of viscous liquid in a circular tube under pressure gradients varying exponentially with time. *Indian J. Phys.* **30**, No. 2, 57. [390]

SARGENT, R. F. See Fage and Sargent (1944), (1947).

SATO, H. (1956). Experimental investigation of the transition of a laminar separated layer. *J. Phys. Soc. Japan,* **11**, 702-9. (Errata p. 1128.) [559]

SATO, H. (1960). The stability and transition of a two-dimensional jet. *J. Fluid Mech.* **7**, 53-80. [561]

SAUNDERS, O. A. See Schmidt and Saunders (1938).

SAVIC, P. (1941). On acoustically effective vortex motion in gaseous jets. *Phil. Mag.* (7), **32**, 245-52. [561]

SAVIC, P., and MURPHY, J. W. (1943). The symmetrical vortex street in sound-sensitive plane jets. *Phil. Mag.* (7), **34**, 139-44. [562]

SCHAEFER, H. (1943). Laminare Grenzschicht zur Potentialströmung $U = u_1 x^m$ mit Absaugen und Ausblasen. I. Teil. *Untersuch. Mitt. dtsch. Luftfahrtf.* No. 2043. [248]

SCHAEFER, H. (1944). Eine Näherungslösung für den Anlauf der laminaren Grenzschicht an der ebenen Platte mit homogener Absaugung. *Ber. Inst. Aero. tech. Hochsch., Braunschweig* No. 44/15. See also *Untersuch. Mitt. dtsch. Luftfahrtf.* No. 2088. [344]

SCHILLER, L. (1922). Die Entwicklung der laminaren Geschwindigkeitsverteilung und ihre Bedeutung für Zähigkeitsmessungen. *Z. angew. Math. Mech.* **2**, 96-106. [442]

SCHLICHTING, H. (1932a). Berechnung ebener periodischer Grenzschichtströmungen. *Phys. Z.* **33**, 327-35. [382, 383, 384, 386, 387, 388]

SCHLICHTING, H. (1932b). Über die Stabilität der Couette-Strömung. *Ann. Phys., Lpz.* **14**, 905-36. [539]

SCHLICHTING, H. (1932c). Über die Entstehung der Turbulenz in einem rotierenden Zylinder. *Nachr. Ges. Wiss. Göttingen, Math.-phys. Kl.* 160-98. [539]

SCHLICHTING, H. (1933a). Laminare Strahlausbreitung. *Z. angew. Math. Mech.* **13**, 260-3. [154, 254, 452]

SCHLICHTING, H. (1933b). Zur Entstehung der Turbulenz bei der Plattenströmung. *Nachr. Ges. Wiss. Göttingen, Math.-phys. Kl.* 181-208. [521, 530, 534, 541]

SCHLICHTING, H. (1935a). Amplitudenverteilung und Energiebilanz der kleinen Störungen bei der Plattengrenzschicht. *Nachr. Ges. Wiss. Göttingen Math.-phys. Kl. Fachgruppe*, **1**, *47–78*. (Translated as 'Amplitude distribution and energy balance of small disturbances in plate flow', *Tech. Memor. nat. adv. Comm. Aero., Wash. No. 1265*.) [521, 534, 541]

SCHLICHTING, H. (1935b). Turbulenz bei Wärmeschichtung. *Z. angew. Math. Mech.* **15**, *313–38*. (Translated in *Tech. Memor. nat. adv. Comm. Aero., Wash. No. 1262*.) [548]

SCHLICHTING, H. (1940). Über die theoretische Berechnung der kritischen Reynoldsschen Zahl einer Reibungsschicht in beschleunigter und verzögerter Strömung. *Jb. dtsch. Luftfahrtf.* **1**, *97–112*. [91, 540, 541, 542, 543]

SCHLICHTING, H. (1943). Ein Näherungsverfahren zur Berechnung der laminaren Grenzschicht mit Absaugung bei beliebiger Körperform. *Ber. Inst. Aero. tech. Hochsch., Braunschweig*, No. *43/13*. (Translated as 'An approximate method for calculation of the laminar boundary layer with suction for bodies of arbitrary shape', *Tech. Memor. nat. adv. Comm. Aero., Wash. No. 1216*.) See also *Ingen.-Arch.* **16**, *201–20* (1948). [336, 344]

SCHLICHTING, H. (1955). *Boundary layer theory*. Pergamon Press, London. [91, 94, 138, 161, 423, 544]

SCHLICHTING, H., and BUSSMANN, K. (1943). Exakte Lösungen für die laminare Grenzschicht mit Absaugung und Ausblasen. *Schr. dtsch. Akad. Luftfahrtf.* **7B**, *25–69*. [242, 248, 334, 336]

SCHLICHTING, H., and TRUCKENBRODT, E. (1952). Die Strömung an einer angeblasenen rotierenden Scheibe. *Z. angew Math. Mech.* **32**, *97–111*. [160]

SCHLICHTING, H., and ULRICH, A. (1940). Zur Berechnung des Umschlages laminar/turbulent. *Ber. Lilienthal-Ges. Luftfahrtf. S10, 75–135*, and *Jb. dtsch. Luftfahrtf.* **1**, *8–35* (1942). [298, 404, 541, 542, 543, 544]

SCHMIDT, R. J., and MILVERTON, S. W. (1935). On the instability of a fluid when heated from below. *Proc. Roy. Soc.* A **152**, *586–94*. [511]

SCHMIDT, R. J., and SAUNDERS, O. A. (1938). On the motion of a fluid heated from below. *Proc. Roy. Soc.* A **165**, *216–28*. [511]

SCHMIEDEL, J. S. (1928). Experimentelle Untersuchungen über die Fallbewegung von Kugeln und Scheiben in reibenden Flüssigkeiten. *Phys. Z.* **29**, *593–610*. 105]

SCHNEIDER, P. J. See Eckert, Soehngen, and Schneider (1955).

SCHOLKEMEIER, F. W. (1949). Lösung der Prandtlschen Grenzschichtdifferentialgleichungen mit Hilfe von Potenzreihenentwicklungen. *Arch. Math., Karlsruhe*, **1**, *270–7*. [422]

SCHRÖDER, K. (1943). Ein einfaches numerisches Verfahren zur Berechnung der laminaren Grenzschicht. *ForschBer. dtsch. Luftfahrtf.* No. *1741*. (Translated as 'A simple numerical method for the calculation of the laminar boundary layer', *Tech. Memor. nat. adv. Comm. Aero., Wash. No. 1317*.) [285]

SCHRÖDER, K. (1951). Verwendung der Differenzenrechnung zur Berechnung der laminaren Grenzschicht. *Math. Nachr.* **4**, *439–67*. [285]

SCHUBAUER, G. B. (1935). Air flow in a separating laminar boundary layer. *Rep. nat. adv. Comm. Aero., Wash. No. 527*. [283, 329, 404]

SCHUBAUER, G. B. (1958). Mechanism of transition at subsonic speeds. *Proc. Symp. boundary layer Res., Int. Union theoret. appl. Mech. Freiburg i. Br.* (1957), *85–109*. [573]

SCHUBAUER, G. B., and KLEBANOFF, P. S. (1955). Contributions on the mechanics of boundary layer transition. *Proc. Symp. boundary layer effects Aerodyn., nat. phys. Lab.* (Also available as *Rep. nat. adv. Comm. Aero., Wash. No. 1289*.) [95, 96, 573, 577, 578, 607]

SCHUBAUER, G. B., and SKRAMSTAD, H. K. (1947). Laminar boundary layer oscillations and transition on a flat plate. *Rep. nat. adv. Comm. Aero., Wash. No. 909*. See also *J. Res. nat. Bur. Stand.* **38**, *251–92*; and *J. aero. Sci.* **14**, *69–78*. [94, 533, 536, 537, 538, 544, 573]

SCHUBAUER, G. B. See Dryden, Schubauer, Mock, and Skramstad (1937); Klebanoff, Schubauer, and Tidstrom (1955).

SCHUH, H. (1947). Über die Lösung der laminaren Grenzschichtgleichung an der ebenen

Platte für Geschwindigkeits- und Temperaturfeld bei veränderlichen Stoffwerten und für das Diffusionsfeld bei höheren Konzentrationen. *Z. angew. Math. Mech.* **25–27**, *54–60*. (Translated as 'The solution of the laminar-boundary-layer equation for the flat plate for velocity and temperature fields for variable physical properties and for the diffusion field at high concentration', *Tech. Memor. nat. adv. Comm. Aero.*, *Wash.* No. *1275*.) [274]

SCHUH, H. (1953a). Calculation of unsteady boundary layers in two-dimensional laminar flow. *Z. Flugwiss.* **1**, *122–31*. [362, 368, 369, 408]

SCHUH, H. (1953b). A new method for calculating the laminar heat transfer on cylinders of arbitrary cross section and on bodies of revolution at constant and variable wall temperature. *Aero. tech. Notes K. tek. Högsk.*, *Stockholm* No. *33*. [506]

SCHUH, H. (1955). Über die 'ähnlichen' Lösungen der instationären laminaren Grenzschichtgleichung in inkompressibler Strömung. *50 Jahre Grenzschichtforschung* (Editors: Görtler, H., and Tollmien, W.), Vieweg, Braunschweig. *147–52*. [360]

SCHULTZ-GRUNOW, F., and HEIN, H. (1956). Beitrag zur Couetteströmung. *Z. Flugwiss.* **4**, *28–30*. [501, 565]

SCHULZE, W. M., ASHBY, G. C., and ERWIN, J. R. (1952). Several combination probes for surveying static and total pressure and flow direction. *Tech. Notes nat. adv. Comm. Aero.*, *Wash.* No. *2830*. [598]

SCHWABE, M. (1935). Über Druckermittlung in der nichtstationären ebenen Strömung. *Ingen.-Arch.* **6**, *34–50*. (Translated as 'Pressure distribution in non-uniform two-dimensional flow', *Tech. Memor. nat. adv. Comm. Aero.*, *Wash.* No. *1039*.) [374, 375]

SCORER, R. S. (1949). Theory of waves in the lee of mountains. *Quart. J. R. met. Soc.* **75**, *41–56*. [33]

SCOTT-WILSON, J. B., and CAPPS, D. S. (1954). Wind tunnel observations of boundary layer transition on two sweptback wings at a Mach number of 1·61. *Rep. aero. Res. Coun.*, *Lond.* No. *17627*. [555]

SEARS, W. R. (1948). The boundary layer of yawed cylinders. *J. aero. Sci.* **15**, *49–52*. [468, 469, 490]

SEARS, W. R. (1950). Potential flow around a rotating cylindrical blade. *J. aero. Sci.* **17**, *183–4*. [480]

SEARS, W. R. (Editor) (1954a). General theory of high speed aerodynamics. *High-speed aerodynamics and jet propulsion*, **VI**. Oxford University Press, London. [8]

SEARS, W. R. (1954b). Boundary layers in three-dimensional flow. *Appl. Mech. Rev.* **7**, *281–5*. [409, 485]

SEARS, W. R. (1955). A brief review of three-dimensional boundary layer flows. *Pap. 7th mtg AGARD wind Tunn. mod. test. Panel Publication* No. *AG 19/P9*, *180–90*. [490]

SEBAN, R. A., and BOND, R. (1951). Skin friction and heat transfer characteristics of a laminar boundary layer on a cylinder in axial incompressible flow. *J. aero. Sci.* **18**, *671–5*. [447, 448]

SEGEL, L. A. (1960). A uniformly valid asymptotic expansion of the solution to an unsteady boundary layer problem. *J. Math. Phys.* **39**, *189–97*. [393]

SEGEL, L. A. (1961). Application of conformal mapping to viscous flow between moving circular cylinders. *Quart. Appl. Math.* **18**, *335–53*. [387–8]

SELLARS, J. R. *See* Corcos and Sellars (1959).

SERRIN, J. B. (1959). On the stability of viscous fluid motions. *Arch. rat. Mech. Anal.*, *Heidelberg*, **3**, *1–13*. [See pp. 492–501]

SEXL, T. (1927a). Zur Stabilitätsfrage der Poiseuilleschen und Couetteschen Strömung. *Ann. Phys.*, *Lpz.* (4), **83**, *835–48*. [539]

SEXL, T. (1927b). Über dreidimensionale Störungen der Poiseuilleschen Strömung. *Ann. Phys.*, *Lpz.* (4), **84**, *807–22*. [539]

SEXL, T. (1930). Über die von E. G. Richardson entdeckten Annulareffekt. *Z. Phys.* **61**, *349–62*. [388]

SEXL, T., and SPIELBERG, K. (1958). Zum Stabilitätsproblem der Poiseuille-Strömung. *Acta. phys. austr.* **12**, *9–28*. [539]

SHANKS, D. (1953). The Blasius and Weyl constants in boundary-layer theory. *Phys. Rev.* **90**, *377*. [226]

SHAPIRO, A. H. *See* Hurd, Chesky, and Shapiro (1953).

SHAW, R. (1960). The influence of hole dimensions on static pressure measurements. *J. Fluid Mech.* **7**, *550–60*. [595]

SHEN, S. F. (1954). Calculated amplified oscillations in plane Poiseuille and Blasius flows. *J. aero. Sci.* **21**, *62–64*. [521, 530, 533, 534]

SHEN, S. F. (1961). Some considerations on the laminar stability of time-dependent basic flows. *J. aero. Space Sci.* **28**, *397–405*. [557]

SHERMAN, A. *See* Abbott and Sherman (1938).

SHERMAN, F. S. (1953). New experiments on impact-pressure interpretation in supersonic and subsonic rarefied air streams. *Tech. Notes nat. adv. Comm. Aero., Wash.* No. *2995*. [594, 595]

SIKKELAND, T. *See* Holtsmark, Johnsen, Sikkeland, and Skavlem (1954).

SILVESTON, P. L. (1958). Wärmedurchgang in waagerechten Flüssigkeitsschichten, I., II. *ForschArb. IngWes.* **24**, *29–32 and 59–69*. [511]

SIMMONS, L. F. G. (1949). A shielded hot-wire anemometer for low speeds. *J. sci. Instrum.* **26**, *407–11*. [606, 607]

SIMMONS, L. F. G., and JONES, R. (1927). The one-foot wind tunnel at the National Physical Laboratory, including particulars of calibrations made with a pitot-tube and vane anemometer at low speeds. *Rep. Memor. aero. Res. Coun., Lond.* No. *1103* (1927–8 Vol.). [602]

SIMPSON, J. H. *See* Rosenhead and Simpson (1936).

SINCLAIR, A. R., and ROBINS, A. W. (1952). A method for the determination of the time lag in pressure measuring systems incorporating capillaries. *Tech. Notes nat. adv. Comm. Aero., Wash.* No. *2793*. [605]

SINHA, K. D. P. (1956). The direction of flow in the laminar boundary layer on an infinite yawed cylinder. *Curr. Pap. aero. Res. Coun., Lond.* No. *295*. [555]

SKAN, S. W. *See* Falkner and Skan (1930); Curle and Skan (1957).

SKAVLEM, S. *See* Holtsmark, Johnsen, Sikkeland, and Skavlem (1954).

SKINNER, G. T. *See* Liepmann and Skinner (1954).

SKRAMSTAD, H. K. *See* Dryden, Schubauer, Mock, and Skramstad (1937); Schubauer and Skramstad (1943), (1947).

SLAVNOV, V. V. (1956). *Zh. Tekh. Fiz.* **26**, *2002–4*. (Translated as 'Free heat convection in metallic vertical tubes of circular section', *Sov. Phys.—tech. Phys.* **1**, *1938–41*.) [511]

SLEZKIN, N. A. (1934). On an exact solution of the equations of viscous flow. *Uch. zap. MGU Sci. Rec., Moscow State Univ.* No. 2 (in Russian). [151]

SMITH, A. M. O. (1954). Improved solutions of the Falkner and Skan boundary-layer equation. *Pap. Fairchild Fund, Inst. aero. Sci. FF—10*. (Quoted by Smith (1956b).) [248]

SMITH, A. M. O. (1955). On the growth of Taylor-Görtler vortices along highly concave walls. *Quart. appl. Math.* **13**, *233–62*. [504]

SMITH, A. M. O. (1956a). Transition, pressure gradient and stability theory. *Proc. 9th int. Congr. appl. Mech., Brussels* **4**, *234–44*. [95]

SMITH, A. M. O. (1956b). Rapid laminar boundary-layer calculations by piecewise application of similar solutions. *J. aero. Sci.* **23**, *901–12*. *See also* Smith (1954). [302]

SMITH, A. M. O., and MURPHY, J. S. (1955a). Micromanometer for measuring boundary layer profiles. *Rev. sci. Instrum.* **26**, *775–81*. [603]

SMITH, A. M. O., and MURPHY, J. S. (1955b). A dust method for locating the separation point. *J. aero. Sci.* **22**, *273–74*. [615]

SMITH, A. M. O. *See* Clutter and Smith (1961); Murphy and Smith (1956).

SMITH, J. H. B. *See* Mangler and Smith (1959).

SMITH, K. (1954). Pressure lag in pipes with special reference to aircraft speed and height measurements. *Rep. aero. Res. Coun., Lond.* No. *17610*. [605]

SMITH, N. H. (1947). Exploratory investigation of laminar boundary-layer oscillations on a rotating disk. *Tech. Notes nat. adv. Comm. Aero., Wash.* No. *1227*. [556]

SMITH, W. E. (1952). Some examples of laminar boundary layer flow of rotating blades. *Thesis Cornell Univ.* See also Rott and Smith (1956). [482]

SOBERMAN, R. K. (1958). Effects of lateral boundaries on natural convection. *J. appl. Phys.* **29**, *872–3.* [511]

SOBERMAN, R. K. (1959). Onset of convection in liquids subject to transient heating from below. *Phys. Fluids,* **2**, *131–8.* [511]

SOEHNGEN, E. *See* Eckert and Soehngen (1951); Eckert, Soehngen, and Schneider (1955).

SOUTHWELL, R. V., and CHITTY, L. (1930). On the problem of hydrodynamic stability. *Phil. Trans.* A **229**, *205–83.* [538]

SOUTHWELL, R. V. *See* Allen and Southwell (1955); Pellew and Southwell (1940).

SOWERBY, L. (1951). The unsteady flow of viscous incompressible fluid inside an infinite channel. *Phil. Mag.* (7), **42**, *176–87.* [138, 363, 488]

SOWERBY, L. (1954). Secondary flow in a boundary layer. *Rep. aero. Res. Coun., Lond.* No. *16832.* [457]

SOWERBY, L., and COOKE, J. C. (1953). The flow of fluid along corners and edges. *Quart. J. Mech.* **6**, *50–70.* [138, 363, 364, 487, 488]

SPALDING, D. B., and EVANS, H. L. (1961). Mass transfer through laminar boundary layers—2. Auxiliary functions for the velocity boundary layer. *Int. J. Heat Mass Transfer,* **2**, *199–221.* [337]

SPARROW, E. M. (1958). Combined effects of unsteady flight velocity and surface temperature on heat transfer. *Jet Prop.* **28**, *403–5.* [408]

SPARROW, E. M., and GREGG, J. L. (1957). Non-steady surface-temperature effects on forced-convection heat transfer. *J. aero. Sci.* **24**, *776–7.* [408]

SPARROW, E. M., and GREGG, J. L. (1958). Prandtl-number effects on unsteady forced-convection heat transfer. *Tech. Notes nat. adv. Comm. Aero., Wash.* No. *4311.* [408]

SPIEGEL, E. VAN. *See* Zaat, Spiegel, and Timman (1955).

SPIELBERG, K. *See* Sexl and Spielberg (1958).

SQUIRE, H. B. (1933). On the stability for three-dimensional disturbances of viscous fluid flow between parallel walls. *Proc. Roy. Soc.* A **142**, *621–8.* [514, 515]

SQUIRE, H. B. (1951). The round laminar jet. *Quart. J. Mech.* **4**, *321–9.* [152, 455]

SQUIRE, H. B. (1952). Some viscous fluid flow problems, I. Jet emerging from a hole in a plane wall. *Phil. Mag.* (7), **43**, *942–5.* [152, 154, 455]

SQUIRE, H. B. (1955). Radial jets. *50 Jahre Grenzschichtforschung* (Editors: Görtler, H., and Tollmien, W.), Vieweg, Braunschweig, *47–54.* [152, 439]

SQUIRE, H. B., and YOUNG, A. D. (1937). The calculation of the profile drag of aerofoils. *Rep. Memor. aero. Res. Coun., Lond.* No. *1838* (1938 Vol.). [479, 627]

SQUIRE, L. C. (1954). Boundary layer growth in three dimensions. *Phil. Mag.* (7), **45**, *1272–83.* [376, 377, 379, 490]

SQUIRE, L. C. (1955). The three-dimensional boundary layer equations and some power series solutions. *Rep. Memor. aero. Res. Coun., Lond.* No. *3006.* [457, 467]

STANTON, T. E., MARSHALL, D., and BRYANT, C. N. (1920). On the conditions at the boundary of a fluid in turbulent motion. *Proc. Roy. Soc,* A **97**, *413–34.* [624]

STEINMAN, H. (1956). The stability of viscous flow between rotating cylinders. *Quart. appl. Math.* **14**, *27–33.* [501]

STEWARTSON, K. (1951). On the impulsive motion of a flat plate in a viscous fluid. *Quart. J. Mech.* **4**, *182–98.* [361]

STEWARTSON, K. (1953). On the flow between two rotating coaxial discs. *Proc. Camb. phil. Soc.* **49**, *333–41.* [162]

STEWARTSON, K. (1954). Further solutions of the Falkner–Skan equation. *Proc. Camb. phil. Soc.* **50**, *454–65.* [248, 249]

STEWARTSON, K. (1955). The asymptotic boundary layer on a circular cylinder in axial incompressible flow. *Quart. appl. Math.* **13**, *113–22.* [449]

STEWARTSON, K. (1957a). On asymptotic expansions in the theory of boundary layers. *J. Math. Phys.* **36**, *173–91.* [280, 281, 343, 449]

STEWARTSON, K. (1957b). On rotating laminar boundary layers. *Proc. Symp. boundary layer Res., Int. Union theoret. appl. Mech. Freiburg i. Br.* (1957) *59–71.* [436, 439]

TAN, H. S. (1953). On laminar boundary layer over a rotating blade. *J. aero. Sci.* **20**, *780–1.* [482]

TANEDA, S. (1956). Experimental investigation of the wakes behind cylinders and plates at low Reynolds numbers. *J. phys. Soc. Japan*, **11**, *302–7.* [562]

TANEDA, S. (1958). Oscillation of the wake behind a flat plate parallel to the flow. *J. phys. Soc. Japan*, **13**, *418–25.* [562]

TANI, I. (1941). A simple method for determining the laminar separation point. *Rep. aero. Res. Inst. Tokyo*, No. *199* (in Japanese—quoted by Tani (1954)). [304]

TANI, I. (1949). On the solution of the laminar boundary layer equations. *J. phys. Soc. Japan*, **4**, *149–54.* [266, 330, 331]

TANI, I. (1954). On the approximate solution of the laminar boundary-layer equations. *J. aero. Sci.* **21**, *487–95* and *504. See also* Tani (1941). [313, 331]

TANI, I. (1958). An example of unsteady laminar boundary-layer flow. *Rep. aero. Res. Inst., Tokyo*, No. *331.* [See pp. 358–60]

TATSUMI, T. (1952a). Stability of the laminar inlet-flow prior to the formation of Poiseuille régime. *J. phys. Soc. Japan*, **7**, *489–502.* [539]

TATSUMI, T. (1952b). Note on discrepancies between two theories on the stability of plane Poiseuille flow. *J. phys. Soc. Japan*, **7**, *619–24.* [521]

TATSUMI, T., and GOTOH, K. (1960). The stability of free boundary layers between two uniform flows. *J. Fluid Mech.* (in the press). [559]

TATSUMI, T., and KAKUTANI, T. (1958). The stability of a two-dimensional laminar jet. *J. Fluid Mech.* **4**, *261–75.* [558, 560]

TAYLOR, G. I. (1915). Eddy motion in the atmosphere. *Phil. Trans.* A **215**, *1–26.* [93, 519]

TAYLOR, G. I. (1923a). On the decay of vortices in a viscous fluid. *Phil. Mag.* **46**, *671–4.* [139]

TAYLOR, G. I. (1923b). Stability of a viscous liquid contained between two rotating cylinders. *Phil. Trans.* A **223**, *289–343.* [496, 497, 498, 501, 511, 563, 564]

TAYLOR, G. I. (1931a). *Rapports et Procès-verbaux du Conseil permanent international pour l'exploration de la mer*, **76**, *35–43.* [548]

TAYLOR, G. I. (1931b). Effect of variation of density on superposed streams of fluid. *Proc. Roy. Soc.* A **132**, *499–523.* [548]

TAYLOR, G. I. (1936). Fluid friction between rotating cylinders. *Proc. Roy. Soc.* A **157**, *546–78.* [539, 571]

TAYLOR, G. I. (1937a). The determination of stresses by means of soap films. *The Mechanical Properties of Fluids* (a collective work). Blackie & Son Ltd., London and Glasgow. [136]

TAYLOR, G. I. (1937b). The determination of drag by the pitot traverse method. *Rep. Memor. aero. Res. Coun., Lond.* No. *1808.* [626, 627]

TAYLOR, G. I. (1950). The boundary layer in the converging nozzle of a swirl atomiser. *Quart. J. Mech.* **3**, *129–39.* [432]

TAYLOR, G. I. (1951). Analysis of the swimming of microscopic organisms. *Proc. Roy. Soc.* A **209**, *447–61.* [172]

TAYLOR, G. I. (1952). The action of waving cylindrical tails in propelling microscopic organisms. *Proc. Roy. Soc.* A **211**, *225–39.* [173]

TAYLOR, G. I. (1954). Diffusion and mass transport in tubes. *Proc. phys. Soc. Lond.* B **67**, *857–69.* [511]

TAYLOR, H. S. *See* Kovásznay (1955).

TERRILL, R. M. (1960). Laminar boundary-layer flow near separation with and without suction. *Phil. Trans.* A **253**, *55–100.* [219, 221, 248, 283, 330, 334]

TETERVIN, N. (1953). A study of the stability of the incompressible boundary layer on infinite wedges. *Tech. Notes nat. adv. Comm. Aero., Wash.* No. *2976.* [541, 542, 543]

TETERVIN, N. (1958). Theoretical distribution of laminar boundary-layer thickness, boundary-layer Reynolds number and stability limit, and roughness Reynolds number for a sphere and disk in incompressible flow. *Tech. Notes nat. adv. Comm. Aero., Wash.* No. *4350.* [557]

TETERVIN, N., and LEVINE, D. A. (1952). A study of the stability of the laminar

TIFFORD, A. N., and CHU, S. T. (1952). Uniform stream past a rotating disc. *J. aero. Sci.* **19**, *284–5.* [160]

TILLMANN, W. *See* Ludwieg and Tillmann (1949).

TIMMAN, R. (1949). A one-parameter method for the calculation of laminar boundary layers. *Rep. Trans. nat. LuchtvLab., Amsterdam,* **15**, *F29–45.* (Also available as *Rep. nat. LuchtvLab., Amsterdam, F35.*) [298, 331]

TIMMAN, R. (1952). A calculation method for three-dimensional laminar boundary layers. Part I. General Theory. *Rep. Trans. nat. LuchtvLab., Amsterdam,* **16**, *F31–F43.* (Also available as *Rep. nat. LuchtvLab., Amsterdam, F66* (1950).) [417]

TIMMAN, R. (1955). The theory of three-dimensional laminar boundary layers. *Proc. Symp. boundary layer effects Aerodyn., nat. phys. Lab.* [411, 415]

TIMMAN, R. *See* Zaat, Spiegel van, and Timman (1955).

TIPPELSKIRCH, H. VON (1956). Über Konvektionszellen, inbesondere im flüssigen Schwefel. *Beitr. Phys. Atmos., Frankfurt a. M.,* **29**, *37–54.* [511]

TOLLMIEN, W. (1929). Über die Enstehung der Turbulenz. *Nachr. Ges. Wiss. Göttingen 21–44.* (Translated as 'The production of turbulence', *Tech. Memor. nat. adv. Comm. Aero., Wash.* No. *609.*) [89, 90, 521, 523, 528, 531, 533, 541, 542, 543]

TOLLMIEN, W. (1931). Grenzschichttheorie. *Handbuch der Experimentalphysik,* **4**, Teil I, *241–87.* Akademische Verlagsgesellschaft, Leipzig. [144, 280, 373, 374]

TOLLMIEN, W. (1935). Ein allgemeines Kriterium der· Instabilität laminarer Geschwindigkeitsverteilungen. *Nachr. Ges. Wiss. Fachgruppe, Göttingen* **1**, *79–114.* [89, 90, 520]

TOLLMIEN, W. (1946). On the behaviour of a flow along a wall at the outer edge of its boundary layer. *Rep. aero. Res. Coun., Lond.* No. *9739.* (From 'Über das Verhalten einer Strömung längs einer Wand am äusseren Rand ihrer Reibungsschicht', *Betz-Festschr. Göttingen, 218–24,* (1945).) [215]

TOLLMIEN, W. (1947). Asymptotische Integration der Störungsdifferentialgleichung ebener laminarer Strömungen bei hohen Reynoldschen Zahlen. *Z. angew. Math. Mech.* **25/27**, *33–50* and *70–83.* [521]

TOLLMIEN, W. (Editor) (1948). Boundary layers. *Monogr. aerodyn. VersAnst. Göttingen B.* (*See also* unpublished translation, Min. Aviation, London.) *See also* Mangler (1948a, b). [251, 337, 429, 430]

TOLLMIEN, W. *See* Görtler and Tollmien (1955).

TOLMAN, R. C. (1948). *The principles of statistical mechanics.* Oxford University Press. [5]

TOMOTIKA, S., and AOI, T. (1950). The steady flow of viscous fluid past a sphere and circular cylinder at small Reynolds numbers. *Quart. J. Mech.* **3**, *140–61.* [176, 178]

TOMOTIKA, S., and AOI, T. (1951). An expansion formula for the drag on a circular cylinder moving through a viscous fluid at small Reynolds numbers. *Quart. J. Mech.* **4**, *401–6.* [180]

TOMOTIKA, S., AOI, T., and YOSINABU, H. (1953). On the forces acting on a circular cylinder set obliquely in a uniform stream at low values of Reynolds numbers. *Proc. Roy. Soc.* A **219**, *233–44.* [193]

TOMOTIKA, S., and IMAI, I. (1938). On the transition from laminar to turbulent flow in the boundary layer of a sphere. *Rep. aero. Res. Inst., Tokyo* **13**, *389–423.* [423]

TÖPFER, K. (1912). Bemerkung zu dem Aufsatz von H. Blasius 'Grenzschichten in Flüssigkeiten mit kleiner Reibung'. *Z. Math. Phys.* **60**, *397–8.* [223]

TORDA, T. P. (1952). Boundary layer control by continuous surface suction or injection. *J. Math. Phys.* **31**, *206–13.* [338]

TOWNEND, H. C. H. (1931). Hot-wire and spark shadowgraphs of the airflow through an airscrew. *Rep. Memor. aero. Res. Coun., Lond.* No. *1434* (1931–2 Vol.). [592]

TOWNEND, H. C. H. (1937a). Abstract of a film illustrating the theory of flight. *Rep. Memor. aero. Res. Coun., Lond.* No. *1767.* [592]

TOWNEND, H. C. H. (1937b). Visual and photographic methods of studying boundary layer flow. *Rep. Memor. aero. Res. Coun., Lond.* No. *1803.* [619]

TOWNEND, H. C. H. *See* Fage and Townend (1932).

TOWNSEND, A. A. (1956). *The structure of turbulent shear flow.* Cambridge University Press. [98, 99, 579]

TRILLING, L. (1950). The incompressible boundary layer with pressure gradient and suction. *J. aero. Sci.* **17**, *335–42*. [286]

TRITTON, D. J. (1959). Experiments on the flow past a circular cylinder at low Reynolds numbers. *J. Fluid Mech.* **6**, *547–67*. [562]

TRUCKENBRODT, E. (1952a). An approximate method for the calculation of the laminar and turbulent boundary layer by simple quadra...ure for two-dimensional and axially symmetric flow. *J. aero. Sci.* **19**, *428–9*. [313, 33.¹

TRUCKENBRODT, E. (1952b). Ein Quadraturverfahren zur Berechnung der laminaren und turbulenten Reibungsschichten bei ebener und rotations-symmetrischer Strömung. *Ingen.-Arch.* **20**, *211–28*. [309, 313, 331]

TRUCKENBRODT, E. *See* Schlichting and Truckenbrodt (1952).

TRUESDELL, C. (1954). The kinematics of vorticity. Indiana University Press, Blooming-ton, Indiana. [47]

TSIEN, L. C. *See* Andrade and Tsien (1937).

TSUJI, H. (1953). Note on the solution of the unsteady laminar boundary-layer equa-tions. *J. aero. Sci.* **20**, *295–6*. [362]

TULIN, M. P. *See* Cooper and Tulin (1955).

TYLER, E. *See* Richardson and Tyler (1929).

TYLER, R. A. *See* Piercy, Whitehead, and Tyler (1948).

UCHIDA, S. (1956). The pulsating viscous flow superposed on the steady laminar motion of incompressible fluid in a circular pipe. *Z. angew. Math. Phys.* **7**, *403–22*. [390]

ULMANN, E. F. *See* Dunning and Ulmann (1955).

ULRICH, A. (1943). Die laminare Reibungsschicht am Kreiszylinder. *ForschBer. dtsch. Luftfahrtf.* No. *1762*. [261, 334]

ULRICH, A. (1944). Theoretische Untersuchungen über die Widerstandsersparnis durch Laminarhaltung mit Absaugung. *Schr. dtsch. Akad. Luftfahrtf.* **8B**, *53*. (Trans-lated as 'Theoretical investigation of drag reduction by maintaining the laminar boundary layer by suction', *Tech. Memor. nat. adv. Comm. Aero., Wash.* No. *1121*.) [545, 547]

ULRICH, A. (1949). Die ebene laminare Reibungsschicht an einem Zylinder. *Arch. Math., Karlsruhe,* **2**, *33–41*. [261]

ULRICH, A. *See* Bussmann and Ulrich (1943), (1944); Schlichting and Ulrich (1940).

VERONIS, G. (1959). Cellular convection with finite amplitude in a rotating fluid. *J. Fluid Mech.* **5**, *401–35*. [565, 572]

VERONIS, G. *See* Malkus and Veronis (1958).

VOLKOVISKY, V. (1939). Étude des tourbillons thermoconvectifs dans les liquides. *Publ. sci. Ministr. Air.* No. *151*. [511]

WADHWA, Y. D. (1958). Boundary-layer growth on a spinning body : accelerated motion. *Phil. Mag.* (8), **3**, *152–8*. [378]

WALKER, G. T. *See* Phillips and Walker (1932).

WALKER, W. S. *See* Fage, Falkner, and Walker (1929); Gregory, Stuart, and Walker (1955); Gregory and Walker (1950); Relf, Pankhurst, and Walker (1954).

WALSHE, D. E. *See* Bryer, Walshe, and Garner (1955).

WALZ, A. (1941). Ein neuer Ansatz für das Geschwindigkeitsprofil der laminaren Reibungsschicht. *Ber. Lilienthal-Ges. Luftfahrtf.* No. *141*, *8–12*. *See also* Mangler (1948b). [294, 301–4, 331]

WALZ, A. (1943). Näherungsverfahren zur Berechnung der laminaren und turbulenten Reibungsschicht. *ForschBer. dtsch. Luftfahrtf.* No. *3060*. [432]

WALZ, A. (1946). Application of Wieghardt's energy theorem to velocity profiles of one parameter in laminar boundary layers. *Rep. aero. Res. Coun., Lond.* No. *10133*. [313]

WALZ, A. (1948). Anwendung des Energiesatzes von Wieghardt auf einparametrige Geschwindigkeitsprofile in laminaren Grenzschichten. *Ingen.-Arch.* **16**, *243–8*. [313]

WASHBURN, E. W. (Editor) (1926). *International critical tables.* McGraw-Hill, New York. [26, 30]

WASIUTINSKI, J. (1946). Studies in hydrodynamics and structure of stars and planets. *Astrophys. norveg.* **4**, *1.* [511]

WASOW, W. (1948). The complex asymptotic theory of a fourth-order differential equation of hydrodynamics. *Ann. Math., Princeton* (2), **49**, *852–71.* [527]

WASOW, W. (1953). On small disturbances of plane Couette flow. *J. Res. nat. Bur. Stand.* **51**, *195–202.* [538]

WATSON, E. J. (1947). The asymptotic theory of boundary-layer flow with suction. *Rep. Memor. aero. Res. Coun., Lond.* No. *2619.* [252, 346]

WATSON, E. J. (1955). Boundary-layer growth. *Proc. Roy. Soc.* A **231**, *104–16.* [359, 371, 374]

WATSON, G. N. (1944). *Theory of Bessel Functions,* 2nd edition. Cambridge University Press. [173, 388, 391]

WATSON, G. N. *See* Whittaker and Watson (1946).

WATSON, J. (1958). A solution of the Navier–Stokes equations illustrating the response of the laminar boundary layer to a given change in the external stream velocity. *Quart. J. Mech.* **11**, *302–25.* [400]

WATSON, J. (1959). The two-dimensional laminar flow near the stagnation point of a cylinder which has an arbitrary transverse motion. *Quart. J. Mech.* **12**, *175–90.* [402]

WATSON, J. (1960a). Three-dimensional disturbances in flow between parallel planes. *Proc. Roy. Soc.* A **254**, *562–9.* [514, 515]

WATSON, J. (1960b). On the non-linear mechanics of wave disturbances in parallel flows : Part 2. The development of a solution for plane Poiseuille flow and for plane Couette flow. *J. Fluid Mech.* **9**, *371–89.* [565, 567]

WAYLAND, H. (1955). Streaming birefringence as a hydrodynamic research tool— applied to a rotating cylinder apparatus above the transition velocity. *J. appl. Phys.* **26**, *1197–1205.* [611]

WEATHERBURN, C. E. (1927). *Differential geometry of three dimensions.* Vol. I. Cambridge University Press. [412]

WEATHERBURN, C. E. (1944). *Advanced vector analysis.* Bell, London. [11, 129]

WEBER, J., and BREBNER, G. G. (1952). A simple estimate of the profile drag of swept wings. *Rep. aero. Res. Coun., Lond.* No. *15246.* [479]

WEHRMANN, O., and WILLE, R. (1958). Beitrag zur Phänomenologie des laminaren turbulenten Übergangs im Freistrahl bei kleinen Reynoldszahlen. *Proc. Symp. boundary layer Res., Int. Union theoret. appl. Mech., Freiburg i. Br.* (1957), *387–403.* [562]

WESKE, J. R. (1957). Experimental study of detail phenomena of transition in boundary layers. *Tech. Notes Inst. Fluid Dyn. appl. Math., Univ. Maryland BN—91.* [578]

WESTERVELT, P. J. (1953a). The theory of steady rotational flow generated by a sound field. *J. acoust. Soc. Amer.* **25**, *60–67.* [387]

WESTERVELT, P. J. (1953b). Acoustic streaming near a small obstacle. *J. acoust. Soc. Amer.* **25**, *1123.* [388]

WEYL, H. (1941). Concerning the differential equations of some boundary-layer problems, I. *Proc. nat. Acad. Sci., Wash.* **27**, *578–83.* [233]

WEYL, H. (1942a). Concerning the differential equations of some boundary-layer problems, II. *Proc. nat. Acad. Sci., Wash.* **28**, *100–2.* [225, 233, 248]

WEYL, H. (1942b). On the differential equations of the simplest boundary-layer problems. *Ann. Math., Princeton* **43**, *381–407.* [233, 239]

WHIPPLE, F. J. W. (1933). The wet and dry-bulb hygrometer. *Proc. phys. Soc. Lond.* **45**, *307–19.* [22]

WHITE, C. M. *See* Davies and White (1928).

WHITEHEAD, A. N. (1889). Second approximations to viscous fluid motion. *Quart. J. Math.* **23**, *143–52.* [186]

WHITEHEAD, L. G. (1949). An integral relationship for boundary layer flow. *Aircr. Engng,* **21**, *14–16.* [317]

WHITEHEAD, L. G., and CANETTI, G. S. (1950). The laminar boundary layer on solids of revolution. *Phil. Mag.* (7), **41**, *988–1000.* [429, 430]